REPRESENTATIVE ELEMENTS | TRANSITION ELEMENTS | REPRESENTATIVE ELEMENTS

Key	
1	Atomic number
H	Symbol
Hydrogen	
1.008	Atomic mass

- Metals (main group)
- Metals (transition)
- Metals (inner transition)
- Metalloids
- Nonmetals

Period	IA (1)	IIA (2)	IIIB (3)	IVB (4)	VB (5)	VIB (6)	VIIB (7)	VIIIB (8)	VIIIB (9)	VIIIB (10)	IB (11)	IIB (12)	IIIA (13)	IVA (14)	VA (15)	VIA (16)	VIIA (17)	VIIIA (18)
1	1 **H** Hydrogen 1.008																	2 **He** Helium 4.003
2	3 **Li** Lithium 6.941	4 **Be** Beryllium 9.012											5 **B** Boron 10.81	6 **C** Carbon 12.01	7 **N** Nitrogen 14.01	8 **O** Oxygen 16.00	9 **F** Fluorine 19.00	10 **Ne** Neon 20.18
3	11 **Na** Sodium 22.99	12 **Mg** Magnesium 24.31											13 **Al** Aluminum 26.98	14 **Si** Silicon 28.09	15 **P** Phosphorus 30.97	16 **S** Sulfur 32.07	17 **Cl** Chlorine 35.45	18 **Ar** Argon 39.95
4	19 **K** Potassium 39.10	20 **Ca** Calcium 40.08	21 **Sc** Scandium 44.96	22 **Ti** Titanium 47.88	23 **V** Vanadium 50.94	24 **Cr** Chromium 52.00	25 **Mn** Manganese 54.94	26 **Fe** Iron 55.85	27 **Co** Cobalt 58.93	28 **Ni** Nickel 58.69	29 **Cu** Copper 63.55	30 **Zn** Zinc 65.39	31 **Ga** Gallium 69.72	32 **Ge** Germanium 72.61	33 **As** Arsenic 74.92	34 **Se** Selenium 78.96	35 **Br** Bromine 79.90	36 **Kr** Krypton 83.80
5	37 **Rb** Rubidium 85.47	38 **Sr** Strontium 87.62	39 **Y** Yttrium 88.91	40 **Zr** Zirconium 91.22	41 **Nb** Niobium 92.91	42 **Mo** Molybdenum 95.94	43 **Tc** Technetium (98)	44 **Ru** Ruthenium 101.1	45 **Rh** Rhodium 102.9	46 **Pd** Palladium 106.4	47 **Ag** Silver 107.9	48 **Cd** Cadmium 112.4	49 **In** Indium 114.8	50 **Sn** Tin 118.7	51 **Sb** Antimony 121.8	52 **Te** Tellurium 127.6	53 **I** Iodine 126.9	54 **Xe** Xenon 131.3
6	55 **Cs** Cesium 132.9	56 **Ba** Barium 137.3	57 **La** Lanthanum 138.9	72 **Hf** Hafnium 178.5	73 **Ta** Tantalum 180.9	74 **W** Tungsten 183.9	75 **Re** Rhenium 186.2	76 **Os** Osmium 190.2	77 **Ir** Iridium 192.2	78 **Pt** Platinum 195.1	79 **Au** Gold 197.0	80 **Hg** Mercury 200.6	81 **Tl** Thallium 204.4	82 **Pb** Lead 207.2	83 **Bi** Bismuth 209.0	84 **Po** Polonium (209)	85 **At** Astatine (210)	86 **Rn** Radon (222)
7	87 **Fr** Francium (223)	88 **Ra** Radium (226)	89 **Ac** Actinium (227)	104 **Rf** Rutherfordium (261)	105 **Db** Dubnium (262)	106 **Sg** Seaborgium (266)	107 **Bh** Bohrium (262)	108 **Hs** Hassium (265)	109 **Mt** Meitnerium (266)	110 **Ds** Darmstadtium (281)	111 **Rg** Roentgenium (272)	112 (277)	113	114 (285)	115	116 (289)	117	118

INNER TRANSITION ELEMENTS

Period															
6	Lanthanides	58 **Ce** Cerium 140.1	59 **Pr** Praseodymium 140.9	60 **Nd** Neodymium 144.2	61 **Pm** Promethium (147)	62 **Sm** Samarium 150.4	63 **Eu** Europium 152.0	64 **Gd** Gadolinium 157.3	65 **Tb** Terbium 158.9	66 **Dy** Dysprosium 162.5	67 **Ho** Holmium 164.9	68 **Er** Erbium 167.3	69 **Tm** Thulium 168.9	70 **Yb** Ytterbium 173.0	71 **Lu** Lutetium 175.0
7	Actinides	90 **Th** Thorium 232.0	91 **Pa** Protactinium (231)	92 **U** Uranium 238.0	93 **Np** Neptunium (237)	94 **Pu** Plutonium (242)	95 **Am** Americium (243)	96 **Cm** Curium (247)	97 **Bk** Berkelium (247)	98 **Cf** Californium (251)	99 **Es** Einsteinium (252)	100 **Fm** Fermium (257)	101 **Md** Mendelevium (258)	102 **No** Nobelium (259)	103 **Lr** Lawrencium (260)

The 1–18 group designation is recommended (International Union of Pure and Applied Chemistry) but not widely used. This text uses standard notation for groups (IA–VIIIA and IB–VIIIB).

List of the Elements with their Symbols and Atomic Masses*

Element	Symbol	Atomic Number	Atomic Mass†	Element	Symbol	Atomic Number	Atomic Mass†
Actinium	Ac	89	(227)	Mendelevium	Md	101	(256)
Aluminum	Al	13	26.98	Mercury	Hg	80	200.6
Americium	Am	95	(243)	Molybdenum	Mo	42	95.94
Antimony	Sb	51	121.8	Neodymium	Nd	60	144.2
Argon	Ar	18	39.95	Neon	Ne	10	20.18
Arsenic	As	33	74.92	Neptunian	Np	93	(237)
Astatine	At	85	(210)	Nickel	Ni	28	58.69
Barium	Ba	56	137.3	Niobium	Nb	41	92.91
Berkelium	Bk	97	(247)	Nitrogen	N	7	14.01
Beryllium	Be	4	9.012	Nobelium	No	102	(253)
Bismuth	Bi	83	209.0	Osmium	Os	76	190.2
Bohrium	Bh	107	(262)	Oxygen	O	8	16.00
Boron	B	5	10.81	Palladium	Pd	46	106.4
Bromine	Br	35	79.90	Phosphorus	P	15	30.97
Cadmium	Cd	48	112.4	Platinum	Pt	78	195.1
Calcium	Ca	20	40.08	Plutonium	Pu	94	(242)
Californium	Cf	98	(249)	Polonium	Po	84	(210)
Carbon	C	6	12.01	Potassium	K	19	39.10
Cerium	Ce	58	140.1	Praseodymium	Pr	59	140.9
Cesium	Cs	55	132.9	Promethium	Pm	61	(147)
Chlorine	Cl	17	35.45	Protactinium	Pa	91	(231)
Chromium	Cr	24	52.00	Radium	Ra	88	(226)
Cobalt	Co	27	58.93	Radon	Rn	86	(222)
Copper	Cu	29	63.55	Rhenium	Re	75	186.2
Curium	Cm	96	(247)	Rhodium	Rh	45	102.9
Darmstadtium	Ds	110	(281)	Roentgenium	Rg	111	(272)
Dubnium	Db	105	(262)	Rubidium	Rb	37	85.47
Dysprosium	Dy	66	162.5	Ruthenium	Ru	44	101.1
Einsteinium	Es	99	(254)	Rutherfordium	Rf	104	(257)
Erbium	Er	68	167.3	Samarium	Sm	62	150.4
Europium	Eu	63	152.0	Scandium	Sc	21	44.96
Fermium	Fm	100	(253)	Seaborgium	Sg	106	(263)
Fluorine	F	9	19.00	Selenium	Se	34	78.96
Francium	Fr	87	(223)	Silicon	Si	14	28.09
Gadolinium	Gd	64	157.3	Silver	Ag	47	107.9
Gallium	Ga	31	69.72	Sodium	Na	11	22.99
Germanium	Ge	32	72.59	Strontium	Sr	38	87.62
Gold	Au	79	197.0	Sulfur	S	16	32.07
Hafnium	Hf	72	178.5	Tantalum	Ta	73	180.9
Hassium	Hs	108	(265)	Technetium	Tc	43	(99)
Helium	He	2	4.003	Tellurium	Te	52	127.6
Holmium	Ho	67	164.9	Terbium	Tb	65	158.9
Hydrogen	H	1	1.008	Thallium	Tl	81	204.4
Indium	In	49	114.8	Thorium	Th	90	232.0
Iodine	I	53	126.9	Thulium	Tm	69	168.9
Iridium	Ir	77	192.2	Tin	Sn	50	118.7
Iron	Fe	26	55.85	Titanium	Ti	22	47.88
Krypton	Kr	36	83.80	Tungsten	W	74	183.9
Lanthanum	La	57	138.9	Uranium	U	92	238.0
Lawrencium	Lr	103	(257)	Vanadium	V	23	50.94
Lead	Pb	82	207.2	Xenon	Xe	54	131.3
Lithium	Li	3	6.941	Ytterbium	Yb	70	173.0
Lutetium	Lu	71	175.0	Yttrium	Y	39	88.91
Magnesium	Mg	12	24.31	Zinc	Zn	30	65.39
Manganese	Mn	25	54.94	Zirconium	Zr	40	91.22
Meitnerium	Mt	109	(266)				

*All atomic masses have four significant figures. These values are recommended by the Committee on Teaching of Chemistry, International Union of Pure and Applied Chemistry.

†Masses of the longest-lived isotope for radioactive elements are given in parentheses.

PRINCIPAL FUNCTIONAL GROUPS IN ORGANIC COMPOUNDS

Type of Compound	Structural Formula	Condensed Formula	Chapter Reference	Example: Structural Formula	Example: IUPAC Name	Example: Common Name
Alcohol	R—O—H	ROH	12	CH_3CH_2—O—H	Ethanol	Ethyl alcohol
Aldehyde	R—C(=O)—H	RCHO	12	CH_3C(=O)—H	Ethanal	Acetaldehyde
Amide	R—C(=O)—N(H)—H	$RCONH_2$	13	CH_3C(=O)—N(H)—H	Ethanamide	Acetamide
Amine	R—N(H)—H	RNH_2	13	CH_3CH_2N(H)—H	Ethanamine	Ethyl amine
Carboxylic acid	R—C(=O)—O—H	RCOOH	13	CH_3C(=O)—O—H	Ethanoic acid	Acetic acid
Ester	R—C(=O)—O—R'	RCOOR'	13	CH_3C(=O)—OCH_3	Methyl ethanoate	Methyl acetate
Ether	R—O—R'	ROR'	12	CH_3OCH_3	Methoxymethane	Dimethyl ether
Halide	—Cl (or —Br, —F, —I)	RCl	10	CH_3CH_2Cl	Chloroethane	Ethyl chloride
Ketone	R—C(=O)—R'	RCOR'	12	CH_3C(=O)CH_3	Propanone	Acetone

METRIC PREFIXES

Multiple	Prefix	Symbol	Submultiple	Prefix	Symbol
10^{12}	tera	T	10^{-1}	deci	d
10^{9}	giga	G	10^{-2}	centi	c
10^{6}	mega	M	10^{-3}	milli	m
10^{3}	kilo	k	10^{-6}	micro	μ
10^{2}	hecto	h	10^{-9}	nano	n
10^{1}	deka	da	10^{-12}	pico	p

CONVERSION FACTORS

Length:
1 meter (m) = 39.37 inches (in)
1 inch (in) = 2.54 centimeters (cm)
1 Ångstrom (Å) = 10^{-10} m

Mass:
1 kilogram (kg) = 2.205 pounds (lb)
1 pound (lb) = 453.5 grams (g)
1 atomic mass unit (amu)
= 1.661×10^{-24} grams (g)

Volume:
1 liter (L) = 1000 milliliters (mL)
= 1000 cm^3
1 liter = 1.057 quarts (qt)

Energy:
1 calorie (cal) = 4.18 joules (J)

Temperature:
$°F = 1.8°C + 32$
$°C = \frac{(°F - 32)}{1.8}$
$K = °C + 273.15$

Pressure:
1 atmosphere (atm) = 14.7 lbs in^{-2} (psi)
1 atm = 760 millimeters of mercury
(760 mm Hg = 760 torr)

PHYSICAL CONSTANTS

Avogadro's number	6.022×10^{23} units $mole^{-1}$
Speed of light	3.0×10^{8} m sec^{-1}
Gas constant (*R*)	0.08205 L-atm K^{-1}-mol^{-1}
Mass of an electron	9.11×10^{-28} g or 5.40×10^{-4} amu
Mass of a proton	1.67×10^{-24} g or 1.007 amu
Mass of a neutron	1.68×10^{-24} g or 1.009 amu
Volume of one mole of ideal gas	22.4 L (@ 273 K)

General, Organic, *and* Biochemistry

EIGHTH EDITION

Katherine J. Denniston
Towson University

Joseph J. Topping
Towson University

Kim R. Woodrum
University of Kentucky

Robert L. Caret
University of Massachusetts

Chemistry 1113
Special Edition for CSCC

Boston Burr Ridge, IL Dubuque, IA New York San Francisco St. Louis
Bangkok Bogotá Caracas Lisbon London Madrid
Mexico City Milan New Delhi Seoul Singapore Sydney Taipei Toronto

1 2 3 4 5 6 7 8 9 0 QVS QVS 16 15 14 13 12

ISBN-13: 978-0-07-337194-8
ISBN-10: 0-07-337194-7

Learning Solutions Consultant: Bradley Ritter
Project Manager: Jeni McAtee
Printer/Binder: Quad Graphics-Versailles

Brief Contents

ORGANIC CHEMISTRY

10 An Introduction to Organic Chemistry: The Saturated Hydrocarbons 326
11 The Unsaturated Hydrocarbons: Alkenes, Alkynes, and Aromatics 363
12 Alcohols, Phenols, Thiols, and Ethers 405
13 Aldehydes and Ketones 439
14 Carboxylic Acids and Carboxylic Acid Derivatives 469
15 Amines and Amides 511

BIOCHEMISTRY

16 Carbohydrates 547
17 Lipids and Their Functions in Biochemical Systems 581
18 Protein Structure and Function 617
19 Enzymes 649
20 Introduction to Molecular Genetics 684
21 Carbohydrate Metabolism 727
22 Aerobic Respiration and Energy Production 761
23 Fatty Acid Metabolism 793

Contents

ORGANIC CHEMISTRY

10 An Introduction to Organic Chemistry: The Saturated Hydrocarbons 326

10.1 The Chemistry of Carbon 327
Important Differences Between Organic and Inorganic Compounds 328
Families of Organic Compounds 329
Green Chemistry: Frozen Methane: Treasure or Threat? 330

10.2 Alkanes 331
Structure 331
Physical Properties 335
Alkyl Groups 336
Chemistry at the Crime Scene: Arson and Alkanes 338
Nomenclature 338
Green Chemistry: Biofuels: A Renewable Resource 340
Constitutional or Structural Isomers 344

10.3 Cycloalkanes 345
cis-trans Isomerism in Cycloalkanes 346

10.4 Conformations of Alkanes and Cycloalkanes 348
Alkanes 349
Cycloalkanes 349
Green Chemistry: The Petroleum Industry and Gasoline Production 350

10.5 Reactions of Alkanes and Cycloalkanes 351
Combustion 351
Halogenation 352
A Medical Perspective: Polyhalogenated Hydrocarbons Used as Anesthetics 354
Chapter Map 355
Summary of Reactions 356
Summary 356
Answers to Practice Problems 357
Questions and Problems 357
Critical Thinking Problems 362

11 The Unsaturated Hydrocarbons: Alkenes, Alkynes, and Aromatics 363

11.1 Alkenes and Alkynes: Structure and Physical Properties 364

11.2 Alkenes and Alkynes: Nomenclature 366

11.3 Geometric Isomers: A Consequence of Unsaturation 369
A Medical Perspective: Killer Alkynes in Nature 370

11.4 Alkenes in Nature 376

11.5 Reactions Involving Alkenes and Alkynes 378
Hydrogenation: Addition of H_2 378
Halogenation: Addition of X_2 380
Hydration: Addition of H_2O 382
Hydrohalogenation: Addition of HX 385
Addition Polymers of Alkenes 386
A Human Perspective: Life Without Polymers? 387
Green Chemistry: Plastic Recycling 388

11.6 Aromatic Hydrocarbons 388
Structure and Properties 390
Nomenclature 390
Polynuclear Aromatic Hydrocarbons 393
Reactions Involving Benzene 393

11.7 Heterocyclic Aromatic Compounds 394
Kitchen Chemistry: Amazing Chocolate 395
Chapter Map 396
Summary of Reactions 397
Summary 398
Answers to Practice Problems 398
Questions and Problems 400
Critical Thinking Problems 403

12 Alcohols, Phenols, Thiols, and Ethers 405

12.1 Alcohols: Structure and Physical Properties 407

12.2 Alcohols: Nomenclature 409
IUPAC Names 409
Common Names 410

12.3 Medically Important Alcohols 411
Methanol 411
Ethanol 411
A Medical Perspective: Fetal Alcohol Syndrome 412
2-Propanol 412
1,2-Ethanediol 412
1,2,3-Propanetriol 413

12.4 Reactions Involving Alcohols 413
Preparation of Alcohols 413
Dehydration of Alcohols 415
Oxidation Reactions 416

12.5 Oxidation and Reduction in Living Systems 419
Chemistry at the Crime Scene: Drinking and Driving 421

12.6 Phenols 421
Kitchen Chemistry: Spicy Phenols 422
A Medical Perspective: Resveratrol: Fountain of Youth? 424

12.7 Ethers 424

12.8 Thiols 427
Kitchen Chemistry: The Magic of Garlic 430
Chapter Map 431

Summary of Reactions 432
Summary 432
Answers to Practice Problems 433
Questions and Problems 434
Critical Thinking Problems 438

13 Aldehydes and Ketones 439

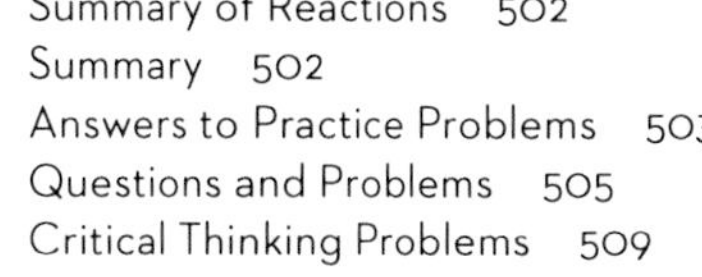

13.1 Structure and Physical Properties 441

13.2 IUPAC Nomenclature and Common Names 442
Naming Aldehydes 442
Naming Ketones 444

13.3 Important Aldehydes and Ketones 447

13.4 Reactions Involving Aldehydes and Ketones 449
Preparation of Aldehydes and Ketones 449
A Medical Perspective: Formaldehyde and Methanol Poisoning 450
Oxidation Reactions 450
Reduction Reactions 452
A Human Perspective: Alcohol Abuse and Antabuse 453
Addition Reactions 455
Kitchen Chemistry: The Allure of Truffles 456
Keto-Enol Tautomers 459
Chapter Map 461
Summary of Reactions 462
Summary 462
Answers to Practice Problems 463
Questions and Problems 464
Critical Thinking Problems 468

14 Carboxylic Acids and Carboxylic Acid Derivatives 469

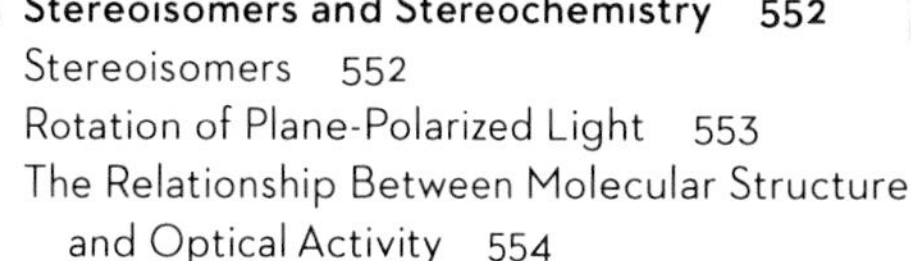

14.1 Carboxylic Acids 471
Structure and Physical Properties 471
Nomenclature 472
Chemistry at the Crime Scene: Carboxylic Acids and the Body Farm 476
Green Chemistry: Garbage Bags from Potato Peels? 478
Some Important Carboxylic Acids 478
Reactions Involving Carboxylic Acids 481

14.2 Esters 484
Structure and Physical Properties 484
Nomenclature 484
Reactions Involving Esters 485
A Human Perspective: The Chemistry of Flavor and Fragrance 488
A Human Perspective: Detergents 492

14.3 Acid Chlorides and Acid Anhydrides 494
Acid Chlorides 494
Acid Anhydrides 495

14.4 Nature's High-Energy Compounds: Phosphoesters and Thioesters 498
A Human Perspective: Carboxylic Acid Derivatives of Special Interest 500
Chapter Map 501
Summary of Reactions 502
Summary 502
Answers to Practice Problems 503
Questions and Problems 505
Critical Thinking Problems 509

15 Amines and Amides 511

15.1 Amines 513
Structure and Physical Properties 513
Nomenclature 516
Medically Important Amines 519
Reactions Involving Amines 520
Chemistry at the Crime Scene: Methamphetamine 523
Quaternary Ammonium Salts 525

15.2 Heterocyclic Amines 525

15.3 Amides 527
Kitchen Chemistry: Browning Reactions and Flavor: The Maillard Reaction 528
Structure and Physical Properties 528
Nomenclature 529
Medically Important Amides 529
Reactions Involving Amides 531
A Medical Perspective: Semisynthetic Penicillins 532

15.4 A Preview of Amino Acids, Proteins, and Protein Synthesis 534

15.5 Neurotransmitters 535
Catecholamines 535
A Medical Perspective: Opiate Biosynthesis and the Mutant Poppy 536
Serotonin 536
Histamine 538
γ-Aminobutyric Acid and Glycine 538
Acetylcholine 539
Nitric Oxide and Glutamate 540
Chapter Map 540
Summary of Reactions 541
Summary 541
Answers to Practice Problems 542
Questions and Problems 542
Critical Thinking Problems 546

BIOCHEMISTRY

16 Carbohydrates 547

16.1 Types of Carbohydrates 548

16.2 Monosaccharides 550
A Medical Perspective: Tooth Decay and Simple Sugars 551

16.3 Stereoisomers and Stereochemistry 552
Stereoisomers 552
Rotation of Plane-Polarized Light 553
The Relationship Between Molecular Structure and Optical Activity 554

Fischer Projection Formulas 554
Racemic Mixtures 556
Diastereomers 556
Meso Compounds 557
The D- and L- System of Nomenclature 558

16.4 **Biologically Important Monosaccharides 559**
Glucose 559
Fructose 563
Galactose 564
Ribose and Deoxyribose, Five-Carbon Sugars 564
Reducing Sugars 565
Kitchen Chemistry: The Chemistry of Caramels 566

16.5 **Biologically Important Disaccharides 567**
Maltose 568
Lactose 568
Sucrose 568
Chemistry at the Crime Scene: Blood Group Antigens 570

16.6 **Polysaccharides 570**
Starch 570
Glycogen 571
Cellulose 572
A Medical Perspective: Monosaccharide Derivatives and Heteropolysaccharides of Medical Interest 573
Chapter Map 574
Summary 575
Answers to Practice Problems 576
Questions and Problems 577
Critical Thinking Problems 579

17 Lipids and Their Functions in Biochemical Systems 581

17.1 **Biological Functions of Lipids 582**
A Medical Perspective: Lifesaving Lipids 583

17.2 **Fatty Acids 584**
Structure and Properties 584
Eicosanoids: Prostaglandins, Leukotrienes, and Thromboxanes 587
Omega-3 Fatty Acids 589

17.3 **Glycerides 590**
Neutral Glycerides 590
Chemical Reactions of Fatty Acids and Glycerides 592
Phosphoglycerides 595
Chemistry at the Crime Scene: Adipocere and Mummies of Soap 597

17.4 **Nonglyceride Lipids 598**
Sphingolipids 598
Steroids 600
A Medical Perspective: Disorders of Sphingolipid Metabolism 601
A Medical Perspective: Steroids and the Treatment of Heart Disease 602
Waxes 604

17.5 **Complex Lipids 605**

17.6 **The Structure of Biological Membranes 608**
Fluid Mosaic Structure of Biological Membranes 608
A Medical Perspective: Liposome Delivery Systems 610
Chapter Map 612
Summary 613
Answers to Practice Problems 613
Questions and Problems 615
Critical Thinking Problems 616

18 Protein Structure and Function 617

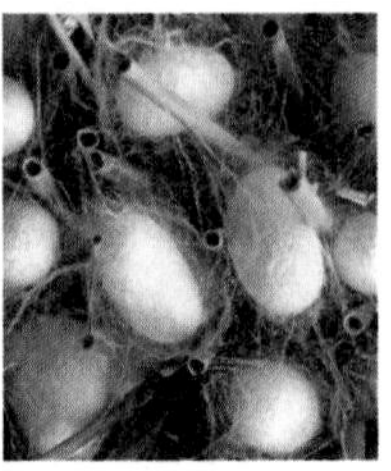

18.1 **Protein Building Blocks: The α-Amino Acids 618**
Structure of Amino Acids 618
Stereoisomers of Amino Acids 619
Classes of Amino Acids 620

18.2 **The Peptide Bond 622**
A Human Perspective: The Opium Poppy and Peptides in the Brain 625

18.3 **The Primary Structure of Proteins 626**

18.4 **The Secondary Structure of Proteins 626**
α-Helix 627
β-Pleated Sheet 628

18.5 **The Tertiary Structure of Proteins 629**
A Medical Perspective: Collagen, Cosmetic Procedures, and Clinical Applications 631

18.6 **The Quaternary Structure of Proteins 632**

18.7 **An Overview of Protein Structure and Function 633**

18.8 **Myoglobin and Hemoglobin 634**
Myoglobin and Oxygen Storage 634
Hemoglobin and Oxygen Transport 634
Oxygen Transport from Mother to Fetus 635
Sickle Cell Anemia 636

18.9 **Proteins in the Blood 636**

18.10 **Denaturation of Proteins 637**
Temperature 637
pH 638
Kitchen Chemistry: Egg Foams: Meringues and Soufflés 639
Organic Solvents 639
A Medical Perspective: Immunoglobulins: Proteins That Defend the Body 640
Detergents 641
Heavy Metals 641
Mechanical Stress 641

18.11 **Dietary Protein and Protein Digestion 641**
Chapter Map 643
Summary 644
Answers to Practice Problems 645
Questions and Problems 645
Critical Thinking Problems 647

19 Enzymes 649

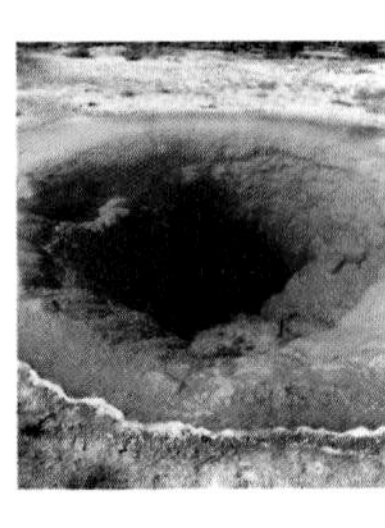

19.1 **Nomenclature and Classification 650**
Classification of Enzymes 650
Nomenclature of Enzymes 652
Kitchen Chemistry: Transglutaminase: aka Meat Glue 655

19.2 **The Effect of Enzymes on the Activation Energy of a Reaction 656**

19.3 **The Effect of Substrate Concentration on Enzyme-Catalyzed Reactions 657**

19.4 The Enzyme-Substrate Complex 658

19.5 Specificity of the Enzyme-Substrate Complex 659

19.6 The Transition State and Product Formation 660
A Medical Perspective: HIV Protease Inhibitors and Pharmaceutical Drug Design 662

19.7 Cofactors and Coenzymes 663

19.8 Environmental Effects 666
Effect of pH 666
A Medical Perspective: α_1-Antitrypsin and Familial Emphysema 667
Effect of Temperature 667

19.9 Regulation of Enzyme Activity 668
Allosteric Enzymes 669
Feedback Inhibition 670
Proenzymes 670
Protein Modification 670

19.10 Inhibition of Enzyme Activity 671
Irreversible Inhibitors 671
Chemistry at the Crime Scene: Enzymes, Nerve Agents, and Poisoning 672
Reversible, Competitive Inhibitors 672
Reversible, Noncompetitive Inhibitors 674

19.11 Proteolytic Enzymes 675

19.12 Uses of Enzymes in Medicine 676
Chapter Map 679
Summary 679
Answers to Practice Problems 681
Questions and Problems 681
Critical Thinking Problems 683

20 Introduction to Molecular Genetics 684

20.1 The Structure of the Nucleotide 685
Chemical Composition of DNA and RNA 686
Nucleosides 686
Nucleotide Structure 687

20.2 The Structure of DNA and RNA 688
DNA Structure: The Double Helix 688
Chromosomes 690
RNA Structure 692
A Medical Perspective: Molecular Genetics and Detection of Human Genetic Disorders 693

20.3 DNA Replication 693
Bacterial DNA Replication 695
Eukaryotic DNA Replication 696

20.4 Information Flow in Biological Systems 698
Classes of RNA Molecules 698
Transcription 698
Post-transcriptional Processing of RNA 700

20.5 The Genetic Code 702

20.6 Protein Synthesis 703
The Role of Transfer RNA 705
The Process of Translation 705

20.7 Mutation, Ultraviolet Light, and DNA Repair 708
The Nature of Mutations 708
The Results of Mutations 708
Mutagens and Carcinogens 709
Ultraviolet Light Damage and DNA Repair 709
A Medical Perspective: The Ames Test for Carcinogens 710
Consequences of Defects in DNA Repair 711

20.8 Recombinant DNA 711
Tools Used in the Study of DNA 711
Genetic Engineering 714

20.9 Polymerase Chain Reaction 717

20.10 The Human Genome Project 717
Genetic Strategies for Genome Analysis 717
Chemistry at the Crime Scene: DNA Fingerprinting 718
DNA Sequencing 718
A Medical Perspective: A Genetic Approach to Familial Emphysema 720
Chapter Map 722
Summary 723
Questions and Problems 724
Critical Thinking Problems 726

21 Carbohydrate Metabolism 727

21.1 ATP: The Cellular Energy Currency 728

21.2 Overview of Catabolic Processes 731
Stage I: Hydrolysis of Dietary Macromolecules into Small Subunits 732
Stage II: Conversion of Monomers into a Form That Can Be Completely Oxidized 732
Stage III: The Complete Oxidation of Nutrients and the Production of ATP 732

21.3 Glycolysis 733
An Overview 733
Biological Effects of Genetic Disorders of Glycolysis 735
Reactions of Glycolysis 736
Entry of Fructose into Glycolysis 740
A Medical Perspective: High Fructose Corn Syrup 741
Regulation of Glycolysis 741

21.4 Fermentations 742
Lactate Fermentation 742
Alcohol Fermentation 743
A Human Perspective: Fermentations: The Good, the Bad, and the Ugly 744

21.5 The Pentose Phosphate Pathway 744

21.6 Gluconeogenesis: The Synthesis of Glucose 746

21.7 Glycogen Synthesis and Degradation 748
The Structure of Glycogen 748
Glycogenolysis: Glycogen Degradation 748
Glycogenesis: Glycogen Synthesis 750
A Medical Perspective: Diagnosing Diabetes 752
Compatibility of Glycogenesis and Glycogenolysis 754
A Human Perspective: Glycogen Storage Diseases 755
Chapter Map 756
Summary 756
Questions and Problems 757
Critical Thinking Problems 760

22 Aerobic Respiration and Energy Production 761

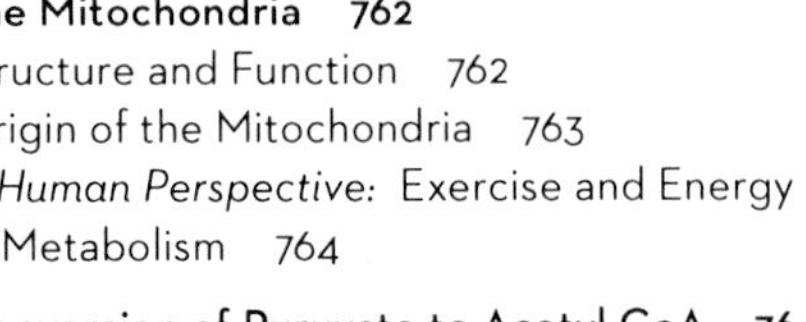

22.1 The Mitochondria 762
Structure and Function 762
Origin of the Mitochondria 763
A Human Perspective: Exercise and Energy Metabolism 764

22.2 Conversion of Pyruvate to Acetyl CoA 764

22.3 An Overview of Aerobic Respiration 767

22.4 The Citric Acid Cycle (The Krebs Cycle) 768
Biological Effects of Disorders of the Citric Acid Cycle 768
Reactions of the Citric Acid Cycle 769

22.5 Control of the Citric Acid Cycle 772

22.6 Oxidative Phosphorylation 774
Electron Transport Systems and the Hydrogen Ion Gradient 774
ATP Synthase and the Production of ATP 775
Summary of the Energy Yield 775
A Human Perspective: Brown Fat: The Fat That Makes You Thin? 776

22.7 The Degradation of Amino Acids 778
Removal of α-Amino Groups: Transamination 779
Removal of α-Amino Groups: Oxidative Deamination 780
The Fate of Amino Acid Carbon Skeletons 782

22.8 The Urea Cycle 782
Reactions of the Urea Cycle 782
A Medical Perspective: Pyruvate Carboxylase Deficiency 785

22.9 Overview of Anabolism: The Citric Acid Cycle as a Source of Biosynthetic Intermediates 786
Chapter Map 788
Summary 789
Answers to Practice Problems 790
Questions and Problems 790
Critical Thinking Problems 792

23 Fatty Acid Metabolism 793

23.1 Lipid Metabolism in Animals 794
Digestion and Absorption of Dietary Triglycerides 794
Lipid Storage 795
A Medical Perspective: Obesity: A Genetic Disorder? 797

23.2 Fatty Acid Degradation 798
An Overview of Fatty Acid Degradation 798
The Reactions of β-Oxidation 799
A Medical Perspective: Carnitine: The Fat Mover 802

23.3 Ketone Bodies 804
Ketosis 805
Ketogenesis 805
A Human Perspective: Losing Those Unwanted Pounds of Adipose Tissue 807

23.4 Fatty Acid Synthesis 808
A Comparison of Fatty Acid Synthesis and Degradation 808

23.5 The Regulation of Lipid and Carbohydrate Metabolism 810
The Liver 810
A Medical Perspective: Diabetes Mellitus and Ketone Bodies 811
Adipose Tissue 812
Muscle Tissue 812
The Brain 813

23.6 The Effects of Insulin and Glucagon on Cellular Metabolism 813
Chapter Map 815
Summary 816
Answers to Practice Problems 816
Questions and Problems 817
Critical Thinking Problems 818

Glossary G-1
Answers to Odd-Numbered Problems AP-1
Credits C-1
Index I-1

Perspectives

A HUMAN PERSPECTIVE

The Scientific Method 5
Food Calories 29
Quick and Useful Analysis 35
Atomic Spectra and the Fourth of July 56
The Chemistry of Automobile Air Bags 152
The Demise of the Hindenburg 168
Gemstones 187
Scuba Diving: Nitrogen and the Bends 198
Too Fast or Too Slow? 243
An Extraordinary Molecule 255
Origin of the Elements 301
An Extraordinary Woman in Science 309
Life Without Polymers? 387
Alcohol Abuse and Antabuse 453
The Chemistry of Flavor and Fragrance 488
Detergents 492
Carboxylic Acid Derivatives of Special Interest 500
The Opium Poppy and Peptides in the Brain 625
Fermentations: The Good, the Bad, and the Ugly 744
Glycogen Storage Diseases 755
Exercise and Energy Metabolism 764
Brown Fat: The Fat That Makes You Thin? 776
Losing Those Unwanted Pounds of Adipose Tissue 807

A MEDICAL PERSPECTIVE

Curiosity and the Technology that Leads to Discovery 26
Assessing Obesity: The Body-Mass Index 34
Copper Deficiency and Wilson's Disease 60
Dietary Calcium 72
Unwanted Crystal Formation 88
Rebuilding Our Teeth 99
Blood Pressure and the Sodium Ion/Potassium Ion Ratio 102
Carbon Monoxide Poisoning: A Case of Combining Ratios 155
Pharmaceutical Chemistry: The Practical Significance of Percent Yield 158
Blood Gases and Respiration 181
Oral Rehydration Therapy 214
Hemodialysis 220
Hot and Cold Packs 234
Drug Delivery 272
Oxidizing Agents for Chemical Control of Microbes 285
Electrochemical Reactions in the Statue of Liberty and in Dental Fillings 290
Magnetic Resonance Imaging 316
Polyhalogenated Hydrocarbons Used as Anesthetics 354
Killer Alkynes in Nature 370
Fetal Alcohol Syndrome 412
Resveratrol: Fountain of Youth? 424
Formaldehyde and Methanol Poisoning 450
Semisynthetic Penicillins 532
Opiate Biosynthesis and the Mutant Poppy 536
Tooth Decay and Simple Sugars 551
Monosaccharide Derivatives and Heteropolysaccharides of Medical Interest 573
Lifesaving Lipids 583
Disorders of Sphingolipid Metabolism 601
Steroids and the Treatment of Heart Disease 602
Liposome Delivery Systems 610
Collagen, Cosmetic Procedures, and Clinical Applications 631
Immunoglobulins: Proteins That Defend the Body 640
HIV Protease Inhibitors and Pharmaceutical Drug Design 662
α_1-Antitrypsin and Familial Emphysema 667

Molecular Genetics and Detection of Human Genetic Disorders 693
The Ames Test for Carcinogens 710
A Genetic Approach to Familial Emphysema 720
High Fructose Corn Syrup 741
Diagnosing Diabetes 752
Pyruvate Carboxylase Deficiency 785
Obesity: A Genetic Disorder? 797
Carnitine: The Fat Mover 802
Diabetes Mellitus and Ketone Bodies 811

GREEN CHEMISTRY

Electromagnetic Radiation and Its Effects on Our Everyday Lives 54
The Greenhouse Effect and Global Climate Change 179
Twenty-First Century Energy 230
Acid Rain 276
Hydrangea, pH, and Soil Chemistry 277
Nuclear Waste Disposal 312
Radon and Indoor Air Pollution 320
Frozen Methane: Treasure or Threat? 330
Biofuels: A Renewable Resource 340
The Petroleum Industry and Gasoline Production 350
Plastic Recycling 388
Garbage Bags from Potato Peels? 478

KITCHEN CHEMISTRY

Solubility, Surfactants, and the Dishwasher 216
Amazing Chocolate 395
Spicy Phenols 422
The Magic of Garlic 430
The Allure of Truffles 456
Browning Reactions and Flavor: The Maillard Reaction 528
The Chemistry of Caramels 566
Egg Foams: Meringues and Soufflés 639
Transglutaminase: aka Meat Glue 655

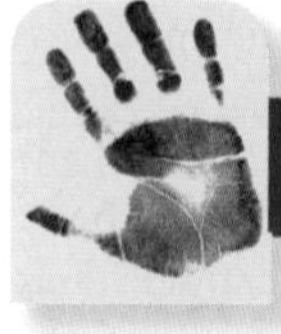

CHEMISTRY AT THE CRIME SCENE

Microbial Forensics 49
Explosives at the Airport 184
Arson and Alkanes 338
Drinking and Driving 421
Carboxylic Acids and the Body Farm 476
Methamphetamine 523
Blood Group Antigens 570
Adipocere and Mummies of Soap 597
Enzymes, Nerve Agents, and Poisoning 672
DNA Fingerprinting 718

Preface

To Our Students

Just as some researchers study chemical change, others study learning. The two are related: there are measurable changes in the brain as learning occurs. While the research on brain chemistry and learning continues, the research on learning has taught us some very successful strategies for teaching and learning chemistry. For instance, we now know that building long-term memory requires "repetitions." When you exercise to build muscle strength, you perform some number of "reps" of each exercise for each muscle that you wish to build. That is exactly what you need to do to build your long-term memory and understanding. The Center for Academic Success at the Louisiana State University has devised study tools that have allowed students to improve their performance by a full letter grade, or higher. The following is the Study Cycle with five stages that provide the "reps" needed to perform well in any course:

1. ***Preview*** the chapter *before* class. Either the evening before or the day of class, skim the material; pay attention to the end-of-chapter summary with boldfaced key terms, chapter map, the learning goals, and headings. Think of questions you would like the instructor to answer. Think of this 10 minutes as your "warm up."
2. ***Attend*** class! Be an active participant in the class, asking and answering questions and taking thoughtful, meaningful notes. Class time is much more meaningful if you have already familiarized yourself with the organization and key concepts to be discussed.
3. ***Review*** your notes as soon as possible after class. Fill in any gaps that exist and note any additional questions that arise. This also takes about 10 minutes; think of it as your "cool down" period.
4. ***Study.*** Since repetition is the key to success, The Center for Academic Success recommends 3–5 short, but intense, study sessions each day. These intense study sessions should have a very structured organization. In the first 2–5 minutes, establish your goal for the session. Spend the next 30–50 minutes studying with focus and action. Organize the material, make flash cards to help you review, draw concept maps to define the relationship among ideas, and practice problem solving. Then reward yourself with a 5–10 minute break. Call a friend, play Angry Birds, or do anything you find enjoyable. Then take 5 minutes to review the material. Finally, about once a week, perhaps on the weekend, review all of the material that you have been studying throughout the week.
5. ***Assess*** your progress. Are you able to solve the questions and problems at the end of the chapter? Can you explain the concepts to others? The assessment will affirm what you know well and reveal what you need to study further.

The Center for Academic Success has many other suggestions to help students learn how to learn. You can find their online tutorials and workshops at www.cas.lsu.edu.

To the Instructor

The eighth edition of *General, Organic, and Biochemistry,* like our earlier editions, has been designed to help undergraduate majors in health-related fields understand key concepts and appreciate significant connections among chemistry, health, and the treatment of disease. We have tried to strike a balance between theoretical and practical chemistry, while emphasizing material that is unique to health-related studies. We have written at a level intended for students whose professional goals do not include a mastery of chemistry, but for whom an understanding of the principles and practice of chemistry is a necessity.

Although our emphasis is the importance of chemistry to the health-related professions, we wanted this book to be appropriate for all students who need a one- or two-semester introduction to chemistry. Students learn best when they are engaged. One way to foster that engagement is to help them see clear relationships between the subject and real life. For these reasons, we have included perspectives and essays that focus on medicine and the function of the human body, as well as the environment, forensic science, and even culinary arts.

We begin that engagement with the book cover. Students may wonder why the cover depicts a coral reef featuring a sponge. Then they learn that one of the first drugs used to treat cancer successfully, *cytosine arabinoside,* was synthesized following the discovery of similar compounds from a Caribbean sponge. Because sponges are sessile, they produce a variety of compounds to protect them from predation. Cytosine arabinoside is now used routinely for treatment of acute myeloid leukemia (AAML), acute lymphocytic leukemia (ALL). In fact, a large number of other compounds from sponges are being tested for anticancer and antimicrobial properties.

The cover sets the theme for the book: chemistry is not an abstract study, but one that has an immediate impact on our lives. We try to spark student interest with an art program that uses relevant photography, clear and focused figures, animations that are available on our website and in the e-book, and perspectives and essays that bring life to abstract ideas. We reinforce key concepts by explaining them in a clear and concise way and encouraging students to apply the concept to solve problems. We provide guidance through the inclusion of a large number of in-chapter examples that are solved in a stepwise fashion and that provide students the opportunity to test their understanding through the practice problems that follow and the suggested end-of-chapter questions and problems that apply the same concepts.

New in This Edition

In the preparation of the eighth edition, we have been guided by the collective wisdom of reviewers who are expert chemists and excellent teachers. They represent experience in community colleges, liberal arts colleges, comprehensive institutions, and research universities. We have followed their recommendations, while remaining true to our overriding goal of writing a readable, student-centered text. The following is a summary of the additions and refinements that we have included in this edition.

Chapter maps are included just before the end-of-chapter summaries to provide students with an overview of the chapter—showing connections among topics, how concepts are related, and outlining the chapter hierarchy.

End-of-chapter summaries have been changed to a bulleted list format of chapter concepts by section, with the boldfaced key terms appearing in context. This more succinct format helps students to quickly identify and review important chapter concepts and to make connections with the incorporated key terms.

Eight new Kitchen Chemistry and two new Green Chemistry applications, and six new Perspectives have been added to the eighth edition to help students see the connections between chemistry and their daily lives and future careers.

Answers to Practice Problems are now supplied at the end of each chapter so that students can quickly check their understanding of important problem-solving skills and chapter concepts.

- **Chapter 1** The chapter includes a new subsection called Problem Solving Strategies, and was also reorganized to provide a discussion of units prior to the discussion of numbers. Section 1.3 was revised to incorporate information about the English versus the metric system and unit prefixes. The material on significant figures was revised to expand and clarify the discussions of making measurements to the correct number of significant figures, of zeros and significant figures, and of scientific notation and adding numbers in scientific notation. Thirty-seven new end-of-chapter problems were added to correlate to the new and revised material within the text.
- **Chapter 2** A new subsection and example on writing shorthand electron configurations were added. Also, based on reviewer feedback, the explanations of ions and ion formation, how to use mass number or atomic number to determine the number of neutrons, how to determine the average atomic mass, and of light and the Bohr model were revised to clarify these discussions. Thirty new end-of-chapter problems were added to correlate to the new and revised material within the text.
- **Chapter 3** New worked examples were added throughout the chapter, including Example 3.3 on how to name ionic compounds using the Stock system and Example 3.16 on exceptions to the octet rule (involving electron pairs on the central atom). The text was revised to expand and clarify the discussion of how to handle molecules with more than one central atom, and a new Example 3.10, Drawing Lewis Structures for Compounds with Multiple Central Atoms was added. Additionally, based on reviewer feedback, the symbol used for electronegativity was changed. Twenty new end-of-chapter problems were added to correlate to the new and revised material within the text.
- **Chapter 4** Several of the chapter examples were modified, with color-coding added, and otherwise enhanced for clarity. A new illustration of the conversion between numbers of moles, particles, and grams was added, and other illustrations were revised and improved.
- **Chapter 5** *A Human Perspective: Gemstones* was added, and *Green Chemistry: The Greenhouse Effect and Global Climate Change* was revised to make the article more current. Six new end-of-chapter problems were added and others revised to correlate to the new and revised material within the text.
- **Chapter 6** Several of the chapter examples were modified, with reworked solutions, and otherwise enhanced for clarity. A new Example 6.11, Calculating Freezing and Boiling Points of Aqueous Solutions of Ionic, Dissociating Solutes and a new *Kitchen Chemistry: Solubility, Surfactants, and the Dishwasher* were also added. Four new in-text and six new end-of-chapter questions and problems were added, and others revised to correlate to the new and revised material within the text.
- **Chapter 7** Based on reviewer feedback, *A Human Perspective: An Extraordinary Molecule* was revised and moved to Chapter 7 from Chapter 6 in the previous edition. Several of the chapter examples were modified and otherwise enhanced for clarity. *Green Chemistry: Twenty-First Century Energy* was revised and made more objective. Seven new end-of-chapter questions and problems were added, and others revised to correlate to the new and revised material within the text.
- **Chapter 8** Based on reviewer feedback, *A Medical Perspective: Control of Blood pH* was made part of the main text in Section 8.4. A new essay *Green Chemistry: Hydrangeas, pH, and Soil Chemistry* was also added. Several of the chapter examples were modified and otherwise enhanced for clarity. Six new in-text and six new end-of-chapter questions and problems were added, and others revised to correlate to the new and revised material within the text.
- **Chapter 9** Two new worked examples, Example 9.2, Predicting the Product of Beta Decay and Example 9.3, Predicting the Product of Positron Emission, and two new practice problems were added to the chapter. Four new in-text and two new end-of-chapter questions and problems were added, and others revised to correlate to the new and revised material within the text.
- **Chapter 10** A new *Green Chemistry: Biofuels: A Renewable Resource*, including two For Further Understanding questions, has been added to the revised Chapter 10. More explicit definitions of aliphatic hydrocarbons, alkenes, and alkynes were also added to the text. The subsections

Families of Organic Compounds Structure, Alkyl Groups, *cis-trans* Isomerism in Cycloalkanes, and Cycloalkanes were revised and expanded for clarity. A new subsection Physical Properties adds deeper understanding of properties and the relationship to structure, and includes a discussion of London dispersion forces, which has been woven into all of the organic chapters where appropriate. Several of the chapter examples were modified, with structures added and revised, to further clarify the relationship between structural and condensed formulas. Line formulas were also added throughout to help students understand relationships between line and condensed formulas, and cycloalkane structures were improved to help students visualize three-dimensional structures. Table 10.2 was revised to include a column for names of functional groups, and Table 10.6 was modified with color coding: highlighting the carbon of the alkyl group that bonds to the parent chain to assist students in identifying classification of 1°, 2°, and 3°. Five new questions and problems were added, and nineteen revised to correspond to revisions within the chapter.

- **Chapter 11** Chapter 11 includes a new *Kitchen Chemistry: Amazing Chocolate* and an increased emphasis on line formulas throughout the chapter text.
- **Chapter 12** A new *A Medical Perspective: Resveratrol: Fountain of Youth?* and a new *Kitchen Chemistry: Spicy Phenols* were added. The chapter was reorganized to include alcohol classification within the section on structure. Color-coding was added to the general equations and to the examples of reactions of alcohols to help students visualize the changes occurring in the reactions. An explanation of oxidation and reduction in biochemical/organic reactions was also added to Section 12.5.
- **Chapter 13** Condensed structures were added to the introduction and line formulas to the text to help students better understand the relationships between line and condensed formulas. A new *Kitchen Chemistry: The Allure of Truffles* was added. Numerous figures were revised and color-coding added to help clarify the concepts portrayed. In addition, many areas of the text were revised to improve the clarity of explanations, based on reviewer feedback: added detail to explain polarity of carbonyl groups; improved explanations of oxidation/reduction in organic systems; revised Addition Reactions to update content; and added text art to clarify intramolecular hemiacetal formation. Two new end-of-chapter problems were added and sixteen revised to correlate to the new and revised material within the text.
- **Chapter 14** Line formulas were added where appropriate to help students see relationships with condensed formulas. A new *A Human Perspective: Detergents* and a table of common dicarboxylic acids were also added. In addition, the subsections Nomenclature and Some Important Carboxylic Acids were revised based on reviewer feedback to add detail and further clarity. Section 14.2 was reorganized to clarify the use of nomenclature, and the coverage of acid chlorides in Section 14.3 was reduced to remove unnecessary material.
- **Chapter 15** A new *Kitchen Chemistry: Browning Reactions and Flavor: The Maillard Reaction* was added. Line formulas were added where appropriate to help students see the relationship with condensed formulas. Many end-of-chapter problems were also revised to use condensed rather than expanded structures.
- **Chapter 16** Chapter 16 includes a new *Kitchen Chemistry: The Chemistry of Caramels* and updated material on intramolecular hemiacetal formation in fructose. Sections 16.2 and 16.3 were also rewritten for clarity and improved comprehension.
- **Chapter 17** Sections 17.2 and 17.3 were reorganized to place Chemical Reactions of Fatty Acids and Glycerides into Section 17.3 for greater clarity. Line formulas were added in Section 17.2 to help students understand the relationship with condensed formulas. Also Examples 17.4 and 17.5 were replaced with clearer examples of the relationship of the reaction (hydrolysis of esters) to monoglycerides. Table 17.1 was revised to add molar mass, and color-coding was added to chemical equations throughout the chapter to better portray chemical changes.
- **Chapter 18** A new *Kitchen Chemistry: Egg Foams: Meringues and Soufflés* was added as well as a new section Proteins in the Blood. Also the sections on stereoisomers, pH, and mechanical stress were revised for greater clarity. One letter codes for the amino acids were added to Table 18.1.
- **Chapter 19** A new *Kitchen Chemistry: Transglutaminase: aka Meat Glue* was added. Also Section 19.12 Uses of Enzymes in Medicine was enhanced to bring greater depth to this topic, which is extremely relevant to health professionals.
- **Chapter 20** New subsections and illustrations of Chemical Composition of DNA and RNA and Nucleosides were added. New material on nucleotide nomenclature was also added.
- **Chapter 21** Chapter 21 includes a new *A Medical Perspective: High Fructose Corn Syrup.* New subsections Biological Effects of Genetic Disorders of Glycolysis and Entry of Fructose into Glycolysis were also added. Section 21.5 The Pentose Phosphate Pathway was revised to focus on key products used in biosynthesis. Four new end-of-chapter problems were added and others revised to correlate to the new and revised material within the text.
- **Chapter 22** A new subsection Biological Effects of Disorders of the Citric Acid Cycle was added to bring medical relevance to the reactions within the chapter. New transition text introduces Summary of the Energy Yield. Five new end-of-chapter problems were added and others revised to correlate to the new and revised material within the text.
- **Chapter 23** A new *A Medical Perspective: Carnitine: The Fat Mover* was added to the revised Chapter 23. Also a new Figure 23.7 illustrates acylation of carnitine and the transport of fatty acids from the cytoplasm into the mitochondria.

Applications

Each chapter contains applications that present short stories about real-world situations involving one or more topics students will encounter within the chapter. There are over 100 applications throughout the text, so students are sure to find many topics that spark their interest. Global climate change, fingerprinting, the benefits of garlic, and gemstones are just a few examples of application topics.

- **Medical Perspectives** relate chemistry to a health concern or a diagnostic application.
- **Green Chemistry** explores environmental topics, including the impact of chemistry on the ecosystem and how these environmental changes affect human health.
- **Human Perspectives** delve into chemistry and society and include such topics as gender issues in science and historical viewpoints.
- **Chemistry at the Crime Scene** focuses on forensic chemistry, applying the principles of chemistry to help solve crimes.
- **Kitchen Chemistry** discusses the chemistry associated with everyday foods and cooking methods.

CHEMISTRY AT THE CRIME SCENE

Adipocere and Mummies of Soap

One November evening in 1911, widower Patrick Higgins stepped into his local pub in Abercorn, Scotland. To the surprise of his drinking companions, he did not have his two young boys with him. Neighbors knew that the boys had been a great burden on Patrick since the death of his wife; so they believed Patrick's story that he left William, age 6, and John, age 4, with two women in Edinburgh who had offered to adopt the boys.

More than 18 months had passed when an object was seen floating in the Hopetoun Quarry, an unused, flooded quarry near town. When the object was fished out, it was obvious that it was the body of a young boy; the rescuers were stunned to find another small body tied to the first by a rope. How were these bodies preserved after such a long time and why did they float? The answer is that their bodies had almost completely turned into adipocere, or more simply, soap.

Forensic scientists are trying to understand the nature of the reaction that creates *adipocere,* the technical term for the yellowish-white, greasy, waxlike substance that results from the saponification of fatty tissue. Some researchers hope that this information may allow determination of the postmortem interval (length of time since death). Others simply value the process because it helps preserve the body so well that even after long periods, it can be easily recognized and any wounds or injuries can be observed.

It is known that adipocere is produced when body fat is hydrolyzed (water is needed) to release fatty acids. Because the fatty acids lower the pH in the tissues, they inhibit many of the bacteria that would begin the process of decay. Certain other bacteria, particularly *Clostridium welchii,* an organism that cannot grow in the presence of oxygen, is known to speed up the formation of adipocere in moist, warm, anaerobic (oxygenless) environments. Adipocere forms first in subcutaneous tissues, including the cheeks, breasts, and buttocks. Given appropriate warmth and damp conditions, it may be seen as early as 3 to 4 weeks after death; but more commonly it is not observed until 5 to 6 months after death.

Adipocere formation in John and William Higgins was so extensive that their former neighbors had no trouble recognizing them. At the postmortem, another advantage of adipocere formation became obvious—it had preserved the stomach contents of the boys! From this, the coroner learned that the boys

had eaten Scotch broth about an hour before they died. Investigators were able to find the woman who had given the broth to the boys and, from her testimony, learned that she had fed them on the last day they were seen in the village. Clearly their father had lied about the adoption by two Edinburgh women! In under one and one-half hours, a jury convicted the father of murdering his sons and he was hanged in October 1913.

For Further Understanding

- Adipocere is the technical term for "soap mummification." It comes from the Latin words *adipis* or fat, as in adipose tissue, and *cera,* which means wax. Draw a triglyceride composed of the fatty acids myristic acid, stearic acid, and oleic acid. Write a balanced equation showing a possible reaction that would lead to the formation of adipocere.
- Forensic scientists are studying adipocere formation as a possible source of information to determine postmortem interval (length of time since death) of bodies of murder or accident victims. Among the factors being studied are the type of soil, including pH, moisture, temperature, and presence or absence of lime. How might each of these factors influence the rate of adipocere formation and hence the determination of the postmortem interval?

Learning Tools

In designing the original learning system we asked ourselves: "If we were students, what would help us organize and understand the material covered in this chapter?" Based on the feedback of reviewers and users of our text, we include a variety of learning tools:

- **Chapter Overview** pages begin each chapter, listing learning goals and the chapter outline. Both students and professor can see, all in one place, the plan for the chapter.
- **Learning Goal Icons** mark the sections and examples in the chapter that focus on each learning goal.
- **Chapter Cross-References** help students locate pertinent background material. These references to previous chapters, sections, and perspectives are noted in the margins of the text. Marginal cross references also alert students to upcoming topics related to the information currently being studied.
- **End-of-Chapter Questions and Problems** are arranged according to the headings in the chapter outline, with further subdivision into Foundations (basic concepts) and Applications.
- **New Chapter Maps** are included just before the End-of-Chapter Summaries to provide students with an overview of the

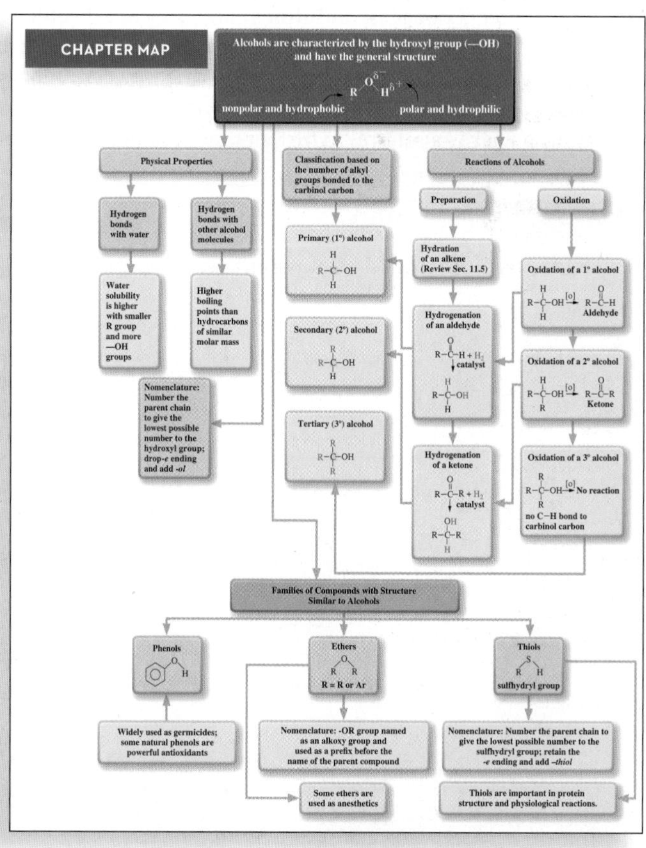

Question 7.7 Using the conversion factor in Chapter 1, convert the energy released in Example 7.3 to joules (J).

Question 7.8 Using the conversion factor in Chapter 1, convert the energy absorbed in Example 7.4 to J.

Many chemical reactions that produce heat are combustion reactions. In our bodies many food substances (carbohydrates, proteins, and fats; Chapters 21 and 22) are oxidized to release energy. **Fuel value** is the amount of energy per g of food.

Note: Refer to A Human Perspective: Food Calories, Section 1.6.

The fuel value of food is an important concept in nutrition science. The fuel value is generally reported in units of *nutritional Calories.* One **nutritional Calorie (Cal)** is equivalent to one kilocalorie (1000 cal). It is also known as the *large Calorie* (uppercase C).

LEARNING GOAL

3 Describe experiments that yield thermochemical information and calculate fuel values based on experimental data.

Energy necessary for our daily activity and bodily function comes largely from the reaction of oxygen with carbohydrates. Chemical energy from foods that is not used to maintain normal body temperature or in muscular activity is stored in the bonds of chemical compounds known collectively as fat. Thus consumption of "high-calorie" foods is implicated in the problem of obesity.

A special type of calorimeter, a *bomb calorimeter,* is useful for the measurement of the fuel value (Cal) of foods. Such a device is illustrated in Figure 7.6. Its design is similar, in principle, to that of the "coffee cup" calorimeter discussed earlier.

chapter—showing connections among topics, how concepts are related, and outlining the chapter hierarchy.

- **Chapter Summaries** are now a bulleted list format of chapter concepts by major sections, with the integrated bold-faced **Key Terms** appearing in context. This more succinct format helps students to quickly identify and review important chapter concepts and to make connections with the incorporated Key Terms. Each Key Term is defined and listed alphabetically in the **Glossary Terms** at the end of the book.
- **New Answers to Practice Problems** are supplied at the end of each chapter so that students can quickly check their understanding of important problem solving skills and chapter concepts.
- **Summary of Reactions** in the organic chemistry chapters highlight each major reaction type on a tan background. Major chemical reactions are summarized by equations at the end of the chapter, facilitating review.

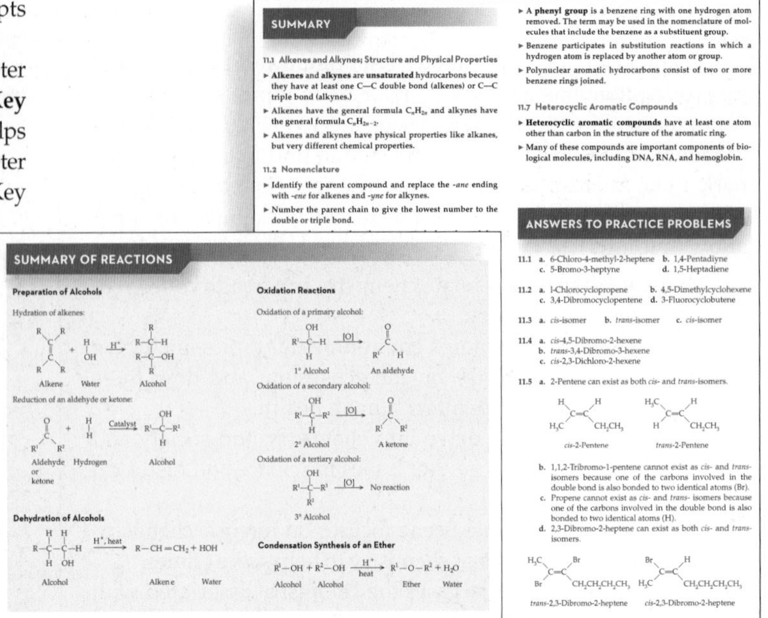
SUMMARY

11.1 Alkenes and Alkynes; Structure and Physical Properties

- **Alkenes** and **alkynes** are **unsaturated** hydrocarbons because they have at least one C—C double bond (alkenes) or C—C triple bond (alkynes.)
- Alkenes have the general formula C_nH_{2n} and alkynes have the general formula C_nH_{2n-2}.
- Alkenes and alkynes have physical properties like alkanes, but very different chemical properties.

11.2 Nomenclature

- Identify the parent compound and replace the *-ane* ending with *-ene* for alkenes and *-yne* for alkynes.
- Number the parent chain to give the lowest number to the double or triple bond.

- A **phenyl group** is a benzene ring with one hydrogen atom removed. The term may be used in the nomenclature of molecules that include the benzene as a substituent group.
- Benzene participates in substitution reactions in which a hydrogen atom is replaced by another atom or group.
- Polynuclear aromatic hydrocarbons consist of two or more benzene rings joined.

11.7 Heterocyclic Aromatic Compounds

- **Heterocyclic aromatic compounds** have at least one atom other than carbon in the structure of the aromatic ring.
- Many of these compounds are important components of biological molecules, including DNA, RNA, and hemoglobin.

SUMMARY OF REACTIONS

Preparation of Alcohols

Hydration of alkenes:

Alkene + Water $\xrightarrow{H^+}$ Alcohol

Reduction of an aldehyde or ketone:

Aldehyde or ketone + Hydrogen $\xrightarrow{Catalyst}$ Alcohol

Dehydration of Alcohols

Alcohol $\xrightarrow{H^+, heat}$ $R-CH=CH_2 + HOH$ (Alkene, Water)

Oxidation Reactions

Oxidation of a primary alcohol: 1° Alcohol $\xrightarrow{[O]}$ An aldehyde

Oxidation of a secondary alcohol: 2° Alcohol $\xrightarrow{[O]}$ A ketone

Oxidation of a tertiary alcohol: 3° Alcohol $\xrightarrow{[O]}$ No reaction

Condensation Synthesis of an Ether

$R^1-OH + R^2-OH \xrightarrow[heat]{H^+} R^1-O-R^2 + H_2O$ (Alcohol, Alcohol, Ether, Water)

ANSWERS TO PRACTICE PROBLEMS

11.1 a. 6-Chloro-4-methyl-2-heptene b. 1,4-Pentadiyne c. 5-Bromo-3-heptyne d. 1,5-Heptadiene

11.2 a. 1-Chlorocyclopropene b. 4,5-Dimethylcyclohexene c. 3,4-Dibromocyclopentene d. 3-Fluorocyclobutene

11.3 a. *cis*-isomer b. *trans*-isomer c. *cis*-isomer

11.4 a. *cis*-4,5-Dibromo-2-hexene b. *trans*-3,4-Dibromo-3-hexene c. *cis*-2,3-Dichloro-2-hexene

11.5 a. 2-Pentene can exist as both *cis*- and *trans*-isomers.

cis-2-Pentene *trans*-2-Pentene

b. 1,1,2-Tribromo-1-pentene cannot exist as *cis*- and *trans*-isomers because one of the carbons involved in the double bond is also bonded to two identical atoms (Br).
c. Propene cannot exist as *cis*- and *trans*- isomers because one of the carbons involved in the double bond is also bonded to two identical atoms (H).
d. 2,3-Dibromo-2-heptene can exist as both *cis*- and *trans*-isomers.

trans-2,3-Dibromo-2-heptene *cis*-2,3-Dibromo-2-heptene

Problem Solving and Critical Thinking

Perhaps the best preparation for a successful and productive career is the development of problem-solving and critical thinking skills. To this end, we created a variety of problems that require recall, fundamental calculations, and complex reasoning. In this edition we have used suggestions from our reviewers, as well as from our own experience, to enhance our 2300 problems. This edition includes new problems and hundreds of example problems with step-by-step solutions.

- **In-Chapter Examples, Solutions, and Practice Problems:** Each chapter includes examples that show the student, step-by-step, how to properly reach the correct solution to model problems. Each example contains a practice problem, as well as a referral to further practice questions. These questions allow students to test their mastery of information and to build self-confidence. The answers to the practice problems can be found at the end of each chapter so students can check their understanding.
- **In-Chapter and End-of-Chapter Questions and Problems:** We have created a wide variety of paired concept problems. The answers to the odd-numbered questions are found in the back of the book as reinforcement for students as they develop problem-solving skills. However, students must then be able to apply the same principles to the related even-numbered problems.
- **Critical Thinking Problems:** Each chapter includes a set of critical thinking problems. These problems are intended to challenge students to integrate concepts to solve more complex problems. They make a perfect complement to the classroom lecture because they provide an opportunity for in-class discussion of complex problems dealing with daily life and the health care sciences.

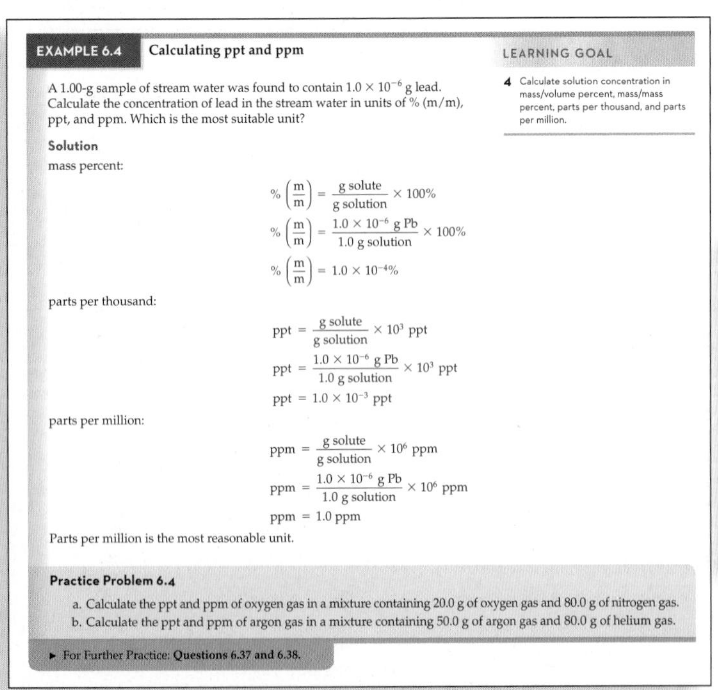
EXAMPLE 6.4 Calculating ppt and ppm

LEARNING GOAL

4 Calculate solution concentration in mass/volume percent, mass/mass percent, parts per thousand, and parts per million.

A 1.00-g sample of stream water was found to contain 1.0×10^{-6} g lead. Calculate the concentration of lead in the stream water in units of % (m/m), ppt, and ppm. Which is the most suitable unit?

Solution

mass percent:

$$\%\left(\frac{m}{m}\right) = \frac{\text{g solute}}{\text{g solution}} \times 100\%$$

$$\%\left(\frac{m}{m}\right) = \frac{1.0 \times 10^{-6}\ \text{g Pb}}{1.0\ \text{g solution}} \times 100\%$$

$$\%\left(\frac{m}{m}\right) = 1.0 \times 10^{-4}\%$$

parts per thousand:

$$\text{ppt} = \frac{\text{g solute}}{\text{g solution}} \times 10^3\ \text{ppt}$$

$$\text{ppt} = \frac{1.0 \times 10^{-6}\ \text{g Pb}}{1.0\ \text{g solution}} \times 10^3\ \text{ppt}$$

$$\text{ppt} = 1.0 \times 10^{-3}\ \text{ppt}$$

parts per million:

$$\text{ppm} = \frac{\text{g solute}}{\text{g solution}} \times 10^6\ \text{ppm}$$

$$\text{ppm} = \frac{1.0 \times 10^{-6}\ \text{g Pb}}{1.0\ \text{g solution}} \times 10^6\ \text{ppm}$$

$$\text{ppm} = 1.0\ \text{ppm}$$

Parts per million is the most reasonable unit.

Practice Problem 6.4

a. Calculate the ppt and ppm of oxygen gas in a mixture containing 20.0 g of oxygen gas and 80.0 g of nitrogen gas.
b. Calculate the ppt and ppm of argon gas in a mixture containing 50.0 g of argon gas and 80.0 g of helium gas.

► For Further Practice: **Questions 6.37 and 6.38.**

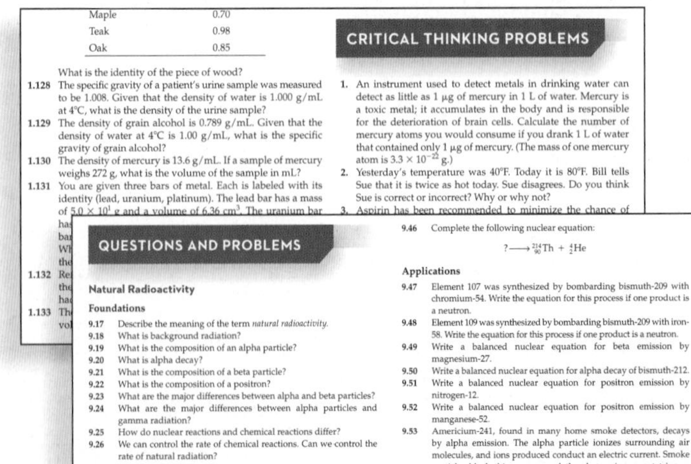

Maple	0.70
Teak	0.98
Oak	0.85

What is the identity of the piece of wood?

1.128 The specific gravity of a patient's urine sample was measured to be 1.008. Given that the density of water is 1.000 g/mL at 4°C, what is the density of the urine sample?

1.129 The density of grain alcohol is 0.789 g/mL. Given that the density of water at 4°C is 1.00 g/mL, what is the specific gravity of grain alcohol?

1.130 The density of mercury is 13.6 g/mL. If a sample of mercury weighs 272 g, what is the volume of the sample in mL?

1.131 You are given three bars of metal. Each is labeled with its identity (lead, uranium, platinum). The lead bar has a mass of 5.0×10^1 g and a volume of 6.36 cm^3. The uranium bar

CRITICAL THINKING PROBLEMS

1. An instrument used to detect metals in drinking water can detect as little as 1 μg of mercury in 1 L of water. Mercury is a toxic metal; it accumulates in the body and is responsible for the deterioration of brain cells. Calculate the number of mercury atoms you would consume if you drank 1 L of water that contained only 1 μg of mercury. (The mass of one mercury atom is 3.3×10^{-22} g.)
2. Yesterday's temperature was 40°F. Today it is 80°F. Bill tells Sue that it is twice as hot today. Sue disagrees. Do you think Sue is correct or incorrect? Why or why not?
3. Aspirin has been recommended to minimize the chance of

QUESTIONS AND PROBLEMS

Natural Radioactivity

Foundations

9.17 Describe the meaning of the term *natural radioactivity*.
9.18 What is background radiation?
9.19 What is the composition of an alpha particle?
9.20 What is alpha decay?
9.21 What is the composition of a beta particle?
9.22 What is the composition of a positron?
9.23 What are the major differences between alpha and beta particles?
9.24 What are the major differences between alpha particles and gamma radiation?
9.25 How do nuclear reactions and chemical reactions differ?
9.26 We can control the rate of chemical reactions. Can we control the rate of natural radiation?

9.46 Complete the following nuclear equation:

$$? \longrightarrow {}^{214}_{90}\text{Th} + {}^{4}_{2}\text{He}$$

Applications

9.47 Element 107 was synthesized by bombarding bismuth-209 with chromium-54. Write the equation for this process if one product is a neutron.
9.48 Element 109 was synthesized by bombarding bismuth-209 with iron-58. Write the equation for this process if one product is a neutron.
9.49 Write a balanced nuclear equation for beta emission by magnesium-27.
9.50 Write a balanced nuclear equation for alpha decay of bismuth-212.
9.51 Write a balanced nuclear equation for positron emission by nitrogen-12.
9.52 Write a balanced nuclear equation for positron emission by manganese-52.
9.53 Americium-241, found in many home smoke detectors, decays by alpha emission. The alpha particle ionizes surrounding air molecules, and ions produced conduct an electric current. Smoke

Over the course of the last seven editions, hundreds of reviewers have shared their knowledge and wisdom with us, as well as the reactions of their students to elements of this book. Their contributions, as well as our own continuing experience in the area of teaching and learning science, have resulted in a text that we are confident will provide a strong foundation in chemistry, while enhancing the learning experience of students.

The Art Program

Today's students are much more visually oriented than previous generations. We have built upon this observation through the use of color, figures, and three-dimensional computer-generated models. This art program enhances the readability of the text and provides alternative pathways to learning.

- **Dynamic Illustrations:** Each chapter is amply illustrated using figures, tables, and chemical formulas. All of these illustrations are carefully annotated for clarity. To help students better understand difficult concepts, there are approximately 350 illustrations and 250 photos in the eighth edition.

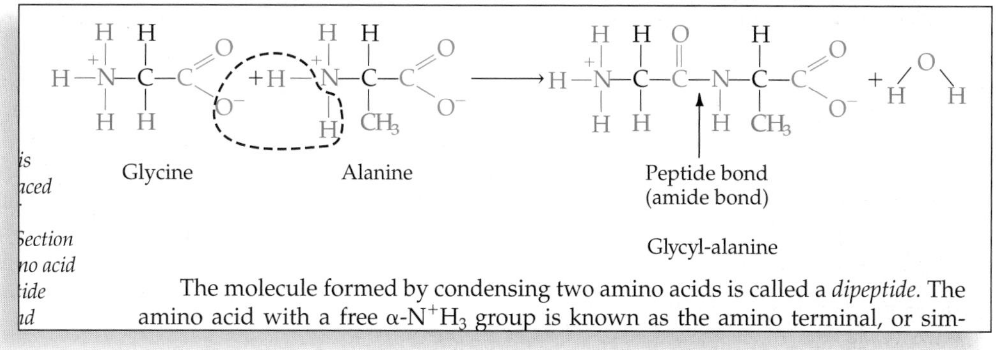

- **Color-Coding Scheme:** We have color-coded equations so that chemical groups being added or removed in a reaction can be quickly recognized. 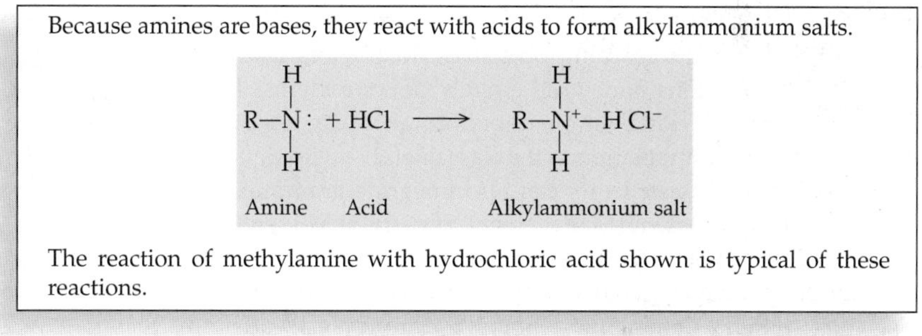
  1. **Red print** is used in chemical equations or formulas to draw the reader's eye to key elements or properties in a reaction or structure.
  2. **Blue print** is used when additional features must be highlighted.
  3. **Green background** screens denote generalized chemical and mathematical equations. In the organic chemistry chapters, the Summary of Reactions at the end of the chapter is also highlighted for ease of recognition.
  4. Yellow backgrounds illustrate energy, stored either in electrons or groups of atoms, in the general and biochemistry sections of the text. In the organic chemistry section of the text, yellow background screens also reveal the parent chain of an organic compound. 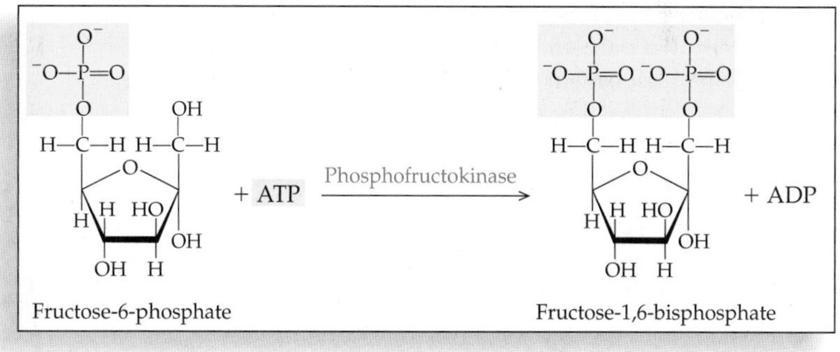
  5. There are situations in which it is necessary to adopt a unique color convention tailored to the material in a particular chapter. For example, in Chapter 18, the structures of amino acids require three colors to draw attention to key features of these molecules. For consistency, blue is used to denote the acid portion of an amino acid and red is used to denote the basic portion of an amino acid. Green print is used to denote the R groups, and a yellow background screen directs the eye to the α-carbon.

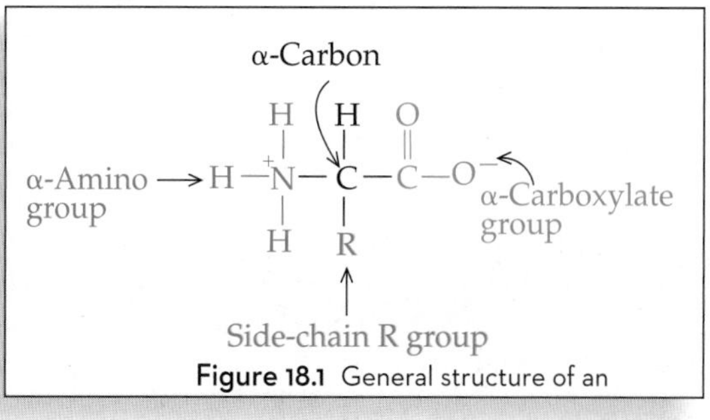

- **Computer-Generated Models:** The ability of students to understand the geometry and three-dimensional structure of molecules is essential to the understanding of organic and biochemical reactions. Computer-generated models are used throughout the text because they are both accurate and easily visualized.

Learning Resources

This text is supported by a complete package for instructors and students. Several print and media ancillaries have been prepared to accompany the text and make learning as meaningful and up-to-date as possible.

For the Instructor and Student:

- **McGraw-Hill Connect Chemistry**

McGraw-Hill Connect® Chemistry is a web-based assignment and assessment platform that gives students the means to better connect with their coursework, with their instructors, and with the important concepts that they need to know for success now and in the future.

With Connect Chemistry, instructors can deliver assignments, quizzes, and tests online. Nearly all the questions from the text are presented in an auto-gradable format and tied to the text's learning objectives. Instructors can edit existing questions and write entirely new problems. They can track individual student performance—by question, assignment, or in relation to the class overall—with detailed grade reports. Instructors can also integrate grade reports easily with Learning Management Systems (LMS) such as WebCT and Blackboard, and much more.

By choosing Connect Chemistry, instructors provide their students with a powerful tool for improving academic performance and truly mastering course material. Connect Chemistry allows students to practice important skills at their own pace and on their own schedule. Importantly, students' assessment results and instructors' feedback are all saved online—so students can continually review their progress and plot their course to success.

- **McGraw-Hill ConnectPlus® Chemistry**
  Like Connect Chemistry, ConnectPlus Chemistry provides students with online assignments and assessments, plus 24/7 online access to an eBook—an online edition of the text—to aid them in successfully completing their work, wherever and whenever they choose.
- **McGraw-Hill LearnSmart™**
  McGraw-Hill LearnSmart is available as a stand-alone product as well as an integrated feature of McGraw-Hill Connect Chemistry. It is an adaptive learning system designed to help students learn faster, study more efficiently, and retain more knowledge for greater success. LearnSmart assesses a student's knowledge of course content through a series of probes, pinpointing concepts the student does not understand. This innovative study tool also has features that allow instructors to see exactly what students have accomplished and a built-in assessment tool for graded assignments. Visit the following site for a demonstration. www.mhlearnsmart.com

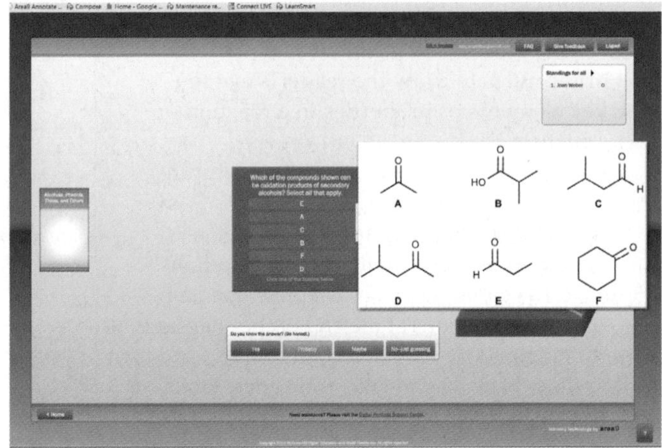

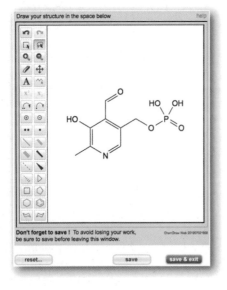

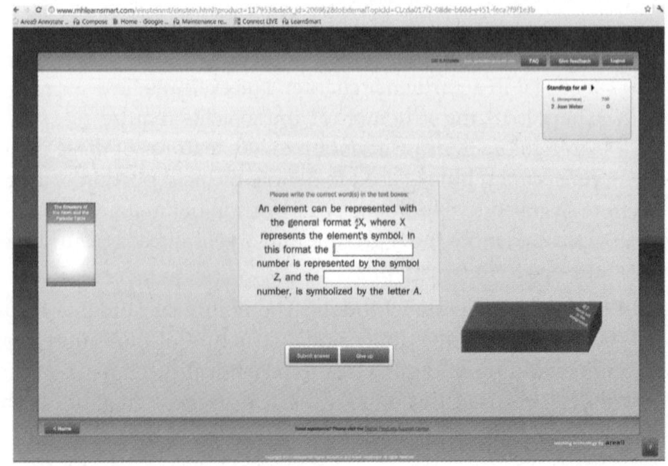

For the Instructor

- **Instructor's Manual:** Written by the authors and developed for the eighth edition by Cheryl Vaughn and Danae Quirk Dorr, this ancillary contains suggestions for organizing lectures, instructional objectives, perspectives on readings from the text, answers to the even-numbered problems from the text, a list of each chapter's key problems and concepts, and more. The Instructor's Manual is available through the Connect website for this text.
- **Test Bank:** The electronic test bank offers questions that can be used for homework assignments or the preparation of exams. The test bank can be utilized to quickly create customized exams. It allows instructors to sort questions by format or level of difficulty, edit existing questions or add new ones, and scramble questions and answer keys for multiple versions of the same test.
- **Laboratory Manual for General, Organic, and Biochemistry:** The seventh edition, by Charles H. Henrickson, Larry C. Byrd, and Norman W. Hunter of Western Kentucky University, offers clear and concise laboratory experiments to reinforce students' understanding of concepts. Pre-laboratory exercises, questions, and report sheets are coordinated with each experiment to ensure active student involvement and comprehension. An updated student tutorial on graphing with Excel has been added to this edition.
- **Laboratory Instructor's Manual:** Written by Charles H. Henrickson, Larry C. Byrd, and Norman W. Hunter of Western Kentucky University, this helpful guide contains hints that the authors have learned over the years to ensure students' success in the laboratory. This Resource Guide is available through the Connect Chemistry website for this text.
- **McGraw-Hill Presentation Center:** Build instructional material wherever, whenever, and however you want! McGraw-Hill Presentation Center is an online digital library containing assets such as photos, artwork, and other media that can be used to create customized lectures, visually enhanced tests and quizzes, compelling course websites, or attractive printed support materials. The McGraw-Hill Presentation Center Library includes thousands of assets from many McGraw-Hill titles. This ever-growing resource gives instructors the power to use assets specific to an adopted textbook as well as content from all other books in the library. The Presentation Center can be accessed from the instructor side of your textbook's Connect website, and the Presentation Center's dynamic search engine allows you to explore by discipline, course, textbook chapter, asset type, or key word. Simply browse, select, and download the files you need to build engaging course materials. All assets are copyrighted by McGraw-Hill Higher Education but can be used by instructors for classroom purposes.
- **More than 300 animations available through the Connect website:** Many animations are linked to appropriate sections of the textbook using the ▸. They supplement the textbook material in much the same way as instructor demonstrations. However, for students, they are only a few mouse-clicks away, any time, day or night. Because many students are visual learners and quite computer-literate, the animations add another dimension of learning; they bring a greater degree of reality to the written word.

Customizable Textbooks: Create™

Create what you've only imagined. Introducing **McGraw-Hill Create**—new, self-service website that allows you to create custom course materials—print and eBooks—by drawing upon McGraw-Hill's comprehensive, cross-disciplinary content. Add your own content quickly and easily. Tap into other rights-secured third party sources as well. Then, arrange the content in a way that makes the most sense for your course, and if you wish, personalize your book with your course name and information. Choose the best delivery format for your course: color print, black and white print, or eBook. The eBook is now viewable for the iPad! And when you are finished customizing, you will receive a free PDF review copy in just minutes! Visit McGraw-Hill Create-www.mcgrawhillcreate.com-today and begin building your perfect book.

Digital Lecture Capture: Tegrity®

McGraw-Hill Tegrity records and distributes your lecture with just a click of a button. Students can view anytime/anywhere via computer, iPod, or mobile device. Tegrity indexes as it records your slideshow presentations and anything shown on your computer, so students can use keywords to find exactly what they want to study.

For the Student

- **Student Study Guide/Solutions Manual:** A separate Student Study Guide/Solutions Manual, prepared by Cheryl Vaughn and Danae Quirk Dorr, is available. It contains the answers and complete solutions for the odd-numbered problems. It also offers students a variety of exercises and keys for testing their comprehension of basic, as well as difficult, concepts.
- **Schaum's Outline of General, Organic, and Biological Chemistry:** Written by George Odian and Ira Blei, this supplement provides students with more than 1400 solved problems with complete solutions. It also teaches effective problem-solving techniques.

Acknowledgments

We are thankful to our families, whose patience and support made it possible for us to undertake this project. We are also grateful to our many colleagues at McGraw-Hill for their support, guidance, and assistance. In particular, we would like to thank Sandy Wille, Content Project Manager, Mary Hurley, Developmental Editor, Todd Turner, Brand Manager, and Heather Wagner, Marketing Manager. **Connect Chemistry** has been greatly enhanced by the efforts of Danaé Quirk Dorr of Minnesota State University, Mankato, who worked to improve the content, author feedback and hints, and select problems for the eighth edition site, and Shirley Hino of Santa Rosa Junior College, who authored the interactive problem content, also authored feedback and hints, and performed accuracy checking of all Connect Chemistry content.

In addition, the following instructors also did a masterful job of authoring hints and feedback to augment all of the Connect Chemistry homework problems: Eric Elisabeth of Johnson County Community College; Patrick Greco of Sinclair Community College; Paul Root of Henry Ford Community College; Emily Tansey of Otterbein College; John Tansey of Otterbein College; and Dave Tramontozzi of Macomb Community College. The following instructors performed accuracy checks of the Connect Chemistry content to ensure the reliability and correctness: Jennifer Adamski (formally of Old Dominion University); Eric Elisabeth of Johnson County Community College; and Annise Goodman of Eastern Michigan University.

The following individuals helped write and review learning goal-oriented content for **LearnSmart for General, Organic, & Biochemistry:** Susan Bane, Binghamton University; Claire Cohen, University of Toledo; Peter de Lijser, California State University, Fullerton; Anne M. Distler, Cuyahoga Community College; Cynthia Jolly Harwood, Purdue University; David G. Jones, North Carolina Central University; Adam I. Keller, Columbus State Community College; Julia M. Keller, Florida State College at Jacksonville; Jason C. Myers, University of Minnesota; Paul D. Root, Henry Ford Community College; Kathleen Thrush Shaginaw, Particular Solutions, Inc. and the Community College of Philadelphia; and Erin Whitteck.

We are also extremely grateful to the authors of the other ancillaries to accompany *General, Organic, & Biochemistry,* Eighth Edition: Danaé Quirk Dorr of Minnesota State University, Mankato for her authoring of the Instructors' and Students' Solutions Manuals; Cheryl Vaughn of Columbus State Community College for authoring the Student Study Guide and Instructor's Manual; Andrea Leonard of the University of Louisiana at Lafayette for her authoring of the PowerPoint Lecture Outlines; and Jennifer Adamski for her authoring of the Test Bank.

A revision cannot move forward without the feedback of professors teaching the course. The following reviewers have our gratitude and assurance that their comments received serious consideration. The following professors provided reviews, participated in focus groups, or otherwise provided valuable advice for the preparation of the eighth edition:

Augustine Agyeman, *Clayton State University*
Phyllis Arthasery, *Ohio University*
EJ Behrman, *The Ohio State University*
C. Bruce Bradley, *Spartanburg Community College*
Mary Hadley, *Minnesota State University, Mankato*
Thomas Gilbert, *Northern Illinois University*
Emily Halvorson, *Pima Community College*
James Hardy, *The University of Akron*
Amy Hanks, *Brigham Young University-Idaho*
Theresa Hill, *Rochester Community and Technical College*
Shirley Hino, *Santa Rosa Junior College*
Narayan Hosmane, *Northern Illinois University*
Colleen Kelley, *Pima Community College*
Myung-Hoon Kim, *Georgia Perimeter College*
Charlene Kozerow, *University of Maine*
Andrea Leonard, *University of Louisiana at Lafayette*
Lauren E. H. McMills, *Ohio University*
Jonathan McMurry, *Kennesaw State University*
Cynthia Molitor, *Lourdes College*
Matthew Morgan, *Georgia Perimeter College, Covington*
Melekeh Nasiri, *Woodland Community College*
Glenn Nomura, *Georgia Perimeter College*
Kenneth O'Connor, *Marshall University*
Dwight Patterson, *Middle Tennessee State University*
Allan Pinhas, *University of Cincinnati, Cincinnati*
Jerry Poteat, *Georgia Perimeter College*
Danaé R. Quirk Dorr, *Minnesota State University, Mankato*
Michael E. Rennekamp, *Columbus State Community College*
Raymond Sadeghi, *University of Texas at San Antonio*
Paul Sampson, *Kent State University*
Shirish Shah, *Towson University*
Buchang Shi, *Eastern Kentucky University*
Heather Sklenicka, *Rochester Community and Technical College*
Sara Tate, *Northeast Lakeview College*
Kimberley Taylor, *University of Arkansas at Little Rock*
Susan Tansey Thomas, *University of Texas at San Antonio*
Nathan Tice, *Eastern Kentucky University*
Steven Trail, *Elgin Community College*
David A. Tramontozzi, *Macomb Community College*
Pearl Tsang, *University of Cincinnati*
Michael Van Dyke, *Western Carolina University*
Wendy Weeks, *Pima Community College*
Gregg Wilmes, *Eastern Michigan University*
Yakov Woldman, *Valdosta State University*

THE SATURATED HYDROCARBONS

An Introduction to Organic Chemistry

The origins of fossil fuels.

OUTLINE

Introduction 327

10.1 The Chemistry of Carbon 327

Green Chemistry: Frozen Methane: Treasure or Threat? 330

10.2 Alkanes 331

Chemistry at the Crime Scene: Arson and Alkanes 338

Green Chemistry: Biofuels: A Renewable Resource 340

10.3 Cycloalkanes 345

10.4 Conformations of Alkanes and Cycloalkanes 348

Green Chemistry: The Petroleum Industry and Gasoline Production 350

10.5 Reactions of Alkanes and Cycloalkanes 351

A Medical Perspective: Polyhalogenated Hydrocarbons Used as Anesthetics 354

LEARNING GOALS

1. Compare and contrast organic and inorganic compounds.
2. Recognize structures that represent each of the families of organic compounds.
3. Write the names and draw the structures of the common functional groups that characterize the families of organic compounds.
4. Write condensed, structural, and line formulas for saturated hydrocarbons.
5. Describe the relationship between the structure and physical properties of saturated hydrocarbons.
6. Use the basic rules of the IUPAC nomenclature system to name alkanes and substituted alkanes.
7. From the IUPAC name of an alkane or substituted alkane, be able to draw the structure.
8. Draw constitutional (structural) isomers of simple organic compounds.
9. Write the names and draw the structures of simple cycloalkanes.
10. Draw *cis*- and *trans*-isomers of cycloalkanes.
11. Describe conformations of alkanes.
12. Draw the chair and boat conformations of cyclohexane.
13. Write balanced equations for combustion reactions of alkanes.
14. Write balanced equations for halogenation reactions of alkanes.

INTRODUCTION

Organic chemistry is the study of carbon-containing compounds. The term *organic* was coined in 1807 by the Swedish chemist Jöns Jakob Berzelius. At that time it was thought that all organic compounds, such as fats, sugars, coal, and petroleum, were formed by living or once living organisms. All early attempts to synthesize these compounds in the laboratory failed, and it was thought that a vital force, available only in living cells, was needed for their formation.

This idea began to change in 1828 when a 27-year-old German physician, whose first love was chemistry, synthesized the organic molecule urea from inorganic starting materials. This man was Friedrich Wöhler, the "father of organic chemistry."

As a child, Wöhler didn't do particularly well in school because he spent so much time doing chemistry experiments at home. Eventually, he did earn his medical degree, but he decided to study chemistry in the laboratory of Berzelius rather than practice medicine.

After a year he returned to Germany to teach and, as it turned out, to do the experiment that made him famous. The goal of the experiment was to prepare ammonium cyanate from a mixture of potassium cyanate and ammonium sulfate. Wöhler heated a solution of the two salts and crystallized the product. But the product didn't look like ammonium cyanate. It was a white crystalline material that looked exactly like urea! Urea is a waste product of protein breakdown in the body and is excreted in the urine. Wöhler recognized urea crystals because he had previously purified them from the urine of dogs and humans. Excited about his accidental discovery, he wrote to his teacher and friend Berzelius, "I can make urea without the necessity of a kidney, or even an animal, whether man or dog."

$$NH_4^+ [N{=}C{=}O]^- \qquad\qquad H_2N{-}C({=}O){-}NH_2$$

Ammonium cyanate (inorganic salt) — Urea (organic compound)

Ironically, Wöhler, the first person to synthesize an organic compound from inorganic substances, devoted the rest of his career to inorganic chemistry. However, other chemists continued this work, and as a result, the "vital force theory" was laid to rest, and modern organic chemistry was born.

In this and later chapters, we will study the amazing array of organic molecules (molecules made up of carbon, hydrogen, and a few other elements), many of which are essential to life. As we will see, all of the structural and functional molecules of the cell, including the phospholipids that make up the cell membrane and the enzymes that speed up biological reactions, are organic molecules. Smaller organic molecules, such as the sugars glucose and fructose, are used as fuel by our cells. Others, such as penicillin and aspirin are useful in the treatment of disease. All these organic compounds, and many more, are the subject of the remaining chapters of this text.

10.1 The Chemistry of Carbon

The number of possible carbon-containing compounds is almost limitless. The importance of these organic compounds is reflected in the fact that over half of this book is devoted to the study of molecules made with this single element.

Why are there so many organic compounds? There are several reasons. First, carbon can form *stable, covalent* bonds with other carbon atoms. This characteristic can be seen in three inorganic *allotropic forms* of elemental carbon: graphite, diamond, and buckminsterfullerene. Models of these allotropes are shown in Figure 10.1.

Allotropes are forms of an element that have the same physical state but different properties.

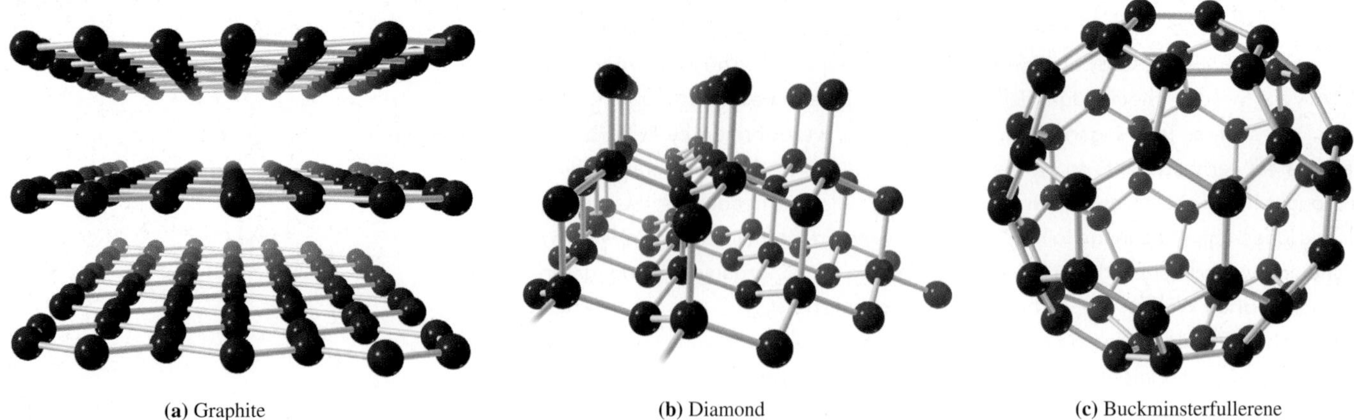

(a) Graphite (b) Diamond (c) Buckminsterfullerene

Figure 10.1 Three allotropic forms of elemental carbon.

Coal is a rock composed largely of carbon, with some other impurities. Investigate the conditions required to convert coal into a diamond.

Graphite consists of planar layers in which all carbon-to-carbon bonds extend in two dimensions. Because the planar units can slide over one another, graphite is an excellent lubricant. In contrast, diamond consists of a large, three-dimensional network of carbon-to-carbon bonds. As a result, it is an extremely hard substance used in jewelry and cutting tools.

The third allotropic form of carbon is buckminsterfullerene, affectionately called the *buckey ball.* The buckey ball consists of sixty carbon atoms in the shape of a soccer ball. Discovered in the 1980s, buckminsterfullerene was named for Buckminster Fuller, who used such shapes in the design of geodesic domes.

A second reason for the vast number of organic compounds is that carbon atoms can form stable bonds with other elements. Several families of organic compounds (alcohols, aldehydes, ketones, esters, and ethers) contain oxygen atoms bonded to carbon. Others contain nitrogen, sulfur, or halogens (Group VIIA(17) elements). The presence of these elements confers a wide variety of new chemical and physical properties on an organic compound.

Third, carbon can form double or triple covalent bonds with other carbon atoms to produce a variety of organic molecules with very different properties. Finally, the number of ways in which carbon and other atoms can be arranged is nearly limitless. In addition to linear chains of carbon atoms, ring structures and branched chains are common. Two organic compounds may even have the same number and kinds of atoms but completely different structures and thus different properties. Such organic molecules are called *isomers.*

Important Differences Between Organic and Inorganic Compounds

LEARNING GOAL

1 Compare and contrast organic and inorganic compounds.

The bonds between carbon and another atom are almost always *covalent bonds,* whereas the bonds in many inorganic compounds are *ionic bonds.* Ionic bonds result from the *transfer* of one or more electrons from one atom to another. Thus, ionic bonds are electrostatic, resulting from the attraction between the positive and negative ions formed by the electron transfer. Covalent bonds are formed by sharing one or more pairs of electrons.

Ionic compounds often form three-dimensional crystals made up of many positive and negative ions. Covalent compounds exist as individual units called molecules. Water-soluble ionic compounds often dissociate in water to form ions and are called electrolytes. Most covalent compounds are nonelectrolytes, remaining intact in solution.

Polar covalent compounds, such as HCl, dissociate in water and, thus, are electrolytes. Carboxylic acids, the family of organic compounds we will study in Chapter 14, are weak electrolytes when dissolved in water.

As a result of these differences, ionic substances usually have much higher melting and boiling points than covalent compounds. They are more likely to dissolve

TABLE 10.1 Comparison of the Major Properties of a Typical Organic and an Inorganic Compound: Butane Versus Sodium Chloride

Property	Organic Compound (e.g., Butane)	Inorganic Compound (e.g., Sodium Chloride)
Molar mass	58	58.5
Bonding	Covalent (C_4H_{10})	Ionic (Na^+ and Cl^- ions)
Physical state at room temperature and atmospheric pressure	Gas	Solid
Boiling point	Low (−0.5°C)	High (1413°C)
Melting point	Low (−139°C)	High (801°C)
Solubility in water	Insoluble	High (36 g/100 mL)
Solubility in organic solvents (e.g., hexane)	High	Insoluble
Flammability	Flammable	Nonflammable
Electrical conductivity	Nonconductor	Conducts electricity in solution and in molten liquid

in water than in a less-polar solvent, whereas organic compounds, which are typically nonpolar or only moderately polar, are less soluble, or insoluble in water. In Table 10.1, the physical properties of the organic compound butane are compared with those of sodium chloride, an inorganic compound of similar molar mass.

Question 10.1 A student is presented with a sample of an unknown substance and asked to classify the substance as organic or inorganic. What tests should the student carry out?

Question 10.2 What results would the student expect if the sample in Question 10.1 were an inorganic compound? What results would the student expect if it were an organic compound?

Families of Organic Compounds

LEARNING GOAL

2 Recognize structures that represent each of the families of organic compounds.

The most general classification of organic compounds divides them into hydrocarbons and substituted hydrocarbons. A **hydrocarbon** molecule contains only carbon and hydrogen. A **substituted hydrocarbon** is one in which one or more hydrogen atoms is replaced by another atom or group of atoms.

The hydrocarbons can be further subdivided into aliphatic and aromatic hydrocarbons (Figure 10.2). **Aliphatic hydrocarbons** are non-aromatic compounds. This means they do not have a benzene ring in the structure. The four families of aliphatic hydrocarbons are the alkanes, cycloalkanes, alkenes, and alkynes.

Saturated hydrocarbons contain only carbon and hydrogen and have only carbon-to-hydrogen and carbon-to-carbon single bonds. Alkanes and cycloalkanes are saturated hydrocarbons. **Unsaturated hydrocarbons** contain at least one

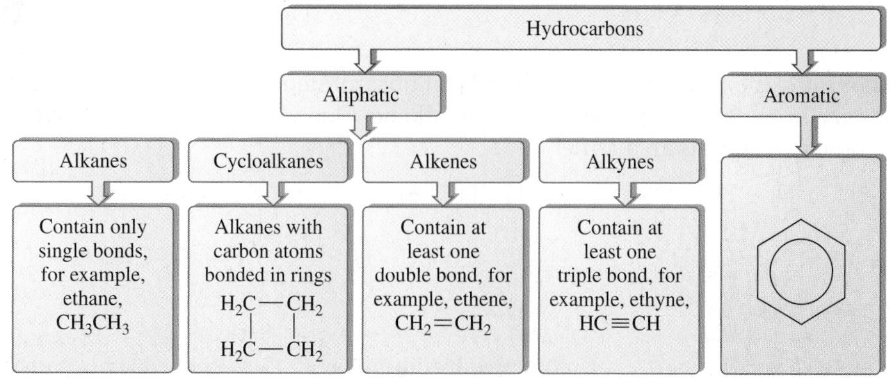

Figure 10.2 The family of hydrocarbons is divided into two major classes: aliphatic and aromatic. The aliphatic hydrocarbons are further subdivided into four major subclasses: alkanes, cycloalkanes, alkenes, and alkynes.

GREEN CHEMISTRY

Frozen Methane: Treasure or Threat?

Methane is the simplest hydrocarbon, but it has some unusual behaviors. One of these is the ability to form a clathrate, which is an unusual type of matter in which molecules of one substance form a cage around molecules of another substance. For instance, water molecules can form a latticework around methane molecules to form frozen methane hydrate, possibly one of the biggest reservoirs of fossil fuel on earth.

Typically we wouldn't expect a nonpolar molecule, such as methane, to interact with a polar molecule, such as water. So, then, how is this structure formed? As we have studied earlier, water molecules interact with one another by strong hydrogen bonding. In the frozen state, these hydrogen-bonded water molecules form an open latticework. The nonpolar methane molecule is simply trapped inside one of the spaces within the lattice.

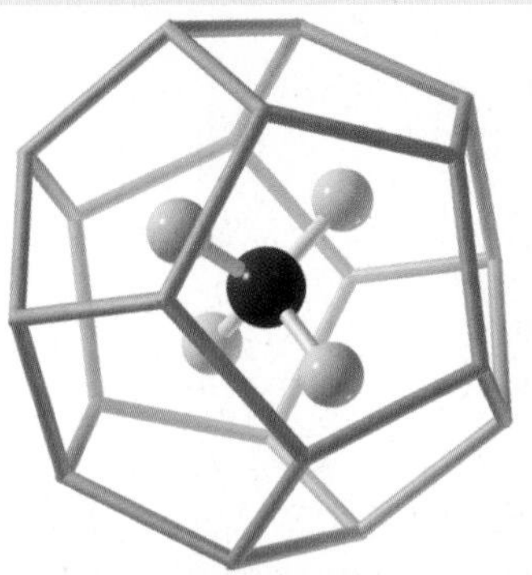

Three-dimensional structure of methane hydrate.

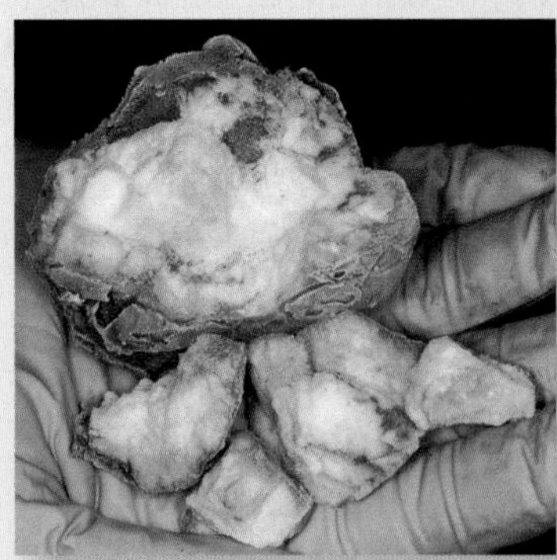

A sample of frozen methane hydrate.

Vast regions of the ocean floor are covered by ice fields of frozen methane. Scientists would like to "mine" this ice to use the methane as a fuel. In fact, the U.S. Geological Survey estimates that the amount of methane hydrate in the United States is worth over 200 times the conventional natural gas resources in this country!

But is it safe to harvest the methane from this ice? Caution will certainly be required. Methane is flammable, and, like carbon dioxide, it is a greenhouse gas. In fact, it is about twenty times more efficient at trapping heat than carbon dioxide. (Greenhouse gases are discussed in greater detail in Green Chemistry: The Greenhouse Effect and Global Climate Change in Chapter 5.) So the U.S. Department of Energy, which is working with industry to develop ways to harvest the methane, must figure out how to do that without releasing much into the atmosphere where it could intensify global warming.

It may be that a huge release of methane from these frozen reserves was responsible for a major global warming that occurred fifty-five million years ago and lasted for one hundred thousand years. NASA scientists using computer simulations hypothesize that a shift of the continental plates may have released vast amounts of methane gas from the ocean floor. This methane raised the temperature of earth by about 13°F. In fact, the persistence of the methane in the atmosphere warmed earth enough to melt the ice in the oceans and at polar caps and completely change the global climate. This theory, if it turns out to be true, highlights the importance of controlling the amount of methane, as well as carbon dioxide, that we release into the air. Certainly, harvesting the frozen methane of the oceans, if we choose to do it, must be done with great care.

For Further Understanding

- News stories alternatively describe frozen methane as a "New Frontier" and "Armageddon." Explain these opposing views.
- What are the ethical considerations involved in mining frozen methane?

carbon-to-carbon double or triple bond. An unsaturated hydrocarbon with at least one carbon-to-carbon double bond is an alkene. One with at least one carbon-to-carbon triple bond is an alkyne.

Recall that each of the lines in these structures represents a shared pair of electrons. See Chapter 3.

$$\begin{array}{ccccc} & H & H & H & \\ & | & | & | & \\ H- & C- & C- & C & -H \\ & | & | & | & \\ & H & H & H & \end{array}$$

Saturated Hydrocarbon (Alkane)

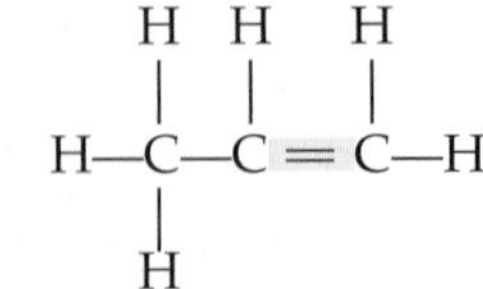

Unsaturated Hydrocarbon (Alkene)

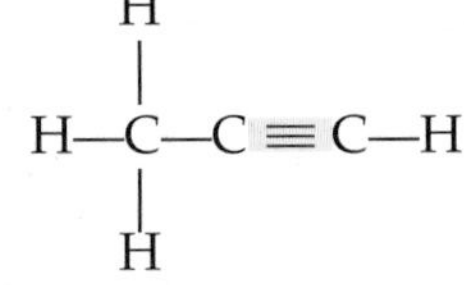

Unsaturated Hydrocarbon (Alkyne)

Some hydrocarbons are cyclic. Cycloalkanes consist of carbon atoms bonded to one another to produce a ring. **Aromatic hydrocarbons** contain a benzene ring or a derivative of the benzene ring.

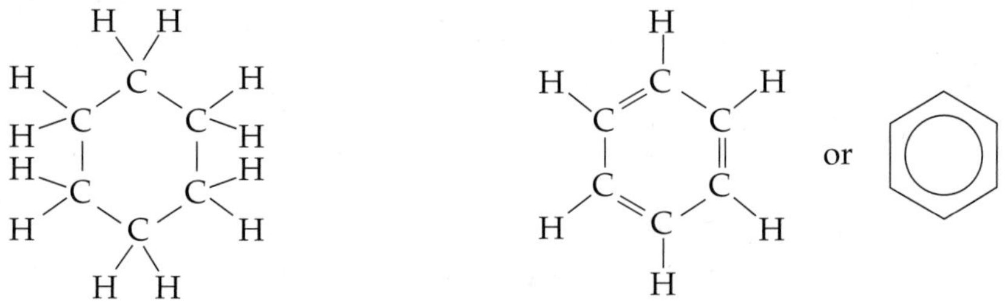

A Cycloalkane (Cyclohexane)

Benzene

LEARNING GOAL

3 Write the names and draw the structures of the common functional groups that characterize the families of organic compounds.

A substituted hydrocarbon is produced by replacing one or more hydrogen atoms with a functional group. A **functional group** is an atom or group of atoms arranged in a particular way that is primarily responsible for the chemical and physical properties of the molecule in which it is found. The importance of functional groups becomes more apparent when we consider that hydrocarbons have little biological activity. However, the addition of a functional group confers unique and interesting properties that give the molecule important biological or medical properties.

All compounds that have a particular functional group are members of the same family. We have just seen that the alkenes are characterized by the presence of carbon-to-carbon double bonds. Similarly, all alcohols contain a hydroxyl group (—OH). Since this group is polar and can form hydrogen bonds, an alcohol such as ethanol (CH_3CH_2OH) is liquid at room temperature and highly soluble in water, while the alkane of similar molar mass, propane ($CH_3CH_2CH_3$), is nonpolar and is a gas at room temperature and completely insoluble in water. Other common functional groups are shown in Table 10.2, along with an example of a molecule from each family.

The chemistry of organic and biological molecules is usually controlled by the functional group found in the molecule. Just as members of the same family of the periodic table exhibit similar chemistry, organic molecules with the same functional group exhibit similar chemistry. Although it would be impossible to learn the chemistry of each organic molecule, it is relatively easy to learn the chemistry of each functional group. In this way you can learn the chemistry of all members of a family of organic compounds, or biological molecules, just by learning the chemistry of its characteristic functional group or groups.

10.2 Alkanes

Alkanes are saturated hydrocarbons; that is, alkanes contain only carbon and hydrogen bonded together through carbon-hydrogen and carbon-carbon single bonds. C_nH_{2n+2} is the general formula for alkanes. In this formula, n is the number of carbon atoms in the molecule.

Structure

LEARNING GOAL

4 Write condensed, structural, and line formulas for saturated hydrocarbons.

Four types of formulas, each providing different information, are used in organic chemistry: the molecular formula, the structural formula, the condensed formula, and the line formula.

The **molecular formula** tells the kind and number of each type of atom in a molecule but does not show the bonding pattern. Consider the molecular formulas for simple alkanes:

CH_4	C_2H_6	C_3H_8	C_4H_{10}
Methane	Ethane	Propane	Butane

TABLE 10.2 Common Functional Groups

Type of Compound	Functional Group	Structural Formula	Condensed Formula	Example Structural Formula	Example IUPAC Name	Common Name
Alcohol	Hydroxyl	*R—O—H	ROH	CH_3CH_2—O—H	Ethanol	Ethyl alcohol
Aldehyde	Carbonyl	$R{-}\overset{\overset{\displaystyle O}{\|}}{C}{-}H$	RCHO	$CH_3\overset{\overset{\displaystyle O}{\|}}{C}{-}H$	Ethanal	Acetaldehyde
Amide	Carboxamide	$R{-}\overset{\overset{\displaystyle O}{\|}}{C}{-}\overset{\overset{\displaystyle H}{\mid}}{N}{-}H$	$RCONH_2$	$CH_3\overset{\overset{\displaystyle O}{\|}}{C}{-}\overset{\overset{\displaystyle H}{\mid}}{N}{-}H$	Ethanamide	Acetamide
Amine	Amino	$R{-}\overset{\overset{\displaystyle H}{\mid}}{N}{-}H$	RNH_2	$CH_3CH_2\overset{\overset{\displaystyle H}{\mid}}{N}{-}H$	Aminoethane	Ethyl amine
Carboxylic acid	Carboxyl	$R{-}\overset{\overset{\displaystyle O}{\|}}{C}{-}O{-}H$	RCOOH	$CH_3\overset{\overset{\displaystyle O}{\|}}{C}{-}O{-}H$	Ethanoic acid	Acetic acid
Ester	Ester	$R{-}\overset{\overset{\displaystyle O}{\|}}{C}{-}O{-}R'$	RCOOR′	$CH_3\overset{\overset{\displaystyle O}{\|}}{C}{-}OCH_3$	Methyl ethanoate	Methyl acetate
Ether	Ether	R—O—R′	ROR′	CH_3OCH_3	Methoxymethane	Dimethyl ether
Halide	Halogen atom	R—Cl (or —Br, —F, —I)	RCl	CH_3CH_2Cl	Chloroethane	Ethyl chloride
Ketone	Carbonyl	$^{\dagger}R{-}\overset{\overset{\displaystyle O}{\|}}{C}{-}R'$	RCOR′	$CH_3\overset{\overset{\displaystyle O}{\|}}{C}CH_3$	Propanone	Acetone
Alkene	Double bond	$\begin{matrix}R & & R\\ & C{=}C & \\ R & & R\end{matrix}$	R_2CCR_2	$CH_3CH{=}CH_2$	Propene	Propylene
Alkyne	Triple bond	R—C≡C—R	RCCR	$CH_3C{\equiv}CH$	Propyne	Methyl acetylene

*R and R′ represent an alkyl group, an aryl group, or H.
†In a ketone, R and R′ must be alkyl or aryl groups.

For the first three compounds, there is only one possible arrangement of the atoms. However, for C_4H_{10} there are two possible arrangements. How do we know which is correct? The problem is solved by using the **structural formula,** which shows each atom and bond in a molecule. The following are the structural formulas for methane, ethane, propane, and the two isomers of butane:

$$\begin{matrix} & H & \\ & \mid & \\ H{-} & C & {-}H \\ & \mid & \\ & H & \end{matrix}\qquad \begin{matrix} & H & H & \\ & \mid & \mid & \\ H{-} & C{-} & C & {-}H \\ & \mid & \mid & \\ & H & H & \end{matrix}\qquad \begin{matrix} & H & H & H & \\ & \mid & \mid & \mid & \\ H{-} & C{-} & C{-} & C & {-}H \\ & \mid & \mid & \mid & \\ & H & H & H & \end{matrix}\qquad \begin{matrix} & H & H & H & H & \\ & \mid & \mid & \mid & \mid & \\ H{-} & C{-} & C{-} & C{-} & C & {-}H \\ & \mid & \mid & \mid & \mid & \\ & H & H & H & H & \end{matrix}\qquad \begin{matrix} & & H & & \\ & & \mid & & \\ & H{-} & C & {-}H & \\ & H & \mid & H & \\ & \mid & \mid & \mid & \\ H{-} & C{-} & C{-} & C & {-}H \\ & \mid & \mid & \mid & \\ & H & H & H & \end{matrix}$$

Methane Ethane Propane Butane Methylpropane (isobutane)

Recall that a covalent bond, representing a pair of shared electrons, can be drawn as a line between two atoms. For the structure to be correct, each carbon atom must show four pairs of shared electrons.

The advantage of a structural formula is that it shows the complete structure, but for large molecules it is time-consuming to draw and requires too much space. The compromise is the **condensed formula.** It shows all the atoms in a molecule and places them in a sequential order that indicates which atoms are bonded to which. The following are the condensed formulas for the preceding five compounds.

CH_4	CH_3CH_3	$CH_3CH_2CH_3$	$CH_3(CH_2)_2CH_3$	$(CH_3)_3CH$
Methane	Ethane	Propane	Butane	Methylpropane (isobutane)

The names and formulas of the first ten straight-chain alkanes are shown in Table 10.3.

The simplest representation of a molecule is the **line formula.** In the line formula we assume that there is a carbon atom at any location where two or more lines intersect. We also assume that there is a methyl group at the end of any line and that each carbon in the structure is bonded to the correct number of hydrogen atoms. Compare the structural and line formulas for butane and methylpropane, shown here:

```
                                              H
                                              |
                                            H-C-H
   H  H  H  H                              H  |  H
   |  |  |  |                              |  |  |
 H-C--C--C--C-H =                        H-C--C--C-H =
   |  |  |  |                              |  |  |
   H  H  H  H                              H  H  H
```

Butane
(Straight chain alkane)

Methylpropane
(Branched alkane)

Each carbon atom forms four single covalent bonds, but each hydrogen atom has only a single covalent bond. Although a carbon atom may be involved in single, double, or triple bonds, it always shares four pairs of electrons. The Lewis structure of the simplest alkane, methane, shows the four shared pairs of electrons (Figure 10.3a). When carbon is involved in four single bonds, the *bond angle,* the angle between two atoms or substituents attached to carbon, is 109.5°, as predicted by the valence-shell electron-pair repulsion (VSEPR) theory. Thus, alkanes contain carbon atoms that have tetrahedral geometry.

ANIMATIONS

- The Geometry of CH_4
- Valence-Shell Electron-Pair Repulsion Theory
- VSEPR and Molecular Geometry

Molecular geometry is described in Section 3.4.

TABLE 10.3 Names and Formulas of the First Ten Straight-Chain Alkanes

Name	Molecular Formula	Condensed Formula	Melting Point, °C*	Boiling Point, °C*
Alkanes	C_nH_{2n+2}			
Methane	CH_4	CH_4	−182.5	−162.2
Ethane	C_2H_6	CH_3CH_3	−183.9	−88.6
Propane	C_3H_8	$CH_3CH_2CH_3$	−187.6	−42.1
Butane	C_4H_{10}	$CH_3CH_2CH_2CH_3$ or $CH_3(CH_2)_2CH_3$	−137.2	−0.5
Pentane	C_5H_{12}	$CH_3CH_2CH_2CH_2CH_3$ or $CH_3(CH_2)_3CH_3$	−129.8	36.1
Hexane	C_6H_{14}	$CH_3CH_2CH_2CH_2CH_2CH_3$ or $CH_3(CH_2)_4CH_3$	−95.2	68.8
Heptane	C_7H_{16}	$CH_3CH_2CH_2CH_2CH_2CH_2CH_3$ or $CH_3(CH_2)_5CH_3$	−90.6	98.4
Octane	C_8H_{18}	$CH_3CH_2CH_2CH_2CH_2CH_2CH_2CH_3$ or $CH_3(CH_2)_6CH_3$	−56.9	125.6
Nonane	C_9H_{20}	$CH_3CH_2CH_2CH_2CH_2CH_2CH_2CH_2CH_3$ or $CH_3(CH_2)_7CH_3$	−53.6	150.7
Decane	$C_{10}H_{22}$	$CH_3CH_2CH_2CH_2CH_2CH_2CH_2CH_2CH_2CH_3$ or $CH_3(CH_2)_8CH_3$	−29.8	174.0

*Melting and boiling points as reported in the National Institute of Standards and Technology Chemistry Webbook, which can be found at http://webbook.nist.gov/.

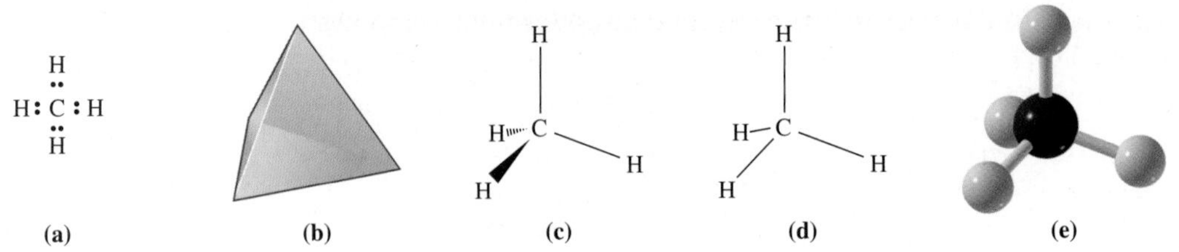

(a) (b) (c) (d) (e)

Figure 10.3 The tetrahedral carbon atom: (a) Lewis structure; (b) a tetrahedron; (c) the tetrahedral carbon drawn with dashes and wedges; (d) the stick drawing of the tetrahedral carbon atom; (e) ball-and-stick model of methane.

A tetrahedron is a geometric solid having the structure shown in Figure 10.3b. There are many different ways to draw the tetrahedral carbon (Figures 10.3c–10.3e). In Figure 10.3c, solid lines, dashes, and wedges are used to represent the structure of methane. Dashes go back into the page away from you; wedges come out of the page toward you; and solid lines are in the plane of the page. The structure in Figure 10.3d is the same as that in Figure 10.3c; it just leaves a lot more to the imagination. Figure 10.3e is a ball-and-stick model of the methane molecule. Three-dimensional drawings of two other simple alkanes are shown in Figure 10.4.

EXAMPLE 10.1 Using Different Types of Formulas to Represent Organic Compounds

LEARNING GOAL

4 Write condensed, structural, and line formulas for saturated hydrocarbons.

The following line structure represents 2,2,4-trimethylpentane (also called isooctane), which is the standard of excellence used in determining the octane rating of gasoline. See also Green Chemistry: The Petroleum Industry and Gasoline Production later in this chapter.

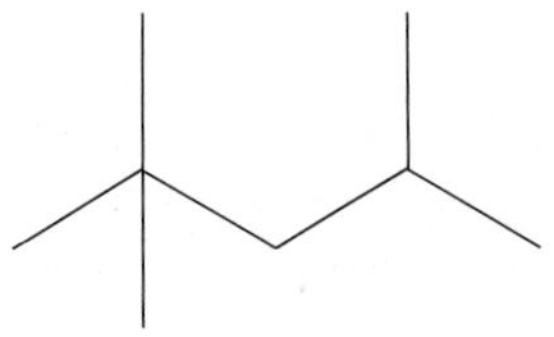

2,2,4-Trimethylpentane
(isooctane)

Draw the structural and condensed formulas of this molecule.

Solution

Remember that each intersection of lines represents a carbon atom and that each line ends in a methyl group. This gives us the following carbon skeleton:

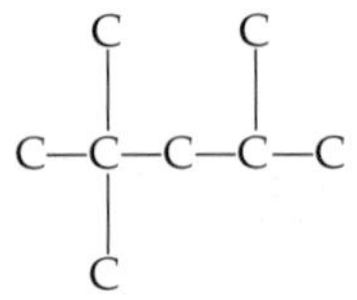

By adding the correct number of hydrogen atoms to the carbon skeleton, we are able to complete the structural formula of this compound.

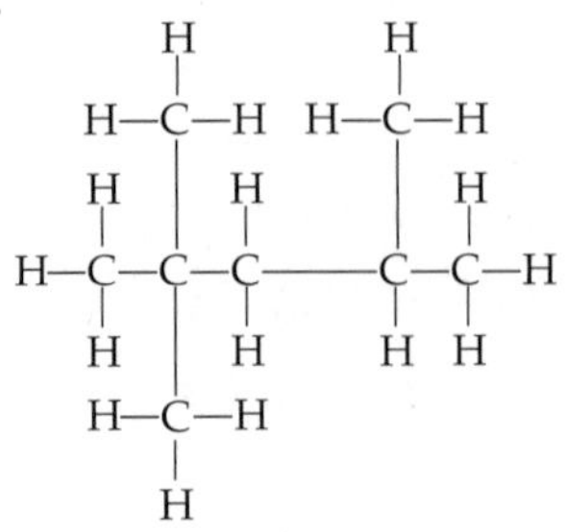

From the structural formula, we can write the condensed formula as follows:

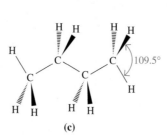

$$CH_3C(CH_3)_2CH_2CH(CH_3)CH_3$$

Practice Problem 10.1

For each of the molecules in Table 10.4, draw the structural and the line formulas.

▸ For Further Practice: **Questions 10.20 and 10.21.**

Physical Properties

LEARNING GOAL

5 Describe the relationship between the structure and physical properties of saturated hydrocarbons.

All hydrocarbons are nonpolar molecules. As a result, they are not water soluble but are soluble in nonpolar organic solvents. Furthermore, they have relatively low melting points and boiling points and are generally less dense than water. In general, the longer the hydrocarbon chain (greater the molar mass), the higher the melting and boiling points and the greater the density (see Table 10.3).

At room temperature, alkanes with 1 to 4 carbon atoms are gases, those with 5 to 17 carbon atoms are colorless liquids, and those containing more than 18 carbon atoms are white, waxy solids. These trends in physical properties are the result of London dispersion forces. These attractive forces increase as the mass of the molecule and the number of electrons increase. Knowing this, we can predict that London dispersion forces will be stronger and the attraction greater for molecules having a larger surface area. The longer, higher molar mass alkanes would be expected to exhibit stronger London dispersion forces and therefore higher boiling and melting points.

See Section 5.2 for a discussion of the forces responsible for the physical properties of a substance.

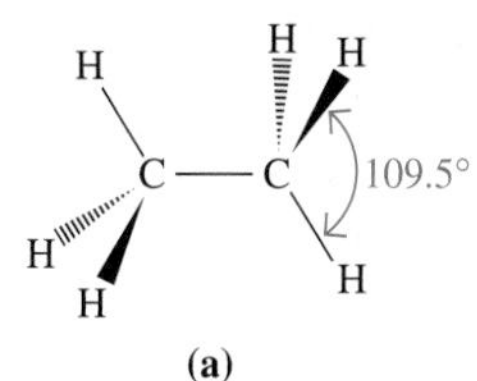

(a)

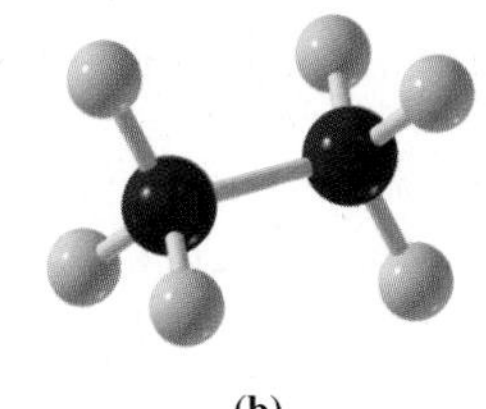

(b)

(c)

(d)

Figure 10.4 (a) Drawing and (b) ball-and-stick model of ethane. All the carbon atoms have a tetrahedral arrangement, and all bond angles are approximately 109.5°. (c) Drawing and (d) ball-and-stick model of a more complex alkane, butane.

TABLE 10.4 Melting and Boiling Points of Five Alkanes of Molecular Formula C_6H_{14}

Name	Condensed Formula	Boiling Point* °C	Melting Point* °C
Hexane	$CH_3(CH_2)_4CH_3$	68.8	−95.2
2-Methylpentane	$CH_3CH(CH_3)(CH_2)_2CH_3$	60.9	−153.2
3-Methylpentane	$CH_3CH_2CH(CH_3)CH_2CH_3$	63.3	−118
2,3-Dimethylbutane	$CH_3CH(CH_3)CH(CH_3)CH_3$	58.1	−130.2
2,2-Dimethylbutane	$CH_3C(CH_3)_2CH_2CH_3$	49.8	−100.2

*Melting and boiling points as reported in the National Institute of Standards and Technology Chemistry Webbook, which can be found at http://webbook.nist.gov/.

Some alkanes have one or more carbon atoms branching from the main carbon chain. Compare the following two molecules with molecular formula C_9H_{20}.

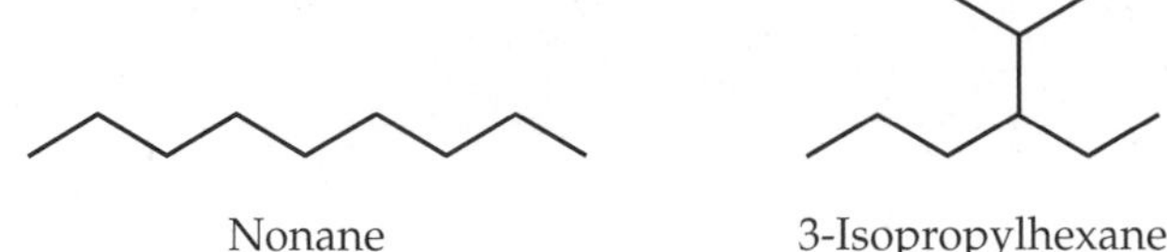

Nonane 3-Isopropylhexane

The branched-chain form, 3-isopropylhexane, has a much smaller surface area than the straight chain. As a result, the London dispersion forces attracting the molecules to one another are less strong and these molecules have lower melting and boiling points than the straight-chain isomers. The melting and boiling points of the five structural isomers of C_6H_{14} are found in Table 10.4.

Alkyl Groups

Alkyl groups are alkanes with one fewer hydrogen atom. The name of the alkyl group is derived from the name of the alkane containing the same number of carbon atoms. The *-ane* ending of the alkane name is replaced by the *-yl* ending. Thus, —CH_3 is a methyl group and —CH_2CH_3 is an ethyl group. The dash at the end of these two structures represents the point at which the alkyl group can bond to another atom. The first five continuous-chain alkyl groups are presented in Table 10.5.

Carbon atoms are classified according to the number of other carbon atoms to which they are attached. A **primary (1°) carbon** is directly bonded to one other carbon. A **secondary (2°) carbon** is bonded to two other carbon atoms; a **tertiary (3°) carbon** is bonded to three other carbon atoms, and a **quaternary (4°) carbon** to four.

Alkyl groups are classified according to the number of carbons attached to the carbon atom that joins the alkyl group to a molecule.

TABLE 10.5 Names and Formulas of the First Five Continuous-Chain Alkyl Groups

Alkyl Group Structure	Name
—CH_3	Methyl
—CH_2CH_3	Ethyl
—$CH_2CH_2CH_3$	Propyl
—$CH_2CH_2CH_2CH_3$	Butyl
—$CH_2CH_2CH_2CH_2CH_3$	Pentyl

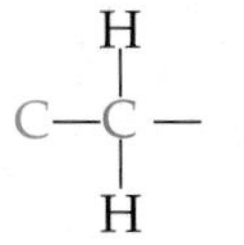

```
    H              C              C
    |              |              |
 C—C—           C—C—           C—C—
    |              |              |
    H              H              C
 Primary       Secondary       Tertiary
alkyl group   alkyl group    alkyl group
```

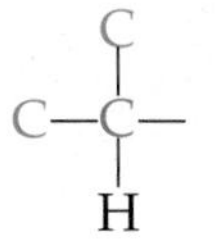

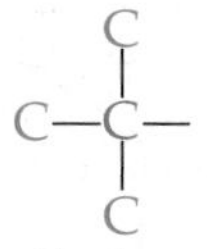

All of the continuous-chain alkyl groups are primary alkyl groups (see Table 10.5). Several branched-chain alkyl groups are shown in Table 10.6. The carbon atom that attaches the alkyl group to the parent compound is highlighted in red in these structures above and in Table 10.6. Notice that the isopropyl and *sec*-butyl groups are secondary alkyl groups; the isobutyl group is a primary alkyl group; and the *t*-butyl (*tert*-butyl) is a tertiary alkyl group.

TABLE 10.6 Structures and Names of Some Branched-Chain Alkyl Groups

Structure	Classification	Common Name	IUPAC Name
$CH_3CH—$ with CH_3 on CH	2°	Isopropyl*	1-Methylethyl
$CH_3CHCH_2—$ with CH_3 on CH	1°	Isobutyl*	2-Methylpropyl
$CH_3CH_2CH—$ with CH_3 on CH	2°	*sec*-Butyl†	1-Methylpropyl
$CH_3C—$ with two CH_3 on C	3°	*t*-Butyl or *tert*-Butyl‡	1,1-Dimethylethyl

*The prefix *iso*- (isomeric) is used when there are two methyl groups at the end of the alkyl group.
†The prefix sec- (secondary) indicates that there are two carbons bonded to the carbon that attaches the alkyl group to the parent molecule.
‡The prefix *t*- or *tert*- (tertiary) means that three carbons are attached to the carbon that attaches the alkyl group to the parent molecule.

Question 10.3 Classify each of the carbon atoms in the following structures as primary, secondary, tertiary, or quaternary.

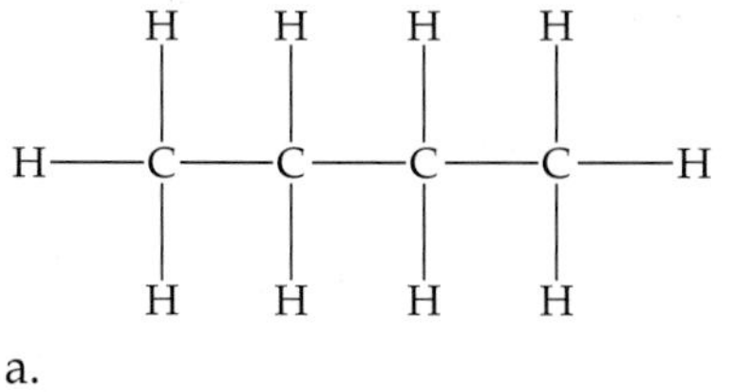

```
                                   H                            H
                                   |                            |
                               H—C—H                        H—C—H
                                   |                            |
                              H    |    H                 H    |    H    H    H
                              |    |    |                 |    |    |    |    |
                          H—C—C—C—H                 H—C—C—C—C—C—H
   H   H   H   H              |    |    |                 |    |    |    |    |
   |   |   |   |              H    |    H                 H    H    |    H    H
H—C—C—C—C—H                    |                                 |
   |   |   |   |               H—C—H                          H—C—H
   H   H   H   H                   |                              |
a.                        b.       H                  c.          H
```

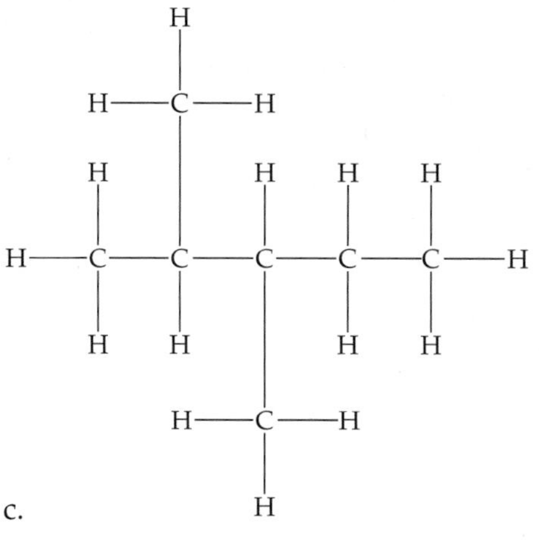

Question 10.4 Classify each of the carbon atoms in the following structures as primary, secondary, tertiary, or quaternary.

a. $CH_3CH_2C(CH_3)_2CH_2CH_3$
b. $CH_3CH_2CH_2CH_2CH(CH_3)CH(CH_3)CH_3$

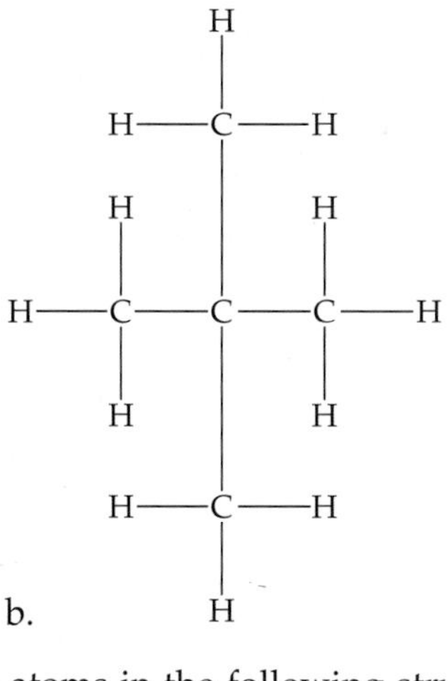

CHEMISTRY AT THE CRIME SCENE

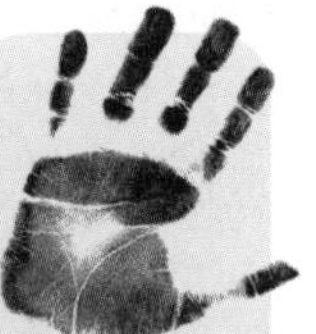

Arson and Alkanes

In September of 2005, Thomas Sweatt was sentenced to life in prison for setting forty-five fires in the Washington, D.C. area. Aside from millions of dollars in property damage, two people died as a result of these fires. Mr. Sweatt confessed to the fires, which terrorized the Washington metropolitan area over a 2-year period, stating that he was "addicted to setting fires."

Authorities estimate that one-third of all fires are arson, and the Federal Bureau of Investigation (FBI) reports that arson is more common in the United States than anywhere else in the world. Although arsonists may set fires as terrorist acts, to defraud insurance companies, to gain revenge, or to cover up another crime, other arsonists are mentally ill pyromaniacs like Mr. Sweatt.

As soon as a fire is extinguished and the scene is secure, investigators gather evidence to determine the cause of the fire. They study the pattern of the fire to determine the point of origin. This is critical, because this is where they must sample for the presence of accelerants, flammable substances that cause fires to burn hotter and spread more quickly. The most common accelerants are mixtures of hydrocarbons, including gasoline, kerosene, or diesel fuel.

Because all of these accelerants contain molecules that evaporate, they may be detected at the point of origin by trained technicians or "sniffer dogs." However, a much more advanced technology is also available; it is called *headspace gas chromatography.* Gas chromatography separates and identifies components of a sample based on differences in their boiling points. Each gas mixture produces its own unique "chemical fingerprint" or chromatogram. Crime scene technicians collect debris from the point of origin and seal it in an airtight vial. In the laboratory, they heat the vial so the hydrocarbons evaporate and are trapped in the headspace of the vial. These gases are then collected with a needle and syringe and injected into the gas chromatograph for analysis and identification.

To be absolutely certain that an accelerant has been used, the crime scene technicians also collect debris from control sites away from the point of origin. The reason for this is that pyrolysis, the decomposition or transformation of a compound caused by heat, may produce products that simulate accelerants. If an accelerant is found at the point of origin and not among the other pyrolysis products, it can be concluded that arson was the cause of the blaze.

Of course, the next priority is to catch the arsonist. Crime scene technicians collect and analyze physical evidence, including fingerprints, footprints, and other artifacts, found at the crime scene. In the case of Mr. Sweatt, it was DNA fingerprint evidence from articles of clothing left at the crime scenes that led to his capture and conviction and ended his 2-year arson spree.

For Further Understanding

- Investigate the composition of gasoline, diesel fuel, and kerosene and explain how they can be distinguished from one another using gas chromatography.
- Other accelerants that have been used by arsonists include nail polish remover (acetone), grain alcohol (ethanol), and rubbing alcohol (2-propanol or isopropyl alcohol). What properties do these substances share that make them useful as accelerants?

c.

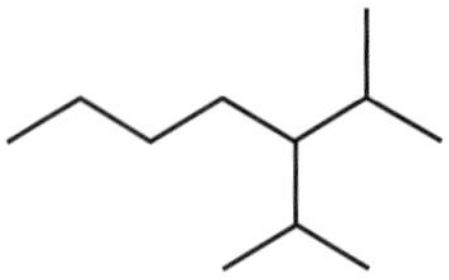

d.

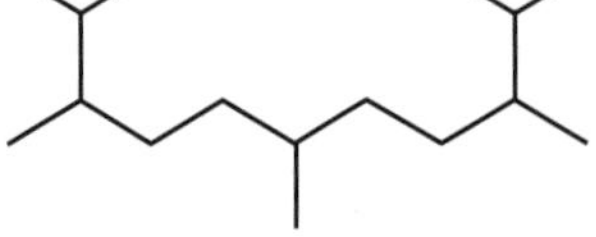

Nomenclature

Historically, organic compounds were named by the chemist who discovered them. Often the names reflected the source of the compound. For instance, the antibiotic penicillin is named for the mold *Penicillium notatum,* which produces it. The pain reliever aspirin was made by adding an acetate group to a compound first purified from the bark of a willow tree and later from the meadowsweet plant (*Spirea ulmaria*). Thus, the name aspirin comes from *a* (acetate) and *spir* (genus of meadowsweet).

These names are easy for us to remember because we come into contact with these compounds often. However, as the number of compounds increased, organic chemists realized that historical names were not adequate because they revealed nothing about the structure of a compound. Thousands of such compounds and their common names had to be memorized! What was needed was a set of nomenclature (naming) rules that would produce a unique name for every organic compound. Furthermore, the name should be so descriptive that, by knowing the name, a student or scientist could write the structure.

The International Union of Pure and Applied Chemistry (IUPAC) is the organization responsible for establishing and maintaining a standard, universal system for naming organic compounds. The system of nomenclature developed by this group is called the **IUPAC Nomenclature System.** The following rules are used for naming alkanes by the IUPAC system.

LEARNING GOAL

6 Use the basic rules of the IUPAC Nomenclature System to name alkanes and substituted alkanes.

It is important to learn the prefixes for the carbon chain lengths. We will use them in the nomenclature for all organic molecules.

1. Determine the name of the **parent compound,** the longest continuous carbon chain in the compound. Refer to Tables 10.3 and 10.7 to determine the parent name. Notice that these names are made up of a prefix related to the number of carbons in the chain and the suffix *-ane,* indicating that the molecule is an alkane (Table 10.7). Write down the name of the parent compound, leaving space before the name to identify the substituents. Parent chains are highlighted in yellow in the following examples, and the names of the parent compounds are shown below each structure.

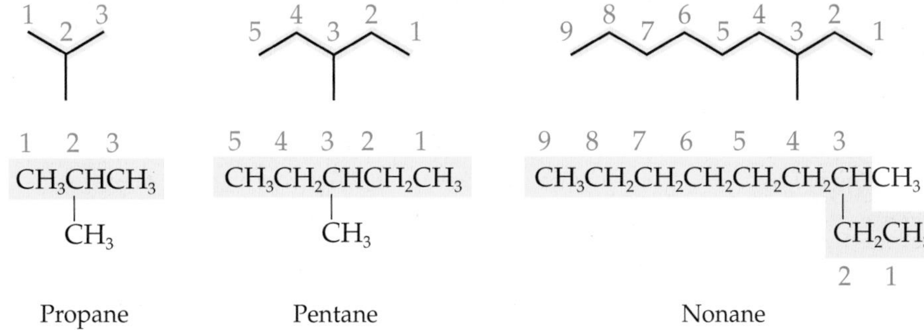

Propane Pentane Nonane

2. Number the parent chain to give the lowest number to the carbon bonded to the first group encountered on the parent chain, regardless of the numbers that result for the other substituents.
3. Name and number each atom or group attached to the parent compound. The number tells you the position of the group on the main chain, and the name tells you what type of substituent is present at that position. For

TABLE 10.7 Carbon Chain Length and Prefixes Used in the IUPAC Nomenclature System

Carbon Chain Length	Prefix	Alkane Name
1	Meth-	Meth*ane*
2	Eth-	Eth*ane*
3	Prop-	Prop*ane*
4	But-	But*ane*
5	Pent-	Pent*ane*
6	Hex-	Hex*ane*
7	Hept-	Hept*ane*
8	Oct-	Oct*ane*
9	Non-	Non*ane*
10	Dec-	Dec*ane*

GREEN CHEMISTRY

Biofuels: A Renewable Resource

What do a high school science project and a train in the Midwest have in common: biofuels. For their senior project, two young Florida women re-engineered one of the school's maintenance trucks to run on the used oil from a local Chinese restaurant. Aside from the aroma of egg rolls frying, the truck performs very well. There are complications, however. The oil is too viscous to use until the truck engine has warmed up. So the driver needs to start the truck with diesel fuel, warm up the engine, then switch to the cooking oil fuel. Similarly, when preparing to stop the truck, the driver must switch back to diesel fuel so that the biofuel is no longer in the engine when it cools.

In 2010 Amtrak unveiled its first biodiesel-fueled train. The biodiesel fuel is a B20 blend, which means that it is **20%** biodiesel and **80%** regular diesel. The biodiesel is a complex mixture of fatty acids that are a by-product of the beef industry. So it is fitting that this train runs the Oklahoma City to Fort Worth route. This source works well in Texas and Oklahoma, which both produce large numbers of cattle, but what of other locations? Some have suggested corn or soybeans for biodiesel production. The question there is whether it is wise to rely on food crops that, in the event of widespread famine, may be needed for food.

The options are as creative as the minds that have envisioned them. As it turns out, 15 million pounds of alligator fat are dumped into landfills each year as a by-product of processing the meat. Over 60% of that fat can be extracted by microwaving and the resultant fatty acid profile makes it an excellent biodiesel fuel. NASA scientists are developing biodiesel from halophytic (salt-loving) plants. These plants can grow in the desert and can be irrigated with seawater. Thus they take advantage of environments and conditions that traditionally have not been usefully employed. The scientists even predict that this would create a cooler, wetter land surface that would promote rainfall in areas that are extremely arid.

Boeing Corporation scientists think that biodiesel could cut aircraft emissions by 60–80%, which is a considerable improvement when you consider that 2% of all human emissions are from the aviation industry. Several test flights have shown that aircraft fly very well on fuels that are a mixture of 50% jet fuel and 50% biodiesel produced from a variety of sources including algae, the jatropha plant, and *Camelina* seed.

Biodiesel is much more common in Europe than elsewhere in the world and is produced from palm oil, rapeseed, flax, sunflower, and jatropha. These oils are treated by a transesterification process that produces fatty acid methyl or ethyl esters (FAMES). The resultant fuels are considered safer than traditional diesel because they are biodegradable, are ten times less toxic than table salt, and have high flash points.

We have much to learn about biofuels and their production before we can hope to replace the use of fossil fuels. However, knowing that fossil fuels are a limited resource, it is important to study renewable energy sources so that we can make wise decisions about those processes that provide the greatest benefit with the least negative impact on our environment.

For Further Understanding

- What are some of the environmental issues that must be studied when considering biodiesel from a variety of sources?
- What are some of the economic issues that need to be analyzed when considering biodiesel as a replacement for fossil fuels?

example, it may be one of the halogens [F—fluoro), Cl—(chloro), Br—(bromo), and I—(iodo)] or an alkyl group (Tables 10.5 and 10.6). In the following examples the parent chain is highlighted in yellow:

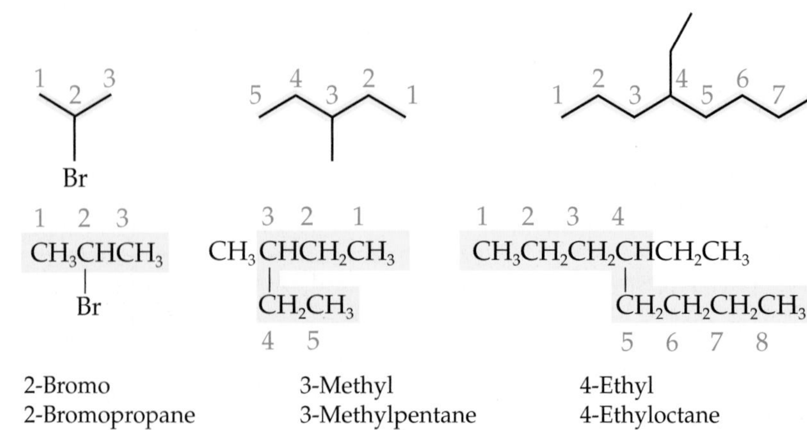

Substituent:	2-Bromo	3-Methyl	4-Ethyl
IUPAC name:	2-Bromopropane	3-Methylpentane	4-Ethyloctane

4. If the same substituent occurs more than once in the compound, a separate position number is given for each, and the prefixes *di-*, *tri-*, *tetra-*, *penta-*, and so forth are used, as shown in the following examples:

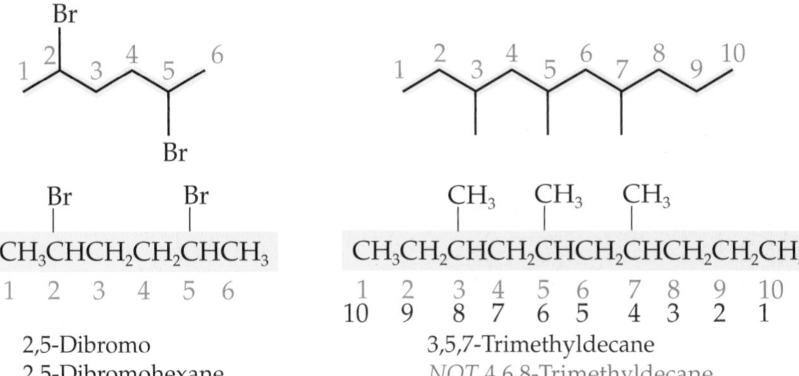

2,5-Dibromo
2,5-Dibromohexane

3,5,7-Trimethyldecane
NOT 4,6,8-Trimethyldecane

Throughout this book we will primarily use the IUPAC Nomenclature System. When common names are used, they will be shown in parentheses beneath the IUPAC name.

5. Place the names of the substituents in alphabetical order before the name of the parent compound, which you wrote down in step 1. Numbers are separated by commas, and numbers are separated from names by hyphens. By convention, halogen substituents are placed before alkyl substituents.

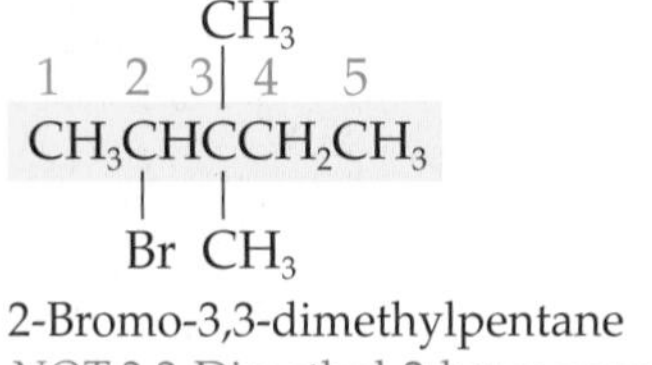

2-Bromo-3,3-dimethylpentane
NOT 3,3-Dimethyl-2-bromopentane

$CH_3CHCHCHCH_2CH_3$ (F on C-3; CH_3 on C-2 and C-4)

3-Fluoro-2,4-dimethylhexane
NOT 2,4-Dimethyl-3-fluorohexane

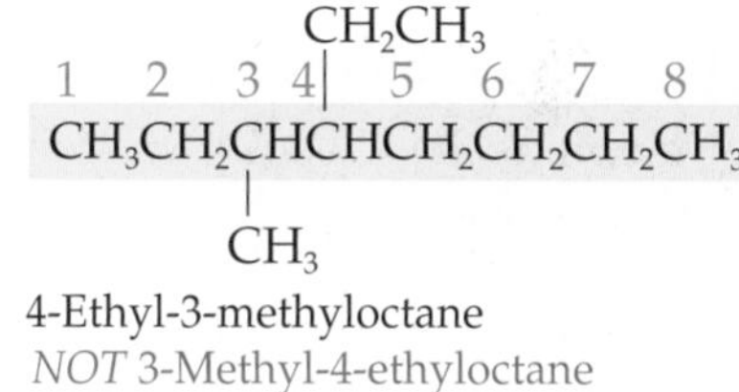

4-Ethyl-3-methyloctane
NOT 3-Methyl-4-ethyloctane

EXAMPLE 10.2 Naming Substituted Alkanes Using the IUPAC System

LEARNING GOAL

6 Use the basic rules of the IUPAC Nomenclature System to name alkanes and substituted alkanes.

a. What is the IUPAC name of the molecule below, which is commonly called Freon-12? This compound is a chlorofluorocarbon (CFC) once used as a refrigerant and aerosol propellant. It has not been manufactured in the United States since 1995 because of the CFC damage to the ozone layer.

$$CCl_2F_2$$

(F—C—Cl with Cl above and F below the carbon)

Solution

Helpful Hint: No numbers are necessary if there is only one carbon or if the numbering is clear cut.

Parent chain: methane
Substituents: dichlorodifluoro (no numbers are necessary)
Name: Dichlorodifluoromethane

b. What is the IUPAC name of the following molecule, which is a component of the tsetse fly pheromone? Molecules such as this are used as attractants in tsetse fly control measures.

$$CH_3(CH_2)_{14}CHCH_3$$

(with CH_3 on the CH carbon)

Continued...

Solution

Helpful Hint: For alkanes of between eleven and nineteen carbons, a prefix is used before the word decane (see Table 10.8).

Parent chain: heptadecane
Substituent: 2-methyl
Name: 2-Methylheptadecane

c. What is the IUPAC name of the following molecule, which is the standard of excellence used in determining the octane rating of gasoline?

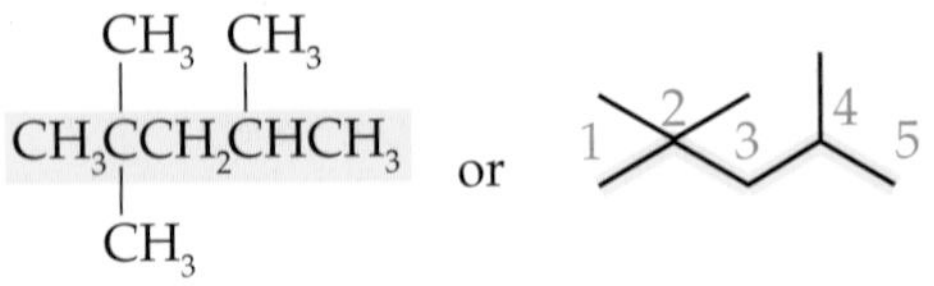

$$\begin{array}{c} CH_3\ \ CH_3 \\ |\qquad | \\ CH_3CCH_2CHCH_3 \\ | \\ CH_3 \end{array}$$

or (skeletal structure numbered 1–5)

Solution

Parent chain: pentane
Substituents: 2,2,4-trimethyl
Name: 2,2,4-Trimethylpentane

Practice Problem 10.2

Determine the IUPAC name for each of the following molecules.

a. 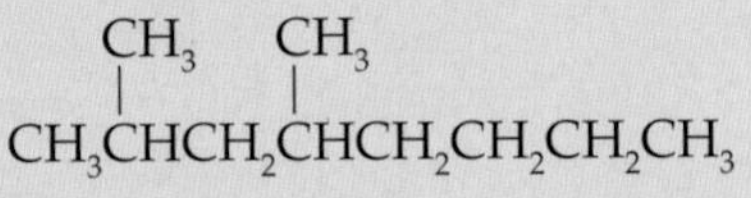 $CH_3CH(CH_3)CH_2CH(CH_3)CH_2CH_2CH_2CH_3$

b. 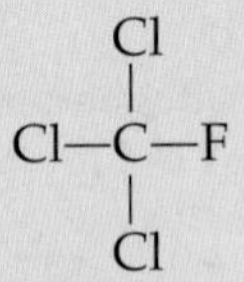 $Cl-C(Cl)(Cl)-F$

c. $CH_3CH_2CH_2CH(F)CH(Cl)CH(CH_3)CH_3$

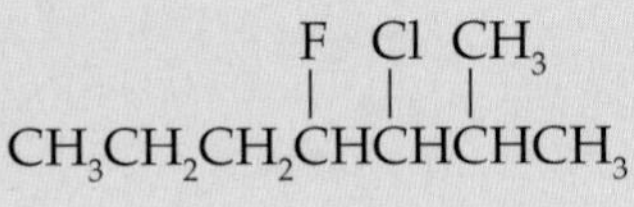

▶ For Further Practice: **Questions 10.57, 10.58, and 10.61.**

Having learned to name a compound using the IUPAC system, we can easily write the structural formula of a compound, given its name. First, draw and number the parent carbon chain. Add the substituent groups to the correct carbon, and finish the structure by adding the correct number of hydrogen atoms.

TABLE 10.8 IUPAC Nomenclature for Alkane Parent Chains Longer Than Ten Carbons

Number of Carbons	IUPAC Name
11	*Un*decane
12	*Do*decane
13	*Tri*decane
14	*Tetra*decane
15	*Penta*decane
16	*Hexa*decane
17	*Hepta*decane
18	*Octa*decane
19	*Nona*decane

EXAMPLE 10.3 Drawing the Structure of a Compound Using the IUPAC Name

LEARNING GOAL

7 From the IUPAC name of an alkane or substituted alkane, be able to draw the structure.

Draw the structural formula for 1-bromo-4-methylhexane.

Solution

Begin by drawing the six-carbon parent chain and indicating the four bonds for each carbon atom.

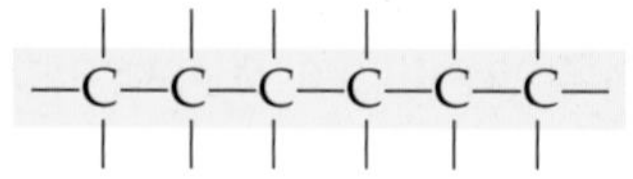

```
  |  |  |  |  |  |
—C—C—C—C—C—C—
  |  |  |  |  |  |
```

Next, number each carbon atom:

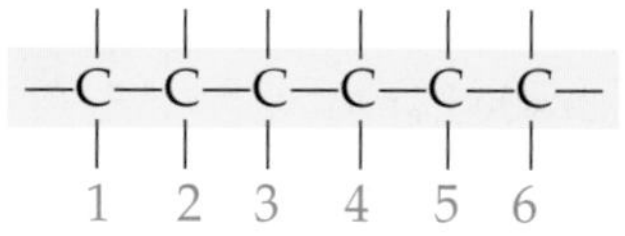

```
  |  |  |  |  |  |
—C—C—C—C—C—C—
  |  |  |  |  |  |
  1  2  3  4  5  6
```

Now add the substituents. In this example a bromine atom is bonded to carbon-1, and a methyl group is bonded to carbon-4:

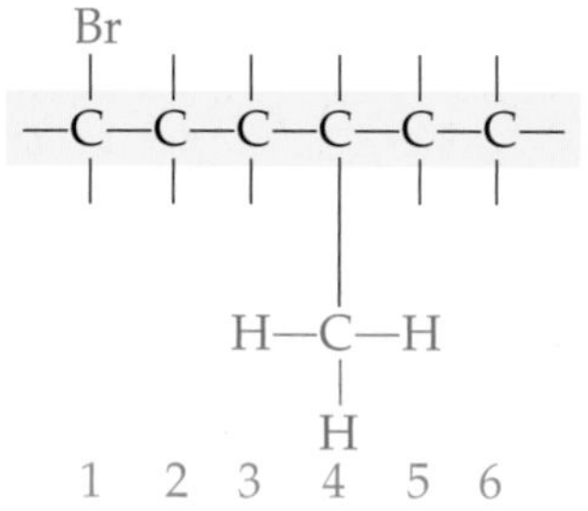

```
  Br
  |  |  |  |  |  |
—C—C—C—C—C—C—
  |  |  |  |  |  |
           |
         H—C—H
           |
           H
  1  2  3  4  5  6
```

Finally, add the correct number of hydrogen atoms so that each carbon has four covalent bonds:

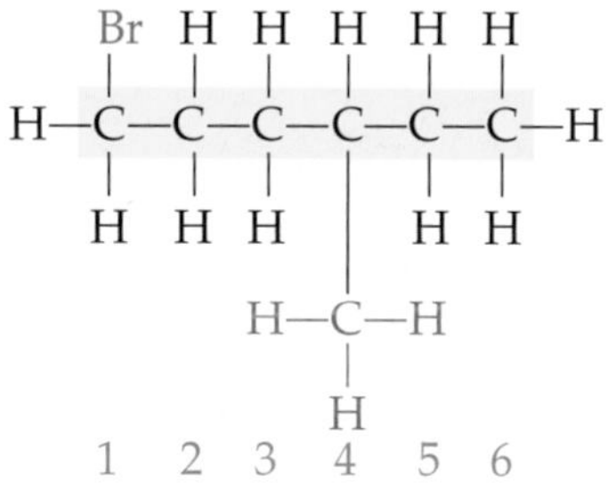

```
  Br H  H  H  H  H
  |  |  |  |  |  |
H—C—C—C—C—C—C—H
  |  |  |  |  |  |
  H  H  H  |  H  H
           |
         H—C—H
           |
           H
  1  2  3  4  5  6
```

As a final check of your accuracy, use the IUPAC system to name the compound that you have just drawn, and compare the name with that in the original problem.

The molecular, condensed, and line formulas can be written from the structural formula shown. The molecular formula is $C_7H_{15}Br$, the condensed formula is $BrCH_2(CH_2)_2CH(CH_3)CH_2CH_3$, and the line formula for 1-bromo-4-methylhexane is

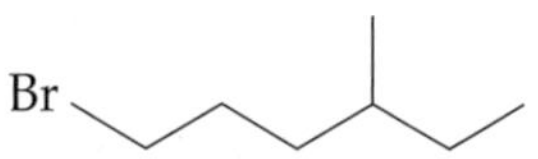

Br

Practice Problem 10.3

Draw the condensed formula of each of the following compounds:

a. 1-Bromo-2-chlorohexane
b. 2,3-Dimethylpentane
c. 1,3,5-Trichloroheptane
d. 3-Chloro-5-iodo-4-methyloctane
e. 1,2-Dibromo-3-chlorobutane
f. Trifluorochloromethane

► For Further Practice: **Questions 10.51, 10.52, and 10.53.**

LEARNING GOAL

8 Draw constitutional (structural) isomers of simple organic compounds.

ANIMATION
- Structural Isomers of Hexane

Constitutional or Structural Isomers

As we saw earlier, there are two arrangements of the atoms represented by the molecular formula C_4H_{10}: butane and methylpropane. Molecules having the same molecular formula but a different arrangement of atoms are called **constitutional,** or **structural, isomers.** These isomers are unique compounds because of their structural differences, and they have different physical and chemical properties. For instance, the data in Table 10.4 show that the branched-chain isomers of C_6H_{14} have lower boiling and melting points than the straight-chain isomer, hexane. These differences reflect the different shapes of the molecules.

EXAMPLE 10.4 Drawing Constitutional or Structural Isomers of Alkanes

LEARNING GOAL

8 Draw constitutional (structural) isomers of simple organic compounds.

Write all the constitutional isomers having the molecular formula C_6H_{14}.

Solution

1. Begin with the continuous six-carbon chain structure:

```
 1  2  3  4  5  6
CH3CH2CH2CH2CH2CH3
```

Isomer A

2. Now try five-carbon chain structures with a methyl group attached to one of the internal carbon atoms of the chain:

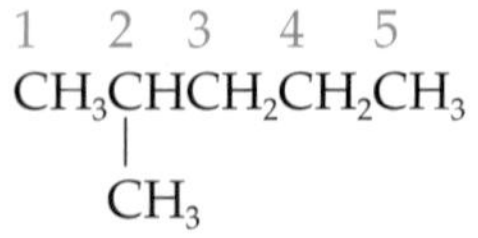

```
 1  2 3  4  5               1  2  3  4  5
CH3CHCH2CH2CH3     and     CH3CH2CHCH2CH3
    |                            |
    CH3                          CH3
```

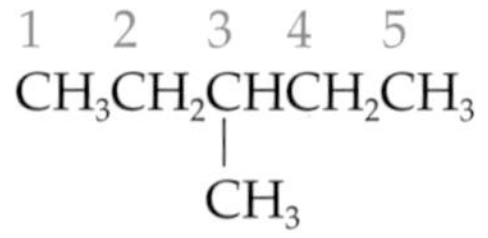

Isomer B　　　　　Isomer C

3. Next consider the possibilities for a four-carbon structure to which two methyl groups (—CH_3) may be attached:

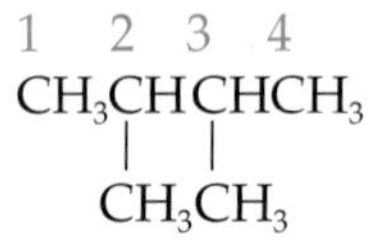

```
                            CH3
 1  2  3  4               1  2|3  4
CH3CHCHCH3        and    CH3CCH2CH3
    |  |                     |
   CH3 CH3                   CH3
```

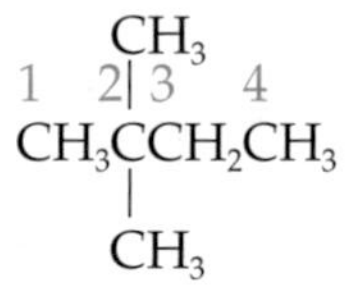

Isomer D　　　　　Isomer E

These are the five possible constitutional isomers of C_6H_{14}. At first it may seem that other isomers are also possible. But careful comparison will show that they are duplicates of those already constructed. For example, rather than add two methyl groups, a single ethyl group (—CH_2CH_3) could be added to the four-carbon chain:

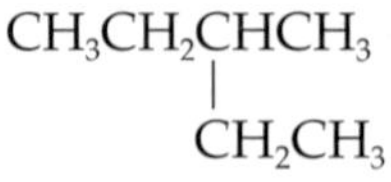

```
CH3CH2CHCH3
      |
      CH2CH3
```

But close examination will show that this is identical to isomer C. Perhaps we could add one ethyl group and one methyl group to a three-carbon parent chain, with the following result:

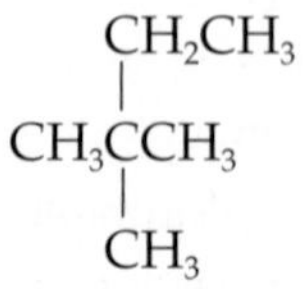

```
    CH2CH3
    |
 CH3CCH3
    |
    CH3
```

Again we find that this structure is the same as one of the isomers we have already identified, isomer E.

To check whether you have accidentally made duplicate isomers, name them using the IUPAC system. All isomers must have different IUPAC names. So if two names are identical, the structures are also identical. Use the IUPAC system to name the isomers in this example, and prove to yourself that the last two structures are simply duplicates of two of the original five isomers.

Practice Problem 10.4

Heptane is a very poor fuel and is given a zero on the octane rating scale. Gasoline octane ratings are determined in test engines by comparison with 2,2,4-trimethylpentane (the standard of high quality) and heptane (standard of poor quality). Draw line formula and give the IUPAC name for each of the nine isomers of heptane.

► For Further Practice: **Questions 10.62 and 10.63.**

10.3 Cycloalkanes

The **cycloalkanes** are a family having C—C single bonds in a ring structure. They have the general molecular formula C_nH_{2n} and thus have two fewer hydrogen atoms than the corresponding alkane (C_nH_{2n+2}). The structures and names of some simple cycloalkanes are shown in Figure 10.5.

In the IUPAC system, the cycloalkanes are named by applying the following simple rules.

- Determine the name of the alkane with the same number of carbon atoms as there are within the ring and add the prefix *cyclo-*. For example, cyclopentane is the cycloalkane that has five carbon atoms.
- If the cycloalkane is substituted, place the names of the groups in alphabetical order before the name of the cycloalkane. No number is needed if there is only one substituent.
- If more than one group is present, use numbers that result in the *lowest possible position numbers.*

EXAMPLE 10.5 Naming a Substituted Cycloalkane Using the IUPAC Nomenclature System

LEARNING GOAL

9 Write the names and draw the structures of simple cycloalkanes.

Name the following cycloalkanes using IUPAC nomenclature.

Solution

```
     H   H                          CH3
     |   |                           |
   H C———C                       H   C   H
  H/ |   |\ Cl                   |  /|\  |
  |/ H   H \|                    C   H   C
  C         C                    |\H   H/|
  |\ H   H /|                    H       H
  H\ |   | / H                     C———C
     C———C                         |   |
     |   |                         H   H
     H   H
```

Parent chain: cyclohexane
Substituent: chloro (no number is required because there is only one substituent)
Name: Chlorocyclohexane

Parent chain: cyclopentane
Substituent: methyl (no number is required because there is only one substituent)
Name: Methylcyclopentane

These cycloalkanes could also be shown as line formulas, as shown on the next page. Each line represents a carbon-carbon bond. A carbon atom and the correct number of hydrogen atoms are assumed to be at the point where the lines meet and at the end of a line.

Continued...

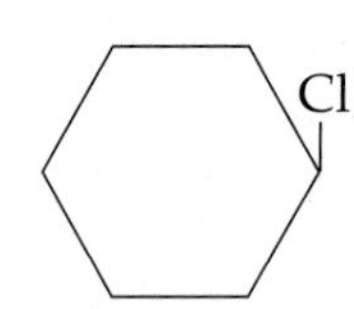

Chlorocyclohexane

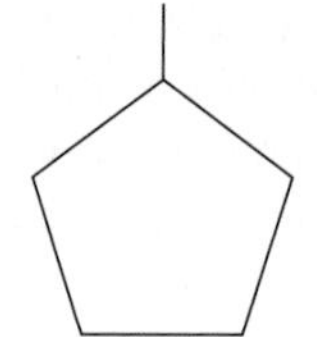

Methylcyclopentane

Practice Problem 10.5

Name each of the following cycloalkanes using IUPAC nomenclature:

a.

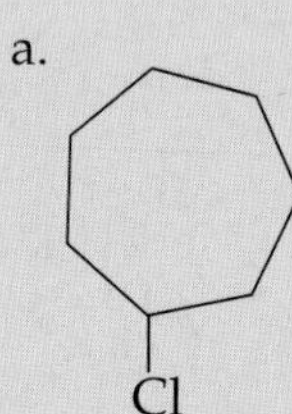

b.

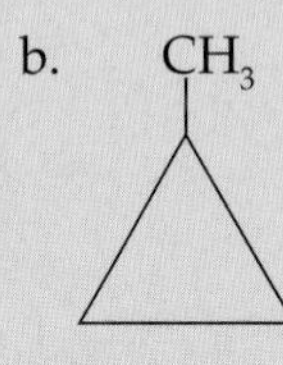

c.

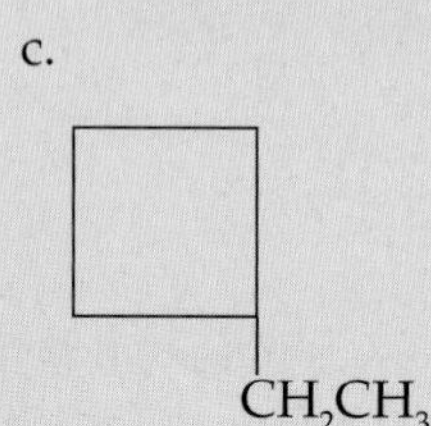

d.

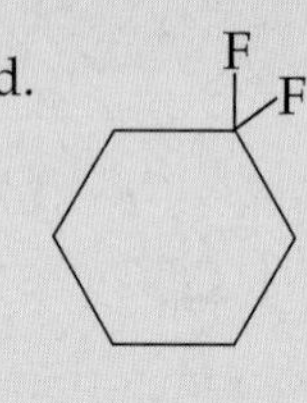

▶ For Further Practice: **Questions 10.77 and 10.78.**

Figure 10.5 Cycloalkanes: (a) cyclopropane; (b) cyclobutane; (c) cyclohexane. All of the cycloalkanes are shown using structural formulas (left column), and line formulas (right column).

(a) (b) (c)

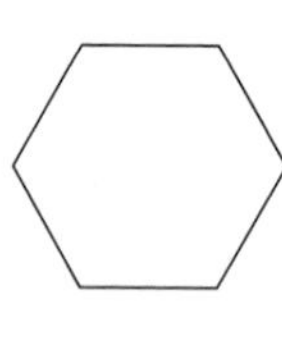

LEARNING GOAL

10 Draw *cis*- and *trans*-isomers of cycloalkanes.

cis-trans Isomerism in Cycloalkanes

Atoms of an alkane can rotate freely around the carbon-carbon single bond, resulting in an unlimited number of arrangements. However, rotation around the bonds in a cyclic structure is limited by the fact that the carbons of the ring are all bonded to another carbon within the ring. The formation of ***cis-trans*** **isomers,** or **geometric isomers,** is a consequence of the absence of free rotation.

Stereoisomers are discussed in detail in Section 16.3.

Geometric isomers are a type of *stereoisomer.* **Stereoisomers** are molecules that have the same structural formulas and bonding patterns but different arrangements of atoms in space. The *cis-trans* isomers of cycloalkanes are stereoisomers that differ from one another in the arrangement of substituents in space. Consider the following two views of the *cis-* and *trans-*isomers of 1,2-dichlorocyclohexane:

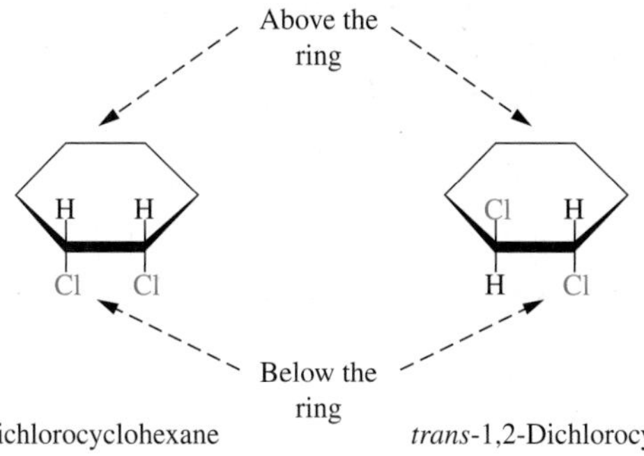

Above the ring

Below the ring

cis-1,2-Dichlorocyclohexane

trans-1,2-Dichlorocyclohexane

cis-1,2-Dichlorocyclohexane

trans-1,2-Dichlorocyclohexane

In the wedge diagram at the top, it is easy to imagine that you are viewing the ring structures as if an edge were projecting toward you. This will help you understand the more common structural formulas, shown beneath them. In the structure on the left, both Cl atoms are beneath the ring. They are termed *cis* (*Latin,* "on the same side"). The complete name for this compound is *cis*-1,2-dichlorocyclohexane. In the structure on the right, one Cl is above the ring and the other is below it. They are said to be *trans* (*Latin,* "across from") to one another and the complete name of this compound is *trans*-1,2-dichlorocyclohexane. In the line structures, the wedges tell us the same information. The dashed wedges indicate that the bond projects away from you. The solid wedges indicate that the bond is projecting toward you.

Geometric isomers do not readily interconvert. The cyclic structure prevents unrestricted free rotation and, thus, prevents interconversion. Only by breaking carbon-carbon bonds of the ring could interconversion occur. As a result, geometric isomers may be separated from one another in the laboratory.

EXAMPLE 10.6 Naming *cis-trans* Isomers of Substituted Cycloalkanes

LEARNING GOAL

10 Draw *cis-* and *trans-*isomers of cycloalkanes.

Determine whether the following substituted cycloalkanes are *cis-* or *trans-*isomers and write the complete name for each.

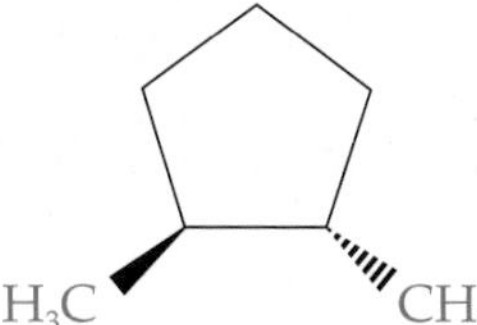

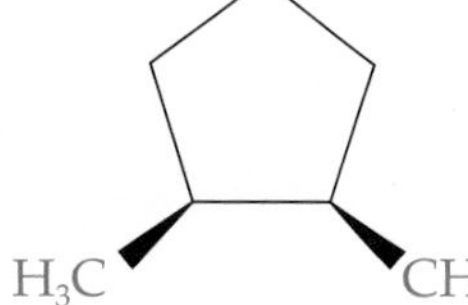

Solution

Both molecules are cyclopentanes having two methyl group substituents. Thus both would be named 1,2-dimethylcyclopentane. In the structure on the left, one methyl group is above the ring and the other is below the ring; they are in the *trans* configuration, and the structure is named *trans*-1,2-dimethylcyclopentane. In the structure on the right, both methyl groups are on the same side of the ring (above it, in this case); they are *cis* to one another, and the complete name of this compound is *cis*-1,2-dimethylcyclopentane.

Continued...

Practice Problem 10.6

Determine whether each of the following is a *cis*- or a *trans*-isomer.

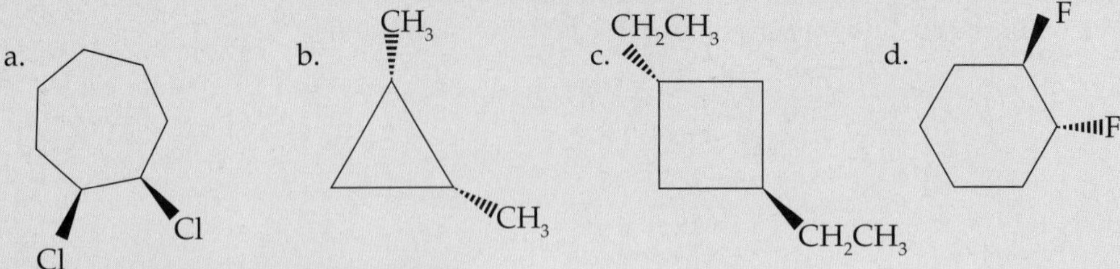

▸ For Further Practice: **Questions 10.85 and 10.86.**

EXAMPLE 10.7 Naming a Cycloalkane Having Two Substituents Using the IUPAC Nomenclature System

LEARNING GOAL

9 Write the names and draw the structures of simple cycloalkanes.

Name the following cycloalkanes using IUPAC nomenclature.

Solution

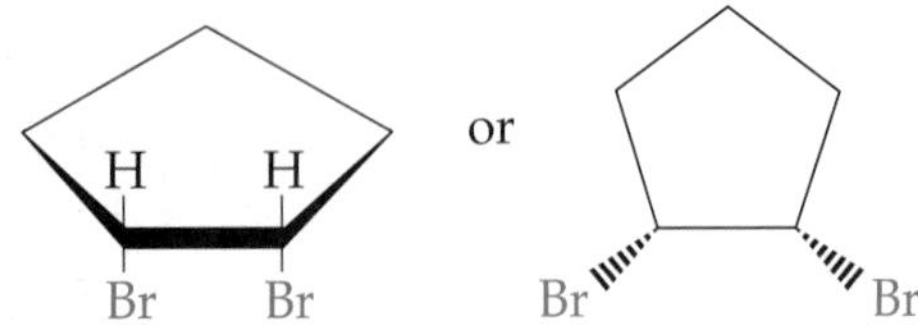

Parent chain: cyclopentane
Substituent: 1,2-dibromo
Isomer: *cis*
Since both bromine atoms are below the ring, the name is: *cis*-1,2-Dibromocyclopentane

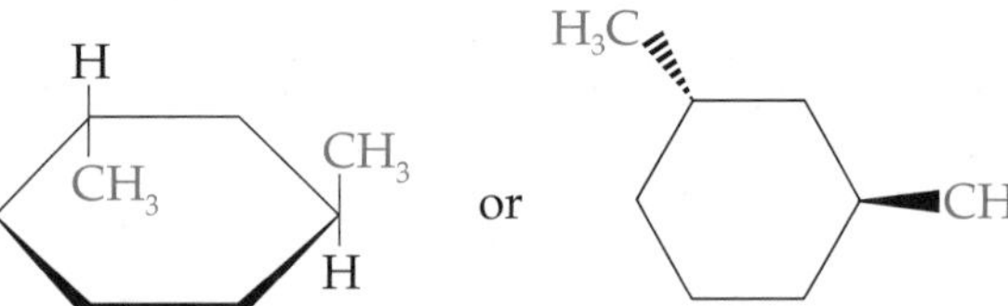

Parent chain: cyclohexane
Substituent: 1,3-dimethyl
Isomer: *trans*
Since one of the methyl groups is above the ring and the other is below, the name is: *trans*-1,3-Dimethylcyclohexane

Practice Problem 10.7

Write the complete IUPAC name for each of the following cycloalkanes.

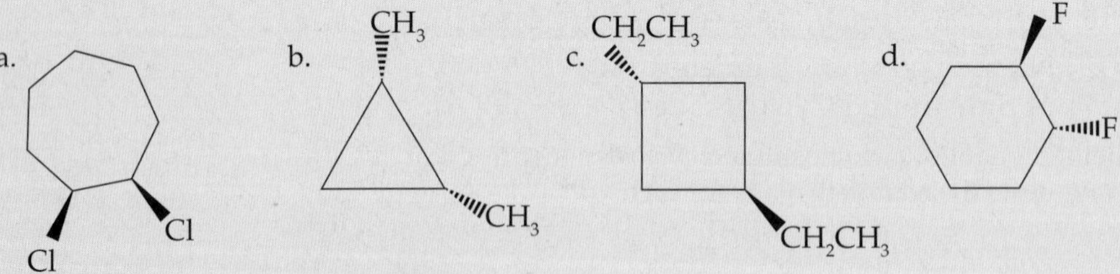

▸ For Further Practice: **Questions 10.83 and 10.84.**

10.4 Conformations of Alkanes and Cycloalkanes

LEARNING GOAL

11 Describe conformations of alkanes.

Because there is *free rotation* around a carbon-carbon single bond, even a very simple alkane, like ethane, can exist in an unlimited number of forms (Figures 10.6a and 10.6b). These different arrangements are called **conformations,** or **conformers.**

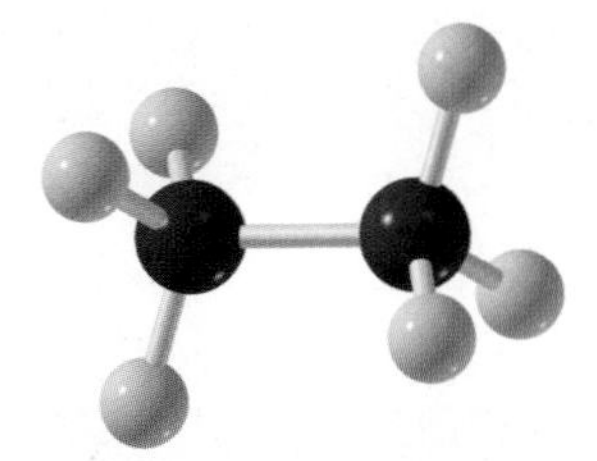

(a) Staggered conformation of ethane

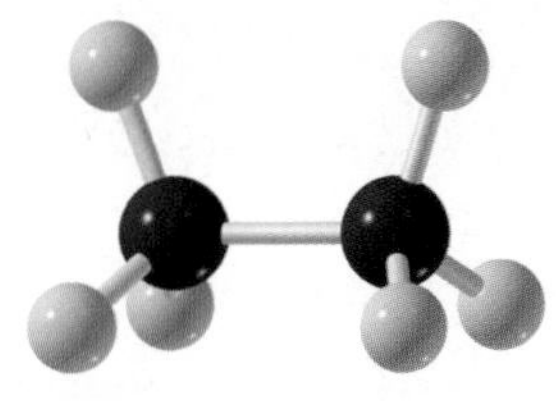

(b) Eclipsed conformation of ethane

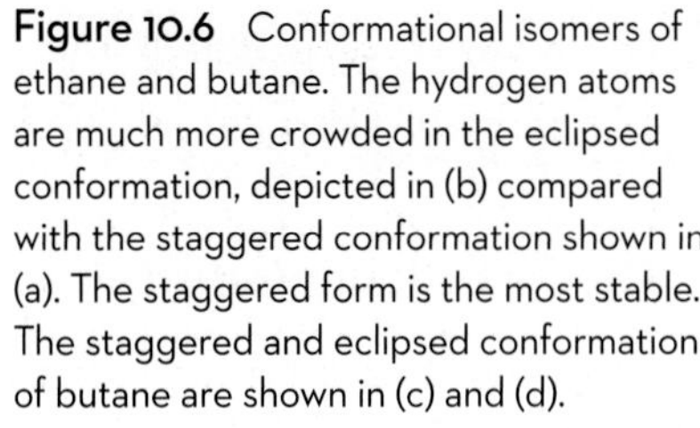

Figure 10.6 Conformational isomers of ethane and butane. The hydrogen atoms are much more crowded in the eclipsed conformation, depicted in (b) compared with the staggered conformation shown in (a). The staggered form is the most stable. The staggered and eclipsed conformations of butane are shown in (c) and (d).

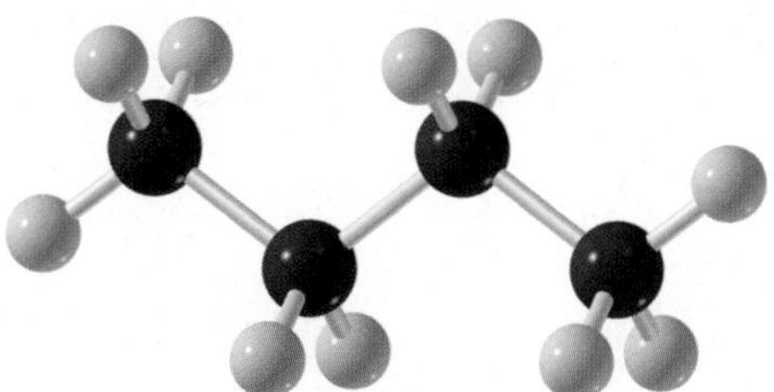

(c) Staggered conformation of butane

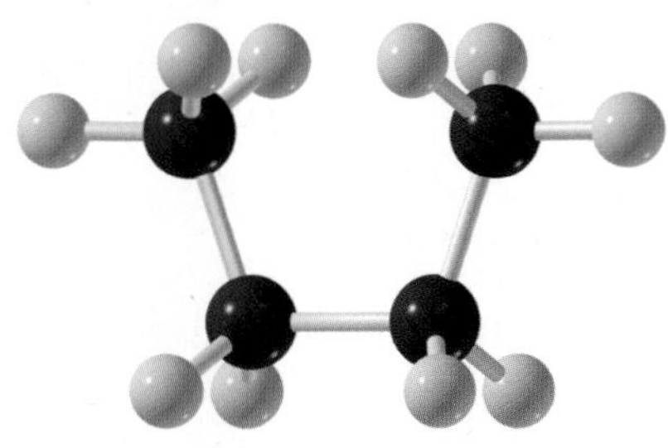

(d) Eclipsed conformation of butane

Alkanes

Figures 10.6c and 10.6d show two conformations of a more complex alkane, butane. In addition to these two conformations, an infinite number of intermediate conformers exist. Keep in mind that all these conformations are simply different forms of the same molecule produced by rotation around the carbon-carbon single bonds. Even at room temperature these conformers interconvert rapidly. As a result, they cannot be separated from one another.

Make a ball-and-stick model of butane and demonstrate these rotational changes for yourself.

Although all conformations can be found in a population of molecules, the *staggered* conformation (see Figures 10.6a and 10.6c) is the most common. One reason for this is that the bonding electrons are farthest from one another in this conformation. Because this minimizes the repulsion between these bonding electrons, the staggered conformation is the most stable of the possible conformations. In the *eclipsed* conformation (Figures 10.6b and 10.6d, the hydrogen atoms are closest to one another. This maximizes the repulsion between electrons. As a result, the eclipsed conformation is the least stable of the conformations.

Cycloalkanes

LEARNING GOAL

12 Draw the chair and boat conformations of cyclohexane.

Cycloalkanes also exist in different conformations. The only exception to this is cyclopropane. Because it has only three carbon atoms, it is always planar.

The conformations of six-member rings have been the most thoroughly studied. One reason is that many important and abundant biological molecules have six-member ring structures. Among these is the simple sugar glucose, also called *blood sugar.* Glucose is the most important sugar in the human body. It is absorbed by the cells of the body and broken down to provide energy for cellular activities.

The structure of glucose is found in Section 16.4. The physiological roles of glucose are discussed in Chapters 21 and 22.

The most energetically favorable conformation for a six-member ring is the **chair conformation.** In this conformation the hydrogen atoms are perfectly staggered; that is, they are as far from one another as possible. In addition, the bond angle between carbons is 109.5°, exactly the angle expected for tetrahedral carbon atoms. Because the hydrogen atoms are as far from one another as possible the repulsion between the bonding electrons is minimized. As a result, the chair conformation is the most stable conformation of cyclohexane.

GREEN CHEMISTRY

The Petroleum Industry and Gasoline Production

Petroleum consists primarily of alkanes and small amounts of alkenes and aromatic hydrocarbons. Substituted hydrocarbons, such as phenol, are also present in very small quantities. Although the composition of petroleum varies with the source (United States, Persian Gulf, etc.), the mixture of hydrocarbons can be separated into its component parts on the basis of differences in the boiling points of various hydrocarbons (distillation). Often several successive distillations of various fractions of the original mixture are required to completely purify the desired component. In the first distillation, the petroleum is separated into several fractions, each of which consists of a mix of hydrocarbons. Each fraction can be further purified by successive distillations. On an industrial scale, these distillations are carried out in columns that may be hundreds of feet (ft) in height.

The gasoline fraction of petroleum, called straight-run gasoline, consists primarily of alkanes and cycloalkanes with six to twelve carbon atoms in the skeleton. This fraction has very poor fuel performance. In fact, branched-chain alkanes are superior to straight-chain alkanes as fuels because they are more volatile, burn less rapidly in the cylinder, and thus reduce "knocking." Alkenes and aromatic hydrocarbons are also good fuels. Methods have been developed to convert hydrocarbons of higher and lower molar masses than gasoline to the appropriate molar mass range and to convert straight-chain hydrocarbons into branched ones. *Catalytic cracking* fragments a large hydrocarbon into smaller ones. *Catalytic re-forming* results in the rearrangement of a hydrocarbon into a more useful form.

The antiknock quality of a fuel is measured as its octane rating. Heptane is a very poor fuel and is given an octane rating of zero. 2,2,4-Trimethylpentane (commonly called isooctane) is an excellent fuel and is given an octane rating of one hundred. Gasoline octane ratings are experimentally determined by comparison with these two compounds in test engines.

Mining the sea for hydrocarbons.

ANIMATION

- Oil Refining Processes

For Further Understanding

- Explain why the mixture of hydrocarbons in crude oil can be separated by distillation.
- Draw the structures of heptane and 2,2,4-trimethylpentane (isooctane).

Compare the structure of this deck chair to the conformation of cyclohexane shown to the right. Explain why this conformation is called the chair conformation.

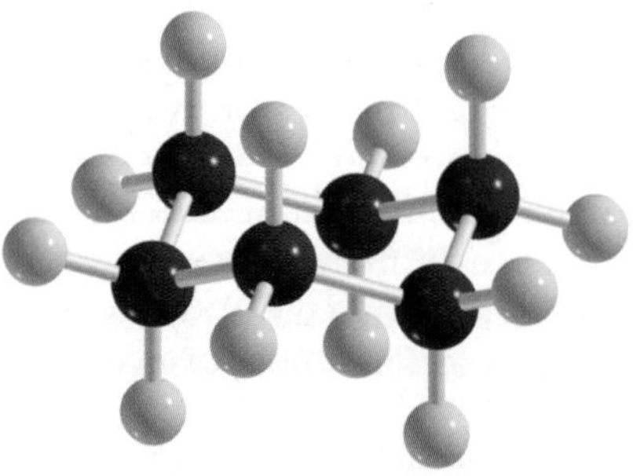

Chair conformation

Six-member rings can also exist in a **boat conformation,** so-called because it resembles a rowboat. This form is much less stable than the chair conformation because the hydrogen atoms are much more crowded, creating much more repulsion between the electrons.

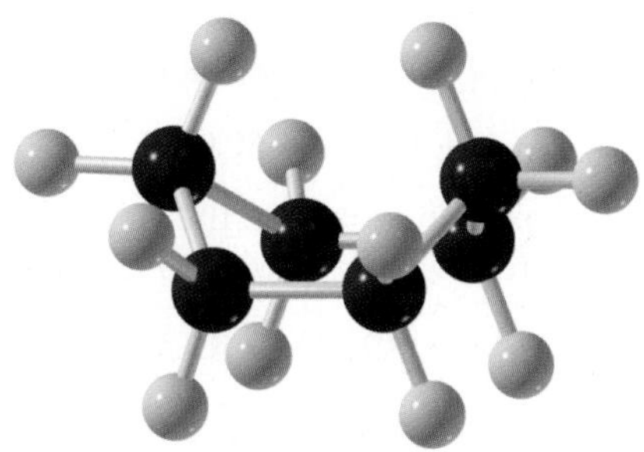

Boat conformation

Compare the structure of these boats to the conformation of cyclohexane shown to the left. Explain why this conformation is called the boat conformation.

10.5 Reactions of Alkanes and Cycloalkanes

Combustion

Alkanes, cycloalkanes, and other hydrocarbons can be oxidized (by burning) in the presence of excess molecular oxygen. In this reaction, called **combustion,** they burn at high temperatures, producing carbon dioxide and water and releasing large amounts of energy as heat.

LEARNING GOAL

13 Write balanced equations for combustion reactions of alkanes.

C_nH_{2n+2}	+	O_2	$\longrightarrow$	CO_2	+	H_2O	+	heat energy
Alkane		Oxygen	$\longrightarrow$	Carbon dioxide		Water		

The following examples show a combustion reaction for a simple alkane and a simple cycloalkane:

Combustion reactions are discussed in Section 4.4.

$$CH_4 + 2O_2 \longrightarrow CO_2 + 2H_2O + \text{heat energy}$$

Methane

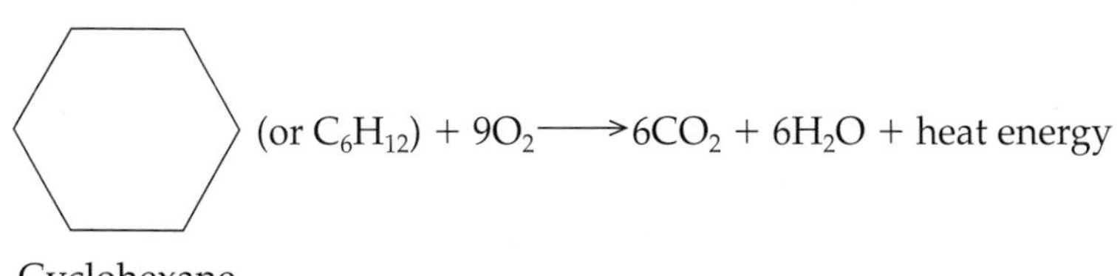

$$\text{(or } C_6H_{12}) + 9O_2 \longrightarrow 6CO_2 + 6H_2O + \text{heat energy}$$

Cyclohexane

EXAMPLE 10.8 Balancing Equations for the Combustion of Alkanes

Balance the following equation for the combustion of hexane:

$$C_6H_{14} + O_2 \longrightarrow CO_2 + H_2O$$

LEARNING GOAL

13 Write balanced equations for combustion reactions of alkanes.

Solution

First, balance the carbon atoms; there are 6 moles (mol) of carbon atoms on the left and only 1 mol of carbon atoms on the right:

$$C_6H_{14} + O_2 \longrightarrow 6CO_2 + H_2O$$

Continued...

Explain why the butane found in the lighter is a liquid only when maintained under pressure. Write an equation representing the complete combustion of butane.

Next, balance hydrogen atoms; there are 14 mol of hydrogen atoms on the left and only 2 mol of hydrogen atoms on the right:

$$C_6H_{14} + O_2 \longrightarrow 6CO_2 + 7H_2O$$

Now there are 19 mol of oxygen atoms on the right and only 2 mol of oxygen atoms on the left. Therefore, a coefficient of 9.5 is needed for O_2.

$$C_6H_{14} + 9.5O_2 \longrightarrow 6CO_2 + 7H_2O$$

Although decimal coefficients are sometimes used, it is preferable to have all integer coefficients. Multiplying each term in the equation by 2 will satisfy this requirement, giving us the following balanced equation:

$$2C_6H_{14} + 19O_2 \longrightarrow 12CO_2 + 14H_2O$$

The equation is now balanced with 12 mol of carbon atoms, 28 mol of hydrogen atoms, and 38 mol of oxygen atoms on each side of the equation.

Practice Problem 10.8

Write a balanced equation for the complete combustion of each of the following hydrocarbons:

a. cyclobutane b. ethane c. decane

▸ For Further Practice: **Questions 10.93 and 10.94.**

See Green Chemistry: The Greenhouse Effect and Global Climate Change in Chapter 5.

The energy released, along with their availability and relatively low cost, makes hydrocarbons very useful as fuels. In fact, combustion is essential to our very existence. It is the process by which we heat our homes, run our cars, and generate electricity. Although combustion of fossil fuels is vital to industry and society, it also represents a threat to the environment. The buildup of CO_2 may contribute to global warming and change the face of the earth in future generations.

LEARNING GOAL

14 Write balanced equations for halogenation reactions of alkanes.

Halogenation

Alkanes and cycloalkanes can also react with a halogen (usually chlorine or bromine) in a reaction called **halogenation.** Halogenation is a **substitution reaction,** that is, a reaction that results in the replacement of one group for another. In this reaction a halogen atom is substituted for one of the hydrogen atoms in the alkane. The products of this reaction are an **alkyl halide** or *haloalkane* and a hydrogen halide. Alkanes are not very reactive molecules. However, alkyl halides are very useful reactants for the synthesis of other organic compounds. Thus, the halogenation reaction is of great value because it converts unreactive alkanes into versatile starting materials for the synthesis of desired compounds. This is important in the pharmaceutical industry for the synthesis of some drugs. In addition, alkyl halides having two or more halogen atoms are useful solvents, insecticides, and herbicides.

Halogenation can occur only in the presence of heat and/or light, as indicated by the reaction conditions noted over the reaction arrows. The general equation for the halogenation of an alkane follows. The R in the general structure for the alkane may be either a hydrogen atom or an alkyl group.

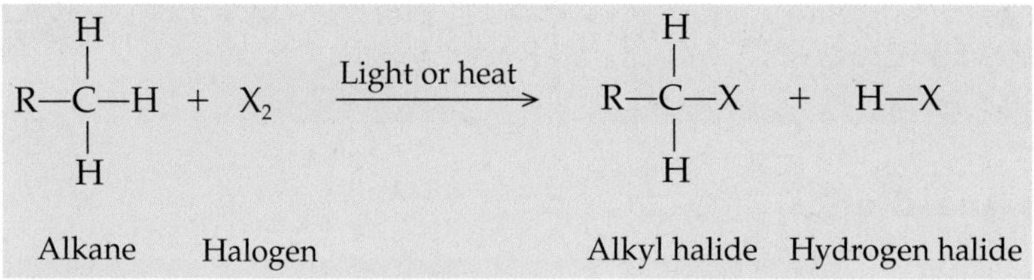

$$R{-}\overset{\displaystyle H}{\underset{\displaystyle H}{\overset{|}{\underset{|}{C}}}}{-}H + X_2 \xrightarrow{\text{Light or heat}} R{-}\overset{\displaystyle H}{\underset{\displaystyle H}{\overset{|}{\underset{|}{C}}}}{-}X + H{-}X$$

Alkane Halogen Alkyl halide Hydrogen halide

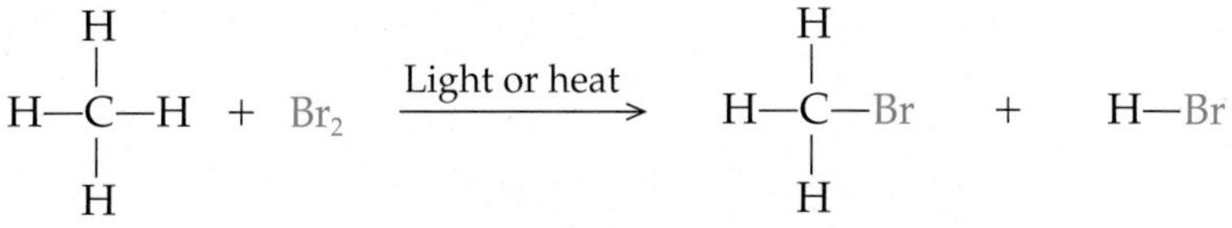

$$H{-}\overset{\displaystyle H}{\underset{\displaystyle H}{\overset{|}{\underset{|}{C}}}}{-}H + Br_2 \xrightarrow{\text{Light or heat}} H{-}\overset{\displaystyle H}{\underset{\displaystyle H}{\overset{|}{\underset{|}{C}}}}{-}Br + H{-}Br$$

Methane Bromine Bromomethane Hydrogen bromide

$$CH_3CH_3 + Cl_2 \xrightarrow{\text{Light}} CH_3CH_2{-}Cl + H{-}Cl$$

Ethane Chlorine Chloroethane Hydrogen chloride

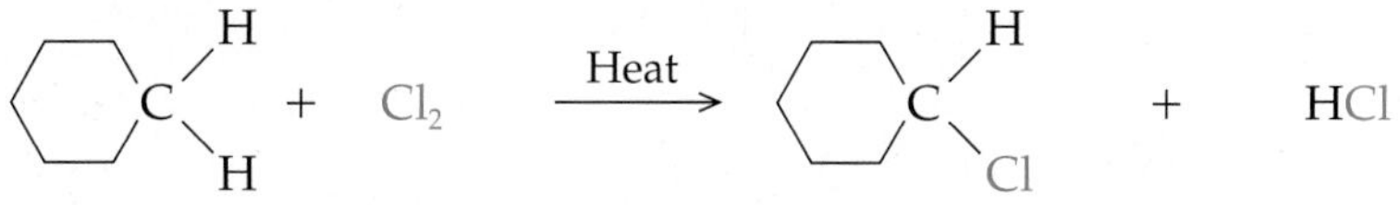

$$\text{Cyclohexane (C with H, H)} + Cl_2 \xrightarrow{\text{Heat}} \text{Chlorocyclohexane (C with H, Cl)} + HCl$$

Cyclohexane Chlorine Chlorocyclohexane Hydrogen chloride

If the halogenation reaction is allowed to continue, the alkyl halide formed may react with other halogen atoms. When this happens, a mixture of products may be formed. For instance, bromination of methane will produce bromomethane (CH_3Br), dibromomethane (CH_2Br_2), tribromomethane ($CHBr_3$), and tetrabromomethane (CBr_4).

The alkyl halide may continue to react, forming a mixture of products substituted at multiple sites or substituted multiple times at the same site.

In more complex alkanes, including branched alkanes, halogenation can occur to some extent at all positions to give a mixture of monosubstituted products. For example, bromination of propane produces a mixture of 1-bromopropane and 2-bromopropane. Halogenation of the branched alkane 2-methylpropane results in two alkyl halide products. If the hydrogen atom on carbon-2 is replaced (by chlorine, for example) the product will be 2-chloro-2-methylpropane. If any other hydrogen atom is replaced, the product will be 1-chloro-2-methylpropane.

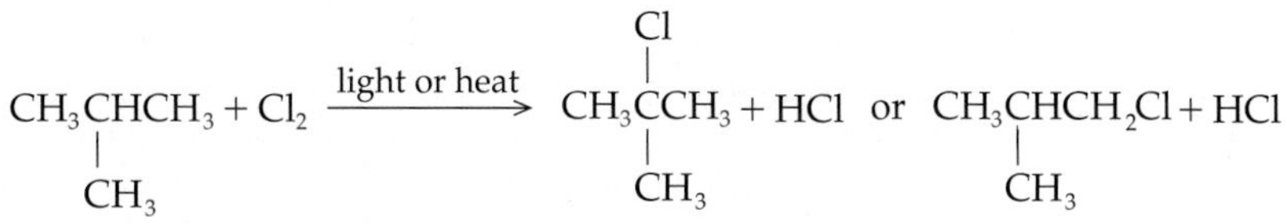

$$CH_3\underset{\displaystyle CH_3}{\underset{|}{C}H}CH_3 + Cl_2 \xrightarrow{\text{light or heat}} CH_3\overset{\displaystyle Cl}{\overset{|}{\underset{\displaystyle CH_3}{\underset{|}{C}}}}CH_3 + HCl \text{ or } CH_3\underset{\displaystyle CH_3}{\underset{|}{C}H}CH_2Cl + HCl$$

2-Chloro-2-methylpropane 1-Chloro-2-methylpropane

Question 10.5 Write a balanced equation for each of the following reactions. Show all possible products.

a. the monobromination of propane
b. the monochlorination of butane
c. the monochlorination of cyclobutane
d. the monobromination of pentane

Question 10.6 Provide the IUPAC names for the products of the reactions in Question 10.5.

A MEDICAL PERSPECTIVE

Polyhalogenated Hydrocarbons Used as Anesthetics

Polyhalogenated hydrocarbons are hydrocarbons containing two or more halogen atoms. Some polyhalogenated compounds are notorious for the problems they have caused. For instance, some insecticides such as DDT, chlordane, kepone, and lindane do not break down rapidly in the environment. As a result, these toxic compounds accumulate in biological tissue of a variety of animals, including humans, and may cause neurological damage, birth defects, or even death.

Other halogenated hydrocarbons are very useful in medicine. They were among the first anesthetics (pain relievers) used routinely in medical practice. These chemicals played a central role as the studies of medicine and dentistry advanced into modern times.

CH_3CH_2Cl
Chloroethane
(ethyl chloride)

CH_3Cl
Chloromethane
(methyl chloride)

Chloroethane and chloromethane are local anesthetics. A local anesthetic deadens the feeling in a portion of the body. Applied topically (on the skin), chloroethane and chloromethane numb the area. Rapid evaporation of these anesthetics lowers the skin temperature, deadening the local nerve endings. They act rapidly, but the effect is brief, and feeling is restored quickly.

$CHCl_3$
Trichloromethane
(chloroform)

In the past, chloroform was used as both a general and a local anesthetic. When administered through inhalation, it rapidly causes loss of consciousness. However, the effects of this powerful anesthetic are of short duration. Chloroform is no longer used because it was shown to be carcinogenic.

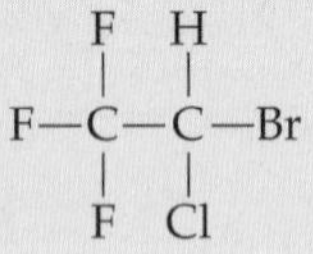

```
   F  H
   |  |
F—C—C—Br
   |  |
   F  Cl
```

2-Bromo-2-chloro-1,1,1-trifluoroethane
(Halothane)

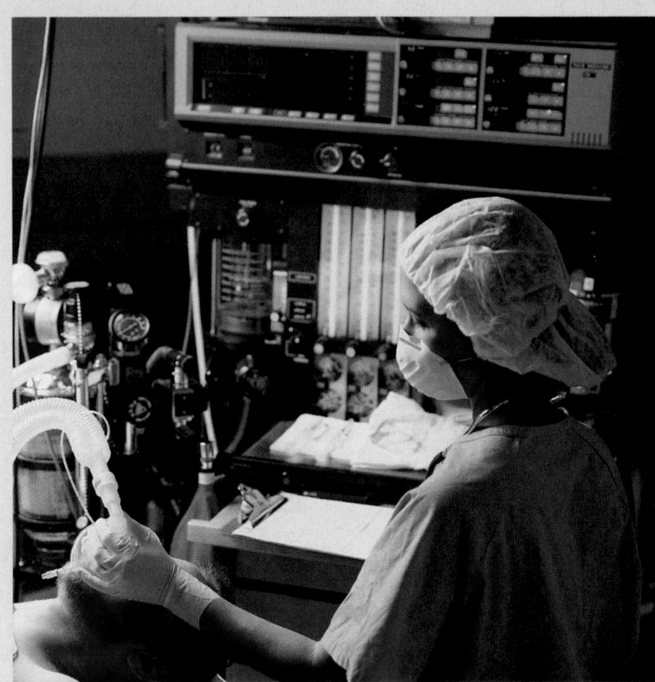

Halothane is administered to a patient.

Halothane is a general anesthetic that is administered by inhalation. It is considered to be a very safe anesthetic and is widely used.

For Further Understanding

- In the first 24 hours (h) following administration, 70% of the halothane is eliminated from the body in exhaled gases. Explain why halothane is so readily eliminated in exhaled gases.
- Rapid evaporation of chloroethane from the skin surface causes cooling that causes local deadening of nerve endings. Explain why the skin surface cools dramatically as a result of evaporation of chloroethane.

CHAPTER MAP

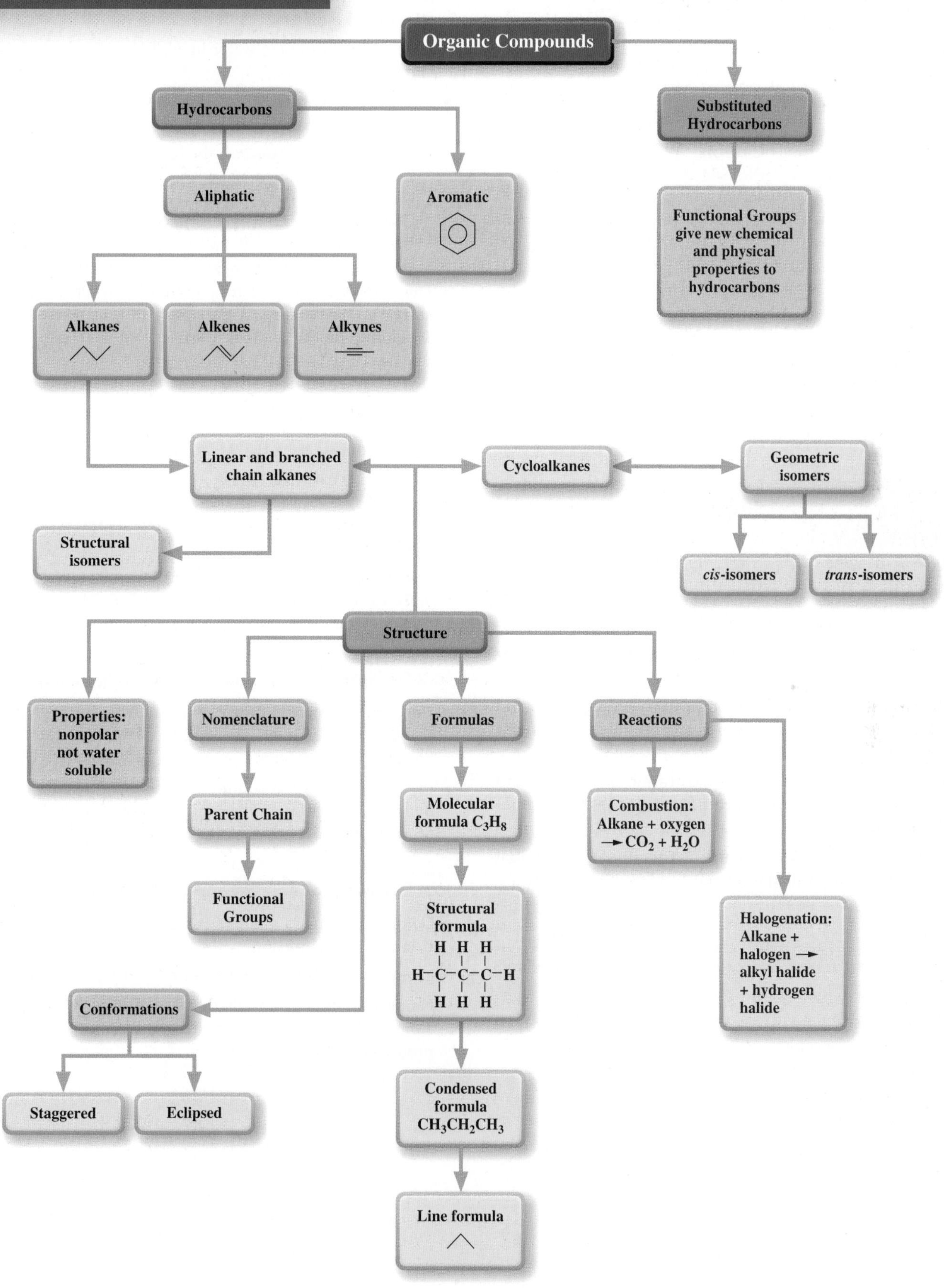

Organic Compounds
Hydrocarbons
Substituted Hydrocarbons
Aliphatic
Aromatic
Functional Groups give new chemical and physical properties to hydrocarbons
Alkanes
Alkenes
Alkynes
Linear and branched chain alkanes
Cycloalkanes
Geometric isomers
Structural isomers
cis-isomers
trans-isomers
Structure
Properties: nonpolar not water soluble
Nomenclature
Formulas
Reactions
Parent Chain
Molecular formula C_3H_8
Combustion: Alkane + oxygen → $CO_2 + H_2O$
Functional Groups
Structural formula
Halogenation: Alkane + halogen → alkyl halide + hydrogen halide
Conformations
Staggered
Eclipsed
Condensed formula $CH_3CH_2CH_3$
Line formula

SUMMARY OF REACTIONS

Reactions of Alkanes
Combustion:

$$\underset{\text{Alkane}}{C_nH_{2n+2}} + \underset{\text{Oxygen}}{O_2} \longrightarrow \underset{\text{Carbon dioxide}}{CO_2} + \underset{\text{Water}}{H_2O} + \text{heat energy}$$

Halogenation:

$$\underset{\text{Alkane}}{R{-}\overset{\displaystyle H}{\underset{\displaystyle H}{\overset{|}{\underset{|}{C}}}}{-}H} + \underset{\text{Halogen}}{X_2} \xrightarrow{\text{light or heat}} \underset{\text{Alkyl halide}}{R{-}\overset{\displaystyle H}{\underset{\displaystyle H}{\overset{|}{\underset{|}{C}}}}{-}X} + \underset{\text{Hydrogen halide}}{H{-}X}$$

SUMMARY

10.1 The Chemistry of Carbon

- Organic chemistry is the study of carbon-containing compounds.
- All organic compounds are classified as **hydrocarbons** or **substituted hydrocarbons.**
- Hydrocarbons contain only carbon and hydrogen atoms and may be **aliphatic** (alkanes, alkenes, and alkynes) or **aromatic** (containing a benzene ring.)
- Aliphatic hydrocarbons may be **saturated** (only C—C and C—H single bonds) or **unsaturated** (at least one C—C double or triple bond.)
- Substituted hydrocarbons include a **functional group** that gives the molecule particular chemical and physical properties.

10.2 Alkanes

- **Alkanes** are **saturated hydrocarbons** with the general formula C_nH_{2n+2}.
- Four types of formulas are used to represent organic molecules:
  - **Molecular formulas**
  - **Structural formulas**
  - **Condensed formulas**
  - **Line formulas**
- Two organic molecules with the same molecular formula but different bonding patterns have different physical and chemical properties. Such molecules are **structural** or **constitutional isomers.**
- Alkanes are nonpolar, water-insoluble, and have low melting and boiling points.
- The **IUPAC Nomenclature System** is the universal system for naming organic compounds.
  - The **parent compound,** the longest carbon chain with the characteristic functional group, gives the molecule its primary name.
  - Attached to the parent chain, **alkyl groups** (alkanes with one fewer hydrogen atom), halogens, or other functional groups may replace one or more of the hydrogen atoms in the alkane.
- The carbon atoms within a molecule are classified as **primary (1°), secondary (2°), tertiary (3°), or quaternary (4°),** depending on the number of carbon atoms to which they are attached.

10.3 Cycloalkanes

- **Cycloalkanes** are organic molecules having C—C single bonds in a ring structure.
- There is very limited rotation around the C—C bonds in a cycloalkane. As a result, **geometric isomers,** also called *cis-trans* isomers, occur.
- Geometric isomers are a type of stereoisomers, which are molecules with the same molecular formulas and bonding patterns, but different arrangements of atoms in space.

10.4 Conformations of Alkanes and Cycloalkanes

- **Conformations** or **conformers** result from the free rotation of the C—C bonds in alkanes and the limited rotation of C—C bonds in **cycloalkanes.**
- In cyclohexane, two common conformers are the **chair** and **boat conformations.** The chair conformation is the most stable and therefore is the more common conformation.

10.5 Reactions of Alkanes and Cycloalkanes

- Common reactions of alkanes and cycloalkanes are **combustion** and **halogenation.**
- Complete combustion produces CO_2, H_2O, and heat.
- Halogenation is a **substitution reaction** in which a halogen atom replaces one of the hydrogen atoms in the molecule, producing an **alkyl halide.**

ANSWERS TO PRACTICE PROBLEMS

10.1 Structural Formulas:

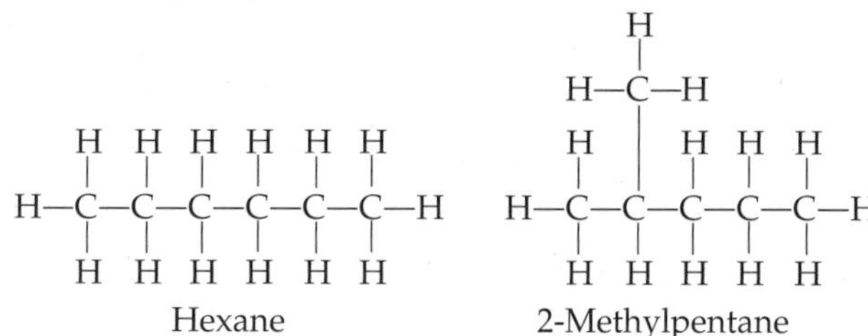

Hexane 2-Methylpentane

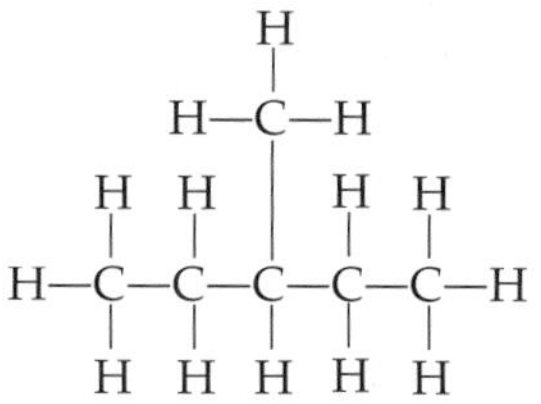

3-Methylpentane

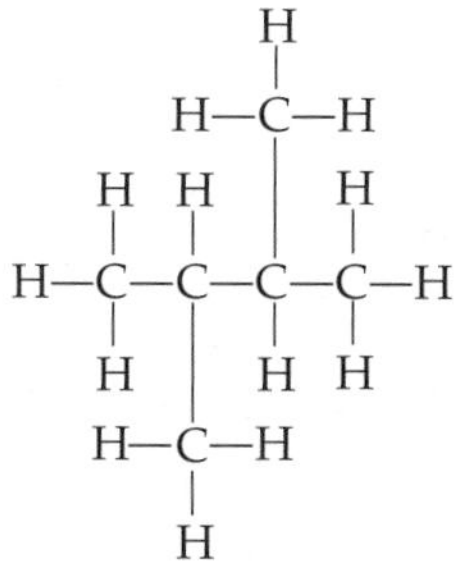

2,3-Dimethylbutane 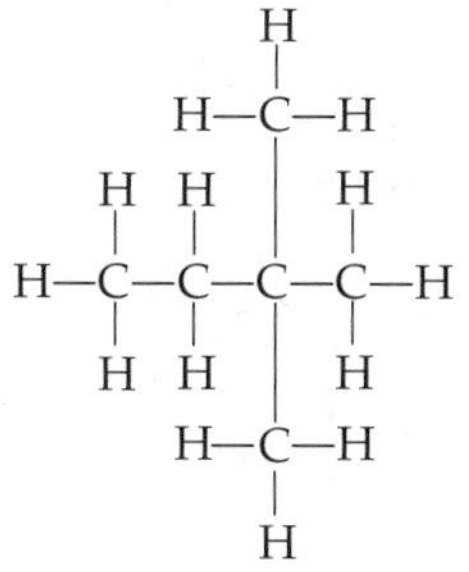 2,2-Dimethylbutane

Line Formulas

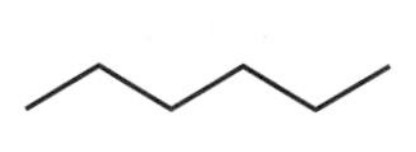

Hexane

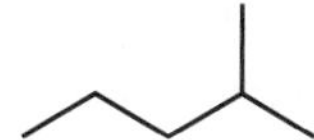

2-Methylpentane

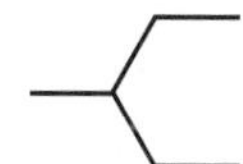

3-Methylpentane

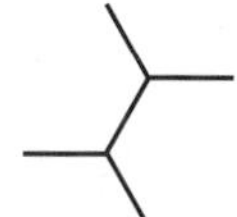

2,3-Dimethylbutane

2,2-Dimethylbutane

10.2 a. 2,4-Dimethyloctane
b. Trichlorofluoromethane
c. 3-Chloro-4-fluoro-2-methylheptane

10.3 a. $CH_2BrCHCl(CH_2)_3CH_3$
b. $CH_3CH(CH_3)CH(CH_3)CH_2CH_3$
c. $CH_2ClCH_2CHClCH_2CHClCH_2CH_3$
d. $CH_3CH_2CHClCH(CH_3)CHI(CH_2)_2CH_3$
e. $CH_2BrCHBrCHClCH_3$
f. CF_3Cl

10.4 The following are the line structures and IUPAC names of the nine isomers of heptane:

Heptane 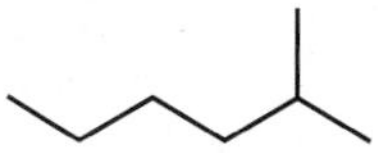 2-Methylhexane 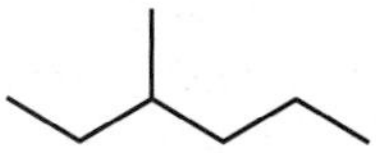 3-Methylhexane

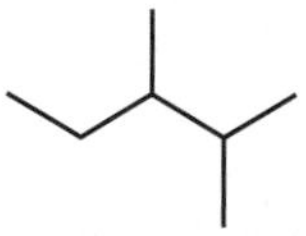

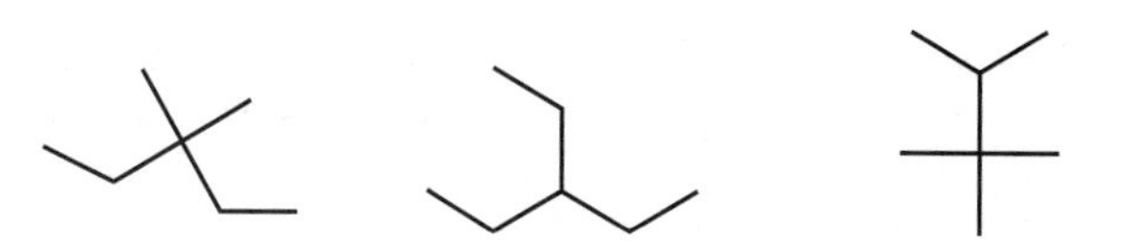

2,3-Dimethylpentane 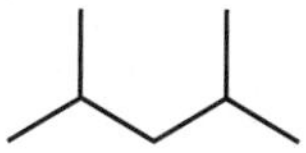 2,4-Dimethylpentane 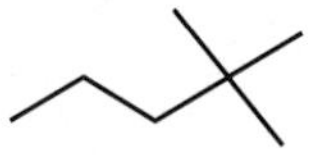 2,2-Dimethylpentane

3,3-Dimethylpentane 3-Ethylpentane 2,2,3-Trimethylbutane

10.5 a. Chlorocycloheptane c. Ethylcyclobutane
b. Methylcyclopropane d. 1,1-Difluorocyclohexane

10.6 a. *cis*-isomer c. *trans*-isomer
b. *cis*-isomer d. *trans*-isomer

10.7 a. *cis*-1,2-Dichlorocycloheptane
b. *cis*-1,2-Dimethylcyclopropane
c. *trans*-1,3-Diethylcyclobutane
d. *trans*-1,2-Difluorocyclohexane

10.8 a. The complete combustion of cyclobutane:

$$\square + 6O_2 \longrightarrow 4CO_2 + 4H_2O + \text{heat energy}$$

b. The complete combustion of ethane:

$$2CH_3CH_3 + 7O_2 \rightarrow 4CO_2 + 6H_2O + \text{heat energy}$$

c. The complete combustion of decane:

$$2C_{10}H_{22} + 31O_2 \rightarrow 20CO_2 + 22H_2O + \text{heat energy}$$

QUESTIONS AND PROBLEMS

The Chemistry of Carbon

Foundations

10.7 Why is the number of organic compounds nearly limitless?
10.8 Describe the three allotropes of carbon.
10.9 Why do ionic substances generally have higher melting and boiling points than covalent substances?
10.10 Why are ionic substances more likely to be water-soluble?

Applications

10.11 Based on intermolecular forces or ionic interactions, rank the following compounds from highest to lowest boiling points:
a. H_2O CH_4 LiCl **b.** C_2H_6 C_3H_8 NaCl

10.12 Based on intermolecular forces or ionic interactions, rank the following compounds from highest to lowest melting points:
a. H_2O CH_4 KCl **b.** C_6H_{14} $C_{18}H_{38}$ NaCl

10.13 What would the physical state of each of the compounds in Question 10.11 be at room temperature?

10.14 Which of the compounds in Question 10.12 would be soluble in water?

10.15 Consider the differences between organic and inorganic compounds as you answer each of the following questions.
a. Which compounds make good electrolytes?
b. Which compounds exhibit ionic bonding?
c. Which compounds have lower melting points?
d. Which compounds are more likely to be soluble in water?
e. Which compounds are flammable?

10.16 Describe the major differences between ionic and covalent bonds.

10.17 For centuries, fishermen have used shark liver oil to treat a variety of ailments, including general weakness, wounds, and inflammation of the respiratory and gastrointestinal tracts. In fact, it is an ingredient in the hemorrhoid cream Preparation H. In addition to chemicals such as vitamins A and D, omega-3 fatty acids, and triglycerides, shark liver oil contains approximately 14% 2,6,10,14-tetramethylpentadecane, also known as pristane.
a. Write the molecular formula for pristane.
b. Draw the line and condensed formulas for pristane.
c. Calculate the molar mass of pristane.

10.18 The tsetse fly *Glossina morsitans* is a large biting fly found in regions of Africa. They carry sleeping sickness, a deadly disease caused by a parasitic protozoan. The pheromone secreted by the tsetse fly contains four straight-chain alkanes: 2-methylheptadecane ($C_{18}H_{38}$), 17,21-dimethylheptatriacontane ($C_{39}H_{80}$), 15,19-dimethylheptatriacontane ($C_{39}H_{80}$), and 15,19,23-trimethylheptatriacontane ($C_{40}H_{82}$). Because this pheromone works by smell over long distances, it has proved useful as an agent to control tsetse fly populations.
a. Draw the line formula for each of these alkanes.
b. Calculate the molar mass of each of these alkanes.

10.19 Condense each of the following structural formulas:

```
     H H H H
     | | | |
a. H—C—C—C—C—H
     | | | |
     H H | H
       H—C—H
         |
         H
```

```
         H     H
         |     |
       H—C—H H—C—H
     H H | H H | H
     | | | | | | |
b. H—C—C—C—C—C—C—C—H
     | | | | | | |
     H H | H H H H
       H—C—H
         |
         H
```

```
         H       H
         |       |
       H—C—H   H—C—H
     H H | H H H | H H
     | | | | | | | | |
c. H—C—C—C—C—C—C—C—C—C—H
     | | | | | | | | |
     H H | H H H H | H
       H—C—H     H—C—H
         |         |
         H         H
```

10.20 Condense each of the following structural formulas:

```
       H
       |
     H—C—H
     H | H H H
     | | | | |
a. H—C—C—C—C—C—H
     | | | | |
     H H H H H
```

```
       H
       |
     H—C—H
     H | H
     | | |
b. H—C—C—C—H
     | | |
     H | H
     H—C—H
       |
       H
```

```
         H
         |
       H—C—H
     H H | H H H H H H H
     | | | | | | | | | |
c. H—C—C—C—C—C—C—C—C—C—C—H
     | | | | | | | | | |
     H H | H H H H | H H
       H—C—H     H—C—H
         |         |
         H         H
```

10.21 Convert the following structural formulas into line formulas:

```
     H H H H H
     | | | | |
   H—C—C—C—C—C—H
     | | | | |
     H H | H H
       H | H
       | | |
a.   H—C—C—C—H
       | | |
       H | H
       H—C—H
         |
         H
```

```
     H H H
     | | |
b. H—C—C=C
     |   |
     H   H
```

```
     H H H
     | | |
c. H—C—C—C—H
     | | |
     H H H
```

10.22 Convert the following structural formulas into line formulas:

```
       H       H
       |       |
     H—C—H   H—C—H
     H | H   H | H
     | | |   | |   |
a. H—C—C—C=C—C—C—C=C—H
     | |   | | | |
     H |   H H H |
     H—C—H     H—C—H
       |         |
       H         H
```

```
         H
         |
       H—C—H
         |   H   H H   H
         |   |   | |   |
b. H—C=C—C—C=C—C=C—C—C=C—H
     | | | |   |   | |
     H H | H   H   | H
       H—C—H     H—C—H
         |         |
         H         H
```

```
       H H   H
       | |   |
c. H—C=C—C—C=C—H
     |   | | |
     H   | H H
       H—C—H
         |
         H
```

10.23 Convert the structural formulas in Question 10.21 into condensed formulas.

10.24 Convert the structural formulas in Question 10.22 into condensed formulas.

10.25 Draw a line formula for each of the following alkanes:
- **a.** 4-Ethyl-2-methylhexane
- **b.** 2,3-Dimethylhexane
- **c.** 3,3-Dimethylhexane
- **d.** 3-Ethylpentane

10.26 Convert the following line formulas into condensed formulas:

a. 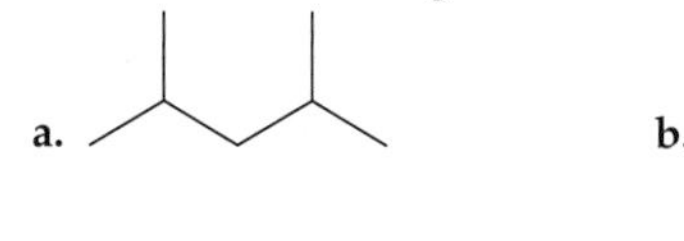

b.

c.

d.

10.27 Certain spider orchids can only be pollinated by a particular sand bee. To ensure pollination, the spider orchid emits a mixture of straight-chain alkanes that is identical to the sex pheromone produced by the female sand bee. The pheromone, a mixture of tricosane ($C_{23}H_{48}$), pentacosane ($C_{25}H_{52}$), and heptacosane ($C_{27}H_{56}$) in the ratio 3:3:1 lures the male sand bee to the spider orchid blooms.
- **a.** Draw the line formula for each of these alkanes.
- **b.** Calculate the molar mass of each of these alkanes.

10.28 Using the octet rule, explain why carbon forms four bonds in a stable compound.

10.29 Convert the following condensed formulas into structural formulas:
- **a.** $CH_3CH(CH_3)CH(CH_3)CH_2CH_3$
- **b.** $CH_3CH_2CH_2CH_2CH_3$

10.30 Convert the following condensed formulas into structural formulas:
- **a.** $CH_3CH_2CH(CH_2CH_3)CH_2CH_2CH_3$
- **b.** $CH_3CH(CH_3)CH(CH_3)CH_2CH_2CH_2CH_3$

10.31 Convert the following condensed formulas into structural formulas:
- **a.** $CH_3CH_2CH(CH_3)(CH_2)_3CH(CH_3)CH_2CH_3$
- **b.** $CH_3C(CH_3)_2CH_2CH_3$

10.32 Convert the following condensed formulas into structural formulas:
- **a.** $CH_3CH(CH_3)CH(CH_3)CH(CH_3)CH_2CH_3$
- **b.** $CH_3C(CH_3)_2CH(CH_2CH_3)CH_2CH_2CH_3$

10.33 Name the functional group in each of the following molecules:
- **a.** $CH_3CH_2CH_2OH$
- **b.** $CH_3CH_2CH_2NH_2$
- **c.** $CH_3CH_2CH_2C{=}O$ (with H on the C)
- **d.** $CH_3CH_2CH_2C{=}O$ (with OH on the C)
- **e.** $CH_3CH_2CH_2C{=}O$ (with OCH_2CH_3 on the C)
- **f.** $CH_3CH_2OCH_2CH_3$
- **g.** $CH_3CH_2CH_2I$

10.34 Convert the condensed structures in Question 10.33 into line formulas.

10.35 Give the general formula for each of the following:
- **a.** An alkane
- **b.** An alkyne
- **c.** An alkene
- **d.** A cycloalkane
- **e.** A cycloalkene

10.36 Of the classes of compounds listed in Question 10.35, which are saturated? Which are unsaturated?

10.37 What major structural feature distinguishes the alkanes, alkenes, and alkynes? Give examples.

10.38 What is the major structural feature that distinguishes between saturated and unsaturated hydrocarbons?

10.39 Give an example, using condensed formulas, of each of the following families of organic compounds. Each of your examples should contain a minimum of three carbons. (*Hint:* Refer to Table 10.2.)
- **a.** A carboxylic acid
- **b.** An amine
- **c.** An alcohol
- **d.** An ether

10.40 Folic acid is a vitamin required by the body for nucleic acid synthesis. The structure of folic acid is given below. Circle and identify as many functional groups as possible.

Folic acid

10.41 The following structure is the artificial sweetener aspartame, found in Equal. Circle and name the functional groups found in this molecule.

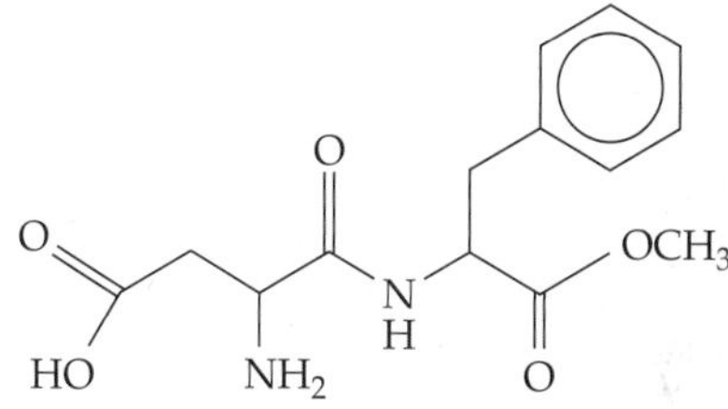

10.42 The following is the structure of the pain reliever ibuprofen, found in Advil. Circle and label the functional groups of the ibuprofen molecule.

Ibuprofen

Alkanes

Foundations

10.43 Why are hydrocarbons not water-soluble?

10.44 Describe the relationship between the length of hydrocarbon chains and the melting points of the compounds.

Applications

10.45 Based on intermolecular forces, rank the following compounds from highest to lowest boiling points:
- **a.** heptane butane hexane ethane
- **b.** $CH_3CH_2CH_2CH_2CH_3$ $CH_3CH_2CH_3$ $CH_3CH_2CH_2CH_2CH_2CH_2CH_2CH_2CH_3$

10.46 Based on intermolecular forces, rank the following compounds from highest to lowest melting points:
- **a.** decane propane methane ethane
- **b.** $CH_3CH_2CH_2CH_2CH_3$ $CH_3(CH_2)_8CH_3$ $CH_3(CH_2)_6CH_3$

10.47 What would the physical state of each of the compounds in Question 10.45 be at room temperature?

10.48 What would the physical state of each of the compounds in Question 10.46 be at room temperature?

10.49 Name each of the compounds in Question 10.45b.

10.50 Name each of the compounds in Question 10.46b.

10.51 Draw each of the following using line formulas:
- **a.** 2-Bromobutane
- **b.** 2-Chloro-2-methylpropane
- **c.** 2,2-Dimethylhexane

10.52 Draw each of the following using line formulas:

a. Dichlorodiiodomethane
b. 1,4-Diethylcyclohexane
c. 2-Iodo-2,4,4-trimethylpentane

10.53 Draw each of the following compounds using structural formulas:

a. 2,2-Dibromobutane c. 1,2-Dichloropentane
b. 2-Iododecane d. 1-Bromo-2-methylpentane

10.54 Draw each of the following compounds using structural formulas:

a. 1,1,1-Trichlorodecane
b. 1,2-Dibromo-1,1,2-trifluoroethane
c. 3,3,5-Trimethylheptane
d. 1,3,5-Trifluoropentane

10.55 Name each of the following using the IUPAC Nomenclature System:

a. $CH_3CH_2CHCH_2CH_3$
      |
   CH_3

b. $CH_3CHCH_2CH_2CHCH_3$
   | |
 CH_3 CH_3

c. $CH_2CH_2CH_2CH_2Br$
   |
 $CH_2CH_2CH_3$

d. $CH_2ClCH_2CHCH_3$
      |
    CH_3

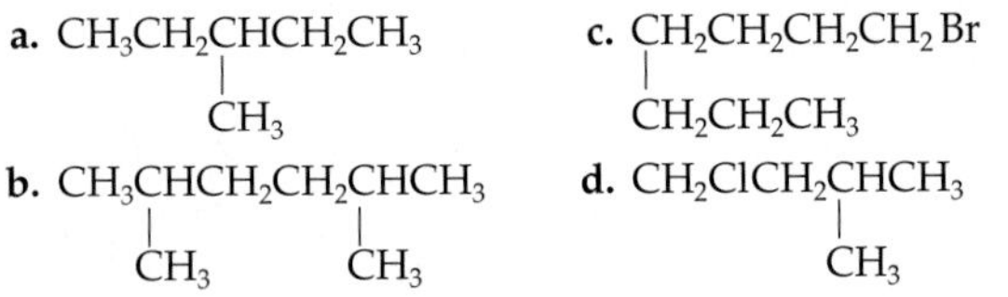

10.56 Provide the IUPAC name for each of the following compounds:

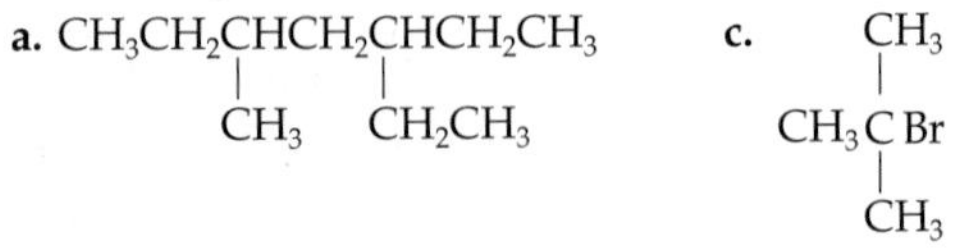

a. $CH_3CH_2CHCH_2CHCH_2CH_3$
   | |
 CH_3 CH_2CH_3

b. $CH_3CHClCH_2CH_2CH_2Cl$

c. CH_3
   |
 CH_3CBr
   |
 CH_3

10.57 Give the IUPAC name for each of the following:

a. CH_3
   |
 CH_3CHCl

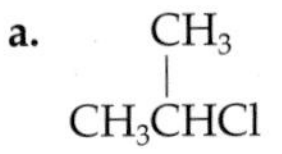

b. $CH_3CHICH_2CH_3$

c. $CH_3CBr_2CH_3$

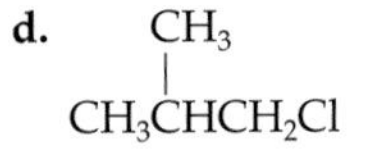

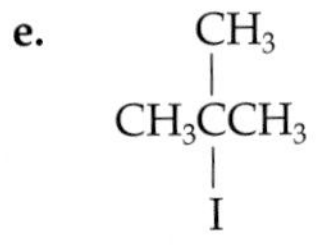

d. CH_3
   |
 CH_3CHCH_2Cl

e. CH_3
   |
 CH_3CCH_3
   |
   I

10.58 Name the following using the IUPAC Nomenclature System:

a. Cl
   |
 $CH_3CHCHCH_2CH_3$
   |
   Cl

b. CH_3
   |
 $CH_3CH_2CCH_2CHCH_3$
   | |
 CH_3 CH_3

c. CH_3 CH_3
   | |
 $CH_3CH_2CHCHCHCH_3$
   |
 CH_3

d. Br
   |
 $CHCH_2CH_2CH_3$
   |
   Br

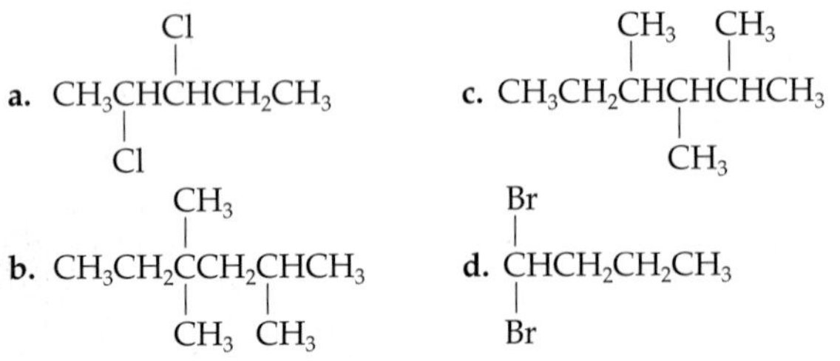

10.59 Draw a complete structural formula for each of the straight-chain isomers of the following alkanes:

a. C_4H_9Br b. $C_4H_8Br_2$

10.60 Name all of the isomers that you obtained in Question 10.59.

10.61 Name the following using the IUPAC Nomenclature System:

a. $CH_3(CH_2)_3CHClCH_3$ c. $CH_3CH_2CHClCH_2CH_3$
b. $CH_2Br(CH_2)_2CH_2Br$ d. $CH_3CH(CH_3)(CH_2)_4CH_3$

10.62 Which of the following pairs of compounds are identical? Which are constitutional isomers? Which are completely unrelated?

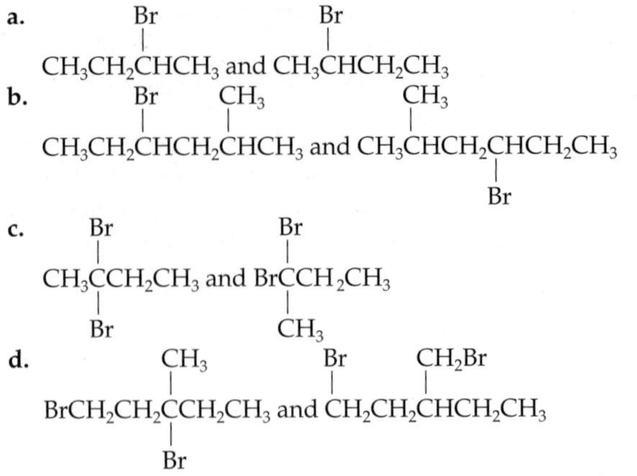

a. Br Br
   | |
 $CH_3CH_2CHCH_3$ and $CH_3CHCH_2CH_3$

b. Br CH_3 CH_3
   | | |
 $CH_3CH_2CHCH_2CHCH_3$ and $CH_3CHCH_2CHCH_2CH_3$
   |
   Br

c. Br Br
   | |
 $CH_3CCH_2CH_3$ and $BrCCH_2CH_3$
   | |
   Br CH_3

d. CH_3 Br CH_2Br
   | | |
 $BrCH_2CH_2CCH_2CH_3$ and $CH_2CH_2CHCH_2CH_3$
   |
   Br

10.63 Which of the following pairs of molecules are identical compounds? Which are constitutional isomers?

a. $CH_3CH_2CH_2$ $CH_3CHCH_2CH_2CH_3$
   | |
 $CH_3CH_2CH_2$ CH_3

b. $CH_3CH_2CH_2CH_2CH_2CH_2CH_3$ $CH_3CH_2CH_2CH_2CH_2$
   |
 CH_3CH_2

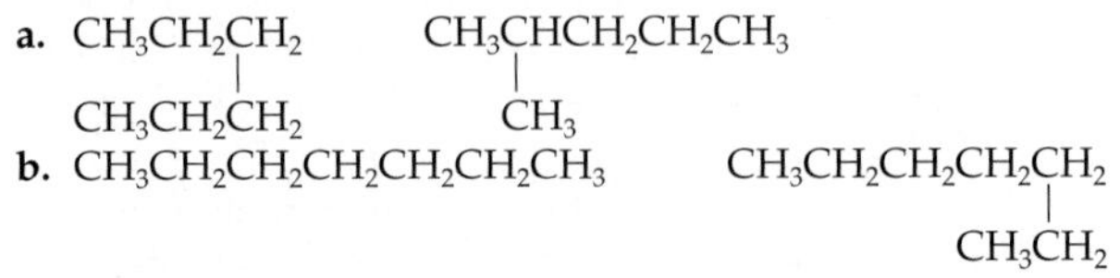

10.64. Which of the following pairs of molecules are identical compounds? Which are constitutional isomers?

a. $CH_3CH_2CH(CH_3)CH_2CH_3$ $CH_3C(CH_3)_2CH_2CH_2CH_3$
b. $CH_3CH_2CH_2CH_2C(CH_3)_2CH_2CH(CH_3)CH_3$
 $CH_3CH(CH_3)CH_2CH_2C(CH_3)_2CH_2CH_2CH_3$

10.65 Which of the following structures are incorrect?

a. CH_3 Br
   | |
 $CH_3CCH_2CH_2$

b. H
   |
 $CH_3CH_2CCH_3$
   |
   Br

c. CH_3
   |
 $CH_3CH_2CH_2CH_3$
   |
   Br

d. Br
   |
 $CH_3CHCH_2CHCH_3$
   |
   Br

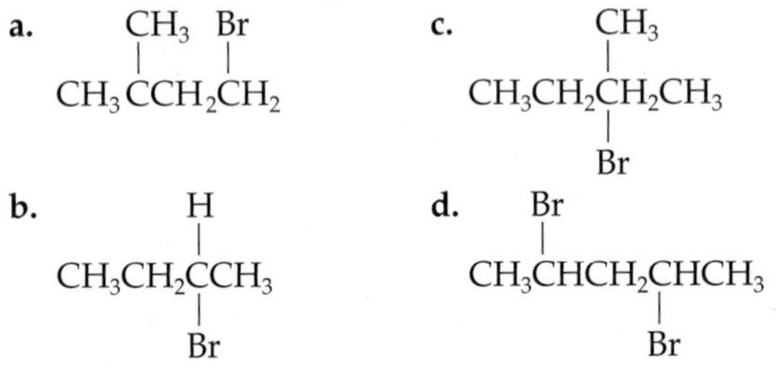

10.66. Which of the following structures are incorrect? Describe the problem in those that are incorrect.

a. $CH_3CH(CH_3)_2CH_2CH_3$ c. $CH_2CH_2C(CH_3)CH_2CH_2CH_3$
b. $CH_3(CH_2)_5CH_3$ d. $CH_3CH_2CH(CH_3)_3CH_3$

10.67 Are the following names correct or incorrect? If they are incorrect, give the correct name.

a. 1,3-Dimethylpentane c. 3-Butylbutane
b. 2-Ethylpropane d. 3-Ethyl-4-methyloctane

10.68 In your own words, describe the steps used to name a compound, using IUPAC nomenclature.

10.69 Draw the structures of the following compounds. Are the names provided correct or incorrect? If they are incorrect, give the correct name.

a. 2,4-Dimethylpentane d. 1,4-Diethylheptane
b. 1,3-Dimethylhexane e. 1,6-Dibromo-6-methyloctane
c. 1,5-Diiodopentane

10.70 Draw the structures of the following compounds. Are the names provided correct or incorrect? If they are incorrect, give the correct name.

a. 1,4-Dimethylbutane c. 2,3-Dimethylbutane
b. 1,2-Dichlorohexane d. 1,2-Diethylethane

Cycloalkanes

Foundations

10.71 Describe the structure of a cycloalkane.

10.72 Describe the IUPAC rules for naming cycloalkanes.

10.73 What is the general formula for a cycloalkane?

10.74 How does the general formula of a cycloalkane compare with that of an alkane?

Applications

10.75 Name each of the following cycloalkanes, using the IUPAC system:

a. 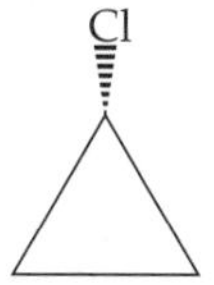 Cl

c.
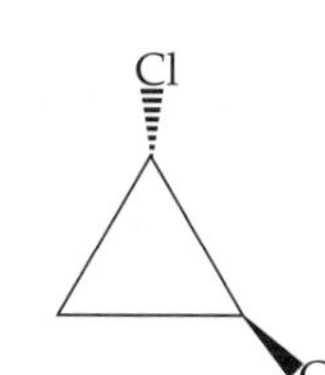

b.
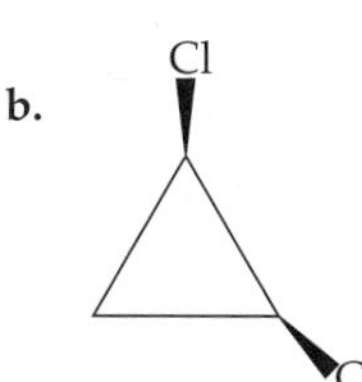

d.
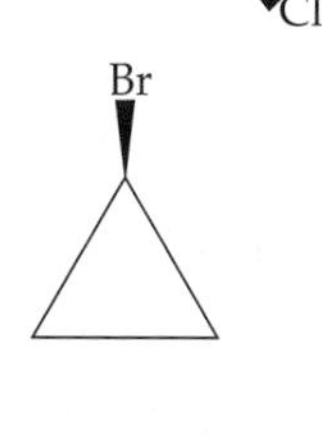

10.76 Name each of the following cycloalkanes, using the IUPAC system:

a. 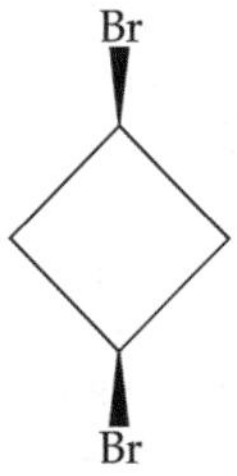 Br Br

c.
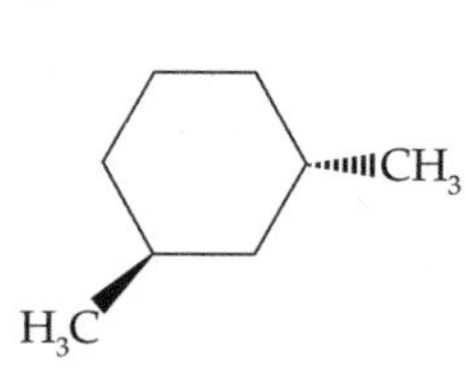

b.

d.
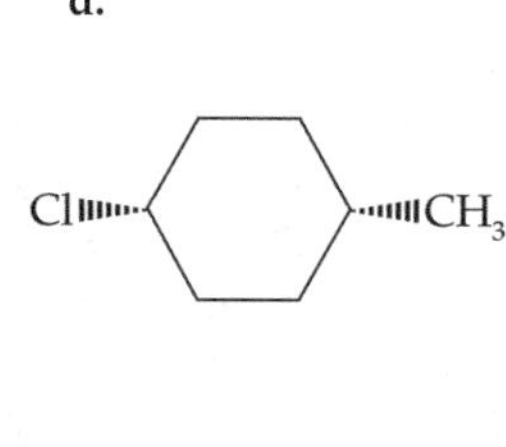

10.77 Draw the structure of each of the following cycloalkanes:
a. 1-Bromo-2-methylcyclobutane
b. Iodocyclopropane
c. 1-Bromo-3-chlorocyclopentane
d. 1,2-Dibromo-3-methylcyclohexane

10.78 Draw each of the following cycloalkanes:
a. 1,2,3-Trichlorocyclopropane
b. 1,1-Dibromo-3-chlorocyclobutane
c. 1,2,4-Trimethylcycloheptane
d. 1,2-Dichloro-3,3-dimethylcyclohexane

10.79 How many geometric and structural isomers of dichlorocyclopropane can you construct? Use a set of molecular models to construct the isomers and to contrast their differences. Draw all these isomers.

10.80 How many isomers of dibromocyclobutane can you construct? As in Question 10.79, use a set of molecular models to construct the isomers and then draw them.

10.81 Which of the following names are correct and which are incorrect? If incorrect, write the correct name.
a. 2,3-Dibromocyclobutane
b. 1,4-Diethylcyclobutane
c. 1,2-Dimethylcyclopropane
d. 4,5,6-Trichlorocyclohexane

10.82 Which of the following names are correct and which are incorrect? If incorrect, write the correct name.
a. 1,4,5-Tetrabromocyclohexane
b. 1,3-Dimethylcyclobutane
c. 1,2-Dichlorocyclopentane
d. 3-Bromocyclopentane

10.83 Draw the structures of each of the following compounds:
a. *cis*-1,3-Dibromocyclopentane
b. *trans*-1,2-Dimethylcyclobutane
c. *cis*-1,2-Dichlorocyclopropane
d. *trans*-1,4-Diethylcyclohexane

10.84 Draw the structures of each of the following compounds:
a. *trans*-1,4-Dimethylcyclooctane
b. *cis*-1,3-Dichlorocyclohexane
c. *cis*-1,3-Dibromocyclobutane

10.85 Name each of the following compounds:

a. 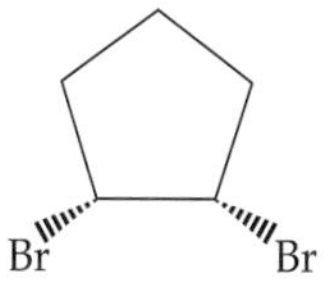 Br Br

c.
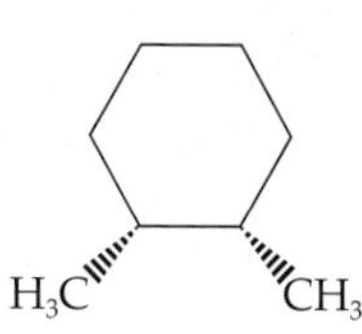

b.
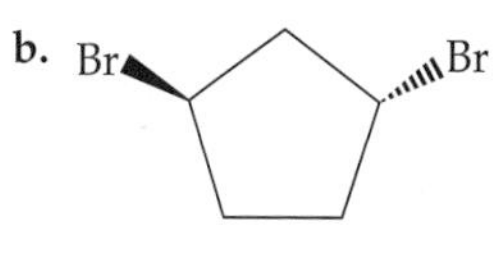

d.
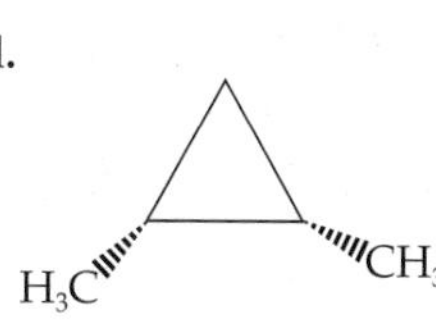

10.86 Name each of the following compounds:

a. 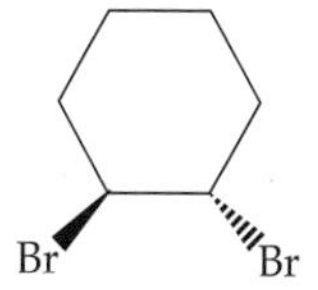 Br Br

c.
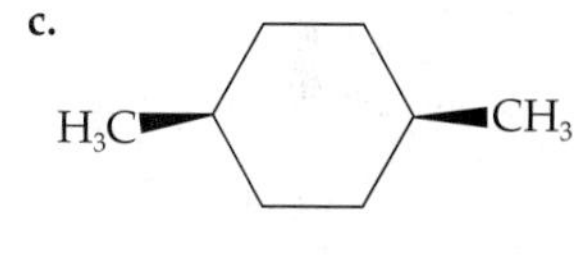

b.
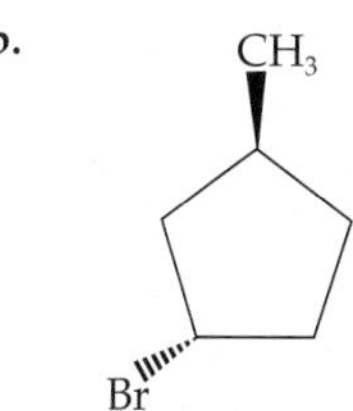

d.
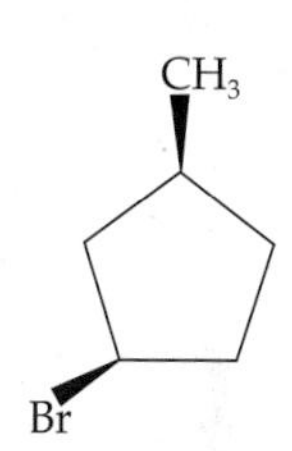

Conformations of Alkanes and Cycloalkanes

Foundations

10.87 What are conformational isomers?

10.88 Why is the staggered conformation of ethane more stable than the eclipsed conformation?

Applications

10.89 Make a model of cyclohexane and compare the boat and chair conformations. Use your model to explain why the chair conformation is more stable.

10.90 What is meant by free rotation around a carbon-carbon single bond? Why can't conformations be separated from one another?

Reactions of Alkanes and Cycloalkanes

Foundations

10.91 Define the term *combustion*.

10.92 Explain why halogenation of an alkane is a substitution reaction.

Applications

10.93 Write a balanced equation for the complete combustion of each of the following:
a. propane
b. heptane
c. nonane
d. decane

10.94 Write a balanced equation for the complete combustion of each of the following:
a. pentane **c.** octane
b. hexane **d.** ethane

10.95 Just as an octane rating is applied to gasoline, a cetane number is used as the measure of the combustion quality of diesel fuel. Cetane, or hexadecane, is an unbranched alkane that ignites easily in a combustion engine. Write a balanced equation for the complete combustion of cetane.

10.96 For gasoline, isooctane, 2,2,4-trimethylpentane, is the standard of excellence. Write a balanced equation for the complete combustion of isooctane.

10.97 Complete each of the following equations by supplying the missing reactant or product as indicated by a question mark:

a. $2CH_3CH_2CH_2CH_3 + 13O_2 \xrightarrow{\text{Heat}}$? (Complete combustion)

b. $CH_3CH(CH_3)_2 + Br_2 \xrightarrow{\text{Light}}$? (Give all possible monobrominated products)

c. (cyclohexane) + ? $\xrightarrow{?}$ Cl–(cyclohexane) + HCl

10.98 Give all the possible monochlorinated products for the following reaction:

$$CH_3CH(CH_3)CH_2CH_3 + Cl_2 \xrightarrow{\text{Light}} ?$$

Name the products, using IUPAC nomenclature.

10.99 Draw the constitutional isomers of molecular formula C_6H_{14} and name each using the IUPAC system.
a. Which one gives two and only two monobromo derivatives when it reacts with Br_2 and light? Name the products, using the IUPAC system.
b. Which give three and only three monobromo products? Name the products, using the IUPAC system.
c. Which give four and only four monobromo products? Name the products, using the IUPAC system.

10.100 **a.** Draw and name all of the isomeric products obtained from the monobromination of propane with Br_2/light. If halogenation were a completely random reaction and had an equal probability of occurring at any of the C—H bonds in a molecule, what percentage of each of these monobromo products would be expected?
b. Answer part (a) using 2-methylpropane as the starting material.

10.101 A mol of hydrocarbon formed 8 mol of CO_2 and 8 mol of H_2O upon combustion. Determine the molecular formula of the hydrocarbon and write the balanced equation for the combustion reaction. Use line formulas.

10.102 Highly substituted alkyl fluorides, called perfluoroalkanes, are often used as artificial blood substitutes. These perfluoroalkanes have the ability to transport O_2 through the bloodstream as blood does. Some even have twice the O_2 transport capability and are used to treat gangrenous tissue. The structure of perfluorodecalin is shown below. How many mol of fluorine must be reacted with 1 mol of decalin to produce perfluorodecalin?

(Decalin) + ? F_2 ⟶ (Perfluorodecalin)

Decalin Perfluorodecalin

CRITICAL THINKING PROBLEMS

1. You are given two unlabeled bottles, each of which contains a colorless liquid. One contains hexane and the other contains water. What physical properties could you use to identify the two liquids? What chemical property could you use to identify them?
2. You are given two beakers, each of which contains a white crystalline solid. Both are soluble in water. How would you determine which of the two solids is an ionic compound and which is a covalent compound?
3. Chlorofluorocarbons (CFCs) are man-made compounds made up of carbon and the halogens fluorine and chlorine. One of the most widely used is Freon-12 (CCl_2F_2). It was introduced as a refrigerant in the 1930s. This was an important advance because Freon-12 replaced ammonia and sulfur dioxide, two toxic chemicals that were previously used in refrigeration systems. Freon-12 was hailed as a perfect replacement because it has a boiling point of −30°C and is almost completely inert. To what family of organic molecules do CFCs belong? Design a strategy for the synthesis of Freon-12.
4. Over time, CFC production increased dramatically as their uses increased. They were used as propellants in spray cans, as gases to expand plastic foam, and in many other applications. By 1985 production of CFCs reached 850,000 tons (t). Much of this leaked into the atmosphere and in that year the concentration of CFCs reached 0.6 parts per billion (ppb). Another observation was made by groups of concerned scientists: as the level of CFCs rose, the ozone level in the upper atmosphere declined. Does this correlation between CFC levels and ozone levels prove a relationship between these two phenomena? Explain your reasoning.
5. Although manufacture of CFCs was banned on December 31, 1995, the C—F and C—Cl bonds of CFCs are so strong that the molecules may remain in the atmosphere for 120 years. Within 5 years they diffuse into the upper stratosphere where ultraviolet photons can break the C—Cl bonds. This process releases chlorine atoms, as shown here for Freon-12:

$$CCl_2F_2 + \text{photon} \longrightarrow CClF_2 + Cl$$

The chlorine atoms are extremely reactive because of their strong tendency to acquire a stable octet of electrons. The following reactions occur when a chlorine atom reacts with an ozone molecule (O_3). First, chlorine pulls an oxygen atom away from ozone:

$$Cl + O_3 \longrightarrow ClO + O_2$$

Then ClO, a highly reactive molecule, reacts with an oxygen atom:

$$ClO + O \longrightarrow Cl + O_2$$

Write an equation representing the overall reaction (sum of the two reactions). How would you describe the role of Cl in these reactions?

ALKENES, ALKYNES, AND AROMATICS
The Unsaturated Hydrocarbons

Ethene gas causes fruit ripening.

LEARNING GOALS

1. Describe the physical properties of alkenes and alkynes.
2. Draw the structures and write the IUPAC names for simple alkenes and alkynes.
3. Write the names and draw the structures of simple geometric isomers of alkenes.
4. Write equations predicting the products of addition reactions of alkenes and alkynes: hydrogenation, halogenation, hydration, and hydrohalogenation.
5. Apply Markovnikov's rule to predict the major and minor products of the hydration and hydrohalogenation reactions of unsymmetrical alkenes.
6. Write equations representing the formation of addition polymers of alkenes.
7. Draw the structures and write the names of common aromatic hydrocarbons.
8. Write equations for substitution reactions involving benzene.
9. Describe heterocyclic aromatic compounds and list several biological molecules in which they are found.

OUTLINE

Introduction 364

11.1 Alkenes and Alkynes: Structure and Physical Properties 364

11.2 Alkenes and Alkynes: Nomenclature 366

11.3 Geometric Isomers: A Consequence of Unsaturation 369

A Medical Perspective: Killer Alkynes in Nature 370

11.4 Alkenes in Nature 376

11.5 Reactions Involving Alkenes and Alkynes 378

A Human Perspective: Life Without Polymers? 387

Green Chemistry: Plastic Recycling 388

11.6 Aromatic Hydrocarbons 388

11.7 Heterocyclic Aromatic Compounds 394

Kitchen Chemistry: Amazing Chocolate 395

Oleic acid, the major fatty acid in olive oil, is a monounsaturated fatty acid. What does the term "monounsaturated" mean?

INTRODUCTION

For many years it was suspected that there existed a gas that stimulated fruit ripening and had other effects on plants. The ancient Chinese observed that their fruit ripened more quickly if incense was burned in the same room. Early in the last century, shippers realized that they could not store oranges and bananas on the same ships because some "emanation" given off by the oranges caused the bananas to ripen too early.

Puerto Rican pineapple growers and Philippine mango growers independently developed a traditional practice of building bonfires near their crops. They believed that the smoke caused the plants to bloom synchronously.

In the mid-nineteenth century, streetlights were fueled with natural gas. Occasionally the pipes leaked, releasing gas into the atmosphere. On some of these occasions, the leaves fell from all the shade trees in the region surrounding the gas leak.

What is the gas responsible for these diverse effects on plants? In 1934, R. Gane demonstrated that the simple alkene ethene (ethylene) was the "emanation" responsible for fruit ripening. More recently, it has been shown that ethene induces and synchronizes flowering in pineapples and mango, induces senescence (aging) and loss of leaves in trees, and effects a wide variety of other responses in various plants.

We can be grateful to ethene for the fresh, unbruised fruits that we purchase at the grocery store. These fruits are picked when they are not yet ripe, while they are still firm. They then can be shipped great distances and gassed with ethene when they reach their destination. Under the influence of ethene, the fruit ripens for display in the store.

In this chapter, we will study the **unsaturated hydrocarbons.** This group of organic compounds includes the alkenes, such as ethene, which all contain at least one carbon-carbon double bond; the alkynes, which all contain at least one carbon-carbon triple bond; and aromatic compounds, particularly stable compounds that contain a benzene ring. The benzene ring is often depicted as having alternating double and single bonds. This arrangement is called a *conjugated system* of double bonds.

11.1 Alkenes and Alkynes: Structure and Physical Properties

LEARNING GOAL

1 Describe the physical properties of alkenes and alkynes.

Many important biological molecules are characterized by the presence of double bonds or a linear or cyclic conjugated system of double bonds (Figure 11.1). For instance, we classify fatty acids as either monounsaturated (having one double bond), polyunsaturated (having two or more double bonds), or saturated (having single bonds only). Vitamin A (retinol), a vitamin required for vision, contains a nine-carbon conjugated hydrocarbon chain. Vitamin K, a vitamin required for blood clotting, contains an aromatic ring.

Fatty acids are long hydrocarbon chains having a carboxyl group at the end. Thus by definition they are carboxylic acids. See Chapters 14 and 17.

Alkenes and **alkynes** are unsaturated hydrocarbons. The characteristic functional group of an alkene is the carbon-carbon double bond. The functional group that characterizes the alkynes is the carbon-carbon triple bond. The general formulas shown below compare the structures of alkanes, alkenes, and alkynes.

LIPID-SOLUBLE VITAMINS

	Alkane	Alkene	Alkyne
General formulas:	C_nH_{2n+2}	C_nH_{2n}	C_nH_{2n-2}
Structural formulas:	H–C(H)(H)–C(H)(H)–H	(H)(H)C=C(H)(H)	H–C≡C–H
	Ethane (ethane)	Ethene (ethylene)	Ethyne (acetylene)
Molecular formulas:	C_2H_6	C_2H_4	C_2H_2
Condensed formulas:	CH_3CH_3	$H_2C{=}CH_2$	$HC{\equiv}CH$

O
C
OH
Oleic acid

(a)

CH_2OH
Vitamin A

(b)

O
O
Vitamin K

(c)

Figure 11.1 (a) Line formula of the eighteen-carbon monounsaturated fatty acid oleic acid. (b) Line formula of vitamin A, which is required for vision. Notice that the carbon chain of vitamin A is a conjugated system of double bonds. (c) Line formula of vitamin K, a lipid-soluble vitamin required for blood clotting. The six-member ring with the circle represents a benzene ring. See Figure 11.6 for other representations of the benzene ring.

Alkanes, alkenes, and alkynes have the same number of carbon atoms but differ in the number of hydrogen atoms. Alkenes contain two fewer hydrogens than the corresponding alkanes, and alkynes contain two fewer hydrogens than the corresponding alkenes.

In alkanes, the central carbon has four bonds, giving it a tetrahedral molecular geometry. When carbon is bonded by one double bond and two single bonds, as in ethene (an alkene), the molecule is *trigonal planar,* because all atoms lie in a single plane. Each bond angle is approximately 120°. When two carbon atoms are bonded by a triple bond, as in ethyne (an alkyne), each bond angle is 180°. Thus, the molecule is linear, and all atoms are positioned in a straight line. For comparison, examples of a five-carbon alkane, alkene, and alkyne are shown in Figure 11.2.

Alkenes, alkynes, and aromatic compounds are nonpolar and have properties similar to alkanes of the same carbon chain length. They have relatively low melting points and boiling points and are generally less dense than water. In general, the longer the hydrocarbon chain (greater the molar mass), the higher the melting and boiling points and the greater the density. For comparison, the melting points and boiling points of several alkenes and alkynes are presented in Table 11.1. As we saw for the alkanes, these trends in physical properties are the result of London dispersion forces. These attractive forces increase as the mass of the molecule and the

Bananas are picked and shipped while still green. They are treated with the fruit-ripening agent, ethene, once they reach the grocery store. Describe the geometry and bonding of ethene. What is the common name of ethene?

TABLE 11.1 Physical Properties of Selected Alkenes and Alkynes

Name	Molecular Formula	Structural Formula	Melting Point (°C)	Boiling Point (°C)
Ethene	C_2H_4	$CH_2{=}CH_2$	−169.1	−103.7
Propene	C_3H_6	$CH_2{=}CHCH_3$	−185.0	−47.6
1-Butene	C_4H_8	$CH_2{=}CHCH_2CH_3$	−185.0	−6.1
Methylpropene	C_4H_8	$CH_2{=}C(CH_3)_2$	−140.0	−6.6
Ethyne	C_2H_2	$HC{\equiv}CH$	−81.8	−84.0
Propyne	C_3H_4	$HC{\equiv}CCH_3$	−101.5	−23.2
1-Butyne	C_4H_6	$HC{\equiv}CCH_2CH_3$	−125.9	8.1
2-Butyne	C_4H_6	$CH_3C{\equiv}CCH_3$	−32.3	27.0

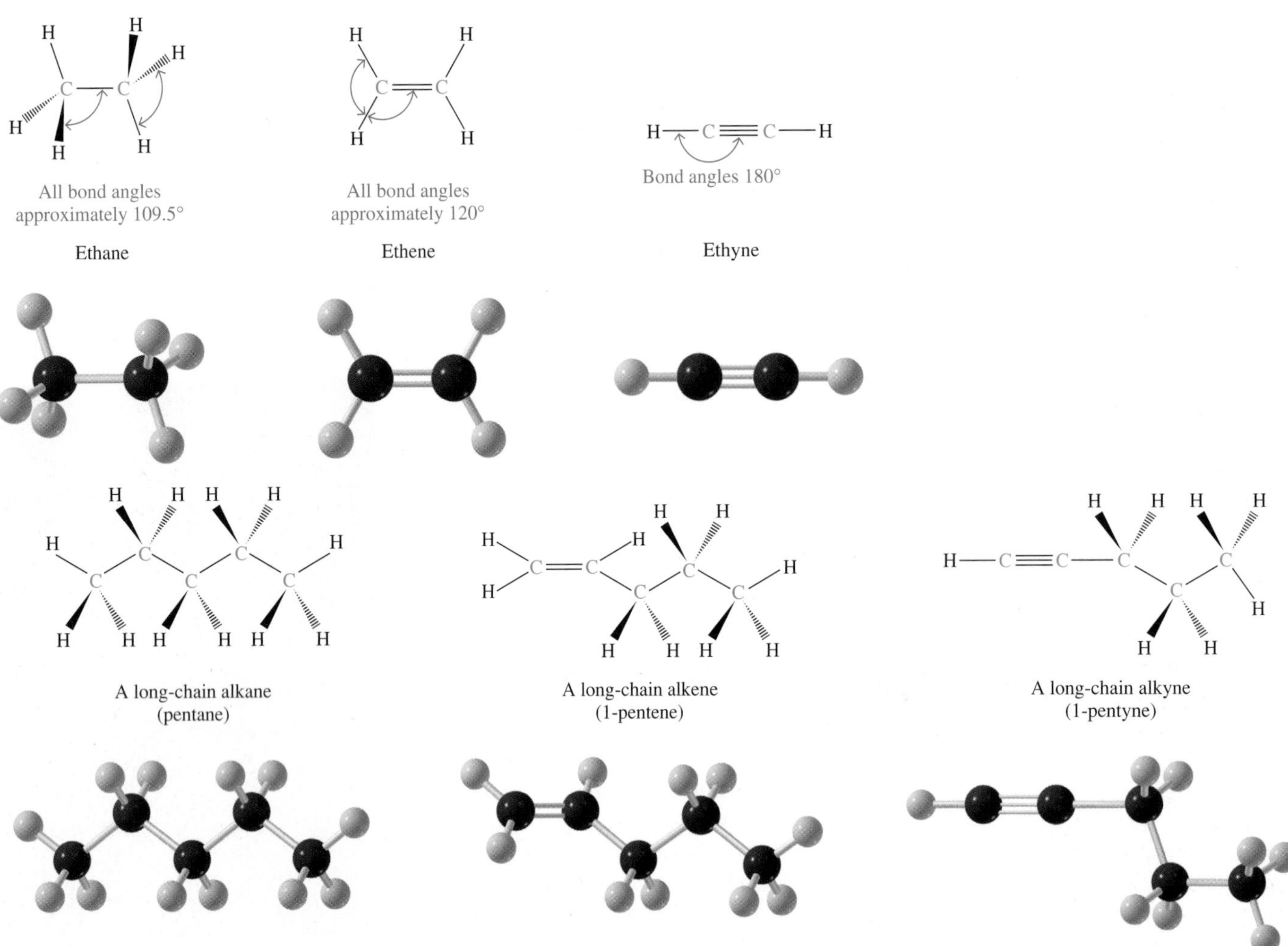

Figure 11.2 Three-dimensional drawings and ball-and-stick models of typical alkanes, alkenes, and alkynes.

number of electrons increase. Thus, the London dispersion forces are stronger and the attraction greater for molecules having a larger surface area. The longer, higher molar mass alkenes and alkynes would be expected to exhibit stronger London dispersion forces and therefore higher boiling and melting points.

Since they are nonpolar, the "like dissolves like" rule tells us that they are not soluble in water. Like the alkanes, they are very soluble in nonpolar solvents such as other hydrocarbons.

11.2 Alkenes and Alkynes: Nomenclature

LEARNING GOAL

2 Draw the structures and write the IUPAC names for simple alkenes and alkynes.

To determine the name of an alkene or alkyne using the IUPAC. Nomenclature System, use the following simple rules:

- Name the parent compound using the longest continuous carbon chain containing the double bond (alkenes) or triple bond (alkynes).
- Replace the *-ane* ending of the alkane with the *-ene* ending for an alkene or the *-yne* ending for an alkyne. For example:

$CH_3{-}CH_3$	$CH_2{=}CH_2$	$CH{\equiv}CH$
Ethane	Ethene	Ethyne
$CH_3{-}CH_2{-}CH_3$	$CH_2{=}CH{-}CH_3$	$CH{\equiv}C{-}CH_3$
Propane	Propene	Propyne

- Number the parent chain to give the double or triple bond the lowest number. For example:

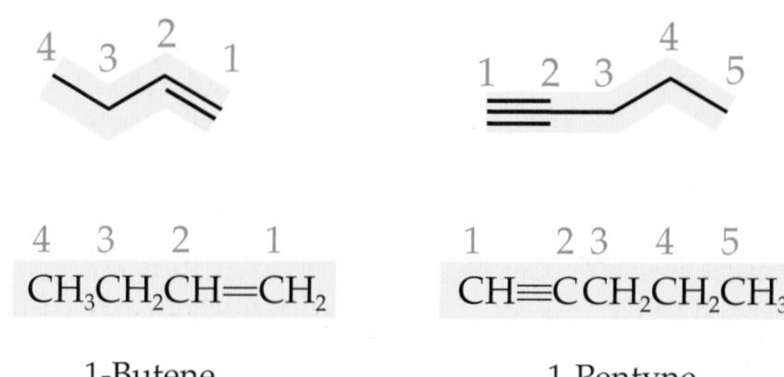

$CH_3CH_2CH{=}CH_2$ (4 3 2 1)

1-Butene

$CH{\equiv}CCH_2CH_2CH_3$ (1 2 3 4 5)

1-Pentyne

Remember, it is the position of the double bond, not the substituent, that determines the numbering of the carbon chain.

- Determine the name and carbon number of each group bonded to the parent alkene or alkyne, and place the name and number in front of the name of the parent compound. Remember that with alkenes and alkynes the double or triple bond takes precedence over a halogen or alkyl group, as shown in the following examples:

$CH_3CH{=}CClCH_3$ (4 3 2 1)

2-Chloro-2-butene

$CH_3CHBr\,C{\equiv}CCH_2CH_3$ (1 2 3 4 5 6)

2-Bromo-3-hexyne

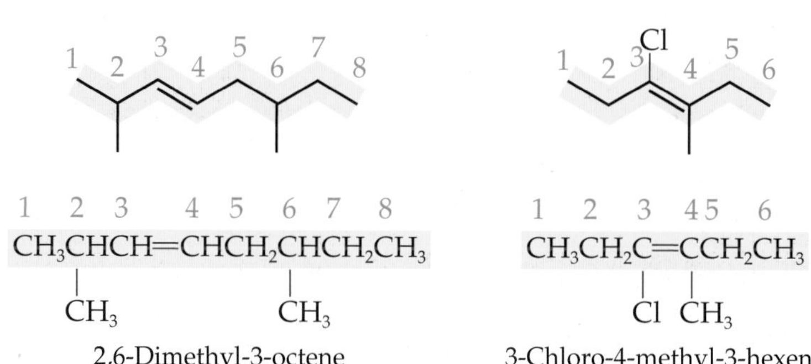

$CH_3CH(CH_3)CH{=}CHCH_2CH(CH_3)CH_2CH_3$ (1 2 3 4 5 6 7 8)

2,6-Dimethyl-3-octene

$CH_3CH_2C(Cl){=}C(CH_3)CH_2CH_3$ (1 2 3 4 5 6)

3-Chloro-4-methyl-3-hexene

- Alkenes having more than one double bond are called alkadienes (two double bonds) or alkatrienes (three double bonds), as seen in these examples:

Alkenes with many double bonds are often referred to as polyenes (*poly*—many *enes*—double bonds).

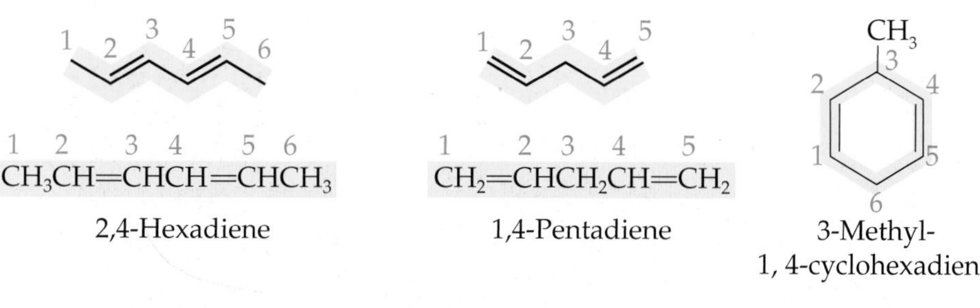

$CH_3CH{=}CHCH{=}CHCH_3$ (1 2 3 4 5 6)

2,4-Hexadiene

$CH_2{=}CHCH_2CH{=}CH_2$ (1 2 3 4 5)

1,4-Pentadiene

3-Methyl-1, 4-cyclohexadiene

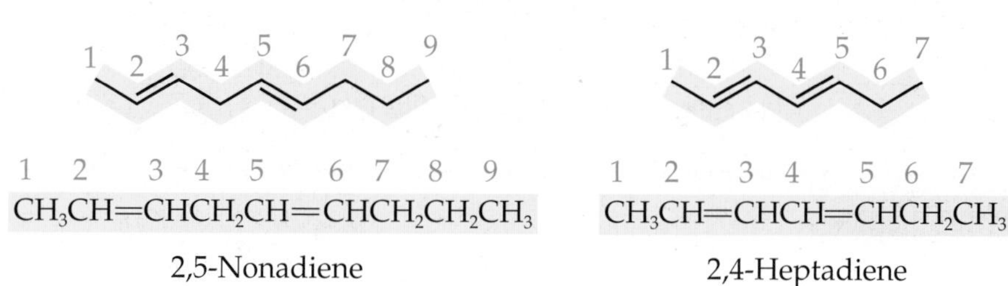

$CH_3CH{=}CHCH_2CH{=}CHCH_2CH_2CH_3$ (1 2 3 4 5 6 7 8 9)

2,5-Nonadiene

$CH_3CH{=}CHCH{=}CHCH_2CH_3$ (1 2 3 4 5 6 7)

2,4-Heptadiene

EXAMPLE 11.1 Naming Alkenes and Alkynes Using IUPAC Nomenclature

LEARNING GOAL

2 Draw the structures and write the IUPAC names for simple alkenes and alkynes.

Name the following alkenes and alkyne using IUPAC nomenclature.

Solution

To determine the IUPAC name, identify the parent chain, number it to give the lowest possible positions for the carbon or carbons with the double bonds, and finally, identify and number each functional group.

The common name of the first molecule below is isoprene. It is the major building block for many important biological molecules, including cholesterol and other steroids, β-carotene, and vitamins A, D, E, and K.

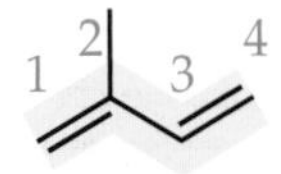

$$CH_2{=}\overset{\overset{\displaystyle CH_3}{|}}{C}CH{=}CH_2$$

1 2 3 4

Isoprene

Longest chain containing the double bond: butene

Positions of the double bonds: 1,3-butadiene

Substituents: 2-methyl

Name: 2-Methyl-1,3-butadiene

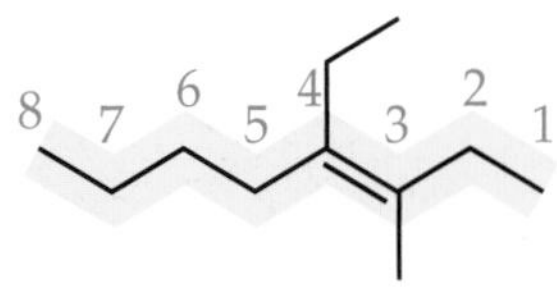

$$\underset{8\ \ 7\ \ 6\ \ 5}{CH_3CH_2CH_2CH_2}\overset{\overset{\displaystyle CH_2CH_3}{|}}{\underset{4}{C}}{=}\underset{\underset{\displaystyle CH_3}{|}}{\underset{3}{C}}\underset{2\ \ 1}{CH_2CH_3}$$

Longest chain containing the double bond: octene

Position of double bond: 3-octene (*not* 5-octene)

Substituents: 3-methyl and 4-ethyl

Name: 4-Ethyl-3-methyl-3-octene

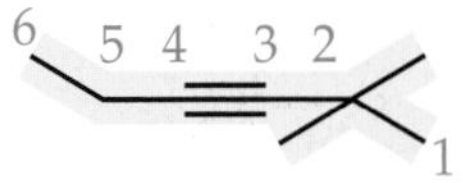

$$\underset{6\ \ 5\ \ 4}{CH_3CH_2C}{\equiv}\underset{3}{C}\overset{\overset{\displaystyle CH_3}{|}}{\underset{\underset{\displaystyle CH_3}{|}}{\underset{2}{C}}}\underset{1}{CH_3}$$

Longest chain containing the triple bond: hexyne

Position of triple bond: 3-hexyne

Substituents: 2,2-dimethyl

Name: 2,2-Dimethyl-3-hexyne

Practice Problem 11.1

Name each of the following alkenes and alkynes using IUPAC nomenclature.

a. $CH_3CH{=}CH\overset{\overset{\displaystyle CH_3}{|}}{C}HCH_2\overset{\overset{\displaystyle Cl}{|}}{C}HCH_3$

b. $CH{\equiv}CCH_2C{\equiv}CH$

c. $CH_3CH_2C{\equiv}C\overset{\overset{\displaystyle Br}{|}}{C}HCH_2CH_3$

d. $CH_3CH{=}CHCH_2CH_2CH{=}CH_2$

► For Further Practice: **Questions 11.43a-c and 11.44a-c.**

EXAMPLE 11.2 Naming Cycloalkenes Using IUPAC Nomenclature

LEARNING GOAL

2 Draw the structures and write the IUPAC names for simple alkenes and alkynes.

Name the following cycloalkenes using IUPAC nomenclature.

Solution

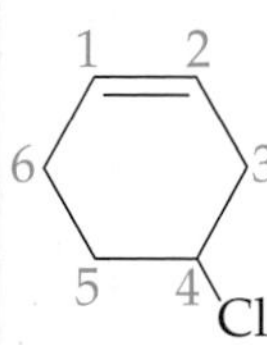

Parent chain: cyclohexene

Position of double bond: carbon-1 (carbons of the double bond are numbered 1 and 2)

Substituents: 4-chloro

Name: 4-Chlorocyclohexene

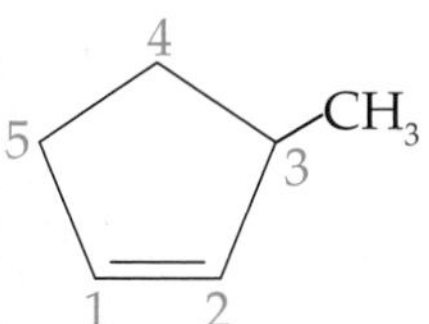

Parent chain: cyclopentene

Position of double bond: carbon-1

Substituent: 3-methyl

Name: 3-Methylcyclopentene

Practice Problem 11.2

Name each of the following cycloalkenes using IUPAC nomenclature.

a. 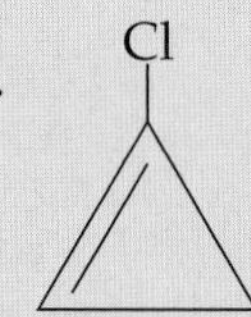

b. 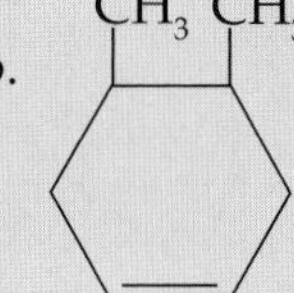

c. 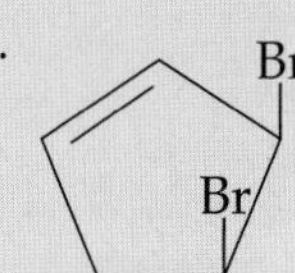

d. 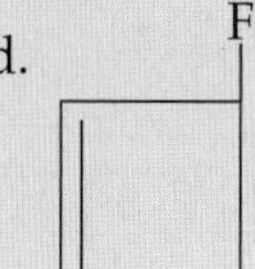

► For Further Practice: **Questions 11.43d and 11.44d.**

Question 11.1 Draw a condensed formula and line formula for each of the following compounds:

a. 1-Bromo-3-hexyne
b. 2-Butyne
c. Dichloroethyne
d. 9-Iodo-1-nonyne

Question 11.2 Name the following compounds using the IUPAC Nomenclature System:

a. $CH_3C\equiv CCH_2CH_3$
b. $CH_3CH_2CHBrCHBrCH_2C\equiv CH$
c. $CH_3CH(CH_3)CCl=C(CH_3)CH(CH_3)_2$
d. $CH_3CH(CH_2CH_3)C\equiv CCHClCH_3$

11.3 Geometric Isomers: A Consequence of Unsaturation

LEARNING GOAL

3 Write the names and draw the structures of simple geometric isomers of alkenes.

The carbon-carbon double bond is rigid because of the shapes of the orbitals involved in its formation. As a result, rotation around the carbon-carbon double bond is restricted. In Section 10.3, we saw that the rotation around the carbon-carbon bonds of cycloalkanes is also restricted. As a consequence, these molecules

A MEDICAL PERSPECTIVE

Killer Alkynes in Nature

There are many examples of alkynes that are beneficial to humans. Among these are *parsalmide,* a pain reliever, *pargyline,* an antihypertensive, and *17-ethynylestradiol,* a synthetic estrogen that is used as an oral contraceptive.

But in addition to these medically useful alkynes, there are in nature a number that are toxic. Some are extremely toxic to mammals, including humans; others are toxic to fungi, fish, or insects. All of these compounds are plant products that may help protect the plant from destruction by predators.

Capillin is produced by the oriental wormwood plant. Research has shown that a dilute solution of capillin inhibits the growth of certain fungi. Since fungal growth can damage or destroy a plant, the ability to make capillin may provide a survival advantage to the plants. Perhaps it may one day be developed to combat fungal infections in humans.

Ichthyothereol is a fast-acting poison commonly found in plants referred to as fish-poison plants. Ichthyothereol is a very toxic polyacetylenic alcohol that inhibits energy production in the mitochondria. Latin American native tribes use these plants to coat the tips of the arrows used to catch fish. Although ichthyothereol is poisonous to the fish, fish caught by this method pose no risk to the people who eat them!

An extract of the leaves of English ivy has been reported to have antibacterial, analgesic, and sedative effects. The compound thought to be responsible for these characteristics, as well as antifungal activity, is *falcarinol.* Falcarinol, isolated from a tree in Panama, also has been reported by the Molecular Targets Drug Discovery Program to have antitumor activity.

Falcarinol is extracted from English ivy, like that covering this stone house.

O ‖ C—$NHCH_2CH_2CH_3$, O—$CH_2C{\equiv}CH$, H_2N

Parsalmide

—CH_2—C(=O)—N(CH_3)—$CH_2C{\equiv}CH$

Pargyline

OH, CH_3, —$C{\equiv}CH$, HO

17-Ethynylestradiol

Alkynes used for medicinal purposes.

form geometric or *cis-trans* isomers. The *cis*-isomers of cycloalkanes have substituent groups on the same side of the ring (*Latin, cis,* "on the same side"). The *trans*-isomers of cycloalkanes have substituent groups located on opposite sides of the ring (*Latin, trans,* "across from").

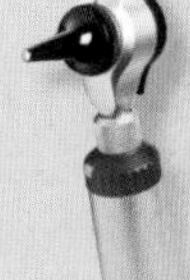

Capillin

Ichthyothereol

$CH_2{=}CH{-}CH(OH){-}C{\equiv}C{-}C{\equiv}C{-}CH_2{-}CH{=}CH{-}(CH_2)_7CH_3$

Falcarinol

Cicutoxin

Alkynes that exhibit toxic activity.

Cicuta maculata, or water hemlock, produces the most deadly toxin indigenous to North America.

Perhaps one day this compound, or a derivative of it, will be useful in treating cancer in humans.

Cicutoxin has been described as the most lethal toxin native to North America. It is a neurotoxin that is produced by the water hemlock (*Cicuta maculata*), which is in the same family of plants as parsley, celery, and carrots. Cicutoxin is present in all parts of the plants, but is most concentrated in the root. Eating a portion as small as 2–3 square centimeters (cm^2) can be fatal to adults. Cicutoxin acts directly on the nervous system. Signs and symptoms of cicutoxin poisoning include dilation of pupils, muscle twitching, rapid pulse and breathing, violent convulsions, coma, and death. Onset of symptoms is rapid and death may occur within 2 to 3 hours (h). No antidote exists for cicutoxin poisoning. The only treatment involves controlling convulsions and seizures in order to preserve normal heart and lung function. Fortunately, cicutoxin poisoning is a very rare occurrence. Occasionally animals may graze on the plants in the spring, resulting in death within 15 minutes (min). Humans seldom come into contact with the water hemlock. The most recent cases have involved individuals foraging for wild ginseng, or other wild roots, and mistaking the water hemlock root for an edible plant.

For Further Understanding

- Circle and name the functional groups in parsalmide and pargyline.
- The fungus *Tinea pedis* causes athlete's foot. Describe an experiment you might carry out to determine whether capillin might be effective against athlete's foot.

In alkenes, **geometric isomers** occur when there are two different groups or atoms on each of the carbon atoms attached by the double bond. If both groups or atoms are on the same side of the double bond, the molecule is a *cis*-isomer. If the groups or atoms are on opposite sides of the double bond, the molecule is a *trans*-isomer.

Restricted rotation around double bonds is partially responsible for the conformation and hence the activity of many biological molecules that we will study later.

Consider the two isomers of 1,2-dichloroethene:

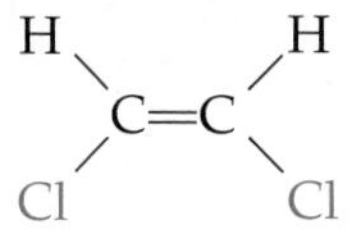

H H — C=C — Cl Cl

cis-1,2-Dichloroethene

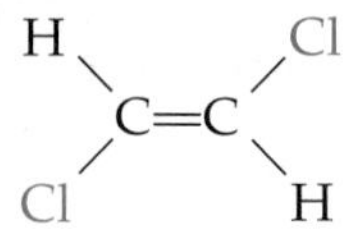

H Cl — C=C — Cl H

trans-1,2-Dichloroethene

In these molecules, each carbon atom of the double bond is also bonded to two different atoms: a hydrogen atom and a chlorine atom. In the molecule on the left, both chlorine atoms are on the same side of the double bond; this is the *cis*-isomer and the complete name for this molecule is *cis*-1,2-dichloroethene. In the molecule on the right, the chlorine atoms are on opposite sides of the double bond; this is the *trans*-isomer and the complete name of this molecule is *trans*-1,2-dichloroethene.

If one of the two carbon atoms of the double bond has two identical substituents, there are no *cis-trans* isomers for that molecule. Consider the example of 1,1-dichloroethene:

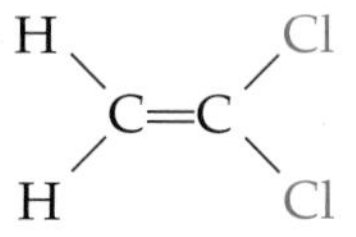

H Cl — C=C — H Cl

1,1-Dichloroethene

EXAMPLE 11.3 Identifying *cis*- and *trans*-Isomers of Alkenes

LEARNING GOAL

3 Write the names and draw the structures of simple geometric isomers of alkenes.

Two isomers of 2-butene are shown below. Which is the *cis*-isomer and which is the *trans*-isomer?

H H — C=C — H_3C CH_3

H CH_3 — C=C — H_3C H

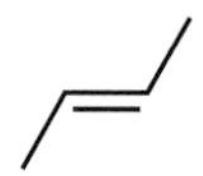

Solution

As we saw with cycloalkanes, the prefixes *cis* and *trans* refer to the placement of the substituents attached to a bond that cannot undergo free rotation. In the case of alkenes, it is the groups attached to the carbon-carbon double bond (in this example, the H and CH_3 groups). When the groups are on the same side of the double bond, as in the structure on the left, the prefix *cis* is used. When the groups are on the opposite sides of the double bond, as in the structure on the right, *trans* is the appropriate prefix.

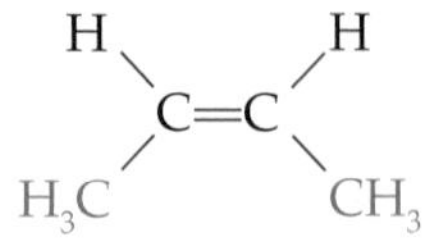

H H — C=C — H_3C CH_3

cis-2-Butene

H CH_3 — C=C — H_3C H

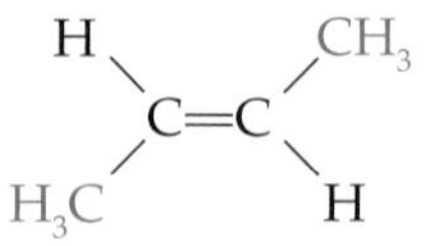

trans-2-Butene

Practice Problem 11.3

Which of the following alkenes are *cis*-isomers and which are *trans*-isomers?

a. 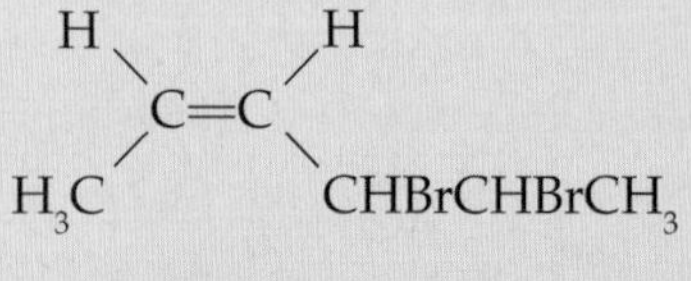 H H — C=C — H_3C $CHBrCHBrCH_3$

b. CH_3CH_2 Br — C=C — Br CH_2CH_3

c. Cl Cl — C=C — H_3C $CH_2CH_2CH_3$

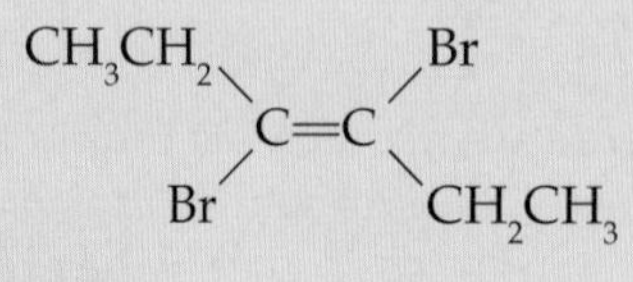

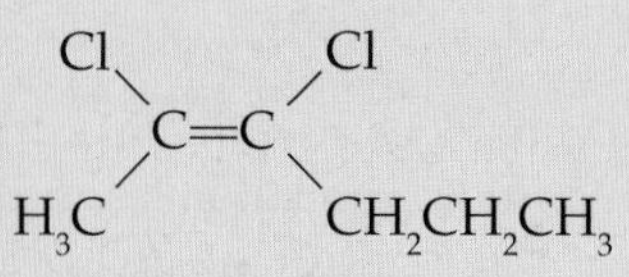

► For Further Practice: **Questions 11.47 and 11.48.**

In alkenes, the orientation of the carbon atoms of the parent chain relative to the double bond determines the *cis*- or *trans*- configuration of the alkene. If the carbon atoms of the parent chain are on opposite sides of the double bond, the alkene is in the *trans*- configuration. If the carbon atoms of the parent chain are on the same side of the double bond, the alkene is in the *cis*- configuration. This can be seen in the *cis*- and *trans*- configurations of 4-nonene shown here:

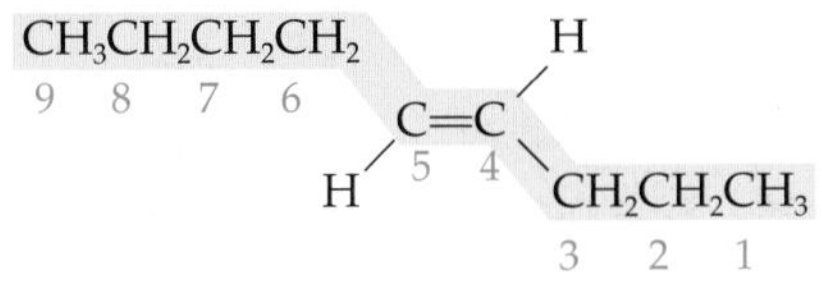

$CH_3CH_2CH_2CH_2$ (9 8 7 6), H — C=C (5 4) — H, $CH_2CH_2CH_3$ (3 2 1)

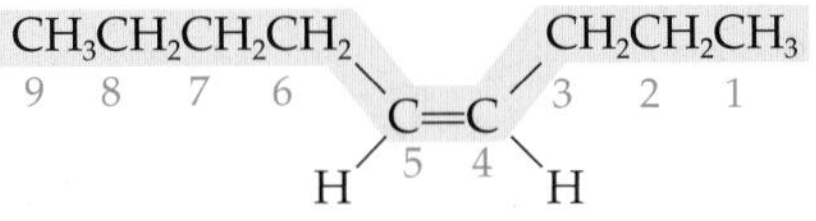

$CH_3CH_2CH_2CH_2$ (9 8 7 6), $CH_2CH_2CH_3$ (3 2 1) — C=C (5 4) — H, H

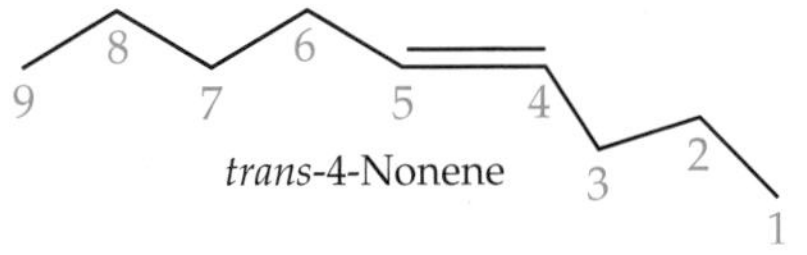

trans-4-Nonene

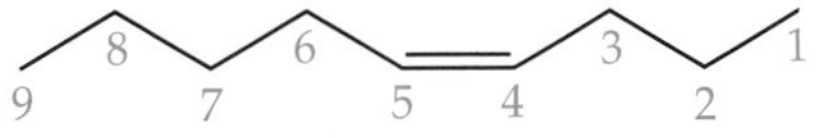

cis-4-Nonene

EXAMPLE 11.4 Naming *cis*- and *trans*-Isomers of Alkenes

LEARNING GOAL

3 Write the names and draw the structures of simple geometric isomers of alkenes.

Name the following geometric isomers.

Solution

The longest chain of carbon atoms in each of the following molecules is highlighted in yellow. *The chain must also contain the carbon-carbon double bond.* The orientation of the carbon atoms of the parent chain relative to the double bond is used in determining the appropriate prefix, *cis* or *trans,* to be used in naming each of the molecules.

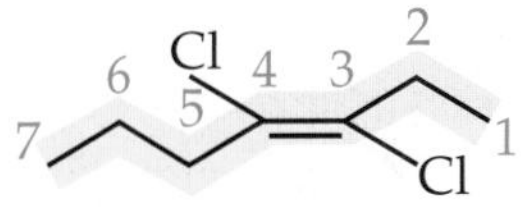

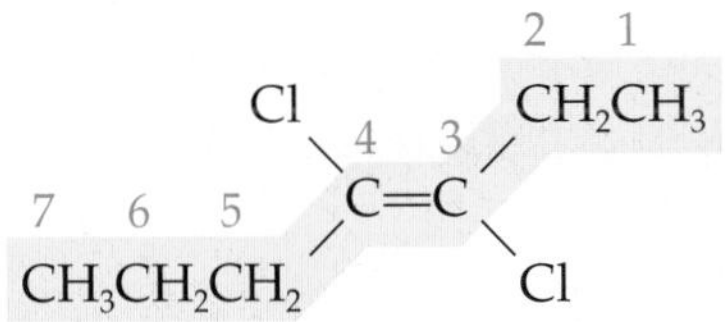

Parent chain: heptene

Position of double bond: 3-

Substituents: 3,4-dichloro

Configuration: *trans* (the carbon atoms of the parent chain are on opposite sides of the double bond)

Name: *trans*-3,4-Dichloro-3-heptene

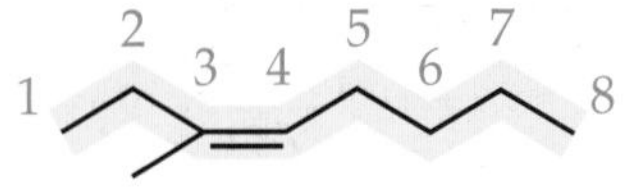

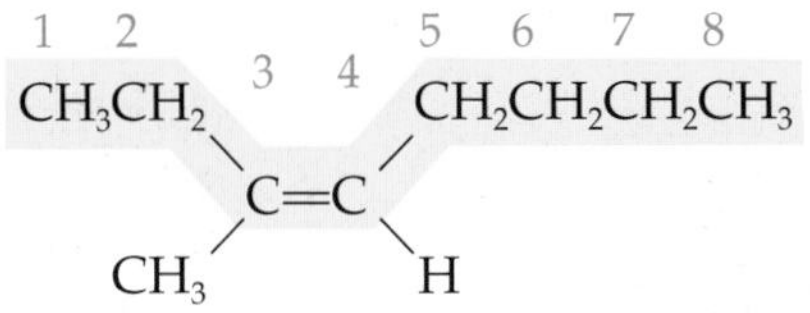

Cl, CH_2CH_3 (2 1) — C=C (4 3) — $CH_3CH_2CH_2$ (7 6 5), Cl

Parent chain: octene

Position of double bond: 3-

Substituents: 3-methyl

Configuration: *cis* (the carbon atoms of the parent chain are on the same side of the double bond)

Name: *cis*-3-Methyl-3-octene

CH_3CH_2 (1 2), $CH_2CH_2CH_2CH_3$ (5 6 7 8) — C=C (3 4) — CH_3, H

Practice Problem 11.4

Name each of the following geometric isomers:

a. 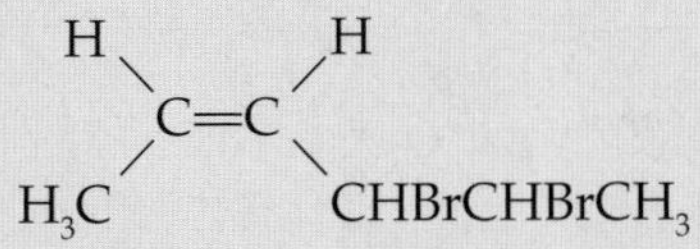 H, H — C=C — H_3C, $CHBrCHBrCH_3$

b. 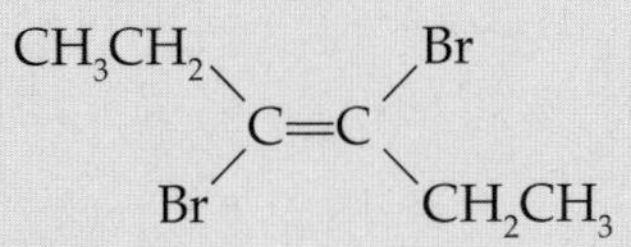 CH_3CH_2, Br — C=C — Br, CH_2CH_3

c. Cl, Cl_3 — C=C — H_3C, $CH_2CH_2CH_3$

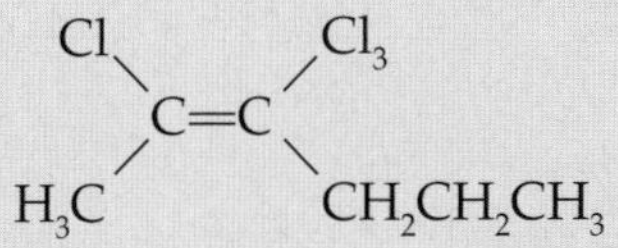

▸ For Further Practice: **Questions 11.51 and 11.52.**

EXAMPLE 11.5 Identifying Geometric Isomers

LEARNING GOAL

3 Write the names and draw the structures of simple geometric isomers of alkenes.

Determine whether each of the following molecules can exist as *cis-trans* isomers: (a) 1-pentene and (b) 3-methyl-2-pentene.

Solution

a. Examine the structure of 1-pentene,

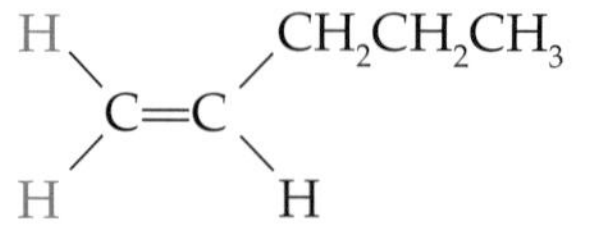

$$\begin{array}{ccc} H & & CH_2CH_2CH_3 \\ & C{=}C & \\ H & & H \end{array}$$

We see that carbon-1 is bonded to two hydrogen atoms, rather than to two different substituents. In this case there can be no *cis-trans* isomers.

b. Examination of the structure of 3-methyl-2-pentene reveals that both a *cis-* and *trans*-isomer can be drawn.

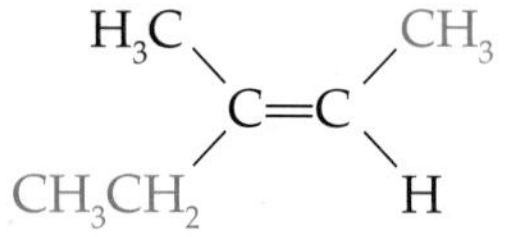

$$\begin{array}{ccc} H_3C & & CH_3 \\ & C{=}C & \\ CH_3CH_2 & & H \end{array} \qquad \begin{array}{ccc} H_3C & & H \\ & C{=}C & \\ CH_3CH_2 & & CH_3 \end{array}$$

trans-3-Methyl-2-pentene 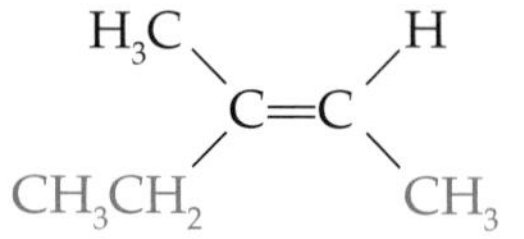 *cis*-3-Methyl-2-pentene

Each of the carbon atoms involved in the double bond is attached to two different groups. In *trans*-3-methyl-2-pentene the carbons of the parent chain are on opposite sides of the double bond. In the *cis*-configuration, the carbons of the parent chain are on the same side of the double bond.

Practice Problem 11.5

Which of the following molecules can exist as *cis-* and *trans*-isomers? Draw the *cis-* and *trans*-isomers, where possible. For those molecules that cannot exist as *cis-* and *trans*-isomers, explain why.

a. $CH_3CH{=}CHCH_2CH_3$
b. $CBr_2{=}CBrCH_2CH_2CH_3$
c. $CH_2{=}CHCH_3$
d. $CH_3CBr{=}CBrCH_2CH_2CH_2CH_3$

► For Further Practice: **Questions 11.49 and 11.50.**

The recent debate over the presence of *cis-* and *trans*-isomers of fatty acids in our diet points out the relevance of geometric isomers to our lives. Fatty acids are long-chain carboxylic acids found in vegetable oils (unsaturated fats) and animal fats (saturated fats). Oleic acid,

$$CH_3(CH_2)_7CH{=}CH(CH_2)_7\overset{\overset{\displaystyle O}{\|}}{C}{-}OH$$

is the naturally occurring fatty acid in olive oil. Its IUPAC name, *cis*-9-octadecenoic acid, reveals that this is a *cis*-fatty acid.

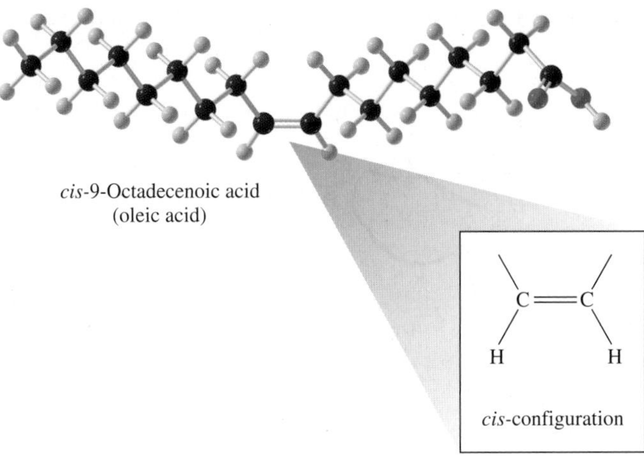

cis-9-Octadecenoic acid
(oleic acid)

The *cis*-isomer of oleic acid is V-shaped as a result of the configuration of the double bond and the molecule is more flexible. Its geometric isomer, *trans*-9-octadecenoic acid is a rigid linear molecule.

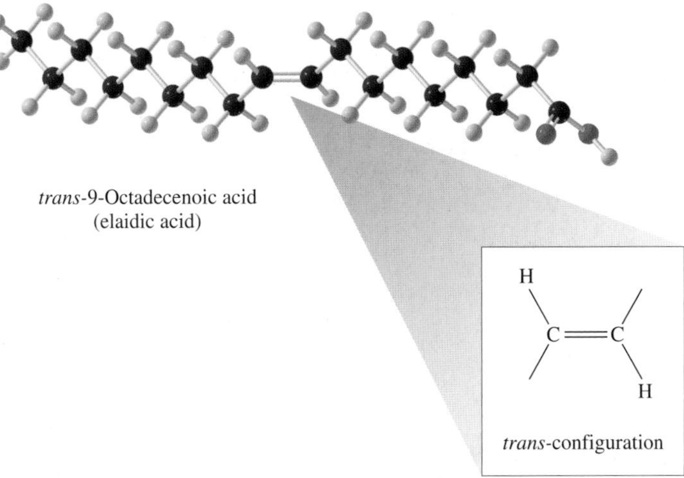

trans-9-Octadecenoic acid
(elaidic acid)

The majority of *trans*-fatty acids found in the diet result from hydrogenation, which is a reaction used to convert oils into solid fats, such as margarine. It has recently been reported that *trans*-fatty acids in the diet elevate levels of "bad" or LDL cholesterol and lower the levels of "good" or HDL cholesterol, thereby increasing the risk of heart disease. Other studies suggest that *trans*-fatty acids may also increase the risk of type 2 diabetes.

cis- *and* trans-*Fatty acids will be discussed in greater detail in Chapter 17. Hydrogenation is described in Section 11.5.*

Question 11.3 In each of the following pairs of molecules, identify the *cis*-isomer and the *trans*-isomer.

a. H(upper left), H(upper right) C=C CH_3CH_2(lower left), CH_2CH_3(lower right) — H(upper left), CH_2CH_3(upper right) C=C CH_3CH_2(lower left), H(lower right)

b. Br(upper left), CH_3(upper right) C=C H_3C(lower left), Br(lower right) — Br(upper left), Br(upper right) C=C H_3C(lower left), CH_3(lower right)

Question 11.4 Provide the complete IUPAC name for each of the compounds in Question 11.3.

Question 11.5 Which of the following molecules can exist as both *cis-* and *trans-* isomers? Explain your reasoning.

a. $CH_3CH_2CCl{=}C(CH_2CH_3)_2$ b. $CH_3CH_2CBr{=}CBr_2$ c. $CH_3CCl{=}CClCH_3$

Question 11.6 Draw each of the *cis-trans* isomers in Question 11.5 and provide the complete names using the IUPAC Nomenclature System.

Question 11.7 Draw condensed formulas for each of the following compounds:

a. *cis*-3-Octene
b. *trans*-5-Chloro-2-hexene
c. *trans*-2,3-Dichloro-2-butene

Question 11.8 Name each of the following compounds, using the IUPAC system. Be sure to indicate *cis* or *trans* where applicable.

a. CH_3 and H on one carbon; CH_3 and CH_3 on the other: $(CH_3)(H)C{=}C(CH_3)(CH_3)$

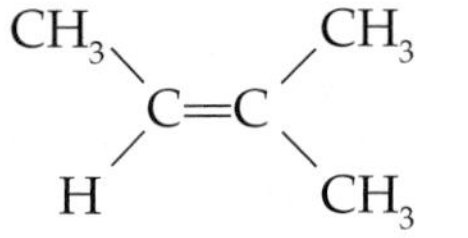

c. CH_3 and H on one carbon; H and $CH_2C(CH_3)_3$ on the other: $(CH_3)(H)C{=}C(H)(CH_2C(CH_3)_3)$

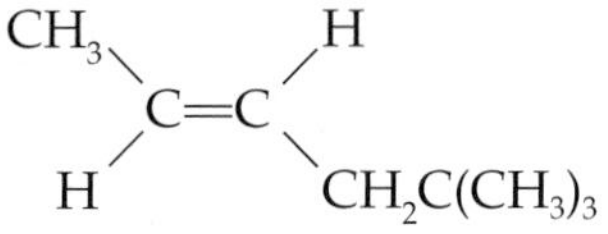

b. CH_3CH_2 and CH_3 on one carbon; CH_2CH_3 and H on the other: $(CH_3CH_2)(CH_3)C{=}C(CH_2CH_3)(H)$

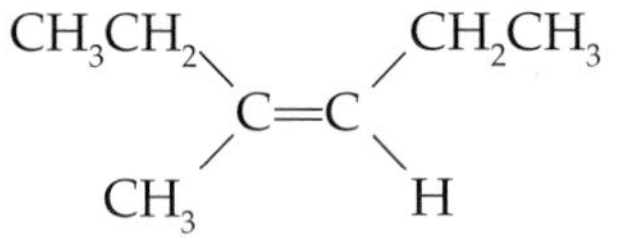

11.4 Alkenes in Nature

Folklore tells us that placing a ripe banana among green tomatoes will speed up the ripening process. In fact, this phenomenon has been demonstrated experimentally. The key to the reaction is *ethene*, the simplest alkene. Ethene, produced by ripening fruit, is a plant growth substance. It is produced in the greatest abundance in areas of the plant where cell division is occurring. It is produced during fruit ripening, during leaf fall and flower senescence, as well as under conditions of stress, including wounding, heat, cold, or water stress, and disease.

There are surprising numbers of polyenes, alkenes with several double bonds, found in nature. These molecules, which have wildly different properties and functions, are built from one or more five-carbon units called *isoprene*.

$$CH_2{=}\overset{\displaystyle CH_3}{\overset{|}{C}}CH{=}CH_2$$

Isoprene

The molecules that are produced are called *isoprenoids*, or *terpenes*. Terpenes include the steroids; chlorophyll and carotenoid pigments that function in photosynthesis; and the lipid-soluble vitamins A, D, E, and K (see Figure 11.1).

Many other terpenes are plant products familiar to us because of their distinctive aromas. *Geraniol*, the familiar scent of geraniums, is a molecule made up of two isoprene units. Purified from plant sources, geraniol is the active ingredient in several natural insect repellants. These can be applied directly to the skin to provide 4 h of protection against a variety of insects, including mosquitoes, ticks, and fire ants.

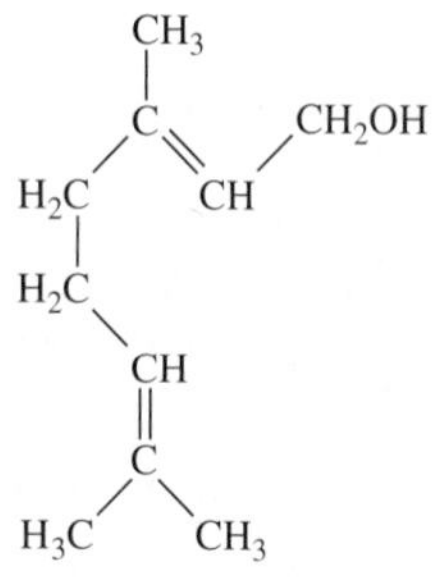

Geraniol
(Roses and geraniums)

D-*Limonene* is the most abundant component of the oil extracted from the rind of citrus fruits. Because of its pleasing orange aroma, D-limonene is used as a flavor and fragrance additive in foods. However, the most rapidly expanding use of the compound is as a solvent. In this role, D-limonene can be used in place of more toxic solvents, such as mineral spirits, methyl ethyl ketone, acetone, toluene, and fluorinated and chlorinated organic solvents. It can also be formulated as a water-based cleaning product, such as Orange Glo, that can be used in place of more caustic cleaning solutions. There is a form of limonene that is a molecular mirror image of D-limonene. It is called L-limonene and has a pine or turpentine aroma.

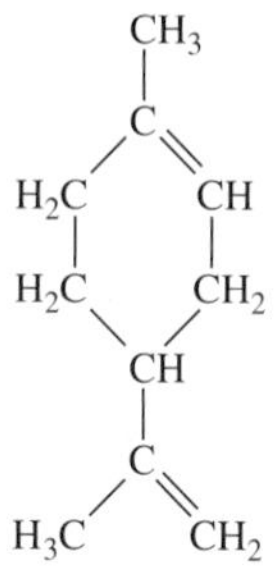

D-Limonene
(Oil of lemon and orange)

The terpene *myrcene* is found in bayberry. It is used in perfumes and scented candles because it adds a refreshing, spicy aroma to them. Trace amounts of myrcene may be used as a flavor component in root beer.

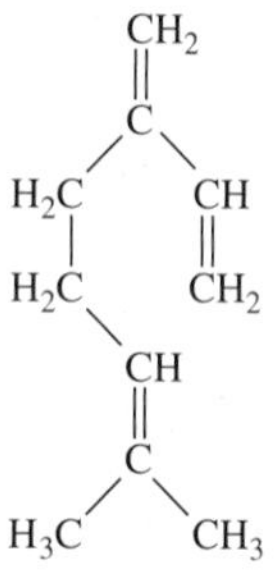

Myrcene
(Oil of bayberry)

Farnesol is a terpene found in roses, orange blossom, wild cyclamen, and lily of the valley. Cosmetics companies began to use farnesol in skin care products in the early 1990s. It is claimed that farnesol smoothes wrinkles and increases skin elasticity. It is also thought to reduce skin aging by promoting regeneration of cells and activation of the synthesis of molecules, such as collagen, that are required for healthy skin.

$$(CH_3)_2C{=}CH{-}CH_2{-}CH_2{-}C(CH_3){=}CH{-}CH_2{-}CH_2{-}C(CH_3){=}CH{-}CH_2OH$$

Farnesol
(Lily of the valley)

Another terpene, *retinol,* is a form of vitamin A (see Figure 11.1). It is able to penetrate the outer layers of skin and stimulate the formation of collagen and elastin. This reduces wrinkles by creating skin that is firmer and smoother.

11.5 Reactions Involving Alkenes and Alkynes

LEARNING GOAL

4 Write equations predicting the products of addition reactions of alkenes and alkynes: hydrogenation, halogenation, hydration, and hydrohalogenation.

Reactions of alkenes involve the carbon-carbon double bond. The key reaction of the double bond is the **addition reaction.** This involves the addition of two atoms or groups of atoms to a double bond. The major alkene addition reactions include addition of hydrogen (H_2), halogens (Cl_2 or Br_2), water (HOH), or hydrogen halides (HBr or HCl). A generalized addition reaction is shown here. The R in these structures represents a hydrogen atom or any alkyl or aryl group.

$$R_2C{=}CR_2 + A{-}B \longrightarrow R_2C(A){-}C(B)R_2$$

Note that the double bond is replaced by a single bond. The former double bond carbons receive a new single bond to a new atom, producing either an alkane or a substituted alkane.

Hydrogenation: Addition of H_2

Recall that a catalyst itself undergoes no net change in the course of a chemical reaction (see Section 7.3).

Hydrogenation is the addition of a molecule of hydrogen (H_2) to a carbon-carbon double bond to give an alkane. In this reaction the double bond is broken, and two new C—H single bonds result. One hydrogen molecule is required for each double bond in the alkene. Platinum, palladium, or nickel is needed as a catalyst to speed up the reaction. Heat and/or pressure may also be required.

$$\underset{\text{Alkene}}{R_2C{=}CR_2} + \underset{\text{Hydrogen}}{H{-}H} \xrightarrow[\text{Heat or pressure}]{\text{Pt, Pd, or Ni}} \underset{\text{Alkane}}{R_2C(H){-}C(H)R_2}$$

Note that the alkene is gaining two hydrogens. Thus, hydrogenation is a reduction reaction (see Sections 8.5 and 12.6).

EXAMPLE 11.6 Writing Equations for the Hydrogenation of Alkenes

LEARNING GOAL

4 Write equations predicting the products of addition reactions of alkenes and alkynes: hydrogenation, halogenation, hydration, and hydrohalogenation.

Linoleic acid (*cis, cis*-9,12-octadecadienoic acid) is an essential fatty acid. This means that we must obtain it in the diet, because we cannot make it. Fortunately, it is found in abundance in sunflower, safflower, and corn oil. These oils are often hydrogenated to produce margarine. Write a balanced equation showing the hydrogenation of linoleic acid.

Solution

First, notice that there are two double bonds. This means that we will need two molecules of H_2 for every molecule of linoleic acid that is hydrogenated.

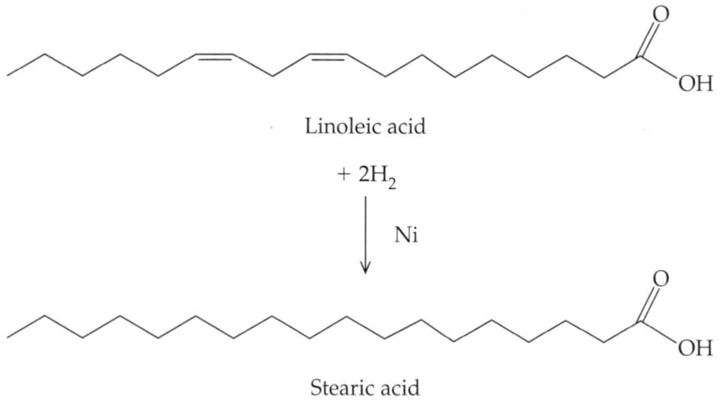

O

OH

Linoleic acid

$+ 2H_2$

$\downarrow$ Ni

O

OH

Stearic acid

The liquid linoleic acid is converted to stearic acid, which is a rather hard solid. In margarine production today, partial hydrogenation is generally used because it produces a fat that can be more easily spread and has a better "mouth feel." Producers may then add butter flavoring, milk solids, salt, an emulsifying agent, preservatives, vitamin A for nutritional value, and a bit of β-carotene for color.

Practice Problem 11.6

Write a balanced equation for the hydrogenation of each of the following alkenes.

a. *cis*-2-Heptene
b. *trans*-2-Pentene
c. 3-Hexene
d. Propene

► For Further Practice: **Questions 11.55, 11.67a, and 11.83.**

The conditions for the hydrogenation of alkynes are very similar to those for the hydrogenation of alkenes. Two molecules of hydrogen add to the triple bond of the alkyne to produce an alkane, as seen in the following general reaction:

$$\text{R—C}\equiv\text{C—R} + 2H_2 \xrightarrow[\text{Heat}]{\text{Pt, Pd, or Ni}} \text{H—}\underset{\text{H}}{\overset{\text{R}}{\text{C}}}\text{—}\underset{\text{R}}{\overset{\text{H}}{\text{C}}}\text{—H}$$

Alkyne Hydrogen Alkane

Margarine and solid shortening are made by partial hydrogenation of vegetable oils. While natural oils contain only *cis*-fatty acids, the hydrogenation reaction produces *trans*-fatty acids. What are the health risks associated with *trans*-fats?

Question 11.9 The *trans*-isomer of 2-pentene was used in Practice Problem 11.6b. Would the result be any different if the *cis*-isomer had been used?

Question 11.10 Write balanced equations for the hydrogenation of 1-butene and *cis*-2-butene.

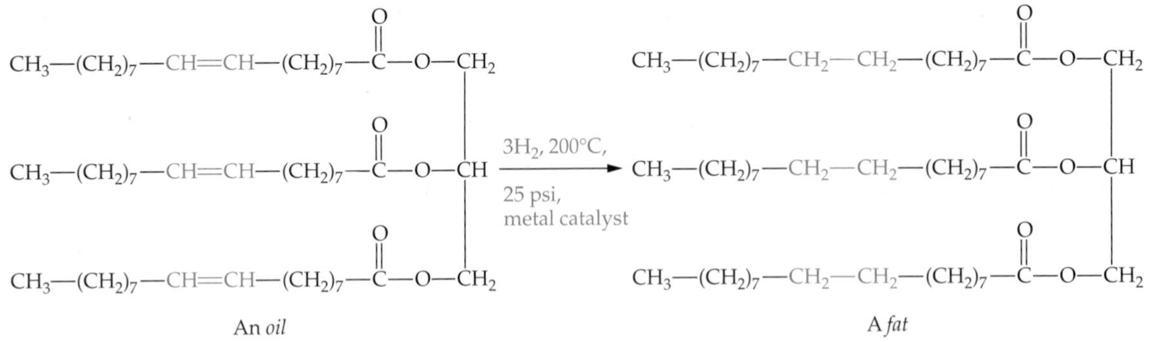

$$
\begin{array}{l}
CH_3{-}(CH_2)_7{-}CH{=}CH{-}(CH_2)_7{-}\overset{O}{\overset{\|}{C}}{-}O{-}CH_2 \\
CH_3{-}(CH_2)_7{-}CH{=}CH{-}(CH_2)_7{-}\overset{O}{\overset{\|}{C}}{-}O{-}CH \\
CH_3{-}(CH_2)_7{-}CH{=}CH{-}(CH_2)_7{-}\overset{O}{\overset{\|}{C}}{-}O{-}CH_2
\end{array}
\xrightarrow[\text{25 psi, metal catalyst}]{3H_2,\ 200^\circ C,}
\begin{array}{l}
CH_3{-}(CH_2)_7{-}CH_2{-}CH_2{-}(CH_2)_7{-}\overset{O}{\overset{\|}{C}}{-}O{-}CH_2 \\
CH_3{-}(CH_2)_7{-}CH_2{-}CH_2{-}(CH_2)_7{-}\overset{O}{\overset{\|}{C}}{-}O{-}CH \\
CH_3{-}(CH_2)_7{-}CH_2{-}CH_2{-}(CH_2)_7{-}\overset{O}{\overset{\|}{C}}{-}O{-}CH_2
\end{array}
$$

An *oil* A *fat*

Figure 11.3 Conversion of a typical oil to a fat involves hydrogenation. In this example, triolein (an oil) is converted to tristearin (a fat).

Question 11.11 Write balanced equations for the complete hydrogenation of each of the following alkynes:

a. $H_3CC{\equiv}CCH_3$ b. $H_3CC{\equiv}CCH_2CH_3$

Question 11.12 Using the IUPAC Nomenclature System, name each of the products and reactants in the reactions described in Question 11.11.

Saturated and unsaturated dietary fats are discussed in Section 17.2.

Hydrogenation is used in the food industry to produce margarine, which is a mixture of hydrogenated vegetable oils (Figure 11.3). Vegetable oils are polyunsaturated, that is, they contain many double bonds and as a result have low melting points and are liquid at room temperature. The hydrogenation of these double bonds to single bonds increases the melting point of these oils and results in a fat, such as Crisco, that remains solid at room temperature. Because saturated fats are extended, rigid chains, they tend to stack. This increases the intermolecular attractions (London dispersion forces) and results in higher melting points, producing a fat that is solid at room temperature. A similar process with highly refined corn oil and added milk solids produces corn oil margarine. As we saw in Section 11.3, such margarine may contain *trans*-fatty acids as a result of hydrogenation.

Halogenation: Addition of X_2

Chlorine (Cl_2) or bromine (Br_2) can be added to a double bond. This reaction, called **halogenation,** proceeds readily and does not require a catalyst:

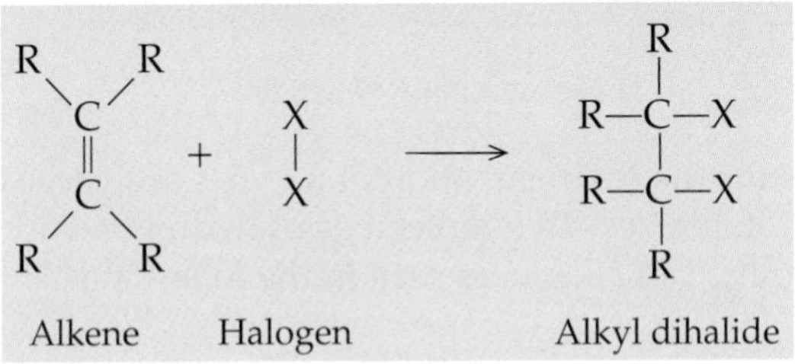

$$
\underset{\text{Alkene}}{R_2C{=}CR_2} + \underset{\text{Halogen}}{X{-}X} \longrightarrow \underset{\text{Alkyl dihalide}}{R{-}\overset{R}{\overset{|}{C}}{-}X \atop R{-}\underset{R}{\underset{|}{C}}{-}X}
$$

EXAMPLE 11.7 Writing Equations for the Halogenation of Alkenes

LEARNING GOAL

4 Write equations predicting the products of addition reactions of alkenes and alkynes: hydrogenation, halogenation, hydration, and hydrohalogenation.

Write a balanced equation showing (a) the chlorination of 1-pentene and (b) the bromination of *trans*-2-butene.

Solution

a. Begin by drawing the structure of 1-pentene and of diatomic chlorine (Cl_2).

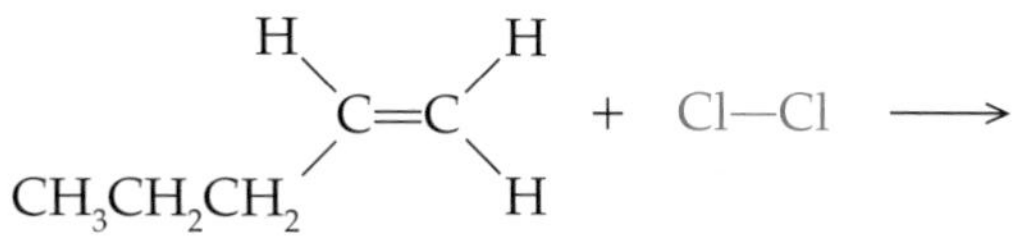

$$\underset{\text{1-Pentene}}{CH_3CH_2CH_2(H)C{=}CH_2} + \underset{\text{Chlorine}}{Cl{-}Cl} \longrightarrow$$

Knowing that one chlorine atom will form a covalent bond with each of the carbon atoms of the carbon-carbon double bond, we can write the product and complete the equation.

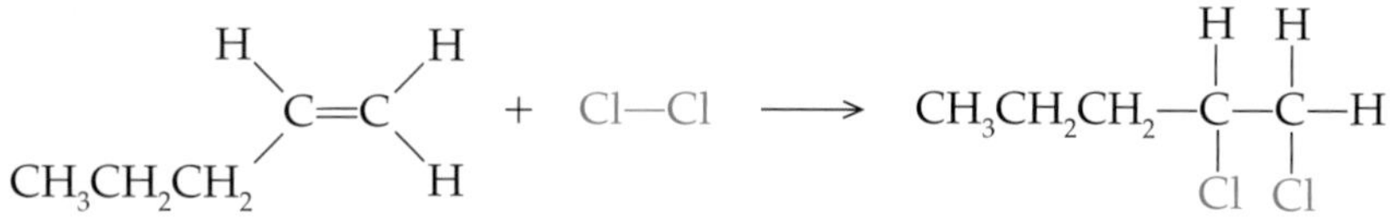

$$\underset{\text{1-Pentene}}{CH_3CH_2CH_2(H)C{=}CH_2} + \underset{\text{Chlorine}}{Cl{-}Cl} \longrightarrow \underset{\text{1,2-Dichloropentane}}{CH_3CH_2CH_2{-}CH(Cl){-}CH_2Cl}$$

b. Begin by drawing the structure of *trans*-2-butene and of diatomic bromine (Br_2).

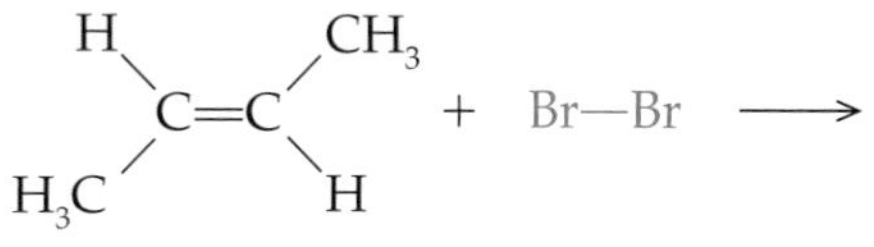

$$\underset{\textit{trans}\text{-2-Butene}}{H_3C(H)C{=}C(H)CH_3} + \underset{\text{Bromine}}{Br{-}Br} \longrightarrow$$

Knowing that one bromine atom will form a covalent bond with each of the carbon atoms of the carbon-carbon double bond, we can write the product and complete the equation.

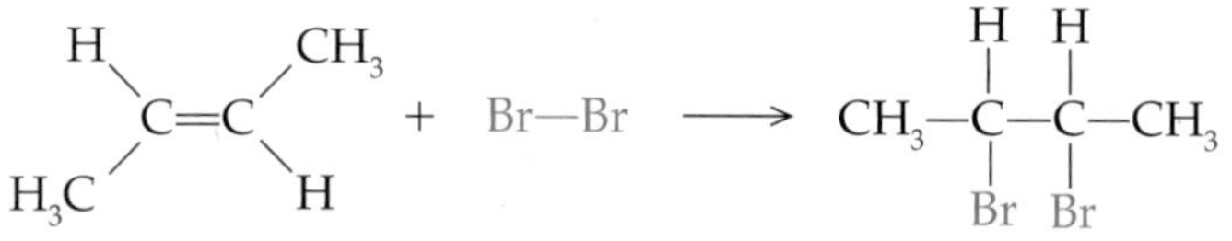

$$\underset{\textit{trans}\text{-2-Butene}}{H_3C(H)C{=}C(H)CH_3} + \underset{\text{Bromine}}{Br{-}Br} \longrightarrow \underset{\text{2,3-Dibromobutane}}{CH_3{-}CH(Br){-}CH(Br){-}CH_3}$$

Practice Problem 11.7

Write a balanced equation for the chlorination of each of the following alkenes.

a. 2,4-Hexadiene

b. 1,5-Dibromo-2-pentene

c. 2,3-Dimethyl-1-butene

d. 4,6-Dimethyl-2-heptene

▸ For Further Practice: **Questions 11.57, 11.67b, and 11.84.**

Alkynes also react with the halogens bromine or chlorine. Two molecules of halogen add to the triple bond to produce a tetrahaloalkane:

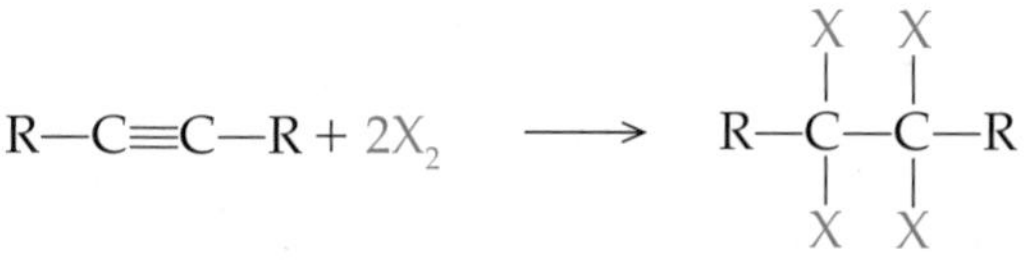

$$\underset{\text{Alkyne}}{R{-}C{\equiv}C{-}R} + \underset{\text{Halogen}}{2X_2} \longrightarrow \underset{\text{Tetrahaloalkane}}{R{-}CX_2{-}CX_2{-}R}$$

Question 11.13 Write a balanced equation for the addition of bromine to each of the following alkenes. Draw the products and reactants for each reaction.

a. $CH_3CH{=}CH_2$ b. $CH_3CH{=}CHCH_3$

Question 11.14 Using the IUPAC Nomenclature System, name each of the products and reactants in the reactions described in Question 11.13.

Question 11.15 Write balanced equations for the complete chlorination of each of the following alkynes:

a. $H_3CC{\equiv}CCH_3$ b. $H_3CC{\equiv}CCH_2CH_3$

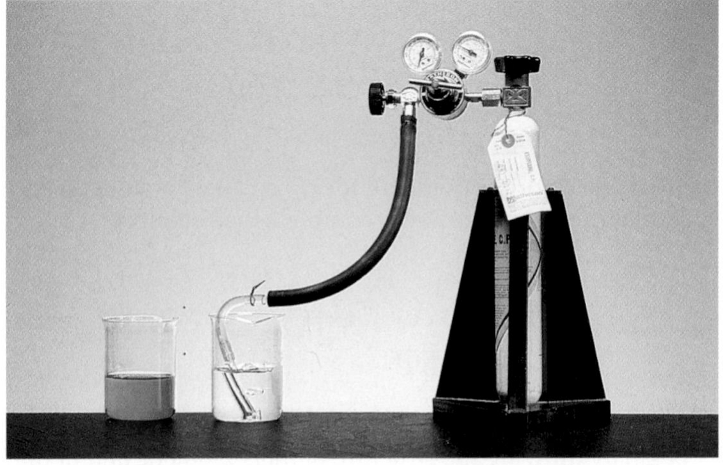

Figure 11.4 Bromination of an alkene. The solution on the left is red because of the presence of bromine and absence of an alkene or alkyne. In the presence of an unsaturated hydrocarbon, the bromine is used in the reaction and the solution becomes colorless.

Question 11.16 Using the IUPAC Nomenclature System, name each of the products and reactants in the reactions described in Question 11.15.

The following equation represents the bromination of 1-pentene:

$$\underset{\substack{\text{1-Pentene}\\\text{(colorless)}}}{CH_3CH_2CH_2CH{=}CH_2} + \underset{\substack{\text{Bromine}\\\text{(red)}}}{Br_2} \longrightarrow \underset{\substack{\text{1,2-Dibromopentane}\\\text{(colorless)}}}{CH_3CH_2CH_2\underset{|\atop Br}{C}H\underset{|\atop Br}{C}H_2}$$

This reaction is represented in Figure 11.4. Notice that the solution of reactants is red because of the presence of bromine. However, the product is colorless.

This bromination reaction can be used to show the presence of double or triple bonds in an organic compound. The reaction mixture is red because of the presence of dissolved bromine. If the red color is lost, the bromine has been consumed. Thus bromination has occurred, and the compound must have had a carbon-carbon double or triple bond. The greater the amount of bromine that must be added to the reaction, the more unsaturated the compound is. For instance, a diene or an alkyne would consume twice as much bromine as an alkene with a single double bond.

Hydration: Addition of H_2O

A water molecule can be added to an alkene. This reaction, termed **hydration,** requires a trace of strong acid (H^+) as a catalyst. The product is an alcohol, as shown in the following equation:

$$\underset{\text{Alkene}}{\begin{array}{c} R\quad R \\ \diagdown\,\diagup \\ C \\ \| \\ C \\ \diagup\,\diagdown \\ R\quad R \end{array}} + \underset{\text{Water}}{\begin{array}{c} H \\ | \\ OH \end{array}} \xrightarrow{H^+} \underset{\text{Alcohol}}{\begin{array}{c} R \\ | \\ R{-}C{-}H \\ | \\ R{-}C{-}OH \\ | \\ R \end{array}}$$

The following equation shows the hydration of ethene to produce ethanol.

$$\underset{\text{Ethene}}{\begin{array}{c} H\quad H \\ \diagdown\,\diagup \\ C \\ \| \\ C \\ \diagup\,\diagdown \\ H\quad H \end{array}} + \underset{\text{Water}}{\begin{array}{c} H \\ | \\ OH \end{array}} \xrightarrow{H^+} \underset{\substack{\text{Ethanol}\\\text{(ethyl alcohol)}}}{\begin{array}{c} H \\ | \\ H{-}C{-}H \\ | \\ H{-}C{-}OH \\ | \\ H \end{array}}$$

With alkenes in which the groups attached to the two carbons of the double bond are different (unsymmetrical alkenes), two products are possible. For example:

```
3  2  1                     3  2     1           3  2  1
H  H                        H  H     H           H  H  H
|  |                        |  |     |           |  |  |
H—C—C=C—H + H—OH  --H+-->   H—C—C————C—H   +   H—C—C—C—H
   |   |                    |  |     |           |  |  |
   H   H                    H  OH    H           H  H  OH
```

Propene (propylene) | Major product 2-Propanol (isopropyl alcohol) | Minor product 1-Propanol (propyl alcohol)

LEARNING GOAL

5 Apply Markovnikov's rule to predict the major and minor products of the hydration and hydrohalogenation reactions of unsymmetrical alkenes.

When hydration of an unsymmetrical alkene, such as propene, is carried out in the laboratory, one product is favored over the other. In this example, 2-propanol is the major product. The Russian chemist Vladimir Markovnikov studied many such reactions and came up with a rule that can be used to predict the major product of such a reaction. **Markovnikov's rule** tells us that the carbon of the carbon-carbon double bond that originally has more hydrogen atoms receives the hydrogen atom being added to the double bond. The remaining carbon forms a bond with the —OH. Simply stated, "the rich get richer"—the carbon with the greater number of hydrogens gets the new one as well. In the preceding example, carbon-1 has two C—H bonds originally, and carbon-2 has only one. The major product, 2-propanol, results from the new C—H bond forming on carbon-1 and the new C—OH bond on carbon-2.

Addition of water to a double bond is a reaction that we find in several biochemical pathways. For instance, the citric acid cycle is a key metabolic pathway in the complete oxidation of the sugar glucose and the release of the majority of the energy used by the body. The citric acid cycle is also the source of starting materials for the synthesis of the biological molecules needed for life. The next-to-last reaction in the citric acid cycle is the hydration of a molecule of fumarate to produce a molecule called malate.

We have seen that hydration of a double bond requires a trace of acid as a catalyst. In the cell, this reaction is catalyzed by an enzyme, or biological catalyst, called fumarase.

```
     COO⁻                                 COO⁻
     |                                    |
     C—H                              HO—C—H
     ||                  Fumarase         |
   H—C      + H2O     ------------->   H—C—H
     |                                    |
     COO⁻                                 COO⁻
   Fumarate                             Malate
```

EXAMPLE 11.8 Writing Equations for the Hydration of Symmetrical and Unsymmetrical Alkenes

LEARNING GOAL

4 Write equations predicting the products of addition reactions of alkenes and alkynes: hydrogenation, halogenation, hydration, and hydrohalogenation.

a. More and more frequently we see ethanol used as an additive in the gasoline we buy. A mixture of 10% ethanol and 90% gasoline significantly raises the octane rating of the fuel. In fact, some cities where auto emissions may reach harmful levels require the use of 10% ethanol gasoline. Bioethanol is produced by fermentation of crops such as corn. However, it can also be manufactured by the hydration of ethene. Write a balanced equation showing the hydration of ethene.

Solution

```
H       H                          H  H
 \     /                  H+       |  |
  C=C      +  HOH      ------>   H—C—C—H
 /     \                           |  |
H       H                          H  OH
  Ethene                          Ethanol
```

Continued...

b. Write an equation showing all the products of the hydration of the unsymmetrical alkene 1-pentene.

LEARNING GOAL

5 Apply Markovnikov's rule to predict the major and minor products of the hydration and hydrohalogenation reactions of unsymmetrical alkenes.

Solution

Begin by drawing the structure of 1-pentene and of water and indicating the catalyst.

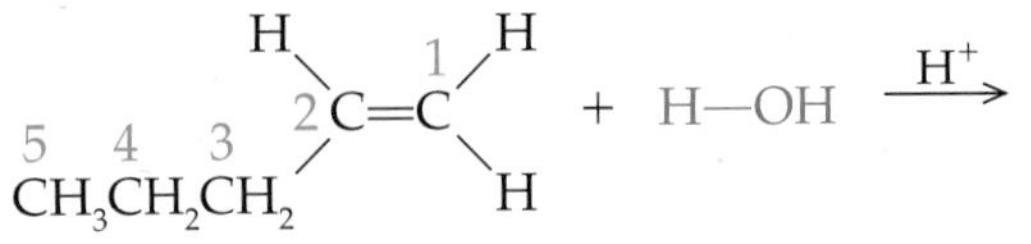

$$\underset{\text{1-Pentene}}{\overset{5\ 4\ 3}{CH_3CH_2CH_2}\!-\!\overset{2}{C}H\!=\!\overset{1}{C}H_2} + \underset{\text{Water}}{H\!-\!OH} \xrightarrow{H^+}$$

Markovnikov's rule tells us that the carbon atom that is already bonded to the greater number of hydrogen atoms is more likely to receive the hydrogen atom from the water molecule. The other carbon atom is more likely to become bonded to the hydroxyl group. Thus we can predict that the major product of this reaction will be 2-pentanol and that the minor product will be 1-pentanol. Now we can complete the equation by showing the products:

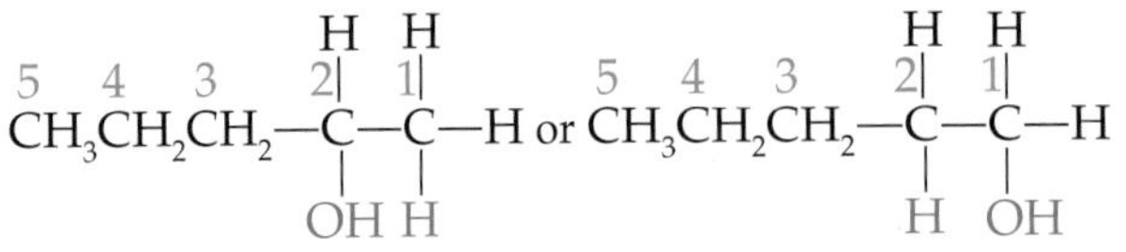

$$\underset{\substack{\text{2-Pentanol}\\ \text{(major product)}}}{CH_3CH_2CH_2-\overset{H}{\underset{OH}{C}}-\overset{H}{\underset{H}{C}}-H} \text{ or } \underset{\substack{\text{1-Pentanol}\\ \text{(minor product)}}}{CH_3CH_2CH_2-\overset{H}{\underset{H}{C}}-\overset{H}{\underset{OH}{C}}-H}$$

Practice Problem 11.8

Write a balanced equation for the hydration of each of the following alkenes.

a. 1-Butene
b. 2-Methyl-3-hexene
c. Propene
d. 1,4-Dichloro-2-butene

► For Further Practice: **Questions 11.59, 11.68, and 11.79.**

The chemistry of enols, aldehydes, and ketones is found in Chapter 13.

Hydration of an alkyne is a more complex process because the initial product is not stable and is rapidly isomerized. As you would expect, the product is an alcohol but, in this case, one in which the hydroxyl group is bonded to one of the carbons of a carbon-carbon double bond. This type of molecule is called an *enol* because it is both an alkene (*ene*) and an alcohol (*ol*). The enol cannot be isolated from the reaction mixture because it is so quickly isomerized into either an aldehyde or ketone, as shown in the following general reaction:

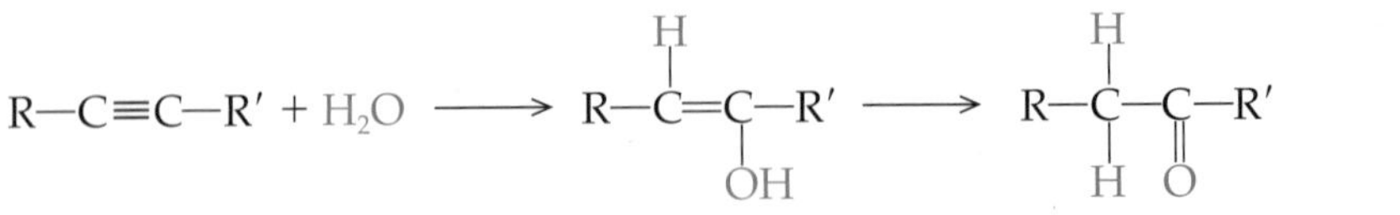

$$\underset{\text{Alkyne}}{R-C\equiv C-R'} + \underset{\text{Water}}{H_2O} \longrightarrow \underset{\text{Enol}}{R-\overset{H}{C}=\underset{OH}{C}-R'} \longrightarrow \underset{\substack{\text{Aldehyde if } R' = H\\ \text{Ketone if } R' = \text{alkyl group}}}{R-\overset{H}{\underset{H}{C}}-\underset{O}{\overset{\|}{C}}-R'}$$

Question 11.17 Write an equation for the hydration of each of the following alkenes. Predict the major product of each of the reactions.

a. $CH_3CH{=}CHCH_3$
b. $CH_2{=}CHCH_2CH_2CH(CH_3)_2$
c. $CH_3CH_2CH_2CH{=}CHCH_2CH_3$
d. $CH_3CHClCH{=}CHCHClCH_3$

Question 11.18 Write an equation for the hydration of each of the following alkenes. Predict the major product of each of the reactions.

a. $CH_2{=}CHCH_2CH_2CH_3$
b. $CH_3CH_2CH_2CH{=}CHCH_3$
c. $CH_3CHBrCH_2CH{=}CHCH_2Cl$
d. $CH_3CH_2CH_2CH_2CH_2CH{=}CHCH_3$

Question 11.19 Write equations for the complete hydration of each of the following alkynes:

a. $H_3CC{\equiv}CH$
b. $H_3CC{\equiv}CCH_2CH_3$

Question 11.20 Is the final product in each of the reactions in Question 11.19 an aldehyde or a ketone?

Hydrohalogenation: Addition of HX

A hydrogen halide (HBr, HCl, or HI) also can be added to an alkene. The product of this reaction, called **hydrohalogenation,** is an alkyl halide:

$$R_2C{=}CR_2 + H{-}X \longrightarrow R_2CH{-}CR_2X$$

Alkene Hydrogen halide Alkyl halide

$$H_2C{=}CH_2 + H{-}Br \longrightarrow H_3C{-}CH_2Br$$

Ethene Hydrogen bromide Bromoethane

This reaction also follows Markovnikov's rule. That is, if HX is added to an unsymmetrical alkene, the hydrogen atom will be added preferentially to the carbon atom that originally had the most hydrogen atoms. Consider the following example:

$$\overset{3}{C}H_3{-}\overset{2}{C}H{=}\overset{1}{C}H_2 + H{-}Br \longrightarrow \overset{3}{C}H_3{-}\overset{2}{C}HBr{-}\overset{1}{C}H_3 \text{ or } \overset{3}{C}H_3{-}\overset{2}{C}H_2{-}\overset{1}{C}H_2Br$$

Propene; Major product 2-Bromopropane; Minor product 1-Bromopropane

EXAMPLE 11.9 Writing Equations for the Hydrohalogenation of Alkenes

LEARNING GOAL

4 Write equations predicting the products of addition reactions of alkenes and alkynes: hydrogenation, halogenation, hydration, and hydrohalogenation.

LEARNING GOAL

5 Apply Markovnikov's rule to predict the major and minor products of the hydration and hydrohalogenation reactions of unsymmetrical alkenes.

Write an equation showing all the products of the hydrohalogenation of 1-pentene with HCl.

Solution

Begin by drawing the structure of 1-pentene and of hydrochloric acid.

$$\overset{5}{C}H_3\overset{4}{C}H_2\overset{3}{C}H_2{-}\overset{2}{C}H{=}\overset{1}{C}H_2 + H{-}Cl \longrightarrow$$

1-Pentene Hydrochloric acid

Continued...

Markovnikov's rule tells us that the carbon atom that is already bonded to the greater number of hydrogen atoms is more likely to receive the hydrogen atom of the hydrochloric acid molecule. The other carbon atom is more likely to become bonded to the chlorine atom. Thus, we can complete the equation by writing the major and minor products.

$$\overset{5}{C}H_3\overset{4}{C}H_2\overset{3}{C}H_2-\overset{2}{C}H(Cl)-\overset{1}{C}H_2-H \quad \text{or} \quad \overset{5}{C}H_3\overset{4}{C}H_2\overset{3}{C}H_2-\overset{2}{C}H_2-\overset{1}{C}H_2-Cl$$

2-Chloropentane (major product) 1-Chloropentane (minor product)

As predicted by Markovnikov's rule, the major product is 2-chloropentane and the minor product is 1-chloropentane.

Practice Problem 11.9

Write a balanced equation for the hydrobromination of each of the following alkenes.

a. 2-Pentene
b. Propene
c. 3-Heptene
d. Ethene

► For Further Practice: **Questions 11.69d, 11.70d, and 11.73.**

Addition Polymers of Alkenes

LEARNING GOAL

6 Write equations representing the formation of addition polymers of alkenes.

ANIMATION
• Natural and Synthetic Polymers

Polymers are macromolecules composed of repeating structural units called **monomers.** A polymer may be made up of several thousand monomers. Many commercially important plastics and fibers are addition polymers made from alkenes or substituted alkenes. They are called **addition polymers** because they are made by the sequential addition of the alkene monomer. The general formula for this addition reaction follows:

$$n\,R_2C{=}CR_2 \xrightarrow[\text{Pressure}]{\text{Catalyst, Heat}} \text{etc.}-CR_2-CR_2-CR_2-CR_2-CR_2-CR_2-\text{etc.}$$

Alkene monomer
R = H, X, or an alkyl group

Addition polymer

The product of the reaction is generally represented in a simplified manner:

$$\sim\left[CR_2-CR_2\right]_n\sim$$

Polyethylene is a polymer made from the monomer ethylene (ethene):

$$nCH_2{=}CH_2 \longrightarrow \sim\left[CH_2-CH_2\right]_n\sim$$

Ethene (ethylene) Polyethylene

It is used to make bottles, injection-molded toys and housewares, and wire coverings.

Polypropylene is a plastic made from propylene (propene). It is used to make indoor-outdoor carpeting, packaging materials, toys, and housewares. When propylene polymerizes, a methyl group is located on every other carbon of the main chain:

A HUMAN PERSPECTIVE

Life Without Polymers?

What do Nike Air-Sole shoes, disposable diapers, tires, shampoo, and artificial joints and skin share in common? These products and a great many other items we use every day are composed of synthetic or natural polymers. Indeed, the field of polymer chemistry has come a long way since the 1920s and 1930s when DuPont chemists invented nylon and Teflon.

Consider the disposable diaper. The outer, waterproof layer is composed of polyethylene. The polymerization reaction that produces polyethylene is shown in Section 11.5. The diapers have elastic to prevent leaking. The elastic is made of a natural polymer, rubber. The monomer from which natural rubber is formed is 2-methyl-1,3-butadiene. The common name of this monomer is *isoprene.* As we will see in coming chapters, isoprene is an important monomer in the synthesis of many natural polymers.

$$n\mathrm{CH_2{=}C(CH_3){-}CH{=}CH_2} \longrightarrow \sim\!\left[\mathrm{CH_2{-}C(CH_3){=}CH{-}CH_2}\right]_n\!\sim$$

2-Methyl-1,3-butadiene (isoprene) — Rubber polymer

The diaper is filled with a synthetic polymer called poly(acrylic acid). This polymer has the remarkable ability to absorb many times its own weight in liquid. Polymers that have this ability are called superabsorbers, but polymer chemists have no idea why they have this property! The acrylic acid monomer and resulting poly(acrylic acid) polymer are shown here:

$$n\,\mathrm{H_2C{=}CH{-}C({=}O){-}O{-}H} \longrightarrow \sim\!\left[\mathrm{CH_2{-}CH(C({=}O){-}O{-}H)}\right]_n\!\sim$$

Acrylic acid monomer — Poly(acrylic acid)

Another example of a useful polymer is Gore-Tex. This amazing polymer is made by stretching Teflon. Teflon is produced from the monomer tetrafluoroethene, as seen in the following equation:

$$n\,\mathrm{F_2C{=}CF_2} \longrightarrow \sim\!\left[\mathrm{CF_2{-}CF_2}\right]_n\!\sim$$

Tetrafluoroethene — Teflon

Clothing made from this fabric is used to protect firefighters because of its fire resistance. Because it also insulates, Gore-Tex clothing is used by military forces and by many amateur athletes, for protection during strenuous activity in the cold. In addition to its use in protective clothing, Gore-Tex has been used in millions of medical procedures for sutures, synthetic blood vessels, and tissue reconstruction.

For Further Understanding

- Visit The Macrogalleria, www.pslc.ws/macrog/index.htm, an Internet site maintained by the Department of Polymer Science of the University of Southern Mississippi, to help you answer these questions:
- Why does shrink wrap shrink?
- What are optical fibers made of and how do they transmit light?

$$n\mathrm{CH_2{=}CH(CH_3)} \longrightarrow \sim\!\left[\mathrm{CH_2{-}CH(CH_3)}\right]_n\!\sim$$

or

$$\sim\mathrm{CH_2{-}CH(CH_3){-}CH_2{-}CH(CH_3){-}CH_2{-}CH(CH_3)}\sim$$

Polymers made from alkenes or substituted alkenes are simply very large alkanes or substituted alkanes. Like the alkanes, they are typically inert. This chemical inertness makes these polymers ideal for making containers to hold juices, chemicals, and fluids used medically. They are also used to make sutures, catheters, and other indwelling devices. A variety of polymers made from substituted alkenes are listed in Table 11.2.

GREEN CHEMISTRY

Plastic Recycling

Plastics, first developed by British inventor Alexander Parkes in 1862, are amazing substances. Some serve as containers for many of our foods and drinks, keeping them fresh for long periods. Other plastics serve as containers for detergents and cleansers or are formed into pipes for our plumbing systems. We have learned to make strong, clear sheets of plastic that can be used as windows, and feather-light plastics that can be used as packaging materials. In the United States alone, seventy-five billion pounds (lb) of plastics are produced each year.

But plastics, amazing in their versatility, are a mixed blessing. One characteristic that makes them so useful, their stability, has created an environmental problem. It may take 40 to 50 years for plastics discarded into landfill sites to degrade. Concern that we could soon be knee-deep in plastic worldwide has resulted in a creative new industry: plastic recycling.

Since there are so many types of plastics, it is necessary to identify, sort, and recycle them separately. To help with this sorting process, manufacturers place recycling symbols on their plastic wares. As you can see in the accompanying table, each symbol corresponds to a different type of plastic.

Polyethylene terephthalate, also known as PETE or simply #1, is a form of polyester often used to make bottles and jars to contain food. When collected, it is ground up into flakes and formed into pellets. The most common use for recycled PETE is the manufacture of polyester carpets. But it may also be spun into a cotton candy–like form that can be used as a fiber filling for pillows or sleeping bags. Reuse to produce bottles and jars is also common.

HDPE, or #2, is high-density polyethylene. Originally used for milk and detergent bottles, recycled HDPE is used to produce pipes, plastic lumber, trash cans, or bottles for storage of materials other than food. Low-density polyethylene (LDPE), or #4, is very similar to HDPE chemically. Because it is a more highly branched polymer, it is less dense and more flexible. Originally used to produce plastic bags, recycled LDPE is also used to make trash bags, grocery bags, and plastic tubing and lumber.

PVC, or #3, is one of the less commonly recycled plastics in the United States, although it is actively recycled in Europe. The recycled material is used to make non-food-bearing containers, shoe soles, flooring, sweaters, and pipes. Polypropylene, PP or #5, is found in margarine tubs, fabrics, and carpets. Recycled polypropylene has many uses, including fabrication of gardening implements.

You probably come into contact with polystyrene, PS or #6, almost every day. It is used to make foam egg cartons and meat

TABLE 11.2 Some Important Addition Polymers of Alkenes

Monomer Name	Formula	Polymer	Uses
Styrene	$CH_2{=}CH{-}C_6H_5$ (benzene ring)	Polystyrene	Styrofoam containers
Acrylonitrile	$CH_2{=}CHCN$	Polyacrylonitrile (Orlon)	Clothing
Methyl methacrylate	$CH_2{=}C(CH_3){-}\overset{O}{\overset{\Vert}{C}}OCH_3$	Polymethyl methacrylate (Plexiglas, Lucite)	Basketball backboards
Vinyl chloride	$CH_2{=}CHCl$	Polyvinyl chloride (PVC)	Plastic pipe, credit cards
Tetrafluoroethene	$CF_2{=}CF_2$	Polytetrafluoroethylene (Teflon)	Nonstick surfaces

LEARNING GOAL

7 Draw the structures and write the names of common aromatic hydrocarbons.

11.6 Aromatic Hydrocarbons

In the early part of the nineteenth century, chemists began to discover organic compounds with chemical properties quite distinct from the alkanes, alkenes, and alkynes. They called these substances *aromatic compounds* because many of the first

Code	Type	Name	Formula	Description	Examples
PETE	1	Polyethylene terephthalate	$-CH_2-CH_2-O-C(=O)-C_6H_4-C(=O)-O-$	Usually clear or green, rigid	Soda bottles, peanut butter jars, vegetable oil bottles
HDPE	2	High-density polyethylene	$-CH_2-CH_2-$	Semirigid	Milk and water jugs, juice and bleach bottles
PVC	3	Polyvinyl chloride	$-CH(Cl)-CH_2-$	Semirigid	Detergent and cleanser bottles, pipes
LDPE	4	Low-density polyethylene	$-CH_2-CH_2-$	Flexible, not crinkly	Six-pack rings, bread bags, sandwich bags
PP	5	Polypropylene	$-CH(CH_3)-CH_2-$	Semirigid	Margarine tubs, straws, screw-on lids
PS	6	Polystyrene	$-CH(C_6H_5)-CH_2-$	Often brittle	Styrofoam, packing peanuts, egg cartons, foam cups
Other	7	Multilayer plastics	N/A	Squeezable	Ketchup and syrup bottles

trays, serving containers for fast food chains, CD "jewel boxes," and "peanuts" used as packing material. At the current time, polystyrene food containers are not recycled. PS from nonfood products can be melted down and converted into pellets that are used to manufacture office desktop accessories, hangers, and plastic trays used to hold plants.

For Further Understanding

- Use the Internet or other resources to investigate recycling efforts in your area.
- In some areas, efforts to recycle plastics and paper have been abandoned. What factors contributed to this?

examples were isolated from the pleasant-smelling resins of tropical trees. The carbon/hydrogen ratio of these compounds suggested a very high degree of unsaturation, similar to the alkenes and alkynes. Imagine, then, how puzzled these early organic chemists must have been when they discovered that these compounds do not undergo the kinds of addition reactions common for the alkenes and alkynes.

$$CH_2{=}CH_2 + Br_2 \longrightarrow \underset{Br}{CH_2}-\underset{Br}{CH_2}$$

$$C_6H_6 \text{ (benzene)} + Br_2 \longrightarrow \text{No reaction}$$

We no longer define aromatic compounds as those having a pleasant aroma; in fact, many do not. We now recognize **aromatic hydrocarbons** as those that exhibit a much higher degree of chemical stability than their chemical composition

(a) (c)

(b) (d)

Figure 11.5 Four ways to represent the benzene molecule. Structure (b) is a simplified diagram of structure (a). Structure (d), a simplified diagram of structure (c), is the most commonly used representation.

Resonance models are described in Section 3.4.

would predict. The most common group of aromatic compounds is based on the six-member aromatic ring, the benzene ring. The structure of the benzene ring is represented in various ways in Figure 11.5.

Structure and Properties

The benzene ring consists of six carbon atoms joined in a planar hexagonal arrangement. Each carbon atom is bonded to one hydrogen atom. Friedrich Kekulé proposed a model for the structure of benzene in 1865. He proposed that single and double bonds alternated around the ring (a conjugated system of double bonds). To explain why benzene did not decolorize bromine—in other words, didn't react like an unsaturated compound—he suggested that the double and single bonds shift positions rapidly.

Actually, the most accurate way to represent the benzene molecules is as a resonance hybrid of two Kekulé structures:

Benzene as a resonance hybrid

The current model of the structure of benzene is based on the idea of overlapping orbitals. Each carbon is bonded to two others by sharing a pair of electrons. Each carbon atom also shares a pair of electrons with a hydrogen atom. The remaining six electrons are located in *p* orbitals that are perpendicular to the plane of the ring. These *p* orbitals overlap laterally to form a cloud of electrons above and below the ring (Figure 11.6).

Two symbols are commonly used to represent the benzene ring. The representation in Figure 11.5b is the structure proposed by Kekulé. The structure in Figure 11.5d uses a circle to represent the electron cloud.

Nomenclature

LEARNING GOAL

7 Draw the structures and write the names of common aromatic hydrocarbons.

Most simple aromatic compounds are named as derivatives of benzene. Thus benzene is the parent ring, and the name of any atom or group bonded to benzene is used as a prefix, as in these examples:

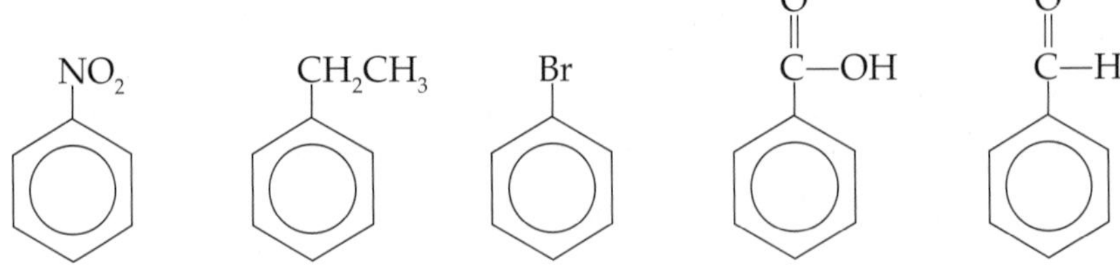

Nitrobenzene Ethylbenzene Bromobenzene Benzoic acid Benzaldehyde

Other members of this family have unique names based on history rather than logic:

CH_3 OH NH_2 OCH_3

Toluene Phenol Aniline Anisole

Other common names include xylene, a benzene ring with two methyl substituents, and cresol, a benzene ring bonded to a methyl group and a hydroxyl group.

When two groups are present on the ring, three possible orientations exist, and they may be named by either the IUPAC Nomenclature System or the common system of nomenclature. If the groups or atoms are located on two adjacent carbons, they are referred to as *ortho* (*o*) in the common system or with the prefix 1,2- in the IUPAC system. If they are on carbons separated by one carbon atom, they are termed *meta* (*m*) in the common system or 1,3- in the IUPAC system. Finally, if the substituents are on carbons separated by two carbon atoms, they are said to be *para* (*p*) in the common system or 1,4- in the IUPAC system. The following examples demonstrate both of these systems:

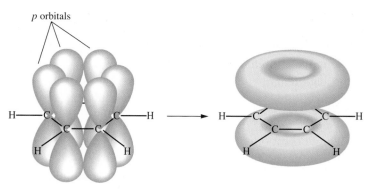

Figure 11.6 The current model of the bonding in benzene. The overlapping *p* orbitals form a cloud of electrons above and below the ring.

Two groups 1,2 or *ortho* Two groups 1,3 or *meta* Two groups 1,4 or *para*

G=Any group

The three orientations of xylene and cresol are shown here:

ortho-Xylene *meta*-Xylene *para*-Xylene *ortho*-Cresol *meta*-Cresol *para*-Cresol

If three or more groups are attached to the benzene ring, numbers must be used to describe their location. The names of the substituents are given in alphabetical order.

EXAMPLE 11.10 Naming Derivatives of Benzene

LEARNING GOAL

7 Draw the structures and write the names of common aromatic hydrocarbons.

Name the following compounds using the IUPAC and common systems of nomenclature.

a. b. c.

Continued...

Solution

IUPAC names:			
Parent compound:	toluene	phenol	aniline
Substituents:	2-chloro	4-nitro	3-ethyl
Name:	2-Chlorotoluene	4-Nitrophenol	3-Ethylaniline
Common names:			
Parent compound:	toluene	phenol	aniline
Substituents:	*ortho*-chloro	*para*-nitro	*meta*-ethyl
Name:	*ortho*-Chlorotoluene	*para*-Nitrophenol	*meta*-Ethylaniline
Abbreviated name:	*o*-Chlorotoluene	*p*-Nitrophenol	*m*-Ethylaniline

Practice Problem 11.10

Name the following compounds using the IUPAC and common nomenclature systems.

a. 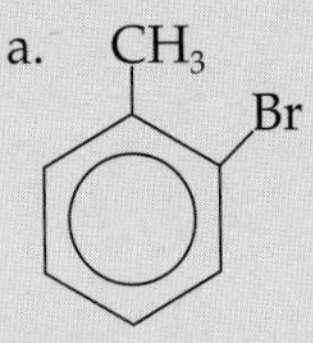 CH_3, Br

b. 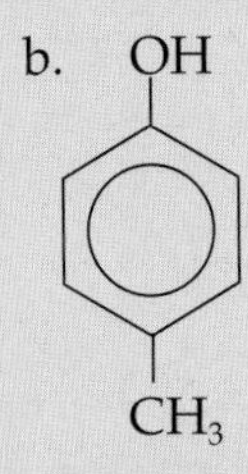

c. 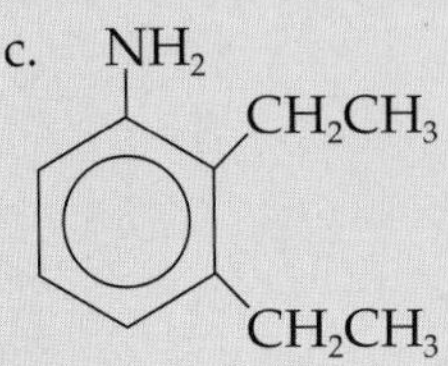

d. 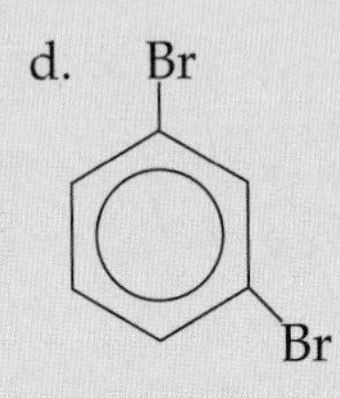

► For Further Practice: **Questions 11.90, 11.91, and 11.92.**

In IUPAC nomenclature, the group derived by removing one hydrogen from benzene (—C_6H_5), is called the **phenyl group.** An aromatic hydrocarbon attached to a long aliphatic group is named as a phenyl substituted hydrocarbon. For example:

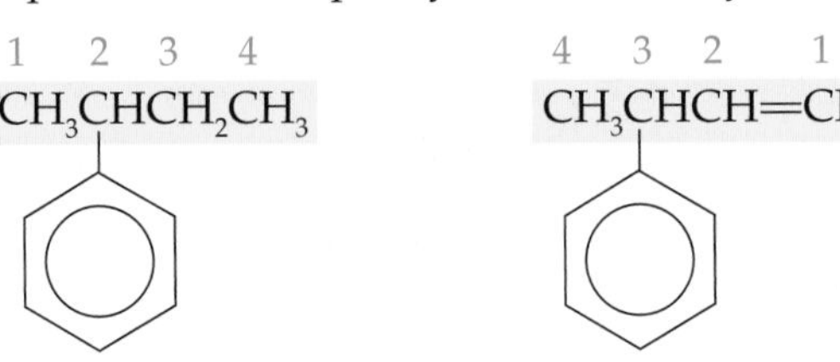

2-Phenylbutane 3-Phenyl-1-butene

One final special name that occurs frequently in aromatic compounds is the benzyl group:

$C_6H_5CH_2$— or —CH_2—

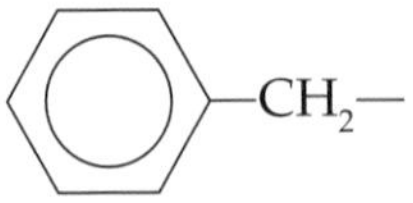

The use of this group name is illustrated by:

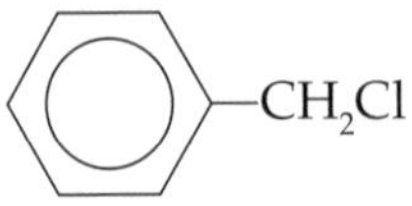

—CH_2Cl —CH_2OH

Benzyl chloride 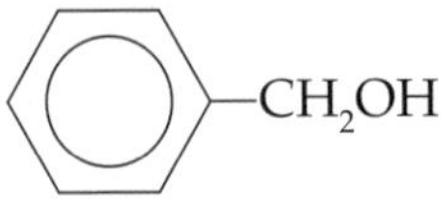 Benzyl alcohol

Question 11.21 Draw each of the following compounds:

a. 1,3,5-Trichlorobenzene
b. *ortho*-Cresol
c. 2,5-Dibromophenol
d. *para*-Dinitrobenzene
e. 2-Nitroaniline
f. *meta*-Nitrotoluene

Question 11.22 Draw each of the following compounds:

a. 2,3-Dichlorotoluene
b. 3-Bromoaniline
c. 1-Bromo-3-ethylbenzene
d. *o*-Nitrotoluene
e. *p*-Xylene
f. *o*-Dibromobenzene

Polynuclear Aromatic Hydrocarbons

The polynuclear aromatic hydrocarbons (PAH) are composed of two or more aromatic rings joined together. Many of them have been shown to be carcinogenic, that is, they cause cancer.

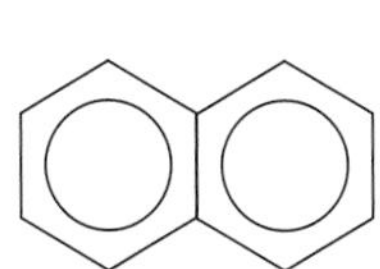
Naphthalene

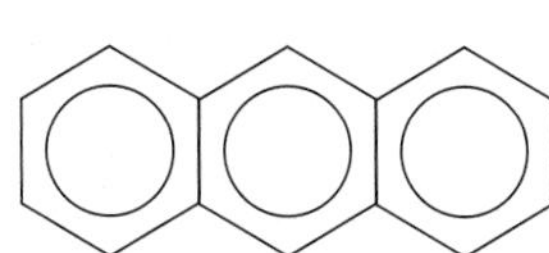
Anthracene

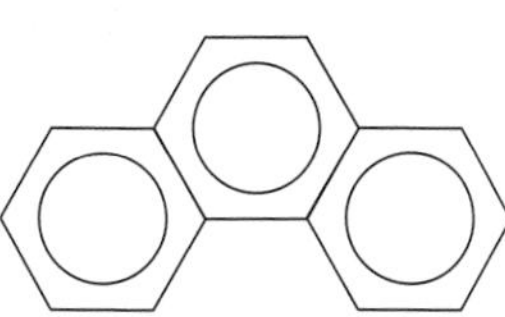
Phenanthrene

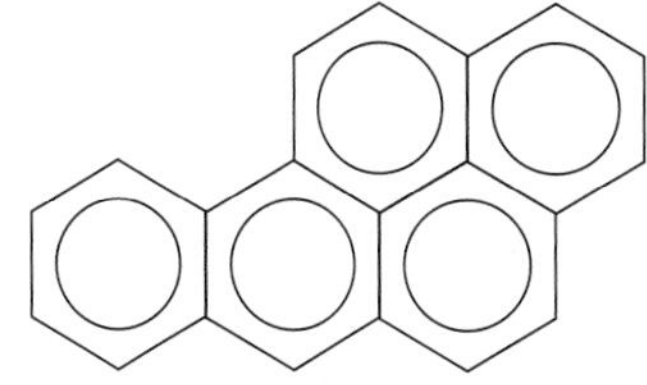
Benzopyrene

Naphthalene has a distinctive aroma. It has been frequently used as mothballs and may cause hemolytic anemia (a condition causing breakdown of red blood cells) in humans, but has not been associated with human or animal cancers. Anthracene, derived from coal tar, is the parent compound of many dyes and pigments. Phenanthrene is common in the environment, although there is no industrial use of the compound. It is a product of incomplete combustion of fossil fuels and wood. Although anthracene is a suspected carcinogen, phenanthrene has not been shown to be one. Benzopyrene is found in tobacco smoke, smokestack effluents, charcoal-grilled meat, and automobile exhaust. It is one of the most potent carcinogens known.

Reactions Involving Benzene

LEARNING GOAL

8 Write equations for substitution reactions involving benzene.

As we have noted, benzene does not readily undergo addition reactions. The typical reactions of benzene are **substitution reactions,** in which a hydrogen atom is replaced by another atom or group of atoms. Unlike addition reactions of alkenes, no carbon-carbon bonds are broken. In substitution reactions of benzene, the carbon-hydrogen bond is broken and the hydrogen is replaced (substituted) with another atom or group of atoms.

Benzene can react (by substitution) with Cl_2 or Br_2. These reactions require either iron or an iron halide as a catalyst. For example:

$$\text{Benzene} + Br_2 \xrightarrow{FeBr_3} \text{C}_6\text{H}_5\text{—Br} + HBr$$

Benzene Bromine Bromobenzene

When a second equivalent of the halogen is added, three isomers—*para, ortho,* and *meta*—are formed.

Benzene also reacts with sulfur trioxide by substitution. Concentrated sulfuric acid is required as the catalyst. Benzenesulfonic acid, a strong acid, is the product:

$$\text{Benzene} + SO_3 \xrightarrow{\text{Concentrated } H_2SO_4} \text{C}_6\text{H}_5\text{—S(=O)(=O)—OH} + H_2O$$

Benzene Sulfur trioxide Benzenesulfonic acid

Benzene can also undergo nitration with concentrated nitric acid dissolved in concentrated sulfuric acid. This reaction requires temperatures in the range of 50–55°C.

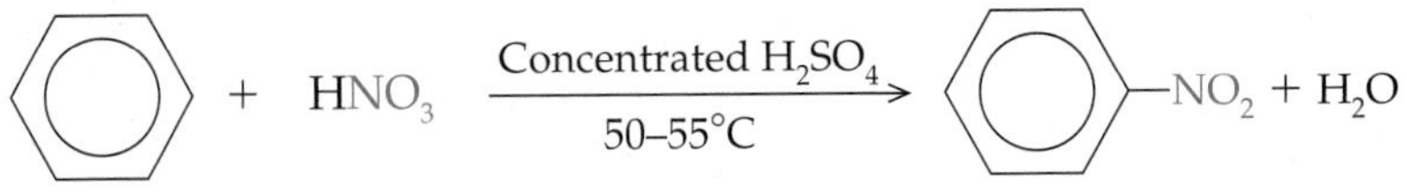

$$\text{Benzene} + \underset{\text{Nitric acid}}{HNO_3} \xrightarrow[50\text{–}55^\circ C]{\text{Concentrated } H_2SO_4} \underset{\text{Nitrobenzene}}{C_6H_5\text{–}NO_2} + H_2O$$

11.7 Heterocyclic Aromatic Compounds

LEARNING GOAL

9 Describe heterocyclic aromatic compounds and list several biological molecules in which they are found.

Heterocyclic aromatic compounds are those having at least one atom other than carbon as part of the structure of the aromatic ring. The structures and common names of several heterocyclic aromatic compounds are shown:

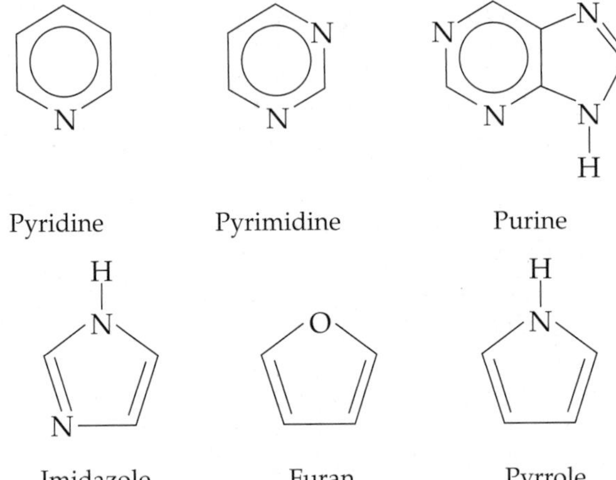

All these compounds are more similar to benzene in stability and chemical behavior than they are to the alkenes. Many of these compounds are components of molecules that have significant effects on biological systems. For instance, the purines and pyrimidines are components of DNA (deoxyribonucleic acid) and RNA (ribonucleic acid). DNA and RNA are the molecules responsible for storing and expressing the genetic information of an organism. The pyridine ring is found in nicotine, the addictive compound in tobacco. The pyrrole ring is a component of the porphyrin ring found in hemoglobin and chlorophyll.

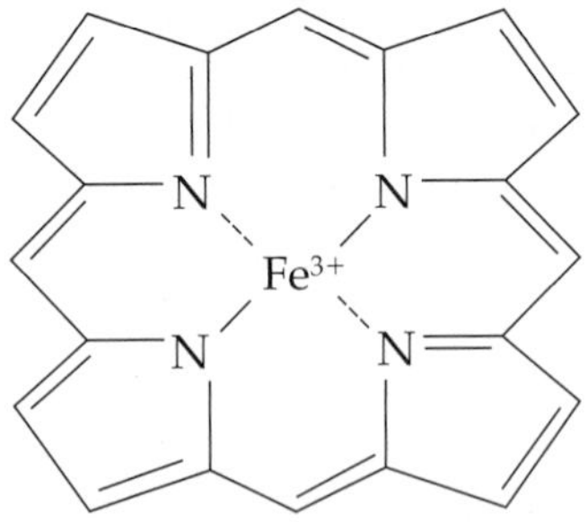

Fe^{3+}

Porphyrin

The imidazole ring is a component of cimetidine, a drug used in the treatment of stomach ulcers. The structure of cimetidine is shown below:

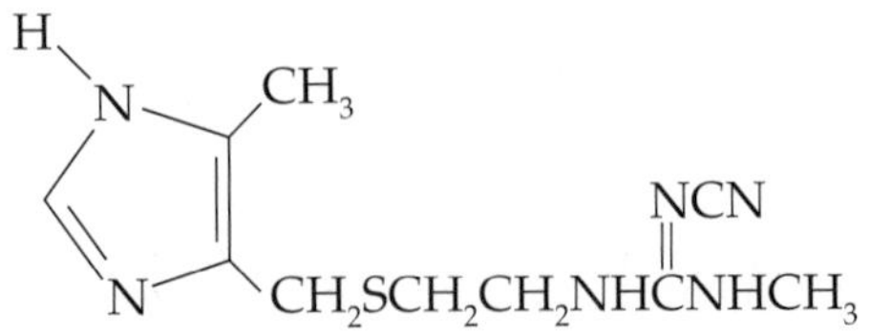

CH_3 ; $CH_2SCH_2CH_2NHC(=NCN)NHCH_3$

Cimetidine

We will discuss a subset of the heterocyclic aromatic compounds, the heterocyclic amines, in Chapter 15.

KITCHEN CHEMISTRY

Amazing Chocolate

Chocolate has been consumed for over 3000 years. The Mayans and Aztecs enjoyed a frothy drink made from ground up cacao beans. The Mayans preferred it hot and the Aztecs drank it cold. Although the Mayans could grow the cacao tree, the Aztecs couldn't. As a result, the beans became very valuable and were even used as money. The drink that the Aztecs and Mayans enjoyed was very bitter and was sometimes enhanced by adding ground chili peppers or vanilla. They thought that the drink would fight fatigue. Both the bitter taste and the mood enhancement that lifted fatigue are caused by theobromine.

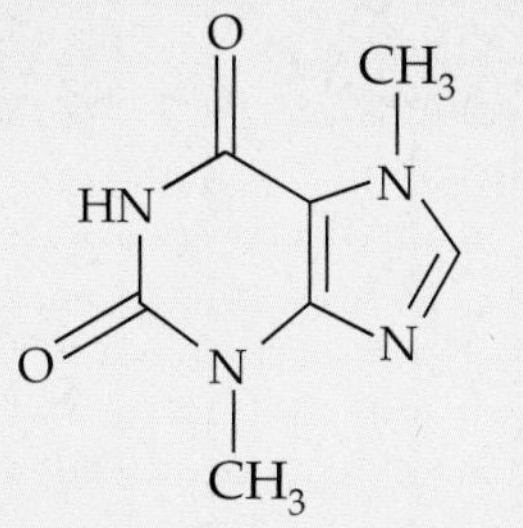

Theobromine

Theobromine is an alkaloid that, in pure form, is a crystalline, bitter powder. Medically it can be used as a vasodilator, a diuretic, and a heart stimulant. One study concluded that theobromine was a better cough suppressant than codeine, and it has been found helpful in the treatment of asthma. As with any pharmacologically active substance, an excess of theobromine can cause theobromine poisoning, which has been observed in some, particularly the elderly, who eat chocolate to excess!

The chocolate that we enjoy is produced by first allowing the cacao seeds to ferment to reduce the bitter taste. The shells are then removed and the inner nib is dried and ground into a powder that is pure chocolate. The powder is generally liquefied, placed in molds to harden, and then processed into cocoa solids and cocoa butter. We can purchase chocolate in many forms. Baking chocolate is generally bitter. No sugar has been added and it primarily consists of the cocoa solids and cocoa butter. Milk chocolate, dark chocolate, and white chocolate are produced by combining the cocoa butter and solids in varying amounts and adding other ingredients, particularly sugar and milk or condensed milk. Dark chocolate has the greatest amount of cocoa solids and, at the extreme, white chocolate has no cocoa solids and is enjoyed by those who have allergies to cocoa solids.

A Mexican sauce made with chili peppers and chocolate brings to mind the drink of the Aztecs. It is a mole sauce (pronounced mole lay). One legend tells us that this sauce was invented by the nuns in Santa Rosa Convent in Puebla, Mexico. The nuns were expecting a visit from the Archbishop. Being poor, they were concerned about the meal that they would prepare for him.

After praying about it, they simply took what they had, some chili peppers, nuts, fruit, bread, tomatillos, spices, and chocolate. They mixed these ingredients into a sauce and served it over turkey. The Archbishop was impressed with the meal and mole sauce over poultry has been a favorite in Mexican cuisine for centuries. It has been said that the secret to the mole sauce is that it combines so many different flavors and sensations; some recipes have 20–30 ingredients! The chili peppers provide "heat;" the tomatillos add a sour note; the dried fruits and sugar contribute sweetness; the spices including cumin, cloves, and anise, add a variety of nuanced flavors; and the nuts and tortillas thicken the sauce. The chocolate, added at the end of the preparation, helps to mellow the heat of the peppers.

Recently scientists have published data to suggest that dark chocolate can reduce blood pressure. Other articles claim that dark chocolate can prevent cancer and heart disease. The molecules responsible for these observed effects are a variety of catechins and derivatives of phenol (see structures below.) Found also in tea, these compounds are antioxidants. It is thought that they prevent the oxidation of lipids in the blood which, in turn, is thought to prevent them from sticking to the surfaces of blood vessels. This reduces the risk of atherosclerosis or hardening of the arteries.

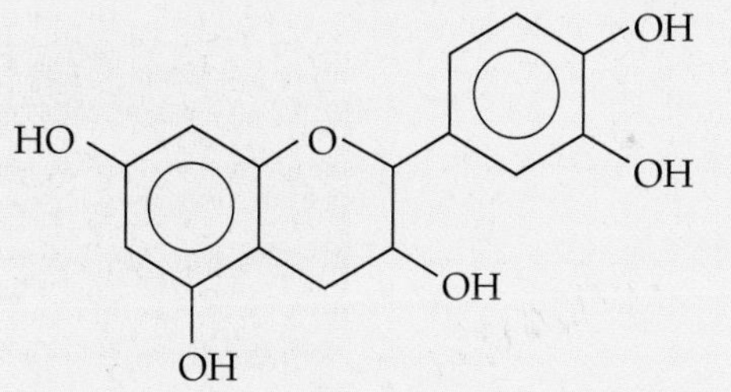

Catechin

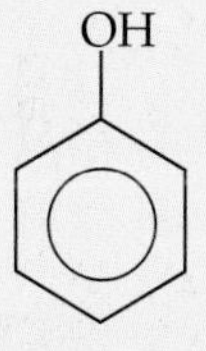

Phenol

We enjoy chocolate in dark, bittersweet form, as creamy milk chocolate, in hot cocoa, and in mole sauces. Whether it is the wide variety of tastes, the melt-in-your mouth sensation, the mild enhancement of mood and energy, or the reported health benefits, chocolate has been enjoyed over the ages and will continue to be a treat in years to come.

For Further Understanding

- Theobromine has a structure very similar to caffeine. It has one fewer methyl group than caffeine. What are some of the similarities in the biological properties of these two substances that can be traced to the similarity in their structures?
- Why is dark chocolate a richer source of antioxidants than milk chocolate or white chocolate?

CHAPTER MAP

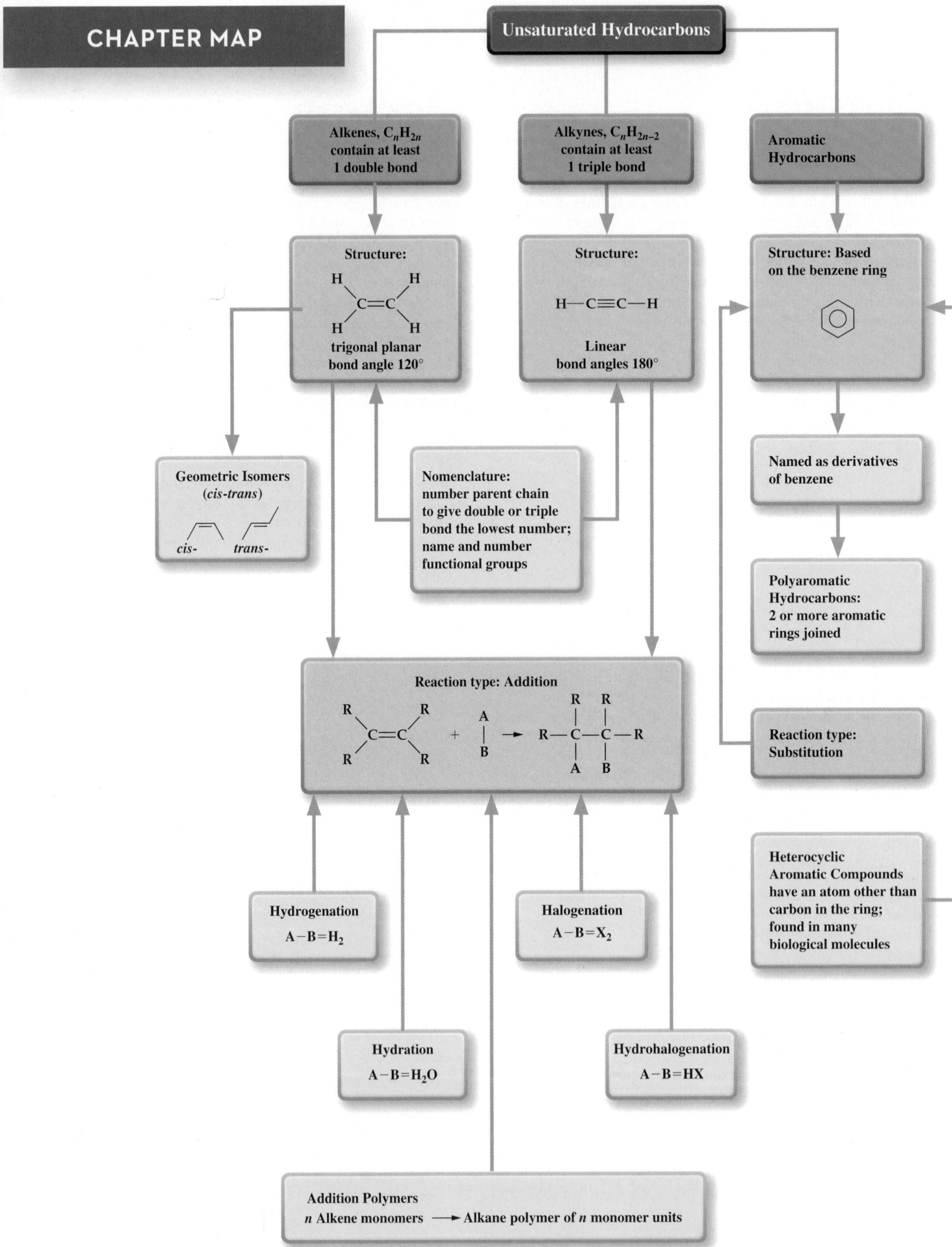

Unsaturated Hydrocarbons
Alkenes, C_nH_{2n} contain at least 1 double bond
Alkynes, C_nH_{2n-2} contain at least 1 triple bond
Aromatic Hydrocarbons
Structure:
trigonal planar bond angle 120°
Structure:
H—C≡C—H
Linear bond angles 180°
Structure: Based on the benzene ring
Geometric Isomers (cis-trans)
cis-
trans-
Nomenclature: number parent chain to give double or triple bond the lowest number; name and number functional groups
Named as derivatives of benzene
Polyaromatic Hydrocarbons: 2 or more aromatic rings joined
Reaction type: Addition
Reaction type: Substitution
Heterocyclic Aromatic Compounds have an atom other than carbon in the ring; found in many biological molecules
Hydrogenation
$A-B=H_2$
Halogenation
$A-B=X_2$
Hydration
$A-B=H_2O$
Hydrohalogenation
$A-B=HX$
Addition Polymers
n Alkene monomers ⟶ Alkane polymer of n monomer units

SUMMARY OF REACTIONS

Addition Reactions of Alkenes

Hydrogenation:

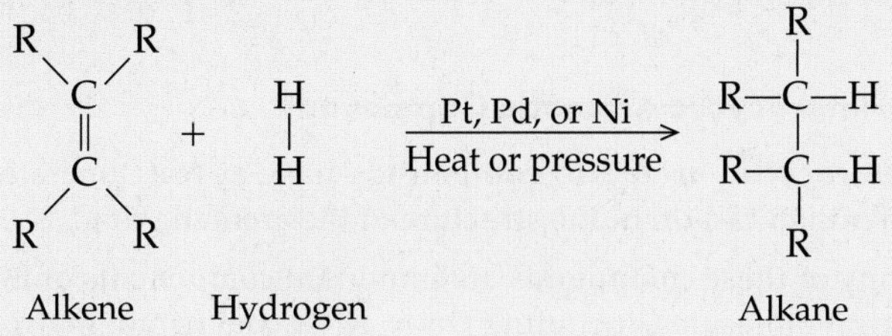

Alkene + Hydrogen $\xrightarrow[\text{Heat or pressure}]{\text{Pt, Pd, or Ni}}$ Alkane

Hydration:

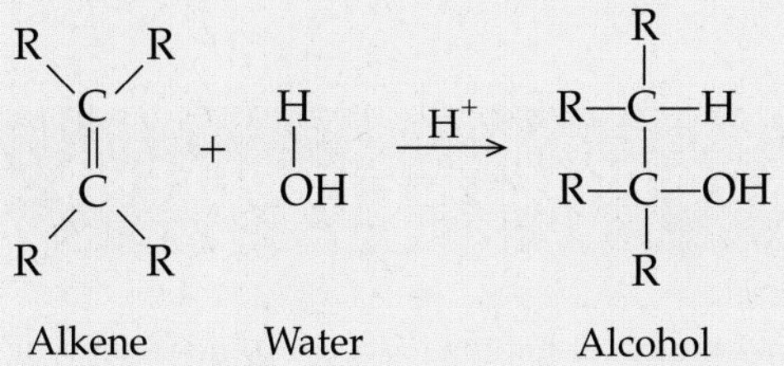

Alkene + Water $\xrightarrow{H^+}$ Alcohol

Halogenation:

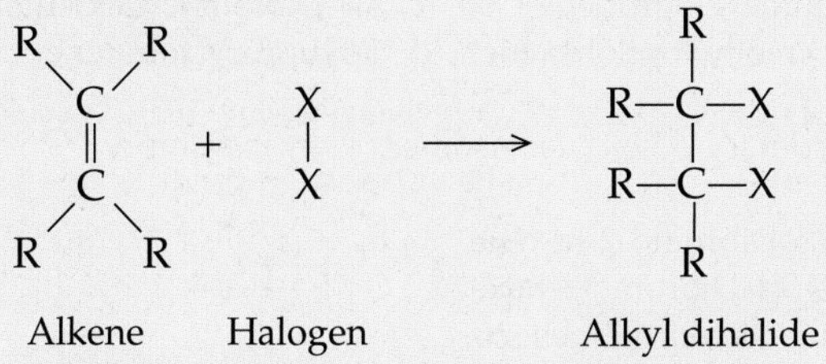

Alkene + Halogen $\longrightarrow$ Alkyl dihalide

Hydrohalogenation:

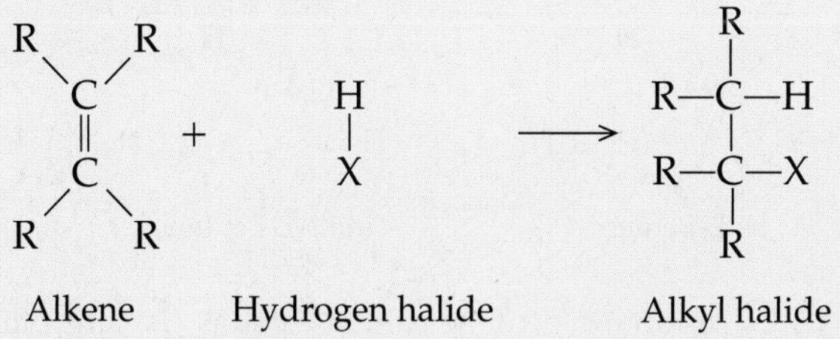

Alkene + Hydrogen halide $\longrightarrow$ Alkyl halide

Addition Polymers of Alkenes

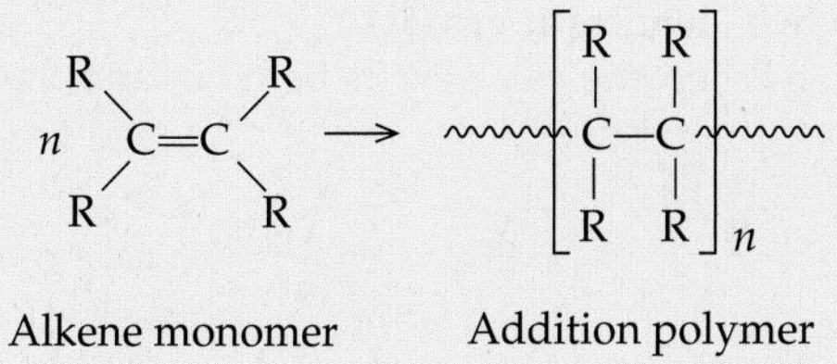

Alkene monomer $\longrightarrow$ Addition polymer

Reactions of Benzene

Halogenation:

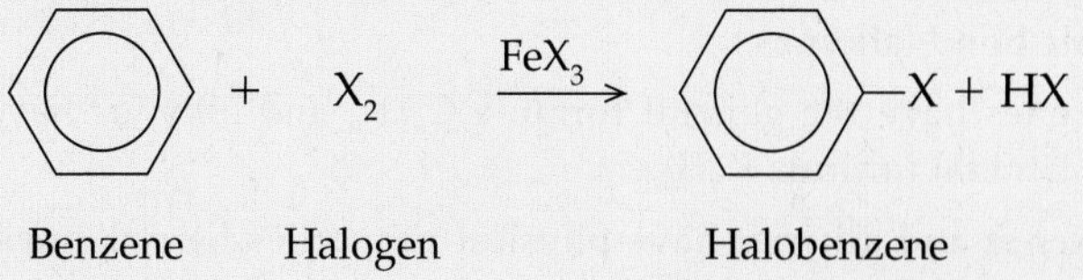

Benzene + Halogen (X_2) $\xrightarrow{FeX_3}$ Halobenzene + HX

Sulfonation:

Benzene + Sulfur trioxide (SO_3) $\xrightarrow{\text{Concentrated } H_2SO_4}$ Benzenesulfonic acid + H_2O

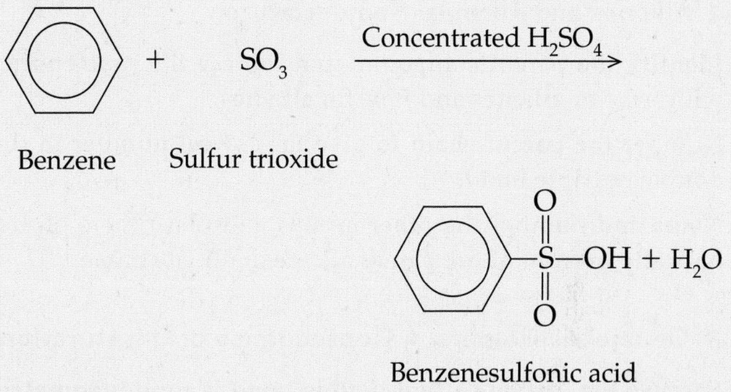

Nitration:

Benzene + Nitric acid (HNO_3) $\xrightarrow[\text{50–55°C}]{\text{Concentrated } H_2SO_4}$ Nitrobenzene ($-NO_2$) + H_2O

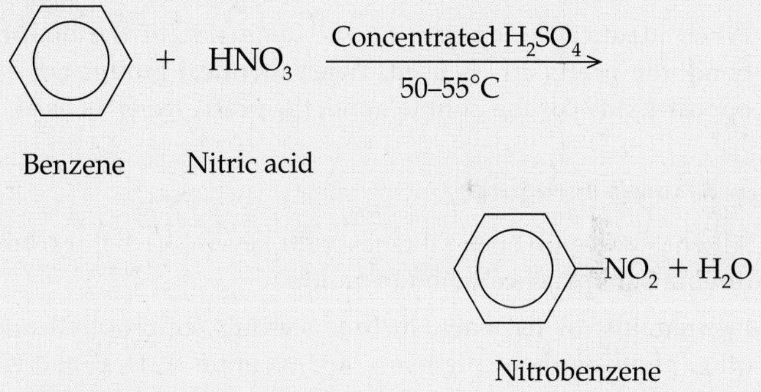

SUMMARY

11.1 Alkenes and Alkynes: Structure and Physical Properties

- **Alkenes** and **alkynes** are **unsaturated** hydrocarbons because they have at least one C—C double bond (alkenes) or C—C triple bond (alkynes.)
- Alkenes have the general formula C_nH_{2n} and alkynes have the general formula C_nH_{2n-2}.
- Alkenes and alkynes have physical properties like alkanes, but very different chemical properties.

11.2 Alkenes and Alkynes: Nomenclature

- Identify the parent compound and replace the *-ane* ending with *-ene* for alkenes and *-yne* for alkynes.
- Number the parent chain to give the lowest number to the double or triple bond.
- Name and number the other groups and place them alphabetically in front of the parent alkene or alkyne name.

11.3 Geometric isomers: A Consequence of Unsaturation

- Because the carbon-carbon double bond is rigid, **geometric isomers** occur when two different groups are bonded to each of the carbons of the double bond.
- When identical groups are on the same side of the double bond, the prefix *cis-* is used. When identical groups are on opposite sides of the double bond, the prefix *trans-* is used.

11.4 Alkenes in Nature

- Alkenes and polyenes (alkenes with several carbon-carbon double bonds) are common in nature.
- Isoprenoids, or terpenes, include steroids, chlorophyll and other photosynthetic pigments, and vitamins A, D, E, and K.

11.5 Reactions Involving Alkenes and Alkynes

- Alkenes and alkynes undergo **addition reactions** in which two atoms or groups of atoms add to the C—C double or triple bond.
- Addition reactions include: **halogenation, hydrohalogenation, hydration,** and **hydrogenation.**
- **Markovnikov's rule** predicts the most abundant products in addition reactions involving unsymmetrical alkenes.
- **Polymers** are formed by the sequential addition of alkene **monomers.** These are called **addition polymers.**

11.6 Aromatic Hydrocarbons

- **Aromatic hydrocarbons** contain benzene rings.
- Simple aromatic compounds are named as derivatives of benzene. Others have historical common names.
- A **phenyl group** is a benzene ring with one hydrogen atom removed. The term may be used in the nomenclature of molecules that include the benzene as a substituent group.
- Benzene participates in substitution reactions in which a hydrogen atom is replaced by another atom or group.
- Polynuclear aromatic hydrocarbons consist of two or more benzene rings joined.

11.7 Heterocyclic Aromatic Compounds

- **Heterocyclic aromatic compounds** have at least one atom other than carbon in the structure of the aromatic ring.
- Many of these compounds are important components of biological molecules, including DNA, RNA, and hemoglobin.

ANSWERS TO PRACTICE PROBLEMS

11.1 a. 6-Chloro-4-methyl-2-heptene c. 5-Bromo-3-heptyne
b. 1,4-Pentadiyne d. 1,5-Heptadiene

11.2 a. l-Chlorocyclopropene c. 3,4-Dibromocyclopentene
b. 4,5-Dimethylcyclohexene d. 3-Fluorocyclobutene

11.3 a. *cis*-isomer b. *trans*-isomer c. *cis*-isomer

11.4 a. *cis*-4,5-Dibromo-2-hexene
b. *trans*-3,4-Dibromo-3-hexene
c. *cis*-2,3-Dichloro-2-hexene

11.5 a. 2-Pentene can exist as both *cis-* and *trans*-isomers.

```
 H         H              H3C        H
   \     /                   \     /
    C=C                       C=C
   /     \                   /     \
H3C       CH2CH3            H       CH2CH3
```

cis-2-Pentene *trans*-2-Pentene

b. 1,1,2-Tribromo-1-pentene cannot exist as *cis-* and *trans*-isomers because one of the carbons involved in the double bond is also bonded to two identical atoms (Br).
c. Propene cannot exist as *cis-* and *trans*-isomers because one of the carbons involved in the double bond is also bonded to two identical atoms (H).
d. 2,3-Dibromo-2-heptene can exist as both *cis-* and *trans*-isomers.

```
H3C        Br                    Br        H
   \     /                         \     /
    C=C                             C=C
   /     \                         /     \
Br        CH2CH2CH2CH3          H3C       CH2CH2CH2CH3
```

trans-2,3-Dibromo-2-heptene *cis*-2,3-Dibromo-2-heptene

11.6 a. 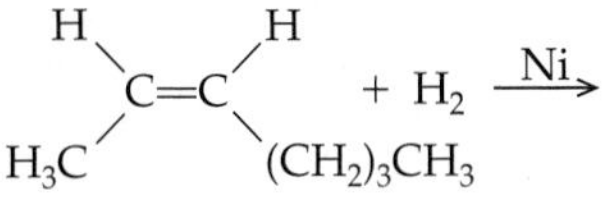 (*cis*-2-Heptene: H, H / H_3C, $(CH_2)_3CH_3$ on C=C) $+ H_2 \xrightarrow{Ni} CH_3(CH_2)_5CH_3$

cis-2-Heptene — Heptene

b. 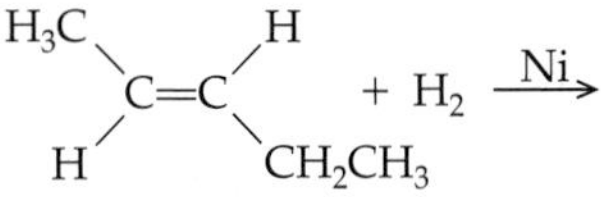 (*trans*-2-Pentene: H_3C, H / H, CH_2CH_3 on C=C) $+ H_2 \xrightarrow{Ni} CH_3CH_2CH_2CH_2CH_3$

trans-2-Pentene — Pentane

c. $CH_3CH_2CH{=}CHCH_2CH_3 + H_2 \xrightarrow{Pt} CH_3CH_2CH_2CH_2CH_2CH_3$

3-Hexene — Hexane

The product, hexane, would be the same regardless of whether this were *cis*- or *trans*-3-hexene.

d. $CH_2{=}CHCH_3 + H_2 \xrightarrow{Pd} CH_3CH_2CH_3$

Propene — Propane

11.7 a. 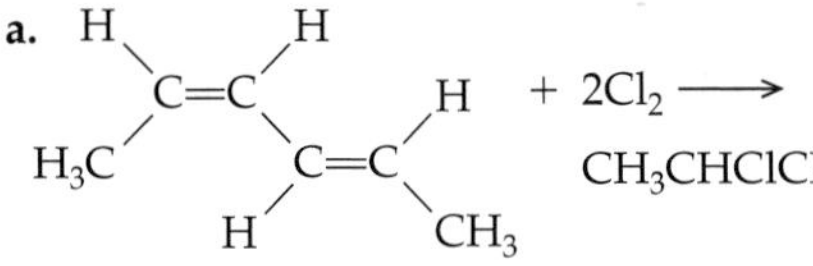 (2,4-Hexadiene: H, H / H_3C on C=C; H / H, CH_3 on C=C) $+ 2Cl_2 \longrightarrow CH_3CHClCHClCHClCHClCH_3$

2,4-Hexadiene — 2,3,4,5-Tetrachlorohexane

b. Both *cis*- and *trans*-1,5-dibromo-2-pentene would produce 1,5-dibromo-2,3-dichloropentane when chlorinated. The *trans*-isomer is shown here:

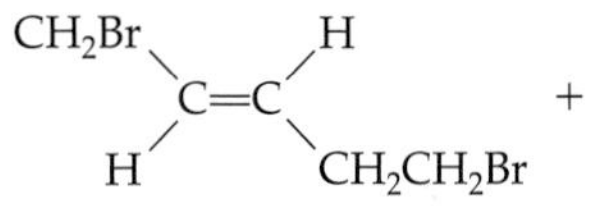

(CH_2Br, H / H, CH_2CH_2Br on C=C) $+ Cl_2 \longrightarrow CH_2BrCHClCHClCH_2CH_2Br$

trans-1,5-Dibromo-2-pentene — 1,5-Dibromo-2,3-dichloropentane

c. (H, CH_3 / H, $CH(CH_3)CH_3$ on C=C) $+ Cl_2 \longrightarrow CH_2ClC(Cl)(CH_3){-}CHCH_3$ (with CH_3 on CH)

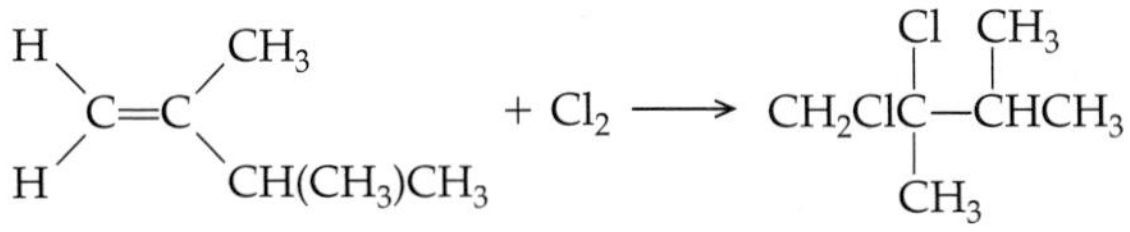

2,3-Dimethyl-1-butene — 1,2-Dichloro-2,3 dimethylbutane

d. Both *cis*- and *trans*-4,6-dimethyl-2-heptene would produce 2,3-dichloro-4,6-dimethylheptane when chlorinated. The *cis*-isomer is shown here:

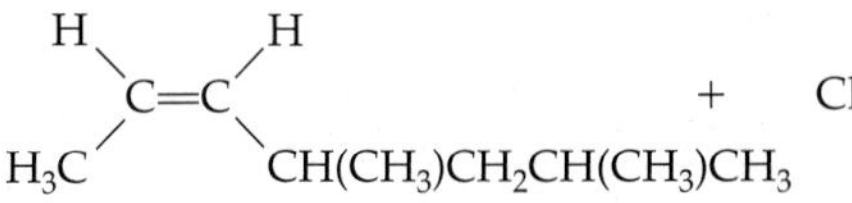

(H, H / H_3C, $CH(CH_3)CH_2CH(CH_3)CH_3$ on C=C) $+ Cl_2 \longrightarrow$

$CH_3CHClCHClCH(CH_3)CH_2CH(CH_3)CH_3$

cis-4,6-Dimethyl-2-heptene — 2,3-Dichloro-4,6-dimethylheptane

11.8 a. 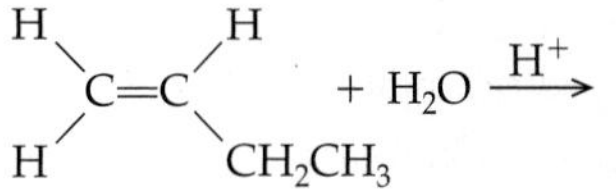 (1-Butene: H, H / H, CH_2CH_3 on C=C) $+ H_2O \xrightarrow{H^+} CH_3CHOHCH_2CH_3$

2-Butanol (major product)

$+ CH_2OHCH_2CH_2CH_3$

1-Butanol (minor product)

1-Butene

b. 2-Methyl-3-hexanol and 5-methyl-3-hexanol would be produced in equal amounts.

$CH_3CH(CH_3)CH{=}CHCH_2CH_3 + H_2O \xrightarrow{H^+}$

$CH_3CH(CH_3)CHOHCH_2CH_2CH_3$

2-Methyl-3-hexene — 2-Methyl-3-hexanol

$CH_3CH(CH_3)CH{=}CHCH_2CH_3 + H_2O \xrightarrow{H^+}$

$CH_3CH(CH_3)CH_2CHOHCH_2CH_3$

2-Methyl-3-hexene — 5-Methyl-3-hexanol

c. $CH_2{=}CHCH_3 + H_2O \xrightarrow{H^+} CH_3CHOHCH_3$

Propene — 2-Propanol (major product)

$+ CH_2OHCH_2CH_3$

1-Propanol (minor product)

d. $CH_2ClCH{=}CHCH_2Cl + H_2O \xrightarrow{H^+} CH_2ClCHOHCH_2CH_2Cl$

1,4-Dichloro-2-butene — 1,4-Dichloro-2-butanol (only product)

11.9 a. 2-Bromopentane and 3-bromopentane would be produced in equal amounts.

$CH_2CH{=}CHCH_2CH_3 + HBr \longrightarrow CH_2CHBrCH_2CH_2CH_3$

2-Pentene — 2-Bromopentane

$+ CH_3CH_2CHBrCH_2CH_3$

3-Bromopentane

b.

$CH_2{=}CHCH_3 + HBr \longrightarrow CH_3CHBrCH_3 + CH_2BrCH_2CH_3$

Propene — 2-Bromopropane (major product) — 3-Bromopropane (minor product)

c. 3-Bromoheptane and 4-bromoheptane would be produced in equal amounts.

$CH_3CH_2CH{=}CHCH_2CH_2CH_3 + HBr \longrightarrow$

3-Heptene

$CH_3CH_2CHBr(CH_2)_3CH_3$

3-Bromoheptane

$CH_3(CH_2)_2CHBr(CH_2)_2CH_3$

+ 4-Bromoheptane

11.10 **a.** IUPAC Name: 2-Bromotoluene
Common name: *ortho*-Bromotoluene or *o*-bromotoluene

b. IUPAC Name: 4-Methylphenol
Common name: *para*-Cresol or *p*-cresol

c. IUPAC Name: 2, 3-Diethylaniline
Common name: 2, 3-Diethylaniline (Numbers must be used since there are three substituents.)

d. IUPAC Name: 1,3-Dibromobenzene
Common name: *meta*-Dibromobenzene or *m*-dibromobenzene

QUESTIONS AND PROBLEMS

Alkenes and Alkynes: Structure and Physical Properties

Foundations

11.23 Explain why the boiling points of alkynes increase as the length of the hydrocarbon chains increases.

11.24 Saturated fatty acids have higher melting points than monounsaturated fatty acids. Polyunsaturated fatty acids have even lower melting points. Develop a hypothesis to explain this observation.

11.25 Write the general formulas for alkanes, alkenes, and alkynes.

11.26 What are the characteristic functional groups of alkenes and alkynes?

Applications

11.27 Describe the geometry of ethene.

11.28 What are the bond angles in ethene?

11.29 Compare the bond angles in ethene with those in ethane.

11.30 Explain the bond angles of ethene in terms of the valence-shell electron-pair repulsion (VSEPR) theory.

11.31 Describe the geometry of ethyne.

11.32 What are the bond angles in ethyne?

11.33 Compare the bond angles in ethane, ethene, and ethyne.

11.34 Explain the bond angles of ethyne in terms of the valence-shell electron-pair repulsion (VSEPR) theory.

11.35 Arrange the following groups of molecules from the highest to lowest boiling points:

a. ethyne propyne 2-pentyne

b. 2-butene 3-decene ethene

11.36 Arrange the following groups of molecules from the highest to the lowest melting points.

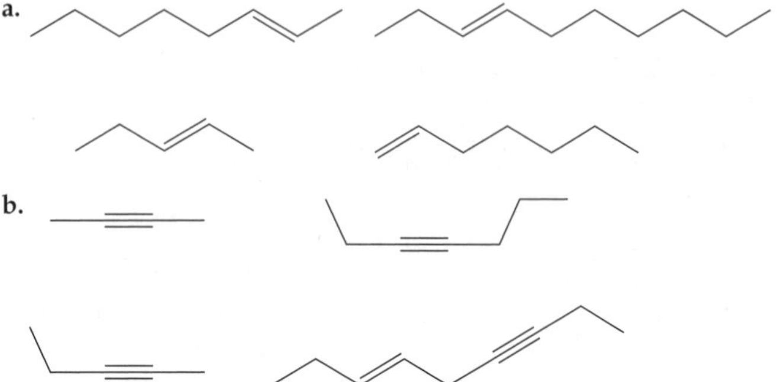

Alkenes and Alkynes: Nomenclature

Foundations

11.37 Briefly describe the rules for naming alkenes and alkynes.

11.38 What is meant by a geometric isomer?

11.39 Describe what is meant by a *cis*-isomer of an alkene.

11.40 Describe what is meant by a *trans*-isomer of an alkene.

Applications

11.41 Draw a condensed formula for each of the following compounds:

a. 2-Methyl-2-hexene

b. *trans*-3-Heptene

c. *cis*-1-Chloro-2-pentene

d. *cis*-2-Chloro-2-methyl-3-heptene

e. *trans*-5-Bromo-2,6-dimethyl-3-octene

11.42 Draw a condensed formula for each of the following compounds:

a. 2-Hexyne

b. 4-Methyl-1-pentyne

c. 1-Chloro-4,4,5-trimethyl-2-heptyne

d. 2-Bromo-3-chloro-7,8-dimethyl-4-decyne

11.43 Name each of the following using the IUPAC Nomenclature System:

a. $CH_3CH_2CH(CH_3)CH{=}CH_2$

b. $CH_2CH_2CH_2CH_2Br$ (with $CH_2CH{=}CH_2$ attached to the first carbon)

c. $CH_3CH_2CH{=}CHCHBrCH_2CH_3$

d. $CH_3{-}C(CH_3)_2{-}$ (cyclohexene ring) ${-}CH_3$

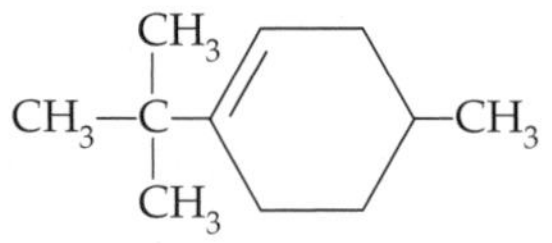

11.44 Name each of the following using the IUPAC Nomenclature System:

a. $CH_3CH(CH_3)CH_2CH{=}C(CH_3)_2$

b. $CH_2ClCH(CH_3)C{\equiv}CH$

c. $CH_3CHClCH_2CH_2CH_2C{\equiv}CH$

d. (cyclopentene ring bearing Br and Cl)

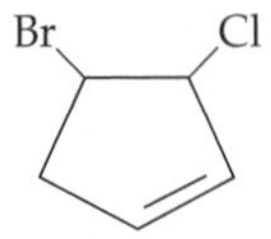

11.45 Draw each of the following compounds using condensed formulas:

a. 1,3,5-Trifluoropentane

b. *cis*-2-Octene

c. Dipropylacetylene

11.46 Draw each of the following compounds using condensed formulas:

a. 3,3,5-Trimethyl-1-hexene

b. 1-Bromo-3-chloro-1-heptyne

c. 3-Heptyne

11.47 Which of the following alkenes can exist as *cis-trans* isomers? Explain your reasoning.

a. 1-Heptene
b. 2-Heptene
c. 3-Heptene
d. 2-Methyl-2-hexene
e. 3-Methyl-2-hexene

11.48 Draw the line formula for each of the alkenes in Question 11.47.

11.49 Which of the following alkenes would not exhibit *cis-trans* geometric isomerism?

a. 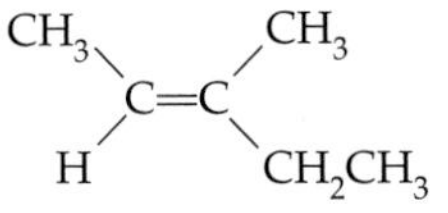 CH_3 CH_3
$C{=}C$
H CH_2CH_3

b. 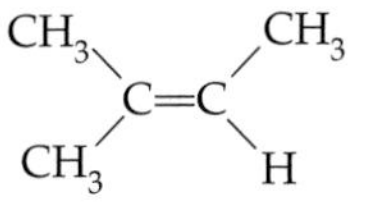 CH_3 CH_3
$C{=}C$
CH_3 H

c. CH_3CH_2 CH_2CH_3 | $CHCH_3$
$C{=}C$
CH_3 $CHCH_2CH_3$ | CH_3

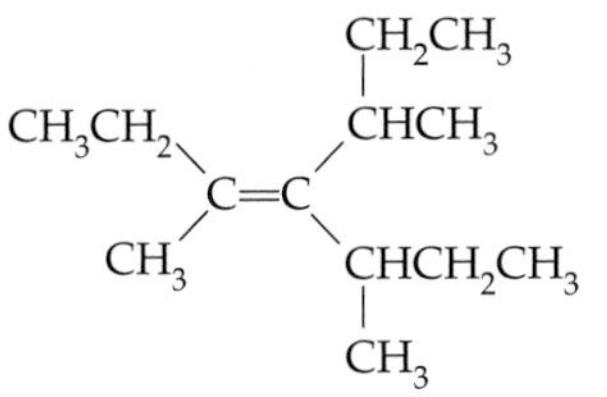

d. 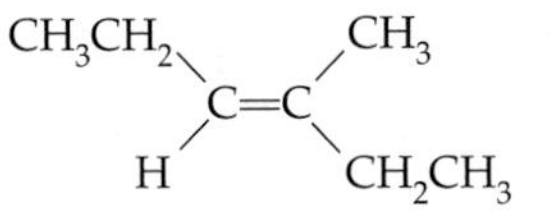 CH_3CH_2 CH_3
$C{=}C$
H CH_2CH_3

11.50 Which of the following structures have incorrect IUPAC names? If incorrect, give the correct IUPAC name.

a. $CH_3C{\equiv}CCH_2CH(CH_3)_2$

2-Methyl-4-hexyne

b. 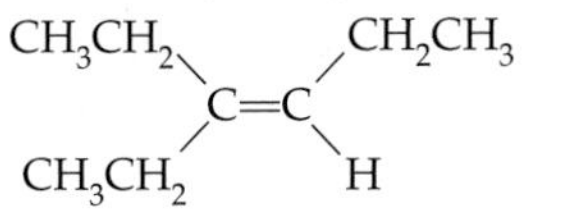 CH_3CH_2 CH_2CH_3
$C{=}C$
CH_3CH_2 H

3-Ethyl-3-hexene

c. $CH_3CH(CH_3)CH_2C{\equiv}CCH_2CH(CH_3)CH_2CH_3$

2-Ethyl-7-methyl-4-octyne

d. 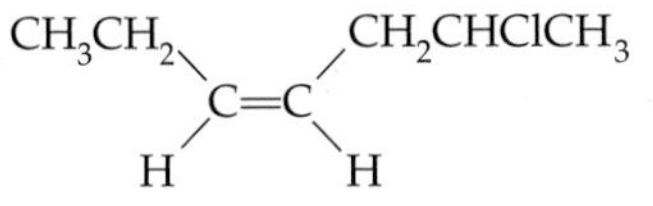 CH_3CH_2 $CH_2CHClCH_3$
$C{=}C$
H H

trans-6-Chloro-3-heptene

e. 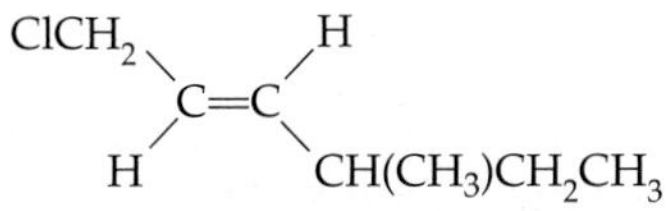 $ClCH_2$ H
$C{=}C$
H $CH(CH_3)CH_2CH_3$

1-Chloro-5-methyl-2-hexene

11.51 Which of the following can exist as *cis*- and *trans*-isomers?

a. $H_2C{=}CH_2$
b. $CH_3CH{=}CHCH_3$
c. $Cl_2C{=}CBr_2$
d. $ClBrC{=}CClBr$
e. $(CH_3)_2C{=}C(CH_3)_2$

11.52 Draw and name all the *cis*- and *trans*-isomers in Question 11.51.

11.53 Provide the IUPAC name for each of the following molecules:

a. $CH_2{=}CHCH_2CH_2CH{=}CHCH_2CH_2CH_3$
b. $CH_2{=}CHCH_2CH{=}CHCH_2CH{=}CHCH_3$
c. $CH_3CH{=}CHCH_2CH{=}CHCH_2CH_3$
d. $CH_3CH{=}CHCH(CH_3)CH{=}CHCH_3$

11.54 Provide the IUPAC name for each of the following molecules:

a. $CH_3CBr{=}CHCH(CH_3)CH{=}CBrCH_3$
b. $CH_2{=}CHCH(CH_3)CH{=}CHCH(CH_2CH_3)CH_2CH_3$
c. $CH_2{=}CHC(CH_3)_2CH{=}CHCH_2CH{=}CHCH(CH_3)_2$
d. $CH_3CH(CH_3)CH(CH_2CH_3)CH{=}CHCH_2CH{=}CHCH(CH_3)CH_2CH_3$

Reactions Involving Alkenes and Alkynes

Foundations

11.55 Write a general equation representing the hydrogenation of an alkene.

11.56 Write a general equation representing the hydrogenation of an alkyne.

11.57 Write a general equation representing the halogenation of an alkene.

11.58 Write a general equation representing the halogenation of an alkyne.

11.59 Write a general equation representing the hydration of an alkene.

11.60 Write a general equation representing the hydration of an alkyne.

11.61 What is the principal difference between the hydrogenation of an alkene and hydrogenation of an alkyne?

11.62 What is the major difference between the hydration of an alkene and hydration of an alkyne?

Applications

11.63 Write an equation representing each of the following reactions:

a. 1-Heptene + H_2O (H^+)
b. 2-Heptene + HBr
c. 3-Heptene + H_2
d. 2-Methyl-2-hexene + HCl

11.64 Write a balanced equation for each of the following reactions:

a. 1,4-Pentadiene + H_2
b. 3-Methyl-1,4-cyclohexadiene + Cl_2
c. 2,4-Heptadiene + Br_2
d. 3-Methylcyclopentene + H_2O (H^+)

11.65 Complete each of the following reactions by supplying the missing reactant or product(s) as indicated by question marks:

a. $CH_3CH_2CH{=}CHCH_2CH_3$ + ? ⟶ $CH_3(CH_2)_4CH_3$

b. 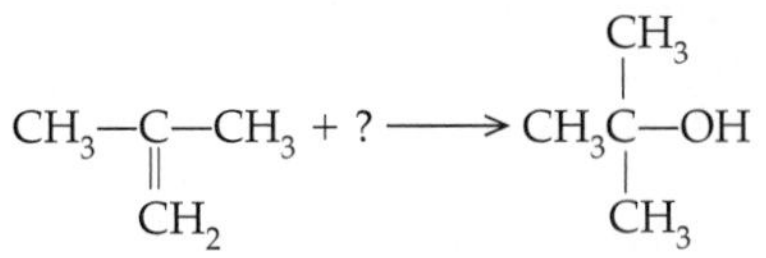 $CH_3{-}C({=}CH_2){-}CH_3$ + ? ⟶ $CH_3C(CH_3)_2{-}OH$

c. ? + (cyclohexene) ⟶ (cyclohexane with Br and H on adjacent carbons)

Br

H

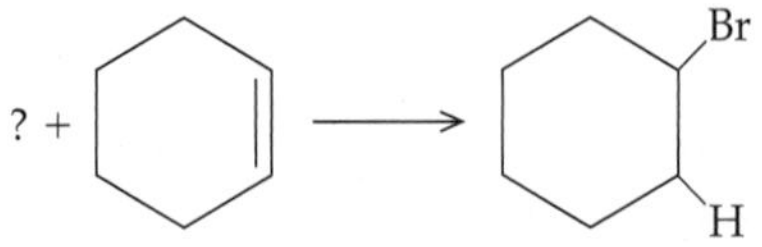

d. $2CH_3CH_2CH_2CH_2CH_2CH_3 + ?O_2 \xrightarrow{\text{Heat}}$? + ? (complete combustion)

e. 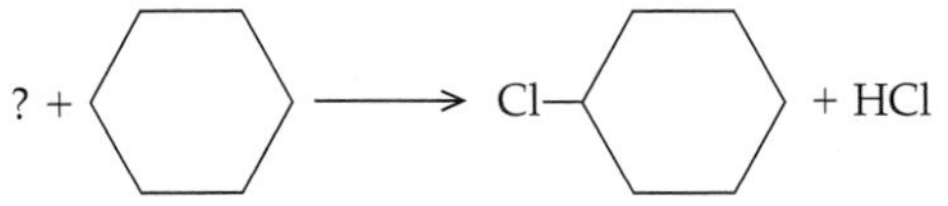 ? + (cyclohexane) ⟶ Cl–(cyclohexane) + HCl

f. 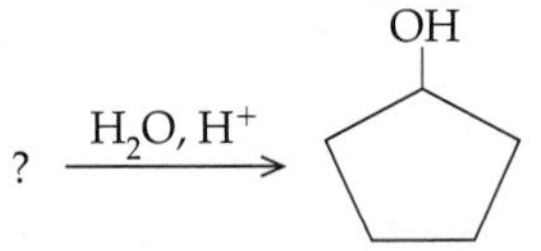 ? $\xrightarrow{H_2O,\ H^+}$ (cyclopentanol)

OH

11.66 Draw and name the product in each of the following reactions:

a. Cyclopentene + H_2O (H^+)

b. Cyclopentene + HCl

c. Cyclopentene + H_2

d. Cyclopentene + HI

11.67 Write a balanced equation for each of the following reactions:

a. Hydrogenation of 2-butyne

b. Halogenation of 2-pentyne

11.68 Write a balanced equation for each of the following reactions:

a. Hydration of 1-butyne

b. Hydration of 2-butyne

11.69 Predict the major product in each of the following reactions. Name the alkene reactant and the product, using IUPAC nomenclature.

a. 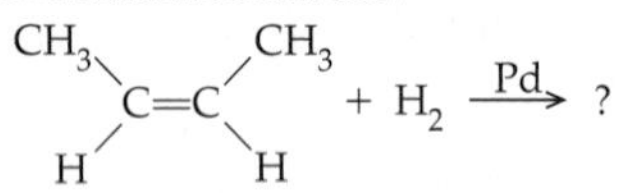 $(CH_3)(H)C{=}C(H)(CH_3)$ (both CH_3 on the same side) + $H_2 \xrightarrow{Pd}$?

b. $CH_3CH_2CH{=}CH_2 + H_2O \xrightarrow{H^+}$?

c. $CH_3CH{=}CHCH_3 + Cl_2 \longrightarrow$?

d. $CH_3CH_2CH_2CH{=}CH_2 + HBr \longrightarrow$?

11.70 Predict the major product in each of the following reactions. Name the alkene reactant and the product, using IUPAC nomenclature.

a. 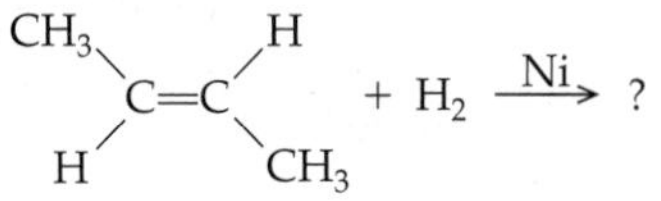 $(CH_3)(H)C{=}C(H)(CH_3)$ (CH_3 groups on opposite sides) + $H_2 \xrightarrow{Ni}$?

b. $(CH_3)_2C{=}CHCH_2CH_2CH_3 + H_2O \xrightarrow{H^+}$?

c. $(CH_3)_2C{=}CHCH_3 + Br_2 \longrightarrow$?

d. $CH_3C(CH_3)_2CH{=}CH_2 + HCl \longrightarrow$?

11.71 A hydrocarbon with the formula C_5H_{10} decolorized Br_2 and consumed 1 mol of hydrogen upon hydrogenation. Draw all the isomers of C_5H_{10} that are possible based on the above information.

11.72 Triple bonds react in a manner analogous to that of double bonds. The extra pair of electrons in the triple bond, however, generally allows 2 mol of a given reactant to *add* to the triple bond in contrast to 1 mol with the double bond. The "rich get richer" rule holds. Predict the major product in each of the following reactions:

a. Acetylene with 2 mol HCl

b. Propyne with 2 mol HBr

c. 2-Butyne with 2 mol HI

11.73 Complete each of the following by supplying the missing product indicated by the question mark:

a. 2-Butene $\xrightarrow{HBr}$?

b. 3-Methyl-2-hexene $\xrightarrow{HI}$?

c. 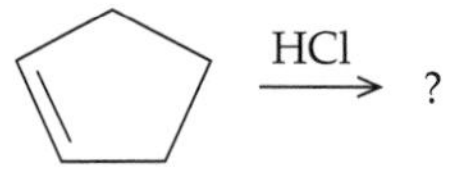 (cyclopentene) $\xrightarrow{HCl}$?

11.74 Bromine is often used as a laboratory spot test for unsaturation in an aliphatic hydrocarbon. Bromine in CCl_4 is red. When bromine reacts with an alkene or alkyne, the alkyl halide formed is colorless; hence, a disappearance of the red color is a positive test for unsaturation. A student tested the contents of two vials, A and B, both containing compounds with a molecular formula, C_6H_{12}. Vial A decolorized bromine, but vial B did not. How may the results for vial B be explained? What class of compound would account for this?

11.75 What is meant by the term *polymer?*

11.76 What is meant by the term *monomer?*

11.77 Write an equation representing the synthesis of polyvinyl chloride from vinyl chloride. (*Hint:* Refer to Table 11.2.) What are some of the uses for polyvinyl chloride?

11.78 Write an equation representing the synthesis of polypropylene from propene. What are some uses for polypropylene?

11.79 Provide the IUPAC name for each of the following molecules. Write a balanced equation for the hydration of each.

a. $CH_3CH{=}CHCH_2CH_3$

b. $CH_2BrCH{=}CH_2$

c. 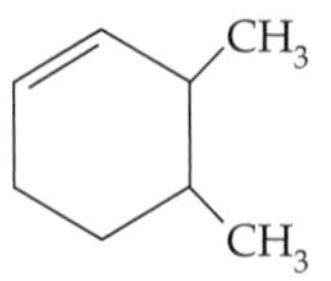 (cyclohexene ring with two adjacent CH_3 substituents)

CH_3

CH_3

11.80 Provide the IUPAC name for each of the following molecules. Write equations for the hydration of each.

a. 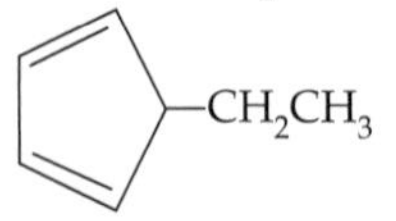 (cyclopentadiene ring)–CH_2CH_3

b. $CH_3CH{=}CHCH_2CH{=}CHCH_2CH{=}CHCH_3$

c. $CH_3CH{=}CHC(CH_3)_2CH_2CH_3$

11.81 Write an equation for the addition reaction that produced each of the following molecules:

a. $CH_2OHCH_2CH_2CH(CH_3)_2$

b. $CH_3CH_2CHBr(CH_2)_2CH_3$

c. 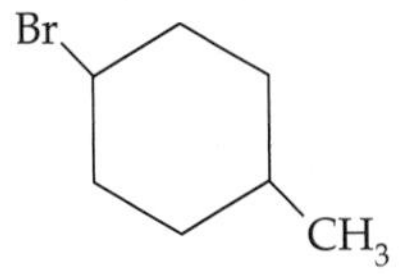 Br, CH_3

d. 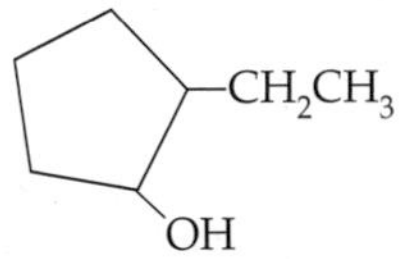 CH_2CH_3, OH

11.82 Write an equation for the addition reaction that produced each of the following molecules:

a. $CH_3CH_2CHOHCH(CH_3)CH_2CH_3$

b. $CH_3CHOHCH_2CH_3$

c. 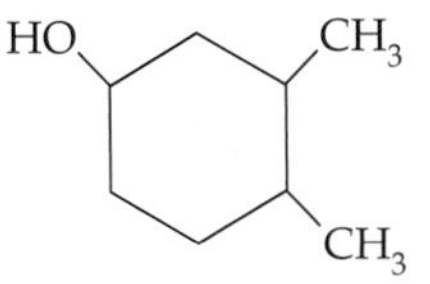 HO, CH_3, CH_3

11.83 Draw the structure of each of the following compounds and write a balanced equation for the complete hydrogenation of each:

a. 1,4-Hexadiene
b. 2,4,6-Octatriene
c. 1,3-Cyclohexadiene
d. 1,3,5-Cyclooctatriene

11.84 Draw the structure of each of the following compounds and write a balanced equation for the bromination of each:

a. 3-Methyl-1,4-hexadiene
b. 4-Bromo-1,3-pentadiene
c. 3-Chloro-2,4-hexadiene
d. 3-Bromo-1,3-cyclohexadiene

Aromatic Hydrocarbons

Foundations

11.85 Where did the term *aromatic hydrocarbon* first originate?

11.86 What chemical characteristic of the aromatic hydrocarbons is most distinctive?

11.87 What is meant by the term *resonance hybrid?*

11.88 Draw a pair of structures to represent the benzene resonance hybrid.

Applications

11.89 Draw the structure for each of the following compounds:

a. 2,4-Dibromotoluene
b. 1,2,4-Triethylbenzene
c. Isopropylbenzene
d. 2-Bromo-5-chlorotoluene

11.90 Name each of the following compounds, using the IUPAC system.

a. 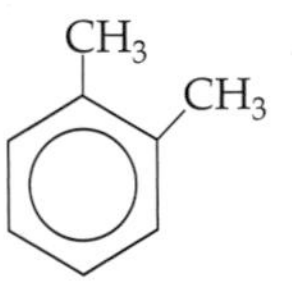 CH_3, CH_3

b. 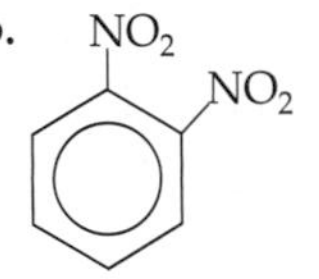 NO_2, NO_2

c. 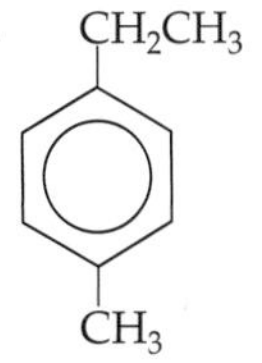 CH_2CH_3, CH_3

d. 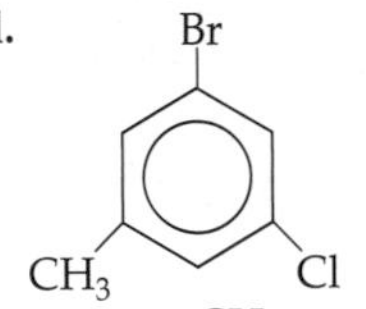 Br, CH_3, Cl

e. 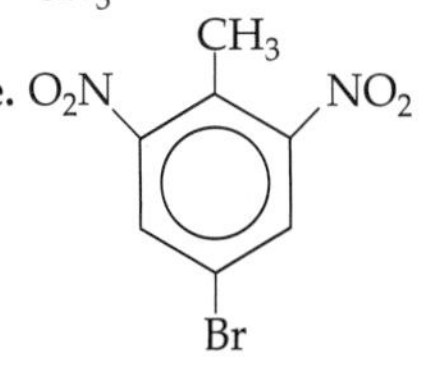 O_2N, CH_3, NO_2, Br

11.91 Draw each of the following compounds, using condensed formulas:

a. *meta*-Cresol
b. Propylbenzene
c. 1,3,5-Trinitrobenzene
d. *m*-Chlorotoluene

11.92 Draw each of the following compounds, using condensed formulas:

a. *p*-Xylene
b. Isopropylbenzene
c. *m*-Nitroanisole
d. *p*-Methylbenzaldehyde

11.93 Describe the Kekulé model for the structure of benzene.

11.94 Describe the current model for the structure of benzene.

11.95 How does a substitution reaction differ from an addition reaction?

11.96 Give an example of a substitution reaction and of an addition reaction.

11.97 Write equations for the reactions that would produce each of the following products:

a. 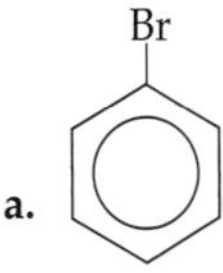

b. 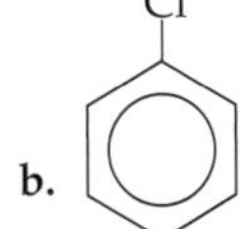

c. 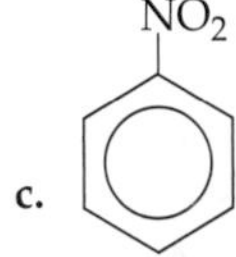

11.98 Draw all of the products that could be formed in a reaction of benzene with each of the following:

a. $2Cl_2$ in the presence of $FeCl_3$
b. $2SO_3$ in the presence of concentrated sulfuric acid
c. $2HNO_3$ in the presence of concentrated sulfuric acid

Heterocyclic Aromatic Compounds

11.99 Draw the general structure of a pyrimidine.

11.100 What biological molecules contain pyrimidine rings?

11.101 Draw the general structure of a purine.

11.102 What biological molecules contain purine rings?

CRITICAL THINKING PROBLEMS

1. There is a plastic polymer called polyvinylidene difluoride (PVDF) that can be used to sense a baby's breath and thus be used to prevent sudden infant death syndrome (SIDS). The secret is that this polymer can be specially processed so that it becomes piezoelectric (produces an electrical current when it is physically deformed) and pyroelectric (develops

an electrical potential when its temperature changes). When a PVDF film is placed beside a sleeping baby, it will set off an alarm if the baby stops breathing. The structure of this polymer is shown here:

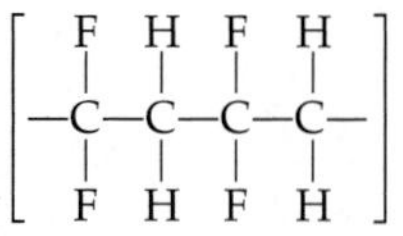

$$\left[\begin{array}{cccc} F & H & F & H \\ | & | & | & | \\ -C- & C- & C- & C- \\ | & | & | & | \\ F & H & F & H \end{array} \right]$$

Go to the library and investigate some of the other amazing uses of PVDF. Draw the structure of the alkene from which this compound is produced.

2. Isoprene is the repeating unit of the natural polymer rubber. It is also the starting material for the synthesis of cholesterol and several of the lipid-soluble vitamins, including vitamin A and vitamin K. The structure of isoprene is seen below.

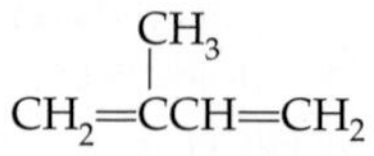

$$\begin{array}{c} \quad CH_3 \\ \quad | \\ CH_2{=}CCH{=}CH_2 \end{array}$$

What is the IUPAC name for isoprene?

3. When polyacrylonitrile is burned, toxic gases are released. In fact, in airplane fires, more passengers die from inhalation of toxic fumes than from burns. Refer to Table 11.2 for the structure of acrylonitrile. What toxic gas would you predict to be the product of the combustion of these polymers?
4. If a molecule of polystyrene consists of 25,000 monomers, what is the molar mass of the molecule?
5. A factory produces one million tons (t) of polypropylene. How many moles (mol) of propene would be required to produce this amount? What is the volume of this amount of propene at 25°C and 1 atmosphere (atm)?

12

Alcohols, Phenols, Thiols, and Ethers

LEARNING GOALS

1 Classify alcohols as primary, secondary, or tertiary.
2 Rank selected alcohols by relative water solubility, boiling points, or melting points.
3 Write the names and draw the structures for common alcohols.
4 Discuss the biological, medical, or environmental significance of several alcohols.
5 Write equations representing the preparation of alcohols by the hydration of an alkene.
6 Write equations representing the preparation of alcohols by hydrogenation (reduction) of aldehydes or ketones.
7 Write equations showing the dehydration of an alcohol.
8 Write equations representing the oxidation of alcohols.
9 Discuss the role of oxidation and reduction reactions in the chemistry of living systems.
10 Discuss the use of phenols as germicides.
11 Write names and draw structures for common ethers and discuss their use in medicine.
12 Write equations representing the condensation reaction between two alcohol molecules to form an ether.
13 Write names and draw structures for simple thiols and discuss their biological significance.

Sugar-free chocolates are not calorie free!

OUTLINE

Introduction 406
12.1 Alcohols: Structure and Physical Properties 407
12.2 Alcohols: Nomenclature 409
12.3 Medically Important Alcohols 411
A Medical Perspective: Fetal Alcohol Syndrome 412
12.4 Reactions Involving Alcohols 413
12.5 Oxidation and Reduction in Living Systems 419
Chemistry at the Crime Scene: Drinking and Driving 421
12.6 Phenols 421
Kitchen Chemistry: Spicy Phenols 422
A Medical Perspective: Resveratrol: Fountain of Youth? 424
12.7 Ethers 424
12.8 Thiols 427
Kitchen Chemistry: The Magic of Garlic 429

List the types of molecules containing the hydroxyl group that are important elements in the meal shown in this photograph.

INTRODUCTION

Research tells us that even as babies, we prefer sweet tastes over all others, and the sugar molecules in our diet that satisfy this sweet tooth are all alcohols and are characterized by the presence of a hydroxyl group (—OH). Glucose (blood sugar) and fructose (fruit sugar), sweet individually, can be chemically combined to produce sucrose, or table sugar. The U.S. Department of Agriculture reports that the average American consumes about 152 pounds (lb) of sucrose each year! It is little wonder that physicians, nutritionists, and dentists are concerned about the obesity and tooth decay caused by so much sugar in our diets.

As a result of these concerns, the food chemistry industry has invested billions of dollars in the synthesis of non-nutritive sugar substitutes, such as aspartame (Equal) and Splenda. You can also find a variety of candies, soft drinks, and gums that are labeled "sugar-free." A quick check of the nutritional label reveals that, although they are sugar-free, they are not calorie-free. These sweets contain sugar alcohols, such as sorbitol or mannitol, instead of sucrose. Sorbitol and mannitol molecules look very much like glucose and fructose, except that they are missing the carbonyl (C=O) group.

```
  O        Carbonyl Group       Hydroxyl Group
  ‖
  C—H                CH2OH            CH2OH             CH2OH
  |                  |                |                 |
H—C—OH               C=O           H—C—OH           HO—C—H
  |                  |                |                 |
HO—C—H            HO—C—H          HO—C—H           HO—C—H
  |                  |                |                 |
H—C—OH             H—C—OH          H—C—OH            H—C—OH
  |                  |                |                 |
H—C—OH             H—C—OH          H—C—OH            H—C—OH
  |                  |                |                 |
  CH2OH              CH2OH            CH2OH             CH2OH
D-Glucose          D-Fructose       D-Sorbitol        D-Mannitol
```

Compared to sucrose, they range in sweetness from about half to nearly the same. They also have fewer calories than table sugar (about one-third to one-half the calories). Sugar alcohols actually absorb heat from the surroundings when they dissolve. As a result, they cause a cooling sensation in the mouth. You may have noticed this when eating certain breath-freshening mints and gums.

In biological systems, the hydroxyl group (—OH) is important to the structures of sugars, fats, and proteins. It allows these biological molecules to undergo a variety of reactions such as oxidation, reduction, hydration, and dehydration, that are essential for life.

An aryl group is an aromatic ring with one hydrogen removed.

In this chapter we will study alcohols and phenols, both of which are characterized by the presence of the hydroxyl group. The difference is that alcohols contain an alkyl group bonded to the hydroxyl group, while phenols have the hydroxyl group bonded to a benzene molecule (aryl group).

General formulas: Example:

R—O—H	C_6H_5—O—H	CH_3—O—H
Alcohol	Phenol	Methanol (methyl alcohol)

We will also be studying ethers, which have two alkyl or aryl groups bonded to oxygen, and thiols, which are similar to alcohols except that the oxygen atom has been replaced by a sulfur atom.

R and R′ = alkyl or aryl groups

R—O—R'	CH_3—O—CH_3	R—SH	CH_3—SH
Ether	Methoxymethane (dimethyl ether)	Thiol	Methanethiol

12.1 Alcohols: Structure and Physical Properties

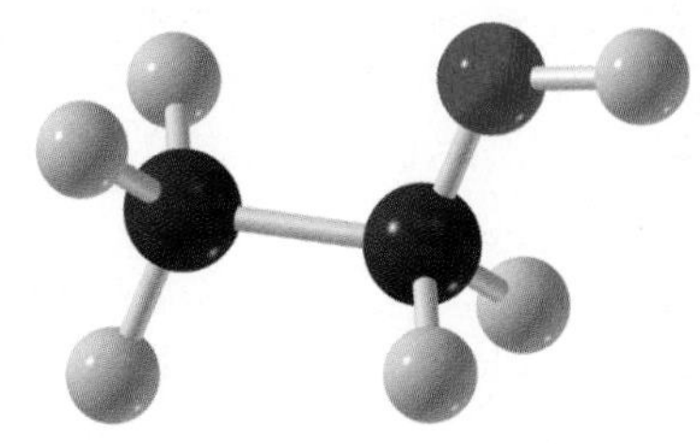

Figure 12.1 Ball-and-stick model of the simple alcohol ethanol.

An **alcohol** is an organic compound that contains a **hydroxyl group** (—OH) attached to an alkyl group (Figure 12.1). The R—O—H portion of an alcohol is similar to the structure of water. The oxygen and the two atoms bonded to it lie in the same plane, and the R—O—H bond angle is approximately 104°, which is very similar to the H—O—H bond angle of water.

Alcohols are classified as **primary (1°), secondary (2°),** or **tertiary (3°),** depending on the number of alkyl groups attached to the **carbinol carbon,** the carbon bearing the hydroxyl (—OH) group. If no alkyl groups are attached, the alcohol is methyl alcohol; if there is a single alkyl group, the alcohol is a primary alcohol; an alcohol with two alkyl groups bonded to the carbon bearing the hydroxyl group is a secondary alcohol, and if three alkyl groups are attached, the alcohol is a tertiary alcohol.

LEARNING GOAL

1 Classify alcohols as primary, secondary, or tertiary.

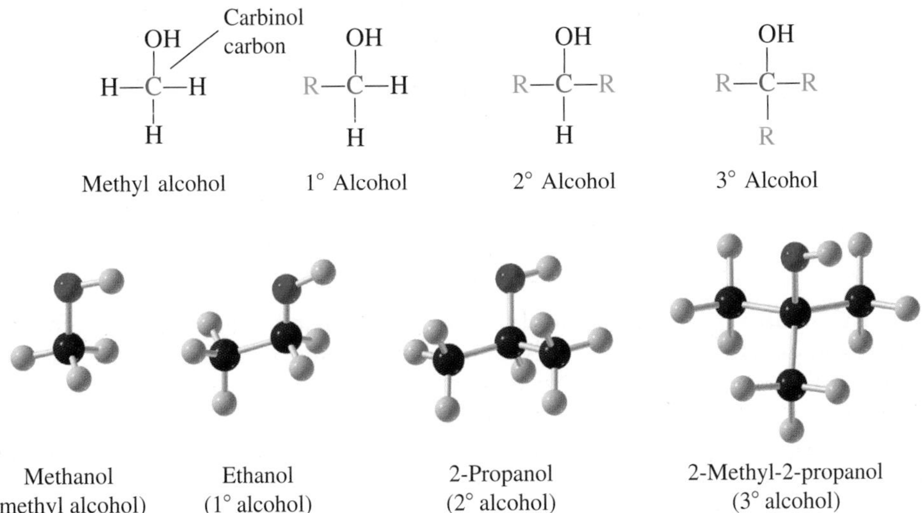

EXAMPLE 12.1 Classifying Alcohols

LEARNING GOAL

1 Classify alcohols as primary, secondary, or tertiary.

Classify each of the following alcohols as primary, secondary, or tertiary.

Solution

a. Two alcohols contribute to the distinctive flavor of mushrooms. These are 1-octanol and 3-octanol. In each of the structures shown below, the carbinol carbon is shown in red:

$$CH_3(CH_2)_6CH_2OH$$

$$\begin{array}{l} CH_3CH_2CH(CH_2)_4CH_3 \\ \quad\quad\quad\;\;| \\ \quad\quad\quad OH \end{array}$$

This alcohol, 1-octanol, is a primary alcohol because there is one alkyl group attached to the carbinol carbon.

This alcohol, 3-octanol, is a secondary alcohol because there are two alkyl groups attached to the carbinol carbon.

Continued…

b.

$$\begin{array}{c} CH_3 \\ | \\ CH_3CCH_3 \\ | \\ OH \end{array}$$

This alcohol, 2-methyl-2-propanol, is a tertiary alcohol because there are three alkyl groups attached to the carbinol carbon.

Practice Problem 12.1

Classify each of the following alcohols as 1°, 2°, 3°, or aromatic (phenol).

a. $CH_3CH_2CH_2CH_2OH$

b. $CH_3CH_2CHCH_2CH_3$ (with OH on the central CH)

c. 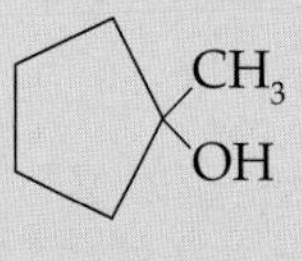 (cyclopentane ring bearing CH_3 and OH on the same carbon)

d. 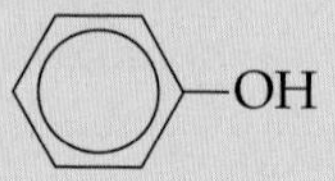 (benzene ring)—OH

e. 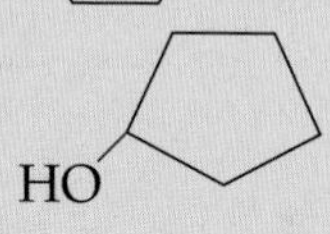 HO—(cyclopentane ring)

▸ For Further Practice: **Questions 12.17 and 12.19.**

Electronegativity is discussed in Section 3.1. Hydrogen bonding is described in detail in Section 5.2.

LEARNING GOAL

2 Rank selected alcohols by relative water solubility, boiling points, or melting points.

The hydroxyl groups of alcohols are very polar because the oxygen and hydrogen atoms have significantly different electronegativities. Because the two atoms involved in this polar bond are oxygen and hydrogen, hydrogen bonds can form between alcohol molecules (Figure 12.2).

As a result of this intermolecular hydrogen bonding, alcohols boil at much higher temperatures than hydrocarbons of similar molar mass. These higher boiling points are caused by the large amount of heat needed to break the hydrogen bonds that attract the alcohol molecules to one another. Compare the boiling points of butane and propanol, which have similar molar masses:

$CH_3CH_2CH_2CH_3$	$CH_3CH_2CH_2OH$
Butane	1-Propanol
M.M. = 58	M.M. = 60
b.p. = −0.5 °C	b.p. = 97.2°C

Alcohols of one to four carbon atoms are very soluble in water, and those with five or six carbons are moderately soluble in water. This is due to the ability of the alcohol to form intermolecular hydrogen bonds with water molecules (see Figure 12.2b). As the nonpolar, or hydrophobic, portion of an alcohol (the carbon chain) becomes larger relative to the polar, hydrophilic, region (the hydroxyl group), the water solubility of the alcohol decreases. As a result, alcohols of seven carbon atoms or more are nearly insoluble in water. The term *hydrophobic,* which literally means "water fearing," is used to describe a molecule or a region of a molecule that is nonpolar and, thus, more soluble in nonpolar solvents than in water. Similarly, the term *hydrophilic,* meaning "water loving," is used to describe a polar molecule or region of a molecule that is more soluble in the polar solvent water than in a nonpolar solvent.

An increase in the number of hydroxyl groups along a carbon chain will increase the influence of the polar hydroxyl group. It follows, then, that diols and triols are more water-soluble than alcohols with only a single hydroxyl group.

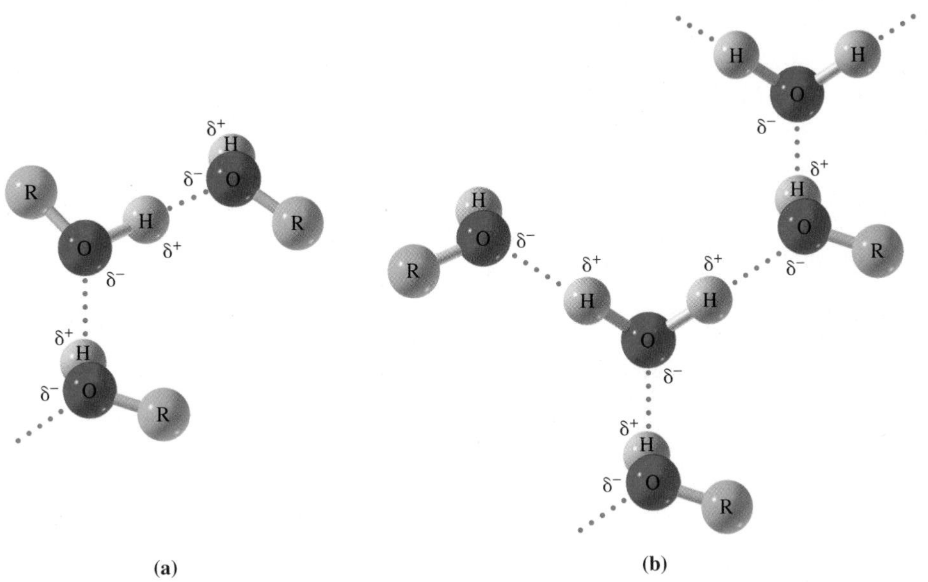

Figure 12.2 (a) Hydrogen bonding between alcohol molecules. (b) Hydrogen bonding between alcohol molecules and water molecules.

The presence of polar hydroxyl groups in large biological molecules—for instance, proteins and nucleic acids—allows *intramolecular* hydrogen bonding that keeps these molecules in the shapes needed for biological function.

Intermolecular hydrogen bonds are attractive forces between two separate molecules. *Intramolecular* hydrogen bonds are attractive forces between polar groups within the same molecule.

12.2 Alcohols: Nomenclature

IUPAC Names

In the IUPAC Nomenclature System, alcohols are named according to the following steps:

- Determine the name of the *parent compound,* the longest continuous carbon chain or the ring containing the —OH group.
- Replace the *-e* ending of the alkane chain with the *-ol* ending of the alcohol. Following this pattern, an alkane becomes an alkanol. For instance, ethan*e* becomes ethan*ol,* and propan*e* becomes propan*ol.*
- Number the parent chain to give the carbon bearing the hydroxyl group the lowest possible number.
- Name and number all substituents, and add them as prefixes to the "alkanol" name.
- Alcohols containing two hydroxyl groups are named *-diols.* Those bearing three hydroxyl groups are called *-triols.* A number giving the position of each of the hydroxyl groups is needed in these cases and the final *-e* of the parent compound is retained.

LEARNING GOAL

3 Write the names and draw the structures for common alcohols.

The way to determine the parent compound was described in Section 10.2.

EXAMPLE 12.2 **Using IUPAC Nomenclature to Name Alcohols**

LEARNING GOAL

3 Write the names and draw the structures for common alcohols.

a. The molecule shown here is an alarm-defense pheromone in certain populations of leaf-cutter ants. Provide the IUPAC name for this molecule.

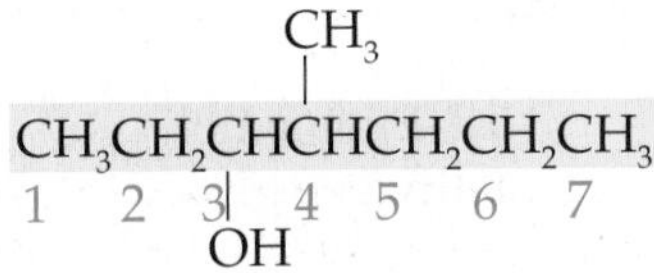

Continued...

Solution

Parent compound: heptane (becomes heptanol)
Position of —OH: carbon-3 (*Not* carbon 5 because the parent chain must be numbered to give the lowest possible number for the carbinol carbon.)
Substituents: 4-methyl
Name: 4-Methyl-3-heptanol

b. Name the following cyclic alcohol using IUPAC nomenclature.

Solution

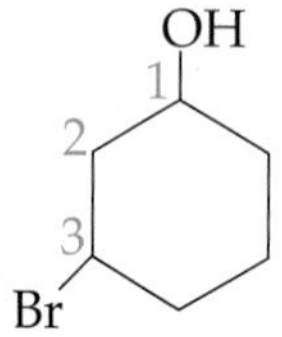

OH
1
2
3
Br

Parent compound: cyclohexane (becomes cyclohexanol)
Position of —OH: carbon-1 (*Not* carbon-3 because the carbinol carbon is defined as carbon-1.)
Substituents: 3-bromo (*Not* 5-bromo because the lowest possible numbering should be used.)
Name: 3-Bromocyclohexanol (it is assumed that the —OH is on carbon-1 in cyclic structures)

Practice Problem 12.2

Use the IUPAC Nomenclature System to name each of the following compounds.

a. $CH_3CHCH_2CH_2CH_2OH$ (with CH_3 on carbon-2)

b. $CH_3CHCH_2CHCH_3$ (with OH on carbon-2 and CH_2CH_3 on carbon-4)

c. CH_2CHCH_2 (with OH on each carbon)
(Common name: Glycerol)

d. $CH_3CH_2CHCHCH_2CH_2OH$ (with Cl on carbon-3 and CH_3 on carbon-4, counting from the left)

▸ For Further Practice: **Questions 12.29 and 12.30.**

See Section 10.2 for the names of the common alkyl groups.

Common Names

The common names for alcohols are derived from the alkyl group corresponding to the parent compound. The name of the alkyl group is followed by the word *alcohol.* For some alcohols, such as ethylene glycol and glycerol, historical names are used. The following examples provide the IUPAC and common names of several alcohols:

CH_3CHCH_3 (with OH on carbon-2)	$HOCH_2CH_2OH$	CH_3CH_2OH
2-Propanol (isopropyl alcohol)	1,2-Ethanediol (ethylene glycol)	Ethanol (ethyl alcohol) (grain alcohol)

Question 12.1 Draw structures for each of the following alcohols.

a. 2-Methyl-1-propanol
b. 2-Chlorocyclopentanol
c. 2,4-Dimethylcyclohexanol
d. 2,3-Dichloro-3-hexanol

Question 12.2 Give the common name and the IUPAC name for each of the following compounds.

a. $CH_3CH_2CH_2CH_2CH_2CH_2CH_2OH$

b. CH_3CHCH_3 with OH on the central carbon

c. Cyclohexane ring with OH at C-1, Br at C-2, Cl at C-3, and Br at C-4

d. Cyclopentane ring with OH at C-1, with H_3C and CH_3 on the two neighbouring carbons

12.3 Medically Important Alcohols

LEARNING GOAL

4 Discuss the biological, medical, or environmental significance of several alcohols.

Methanol

Methanol (methyl alcohol), CH_3OH, is a colorless and odorless liquid that is used as a solvent and as the starting material for the synthesis of methanal (formaldehyde). Methanol is often called *wood alcohol* because it can be made by heating wood in the absence of air. In fact, ancient Egyptians produced methanol by this process and, mixed with other substances, used it for embalming. It was not until 1661 that Robert Boyle first isolated pure methanol, which he called *spirit of box,* because he purified it by distillation from boxwood. Methanol is toxic and can cause blindness and perhaps death if ingested. Methanol may also be used as fuel, especially for "formula" racing cars.

Ethanol

Ethanol (ethyl alcohol), CH_3CH_2OH, is a colorless and odorless liquid and is the alcohol in alcoholic beverages. It is also widely used as a solvent and as a raw material for the preparation of other organic chemicals.

The ethanol used in alcoholic beverages comes from the **fermentation** of carbohydrates (sugars and starches). The beverage produced depends on the starting material and the fermentation process: scotch (grain), bourbon (corn), burgundy wine (grapes and grape skins), and chablis wine (grapes without red skins) (Figure 12.3). The following equation summarizes the fermentation process:

Figure 12.3 Champagne, a sparkling wine, results when fermentation is carried out in a sealed bottle. Under these conditions, the CO_2 produced during fermentation is trapped in the wine.

$$\underset{\text{Sugar (glucose)}}{C_6H_{12}O_6} \xrightarrow[\text{enzyme action}]{\text{Several steps involving}} \underset{\text{Ethanol (ethyl alcohol)}}{2CH_3CH_2OH} + 2CO_2$$

Fermentation reactions are described in detail in Section 21.4 and in A Human Perspective: Fermentations: The Good, the Bad, and the Ugly.

The alcoholic beverages listed have quite different alcohol concentrations. Wines are generally 12–13% alcohol because the yeasts that produce the ethanol are killed by ethanol concentrations of 12–13%. To produce bourbon or scotch with an alcohol concentration of 40–45% ethanol (80 or 90 proof), the original fermentation products must be distilled.

Distillation is the separation of compounds in a mixture based on differences in boiling points.

The sale and use of pure ethanol (100% ethanol) are regulated by the federal government. To prevent illegal use of pure ethanol, it is *denatured* by the addition of a denaturing agent, which makes it unfit to drink but suitable for many laboratory applications.

A MEDICAL PERSPECTIVE

Fetal Alcohol Syndrome

The first months of pregnancy are a time of great joy and anticipation but are not without moments of anxiety. On her first visit to the obstetrician, the mother-to-be is tested for previous exposure to a number of infectious diseases that could damage the fetus. She is provided with information about diet, weight gain, and drugs that could harm the baby. Among the drugs that should be avoided are alcoholic beverages.

The use of alcoholic beverages by a pregnant woman can cause *fetal alcohol syndrome* (*FAS*). A *syndrome* is a set of symptoms that occur together and are characteristic of a particular disease. In this case, physicians have observed that infants born to women with chronic alcoholism showed a reproducible set of abnormalities including mental retardation, poor growth before and after birth, and facial malformations.

Mothers who report only social drinking may have children with *fetal alcohol effects,* a less severe form of fetal alcohol syndrome. This milder form is characterized by a reduced birth weight, some learning disabilities, and behavioral problems.

How does alcohol consumption cause these varied symptoms? No one is exactly sure, but it is well known that the alcohol consumed by the mother crosses the placenta and enters the bloodstream of the fetus. Within about 15 minutes (min), the concentration of alcohol in the blood of the fetus is as high as that of the mother! However, the mother has enzymes to detoxify the alcohol in her blood; the fetus does not. Now consider that alcohol can cause cell division to stop or be radically altered. It is thought that even a single night on the town could be enough to cause FAS by blocking cell division during a critical developmental period.

This raises the question "How much alcohol can a pregnant woman safely drink?" As we have seen, the severity of the symptoms seems to increase with the amount of alcohol consumed by the mother. However, it is virtually impossible to do the scientific studies that would conclusively determine the risk to the fetus caused by different amounts of alcohol. There is some evidence that suggests that there is a risk associated with drinking even 1 ounce (oz) of absolute (100%) alcohol each day. Because of these facts and uncertainties, the American Medical Association and the U.S. Surgeon General recommend that pregnant women completely abstain from alcohol.

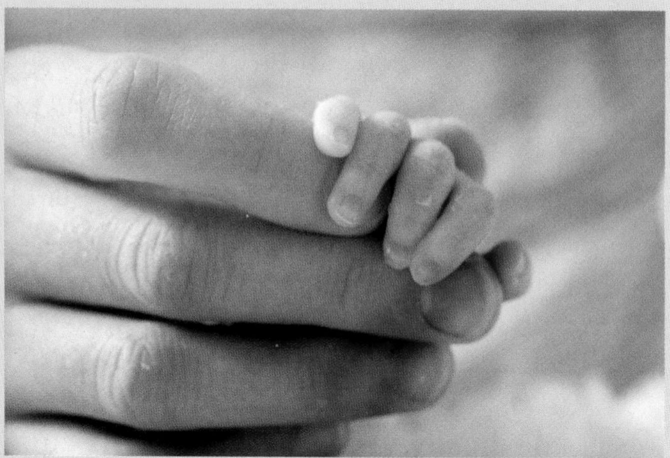

The American Medical Association recommends abstaining from alcohol during pregnancy.

For Further Understanding

- In October 2005, the U.S. Centers for Disease Control issued a document entitled *Guidelines for Identifying and Referring Persons with Fetal Alcohol Syndrome,* which can be found at the following Web address: http://www.cdc.gov/ncbddd/fasd/index.html. Refer to this document when answering the following questions.
- What is the estimate of the number of babies born each year with fetal alcohol syndrome and why is a more accurate number so difficult to determine?
- What are some of the issues, practical and ethical, involved in intervention efforts to prevent fetal alcohol syndrome?

2-Propanol

2-Propanol (isopropyl alcohol),

$$\underset{\displaystyle\text{OH}}{\text{CH}_3\overset{}{\text{C}}\text{HCH}_3}$$

was commonly called *rubbing alcohol* because patients with high fevers were often given alcohol baths to reduce body temperature. Rapid evaporation of the alcohol results in skin cooling. This practice is no longer commonly used.

It is also used as an antiseptic (Figure 12.4), an astringent (skin-drying agent), an industrial solvent, and a raw material in the synthesis of organic chemicals. It is colorless, has a very slight odor, and is toxic when ingested.

1,2-Ethanediol

1,2-Ethanediol (ethylene glycol),

$$\underset{\text{OH}}{\text{CH}_2}-\underset{\text{OH}}{\text{CH}_2}$$

is used as automobile antifreeze. When added to water in the radiator, the ethylene glycol solute lowers the freezing point and raises the boiling point of the water. Ethylene glycol has a sweet taste but is extremely poisonous. For this reason, color additives are used in antifreeze to ensure that it is properly identified.

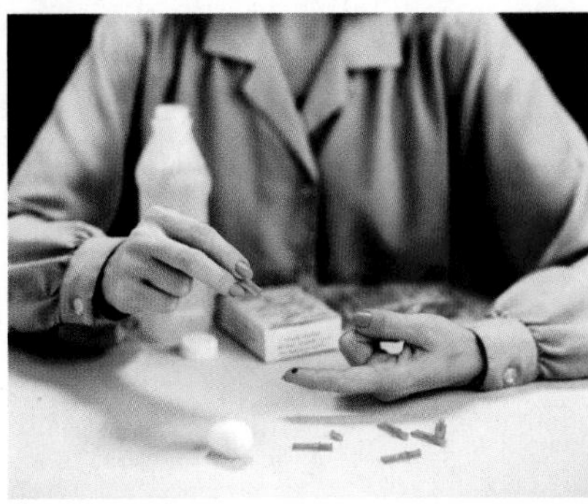

Figure 12.4 Isopropyl alcohol, or rubbing alcohol, is used as an antiseptic before and after an injection or blood test.

1,2,3-Propanetriol

1,2,3-Propanetriol (glycerol),

$$\underset{\text{OH}}{\text{CH}_2}-\underset{\text{OH}}{\text{CH}}-\underset{\text{OH}}{\text{CH}_2}$$

is a viscous, sweet-tasting, nontoxic liquid. It is very soluble in water and is used in cosmetics, pharmaceuticals, and lubricants. Glycerol is obtained as a by-product of the hydrolysis of fats.

12.4 Reactions Involving Alcohols

Preparation of Alcohols

LEARNING GOAL

5 Write equations representing the preparation of alcohols by the hydration of an alkene.

As we saw in the last chapter, the most important reactions of alkenes are *addition reactions.* Addition of a water molecule to the carbon-carbon double bond of an alkene produces an alcohol. This reaction, called **hydration,** requires a trace of acid (H^+) as a catalyst, as shown in the following equation:

$$\underset{\text{Alkene}}{R_2C{=}CR_2} + \underset{\text{Water}}{H{-}OH} \xrightarrow{H^+} \underset{\text{Alcohol}}{R{-}\overset{R}{\underset{H}{C}}{-}\overset{}{\underset{R}{C}}{-}OH}$$

Hydration of alkenes is described in Section 11.5.

Alcohols may also be prepared via the hydrogenation (reduction) of aldehydes and ketones. In organic and biochemical reactions, reduction is recognized as the loss of oxygen or the gain of hydrogen. In the reduction of aldehydes and ketones, it is the gain of hydrogen atoms that allows us to recognize that reduction has occurred. The general equations for these reactions can be summarized as follows:

Hydrogenation of aldehydes and ketones will also be discussed in section 13.4.

$$\underset{\text{Aldehyde}}{R^1{-}\overset{O}{\overset{\|}{C}}{-}H} + \underset{\text{Hydrogen}}{H{-}H} \xrightarrow{\text{Catalyst}} \underset{\text{Primary Alcohol}}{R^1{-}\overset{OH}{\underset{H}{C}}{-}H}$$

$$\underset{\text{Ketone}}{R^1{-}\overset{O}{\overset{\|}{C}}{-}R^2} + \underset{\text{Hydrogen}}{H{-}H} \xrightarrow{\text{Catalyst}} \underset{\text{Secondary Alcohol}}{R^1{-}\overset{OH}{\underset{H}{C}}{-}R^2}$$

EXAMPLE 12.3 **Writing an Equation Representing the Preparation of an Alcohol by the Hydrogenation (Reduction) of an Aldehyde**

Write an equation representing the preparation of 1-propanol from propanal.

LEARNING GOAL

6 Write equations representing the preparation of alcohols by hydrogenation (reduction) of aldehydes or ketones.

Continued...

Solution

Begin by writing the structure of propanal. Propanal is a three-carbon aldehyde. Aldehydes are characterized by the presence of a carbonyl group (—C=O) attached to the end of the carbon chain of the molecule. After you have drawn the structure of propanal, add diatomic hydrogen to the equation.

$$\begin{array}{c}\text{H H} \quad \text{O} \\ \text{H—C—C—C} \\ \text{H H} \quad \text{H}\end{array} + \text{H—H} \xrightarrow{\text{catalyst}}$$

Propanal Hydrogen

Notice that the general equation reveals this reaction to be an example of a hydrogenation reaction. As the hydrogens are added to the carbon-oxygen double bond, it is converted to a carbon-oxygen single bond, and the carbonyl oxygen becomes a hydroxyl group.

$$\begin{array}{c}\text{H H} \quad \text{O} \\ \text{H—C—C—C} \\ \text{H H} \quad \text{H}\end{array} + \text{H—H} \xrightarrow{\text{catalyst}} \begin{array}{c}\text{H H H} \\ \text{H—C—C—C—OH} \\ \text{H H H}\end{array}$$

Propanal Hydrogen 1-Propanol

Practice Problem 12.3

Write an equation representing the reduction of butanal. Provide the structures and names for the reactants and products. *Hint:* Butanal is a four-carbon aldehyde with the structure $CH_3CH_2CH_2C(=O)H$.

► For Further Practice: **Questions 12.65a and c and 12.66a and c.**

EXAMPLE 12.4

Writing an Equation Representing the Preparation of an Alcohol by the Hydrogenation (Reduction) of a Ketone

LEARNING GOAL

6 Write equations representing the preparation of alcohols by hydrogenation (reduction) of aldehydes or ketones.

Write an equation representing the preparation of 2-propanol from propanone.

Solution

Begin by writing the structure of propanone. Propanone is a three-carbon ketone. Ketones are characterized by the presence of a carbonyl group (—C=O) located anywhere within the carbon chain of the molecule. In the structure of propanone, the carbonyl group must be associated with the center carbon. After you have drawn the structure of propanone, add diatomic hydrogen to the equation.

$$\begin{array}{c}\text{H O H} \\ \text{H—C—C—C—H} \\ \text{H} \quad \text{H}\end{array} + \text{H—H} \xrightarrow{\text{catalyst}}$$

Propanone Hydrogen

Notice that this reaction is an example of a hydrogenation reaction. As the hydrogens are added to the carbon-oxygen double bond, it is converted to a carbon-oxygen single bond, and the carbonyl oxygen becomes a hydroxyl group.

$$\begin{array}{c}\text{H O H} \\ \text{H—C—C—C—H} \\ \text{H} \quad \text{H}\end{array} + \text{H—H} \xrightarrow{\text{catalyst}} \begin{array}{c}\text{H OHH} \\ \text{H—C—C—C—H} \\ \text{H H H}\end{array}$$

Propanone Hydrogen 2-Propanol

Practice Problem 12.4

Write an equation representing the reduction of butanone. *Hint:* Butanone is a four-carbon ketone with the structure

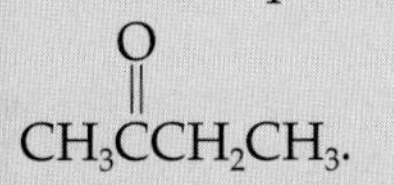

$$CH_3\overset{\overset{\displaystyle O}{\|}}{C}CH_2CH_3.$$

► For Further Practice: **Questions 12.65b and d and 12.66b and d.**

Dehydration of Alcohols

LEARNING GOAL

7 Write equations showing the dehydration of an alcohol.

Alcohols undergo **dehydration** (lose water) when heated with concentrated sulfuric acid (H_2SO_4) or phosphoric acid (H_3PO_4). Dehydration is an example of an **elimination reaction,** that is, a reaction in which a molecule loses atoms or ions from its structure. In this case, the —OH and —H are "eliminated" from adjacent carbons in the alcohol to produce an alkene and water. We have just seen that alkenes can be hydrated to give alcohols. Dehydration is simply the reverse process: the conversion of an alcohol back to an alkene. This is seen in the following general reaction and the examples that follow:

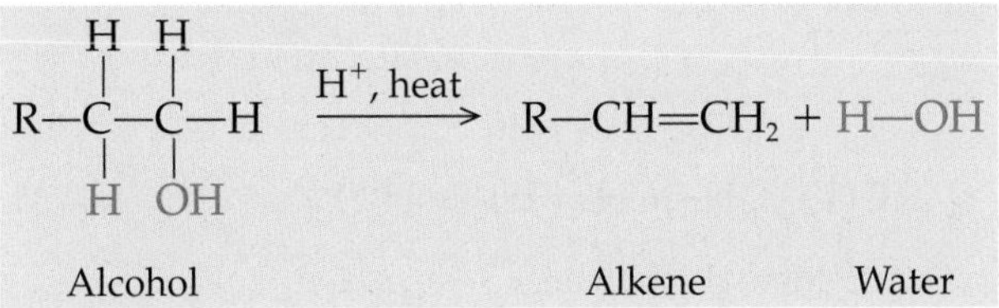

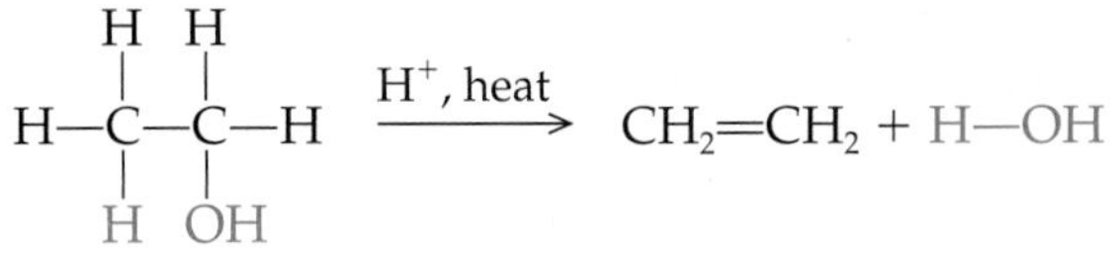

$$\underset{\text{Alcohol}}{R-\underset{H}{\overset{H}{C}}-\underset{OH}{\overset{H}{C}}-H} \xrightarrow{H^+,\text{ heat}} \underset{\text{Alkene}}{R-CH{=}CH_2} + \underset{\text{Water}}{H-OH}$$

$$\underset{\substack{\text{Ethanol}\\ \text{(ethyl alcohol)}}}{H-\underset{H}{\overset{H}{C}}-\underset{OH}{\overset{H}{C}}-H} \xrightarrow{H^+,\text{ heat}} \underset{\substack{\text{Ethene}\\ \text{(ethylene)}}}{CH_2{=}CH_2} + H-OH$$

$$\underset{\substack{\text{1-Propanol}\\ \text{(propyl alcohol)}}}{CH_3CH_2CH_2OH} \xrightarrow{H^+,\text{ heat}} \underset{\substack{\text{Propene}\\ \text{(propylene)}}}{CH_3CH{=}CH_2} + H_2O$$

In some cases, dehydration of alcohols produces a mixture of products, as seen in the following example:

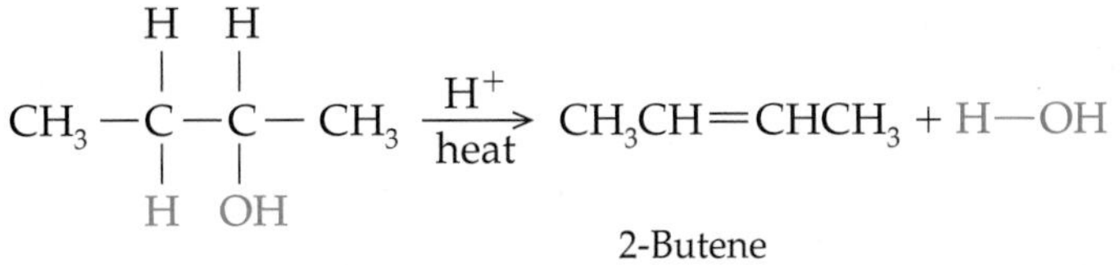

$$\underset{\text{2-Butanol}}{CH_3-\underset{H}{\overset{H}{C}}-\underset{OH}{\overset{H}{C}}-CH_3} \xrightarrow[\text{heat}]{H^+} \underset{\substack{\text{2-Butene}\\ \text{(major product)}}}{CH_3CH{=}CHCH_3} + H-OH$$

$$\underset{\text{2-Butanol}}{CH_3-\underset{H}{\overset{H}{C}}-\underset{OH}{\overset{H}{C}}-CH_3} \xrightarrow[\text{heat}]{H^+} \underset{\substack{\text{1-Butene}\\ \text{(minor product)}}}{CH_3CH_2CH{=}CH_2} + H-OH$$

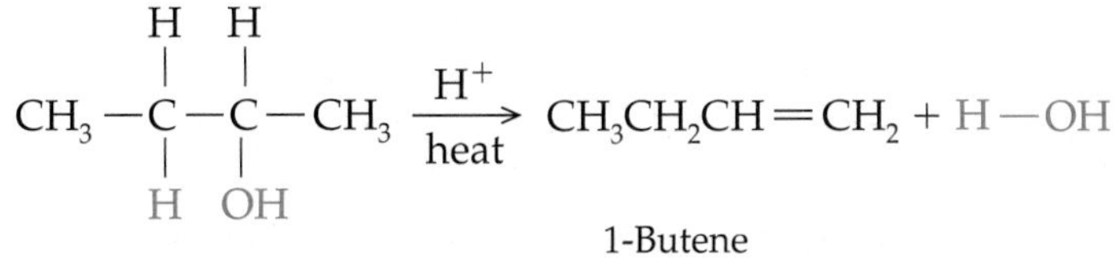

Notice in these equations and in Example 12.5, the major product is the more highly substituted alkene. In 1875 the Russian chemist Alexander Zaitsev developed a rule to describe such reactions. **Zaitsev's rule** states that in an elimination reaction, the alkene with the greatest number of alkyl groups on the double bonded carbons (the more highly substituted alkene) is the major product of the reaction.

EXAMPLE 12.5 Predicting the Products of Alcohol Dehydration

LEARNING GOAL

7 Write equations showing the dehydration of an alcohol.

Predict the products of the dehydration of 3-methyl-2-butanol.

Solution

The product(s) of dehydration of an alcohol will contain a double bond in which one of the carbons was the original carbinol carbon—the carbon to which the hydroxyl group is attached. Consider the following reaction:

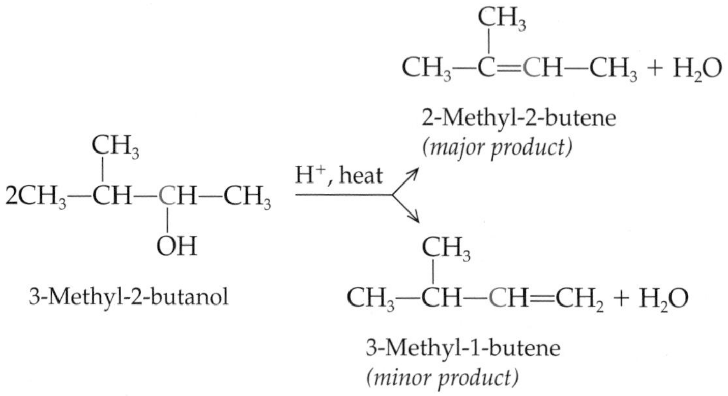

$$2CH_3-\underset{CH_3}{CH}-\underset{OH}{CH}-CH_3 \xrightarrow{H^+,\ heat} \begin{cases} CH_3-\overset{CH_3}{C}=CH-CH_3 + H_2O & \text{2-Methyl-2-butene (major product)} \\ CH_3-\overset{CH_3}{CH}-CH=CH_2 + H_2O & \text{3-Methyl-1-butene (minor product)} \end{cases}$$

3-Methyl-2-butanol

It is clear that both the major and minor products have a double bond to carbon number 2, the carbinol carbon in the original alcohol (shown in red). Zaitsev's rule tells us that in dehydration reactions with more than one product possible, the more highly branched alkene predominates. In the reaction shown, 2-methyl-2-butene has three alkyl groups at the double bond, whereas 3-methyl-1-butene has only one alkyl group at the double bond. The more highly branched alkene is more stable and thus is the major product.

Practice Problem 12.5

Write an equation showing the dehydration of each of the following alcohols. If there are two possible alkene products, indicate which is the major product and which is the minor product.

a. CH_3CH_2OH

b. 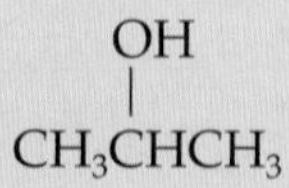 $CH_3\overset{OH}{C}HCH_3$

c. $CH_3CH_2\overset{CH_3}{C}H\underset{OH}{C}HCH_2CH_3$

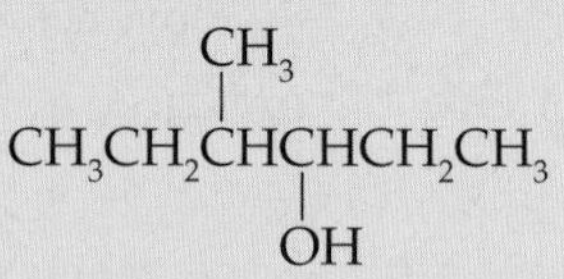

d. 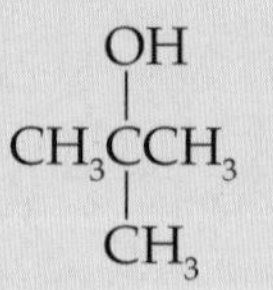 $CH_3\overset{OH}{\underset{CH_3}{C}}CH_3$

▸ For Further Practice: **Questions 12.52 and 12.54.**

Oxidation Reactions

LEARNING GOAL

8 Write equations representing the oxidation of alcohols.

Alcohols may be oxidized with a variety of oxidizing agents to aldehydes, ketones, and carboxylic acids. The most commonly used oxidizing agents are solutions of basic potassium permanganate ($KMnO_4/OH^-$) and chromic acid (H_2CrO_4). The symbol [O] over the reaction arrow is used throughout this book to designate any general oxidizing agent.

Oxidation of methanol produces the aldehyde methanal:

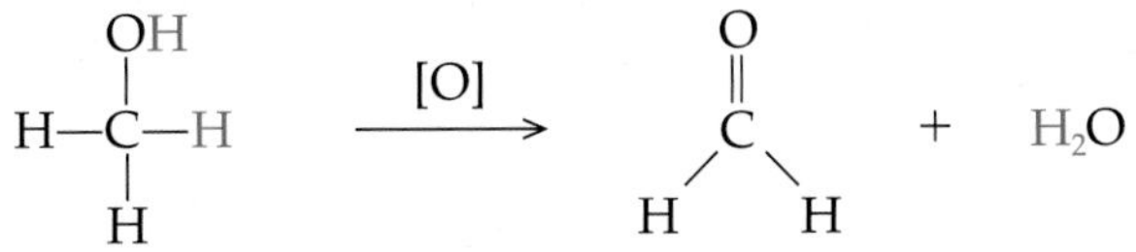

$$\text{H—}\underset{\text{H}}{\overset{\text{OH}}{\overset{|}{\underset{|}{\text{C}}}}}\text{—H} \xrightarrow{[\text{O}]} \text{H—}\overset{\text{O}}{\overset{\|}{\text{C}}}\text{—H} + H_2O$$

Methanol (methyl alcohol) An alcohol → Methanal (formaldehyde) An aldehyde

Note that the symbol [O] is used throughout this book to designate any oxidizing agent.

In organic and biochemical systems, oxidation is recognized by the loss of hydrogen or the gain of oxygen. In the oxidation of alcohols, two hydrogens are removed from the alcohol. One is removed from the hydroxyl group and a second is removed to form the carbinol carbon.

Oxidation of a primary alcohol produces an aldehyde, as seen in the following general equation and Example 12.6:

As we will see in Section 13.4, aldehydes can undergo further oxidation to produce carboxylic acids.

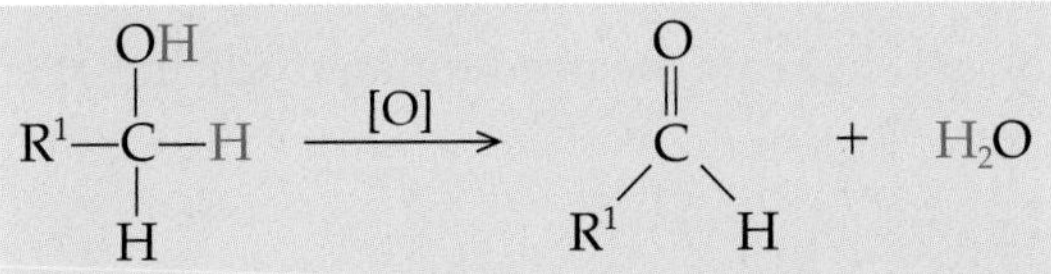

$$R^1\text{—}\underset{\text{H}}{\overset{\text{OH}}{\overset{|}{\underset{|}{\text{C}}}}}\text{—H} \xrightarrow{[\text{O}]} R^1\text{—}\overset{\text{O}}{\overset{\|}{\text{C}}}\text{—H} + H_2O$$

1° Alcohol → An aldehyde

EXAMPLE 12.6 Writing an Equation Representing the Oxidation of a Primary Alcohol

LEARNING GOAL

8 Write equations representing the oxidation of alcohols.

Write an equation showing the oxidation of 2,2-dimethylpropanol to produce 2,2-dimethylpropanal.

Solution

Begin by writing the structure of the reactant, 2,2-dimethylpropanol and indicate the need for an oxidizing agent by placing the designation [O] over the reaction arrow:

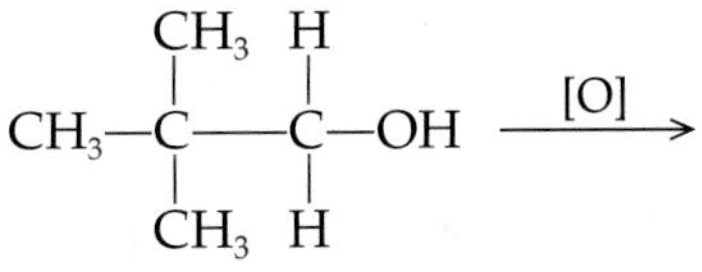

$$CH_3\text{—}\underset{CH_3}{\overset{CH_3}{\overset{|}{\underset{|}{\text{C}}}}}\text{—}\underset{\text{H}}{\overset{\text{H}}{\overset{|}{\underset{|}{\text{C}}}}}\text{—OH} \xrightarrow{[\text{O}]}$$

2,2-Dimethylpropanol

Now show the oxidation of the hydroxyl group to the aldehyde carbonyl group.

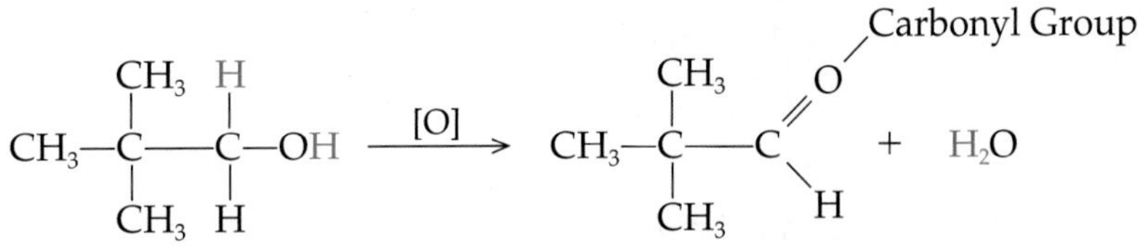

$$CH_3\text{—}\underset{CH_3}{\overset{CH_3}{\overset{|}{\underset{|}{\text{C}}}}}\text{—}\underset{\text{H}}{\overset{\text{H}}{\overset{|}{\underset{|}{\text{C}}}}}\text{—OH} \xrightarrow{[\text{O}]} CH_3\text{—}\underset{CH_3}{\overset{CH_3}{\overset{|}{\underset{|}{\text{C}}}}}\text{—}\overset{\text{O}}{\overset{\|}{\text{C}}}\text{—H} + H_2O$$

2,2-Dimethylpropanol → 2,2-Dimethylpropanal (Carbonyl Group)

Practice Problem 12.6

Write an equation showing the oxidation of the following primary alcohols:

a. $CH_3C(CH_3)_2CH_2CH_2OH$ b. CH_3CH_2OH

▸ For Further Practice: **Questions 12.48 and 12.56.**

Oxidation of a secondary alcohol produces a ketone:

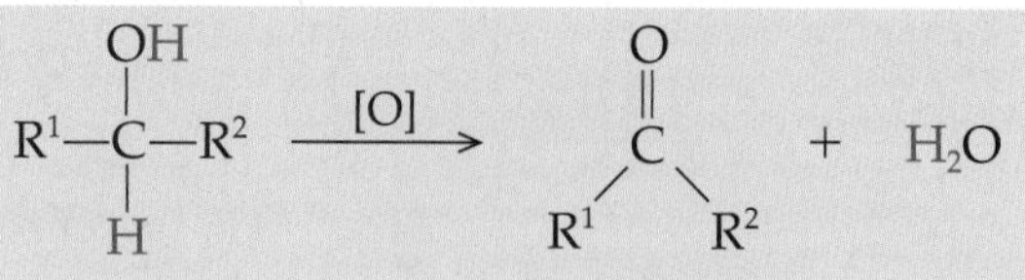

$$R^1{-}\overset{\overset{\large OH}{|}}{\underset{\underset{\large H}{|}}{C}}{-}R^2 \xrightarrow{[O]} \overset{\overset{\large O}{\|}}{C}(R^1)(R^2) + H_2O$$

2° Alcohol → A ketone

EXAMPLE 12.7 Writing an Equation Representing the Oxidation of a Secondary Alcohol

LEARNING GOAL

8 Write equations representing the oxidation of alcohols.

Write an equation showing the oxidation of 2-propanol to produce propanone.

Solution

Begin by writing the structure of the reactant, 2-propanol, and indicate the need for an oxidizing agent by placing the designation [O] over the reaction arrow:

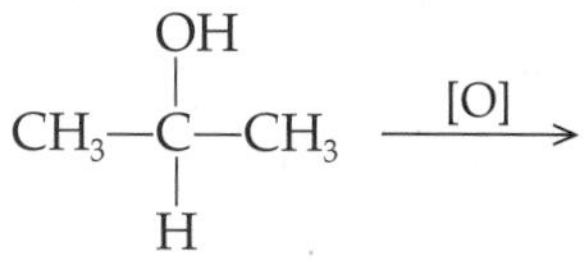

$$CH_3{-}\overset{\overset{\large OH}{|}}{\underset{\underset{\large H}{|}}{C}}{-}CH_3 \xrightarrow{[O]}$$

2-Propanol

Now show the oxidation of the hydroxyl group to the ketone carbonyl group.

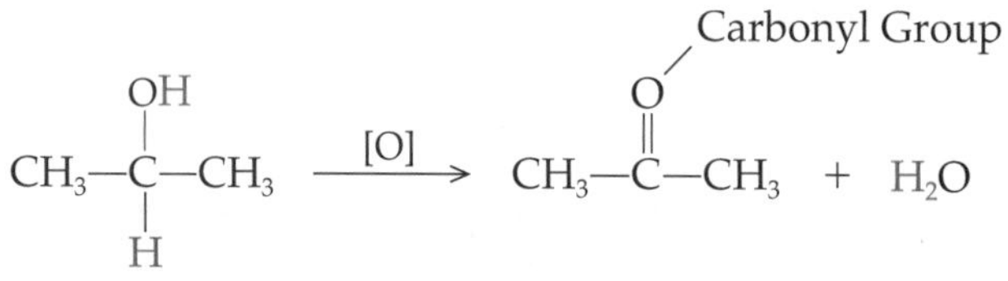

$$CH_3{-}\overset{\overset{\large OH}{|}}{\underset{\underset{\large H}{|}}{C}}{-}CH_3 \xrightarrow{[O]} CH_3{-}\overset{\overset{\large O}{\|}}{C}{-}CH_3 + H_2O$$

2-Propanol → Propanone (Carbonyl Group: C=O)

Practice Problem 12.7

Write an equation showing the oxidation of the following secondary alcohols:

a. 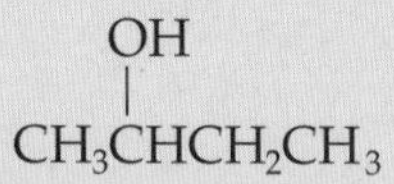 $CH_3\overset{\overset{\large OH}{|}}{C}HCH_2CH_3$

b. 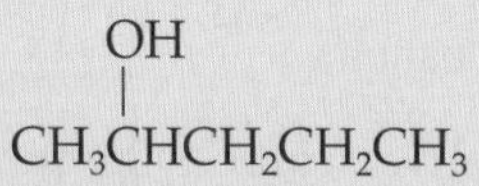 $CH_3\overset{\overset{\large OH}{|}}{C}HCH_2CH_2CH_3$

▸ For Further Practice: **Questions 12.49 and 12.55a, b, and c.**

Tertiary alcohols cannot be oxidized:

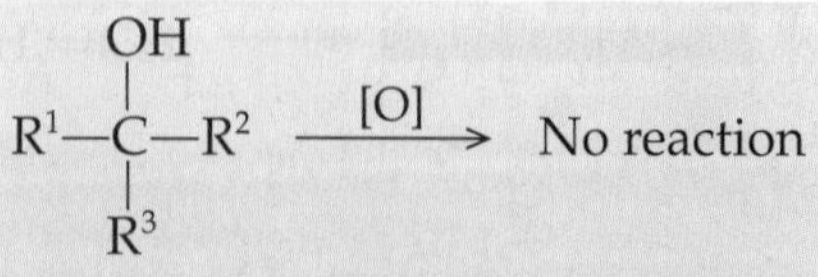

$$R^1{-}\overset{\overset{\large OH}{|}}{\underset{\underset{\large R^3}{|}}{C}}{-}R^2 \xrightarrow{[O]} \text{No reaction}$$

3° Alcohol

For the oxidation reaction to occur, the carbinol carbon must contain at least one C—H bond. Because tertiary alcohols contain three C—C bonds to the carbinol carbon, they cannot undergo oxidation.

Question 12.3 Classify the alcohol product in Practice Problem 12.3 at the end of example 12.3 as primary (1°), secondary (2°), or tertiary (3°) and provide the IUPAC and common names.

Question 12.4 Classify the alcohol product in Practice Problem 12.4, at the end of Example 12.4, as a primary (1°), secondary (2°), or tertiary (3°) alcohol, and provide the IUPAC name.

Question 12.5 Name the alcohol reactants and alkene products in each of the reactions in Practice Problem 12.5, at the end of Example 12.5, using the IUPAC Nomenclature System, and classify each of these alcohols as primary (1°), secondary (2°), or tertiary (3°).

Question 12.6 Name each of the reactant alcohols and product aldehydes in Practice Problem 12.6, at the end of Example 12.6, using the IUPAC Nomenclature System. *Hint:* Refer to Example 12.6, as well as to Section 13.2, to name the aldehyde products.

Question 12.7 Name each of the reactant alcohols and product ketones in Practice Problem 12.7, at the end of Example 12.7, using the IUPAC Nomenclature System. *Hint:* Refer to Example 12.7, as well as to Section 13.2, to name the ketone products.

Question 12.8 Explain why a tertiary alcohol cannot undergo oxidation.

When ethanol is metabolized in the liver, it is oxidized to ethanal (acetaldehyde). If too much ethanol is present in the body, an overabundance of ethanal is formed, which causes many of the adverse effects of the "morning-after hangover." Continued oxidation of ethanal produces ethanoic acid (acetic acid), which is used as an energy source by the cell and eventually oxidized to CO_2 and H_2O. These reactions, summarized as follows, are catalyzed by liver enzymes.

$$CH_3CH_2{-}OH \longrightarrow CH_3\overset{\overset{\displaystyle O}{\|}}{C}{-}H \longrightarrow CH_3\overset{\overset{\displaystyle O}{\|}}{C}{-}OH \longrightarrow CO_2 + H_2O$$

Ethanol (ethyl alcohol) — Ethanal (acetaldehyde) — Ethanoic acid (acetic acid)

12.5 Oxidation and Reduction in Living Systems

LEARNING GOAL

9 Discuss the role of oxidation and reduction reactions in the chemistry of living systems.

Before beginning a discussion of oxidation and reduction in living systems, we must understand how to recognize **oxidation** (loss of electrons) and **reduction** (gain of electrons) in organic compounds. It is easy to determine when an oxidation or a reduction occurs in inorganic compounds because the process is accompanied by a change in charge. For example,

$$Ag^0 \longrightarrow Ag^+ + 1e^-$$

With the loss of an electron, the neutral atom is converted to a positive ion, which is oxidation. In contrast,

$$:\ddot{\underset{..}{Br}}\cdot + e^- \longrightarrow :\ddot{\underset{..}{Br}}:^-$$

With the gain of one electron, the bromine atom is converted to a negative ion, which is reduction.

When organic compounds are involved, however, there may be no change in charge, and it is often difficult to determine whether oxidation or reduction has occurred. The following simplified view may help.

In organic systems, *oxidation* may be recognized as a gain of oxygen or a loss of hydrogen. A *reduction* reaction may involve a loss of oxygen or gain of hydrogen.

Consider the following compounds. A primary or secondary alcohol may be oxidized to an aldehyde or ketone, respectively, by the loss of hydrogen. An aldehyde may be oxidized to a carboxylic acid by gaining an oxygen.

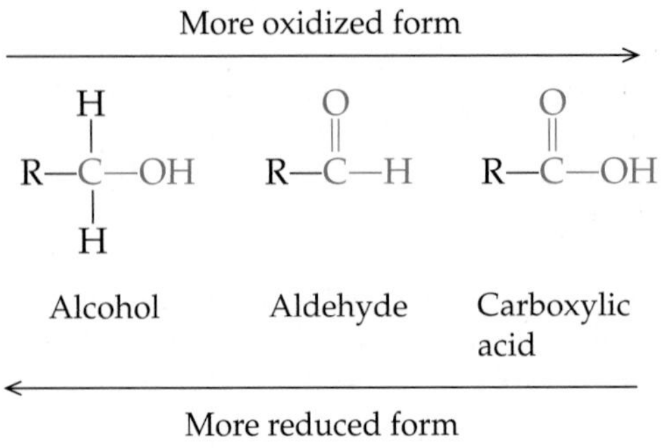

More oxidized form →

$$\underset{\text{Alcohol}}{R{-}CH_2{-}OH} \qquad \underset{\text{Aldehyde}}{R{-}C({=}O){-}H} \qquad \underset{\text{Carboxylic acid}}{R{-}C({=}O){-}OH}$$

← More reduced form

Thus, the conversion of an alcohol to a carbonyl compound, and a carbonyl compound (aldehyde) to a carboxylic acid are both examples of oxidations. Conversions in the opposite direction are reductions.

Oxidation and reduction reactions also play an important role in the chemistry of living systems. In living systems these reactions are catalyzed by the action of various enzymes called *oxidoreductases.* These enzymes require compounds called *coenzymes* to accept or donate hydrogen in the reactions that they catalyze.

Nicotinamide adenine dinucleotide, NAD^+, is a coenzyme commonly involved in biological oxidation-reduction reactions (Figure 12.5). We see NAD^+ in action in the final reaction of the citric acid cycle, an energy-harvesting pathway essential to life. In this reaction, catalyzed by the enzyme malate dehydrogenase, malate is oxidized to produce oxaloacetate:

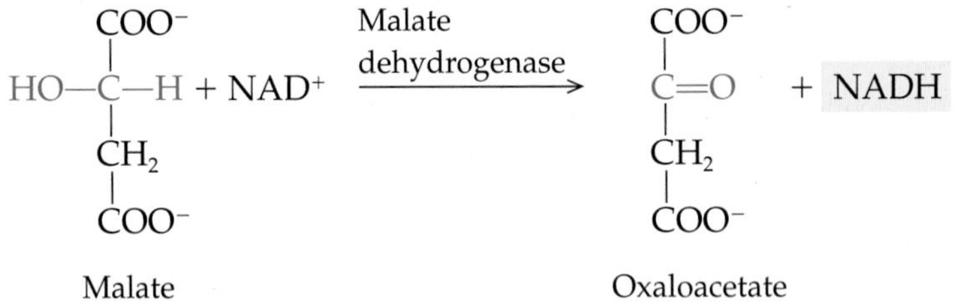

$$\underset{\text{Malate}}{{}^-OOC{-}CH(OH){-}CH_2{-}COO^-} + NAD^+ \xrightarrow{\text{Malate dehydrogenase}} \underset{\text{Oxaloacetate}}{{}^-OOC{-}C({=}O){-}CH_2{-}COO^-} + NADH$$

NAD$^+$ actually accepts a hydride anion, H^-, hydrogen with two electrons.

NAD^+ participates by accepting hydrogen from the malate. As malate is oxidized, NAD^+ is reduced to NADH.

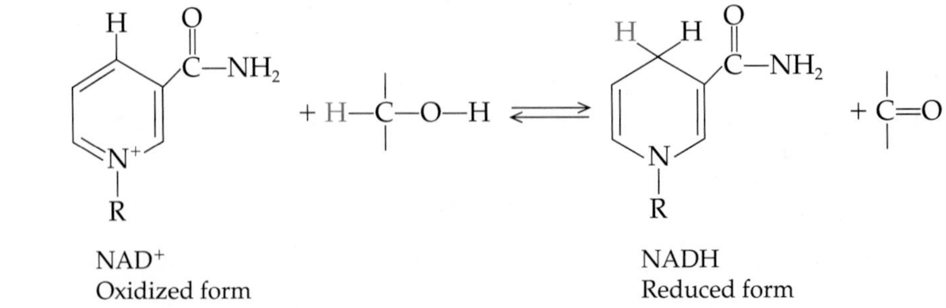

$$\underset{\substack{NAD^+\\ \text{Oxidized form}}}{\text{(pyridinium ring, } N^+{-}R\text{, with } {-}C({=}O){-}NH_2)} + H{-}\overset{|}{\underset{|}{C}}{-}O{-}H \rightleftharpoons \underset{\substack{NADH\\ \text{Reduced form}}}{\text{(dihydropyridine ring, } N{-}R\text{, } CH_2 \text{ with } {-}C({=}O){-}NH_2)} + \overset{|}{\underset{|}{C}}{=}O$$

We will study many other biologically important oxidation-reduction reactions in upcoming chapters.

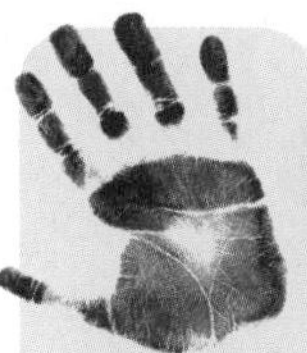

CHEMISTRY AT THE CRIME SCENE

Drinking and Driving

Nearly 41,000 people in the United States are killed each year in alcohol-related automobile accidents that result from the effects of ethanol on behavior, reflexes, and coordination. Blood alcohol levels of 0.05–0.15% seriously inhibit coordination. Blood levels in excess of 0.08% are considered evidence of intoxication in most states. Blood alcohol levels in the range of 0.30–0.50% produce unconsciousness and the risk of death.

One tool in the prevention of alcohol-related traffic deaths and, perhaps, in gathering evidence at the scene of an accident, is the breathalyzer test. The suspect is required to exhale into a solution that will react with the unmetabolized alcohol in the breath. The partial pressure of the alcohol in the exhaled air has been demonstrated to be proportional to the blood alcohol level. The solution is an acidic solution of dichromate ion, which is yellow-orange. The alcohol reduces the chromium in the dichromate ion from +6 to +3, the Cr^{3+} ion, which is green. The intensity of the green color is measured, and it is proportional to the amount of ethanol that was oxidized. The reaction is

$$\underset{\text{Yellow-orange}}{16H^+ + 2Cr_2O_7^{2-}} + 3CH_3CH_2OH \longrightarrow 3CH_3COOH + \underset{\text{Green}}{4Cr^{3+}} + 11H_2O$$

Of course, those with a positive breathalyzer test are given a more accurate blood test to ultimately establish their guilt or innocence. But the breathalyzer technology continues to provide a field-level screen for those endangering the lives of others by drinking and driving.

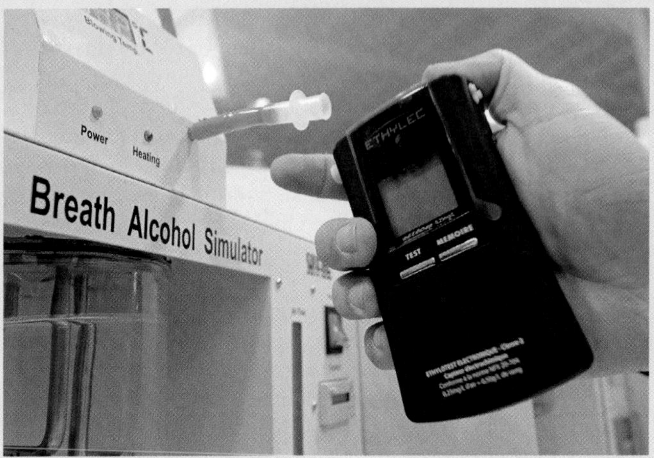

Driving under the influence of alcohol impairs coordination and reflexes.

For Further Understanding

- Explain why the intensity of the green color in the reaction solution is proportional to the level of alcohol in the breath.
- Construct a graph that represents this relationship.

Site of oxidation or reduction

Adenine nucleotide

Nicotinamide nucleotide

Nicotinamide adenine dinucleotide (NAD^+)

Figure 12.5 Nicotinamide adenine dinucleotide.

12.6 Phenols

LEARNING GOAL

10 Discuss the use of phenols as germicides.

Phenols are compounds in which the hydroxyl group is attached to a benzene ring (Figure 12.6). Like alcohols, they are polar compounds because of the polar hydroxyl group. Thus, the simpler phenols are somewhat soluble in water. They

KITCHEN CHEMISTRY

Spicy Phenols

Did you ever wonder why chili peppers are so "hot" or why drinking milk soothes the burning sensation? Why does fresh ginger have such a bite to it? The answer is in the structure of some of the phenols that are found in these foods. In the case of chili peppers, the culprit is capsaicin, which irritates mucous membranes and causes the burning sensation. In the pepper plant, the purpose of capsaicin, and the related molecules found in the peppers, is to protect the plant from herbivores.

The burning sensation when eating foods with capsaicin is caused by binding of the molecule to a receptor on the surface of our sensory nerve cells or neurons. Binding to the receptor causes the same reaction that occurs when the nerve cells are stimulated by excessive heat or abrasion. The reason that milk helps alleviate these symptoms is that capsaicin is hydrophobic and soluble in the milk fat. This removes it from the area of the neurons and eases the burning sensation.

The interaction of capsaicin with the sensory nerve cells is the key to the use of capsaicin to treat a variety of peripheral pain such as that associated with diabetic neuropathy and neuropathy that may follow a shingles infection, as well as pain associated with osteoarthritis and rheumatoid arthritis. Initial use of a capsaicin cream will cause a burning or itching sensation as the sensory neurons are stimulated. This stimulation depletes a neurotransmitter that the neurons need to signal the burning sensation to the brain. When the neurotransmitter is depleted, the pain signals stop. Regular use can significantly decrease chronic pain.

Capsaicins are also used in riot control and personal defense sprays. When the spray comes into contact with the skin and especially with the mucous membranes and eyes, the resulting pain incapacitates the would-be assailant, allowing the victim to run for help.

Ginger is the ingredient that imparts a bite to ginger ale, gingerbread, and ginger cookies. The flavor of ginger is largely due to gingerol, a phenolic compound with a structure very similar to capsaicin. When ginger is cooked, the gingerol is converted into zingerone, which has a less piquant flavor and a spicy-sweet aroma. Zingerone is related structurally to vanillin and is added to some perfumes to give them a spicy aroma. When ginger is dried, the gingerol is converted into shagaol, which is twice as piquant as gingerol. For this reason, dried, powdered ginger is spicier than fresh. Ginger is used in cuisine around the world. It has also been used as a folk medicine, prescribed for gastrointestinal discomfort, including sea sickness and morning sickness. In other cultures it is used to prevent the flu or combat a cold.

Chili peppers and ginger are just two examples of the amazing larder nature provides for us. They bring spice into our lives and, sometimes, relief from our pain.

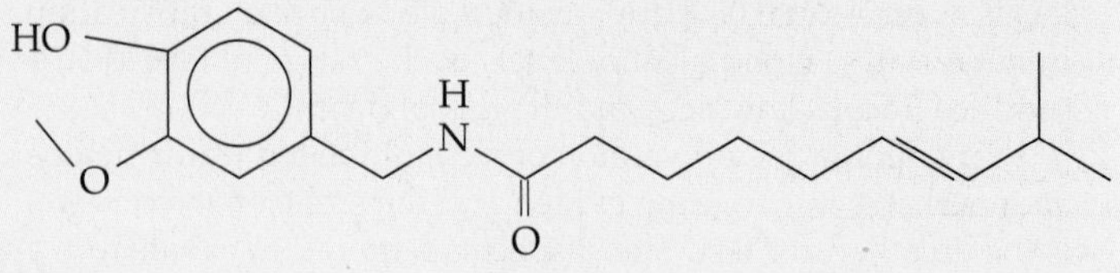

HO H N O O

Capsaicin

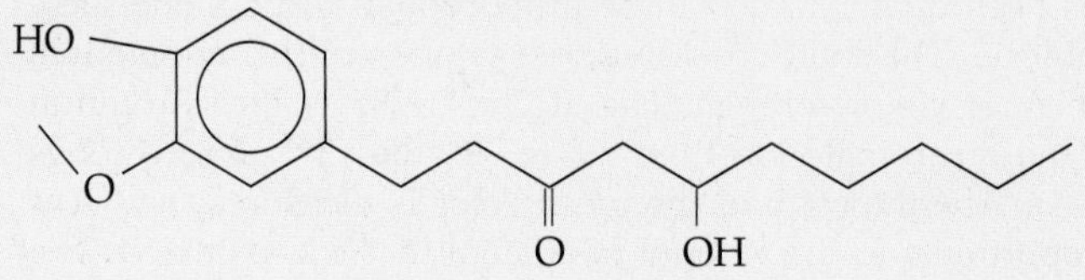

HO O O OH

Gingerol

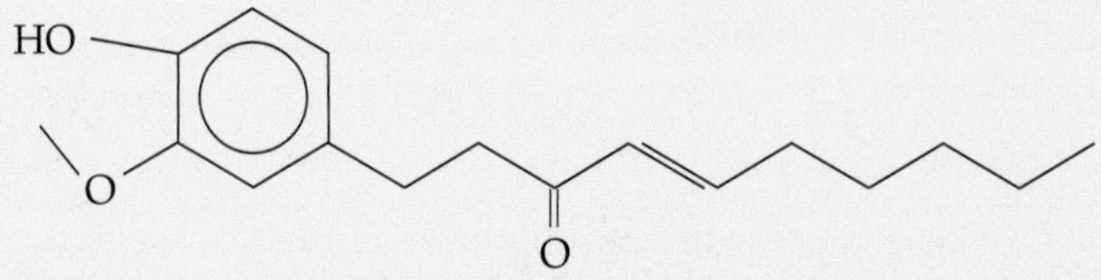

HO O O

Shagaol

HO O O

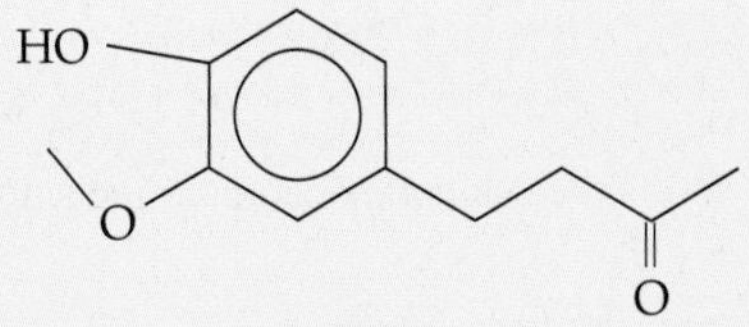

Zingerone

For Further Understanding

- Chili oil is a popular, spicy condiment used in Chinese cooking and sometimes as a dipping sauce. It is prepared by mixing dried chili peppers with oil. Explain why the oil that has been infused with the dried peppers becomes a hot sauce.
- What functional groups do capsaicin, gingerol, shagaol, and zingerone share in common?

are found in flavorings and fragrances (mint and savory) and are used as preservatives (butylated hydroxytoluene, BHT). Examples include:

Thymol (mint) Carvacrol (savory) Butylated hydroxytoluene, BHT (food preservative)

Phenols are also widely used in health care as germicides. In fact, carbolic acid, a dilute solution of phenol, was used as an antiseptic and disinfectant by Joseph Lister in his early work to decrease postsurgical infections. He used carbolic acid to bathe surgical wounds and to "sterilize" his instruments. Other derivatives of phenol that are used as antiseptics and disinfectants include hexachlorophene, hexylresorcinol, and *o*-phenylphenol. The structures of these compounds are shown below:

Phenol (carbolic acid; phenol dissolved in water; antiseptic)

Hexachlorophene (antiseptic)

Hexylresorcinol (antiseptic)

o-Phenylphenol (antiseptic)

In recent years there has been a great deal of discussion about the health benefits of phenols and polyphenols (compounds composed of a large number of phenol rings) from natural sources such as green tea, chocolate, and red wine. Green tea extracts are thought to have antioxidant, antiinflammatory, and anticarcinogenic properties. Two of the polyphenols in green tea are epicatechin gallate (ECG) and epigallocatechin gallate (EGCG) shown here:

Epicatechin gallate Epigallocatechin gallate

Question 12.9 Why are simple phenols somewhat soluble in water?

Question 12.10 What is carbolic acid? How did Joseph Lister use carbolic acid?

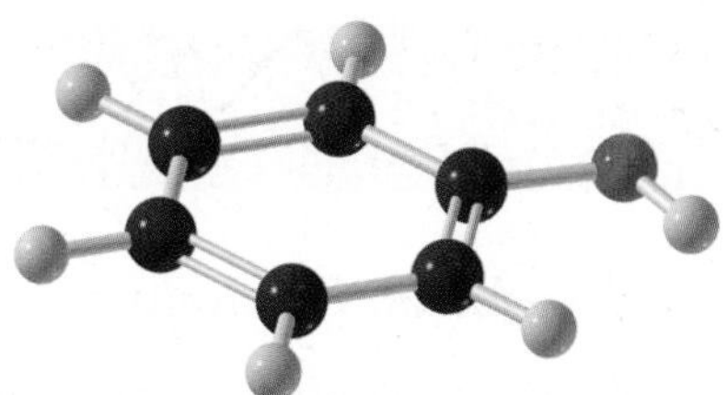

Figure 12.6 Ball-and-stick model of phenol. Keep in mind that this model is not completely accurate because it cannot show the cloud of shared electrons above and below the benzene ring. Review Section 11.6 for a more accurate description of the benzene ring.

A dilute solution of phenol must be used because concentrated phenol causes severe burns and because phenol is not highly soluble in water.

To learn more about nutritional aspects of polyphenols, see A Medical Perspective: Resveratrol: Fountain of Youth? in this chapter and Kitchen Chemistry: Amazing Chocolate in Chapter 11.

A MEDICAL PERSPECTIVE

Resveratrol: Fountain of Youth?

Will a daily snack of dark chocolate and red wine allow us to live longer, healthier lives? Recently such claims have been made based on a compound that is found in both. That compound is resveratrol, which is a type of natural phenol that is produced by plants to protect them from bacterial or fungal infections.

Resveratrol

For quite some time people have thought that red wine in moderation was associated with cardiovascular health. Resveratrol is one of the components in red wine that might help reduce the levels of LDL cholesterol, sometimes referred to as "bad" cholesterol, prevent blood clots and prevent damage to the lining of blood vessels. But how good is the evidence?

Consider that most of the research has been carried out in animals, not in people. There are studies that indicate that resveratrol protected mice from diabetes and obesity, both of which are factors associated with heart disease. These types of experiments have not been reproduced in humans. In fact, to reproduce this experiment with humans would require that each test subject drink 60 liters (L) of wine each day!

Other studies have shown that resveratrol extended the lifespan of yeast, some worms, fruit flies, and a short-lived fish. However, nothing is known about the effect of resveratrol on the human physiology or lifespan. Clinical studies with humans are needed to ensure that there are no negative side effects from consumption of large doses and to determine whether the potential health benefits seen experimentally occur in humans, as well.

As with all nutritional claims, it is important to look at the evidence on which the claims are made before taking a nutritional supplement or changing your lifestyle. Until the data are in, however, it couldn't hurt to have an occasional glass of red wine or piece of dark chocolate.

For Further Understanding

- Resveratrol is described as an antioxidant. Go online to look up further information on what is meant by an antioxidant and how they are thought to act in the body.
- What other types of compounds are described as antioxidants?

12.7 Ethers

LEARNING GOAL

11 Write names and draw structures for common ethers and discuss their use in medicine.

Ethers have the general formula R—O—R, and thus they are structurally related to alcohols (R—O—H). The C—O bonds of ethers are polar, so ether molecules are polar (Figure 12.7). However, ethers do not form hydrogen bonds with one another because there is no —OH group. Therefore, they have much lower boiling points than alcohols of similar molar mass but higher boiling points than alkanes of similar molar mass. Compare the following examples:

$CH_3CH_2CH_2CH_3$	CH_3—O—CH_2CH_3	$CH_3CH_2CH_2OH$
Butane (butane)	Methoxyethane (ethyl methyl ether)	1-Propanol (propyl alcohol)
M.M. = 58	M.M. = 60	M.M. = 60
b.p. = −0.5°C	b.p. = 7.9°C	b.p. = 97.2°C

An alkoxy group is an alkyl group bonded to an oxygen atom (—OR).

In the IUPAC system of naming ethers, the —OR substituent is named as an alkoxy group. This is analogous to the name *hydroxy* for the —OH group. Thus, CH_3—O— is methoxy, CH_3CH_2—O— is ethoxy, and so on.

EXAMPLE 12.8 Using IUPAC Nomenclature to Name an Ether

Name the following ether using IUPAC nomenclature.

Solution

$$\begin{array}{c} \quad O{-}CH_3 \\ | \\ CH_3CH_2CHCH_2CH_2CH_2CH_2CH_2CH_3 \\ 1\ \ 2\ \ 3\ \ 4\ \ 5\ \ 6\ \ 7\ \ 8\ \ 9 \end{array}$$

Parent compound: nonane
Position of alkoxy group: carbon-3 (*Not* carbon-7 because the chain must be numbered to give the lowest number to the carbon bonded to the alkoxy group.)
Substituents: 3-methoxy
Name: 3-Methoxynonane

Practice Problem 12.8

Name the following ethers using IUPAC nomenclature:

a. $CH_3CH_2{-}O{-}CH_2CH_2CH_3$
b. $CH_3{-}O{-}CH_2CH_2CH_3$
c. $CH_3CH_2{-}O{-}CH_2CH_2CH_2CH_2CH_3$
d. $CH_3CH_2CH_2CH_2{-}O{-}CH_2CH_2CH_3$

► For Further Practice: **Questions 12.85 and 12.88.**

LEARNING GOAL

11 Write names and draw structures for common ethers and discuss their use in medicine.

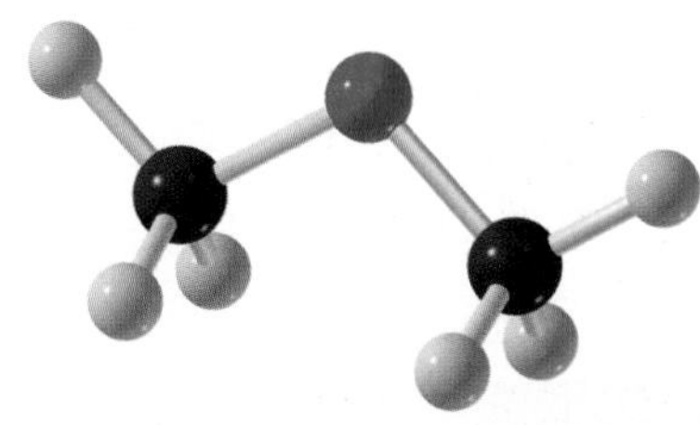

Figure 12.7 Ball-and-stick model of the ether methoxymethane (dimethyl ether).

In the common system of nomenclature, ethers are named by placing the names of the two alkyl groups attached to the ether oxygen as prefixes in front of the word *ether.* The names of the two groups can be placed either alphabetically or by size (smaller to larger), as seen in the following examples:

$CH_3{-}O{-}CH_3$	$CH_3{-}O{-}CH_2CH_3$	$CH_3CH_2{-}O{-}CH(CH_3)_2$
Dimethyl ether or methyl ether	Ethyl methyl ether or methyl ethyl ether	Ethyl isopropyl ether

EXAMPLE 12.9 Naming Ethers Using the Common Nomenclature System

Write the common name for each of the following ethers.

Solution

	$CH_3CH_2{-}O{-}CH_2CH_3$	$CH_3{-}O{-}CH_2CH_2CH_3$
Alkyl groups:	two ethyl groups	methyl and propyl
Name:	Diethyl ether	Methyl propyl ether

Notice that there is only one correct name for methyl propyl ether because the methyl group is smaller than the propyl group and it would be first in an alphabetical listing also.

LEARNING GOAL

11 Write names and draw structures for common ethers and discuss their use in medicine.

Practice Problem 12.9

Write the common name for each of the following ethers:

a. $CH_3CH_2{-}O{-}CH_2CH_2CH_3$
b. $CH_3{-}O{-}CH_2CH_2CH_3$
c. $CH_3CH_2{-}O{-}CH_2CH_2CH_2CH_2CH_3$
d. $CH_3CH_2CH_2CH_2{-}O{-}CH_2CH_2CH_3$

► For Further Practice: **Questions 12.86 and 12.88.**

Chemically, ethers are moderately inert. They do not react with reducing agents or bases under normal conditions. However, they are extremely volatile and highly flammable (easily oxidized in air) and hence must always be treated with great care.

Ethers may be prepared by a condensation reaction (removal of water) between two alcohol molecules, as shown in the following general reaction. The reaction requires heat and acid.

$$\underset{\text{Alcohol}}{R^1-OH} + \underset{\text{Alcohol}}{R^2-OH} \xrightarrow[\text{heat}]{H^+} \underset{\text{Ether}}{R^1-O-R^2} + \underset{\text{Water}}{H_2O}$$

EXAMPLE 12.10 Writing an Equation Representing the Synthesis of an Ether via a Condensation Reaction

LEARNING GOAL

12 Write equations representing the condensation reaction between two alcohol molecules to form an ether.

Write an equation showing the synthesis of dimethyl ether.

Solution

The alkyl substituents of this ether are two methyl groups. Thus, the alcohol that must undergo condensation to produce dimethyl ether is methanol.

$$\underset{\text{Methanol}}{CH_3OH} + \underset{\text{Methanol}}{CH_3OH} \xrightarrow[\text{heat}]{H^+} \underset{\text{Dimethyl ether}}{CH_3-O-CH_3} + \underset{\text{Water}}{H_2O}$$

Practice Problem 12.10

a. Write an equation showing the condensation reaction that would produce diethyl ether. Provide structures and names for all reactants and products.
b. Write an equation showing the condensation reaction between two molecules of 2-propanol. Provide structures and names for all reactants and products.

► For Further Practice: **Questions 12.83 and 12.84.**

Diethyl ether was the first general anesthetic used. The dentist Dr. William Morton is credited with its introduction in the 1800s. Diethyl ether functions as an anesthetic by interacting with the central nervous system. It appears that diethyl ether (and many other general anesthetics) functions by accumulating in the lipid material of the nerve cells, thereby interfering with nerve impulse transmission. This results in analgesia, a lessened perception of pain.

Halogenated ethers are also routinely used as general anesthetics (Figure 12.8). They are less flammable than diethyl ether and are therefore safer to store and work with. *Penthrane* and *Enthrane* (trade names) are two of the more commonly used members of this family:

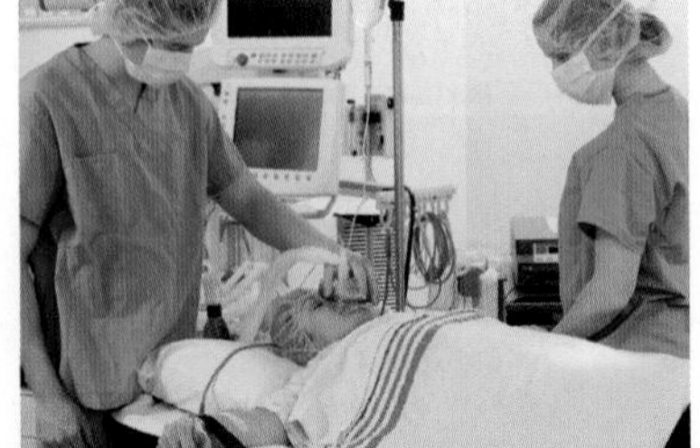

Figure 12.8 An anesthesiologist administers Penthrane to a surgical patient.

$$CH_3-O-\underset{F}{\overset{F}{C}}-\underset{Cl}{\overset{Cl}{C}}-H$$

Penthrane

$$H-\underset{F}{\overset{F}{C}}-O-\underset{F}{\overset{F}{C}}-\underset{Cl}{\overset{F}{C}}-H$$

Enthrane

Figure 12.9 This skunk on a bed of roses is surrounded by scent molecules. The two most common compounds in the defense spray of the striped skunk are the thiols *trans*-2-butene-1-thiol and 3-methyl-1-butanethiol. Two alcohols, 2-phenylethanol and geraniol, are the major components of the scent of roses.

Question 12.11 Why do ethers have much lower boiling points than alcohols?

Question 12.12 Describe the structure of ether molecules.

12.8 Thiols

Compounds that contain the sulfhydryl group (—SH) are called **thiols.** They are similar to alcohols in structure, but the sulfur atom replaces the oxygen atom.

Thiols and many other sulfur compounds have nauseating aromas. They are found in substances as different as the defense spray of the North American striped skunk, onions, and garlic. The structures of the two most common compounds in the defense spray of the striped skunk, *trans*-2-butene-1-thiol and 3-methyl-1-butanethiol, are seen in Figure 12.9. These structures are contrasted with the structures of the two molecules that make up the far more pleasant scent of roses: geraniol, an unsaturated alcohol, and 2-phenylethanol, an aromatic alcohol.

The IUPAC rules for naming thiols are similar to those for naming alcohols, except that the full name of the alkane is retained. The suffix *-thiol* follows the name of the parent compound.

LEARNING GOAL

13 Write names and draw structures for simple thiols and discuss their biological significance.

EXAMPLE 12.11 Naming Thiols Using the IUPAC Nomenclature System

LEARNING GOAL

13 Write names and draw structures for simple thiols and discuss their biological significance.

Write the IUPAC names for the thiols shown below.

Solution

Retain the full name of the parent compound and add the suffix *-thiol.*

	CH_3CH_2—SH	HS—CH_2CH_2—SH
Parent compound:	ethane	ethane
Position of —SH:	carbon-1	carbon-1 and carbon-2
Name:	Ethanethiol	1,2-Ethanedithiol

Continued...

$$\begin{array}{c}CH_3\\|\\CH_3CHCH_2CH_2\\|\\SH\end{array}\qquad\qquad\begin{array}{c}SH\\|\\CH_3CHCH_2CH_2CH_2\\|\\SH\end{array}$$

Parent compound:	butane	pentane
Position of —SH:	carbon-1	carbon-1 and carbon-4
Substituent:	3-methyl	
Name:	3-Methyl-1-butanethiol	1,4-Pentanedithiol

Practice Problem 12.11

Draw the structures of each of the following thiols.

a. 1,3-Butanedithiol
b. 2-Methyl-2-pentanethiol
c. 2-Chloro-2-propanethiol
d. Cyclopentanethiol

▸ For Further Practice: **Questions 12.93 and 12.94.**

Amino acids are the subunits from which proteins are made. A protein is a long polymer, or chain, of many amino acids bonded to one another.

The amino acid cysteine is a thiol that plays an important role in the structure and shape of many proteins. Two cysteine molecules can undergo oxidation to form cystine. The new bond formed is called a **disulfide** (—S—S—) bond.

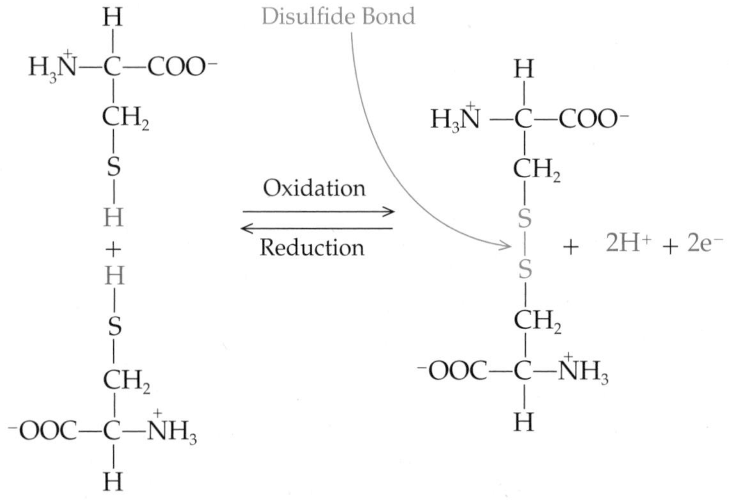

$$\begin{array}{c}H\\|\\H_3\overset{+}{N}—C—COO^-\\|\\CH_2\\|\\S\\|\\H\\+\\H\\|\\S\\|\\CH_2\\|\\{}^-OOC—C—\overset{+}{N}H_3\\|\\H\end{array}\quad\underset{\text{Reduction}}{\overset{\text{Oxidation}}{\rightleftarrows}}\quad\begin{array}{c}H\\|\\H_3\overset{+}{N}—C—COO^-\\|\\CH_2\\|\\S\\|\\S\\|\\CH_2\\|\\{}^-OOC—C—\overset{+}{N}H_3\\|\\H\end{array}+\ 2H^+ + 2e^-$$

Disulfide Bond

2 Cysteine Cystine

If the two cysteines are in different protein chains, the disulfide bond between them forms a bridge joining them together (Figure 12.10). If the two cysteines are in the same protein chain, a loop is formed. An example of the importance of disulfide bonds is seen in the production and structure of the protein hormone insulin, which controls blood sugar levels in the body. Insulin is initially produced as a protein called preproinsulin. Enzymatic removal of twenty-four amino acids and formation of disulfide bonds between cysteine amino acids produce proinsulin (Figure 12.10). Regions of the protein are identified as the A, B, and C chains. Notice that the A and B chains are covalently bonded to one another by two disulfide bonds. A third disulfide bond produces a hairpin loop in the A chain of the molecule. The molecule is now ready for the final stage of insulin synthesis in which the C chain is removed by the action of protein degrading enzymes (proteases). The active hormone, shown at the bottom of Figure 12.10, consists of the twenty-one amino acid A chain bonded to

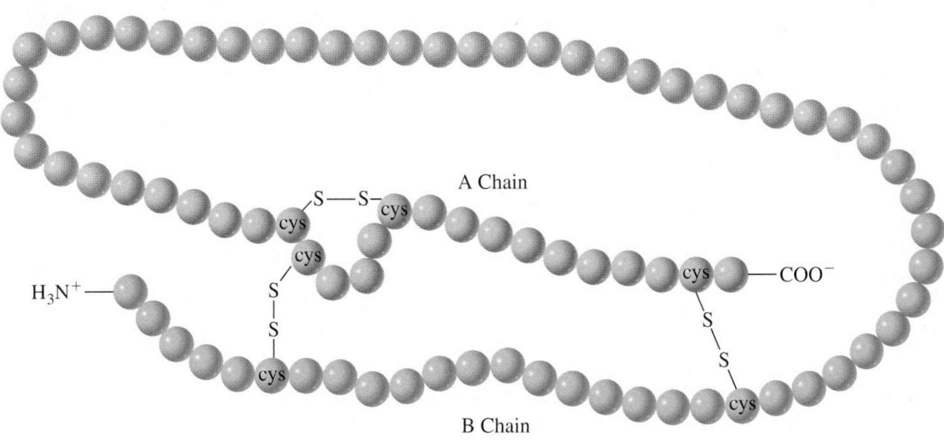

Preproinsulin

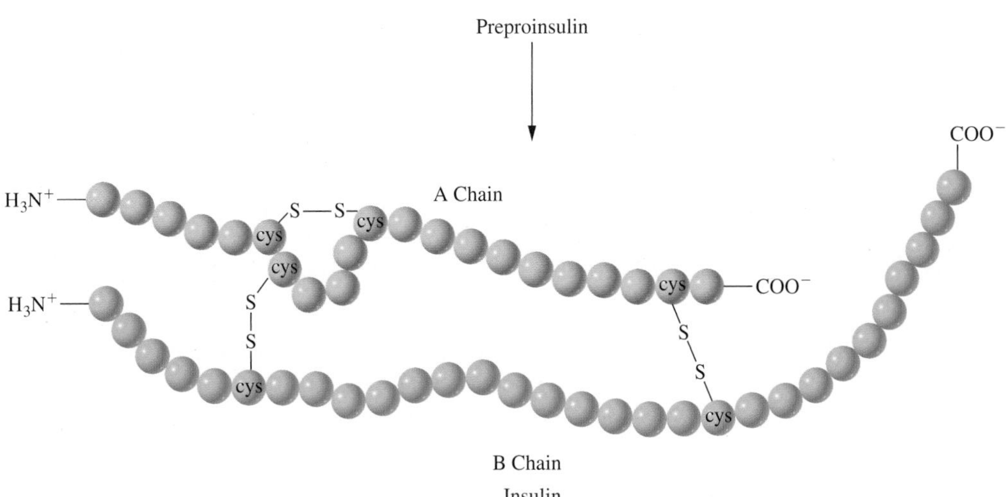

Insulin

Figure 12.10 Two steps in the synthesis of insulin. Disulfide bonds hold the A and B chains together and form a hairpin loop in the A chain.

the thirty amino acid B chain by two disulfide bonds. Without these disulfide bonds, functional insulin molecules could not exist because there would be no way to keep the two chains together in the proper shape.

British Anti-Lewisite (BAL) is a dithiol used as an antidote in mercury poisoning. It was originally developed as an antidote to a mustard gas–like chemical warfare agent called Lewisite, which was developed near the end of World War I and never used. By the onset of World War II, Lewisite was considered to be obsolete because of the discovery of BAL, an effective, inexpensive antidote. The two thiol groups of BAL form a water-soluble complex with mercury (or with the arsenic in Lewisite) that is excreted from the body in the urine.

$$\underset{\text{OH}}{\underset{|}{\text{CH}_2}}-\underset{\text{SH}}{\underset{|}{\text{CH}}}-\underset{\text{SH}}{\underset{|}{\text{CH}_2}}$$

BAL

Coenzyme A is a thiol that serves as a "carrier" of acetyl groups ($CH_3CO—$) in biochemical reactions. It plays a central role in metabolism by shuttling acetyl groups from one reaction to another. When the two-carbon acetate group is attached to coenzyme A, the product is acetyl coenzyme A (acetyl CoA). The bond between coenzyme A and the acetyl group is a high-energy *thioester bond.* In effect, formation of the high-energy thioester bond "energizes" the acetyl group so that it can participate in other biochemical reactions.

The reactions involving coenzyme A are discussed in detail in Chapters 21, 22, and 23.

A high-energy bond is one that releases a great deal of energy when it is broken.

KITCHEN CHEMISTRY

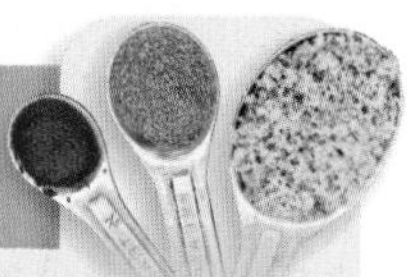

The Magic of Garlic

Chefs have known for centuries that whole roasted garlic cloves impart a sweet flavor to foods and can even be used to make ice cream! But if you chop or crush the clove of garlic before cooking, the flavors are entirely different, much stronger. The chemistry behind this difference was not understood until the 1940s, when two researchers from the Sandoz Company investigated the chemistry of garlic.

They found that the difference between whole cooked garlic cloves and crushed garlic lies in the presence of the compound alliin in certain cells of the garlic clove and the presence of the enzyme allinase in other cells. When the cells are crushed, the enzyme and its substrate are brought together, initiating a chain of chemical reactions that begins with the production of allicin and increases in complexity with time and further cooking. The chemistry becomes even more complex depending on the other ingredients used in the recipe. One set of compounds will form if the garlic is heated in water. Using butter or olive oil or milk will produce quite different products and, thus, quite different flavors in the food.

Some of the compounds produced in these reactions have strong biological activity. For instance, allicin is an antibiotic, having one-fiftieth the power of penicillin and one-tenth the activity of tetracycline. However, allicin is quickly broken down during cooking to produce a complex mixture of compounds that includes propenyl disulfide, which gives onions their aroma, and propenyl sulfenic acid, which causes tears when you cut into an onion. Also among these breakdown products is diallyl disulfide, which has been suggested to have anticancer properties and to be of benefit in reducing cholesterol levels.

For Further Understanding

- Design an experiment to test the suspected anticancer activity of diallyl disulfide.
- Explain why using a variety of ingredients, such as butter or olive oil, will result in different flavors and aromas in the food that is prepared.

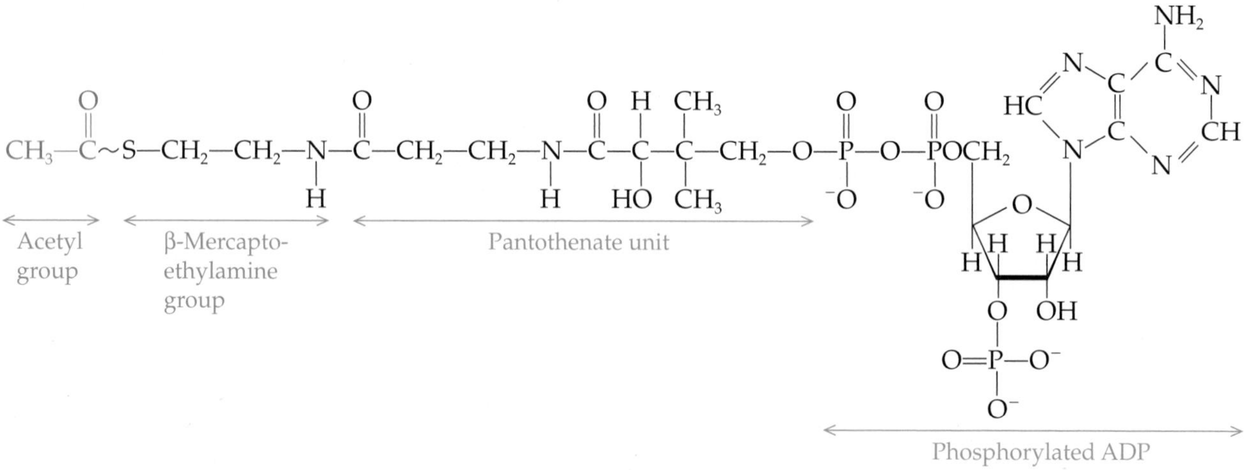

Acetyl group

β-Mercapto-ethylamine group

Pantothenate unit

Phosphorylated ADP

Acetyl coenzyme A
(acetyl CoA)

Acetyl CoA is made and used in the energy-producing reactions that provide most of the energy for life processes. It is also required for the biosynthesis of many biological molecules.

CHAPTER MAP

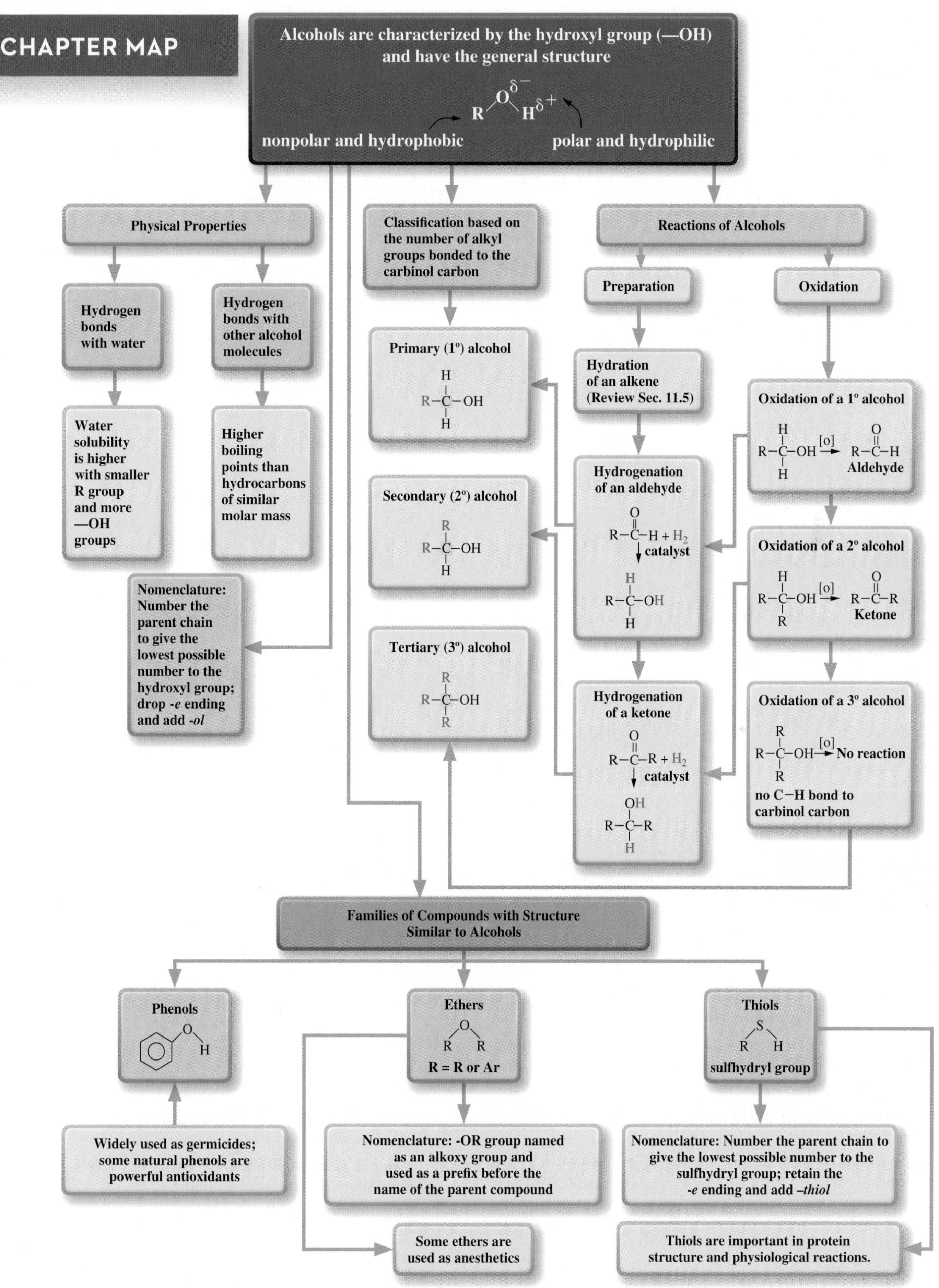

Alcohols are characterized by the hydroxyl group (—OH) and have the general structure
R O H δ− δ+
nonpolar and hydrophobic
polar and hydrophilic
Physical Properties
Hydrogen bonds with water
Hydrogen bonds with other alcohol molecules
Water solubility is higher with smaller R group and more —OH groups
Higher boiling points than hydrocarbons of similar molar mass
Nomenclature: Number the parent chain to give the lowest possible number to the hydroxyl group; drop -e ending and add -ol
Classification based on the number of alkyl groups bonded to the carbinol carbon
Primary (1°) alcohol
Secondary (2°) alcohol
Tertiary (3°) alcohol
Reactions of Alcohols
Preparation
Oxidation
Hydration of an alkene (Review Sec. 11.5)
Hydrogenation of an aldehyde
catalyst
Hydrogenation of a ketone
catalyst
Oxidation of a 1° alcohol
Aldehyde
Oxidation of a 2° alcohol
Ketone
Oxidation of a 3° alcohol
No reaction
no C−H bond to carbinol carbon
Families of Compounds with Structure Similar to Alcohols
Phenols
Ethers
R = R or Ar
Thiols
sulfhydryl group
Widely used as germicides; some natural phenols are powerful antioxidants
Nomenclature: -OR group named as an alkoxy group and used as a prefix before the name of the parent compound
Nomenclature: Number the parent chain to give the lowest possible number to the sulfhydryl group; retain the -e ending and add -thiol
Some ethers are used as anesthetics
Thiols are important in protein structure and physiological reactions.

SUMMARY OF REACTIONS

Preparation of Alcohols

Hydration of alkenes:

$$\underset{\text{Alkene}}{R_2C{=}CR_2} + \underset{\text{Water}}{H{-}OH} \xrightarrow{H^+} \underset{\text{Alcohol}}{R{-}CR_2{-}C(OH)R{-}H}$$

Reduction of an aldehyde or ketone:

$$\underset{\text{Aldehyde or ketone}}{R^1{-}C(=O){-}R^2} + \underset{\text{Hydrogen}}{H{-}H} \xrightarrow{\text{Catalyst}} \underset{\text{Alcohol}}{R^1{-}CH(OH){-}R^2}$$

Dehydration of Alcohols

$$\underset{\text{Alcohol}}{R{-}CH_2{-}CH(OH){-}H} \xrightarrow{H^+,\ \text{heat}} \underset{\text{Alkene}}{R{-}CH{=}CH_2} + \underset{\text{Water}}{HOH}$$

Oxidation Reactions

Oxidation of a primary alcohol:

$$\underset{1°\ \text{Alcohol}}{R^1{-}CH_2{-}OH} \xrightarrow{[O]} \underset{\text{An aldehyde}}{R^1{-}C(=O){-}H}$$

Oxidation of a secondary alcohol:

$$\underset{2°\ \text{Alcohol}}{R^1{-}CH(OH){-}R^2} \xrightarrow{[O]} \underset{\text{A ketone}}{R^1{-}C(=O){-}R^2}$$

Oxidation of a tertiary alcohol:

$$\underset{3°\ \text{Alcohol}}{R^1{-}C(OH)(R^2){-}R^3} \xrightarrow{[O]} \text{No reaction}$$

Condensation Synthesis of an Ether

$$\underset{\text{Alcohol}}{R^1{-}OH} + \underset{\text{Alcohol}}{R^2{-}OH} \xrightarrow[\text{heat}]{H^+} \underset{\text{Ether}}{R^1{-}O{-}R^2} + \underset{\text{Water}}{H_2O}$$

SUMMARY

12.1 Alcohols: Structure and Physical Properties

- **Alcohols** are characterized by the **hydroxyl group (—OH).**
- Alcohols have the general structure R—OH.
- Alcohols are classified as primary, secondary, or tertiary depending on the number of alkyl groups attached to the **carbinol carbon.**
- A **primary alcohol** has one alkyl group attached to the carbinol carbon.
- A **secondary alcohol** has two alkyl groups attached to the carbinol carbon.
- A **tertiary alcohol** has three alkyl groups attached to the carbinol carbon.
- They are very polar because the hydroxyl group is polar.
- Alcohols form intermolecular hydrogen bonds and as a result have higher boiling points than hydrocarbons of comparable molar mass.
- Smaller alcohols are very water-soluble.

12.2 Alcohols: Nomenclature

- In the IUPAC system, alcohols are named by determining the **parent compound** and replacing the *-e* ending with *-ol.*
- The parent chain is numbered to give the hydroxyl group the lowest possible number.
- Common names are derived from the alkyl group corresponding to the parent compound.

12.3 Medically Important Alcohols

- Methanol is a toxic alcohol that is used as a solvent.
- Ethanol is the alcohol consumed in beer, wine, and distilled liquors. It is produced by the alcohol **fermentation** of sugars.
- Isopropanol is used as a an antiseptic.
- Ethylene glycol (1,2-ethanediol) is used as antifreeze.
- Glycerol (1,2,3-propanetriol) is used in cosmetics and pharmaceuticals.

12.4 Reactions Involving Alcohols

- Alcohols can be prepared by the **hydration** of alkenes or the **reduction** of aldehydes and ketones.
- Alcohols can undergo **dehydration** to produce alkenes.
- Dehydration is an example of an **elimination reaction,** that is, one in which a molecule loses atoms or ions from its structure.
- **Zaitsev's rule** states that in an elimination reaction, such as the dehydration of an alcohol, the alkene with the greatest number of alkyl groups on the double-bonded carbons (the more highly substituted alkene) will be the major product in the reaction.
- Primary and secondary alcohols can undergo **oxidation** reactions to yield aldehydes and ketones, respectively.
- Tertiary alcohols do not undergo oxidation.

12.5 Oxidation and Reduction in Living Systems

- In organic and biological systems, **oxidation** involves the gain of oxygen or the loss of hydrogen and **reduction** involves the loss of oxygen or the gain of hydrogen.
- Nicotinamide adenine dinucleotide, NAD^+, is a coenzyme involved in many biological oxidation and reduction reactions.

12.6 Phenols

- **Phenols** are compounds in which the hydroxyl group is attached to a benzene ring.
- Phenols have the general structure Ar—OH.
- Many phenols are important as antiseptics and disinfectants.

12.7 Ethers

- **Ethers** are characterized by the R—O—R functional group.
- Ethers are generally nonreactive but are extremely flammable.
- Diethyl ether was the first general anesthetic used in medical practice.
- Penthrane and enthrane, which are much less flammable, have replaced the use of diethyl ether.

12.8 Thiols

- **Thiols** are characterized by the sulfhydryl group (—SH).
- The amino acid cysteine is a thiol that is extremely important for maintaining the correct shapes of proteins by forming **disulfide bonds** with other cysteine molecules within the same or another protein.
- Coenzyme A is a thiol that serves as a "carrier" of acetyl groups in important biological reactions.

ANSWERS TO PRACTICE PROBLEMS

12.1 a. Primary alcohol
b. Secondary alcohol
c. Tertiary alcohol
d. Aromatic alcohol (phenol)
e. Secondary alcohol

12.2 a. 4-Methyl-1-pentanol
b. 4-Methyl-2-hexanol
c. 1,2,3-Propanetriol
d. 4-Chloro-3-methyl-1-hexanol

12.3 $CH_3CH_2CH_2C(=O)H + H_2 \longrightarrow CH_3CH_2CH_2CH_2OH$

12.4 $CH_3CH_2C(=O)CH_3 + H_2 \longrightarrow CH_3CH_2CH(OH)CH_3$

12.5 a. $CH_3CH_2OH \xrightarrow{H^+,\ heat} CH_2{=}CH_2 + H_2O$

b. $CH_3CHOHCH_3 \xrightarrow{H^+,\ heat} CH_3CH{=}CH_2 + H_2O$

c. There are two possible products

$CH_3CH_2CH(OH)CH(CH_3)CH_2CH_3 \xrightarrow{H^+,\ heat} CH_3CH_2C(CH_3){=}CHCH_2CH_3 + H_2O$

$CH_3CH_2CH(OH)CH(CH_3)CH_2CH_3 \xrightarrow{H^+,\ heat} CH_3CH_2CH(CH_3)CH{=}CHCH_3$

d. $CH_3C(OH)(CH_3)CH_3 \xrightarrow{H^+heat} CH_2{=}C(CH_3)CH_3 + H_2O$

12.6 a. $CH_3C(CH_3)_2CH_2CH_2OH \xrightarrow{[O]} CH_3C(CH_3)_2CH_2C(=O)H$

b. $CH_3CH_2OH \xrightarrow{[O]} CH_3C(=O)H$

12.7 a. 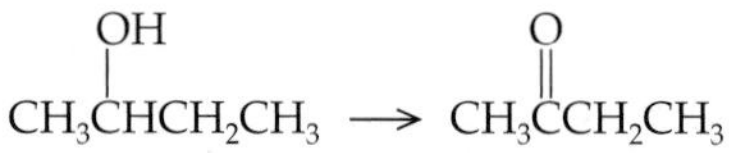 $CH_3CH(OH)CH_2CH_3 \rightarrow CH_3C(=O)CH_2CH_3$

b. 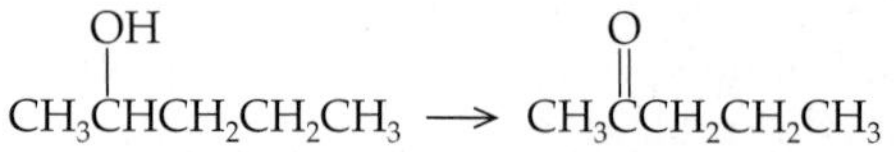 $CH_3CH(OH)CH_2CH_2CH_3 \rightarrow CH_3C(=O)CH_2CH_2CH_3$

12.8 a. 1-Ethoxypropane c. 1-Ethoxypentane
b. 1-Methoxypropane d. 1-Propoxybutane

12.9 a. Ethyl propyl ether c. Ethyl pentyl ether
b. Methyl propyl ether d. Propyl butyl ether

12.10

a.

$$CH_3CH_2OH + CH_3CH_2OH \xrightarrow[\text{heat}]{H^+} CH_3CH_2{-}O{-}CH_2CH_3 + H_2O$$

Ethanol Diethyl ether Water

b.

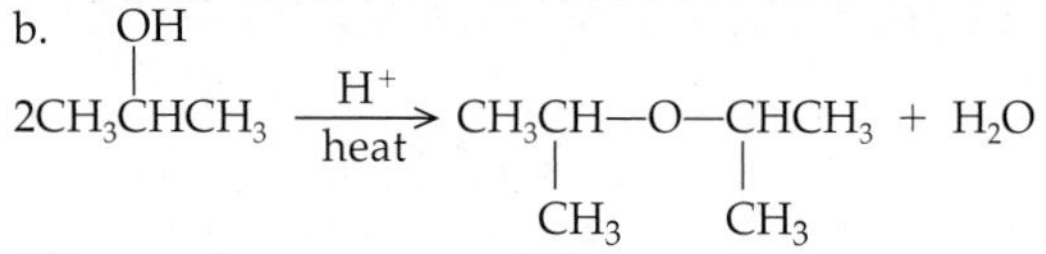

$$2CH_3CH(OH)CH_3 \xrightarrow[\text{heat}]{H^+} CH_3CH(CH_3){-}O{-}CH(CH_3)CH_3 + H_2O$$

2-Propanol Diisopropyl ether

12.11 a. 1,3-Butanedithiol

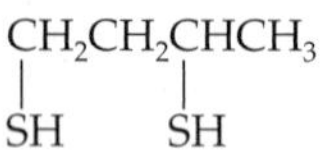

$CH_2(SH)CH_2CH(SH)CH_3$

b. 2-Methyl-2-pentanethiol

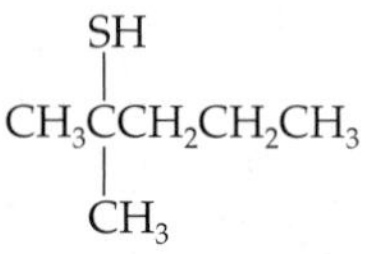

$CH_3C(SH)(CH_3)CH_2CH_2CH_3$

c. 2-Chloro-2-propanethiol

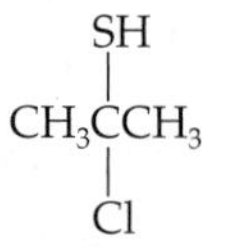

$CH_3C(SH)(Cl)CH_3$

d. Cyclopentanethiol

SH

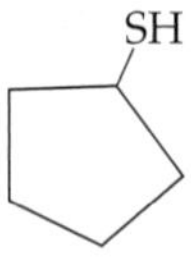

QUESTIONS AND PROBLEMS

Alcohols: Structure and Physical Properties

Foundations

12.13 Describe the relationship between the water solubility of alcohols and their hydrocarbon chain length.

12.14 Explain the relationship between the water solubility of alcohols and the number of hydroxyl groups in the molecule.

12.15 Define the term *carbinol carbon.*

12.16 Define the terms *primary, secondary,* and *tertiary alcohol,* and draw a general structure for each.

Applications

12.17 Classify each of the following as a 1°, 2°, or 3° alcohol:
a. 3-Methyl-1-butanol **d.** 1-Methylcyclopentanol
b. 2-Methylcyclopentanol **e.** 2-Methyl-2-pentanol
c. *t*-Butyl alcohol

12.18 1-Heptanol has a pleasant aroma and is sometimes used in cosmetics to enhance the fragrance. Draw the condensed formula for 1-heptanol. Is this a primary, secondary, or tertiary alcohol?

12.19 Classify each of the following as a 1°, 2°, or 3° alcohol:
a. $CH_3CH_2CH_2CH_2CH_2CH_2CH_2OH$
b. 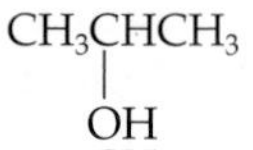 $CH_3CH(OH)CH_3$
c. 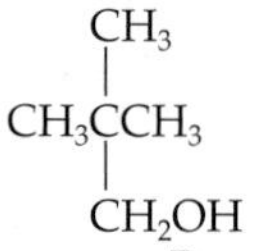 $CH_3C(CH_3)(CH_2OH)CH_3$
d.  $CH_3CH_2CH(Br)CH_2CH_2CH_2OH$
e. 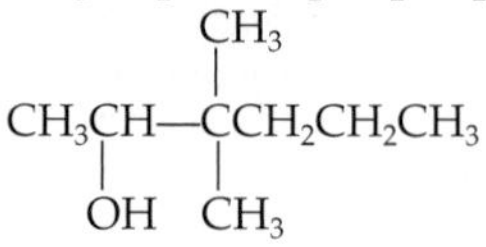 $CH_3CH(OH){-}C(CH_3)(CH_3)CH_2CH_2CH_3$

12.20 Classify each of the following as a primary, secondary, or tertiary alcohol:
a. 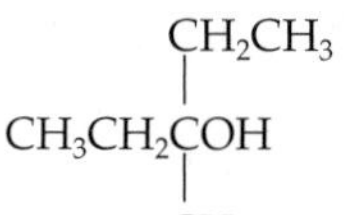 $CH_3CH_2C(CH_2CH_3)(CH_3)OH$
b. 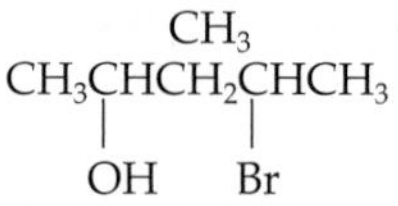 $CH_3CH(OH)CH_2CH(Br)CH_3$
c. $CH_3CH_2CH_2OH$
d. 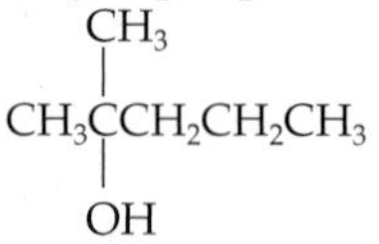 $CH_3C(CH_3)(OH)CH_2CH_2CH_3$

12.21 Stingless bees use complex systems to communicate. One aspect of this communication is chemical: the bees produce 2-nonanol, 2-heptanol, and 2-undecanol in their mouthparts (mandibles) to direct other bees to pollen sources. Draw the condensed structure of each of these alcohols. Classify each as a primary, secondary, or tertiary alcohol.

12.22 Classify each of the following as a primary, secondary, or tertiary alcohol:
a. 2-Methyl-2-butanol
b. 1,2-Dimethylcyclohexanol
c. 2,3,4-Trimethylcyclopentanol
d. 3,3-Dimethyl-2-pentanol

12.23 Arrange the following compounds in order of increasing boiling point, beginning with the lowest:

a. $CH_3CH_2CH_2CH_2CH_3$

b. $CH_3CHCH_2CHCH_3$
OH OH

c. $CH_3CHCH_2CH_2CH_3$
OH

d. $CH_3CH_2CH_2—O—CH_2CH_3$

12.24 Why do alcohols have higher boiling points than alkanes?

12.25 Which member of each of the following pairs is more soluble in water?

a. CH_3CH_2OH or $CH_3CH_2CH_2CH_2OH$

b. $CH_3CH_2CH_2CH_2CH_3$ or $CH_3CH_2CH_2CH_2OH$

c. [cyclopentane ring with OH] or CH_3CHCH_3
OH

12.26 Arrange the three alcohols in each of the following sets in order of increasing solubility in water:

a. $CH_3CH_2CH_2CH_2CH_2OH$ $CH_3CHCH_2CHCH_2CH_3$
OH OH

$CH_3CHCH_2CHCH_2CH_2OH$
OH OH

b. Pentyl alcohol 1-Hexanol Ethylene glycol

Alcohols: Nomenclature

Foundations

12.27 Briefly describe the IUPAC rules for naming alcohols.

12.28 Briefly describe the rules for determining the common names for alcohols.

Applications

12.29 Give the IUPAC name for each of the following compounds:

a. $CH_3CH_2CH(OH)CH_2CH_2CH_2OH$

b. $CH_3CH(OH)CH(OH)CH_2CH_3$

c. $CH_3CH(CH_3)CH(OH)CH_2CH_3$

12.30 Give the IUPAC name for each of the following compounds:

a. $CH_3C(CH_2CH_3)_2CH(CH_3)CH_2CH_2CH_2OH$

b. $CH_3CH_2CH(OH)CH_2CH_2CH_3$

c. $CH_3CH_2CHClCHBrCH_2CH_2OH$

12.31 Draw each of the following, using complete structural formulas and line formulas:

a. 2-Pentanol

b. 1,2,4-Heptanetriol

c. 2-Methylcyclopentanol

12.32 Draw each of the following, using condensed formulas and line formulas:

a. 3-Methyl-4-ethyl-3-hexanol

b. 1-Bromo-2-methyl-3-pentanol

c. 2,4-Dimethylcyclohexanol

12.33 Give the IUPAC name for each of the following compounds:

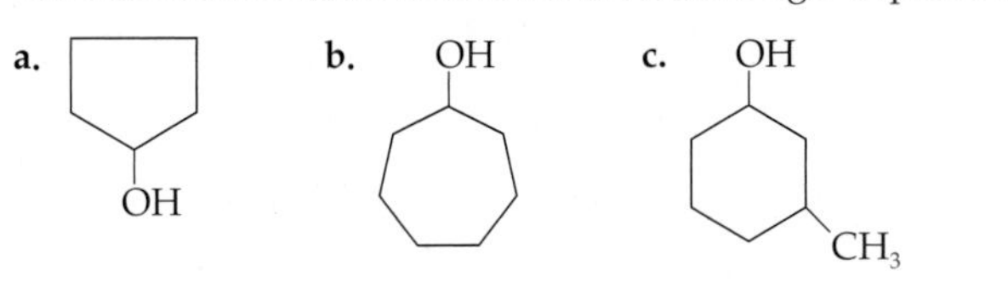

12.34 Draw each of the following alcohols:

a. 1-Iodo-2-butanol

b. 1,2-Butanediol

c. Cyclobutanol

12.35 Give the common name for each of the following compounds:

a. CH_3OH

b. CH_3CH_2OH

c. $CH_2—CH_2$
OH OH

d. $CH_3CH_2CH_2OH$

12.36 Draw the structure of each of the following compounds:

a. Pentyl alcohol

b. Isopropyl alcohol

c. Octyl alcohol

d. Propyl alcohol

12.37 Draw a condensed formula for each of the following compounds:

a. 4-Methyl-2-hexanol

b. Isobutyl alcohol

c. 1,5-Pentanediol

d. 2-Nonanol

e. 1,3,5-Cyclohexanetriol

12.38 Name each of the following alcohols using the IUPAC Nomenclature System:

a. [cyclohexane ring with OH and CH_3 on adjacent carbons]

b. [cyclobutane ring with OH and Br]

c. $CH_3CHCH_2CHCH_2CHCH_3$
OH OH OH

d. $CH_3CH_2CHCHCHCH_3$
(OH above the first CH; OH below each of the second and third CH)

Medically Important Alcohols

12.39 What is denatured alcohol? Why is alcohol denatured?

12.40 What are the principal uses of methanol, ethanol, and isopropyl alcohol?

12.41 What is fermentation?

12.42 Why do wines typically have an alcohol concentration of 12–13%?

12.43 Why must fermentation products be distilled to produce liquors such as scotch?

12.44 If a bottle of distilled alcoholic spirits—for example, scotch whiskey—is labeled as 80 proof, what is the percentage of alcohol in the scotch?

Reactions Involving Alcohols

Foundations

12.45 Write a general equation representing the preparation of an alcohol by hydration of an alkene.

12.46 Write a general equation representing the preparation of an alcohol by hydrogenation of an aldehyde or a ketone.

12.47 Write a general equation representing the dehydration of an alcohol.

12.48 Write a general equation representing the oxidation of a 1° alcohol.

12.49 Write a general equation representing the oxidation of a 2° alcohol.

12.50 Write a general equation representing the oxidation of a 3° alcohol.

Applications

12.51 Predict the products formed by the hydration of the following alkenes:

a. 1-Hexene
b. 2-Hexene
c. 2-Methyl-3-hexene
d. 2,2-Dimethyl-3-heptene

12.52 Draw the alkene products of the dehydration of the following alcohols:

a. 2-Butanol
b. 1-Butanol
c. 2-Propanol
d. 4-Bromo-2-hexanol

12.53 Write an equation showing the hydration of each of the following alkenes. Name each of the products using the IUPAC Nomenclature System.

a. 2-Hexene
b. Cyclopentene
c. 1-Octene
d. 1-Methylcyclohexene

12.54 Write an equation showing the dehydration of each of the following alcohols. Name each of the reactants and products using the IUPAC Nomenclature System.

a. $CH_3\underset{\displaystyle OH}{\underset{|}{C}}HCH_2CH_3$

b. 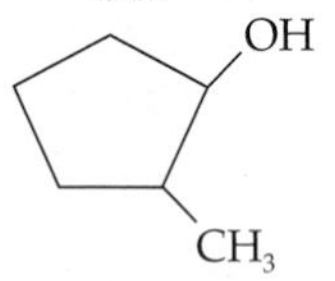 (cyclopentane ring bearing OH and CH_3 on adjacent carbons)

12.55 What product(s) would result from the oxidation of each of the following alcohols with, for example, potassium permanganate? If no reaction occurs, write N.R.

a. 2-Butanol
b. 2-Methyl-2-hexanol
c. Cyclohexanol
d. 1-Methyl-1-cyclopentanol

12.56 We have seen that ethanol is metabolized to ethanal (acetaldehyde) in the liver. What would be the product formed, under the same conditions, from each of the following alcohols?

a. CH_3OH
b. $CH_3CH_2CH_2OH$
c. $CH_3CH_2CH_2CH_2OH$

12.57 Using the IUPAC system, name each of the following alcohols and the product formed when it is oxidized. If no reaction occurs, write N.R.

a. $CH_3CH_2\overset{\displaystyle OH}{\overset{|}{C}}HCH_2CH_3$

b. $CH_3CH_2CH_2OH$

c. $CH_3\overset{\displaystyle OH}{\overset{|}{C}}HCH_2\overset{\displaystyle CH_3}{\overset{|}{C}}HCH_3$

d. $CH_3\overset{\displaystyle OH}{\overset{|}{\underset{\displaystyle CH_3}{\underset{|}{C}}}}CH_2CH_3$

e. 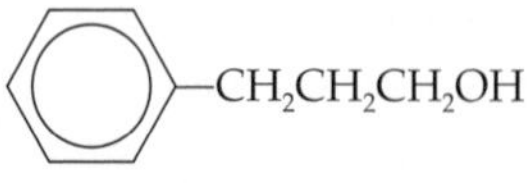 C_6H_5—$CH_2CH_2CH_2OH$ (benzene ring)

12.58 Write an equation demonstrating each of the following chemical transformations:

a. Oxidation of an alcohol to an aldehyde
b. Oxidation of an alcohol to a ketone
c. Dehydration of a cyclic alcohol to a cycloalkene
d. Hydrogenation of an alkene to an alkane

12.59 Write the reaction, occurring in the liver, that causes the oxidation of ethanol. What is the product of this reaction and what symptoms are caused by the product?

12.60 Write the reaction, occurring in the liver, that causes the oxidation of methanol. What is the product of this reaction and what is the possible result of the accumulation of the product in the body?

12.61 Write an equation for the preparation of 2-butanol from 1-butene. What type of reaction is involved?

12.62 Write a general equation for the preparation of an alcohol from an aldehyde or ketone. What type of reaction is involved?

12.63 Show how acetone can be prepared from propene.

$$CH_3\overset{\displaystyle O}{\overset{\|}{C}}CH_3$$
Acetone

12.64 Give the oxidation product for cholesterol.

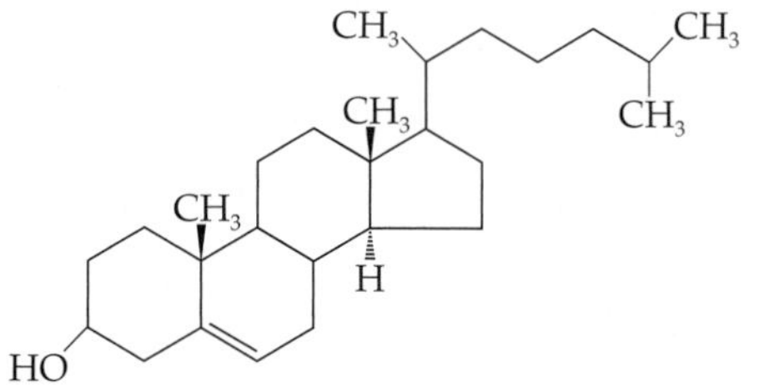

Cholesterol

12.65 Write a balanced equation for the hydrogenation of each of the following:

a. Hexanal (a six-carbon aldehyde)
b. 2-Hexanone (a six-carbon ketone)
c. 2-Methylbutanal (an aldehyde with a four-carbon parent chain)
d. 6-Ethyl-2-octanone (a ketone with an eight-carbon parent chain)

12.66 Write a balanced equation for the hydrogenation of each of the following:

a. Propanal (a three-carbon aldehyde)
b. Propanone (a three-carbon ketone)
c. 2,3-Dimethylheptanal (an aldehyde with a seven-carbon parent chain)
d. 3-Methyl-4-heptanone (a ketone with a seven-carbon parent chain)

Oxidation and Reduction in Living Systems

Foundations

12.67 Define the terms *oxidation* and *reduction.*

12.68 How do we recognize oxidation and reduction in organic compounds?

Applications

12.69 Arrange the following compounds from the most reduced to the most oxidized:

$CH_3CH_2\overset{\displaystyle O}{\overset{\|}{C}}—OH$ $\qquad$ $CH_3CH_2CH_3$

$CH_3CH_2\overset{\displaystyle O}{\overset{\|}{C}}—H$ $\qquad$ $CH_3CH_2CH_2OH$

12.70 What is the role of the coenzyme nicotinamide adenine dinucleotide (NAD^+) in enzyme-catalyzed oxidation-reduction reactions?

Phenols

Foundations

12.71 What are phenols?

12.72 Describe the water solubility of phenols.

Applications

12.73 2,4,6-Trinitrophenol is known by the common name *picric acid.* Picric acid is a solid but is readily soluble in water. In solution it is used as a biological tissue stain. As a solid, it is also known to be unstable and may explode. In this way it is similar to 2,4,6-trinitrotoluene (TNT). Draw the structures of picric acid and TNT. Why is picric acid readily soluble in water whereas TNT is not?

12.74 Name the following aromatic compounds using the IUPAC system:

a. 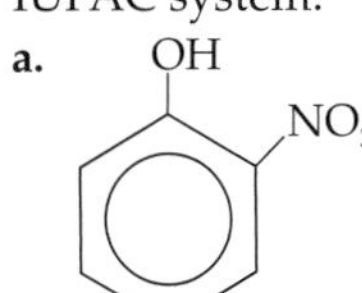

c. 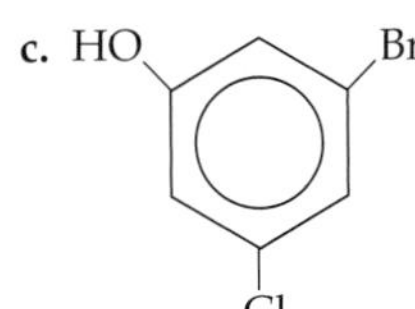

b. 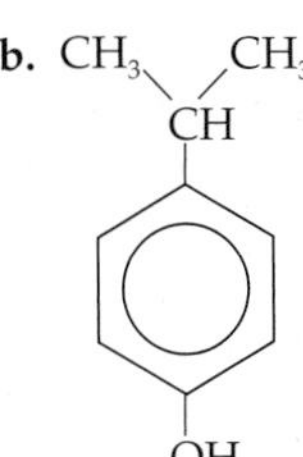

d. (benzene ring with OH, CH_3, Br)

12.75 List some phenol compounds that are commonly used as antiseptics or disinfectants.

12.76 Why must a dilute solution of phenol be used for disinfecting environmental surfaces?

Ethers

Foundations

12.77 Describe the physical properties of ethers.

12.78 Compare the water solubility of ethers and alcohols.

Applications

12.79 Draw all of the alcohols and ethers of molecular formula $C_4H_{10}O$.

12.80 Name each of the isomers drawn for Question 12.79.

12.81 Give the IUPAC names for Penthrane and Enthrane (see Section 12.7).

12.82 Why have Penthrane and Enthrane replaced diethyl ether as a general anesthetic?

12.83 Ethers may be prepared by the removal of water (condensation) between two alcohols, as shown. Give the structure(s) of the ethers formed by the reaction of the following alcohol(s) under acidic conditions with heat. Provide the IUPAC and common names of each reactant and product.

Example: $CH_3OH + HOCH_3 \xrightarrow[\text{Heat}]{H^+} CH_3OCH_3 + H_2O$

a. $2CH_3CH_2OH \longrightarrow ?$

b. $CH_3OH + CH_3CH_2OH \longrightarrow ?$

c. $(CH_3)_2CHOH + CH_3OH \longrightarrow ?$

d. 2 (cyclopentyl)$-CH_2OH \longrightarrow ?$

12.84 Write an equation showing the condensation reaction that would produce each of the following ethers:

a. Diethyl ether b. Ethyl propyl ether

c. Dibutyl ether d. Heptyl hexyl ether

12.85 Name each of the following ethers using the IUPAC Nomenclature System:

a. $CH_3CHCH_2CH_2CH_3$ with OCH_2CH_3 on C-2

b. $CH_3CH_2CHCH_3$ with OCH_3 on C-3

c. $CH_3CH_2CH_2CH_2$ with OCH_2CH_3 on terminal carbon

d. (cyclopentyl)$-OCH_3$

12.86 Provide the common names for each of the following ethers:

a. $CH_3CH_2{-}O{-}CH_2CH_2CH_3$

b. $CH_3{-}O{-}CH_2CH_2CH_2CH_2CH_2CH_2CH_3$

c. $CH_3CH_2CH_2CH_2{-}O{-}CH_2CH_2CH_2CH_3$

d. $CH_3CH_2{-}O{-}CH_2CH_2CH_2CH_2CH_2CH_3$

12.87 Draw the structural formula and line formula for each of the following ethers:

a. Dibutyl ether c. Propyl pentyl ether

b. Ethyl heptyl ether d. *t*-Butyl hexyl ether

12.88 Write the IUPAC and common name for each of the following ethers:

a. $CH_3CH_2{-}O{-}CH_2CH_2CH_2CH_3$

b. $CH_3{-}O{-}CH_2CH_2CH_2CH_2CH_3$

c. $CH_3CH_2CH_2{-}O{-}CH_2CH_2CH_2CH_3$

d. $CH_3CH_2{-}O{-}CH_2CH_2CH_2CH_2CH_3$

Thiols

Foundations

12.89 Compare the structure of thiols and alcohols.

12.90 Describe the IUPAC rules for naming thiols.

Applications

12.91 Cystine is an amino acid formed from the oxidation of two cysteine molecules to form a disulfide bond. The molecular formula of cystine is $C_6H_{12}O_4N_2S_2$. Draw the structural formula of cystine. (*Hint:* For the structure of cysteine, see page 428.)

12.92 Explain the way in which British Anti-Lewisite acts as an antidote for mercury poisoning.

12.93 Give the IUPAC name for each of the following thiols.

a. $CH_3CH_2CH_2{-}SH$

b. $CH_3CHCH_2CH_3$ with SH on C-2

c. CH_3CCH_3 with CH_2CH_3 and SH on the central carbon

d. HS$-$(cyclohexane)$-$SH

12.94 Give the IUPAC name for each of the following thiols.

a.  CH_2CHCH_3 with SH on C1 and C2 (SH SH)

b. 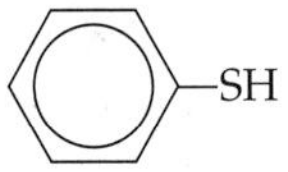 benzene ring–SH

c. 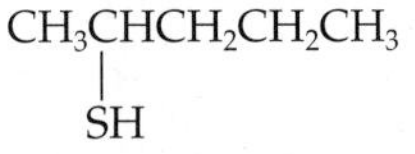 $CH_3CHCH_2CH_2CH_3$ with SH on C2

d. $CH_3CH_2CH_2CH_2CH_2CH_2CH_2SH$

CRITICAL THINKING PROBLEMS

1. You are provided with two solvents: water (H_2O) and hexane ($CH_3CH_2CH_2CH_2CH_2CH_3$). You are also provided with two biological molecules whose structures are shown here:

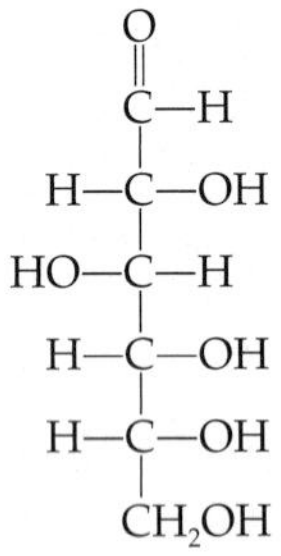

$$\begin{array}{c} O \\ \| \\ C{-}H \\ | \\ H{-}C{-}OH \\ | \\ HO{-}C{-}H \\ | \\ H{-}C{-}OH \\ | \\ H{-}C{-}OH \\ | \\ CH_2OH \end{array}$$

$$\begin{array}{l} H \quad\; O \\ | \quad\;\; \| \\ H{-}C{-}O{-}C{-}CH_2CH_2CH_2CH_2CH_2CH_2CH_2CH_2CH_2CH_2CH_2CH_2CH_2CH_2CH_3 \\ | \qquad\;\; O \\ | \qquad\;\; \| \\ H{-}C{-}O{-}C{-}CH_2CH_2CH_2CH_2CH_2CH_2CH_2CH_2CH_2CH_2CH_2CH_2CH_2CH_2CH_3 \\ | \qquad\;\; O \\ | \qquad\;\; \| \\ H{-}C{-}O{-}C{-}CH_2CH_2CH_2CH_2CH_2CH_2CH_2CH_2CH_2CH_2CH_2CH_2CH_2CH_2CH_3 \\ | \\ H \end{array}$$

Predict which biological molecule would be more soluble in water and which would be more soluble in hexane. Defend your prediction. Design a careful experiment to test your hypothesis.

Consider the digestion of dietary molecules in the digestive tract. Which of the two biological molecules shown in this problem would be more easily digested under the conditions present in the digestive tract?

2. Cholesterol is an alcohol and a steroid (Chapter 17). Diets that contain large amounts of cholesterol have been linked to heart disease and atherosclerosis, hardening of the arteries. The narrowing of the artery, caused by plaque buildup, is very apparent. Cholesterol is directly involved in this buildup. Describe the various functional groups and principal structural features of the cholesterol molecule. Would you use a polar or nonpolar solvent to dissolve cholesterol? Explain your reasoning.

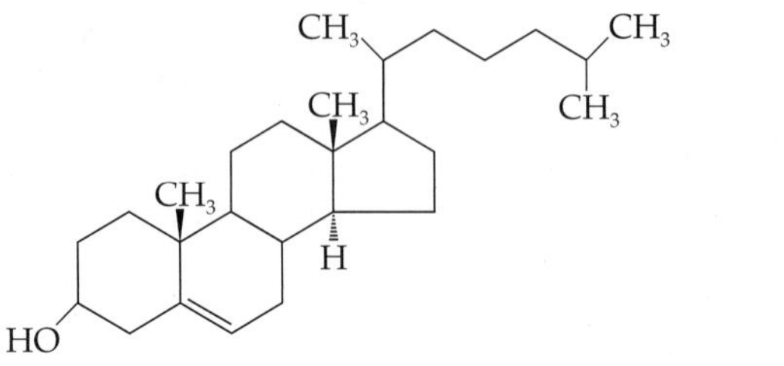

[Structure: cholesterol skeleton with labels CH$_3$, CH$_3$, CH$_3$, CH$_3$, CH$_3$, H, HO]

Cholesterol

3. An unknown compound A is known to be an alcohol with the molecular formula $C_4H_{10}O$. When dehydrated, compound A gave only one alkene product, C_4H_8, compound B. Compound A could not be oxidized. What are the identities of compound A and compound B?

4. Sulfides are the sulfur analogs of ethers, that is, ethers in which oxygen has been substituted by a sulfur atom. They are named in an analogous manner to the ethers with the term *sulfide* replacing *ether*. For example, $CH_3{-}S{-}CH_3$ is dimethyl sulfide. Draw the sulfides that correspond to the following ethers and name them:
   a. diethyl ether
   b. methyl propyl ether
   c. dibutyl ether
   d. ethyl phenyl ether

5. Dimethyl sulfoxide (DMSO) has been used by many sports enthusiasts as a linament for sore joints; it acts as an anti-inflammatory agent and a mild analgesic (pain killer). However, it is no longer recommended for this purpose because it carries toxic impurities into the blood. DMSO is a sulfoxide—it contains the S=O functional group. DMSO is prepared from dimethyl sulfide by mild oxidation, and it has the molecular formula C_2H_6SO. Draw the structure of DMSO.

13

Aldehydes and Ketones

Cinnamon Sticks.

LEARNING GOALS

1. Draw the structures and discuss the physical properties of aldehydes and ketones.
2. From the structures, write the common and IUPAC names of aldehydes and ketones.
3. List several aldehydes and ketones that are of natural, commercial, health, and environmental interest and describe their significance.
4. Write equations for the preparation of aldehydes and ketones by the oxidation of alcohols.
5. Write equations representing the oxidation of carbonyl compounds.
6. Write equations representing the reduction of carbonyl compounds.
7. Write equations for the preparation of hemiacetals and acetals.
8. Draw the keto and enol forms of aldehydes and ketones.

OUTLINE

Introduction 440
13.1 Structure and Physical Properties 441
13.2 IUPAC Nomenclature and Common Names 442
13.3 Important Aldehydes and Ketones 447
13.4 Reactions Involving Aldehydes and Ketones 449
A Medical Perspective: Formaldehyde and Methanol Poisoning 450
A Human Perspective: Alcohol Abuse and Antabuse 453
Kitchen Chemistry: The Allure of Truffles 456

INTRODUCTION

For centuries we have used bloodhounds to locate missing persons or criminals. This works because of the amazing ability of bloodhounds to detect scent molecules, and because individuals have characteristic odor prints that are as unique as their fingerprints or DNA. Forensic scientists are now making the next step in developing this technology for more accurate detection of people associated with a crime scene. The first step is to identify the components of the odor print and an appropriate source of the sample. Some scientists suggest that odor molecules should be collected from the hands, since this is the part of the body that would handle a gun, bomb, or other materials at a crime scene. When samples are collected from hands, complex mixtures of compounds are collected. Among the molecules identified as prominent in these mixtures are some large and complex members of the two groups of compounds we will study in this chapter, the aldehydes and ketones. Among these are the aldehydes nonanal, decanal, and undecanal and the ketones 6-methyl-5-hepten-2-one and 6,10-dimethyl-5,9-undecadien-2-one. The next step in using this information to identify individuals will be the development of an instrument to detect, identify, and quantify these and other components of the human odor print samples found at the scene of a crime so that pattern can be compared with suspects in the case.

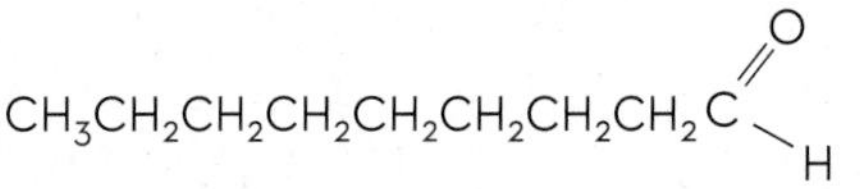

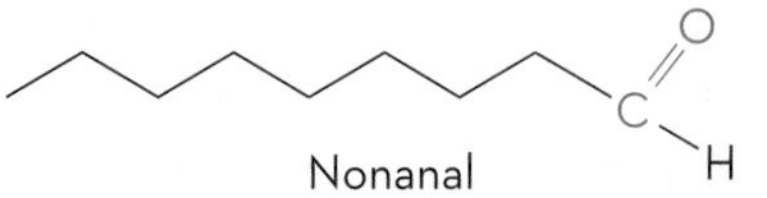

$$CH_3CH_2CH_2CH_2CH_2CH_2CH_2CH_2CHO$$

Nonanal

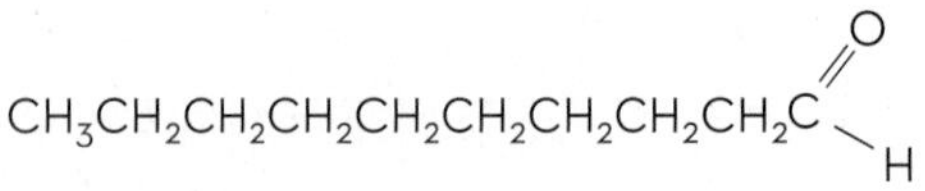

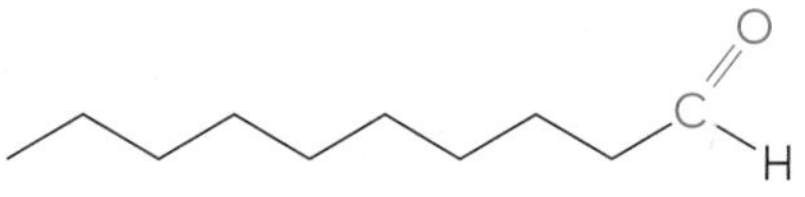

$$CH_3CH_2CH_2CH_2CH_2CH_2CH_2CH_2CH_2CHO$$

Decanal

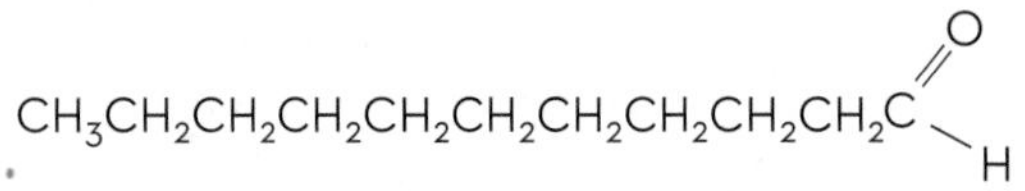

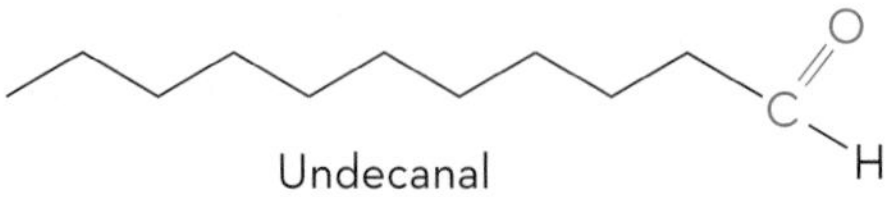

$$CH_3CH_2CH_2CH_2CH_2CH_2CH_2CH_2CH_2CH_2CHO$$

Undecanal

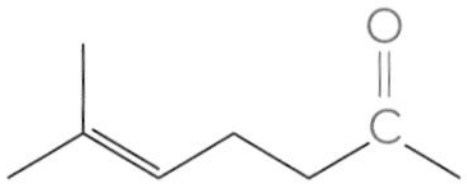

$$CH_3C(CH_3){=}CHCH_2CH_2C({=}O)CH_3$$

6-Methyl-5-hepten-2-one

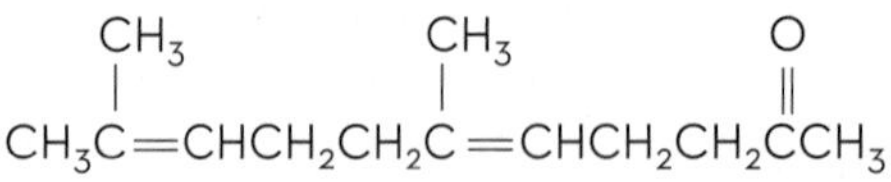

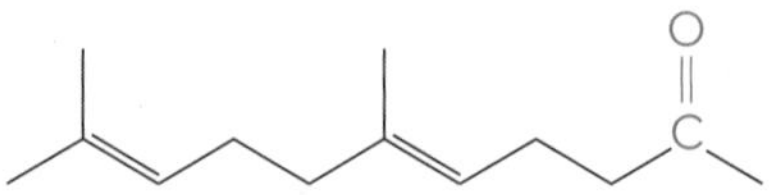

$$CH_3C(CH_3){=}CHCH_2CH_2C(CH_3){=}CHCH_2CH_2C({=}O)CH_3$$

6,10-Dimethyl-5,9-undecadien-2-one

The aldehydes and ketones are characterized by the presence of the **carbonyl group,** which is made up of a carbon atom bonded to an oxygen atom by a double bond.

$$>C{=}O$$

Carbonyl group

Compounds containing a carbonyl group are called carbonyl compounds. These include the aldehydes and ketones covered in this chapter, as well as the carboxylic acids and amides discussed in Chapters 14 and 15.

Aldehyde (R–C(=O)–H) Ketone (R–C(=O)–R′) Carboxylic Acid (R–C(=O)–OH) Amide (R–C(=O)–NR_2)

13.1 Structure and Physical Properties

LEARNING GOAL

1 Draw the structures and discuss the physical properties of aldehydes and ketones.

Aldehydes and **ketones** are carbonyl group–containing compounds distinguished by the location of the carbonyl group within the carbon chain. In aldehydes the carbonyl group is always located at the end of the carbon chain (carbon-1). In ketones the carbonyl group is located within the carbon chain of the molecule. Thus, in ketones the carbonyl carbon is attached to two other carbon atoms. However, in aldehydes the carbonyl carbon is attached to at least one hydrogen atom; the second atom attached to the carbonyl carbon of an aldehyde may be another hydrogen or a carbon atom (Figure 13.1). Aldehydes and ketones are polar compounds because of the polar carbonyl group.

$$\mathrm{C^{\delta+}=O^{\delta-}}$$

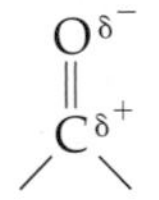

The carbonyl group is polar because oxygen is more electronegative than carbon (3.5 versus 2.5). This produces a dipole in which the oxygen carries a partial negative charge and the carbon carries a partial positive charge.

Because of the dipole-dipole attractions between molecules, aldehydes and ketones boil at higher temperatures than hydrocarbons or ethers that have the same number of carbon atoms or are of equivalent molar mass. Because they cannot form intermolecular hydrogen bonds, their boiling points are lower than those of alcohols of comparable molar mass. These trends are clearly demonstrated in the following examples:

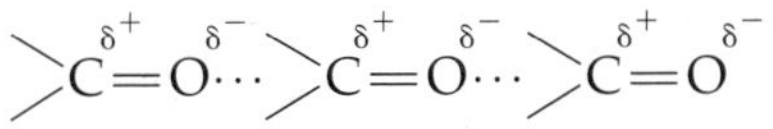

$$\mathrm{>\overset{\delta+}{C}=\overset{\delta-}{O}\cdots>\overset{\delta+}{C}=\overset{\delta-}{O}\cdots>\overset{\delta+}{C}=\overset{\delta-}{O}}$$

Dipole-dipole attraction

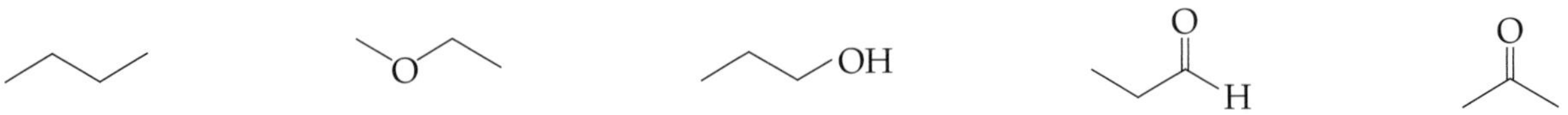

$CH_3CH_2CH_2CH_3$	$CH_3—O—CH_2CH_3$	$CH_3CH_2CH_2—OH$	$CH_3CH_2—C(=O)—H$	$CH_3—C(=O)—CH_3$
Butane (butane)	Methoxyethane (ethyl methyl ether)	1-Propanol (propyl alcohol)	Propanal (propionaldehyde)	Propanone (acetone)
M.M. = 58	M.M. = 60	M.M. = 60	M.M. = 58	M.M. = 58
b.p. −0.5°C	b.p. 7.0°C	b.p. 97.2°C	b.p. 49°C	b.p. 56°C

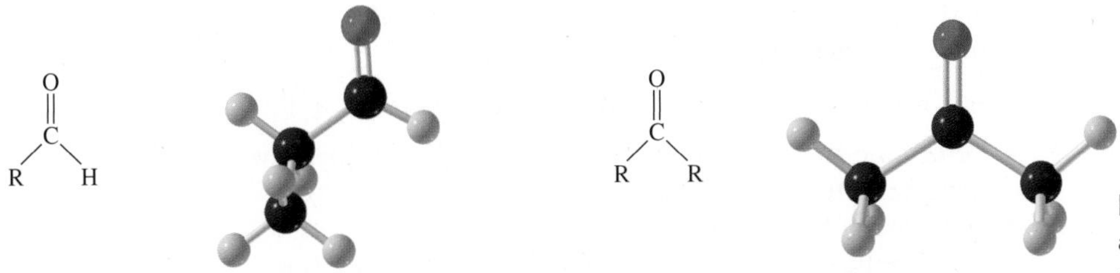

Aldehyde (R–C(=O)–H)
R = H, R, or Ar

An aldehyde
Propanal

(a)

Ketone (R–C(=O)–R)
R = R or Ar

A ketone
Propanone

(b)

Figure 13.1 The structures of aldehydes and ketones. (a) The general structure of an aldehyde and a ball-and-stick model of the aldehyde propanal. (b) The general structure of a ketone and a ball-and-stick model of the ketone propanone.

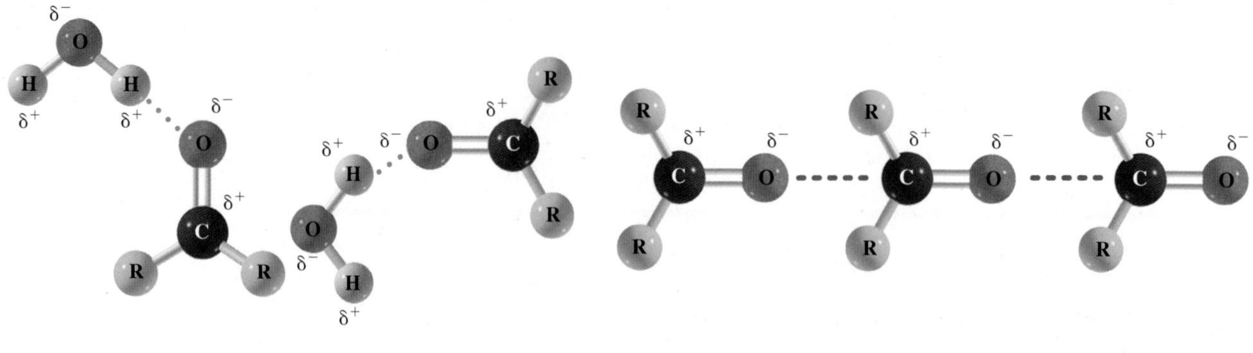

Figure 13.2 (a) Hydrogen bonding between the carbonyl group of an aldehyde or ketone and water. (b) Polar interactions between carbonyl groups of aldehydes or ketones.

Aldehydes and ketones can form intermolecular hydrogen bonds with water (Figure 13.2). As a result, the smaller members of the two families (five or fewer carbon atoms) are reasonably soluble in water. However, as the carbon chain length increases, the compounds become less polar and more hydrocarbonlike. These larger compounds are soluble in nonpolar organic solvents.

Question 13.1 Which member in each of the following pairs will be more water-soluble?

a. $CH_3(CH_2)_2CH_3$ or $CH_3\overset{\overset{O}{\|}}{C}CH_3$

b. $CH_3\overset{\overset{O}{\|}}{C}CH_2CH_2CH_3$ or $CH_3CHOHCH_2CH_2CH_3$

Question 13.2 Which member in each of the following pairs will be more water-soluble?

a. CH_3–cyclopentane (methylcyclopentane) or $H{-}C{=}O$ on cyclopentane (cyclopentanecarbaldehyde)

b. $HOCH_2CH_2OH$ or $H\overset{\overset{O}{\|}}{C}\overset{\overset{O}{\|}}{C}H$

Question 13.3 Which member in each of the following pairs would have a higher boiling point?

a. $CH_3CH_2\overset{\overset{O}{\|}}{C}OH$ or $CH_3CH_2\overset{\overset{O}{\|}}{C}H$

b. $CH_3\overset{\overset{O}{\|}}{C}OH$ or $CH_3\overset{\overset{O}{\|}}{C}CH_3$

Question 13.4 Which member in each of the following pairs would have a higher boiling point?

a. CH_3CH_2OH or $CH_3\overset{\overset{O}{\|}}{C}H$

b. $CH_3(CH_2)_6CH_3$ or $CH_3(CH_2)_5\overset{\overset{O}{\|}}{C}H$

13.2 IUPAC Nomenclature and Common Names

LEARNING GOAL

2 From the structures, write the common and IUPAC names of aldehydes and ketones.

Naming Aldehydes

In the IUPAC system, aldehydes are named according to the following set of rules:

- Determine the parent compound, that is, the longest continuous carbon chain containing the carbonyl group.
- Replace the final *-e* of the parent alkane with *-al.*
- Number the chain beginning with the carbonyl carbon (or aldehyde group) as carbon-1.

- Number and name all substituents as usual. No number is used for the position of the carbonyl group because it is always at the end of the parent chain. Therefore, it must be carbon-1.

Several examples are provided here with common names given in parentheses:

$H{-}\overset{\overset{O}{\|}}{C}{-}H$	$CH_3{-}\overset{\overset{O}{\|}}{C}{-}H$	$CH_3CH_2{-}\overset{\overset{O}{\|}}{C}{-}H$	$CH_3CH_2CH_2\underset{\underset{CH_3}{\|}}{CH}{-}\overset{\overset{O}{\|}}{C}{-}H$
Methanal (formaldehyde)	Ethanal (acetaldehyde)	Propanal (propionaldehyde)	2-Methylpentanal

EXAMPLE 13.1 Using the IUPAC Nomenclature System to Name Aldehydes

For many years, scientists were puzzled about what compounds give the nutty flavor to expensive, aged cheddar cheeses. In 2004, Dr. Mary Anne Drake of North Carolina State University solved this puzzle. She identified a group of aldehydes that impart this desirable flavor. Use the IUPAC Nomenclature System to name two of these aldehydes shown below.

Solution

$$CH_3\underset{\underset{CH_3}{\|}}{CH}\overset{\overset{O}{\|}}{C}{-}H \qquad CH_3\underset{\underset{CH_3}{\|}}{CH}CH_2\overset{\overset{O}{\|}}{C}{-}H$$

Parent compound:	propane (becomes propanal)	butane (becomes butanal)
Position of carbonyl group:	carbon-1	carbon-1
Substituents:	2-methyl	3-methyl
Name:	2-Methylpropanal	3-Methylbutanal

Notice that the position of the carbonyl group is not indicated by a number. By definition, the carbonyl group is located at the end of the carbon chain of an aldehyde. The carbonyl carbon is defined to be carbon-1; thus, it is not necessary to include the position of the carbonyl group in the name of the compound.

Practice Problem 13.1

Many molecules contribute to the complex flavors of olive oils. Among these are hexanal and *trans*-2-hexenal, which have flavors described as "green, grassy" and "green, bitter," respectively. Draw the structures of these two compounds.

► For Further Practice: **Questions 13.5, 13.29, and 13.36a, b, and c.**

LEARNING GOAL

2 From the structures, write the common and IUPAC names of aldehydes and ketones.

Another aldehyde associated with the nutty flavor of cheddar cheese is 2-methylbutanal. Draw the condensed formula of this molecule.

Carboxylic acid nomenclature is described in Section 14.1.

The common names of the aldehydes are derived from the same Latin roots as the corresponding carboxylic acids. The common names of the first five aldehydes are presented in Table 13.1.

In the common system of nomenclature, substituted aldehydes are named as derivatives of the straight-chain parent compound (see Table 13.1). Greek letters are used to indicate the position of the substituents. The carbon atom bonded to the carbonyl group is the α-carbon, the next is the β-carbon, and so on.

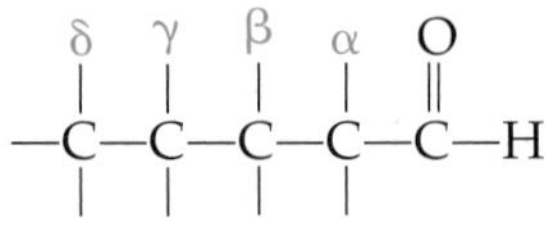

$$\overset{\delta}{-C}-\overset{\gamma}{C}-\overset{\beta}{C}-\overset{\alpha}{C}-\overset{O}{\overset{\|}{C}}-H$$

Consider the following examples:

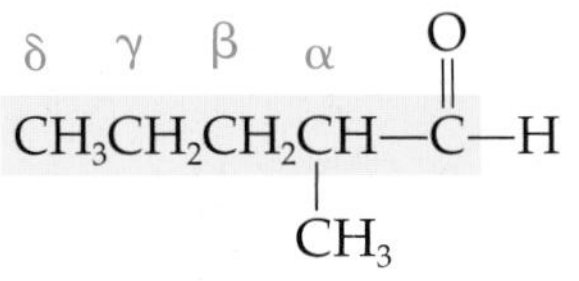

$$\overset{\delta}{CH_3}\overset{\gamma}{CH_2}\overset{\beta}{CH_2}\underset{CH_3}{\overset{\alpha}{CH}}-\overset{O}{\overset{\|}{C}}-H \qquad \overset{\delta}{CH_3}\overset{\gamma}{CH_2}\underset{CH_3}{\overset{\beta}{CH}}\overset{\alpha}{CH_2}-\overset{O}{\overset{\|}{C}}-H$$

2-Methylpentanal (α-methylvaleraldehyde)

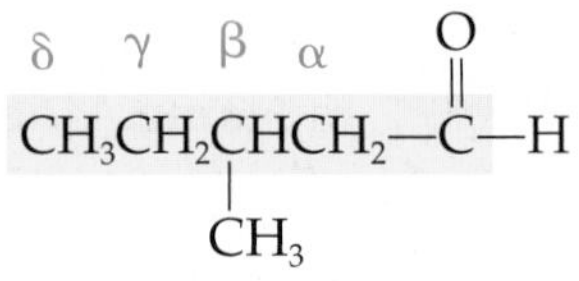

3-Methylpentanal (β-methylvaleraldehyde)

Naming Ketones

LEARNING GOAL

2 From the structures, write the common and IUPAC names of aldehydes and ketones.

The rules for naming ketones in the IUPAC Nomenclature System are directly analogous to those for naming aldehydes. In ketones, however, the *-e* ending of the parent alkane is replaced with the *-one* suffix of the ketone family, and the location of the carbonyl carbon is indicated with a number. The longest carbon chain is numbered to give the carbonyl carbon the lowest possible number. For example,

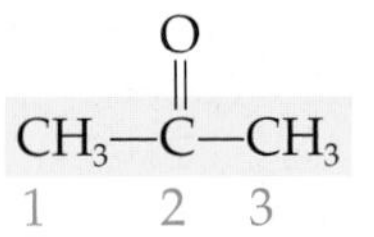

$$\underset{1}{CH_3}-\underset{2}{\overset{O}{\overset{\|}{C}}}-\underset{3}{CH_3} \qquad \underset{4\ \ 3}{CH_3CH_2}-\underset{2}{\overset{O}{\overset{\|}{C}}}-\underset{1}{CH_3} \qquad \underset{8\ \ 7\ \ 6\ \ 5}{CH_3CH_2CH_2CH_2}-\underset{4}{\overset{O}{\overset{\|}{C}}}-\underset{3\ \ 2\ \ 1}{CH_2CH_2CH_3}$$

Propanone (no number necessary) (acetone)

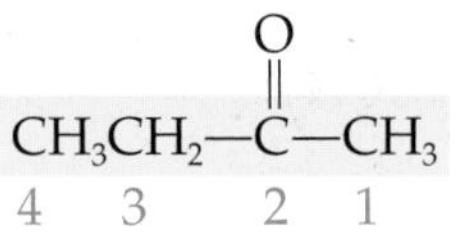

Butanone (no number necessary) (ethyl methyl ketone)

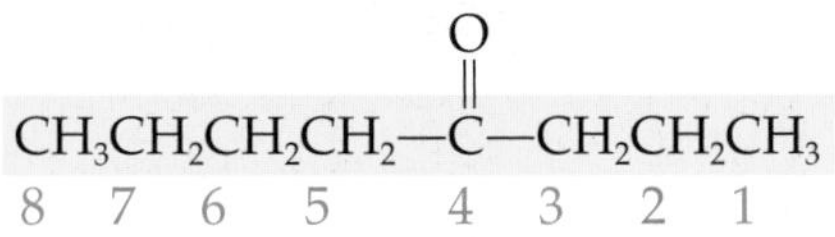

4-Octanone (*not* 5-octanone) (butyl propyl ketone)

TABLE 13.1 IUPAC and Common Names and Formulas for Several Aldehydes

IUPAC Name	Common Name	Formula
Methanal	Formaldehyde	$H-\overset{O}{\overset{\|}{C}}-H$
Ethanal	Acetaldehyde	$CH_3\overset{O}{\overset{\|}{C}}-H$
Propanal	Propionaldehyde	$CH_3CH_2\overset{O}{\overset{\|}{C}}-H$
Butanal	Butyraldehyde	$CH_3CH_2CH_2\overset{O}{\overset{\|}{C}}-H$
Pentanal	Valeraldehyde	$CH_3CH_2CH_2CH_2\overset{O}{\overset{\|}{C}}-H$

EXAMPLE 13.2 Comparing the Common and IUPAC Nomenclature Systems to Name Aldehydes

LEARNING GOAL

2 From the structures, write the common and IUPAC names of aldehydes and ketones.

Name the two aldehydes represented by the following condensed formulas.

Solution

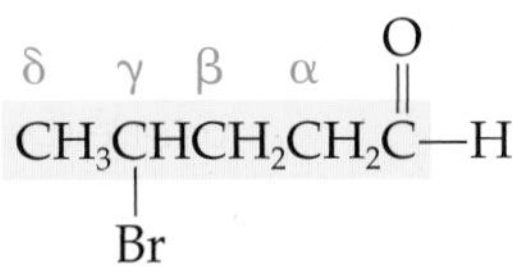

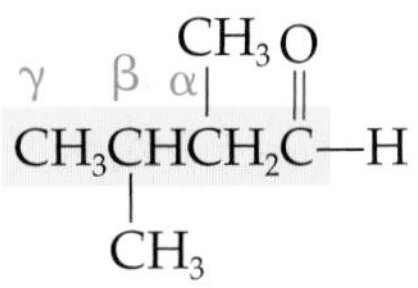

$$\overset{\delta}{C}H_3\overset{\gamma}{C}H(Br)\overset{\beta}{C}H_2\overset{\alpha}{C}H_2C(=O)\text{—}H \qquad \overset{\gamma}{C}H_3\overset{\beta}{C}H(CH_3)\overset{\alpha}{C}H(CH_3)C(=O)\text{—}H$$

Parent compound:	pentane (becomes valeraldehyde)	butane (becomes butyraldehyde)
Position of carbonyl group:	carbon-1	carbon-1
Substituents:	γ-bromo	α, β-dimethyl
Common Name:	γ-Bromovaleraldehyde	α, β-Dimethylbutyraldehyde

In the common system, the carbon atom bonded to the carbonyl group is called the α-carbon, the next is the β-carbon, etc. Greek letters are used to indicate the position of the substituents.

Parent compound:	pentane (becomes pentanal)	butane (becomes butanal)
Position of carbonyl group:	carbon-1	carbon-1
Substituents:	4-bromo	2,3-dimethyl
IUPAC name:	4-Bromopentanal	2,3 Dimethylbutanal

In the IUPAC system, the carbonyl carbon is defined as carbon-1. Any substituents are numbered from that point in the chain to identify their locations.

Also remember that by definition, the carbonyl group is located at the beginning of the carbon chain of an aldehyde. Thus, it is not necessary to include the position of the carbonyl group in the name of the compound.

Practice Problem 13.2

Use the common nomenclature system to name each of the following compounds.

a. 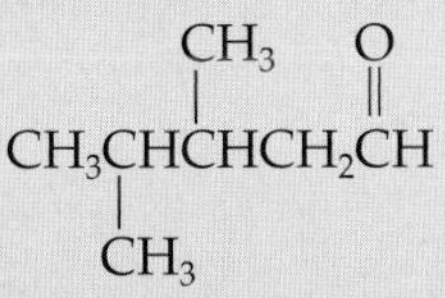 $CH_3CH(CH_3)CH(CH_3)CH_2CH{=}O$

b. 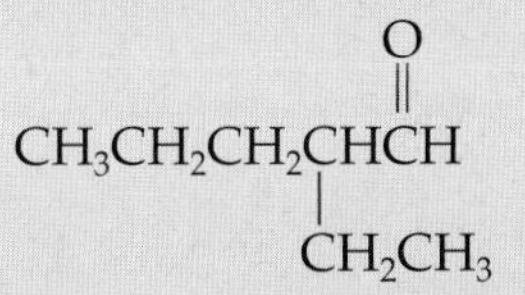 $CH_3CH_2CH_2CH(CH_2CH_3)CH{=}O$

c. 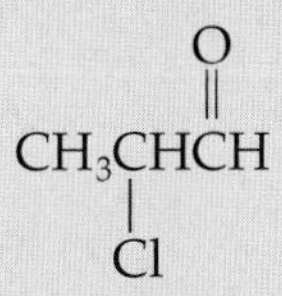 $CH_3CH(Cl)CH{=}O$

d. 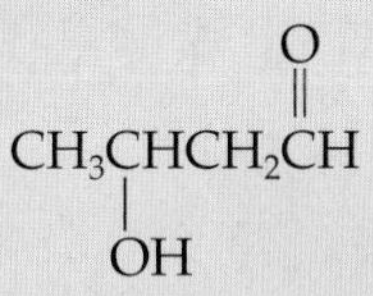 $CH_3CH(OH)CH_2CH{=}O$

▸ For Further Practice: **Questions 13.6b and d, 13.41c and d, 13.42b.**

The common names of ketones are derived by naming the alkyl groups that are bonded to the carbonyl carbon. These are used as prefixes followed by the word *ketone*. The alkyl groups may be arranged alphabetically or by size (smaller to larger).

EXAMPLE 13.3 Using the IUPAC Nomenclature System to Name Ketones

LEARNING GOAL

2 From the structures, write the common and IUPAC names of aldehydes and ketones.

Name the following ketones using the IUPAC Nomenclature System.

Continued...

Solution

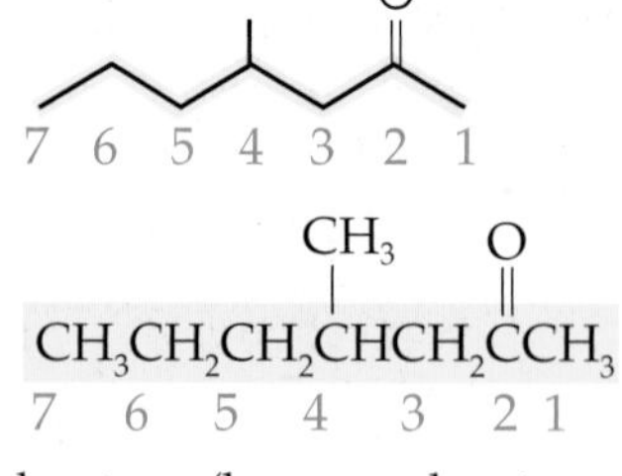

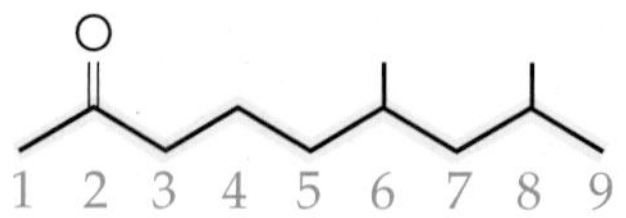

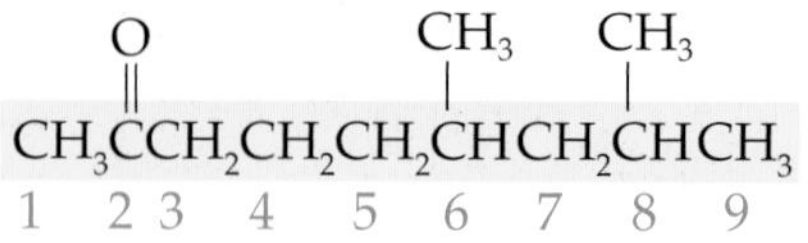

$$\overset{\substack{CH_3\\|}}{} \quad CH_3CH_2CH_2\underset{4}{C}HCH_2\overset{O}{\overset{\|}{C}}CH_3 \qquad (7\ 6\ 5\ 4\ 3\ 2\ 1)$$

$$CH_3\overset{O}{\overset{\|}{C}}CH_2CH_2CH_2\overset{CH_3}{\overset{|}{C}}HCH_2\overset{CH_3}{\overset{|}{C}}HCH_3 \qquad (1\ 2\ 3\ 4\ 5\ 6\ 7\ 8\ 9)$$

Parent compound:	heptane (becomes heptanone)	nonane (becomes nonanone)
Position of carbonyl group:	carbon-2	carbon-2
Substituents:	4-methyl	6, 8-dimethyl
IUPAC Name:	4-Methyl 2-heptanone	6, 8-Dimethyl-2-nonanone

Practice Problem 13.3

Provide the IUPAC name for each of the following ketones.

a. 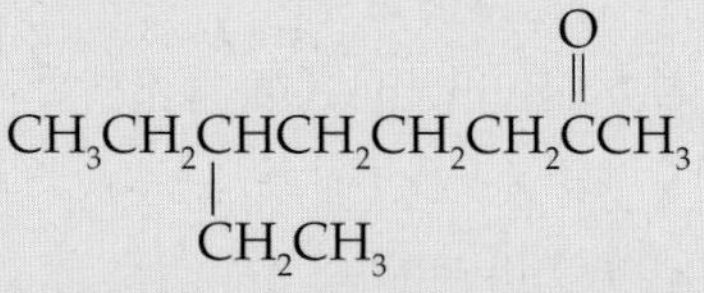 $CH_3CH_2\underset{CH_2CH_3}{\underset{|}{C}}HCH_2CH_2CH_2\overset{O}{\overset{\|}{C}}CH_3$

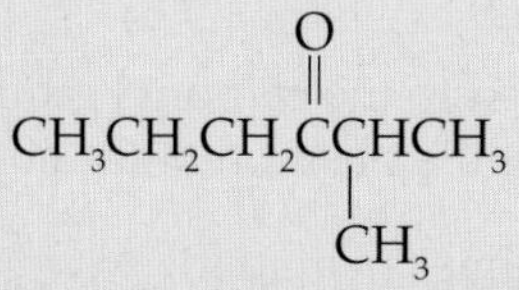

b. $CH_3CH_2CH_2\overset{O}{\overset{\|}{C}}\underset{CH_3}{\underset{|}{C}}HCH_3$

c. $CH_3\underset{CH_3}{\underset{|}{C}}H\overset{O}{\overset{\|}{C}}\underset{CH_3}{\underset{|}{C}}HCH_3$

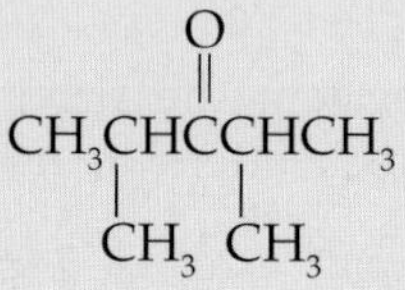

▸ For Further Practice: **Questions 13.7, 13.33a, 13.34a, 13.35b, 13.38, and 13.39.**

LEARNING GOAL

2 From the structures, write the common and IUPAC names of aldehydes and ketones.

Two molecules that contribute to the aroma of blue cheese are 2-heptanone and 2-nonanone. Draw the condensed formula for each of these molecules.

EXAMPLE 13.4 Using the Common Nomenclature System to Name Ketones

Name the ketones represented by the following condensed and line formulas.

Solution

Identify the alkyl groups that are bonded to the carbonyl carbon.

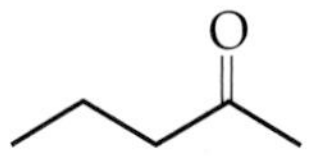

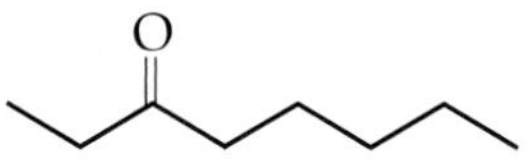

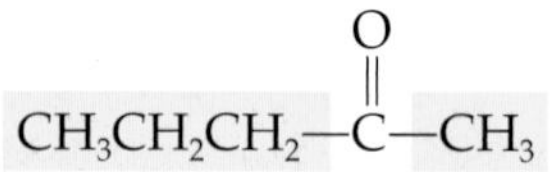

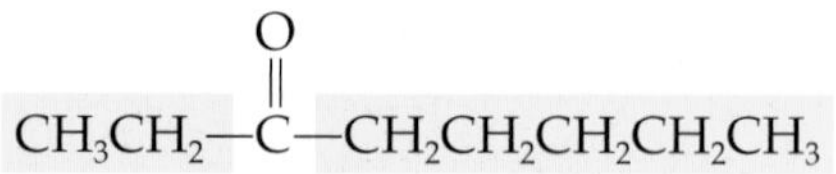

$$CH_3CH_2CH_2-\overset{O}{\overset{\|}{C}}-CH_3 \qquad CH_3CH_2-\overset{O}{\overset{\|}{C}}-CH_2CH_2CH_2CH_2CH_3$$

Alkyl groups:	propyl and methyl	ethyl and pentyl
Common Name:	Methyl propyl ketone	Ethyl pentyl ketone

Practice Problem 13.4

Provide the common names for each of the following ketones:

a. 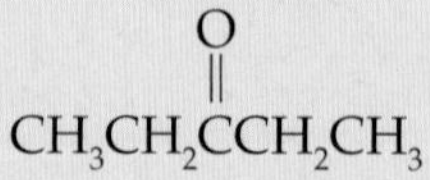 $CH_3CH_2\overset{O}{\overset{\|}{C}}CH_2CH_3$

b. $CH_3CH_2CH_2CH_2\overset{O}{\overset{\|}{C}}CH_2CH_3$

c. $CH_3CH_2CH_2CH_2CH_2CH_2\overset{O}{\overset{\|}{C}}CH_3$

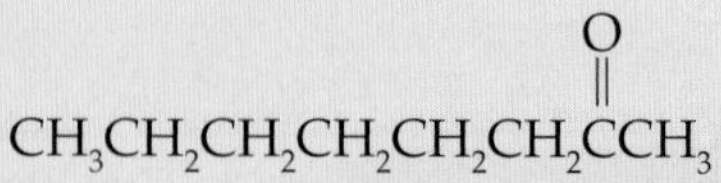

d. 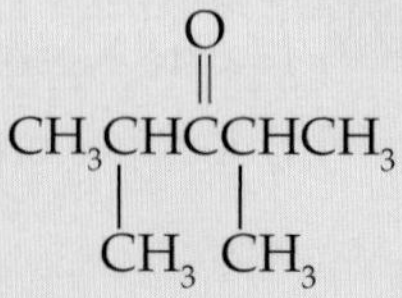 $CH_3\underset{CH_3}{\underset{|}{C}}H\overset{O}{\overset{\|}{C}}\underset{CH_3}{\underset{|}{C}}HCH_3$

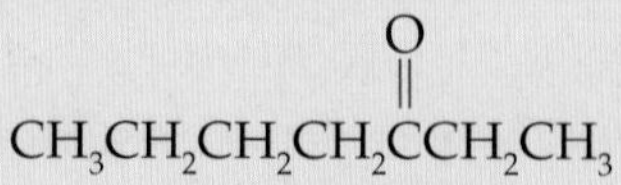

▸ For Further Practice: **Questions 13.41a, b, and e and 13.42a and c.**

Question 13.5 From the IUPAC names, draw the condensed formula for each of the following aldehydes.

a. 2,3-Dichloropentanal
b. 2-Bromobutanal
c. 4-Methylhexanal
d. Butanal
e. 2,4-Dimethylpentanal

Question 13.6 Write the condensed formula for each of the following compounds.

a. 3-Methylnonanal
b. β-Bromovaleraldehyde
c. 4-Fluorohexanal
d. α,β-Dimethylbutyraldehyde

Question 13.7 Use the IUPAC Nomenclature System to name each of the following compounds.

a. $CH_3\underset{\displaystyle I}{\underset{|}{C}}H\overset{\displaystyle O}{\overset{\|}{C}}CH_3$

b. $CH_3\underset{\displaystyle CH_2CH_2CH_2CH_3}{\underset{|}{C}}HCH_2\overset{\displaystyle O}{\overset{\|}{C}}CH_3$

c. $CH_3\underset{\displaystyle CH_3}{\underset{|}{C}}H\overset{\displaystyle O}{\overset{\|}{C}}CH_3$

d. $CH_3\underset{\displaystyle CH_3}{\underset{|}{C}}H\overset{\displaystyle O}{\overset{\|}{C}}CH_2CH_3$

e. $CH_3\underset{\displaystyle F}{\underset{|}{C}}H\overset{\displaystyle O}{\overset{\|}{C}}CH_2CH_3$

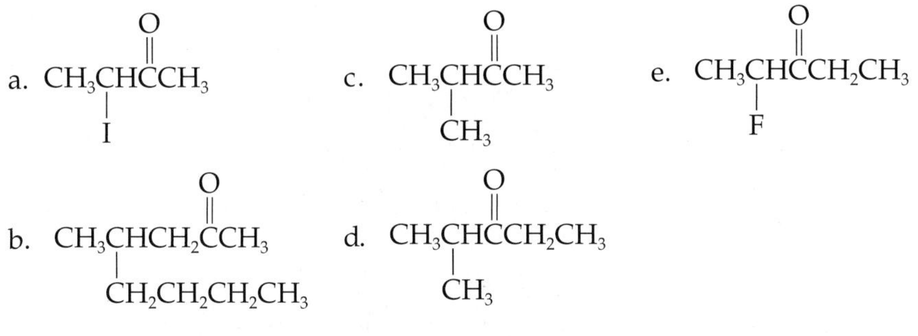

Question 13.8 Write the condensed formula for each of the following compounds.

a. Methyl isopropyl ketone (What is the IUPAC name for this compound?)
b. 4-Heptanone
c. 2-Fluorocyclohexanone
d. Hexachloroacetone (What is the IUPAC name of this compound?)

13.3 Important Aldehydes and Ketones

LEARNING GOAL

3 List several aldehydes and ketones that are of natural, commercial, health, and environmental interest and describe their significance.

Methanal (formaldehyde) is a gas (b.p. −21°C). It is available commercially as an aqueous solution called *formalin*. Formalin has been used as a preservative for tissues and as an embalming fluid. See A Medical Perspective: Formaldehyde and Methanol Poisoning for more information on methanal.

Ethanal (acetaldehyde) is produced from ethanol in the liver. Ethanol is oxidized in this reaction, which is catalyzed by the liver enzyme alcohol dehydrogenase. The ethanal that is produced in this reaction is responsible for the symptoms of a hangover.

Propanone (acetone), the simplest ketone, is an important and versatile solvent for organic compounds. It has the ability to dissolve organic compounds and is also soluble in water. As a result, it has a number of industrial applications and is used as a solvent in adhesives, paints, cleaning solvents, nail polish, and nail polish remover. Propanone is flammable and should therefore be treated with appropriate care. *Butanone,* a four-carbon ketone, is also an important industrial solvent in the manufacture of plastics, paint remover, varnish, and glue.

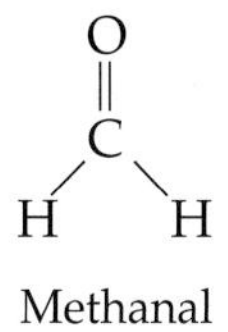

Many aldehydes and ketones are produced industrially as food and fragrance chemicals, medicinals, and agricultural chemicals. They are particularly important to the food industry, in which they are used as artificial and/or natural additives to food. Vanillin, a principal component of natural vanilla, is shown in Figure 13.3. Artificial vanilla flavoring is a dilute solution of synthetic vanillin dissolved in ethanol. Figure 13.3 also shows other examples of important aldehydes and ketones.

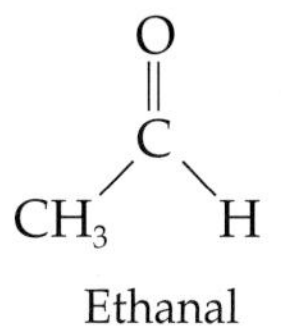

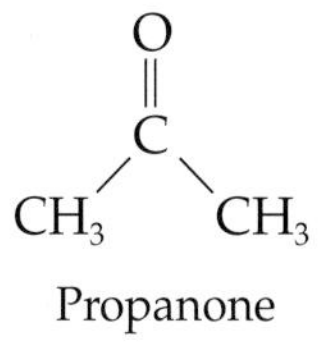

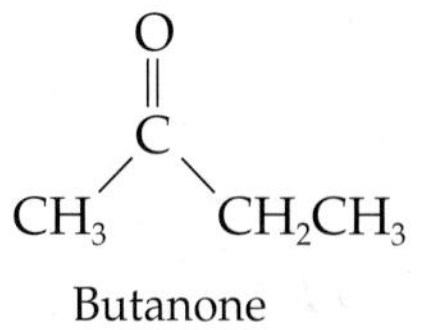

$H-\overset{\displaystyle O}{\overset{\|}{C}}-H$
Methanal

$CH_3-\overset{\displaystyle O}{\overset{\|}{C}}-H$
Ethanal

$CH_3-\overset{\displaystyle O}{\overset{\|}{C}}-CH_3$
Propanone

$CH_3-\overset{\displaystyle O}{\overset{\|}{C}}-CH_2CH_3$
Butanone

Question 13.9 Draw the structure of the aldehyde synthesized from ethanol in the liver.

Question 13.10 Draw the structure of a ketone that is an important, versatile solvent for organic compounds.

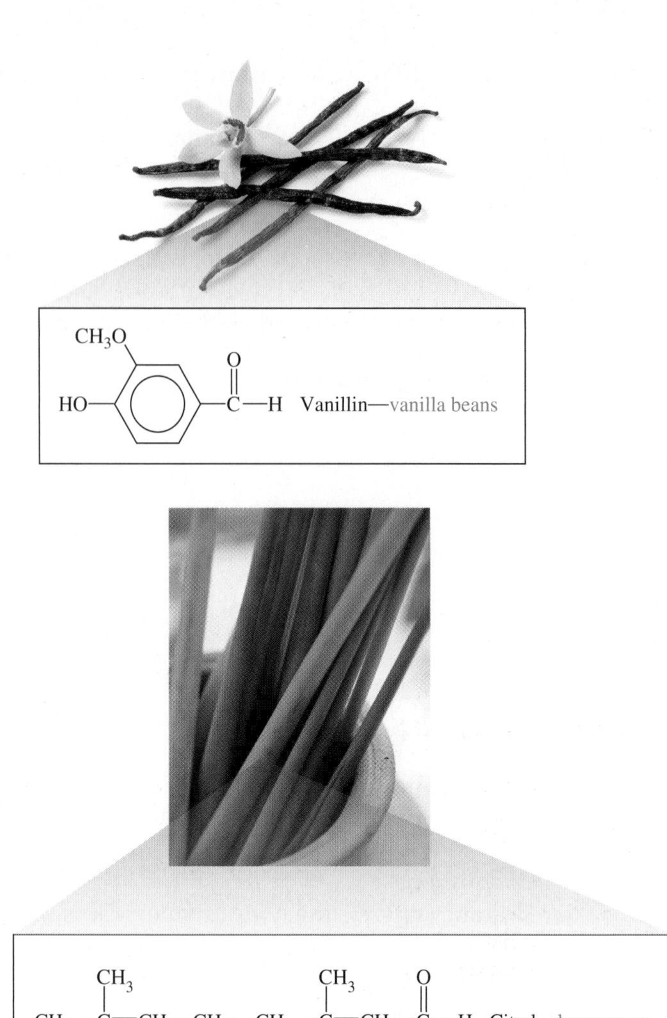

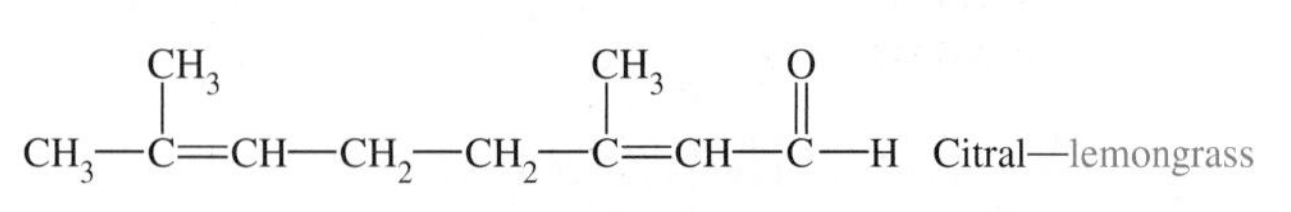

α-Demascone—berry flavoring

$CH_3CH_2CH_2CH_2CH_2CH_2—C(=O)—CH_3$ 2-Octanone—mushroom flavoring

Figure 13.3 Important aldehydes and ketones.

13.4 Reactions Involving Aldehydes and Ketones

Preparation of Aldehydes and Ketones

Aldehydes and ketones are prepared primarily by the **oxidation** of the corresponding alcohol. In organic systems, oxidation is recognized as a loss of hydrogen atoms or the gain of oxygen atoms. As we saw in Chapter 12, the oxidation of methyl alcohol gives methanal (formaldehyde). The oxidation of a primary alcohol produces an aldehyde, and the oxidation of a secondary alcohol yields a ketone. Tertiary alcohols do not undergo oxidation under the conditions normally used.

LEARNING GOAL

4 Write equations for the preparation of aldehydes and ketones by the oxidation of alcohols.

EXAMPLE 13.5 Differentiating the Oxidation of Primary, Secondary, and Tertiary Alcohols

LEARNING GOAL

4 Write equations for the preparation of aldehydes and ketones by the oxidation of alcohols.

Use specific examples to show the oxidation of a primary, a secondary, and a tertiary alcohol.

Solution

The oxidation of a primary alcohol to an aldehyde:

$$CH_3CH_2CH_2{-}\underset{\underset{H}{|}}{\overset{\overset{H}{|}}{C}}{-}OH \xrightarrow{[O]} CH_3CH_2CH_2{-}\overset{\overset{O}{\|}}{C}{-}H$$

1-Butanol (butyl alcohol) — Butanal (butyraldehyde)

The oxidation of a secondary alcohol to a ketone:

$$CH_3CH_2CH_2CH_2{-}\underset{\underset{H}{|}}{\overset{\overset{CH_3}{|}}{C}}{-}OH \xrightarrow{[O]} CH_3CH_2CH_2CH_2{-}\overset{\overset{O}{\|}}{C}{-}CH_3$$

2-Hexanol — 2-Hexanone

Tertiary alcohols cannot undergo oxidation:

$$CH_3CH_2CH_2{-}\underset{\underset{CH_3}{|}}{\overset{\overset{CH_3}{|}}{C}}{-}OH \xrightarrow{[O]} \text{No reaction}$$

2-Methyl-2-pentanol

In all these examples the symbol [O] is used to represent the oxidizing agent.

Practice Problem 13.5

Write equations showing the oxidation of (a) 1-propanol and (b) 2-butanol.

▸ For Further Practice: **Questions 13.57 and 13.58.**

A MEDICAL PERSPECTIVE

Formaldehyde and Methanol Poisoning

Most aldehydes have irritating, unpleasant odors, and formaldehyde is no exception. Formaldehyde is also an extremely toxic substance. As an aqueous solution, called formalin, it has been used to preserve biological tissues and for embalming. It has also been used to disinfect environmental surfaces, body fluids, and feces. Under no circumstances is it used as an antiseptic on human tissue because of its toxic fumes and the skin irritations that it causes.

Formaldehyde is used in the production of some killed-virus vaccines. When a potentially deadly virus, such as polio virus, is treated with heat and formaldehyde, the genetic information (RNA) is damaged beyond repair. The proteins of the virus also react with formaldehyde. However, the shape of the proteins, which is critical for a protective immune response against the virus, is not changed. Thus, when a child is injected with the Salk killed-virus polio vaccine, the immune system recognizes viral proteins and produces antibodies that protect against polio virus infection.

Formaldehyde can also be produced in the body! As we saw in Chapter 12, methanol can be oxidized to produce formaldehyde. In the body, the liver enzyme alcohol dehydrogenase, whose function it is to detoxify alcohols by oxidizing them, catalyzes the conversion of methanol to formaldehyde (methanal). The formaldehyde then reacts with cellular macromolecules, including proteins, causing severe damage (remember, it is used as an embalming agent!). As a result, methanol poisoning can cause blindness, respiratory failure, convulsions, and death.

Clever physicians have devised a treatment for methanol poisoning that is effective if administered soon enough after ingestion. Since the same enzyme that oxidizes methanol to formaldehyde (methanal) also oxidizes ethanol to acetaldehyde (ethanal), doctors reasoned that administering an intravenous solution of ethanol to the patient could protect against the methanol poisoning. If the ethanol concentration in the body is higher than the methanol concentration, most of the alcohol dehydrogenase enzymes of the liver will be carrying out the oxidation of the ethanol. This is called *competitive inhibition* because the methanol and ethanol molecules are competing for binding to the enzymes. The molecule that is in the higher concentration will more frequently bind to the enzyme and undergo reaction. In this case, the result is that the alcohol dehydrogenase enzymes are kept busy oxidizing ethanol and producing the less-toxic (not nontoxic) product, acetaldehyde. This gives the body time to excrete the methanol before it is oxidized to the potentially deadly formaldehyde.

For Further Understanding

- Acetaldehyde is described as less toxic than formaldehyde. Do some background research on the effects of these two aldehydes on biological systems.
- You have studied enzymes in previous biology courses. Using what you learned in those classes with information from Sections 19.4 and 19.10 in this text, put together an explanation of the way in which competitive inhibition works. Can you think of other types of poisoning for which competitive inhibition might be used to develop an effective treatment?

Oxidation Reactions

LEARNING GOAL

5 Write equations representing the oxidation of carbonyl compounds.

Aldehydes are oxidized to carboxylic acids, whereas ketones do not generally undergo further oxidation. The reason is that a carbon-hydrogen bond, present in the aldehyde but not in the ketone, is needed for the reaction to occur. In fact, aldehydes that are liquids are difficult to store because they can be oxidized by oxygen in the air. In some cases they must be stored under nitrogen gas. The following example shows a general equation for the oxidation of an aldehyde to a carboxylic acid:

$$\underset{\text{Aldehyde}}{R{-}\overset{\overset{\displaystyle O}{\|}}{C}{-}H} \xrightarrow{[O]} \underset{\text{Carboxylic acid}}{R{-}\overset{\overset{\displaystyle O}{\|}}{C}{-}OH}$$

Many oxidizing agents can be used. Both basic potassium permanganate and potassium chromate are good oxidizing agents, as the following specific example shows:

In basic solution, the product is the carboxylic acid anion:

$$CH_3{-}\overset{\overset{\displaystyle O}{\|}}{C}{-}O^-$$

$$\underset{\substack{\text{Ethanal}\\\text{(acetaldehyde)}}}{CH_3{-}\overset{\overset{\displaystyle O}{\|}}{C}{-}H} \xrightarrow[OH^-]{KMnO_4} \underset{\substack{\text{Ethanoate anion}\\\text{(acetate anion)}}}{CH_3{-}\overset{\overset{\displaystyle O}{\|}}{C}{-}O^-}$$

The rules for naming carboxylic acid anions are described in Section 14.1.

The oxidation of benzaldehyde to benzoic acid is an example of the conversion of an aromatic aldehyde to the corresponding aromatic carboxylic acid:

$$\text{C}_6\text{H}_5\text{—}\overset{\text{O}}{\overset{\|}{\text{C}}}\text{—H} \xrightarrow{K_2CrO_4} \text{C}_6\text{H}_5\text{—}\overset{\text{O}}{\overset{\|}{\text{C}}}\text{—OH}$$

Benzaldehyde Benzoic acid

Silver ions are very mild oxidizing agents. They will oxidize aldehydes but not alcohols.

Aldehydes and ketones can be distinguished on the basis of the fact that aldehydes are readily oxidized and ketones are not. The most common laboratory test for aldehydes is the **Tollens' test.** When exposed to the Tollens' reagent, a basic solution of $Ag(NH_3)_2^+$, an aldehyde undergoes oxidation. The silver ion (Ag^+) is reduced to silver metal (Ag^0) as the aldehyde is oxidized to a carboxylic acid anion.

$$\text{R—}\overset{\text{O}}{\overset{\|}{\text{C}}}\text{—H} + Ag(NH_3)_2^+ \longrightarrow \text{R—}\overset{\text{O}}{\overset{\|}{\text{C}}}\text{—O}^- + Ag^0$$

Aldehyde	Silver ammonia complex—Tollens' reagent	Carboxylate anion	Silver metal mirror

Silver metal precipitates from solution and coats the flask, producing a smooth silver mirror, as seen in Figure 13.4. The test is therefore often called the Tollens' silver mirror test. The commercial manufacture of silver mirrors uses a similar process. Ketones cannot be oxidized to carboxylic acids and do not react with the Tollens' reagent.

EXAMPLE 13.6 Writing Equations for the Reaction of an Aldehyde and of a Ketone with Tollens' Reagent

LEARNING GOAL

5 Write equations representing the oxidation of carbonyl compounds.

Write equations for the reaction of propanal and 2-pentanone with Tollens' reagent.

Solution

$$CH_3CH_2\overset{\text{O}}{\overset{\|}{\text{C}}}\text{—H} + Ag(NH_3)_2^+ \longrightarrow CH_3CH_2\overset{\text{O}}{\overset{\|}{\text{C}}}\text{—O}^- + Ag^0$$

Propanal Propanoate anion

$$CH_3CH_2CH_2\overset{\text{O}}{\overset{\|}{\text{C}}}CH_3 + Ag(NH_3)_2^+ \longrightarrow \text{No reaction}$$

2-Pentanone

Practice Problem 13.6

Write equations for the reaction of (a) ethanal and (b) propanone with Tollens' reagent.

▸ For Further Practice: **Questions 13.62 and 13.67.**

Another test that is used to distinguish between aldehydes and ketones is **Benedict's test.** Here, a buffered aqueous solution of copper(II) hydroxide and sodium citrate reacts to oxidize aldehydes but does not generally react with ketones. Cu^{2+} is reduced to Cu^+ in the process. Cu^{2+} is soluble and gives a blue solution, whereas the Cu^+ precipitates as the red solid copper(I) oxide, Cu_2O.

Cu(II) is an even milder oxidizing agent than silver ion.

All simple sugars (monosaccharides) are either aldehydes or ketones. Glucose is an aldehyde sugar that is commonly called *blood sugar* because it is the sugar

(a) (b) (c)

Figure 13.4 The silver precipitate produced by the Tollens' reaction is deposited on glass. The progress of the reaction is visualized in panels (a) through (c). Silver mirrors are made in a similar process.

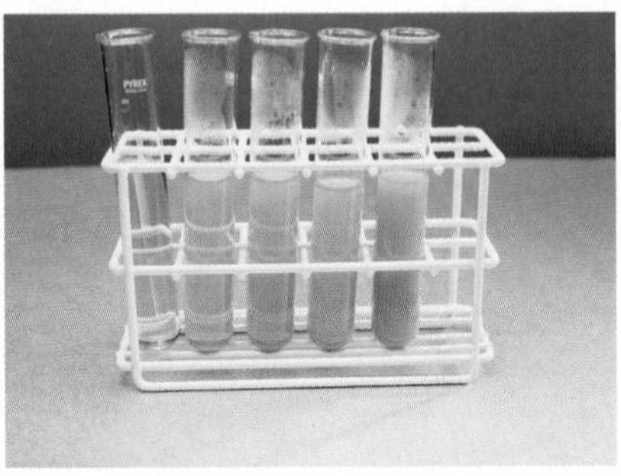

Figure 13.5 The amount of precipitate formed and thus the color change observed in the Benedict's test are directly proportional to the amount of reducing sugar in the sample.

found transported in the blood and used for energy by many cells. In uncontrolled diabetes, glucose may be found in the urine. One early method used to determine the amount of glucose in the urine was to observe the color change of the Benedict's test. The amount of precipitate formed is directly proportional to the amount of glucose in the urine (Figure 13.5). The reaction of glucose with the Benedict's reagent is represented in the following equation:

$$
\begin{array}{c}
\mathrm{O}\;\;\;\mathrm{H} \\
\diagdown\!\!/ \\
\mathrm{C} \\
| \\
\mathrm{H{-}C{-}OH} \\
| \\
\mathrm{HO{-}C{-}H} \\
| \\
\mathrm{H{-}C{-}OH} \\
| \\
\mathrm{H{-}C{-}OH} \\
| \\
\mathrm{CH_2OH} \\
\text{Glucose}
\end{array}
+ 2Cu^{2+} \xrightarrow{OH^-}
\begin{array}{c}
\mathrm{O}\;\;\;\mathrm{O^-} \\
\diagdown\!\!/ \\
\mathrm{C} \\
| \\
\mathrm{H{-}C{-}OH} \\
| \\
\mathrm{HO{-}C{-}H} \\
| \\
\mathrm{H{-}C{-}OH} \\
| \\
\mathrm{H{-}C{-}OH} \\
| \\
\mathrm{CH_2OH}
\end{array}
+ Cu_2O
$$

We should also note that when the carbonyl group of a ketone is bonded to a $-CH_2OH$ group, the molecule will give a positive Benedict's test. This occurs because such ketones are converted to aldehydes under basic conditions. In Chapter 16 we will see that this applies to the ketone sugars, as well. They are converted to aldehyde sugars and react with Benedict's reagent.

Reduction Reactions

LEARNING GOAL

6 Write equations representing the reduction of carbonyl compounds.

One way to recognize reduction, particularly in organic chemistry, is the gain of hydrogen. Oxidation and reduction are discussed in Section 12.5.

Aldehydes and ketones are both readily reduced to the corresponding alcohol by a variety of reducing agents. Throughout the text the symbol [H] over the reaction arrow represents a reducing agent.

The classical method of aldehyde or ketone reduction is **hydrogenation.** The carbonyl compound is reacted with hydrogen gas and a catalyst (nickel, platinum, or palladium metal) in a pressurized reaction vessel. Heating may also be necessary. The carbon-oxygen double bond (the carbonyl group) is reduced to a carbon-oxygen single bond. The addition of hydrogen to a carbon-oxygen double bond is shown in the following general equation:

A HUMAN PERSPECTIVE

Alcohol Abuse and Antabuse

According to a study carried out by the Centers for Disease Control and Prevention,[1] more than 75,000 Americans die each year as a result of alcohol abuse. Of these, nearly 35,000 people died of cirrhosis of the liver, cancer, or other drinking-related diseases. The remaining nearly 41,000 died in alcohol-related automobile accidents. Of those who died, 72% were men and 6% were under the age of twenty-one. In fact, a separate study has estimated that 1400 college-age students die each year of alcohol-related causes.

These numbers are striking. Alcohol abuse is now the third leading cause of preventable death in the United States, outranked only by tobacco use and poor diet and exercise habits. As the study concluded, "These results emphasize the importance of adopting effective strategies to reduce excessive drinking, including increasing alcohol excise taxes and screening for alcohol misuse in clinical settings."

$$(CH_3CH_2)_2N{-}C({=}S){-}S{-}S{-}C({=}S){-}N(CH_2CH_3)_2$$

Tetraethylthiuram disulfide
(disulfiram)
Antabuse

One approach to treatment of alcohol abuse, the drug tetraethylthiuram disulfide or disulfiram, has been used since 1951. The activity of this drug, generally known by the trade name Antabuse, was discovered accidentally by a group of Danish researchers who were testing it for antiparasitic properties. They made the observation that those who had taken disulfiram became violently ill after consuming any alcoholic beverage. Further research revealed that this compound inhibits one of the liver enzymes in the pathway for the oxidation of alcohols.

In Chapter 12 we saw that ethanol is oxidized to ethanal (acetaldehyde) in the liver. This reaction is catalyzed by the enzyme alcohol dehydrogenase. Acetaldehyde, which is more toxic than ethanol, is responsible for many of the symptoms of a hangover. The enzyme acetaldehyde dehydrogenase oxidizes acetaldehyde into ethanoic acid (acetic acid), which then is used in biochemical pathways that harvest energy for cellular work or that synthesize fats.

Antabuse inhibits acetaldehyde dehydrogenase. This inhibition occurs within 1 to 2 hours (h) of taking the drug and continues up to 14 days. When a person who has taken Antabuse drinks an alcoholic beverage, the level of acetaldehyde quickly reaches levels that are five to ten times higher than would normally occur after a drink. Within just a few minutes, the symptoms of a severe hangover are experienced and may continue for several hours.

Experts in drug and alcohol abuse have learned that drugs such as Antabuse are generally not effective on their own. However, when used in combination with support groups and/or psychotherapy to solve underlying behavioral or psychological problems, Antabuse is an effective deterrent to alcohol abuse.

1. Alcohol-Attributable Deaths and Years of Potential Life Lost—United States, 2001, Morbidity and Mortality Weekly Report, 53 (37): 866–870, September 24, 2004, also available at http://www.cdc.gov/mmwr/preview/mmwrhtml/mm5337a2.htm.

For Further Understanding

- Antabuse alone is not a cure for alcoholism. Consider some of the reasons why this is so.
- Write equations showing the oxidation of ethanal to ethanoic acid as a pathway with the product of the first reaction serving as the reactant for the second. Explain the physiological effects of Antabuse in terms of these chemical reactions.

$$R^1{-}\overset{\overset{\displaystyle O}{\|}}{C}{-}R^2 + H{-}H \xrightarrow{Pt} R^1{-}\underset{\underset{\displaystyle R^2}{|}}{\overset{\overset{\displaystyle OH}{|}}{C}}{-}H$$

Aldehyde or ketone — Hydrogen — Alcohol

The hydrogenation (reduction) of a ketone produces a secondary alcohol, as seen in the following equation showing the reduction of the ketone, 3-octanone:

Hydrogenation was first discussed in Section 11.5 for the hydrogenation of alkenes.

$$CH_3CH_2\overset{\overset{\displaystyle O}{\|}}{C}CH_2CH_2CH_2CH_2CH_3 + H_2 \xrightarrow{Ni} CH_3CH_2\underset{\underset{\displaystyle H}{|}}{\overset{\overset{\displaystyle OH}{|}}{C}}CH_2CH_2CH_2CH_2CH_3$$

3-Octanone (A ketone) — Hydrogen — 3-Octanol (A secondary alcohol)

EXAMPLE 13.7 **Writing an Equation Representing the Hydrogenation of a Ketone**

LEARNING GOAL

6 Write equations representing the reduction of carbonyl compounds.

Write an equation showing the hydrogenation of 3-pentanone.

Solution

The product of the reduction of a ketone is a secondary alcohol, in this case, 3-pentanol.

$$CH_3CH_2\overset{\overset{O}{\|}}{C}CH_2CH_3 + H_2 \xrightarrow{Pt} CH_3CH_2\underset{\underset{H}{|}}{\overset{\overset{OH}{|}}{C}}CH_2CH_3$$

3-Pentanone 3-Pentanol

Practice Problem 13.7

Write an equation for the hydrogenation of (a) propanone and (b) butanone.

► For Further Practice: **Question 13.64.**

The hydrogenation of an aldehyde results in the production of a primary alcohol, as seen in the following equation showing the reduction of the aldehyde, butanal:

$$CH_3CH_2CH_2\overset{\overset{O}{\|}}{C}H + H_2 \xrightarrow{Pt} CH_3CH_2CH_2\underset{\underset{H}{|}}{\overset{\overset{OH}{|}}{C}}H$$

Butanal (An aldehyde) Hydrogen 1-Butanol (A primary alcohol)

EXAMPLE 13.8 **Writing an Equation Representing the Hydrogenation of an Aldehyde**

LEARNING GOAL

6 Write equations representing the reduction of carbonyl compounds.

Write an equation showing the hydrogenation of 3-methylbutanal.

Solution

Recall that the reduction of an aldehyde results in the production of a primary alcohol, in this case, 3-methyl-1-butanol.

$$CH_3\underset{\underset{CH_3}{|}}{C}HCH_2\overset{\overset{O}{\|}}{C}H + H_2 \xrightarrow{Pt} CH_3\underset{\underset{CH_3}{|}}{C}HCH_2\underset{\underset{H}{|}}{\overset{\overset{OH}{|}}{C}}H$$

3-Methylbutanal 3-Methyl-1-butanol

Practice Problem 13.8

Write equations for the hydrogenation of 3,4-dimethylhexanal and 2-chloropentanal.

► For Further Practice: **Questions 13.65 and 13.66.**

A biological example of the reduction of a ketone occurs in the body, particularly during strenuous exercise when the lungs and circulatory system may not be able to provide enough oxygen to the muscles. Under these circumstances, the lactate fermentation begins. In this reaction, the enzyme *lactate dehydrogenase* reduces pyruvate, the product of glycolysis (a pathway for the breakdown of glucose) into lactate. The reducing agent for this reaction is nicotinamide adenine dinucleotide (NADH).

The role of the lactate fermentation in exercise is discussed in greater detail in Section 21.4.

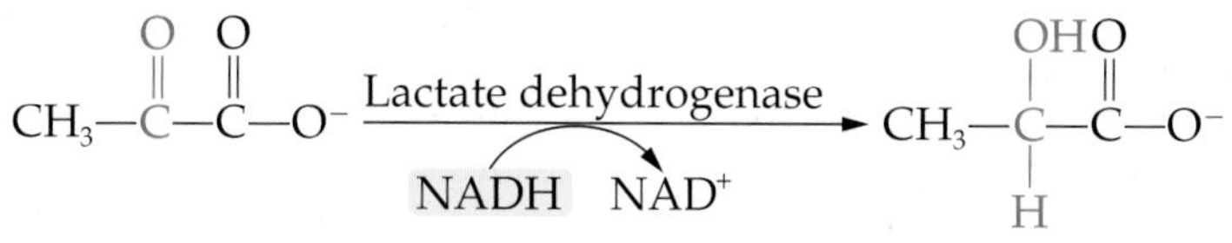

$$\underset{\text{Pyruvate}}{CH_3-\overset{O}{\overset{\|}{C}}-\overset{O}{\overset{\|}{C}}-O^-} \xrightarrow[\text{NADH} \;\; \text{NAD}^+]{\text{Lactate dehydrogenase}} \underset{\text{Lactate}}{CH_3-\underset{H}{\underset{|}{\overset{OH}{\overset{|}{C}}}}-\overset{O}{\overset{\|}{C}}-O^-}$$

NADH is a donor of hydride anions in biological reduction reactions, such as the formation of lactate from pyruvate, and it is oxidized in the reaction. Let's take a closer look at this reaction:

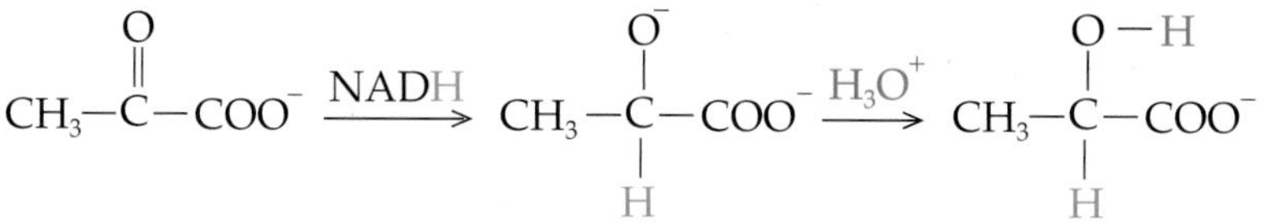

$$\underset{\text{Pyruvate}}{CH_3-\overset{O}{\overset{\|}{C}}-COO^-} \xrightarrow{\text{NADH}} CH_3-\underset{H}{\underset{|}{\overset{O^-}{\overset{|}{C}}}}-COO^- \xrightarrow{H_3O^+} \underset{\text{Lactate}}{CH_3-\underset{H}{\underset{|}{\overset{O-H}{\overset{|}{C}}}}-COO^-}$$

Question 13.11 Label each of the following as an oxidation or a reduction reaction.

a. Ethanal to ethanol
b. Benzoic acid to benzaldehyde
c. Cyclohexanone to cyclohexanol
d. 2-Propanol to propanone
e. 2,3-Butanedione (found in butter) to 2,3-butanediol

Question 13.12 Write an equation for each of the reactions in Question 13.11.

Addition Reactions

LEARNING GOAL

7 Write equations for the preparation of hemiacetals and acetals.

The principal reaction of the carbonyl group is the **addition reaction** across the polar carbon-oxygen double bond. This reaction is very similar to some that we have already studied, addition across the carbon-carbon double bond of alkenes. Such reactions require that a catalytic amount of acid be present in solution, as shown by the H^+ over the arrow for the reactions shown in the following examples.

An example of an addition reaction is the reaction of aldehydes and ketones with alcohols in the presence of catalytic amounts of acid. In this reaction, the hydrogen of the alcohol adds to the carbonyl oxygen. The alkoxy group of the alcohol (—OR) adds to the carbonyl carbon. The predicted product is a **hemiacetal.** A hemiacetal is characterized by a carbon that is bonded to one hydroxyl group (—OH) and one alkoxy group (—OR).

Addition reactions of alkenes are described in detail in Section 11.5.

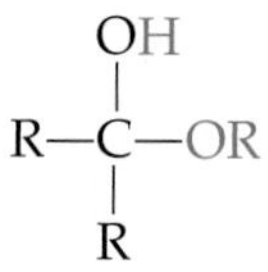

$$R-\underset{R}{\underset{|}{\overset{OH}{\overset{|}{C}}}}-OR$$

General structure of a hemiacetal

KITCHEN CHEMISTRY

The Allure of Truffles

Truffles are the fruiting body of fungi of the genus *Tuber.* They are remarkably ugly, roughly round and warty in appearance, and have an aroma variously described as "nutty," "musky," and "stinky." Nonetheless, truffles are one of the most highly prized ingredients in most of the finest kitchens in the world. In fact, the white truffle has been described as the "diamond of the kitchen."

Truffles grow under a limited variety of trees, including oak, beech, and poplar. They may be as deep as 1 meter (m) underground and only grow in the fall and winter of the year. Traditionally, they were harvested using truffle-sniffing pigs. These pigs were able to detect the smell of the chemicals the truffle produces to attract animals who will eat them and spread their spores to other sites through their feces. Today trained dogs are used to find the truffles because of a tendency of the pigs to eat the truffles before they could be harvested! With prices as high as $500 per pound (lb) for black truffles and $2000 per lb for white truffles, harvesters couldn't afford to have the pigs feasting on them!

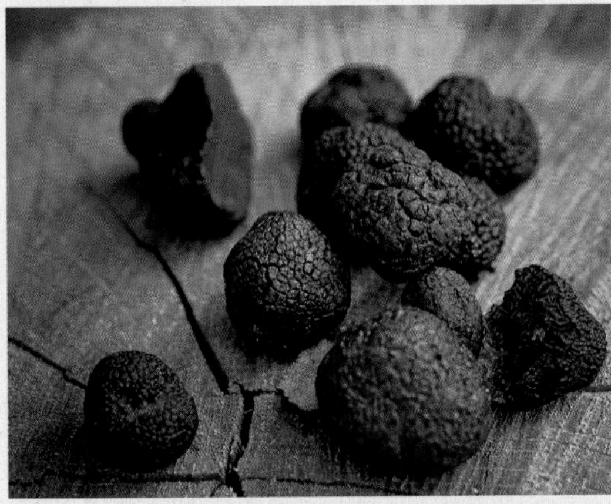

The flavor of the truffles is a direct result of their aroma. The compounds that produce that aroma are only produced as the spores mature, which is why it is useful to use animals to locate the scent of the truffles when they are at their peak. Many have studied the compounds in truffles that produce the aroma, and hence the flavor. They have found as many as thirty-six components of that flavor profile, including alcohols, aldehydes, ketones, carboxylic acids, esters, amines, aromatic compounds, and hydrocarbons—virtually an entire organic chemistry laboratory! Two alcohols and two aldehydes are found in the highest concentrations. These are 2-methylbutanol, 3-methylbutanol, 2-methylbutanal, and 3-methylbutanal. The flavor profile is rounded out by several sulfur compounds, including dimethylsulfide, 2,4-pentanedithiol, and 2,4,6-heptanetrithiol. In fact, it is the dimethylsulfide that attracts animals to the fruiting bodies.

As we have learned in this chapter, alcohols and aldehydes such as these in the truffle flavor profile are easily oxidized. When that happens, the truffle loses the molecules that are characteristic of its aroma and flavor. Fresh truffles must be used quickly and stored carefully to retain the flavor. Often, truffles are sold in a preserved form that has a shelf-life as long as 2 years.

The truffle is becoming much more rare. While it was reported in 1890 that 2200 tons (t) of truffles were harvested, now only about 150 are harvested. The truffle can only grow in association with certain trees and those trees only support truffles for about 15–30 years. To renew the harvest, tree saplings that have been inoculated with spores are being planted in areas with the right type of soil. However, it requires about 7 years before these trees begin to produce the precious fruiting bodies.

Truffles will continue to be a much sought-after delicacy, and science is helping us understand the chemical complexity of this unlovely fungus, as well as ways to ensure that we will be able to enjoy its remarkable flavors in the centuries to come.

For Further Understanding

- Draw the structures of the molecules that are responsible for the flavor profile of truffles.
- Write equations for the oxidation reactions that destroy the complex aroma and flavor of truffles.

In the following reactions notice that the alkoxy group (—OR) of the alcohol adds to the carbonyl carbon and the hydrogen of the hydroxyl group adds to the carbonyl oxygen. The following equations show the addition of ethanol to cyclohexylmethanal and propanone:

$$C_6H_{11}-\overset{\overset{\displaystyle O}{\|}}{\underset{\underset{\displaystyle H}{|}}{C}} + \overset{\overset{\displaystyle H}{|}}{O}-CH_2CH_3 \underset{}{\overset{H^+}{\rightleftarrows}} C_6H_{11}-\overset{\overset{\displaystyle O-H}{|}}{\underset{\underset{\displaystyle H}{|}}{C}}-OCH_2CH_3$$

Cyclohexylmethanal Ethanol A Hemiacetal

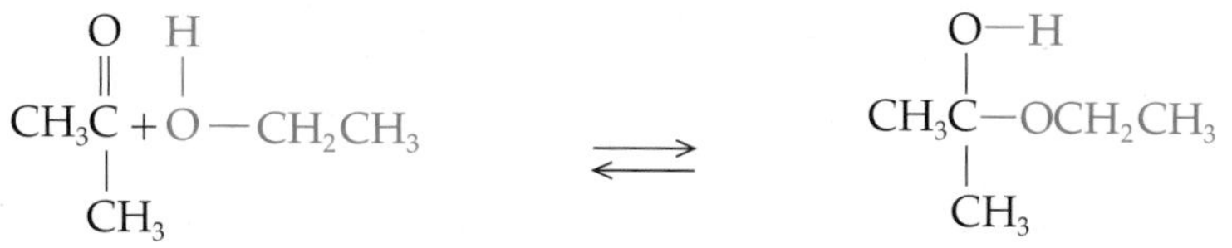

$$\underset{\text{Propanone}}{CH_3\overset{O}{\overset{\|}{C}}\underset{CH_3}{\underset{|}{}}} + \underset{\text{Ethanol}}{\overset{H}{\overset{|}{O}}-CH_2CH_3} \rightleftharpoons \underset{\text{A Hemiacetal}}{CH_3\overset{O-H}{\overset{|}{C}}\underset{CH_3}{\underset{|}{}}-OCH_2CH_3}$$

Hemiacetals are generally unstable. In the presence of acid and excess alcohol, they undergo a substitution reaction in which the —OH group of the hemiacetal is exchanged for another —OR group from the alcohol. The product of this reaction is an **acetal.** Acetal formation is a reversible reaction, as the general equation shows:

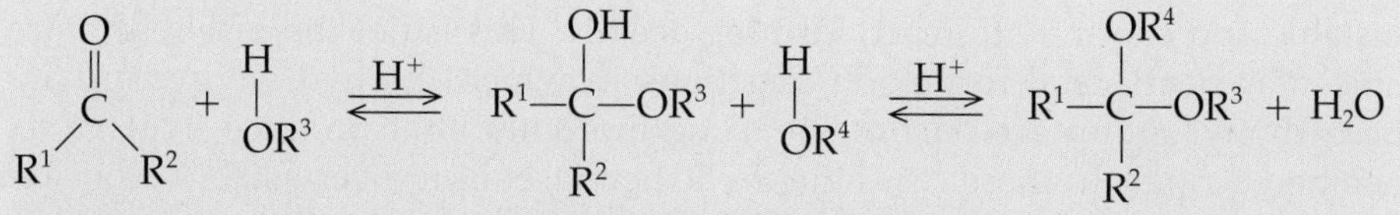

$$\underset{\text{Aldehyde or Ketone}}{R^1-\overset{O}{\overset{\|}{C}}-R^2} + \underset{\text{Alcohol}}{\overset{H}{\overset{|}{O}}R^3} \overset{H^+}{\rightleftharpoons} \underset{\text{Hemiacetal}}{R^1-\overset{OH}{\overset{|}{\underset{R^2}{\underset{|}{C}}}}-OR^3} + \overset{H}{\overset{|}{O}}R^4 \overset{H^+}{\rightleftharpoons} \underset{\text{Acetal}}{R^1-\overset{OR^4}{\overset{|}{\underset{R^2}{\underset{|}{C}}}}-OR^3} + H_2O$$

Notice that the acetal is characterized by a carbon bonded to two alkoxy groups (—OR).

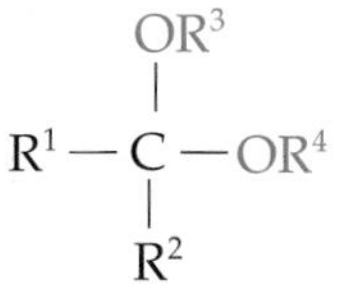

$$R^1-\overset{OR^3}{\overset{|}{\underset{R^2}{\underset{|}{C}}}}-OR^4$$

Acetal formation is seen in the following equations that represent the acid-catalyzed reactions between propanal and methanol and between propanone and ethanol.

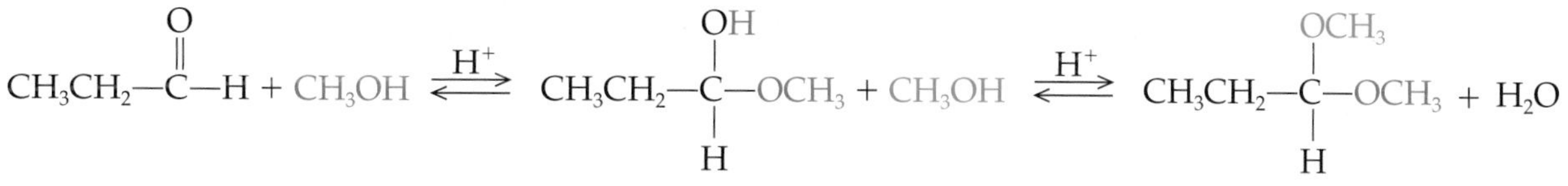

$$\underset{\text{Propanal}}{CH_3CH_2-\overset{O}{\overset{\|}{C}}-H} + \underset{\text{Methanol}}{CH_3OH} \overset{H^+}{\rightleftharpoons} \underset{\text{Hemiacetal}}{CH_3CH_2-\overset{OH}{\overset{|}{\underset{H}{\underset{|}{C}}}}-OCH_3} + CH_3OH \overset{H^+}{\rightleftharpoons} \underset{\text{Acetal}}{CH_3CH_2-\overset{OCH_3}{\overset{|}{\underset{H}{\underset{|}{C}}}}-OCH_3} + H_2O$$

$$\underset{\text{Propanone}}{CH_3-\overset{O}{\overset{\|}{C}}-CH_3} + \underset{\text{Ethanol}}{CH_3CH_2OH} \overset{H^+}{\rightleftharpoons} \underset{\text{Hemiacetal}}{CH_3-\overset{OH}{\overset{|}{\underset{CH_3}{\underset{|}{C}}}}-OCH_2CH_3} + CH_3CH_2OH \overset{H^+}{\rightleftharpoons} \underset{\text{Acetal}}{CH_3-\overset{OCH_2CH_3}{\overset{|}{\underset{CH_3}{\underset{|}{C}}}}-OCH_2CH_3} + H_2O$$

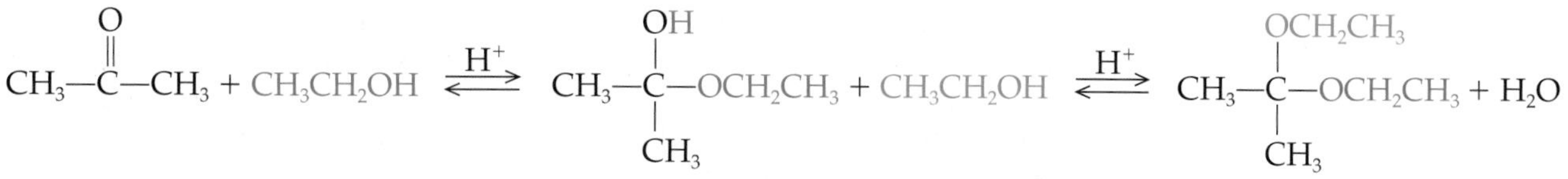

Question 13.13 Identify each of the following structures as a hemiacetal or acetal.

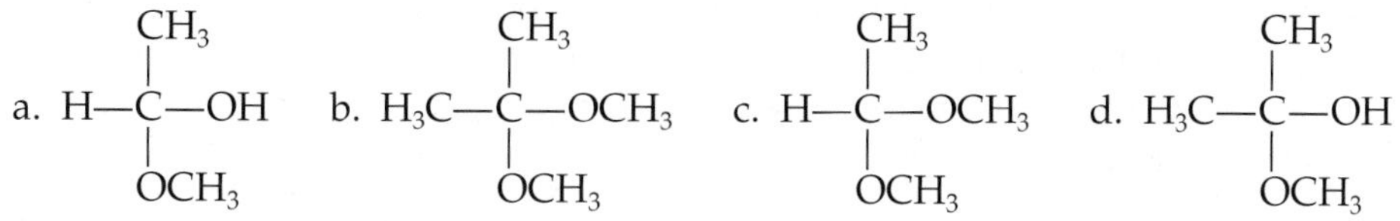

a. $H-\overset{CH_3}{\overset{|}{\underset{OCH_3}{\underset{|}{C}}}}-OH$ b. $H_3C-\overset{CH_3}{\overset{|}{\underset{OCH_3}{\underset{|}{C}}}}-OCH_3$ c. $H-\overset{CH_3}{\overset{|}{\underset{OCH_3}{\underset{|}{C}}}}-OCH_3$ d. $H_3C-\overset{CH_3}{\overset{|}{\underset{OCH_3}{\underset{|}{C}}}}-OH$

Question 13.14 Identify each of the following structures as a hemiacetal or acetal.

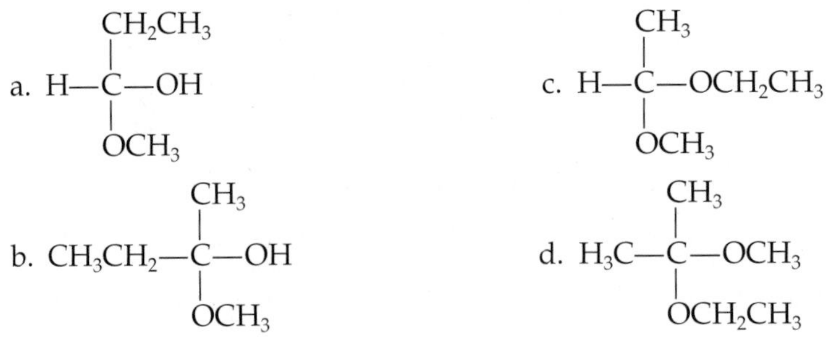

a. $H—\overset{CH_2CH_3}{\underset{OCH_3}{C}}—OH$

b. $CH_3CH_2—\overset{CH_3}{\underset{OCH_3}{C}}—OH$

c. $H—\overset{CH_3}{\underset{OCH_3}{C}}—OCH_2CH_3$

d. $H_3C—\overset{CH_3}{\underset{OCH_2CH_3}{C}}—OCH_3$

Earlier we noted that hemiacetals formed in intermolecular reactions are unstable and continue to react, forming acetals. This is not the case with intramolecular hemiacetal formation, reactions in which the hydroxyl group and the carbonyl group are part of the same molecule, that produce five- or six-membered rings. In these cases the cyclic hemiacetals are very stable. Consider the following reaction in which an intramolecular hemiacetal is formed from 4-hydroxyheptanal:

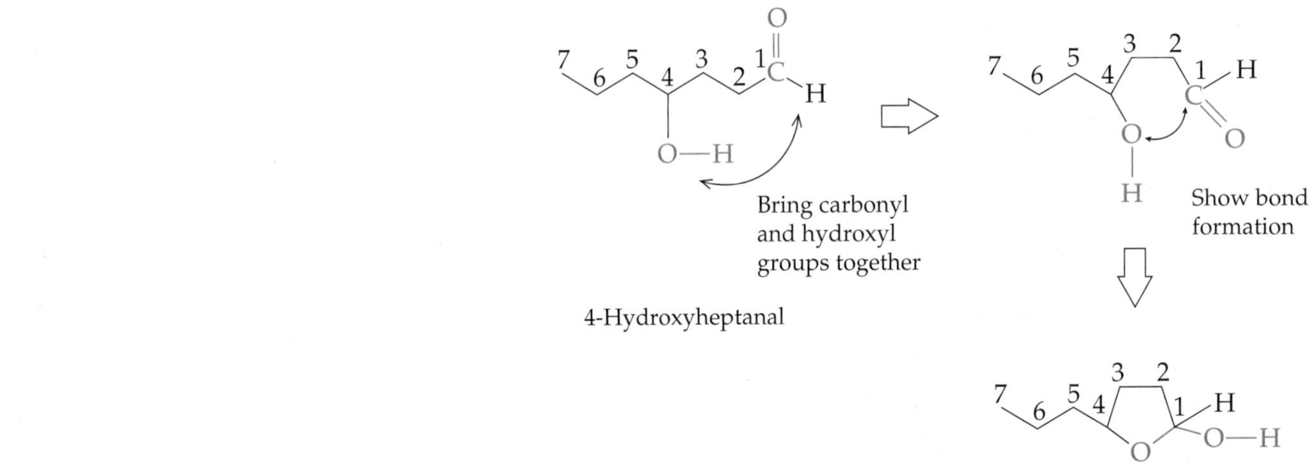

Bring carbonyl and hydroxyl groups together

4-Hydroxyheptanal

Show bond formation

A Cyclic Hemiacetal

This reaction is very important in the chemistry of the carbohydrates, in which hemiacetals are readily formed. Monosaccharides contain several hydroxyl groups and one carbonyl group. The linear form of a monosaccharide quickly undergoes an intramolecular reaction in solution to produce a cyclic hemiacetal. In these reactions the cyclic or ring form of the molecule is more stable than the linear form. This reaction is shown for the sugar glucose (blood sugar) in Figure 13.6 and is discussed in detail in Section 16.2.

When the hemiacetal of one monosaccharide reacts with the hydroxyl group of another monosaccharide, the product is an acetal. A sugar molecule made up of two monosaccharides is called a *disaccharide.* The C—O—C or acetal bond between the two monosaccharides is called a *glycosidic bond.* An example of this is found in Figure 13.7, which depicts the formation of the disaccharide lactose (milk sugar) from the monosaccharides glucose and galactose. Notice that the acetal is formed between the hemiacetal hydroxyl group of galactose (in blue) and an alcohol hydroxyl group of glucose (in red).

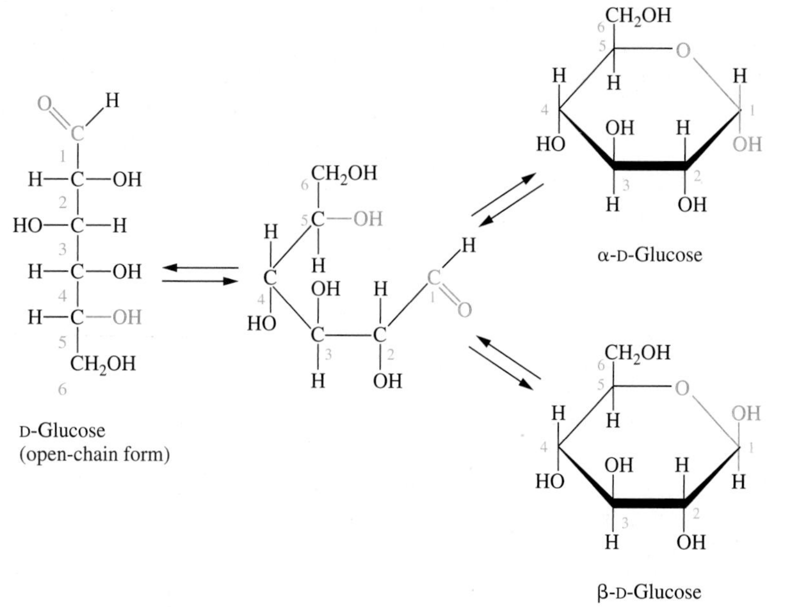

D-Glucose (open-chain form)

α-D-Glucose

β-D-Glucose

Figure 13.6 Hemiacetal formation in sugars, shown for the intramolecular reaction of D-glucose.

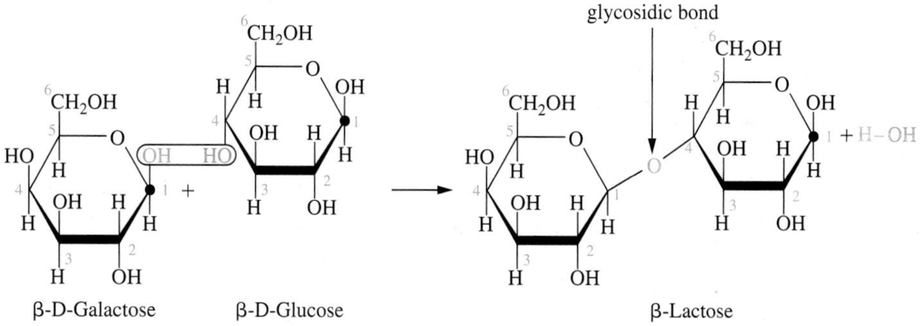

glycosidic bond

β-D-Galactose β-D-Glucose β-Lactose

Figure 13.7 Acetal formation, demonstrated in the formation of the disaccharide lactose, milk sugar. The reaction between the hemiacetal hydroxyl group of the monosaccharide galactose (blue) and an alcohol hydroxyl group of the monosaccharide glucose (red) produces the acetal lactose. The bond between the two sugars is a glycosidic bond.

Keto-Enol Tautomers

LEARNING GOAL

8 Draw the keto and enol forms of aldehydes and ketones.

Many aldehydes and ketones may exist in an equilibrium mixture of two constitutional or structural isomers called tautomers. **Tautomers** differ from one another in the placement of a hydrogen atom and a double bond. One tautomer is the *keto form* (on the left in the following equation). The keto form has the structure typical of an aldehyde or ketone. The other form is called the *enol form* (on the right in the following equation). The **enol** form has a structure containing a carbon-carbon double bond (*en*) and a hydroxyl group, the functional group characteristic of alcohols (*ol*).

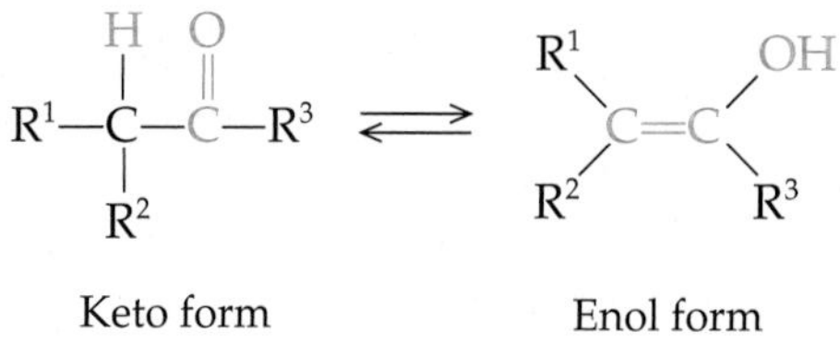

$$R^1{-}\underset{R^2}{\overset{H}{C}}{-}\overset{O}{\overset{\|}{C}}{-}R^3 \rightleftharpoons (R^1)(R^2)C{=}C(OH)(R^3)$$

Keto form Enol form

(R^1, R^2, and R^3 = H or alkyl group)

Because the keto form of most simple aldehydes and ketones is more stable, they exist mainly in that form.

EXAMPLE 13.9 **Writing an Equation Representing the Equilibrium Between the Keto and Enol Forms of a Simple Aldehyde**

LEARNING GOAL

8 Draw the keto and enol forms of aldehydes and ketones.

Draw the keto form of ethanal and write an equation representing the equilibrium between the keto and enol forms of this molecule.

Solution

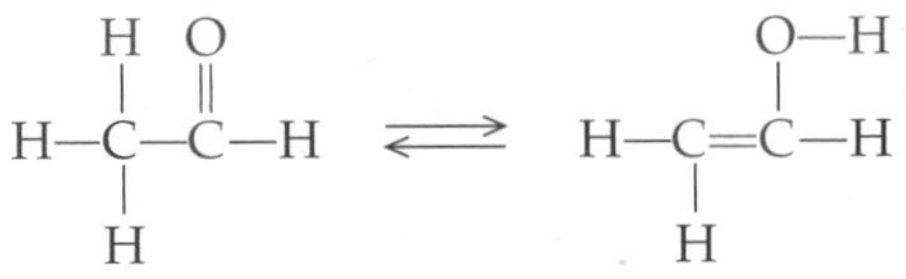

$$H_3C{-}CHO \rightleftharpoons H_2C{=}CH{-}OH$$

Ethanal
Keto form
More stable

Enol form
Less stable

Practice Problem 13.9

Draw the keto and enol forms of (a) propanal and (b) 3-pentanone.

▸ For Further Practice: **Questions 13.79 and 13.80.**

Phosphoenolpyruvate is a biologically important phosphorylated enol. Note that the molecule has a phosphoryl group ($-PO_4^{-2}$) in place of a hydroxyl group (–OH). The bond between the carbon and the phosphoryl group is represented by a "squiggle" (~) to show that this is a high energy bond. In fact, phosphoenolpyruvate is the highest energy phosphorylated compound in living systems.

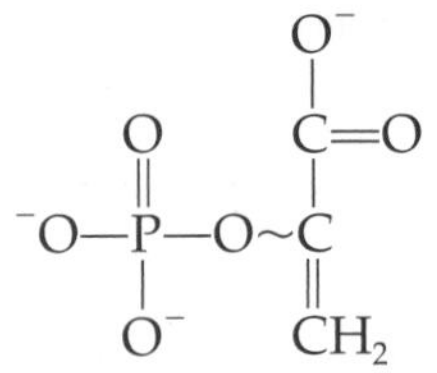

$$^{-}O{-}P(=O)(O^{-}){-}O{\sim}C(=CH_2){-}C(=O){-}O^{-}$$

Phosphoenolpyruvate

Phosphoenolpyruvate is produced in the next-to-last step in the metabolic pathway called *glycolysis,* which is the first stage of carbohydrate breakdown. In the final reaction of glycolysis, the phosphoryl group from phosphoenolpyruvate, along with energy from the high energy bond, are transferred to adenosine diphosphate (ADP). The reaction produces ATP, the major energy currency of the cell.

The glycolysis pathway is discussed in detail in Chapter 21.

CHAPTER MAP

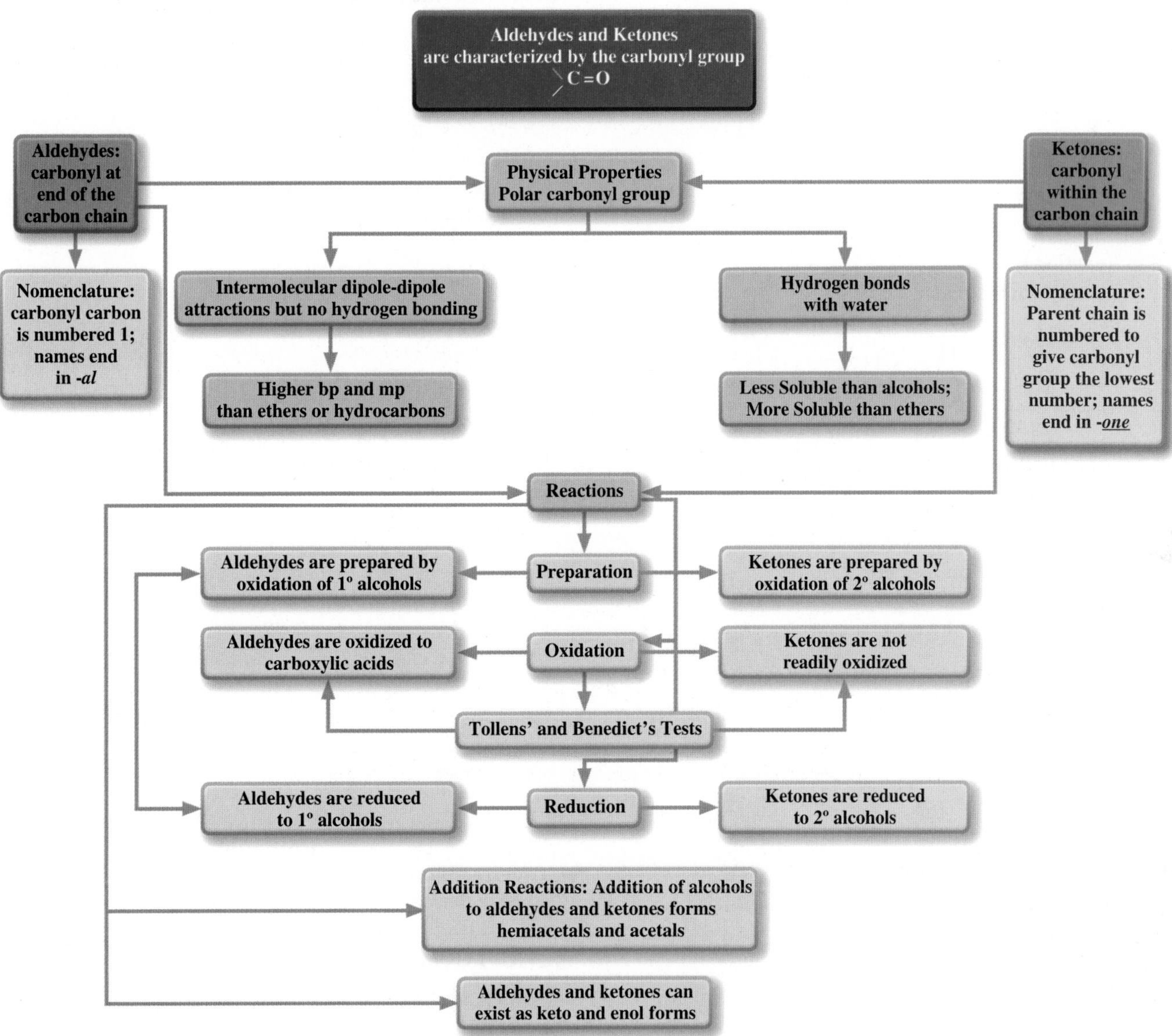
Aldehydes and Ketones
are characterized by the carbonyl group
C=O
Aldehydes: carbonyl at end of the carbon chain
Physical Properties
Polar carbonyl group
Ketones: carbonyl within the carbon chain
Nomenclature: carbonyl carbon is numbered 1; names end in -al
Intermolecular dipole-dipole attractions but no hydrogen bonding
Hydrogen bonds with water
Nomenclature: Parent chain is numbered to give carbonyl group the lowest number; names end in -one
Higher bp and mp than ethers or hydrocarbons
Less Soluble than alcohols; More Soluble than ethers
Reactions
Aldehydes are prepared by oxidation of 1° alcohols
Preparation
Ketones are prepared by oxidation of 2° alcohols
Aldehydes are oxidized to carboxylic acids
Oxidation
Ketones are not readily oxidized
Tollens' and Benedict's Tests
Aldehydes are reduced to 1° alcohols
Reduction
Ketones are reduced to 2° alcohols
Addition Reactions: Addition of alcohols to aldehydes and ketones forms hemiacetals and acetals
Aldehydes and ketones can exist as keto and enol forms

SUMMARY OF REACTIONS

Aldehydes and Ketones

Oxidation of an Aldehyde

$$\underset{\text{Aldehyde}}{R{-}\overset{\overset{\displaystyle O}{\|}}{C}{-}H} \xrightarrow{[O]} \underset{\text{Carboxylic acid}}{R{-}\overset{\overset{\displaystyle O}{\|}}{C}{-}OH}$$

Reduction of Aldehydes and Ketones

$$\underset{\text{Aldehyde or Ketone}}{R^1{-}\overset{\overset{\displaystyle O}{\|}}{C}{-}R^2} + \underset{\text{Hydrogen}}{H{-}H} \xrightarrow{Pt} \underset{\text{Alcohol}}{R^1{-}\overset{OH}{\underset{R^2}{C}}{-}H}$$

Addition Reactions

Addition of an alcohol to an aldehyde or a ketone—acetal formation:

$$\underset{\text{Aldehyde or Ketone}}{R^1{-}\overset{\overset{\displaystyle O}{\|}}{C}{-}R^2} + \underset{\text{Alcohol}}{H{-}OR^3} \underset{}{\overset{H^+}{\rightleftharpoons}} \underset{\text{Hemiacetal}}{R^1{-}\overset{OH}{\underset{R^2}{C}}{-}OR^3} + H{-}OR^4 \overset{H^+}{\rightleftharpoons} \underset{\text{Acetal}}{R^1{-}\overset{OR^4}{\underset{R^2}{C}}{-}OR^3} + H_2O$$

Keto-enol Tautomerization

$$\underset{\text{Keto form}}{R^1{-}\overset{H}{\underset{R^2}{C}}{-}\overset{\overset{\displaystyle O}{\|}}{C}{-}R^3} \rightleftharpoons \underset{\text{Enol form}}{(R^1)(R^2)C{=}C(OH)(R^3)}$$

SUMMARY

13.1 Structure and Physical Properties

- The **carbonyl group** is characteristic of the **aldehydes** and **ketones.**
- The carbonyl group and the two groups attached to it are coplanar.
- In ketones the carbonyl carbon is attached to two carbon-containing groups.
- In aldehydes the carbonyl carbon is attached to at least one hydrogen; the second group may be another hydrogen or a carbon-containing group.
- Because of the polar carbonyl group, aldehydes and ketones are polar compounds. However, they cannot form hydrogen bonds with one another. As a result, they have higher boiling points than comparable hydrocarbons, but lower boiling points than comparable alcohols.
- Aldehydes and ketones can form hydrogen bonds with water and as a result are reasonably soluble in water.
- Larger carbonyl-containing compounds are less polar and thus are more soluble in nonpolar organic solvents.

13.2 IUPAC Nomenclature and Common Names

- In the IUPAC Nomenclature System, aldehydes are named by determining the parent compound and replacing the final *-e* of the parent alkane with *-al.*
  - The chain is numbered beginning with the carbonyl carbon as carbon-1.
- In the IUPAC Nomenclature System, ketones are named by determining the parent compound and replacing the *-e* of the parent alkane with the *-one* suffix of the ketone family.
  - The longest carbon chain is numbered to give the carbonyl carbon the lowest possible number.
- In the common system of nomenclature, substituted aldehydes are named as derivatives of the parent compound. Greek letters indicate the position of substituents.
- Common names of ketones are derived by naming the alkyl groups bonded to the carbonyl carbon. These names are followed by the word *ketone.*

13.3 Important Aldehydes and Ketones

- **Members of the aldehyde and ketone families are important as food and fragrance chemicals, medicinal, and agricultural chemicals.**
- **Methanal (formaldehyde) is used to preserve tissue.**
- **Ethanal causes the symptoms of a hangover and is oxidized to produce acetic acid commercially.**
- **Propanone (acetone) is a useful and versatile solvent for organic compounds.**

13.4 Reactions Involving Aldehydes and Ketones

- **In the laboratory, aldehydes and ketones are prepared by the oxidation of alcohols.**
  - Oxidation of a primary alcohol produces an aldehyde.
  - Oxidation of a secondary alcohol produces a ketone.
- **Aldehydes and ketones can be distinguished from one another on the basis of their ability to undergo oxidation reactions. The Tollens' test and Benedict's test are the most common tests to distinguish aldehydes and ketones.**
  - Aldehydes are relatively easily oxidized to carboxylic acids.
  - Ketones do not undergo further oxidation reactions.
- **Aldehydes and ketones are readily reduced to alcohols by hydrogenation.**
- **The most common reaction of the carbonyl group is addition across the highly polar carbon-oxygen double bond.**
  - The addition of an alcohol to an aldehyde or ketone produces a **hemiacetal.**
  - The hemiacetal may react with a second alcohol to form an **acetal.**
- **Aldehydes and ketones may exist in an equilibrium mixture of keto and enol tautomers.**
  - An **enol** is a molecule having both a carbon-carbon double bond and a hydroxyl group (—OH).
  - **Tautomers** are isomers that differ from one another in the placement of a hydrogen and a double bond.

ANSWERS TO PRACTICE PROBLEMS

13.1

Hexanal: $CH_3CH_2CH_2CH_2CH_2C(=O)—H$

trans-2-Hexanal:

$$\begin{array}{c} H \quad\quad\; C(=O)—H \\ \diagdown \;\; \diagup \\ C{=}C \\ \diagup \;\; \diagdown \\ CH_3CH_2CH_2 \quad\quad H \end{array}$$

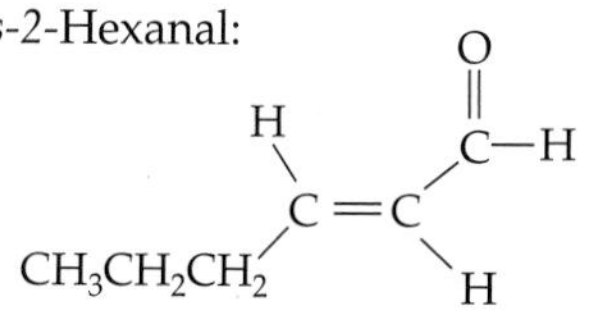

13.2 a. β,γ-Dimethylvaleraldehyde
b. α-Ethylvaleraldehyde
c. α-Chloropropionaldehyde
d. β-Hydroxybutyraldehyde

13.3 a. 6-Ethyl-2-octanone
b. 2-Methyl-3-hexanone
c. 2,4-Dimethyl-3-pentanone

13.4 a. Diethyl ketone c. Methyl hexyl ketone
b. Ethyl butyl ketone d. Diisopropyl ketone

13.5 a. The following equation represents the oxidation of 1-propanol to form propanal:

$$CH_3CH_2CH_2OH \xrightarrow{[O]} CH_3CH_2\overset{O}{\overset{\|}{C}}—H$$

Note that propanal may be further oxidized to form propanoic acid (a carboxylic acid).

b. The following equation represents the oxidation of 2-butanol to form butanone:

$$\underset{\text{2-Butanol}}{CH_3CH_2\overset{OH}{\overset{|}{C}}HCH_3} \xrightarrow{[O]} \underset{\text{Butanone}}{CH_3CH_2\overset{O}{\overset{\|}{C}}CH_3}$$

13.6 a. The following equation represents the reaction between ethanal and Tollens' reagent:

$$\underset{\text{Ethanal}}{CH_3\overset{O}{\overset{\|}{C}}—H} + \underset{\text{Silver ammonia complex}}{Ag(NH_3)_2^+} \longrightarrow \underset{\text{Ethanoate anion}}{CH_3\overset{O}{\overset{\|}{C}}—O^-} + \underset{\text{Silver metal}}{Ag^0}$$

b. Tollens' reagent reacts with aldehydes and not ketones. Therefore, there would be no reaction between propanone and Tollens' reagent.

13.7 a. The following equation represents the hydrogenation of propanone:

$$\underset{\text{Propanone}}{CH_3—\overset{O}{\overset{\|}{C}}—CH_3} + H_2 \xrightarrow{Ni} CH_3—\underset{H}{\underset{|}{\overset{OH}{\overset{|}{C}}}}—CH_3$$

b. The following equation represents the hydrogenation of butanone:

$$\underset{\text{Butanone}}{CH_3CH_2—\overset{O}{\overset{\|}{C}}—CH_3} + H_2 \xrightarrow{Pt} \underset{\text{2 - Butanol}}{CH_3CH_2\underset{OH}{\underset{|}{C}}HCH_3}$$

13.8 a. The following equation shows the hydrogenation of 3,4-dimethylhexanal, which produces 3,4-dimethyl-l-hexanol.

$$\underset{\text{3,4-Dimethylhexanal}}{CH_3CH_2\overset{\overset{CH_3}{|}}{C}H\underset{\underset{CH_3}{|}}{C}HCH_2\overset{\overset{O}{\|}}{C}-H + H_2} \xrightarrow{Pt} \underset{\text{3,4-Dimethtl-1-hexanol}}{CH_3CH_2\overset{\overset{CH_3}{|}}{C}H\underset{\underset{CH_3}{|}}{C}HCH_2CH_2OH}$$

b. The following equation show the hydrogenation of 2-chloropentanal, which produces 2-chloro-l-pentanol.

$$\underset{\text{2-Chloropentanal}}{CH_3CH_2CH_2CHCl\overset{\overset{O}{\|}}{C}-H + H_2} \xrightarrow{Pt} \underset{\text{2-Chloro-1-pentanol}}{CH_3CH_2CH_2CHClCH_2OH}$$

13.9 a. The following structures show the keto and enol forms of propanal:

$$\underset{\substack{\text{Propanal}\\ \text{Keto form}}}{H-\underset{\underset{H}{|}}{\overset{\overset{H}{|}}{C}}-\underset{\underset{H}{|}}{\overset{\overset{H}{|}}{C}}-\overset{\overset{O}{\|}}{C}-H} \rightleftharpoons \underset{\substack{\text{Propanal}\\ \text{Enol form}}}{H-\underset{\underset{H}{|}}{\overset{\overset{H}{|}}{C}}-\underset{\underset{H}{|}}{C}=\overset{\overset{OH}{|}}{C}-H}$$

b. The following structures show the keto and enol forms of 3-pentanone:

$$\underset{\substack{\text{3-Pentanone}\\ \text{(keto form)}}}{H-\underset{\underset{H}{|}}{\overset{\overset{H}{|}}{C}}-\underset{\underset{H}{|}}{\overset{\overset{H}{|}}{C}}-\overset{\overset{O}{\|}}{C}-\underset{\underset{H}{|}}{\overset{\overset{H}{|}}{C}}-\underset{\underset{H}{|}}{\overset{\overset{H}{|}}{C}}-H} \rightleftharpoons \underset{\substack{\text{3-Pentanone}\\ \text{(enol form)}}}{H-\underset{\underset{H}{|}}{\overset{\overset{H}{|}}{C}}-\underset{\underset{H}{|}}{C}=\overset{\overset{OH}{|}}{C}-\underset{\underset{H}{|}}{\overset{\overset{H}{|}}{C}}-\underset{\underset{H}{|}}{\overset{\overset{H}{|}}{C}}-H}$$

QUESTIONS AND PROBLEMS

Structure and Physical Properties

Foundations

13.15 Explain the relationship between carbon chain length and water solubility of aldehydes or ketones.

13.16 Explain the dipole-dipole interactions that occur between molecules containing carbonyl groups.

Applications

13.17 Simple ketones (for example, acetone) are often used as industrial solvents for many organically based products such as adhesives and paints. They are often considered "universal solvents," because they dissolve so many diverse materials. Why are these chemicals such good solvents?

13.18 Explain briefly why simple (containing fewer than five carbon atoms) aldehydes and ketones exhibit appreciable solubility in water.

13.19 Draw intermolecular hydrogen bonding between ethanal and water.

13.20 Draw the polar interactions that occur between acetone molecules.

13.21 Why do alcohols have higher boiling points than aldehydes or ketones of comparable molar mass?

13.22 Why do hydrocarbons have lower boiling points than aldehydes or ketones of comparable molar mass?

13.23 Rank the following from highest to lowest boiling points:

a. O

OH

O

H

b.

O

OH

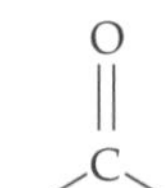

13.24 Rank the following from highest to lowest water solubility:

a.

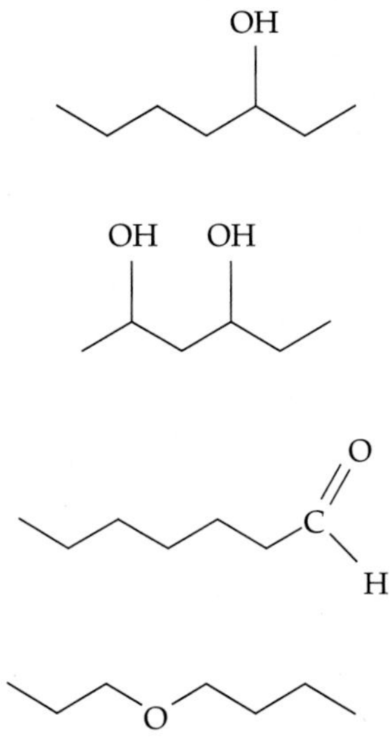

b.

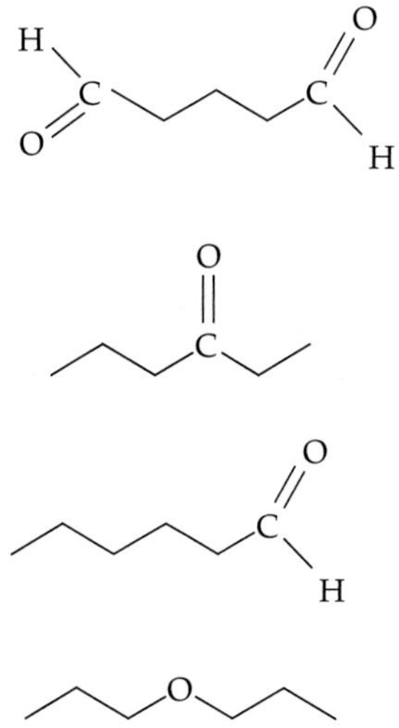

Nomenclature

Foundations

13.25 Briefly describe the rules of the IUPAC Nomenclature System for naming aldehydes.

13.26 Briefly describe the rules of the IUPAC Nomenclature System for naming ketones.

13.27 Briefly describe how to determine the common name of an aldehyde.

13.28 Briefly describe how to determine the common name of a ketone.

Applications

13.29 Draw each of the following using condensed formulas and line formulas:

a. Ethanal c. 2-Ethylheptanal
b. 3,4-Dimethylpentanal d. 5,7-Dichloroheptanal

13.30 Draw each of the following using condensed formulas and line formulas:

a. 2-Nonanone c. 4,6-Diethyl-3-octanone
b. 4-Methyl-2-heptanone d. 5-Bromo-4-octanone

13.31 Draw each of the following using condensed formulas and line formulas:

a. Ethyl isopropyl ketone c. Dibutyl ketone
b. Ethyl propyl ketone d. Heptyl hexyl ketone

13.32 Draw each of the following using condensed formulas and line formulas:

a. β-Methylbutyraldehyde
b. α-Hydroxypropionaldehyde
c. α,β-Dimethylvaleraldehyde
d. γ-Chlorovaleraldehyde

13.33 Use the IUPAC Nomenclature System to name each of the following compounds:

a. 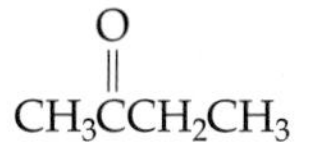 $CH_3C(=O)CH_2CH_3$

b. 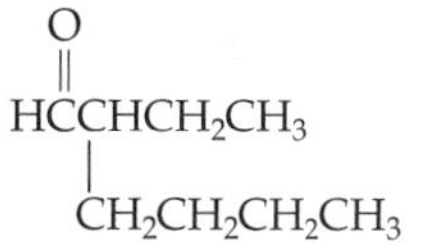 $HC(=O)CH(CH_2CH_2CH_2CH_3)CH_2CH_3$

13.34 Name each of the following using the IUPAC Nomenclature System:

a. 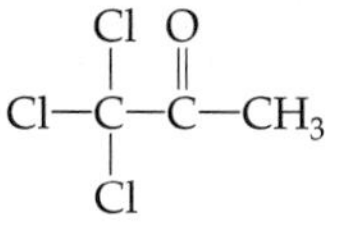 $Cl-CCl_2-C(=O)-CH_3$

b.

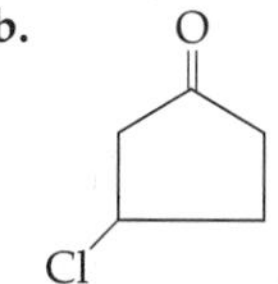

13.35 Name each of the following using the IUPAC Nomenclature System:

a.

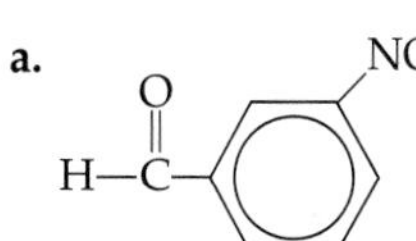

b.

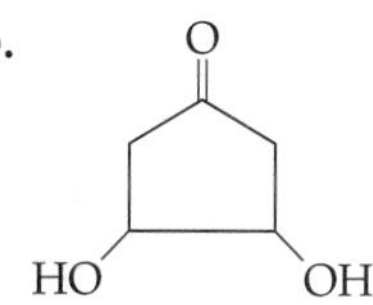

13.36 Name each of the following using the IUPAC Nomenclature System:

a.  $CH_3CH_2CH_2CHO$ (drawn as $CH_3CH_2CH_2C(=O)H$)

b. 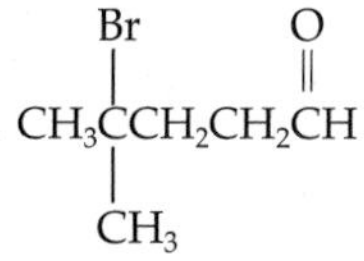 $CH_3C(Br)(CH_3)CH_2CH_2CH(=O)$

c. 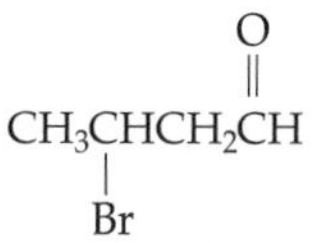 $CH_3CH(Br)CH_2CH(=O)$

d. 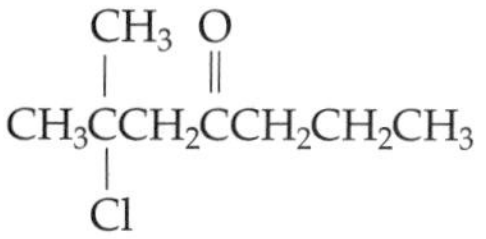 $CH_3C(CH_3)(Cl)CH_2C(=O)CH_2CH_2CH_3$

13.37 The molecule shown below has a lovely aroma of lily-of-the-valley. Discovered in 1908, it has been used in hundreds of perfumes. What is the IUPAC name of this molecule?

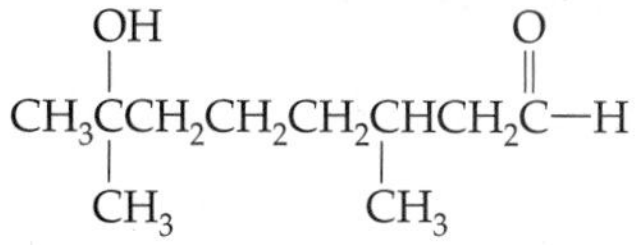

$CH_3C(OH)(CH_3)CH_2CH_2CH_2CH(CH_3)CH_2C(=O)-H$

13.38 Give the IUPAC name for each of the following compounds:

a. 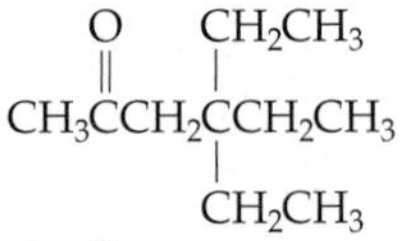 $CH_3C(=O)CH_2C(CH_2CH_3)_2CH_3$

$$\begin{array}{l} \quad\;\; O \quad\;\; CH_2CH_3 \\ \quad\;\; \| \qquad\quad | \\ CH_3CCH_2CCH_2CH_3 \\ \qquad\qquad\;\; | \\ \qquad\qquad CH_2CH_3 \end{array}$$

b.

$$\begin{array}{l} \quad\;\; O \\ \quad\;\; \| \\ CH_3CCH_2CHCH_2CH_3 \\ \qquad\qquad\;\; | \\ \qquad\qquad\; Cl \end{array}$$

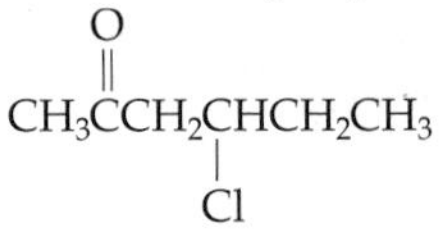

13.39 Give the IUPAC name for each of the following compounds:

a.

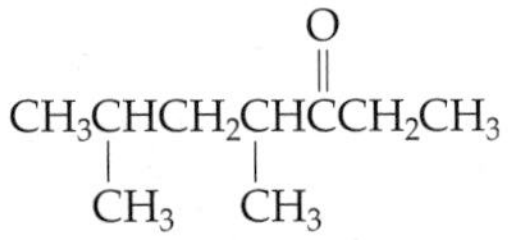

$$\begin{array}{l} \qquad\qquad\qquad\quad\;\; O \\ \qquad\qquad\qquad\quad\;\; \| \\ CH_3CHCH_2CHCCH_2CH_3 \\ \qquad\; | \qquad\;\; | \\ \quad\; CH_3 \quad CH_3 \end{array}$$

b. 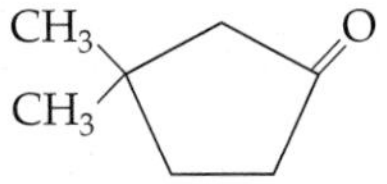 CH₃, CH₃, O (cyclopentanone ring)

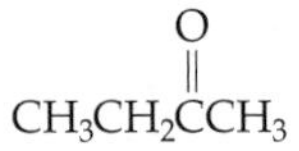

13.40 Give the IUPAC name for each of the following compounds:

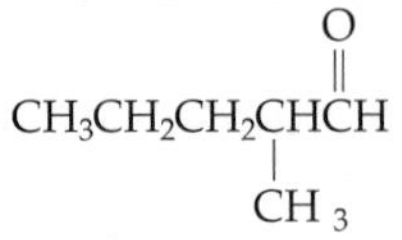

a.

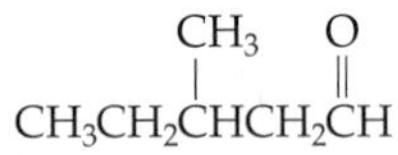

$$\begin{array}{l} \qquad\quad CH_3 \;\; O \\ \qquad\quad\; | \qquad \| \\ CH_3CH_2CHCH_2CH \end{array}$$

b. 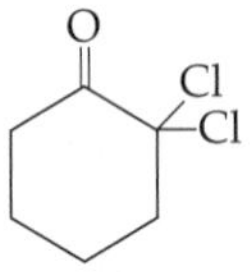 O, Cl, Cl (cyclohexanone ring)

13.41 Give the common name for each of the following compounds:

a. 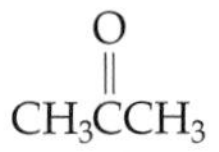 $CH_3\overset{O}{\overset{\|}{C}}CH_3$

b. $CH_3CH_2\overset{O}{\overset{\|}{C}}CH_3$

c. $CH_3\overset{O}{\overset{\|}{C}}H$

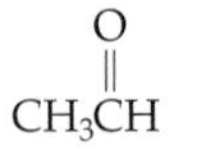

d. 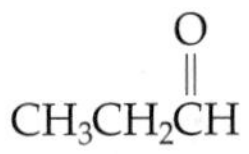 $CH_3CH_2\overset{O}{\overset{\|}{C}}H$

e. 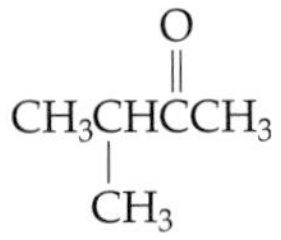 $CH_3\underset{CH_3}{\underset{|}{C}}H\overset{O}{\overset{\|}{C}}CH_3$

13.42 Give the common name for each of the following compounds:

a. 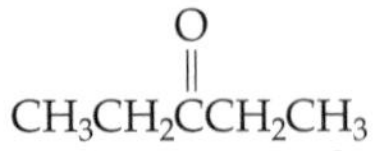 $CH_3CH_2\overset{O}{\overset{\|}{C}}CH_2CH_3$

b. $CH_3CH_2CH_2\underset{CH_3}{\underset{|}{C}}H\overset{O}{\overset{\|}{C}}H$

c. $CH_3\overset{O}{\overset{\|}{C}}CH_2CH_2CH_3$

13.43 Draw the structure of each of the following compounds:

a. 3-Hydroxybutanal
b. 2-Methylpentanal
c. 4-Bromohexanal
d. 3-Iodopentanal
e. 2-Hydroxy-3-methylheptanal

13.44 Draw the structure of each of the following compounds:

a. Propanone
b. 2-Pentanone
c. 3-Heptanone
d. 2,4-Dimethyl-3-pentanone

Important Aldehydes and Ketones

13.45 Why is acetone a good solvent for many organic compounds?

13.46 List several uses for formaldehyde.

13.47 Ethanal is produced by the oxidation of ethanol. Where does this reaction occur in the body?

13.48 List several aldehydes and ketones that are used as food or fragrance chemicals.

Reactions Involving Aldehydes and Ketones

Foundations

13.49 Explain what is meant by oxidation in organic molecules and provide an example of an oxidation reaction involving an aldehyde.

13.50 Explain what is meant by reduction in organic reactions and provide an example of a reduction reaction involving an aldehyde or ketone.

13.51 Define the term *addition reaction*.

13.52 Provide an example of an addition reaction involving an aldehyde or ketone.

13.53 Write a general equation representing the oxidation of an aldehyde. What is the product of this reaction?

13.54 Write a general equation representing the reduction of an aldehyde. What is the product of this reaction?

13.55 Write a general equation representing the addition of one alcohol molecule to an aldehyde or a ketone.

13.56 Write a general equation representing the addition of two alcohol molecules to an aldehyde or a ketone.

Applications

13.57 Draw the structure of each of the following alcohols. Then draw and name the product that you would expect to produce by the oxidation of each.

a. 4-Methyl-2-heptanol
b. 3,4-Dimethyl-1-pentanol
c. 4-Ethyl-2-heptanol
d. 5,7-Dichloro-3-heptanol

13.58 Draw the structure of each of the following alcohols. Then draw and name the product that you would expect to produce by the oxidation of each.

a. 1-Nonanol
b. 4-Methyl-1-heptanol
c. 4,6-Diethyl-3-methyl-3-octanol
d. 5-Bromo-4-octanol

13.59 Draw the generalized equation for the oxidation of a primary alcohol.

13.60 Draw the generalized equation for the oxidation of a secondary alcohol.

13.61 Draw the structures of the reactants and products for each of the following reactions. Label each as an oxidation or a reduction reaction:

a. Ethanal to ethanol
b. Cyclohexanone to cyclohexanol
c. 2-Propanol to propanone

13.62 An unknown has been determined to be one of the following three compounds:

3-Pentanone Pentanal

$CH_3CH_2CH_2CH_2CH_3$

Pentane

The unknown is fairly soluble in water and produces a silver mirror when treated with the silver ammonia complex. A red precipitate appears when it is treated with the Benedict's reagent. Which of the compounds is the correct structure for the unknown? Explain your reasoning.

13.63 Write a balanced equation for the hydrogenation of each of the following aldehydes:
a. 3-Methylpentanal
b. 2-Hydroxypropanal
c. 2,3-Dimethyl pentanal
d. 4-Chloropentanal

13.64 Write a balanced equation for the hydrogenation of each of the following ketones:
a. 2-Methyl-3-pentanone
b. 3-Hexanone
c. 5-Nonanone
d. 7-Tetradecanone

13.65 Write a balanced equation for the hydrogenation of each of the following aldehydes:
a. Butanal
b. 3-Methylpentanal
c. 2-Methylpropanal

13.66 Write a balanced equation for the hydrogenation of each of the following aldehydes:
a. 3-Methylbutanal
b. 4-Bromopentanal
c. Propanal

13.67 Which of the following compounds would be expected to give a positive Tollens' test?
a. 3-Pentanone
b. Cyclohexanone
c. 3-Methylbutanal
d. Cyclopentanol
e. 2,2-Dimethyl-1-pentanol
f. Acetaldehyde

13.68 Write an equation representing the reaction of glucose with the Benedict's reagent. How was this test used in medicine?

13.69 Write an equation for the addition of one ethanol molecule to each of the following aldehydes:

a. $CH_3CH_2\overset{O}{\overset{\|}{C}}H$ b. $CH_3\overset{O}{\overset{\|}{C}}H$

13.70 Write an equation for the addition of one ethanol molecule to each of the following ketones:

b. $CH_3\overset{O}{\overset{\|}{C}}CH_2CH_2CH_3$

13.71 Write an equation for the addition of two methanol molecules to each of the following aldehydes:

b. $CH_3\overset{O}{\overset{\|}{C}}H$

13.72 Write an equation for the addition of two methanol molecules to each of the following ketones:

a. $CH_3\overset{O}{\overset{\|}{C}}CH_3$

13.73 An aldehyde can be oxidized to produce a carboxylic acid. Draw the carboxylic acid that would be produced by the oxidation of each of the following aldehydes:
a. Pentanal
b. Hexanal
c. Heptanal
d. Octanal

13.74 An aldehyde can be oxidized to produce a carboxylic acid. Draw the carboxylic acid that would be produced by the oxidation of each of the following aldehydes:
a. 3-Methylpentanal
b. 2,3-Dichlorobutanal
c. 2,4-Diethylhexanal
d. 2-Methylpropanal

13.75 An alcohol can be oxidized to produce an aldehyde or a ketone. What aldehyde or ketone is produced by the oxidation of each of the following alcohols?
a. Methanol
b. 1-Propanol

13.76 An alcohol can be oxidized to produce an aldehyde or a ketone. What aldehyde or ketone is produced by the oxidation of each of the following alcohols?
a. 3-Pentanol
b. 2-Methyl-2-butanol

13.77 Indicate whether each of the following statements is true or false.
a. Aldehydes and ketones can be oxidized to produce carboxylic acids.
b. Oxidation of a primary alcohol produces an aldehyde.
c. Oxidation of a tertiary alcohol produces a ketone.
d. Alcohols can be produced by the oxidation of an aldehyde or ketone.

13.78 Indicate whether each of the following statements is true or false.
a. Ketones, but not aldehydes, react in the Tollens' silver mirror test.
b. Addition of one alcohol molecule to an aldehyde results in formation of a hemiacetal.
c. The cyclic forms of monosaccharides are intramolecular hemiacetals.
d. Disaccharides (sugars composed of two covalently joined monosaccharides) are acetals.

13.79 Draw the keto and enol forms of propanone.

13.80 Draw the keto and enol forms of butanone.

13.81 Draw the hemiacetal that results from the reaction of each of the following aldehydes or ketones with ethanol:

a. $CH_3CH_2CH_2\overset{O}{\overset{\|}{C}}CH_3$

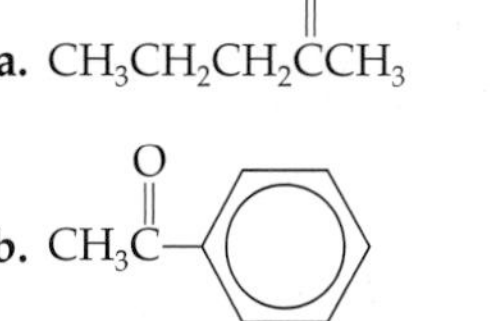

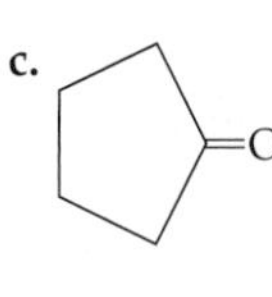

13.82 Identify each of the following compounds as a hemiacetal or acetal:

a. (ring with O, OCH_3, CH_3)

b. (ring with OH, OCH_2CH_3)

c. $CH_3\overset{OH}{\overset{|}{C}}CH_3$ with OCH_2CH_3

d. (ring with O, OH, CH_3)

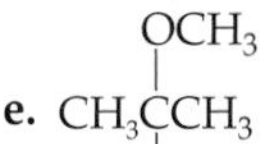

f. $CH_3CH{=}CH\overset{OCH_3}{\overset{|}{C}}CH_3$ with OH

13.83 Complete the following synthesis by supplying the missing reactant(s), reagent(s), or product(s) indicated by the question marks:

$$CH_3\overset{O}{\overset{\|}{C}}CH_3 \xrightarrow{?(1)} CH_3\underset{OCH_2CH_3}{\overset{OCH_2CH_3}{C}}CH_3$$

$$\uparrow ?(2)$$

$$CH_3\underset{OH}{C}HCH_3 \xrightarrow[\text{Heat}]{H_2SO_4} ?(3)$$

13.84 Which alcohol would you oxidize to produce each of the following compounds?

a. $CH_3\overset{CH_3}{C}HCH_2\overset{O}{\overset{\|}{C}}CH_3$

b. $H\overset{O}{\overset{\|}{C}}CH_2CH_2\overset{O}{\overset{\|}{C}}H$

c. $C_6H_5-CH_2\overset{O}{\overset{\|}{C}}H$

d. $H\overset{O}{\overset{\|}{C}}CH_2\overset{O}{\overset{\|}{C}}CH_3$

e. $CH_3\underset{CH_3}{\overset{CH_3}{C}}CH_2CH_2\overset{O}{\overset{\|}{C}}H$

f. O=(cyclohexane)=O

CRITICAL THINKING PROBLEMS

THE CHEMISTRY OF VISION

1. Review the material on the chemistry of vision found on the Web at www.mhhe.com/denniston and, with respect to the isomers of retinal, discuss the changes in structure that occur as the nerve impulses that result in vision are produced. Provide condensed formulas of the retinal isomers that you discuss.
2. Classify the structure of β-D-fructose as a hemiacetal or acetal. Explain your choice.

(Structure of β-D-fructose: CH_2OH, O, OH, H, HO, H, CH_2OH, OH, H)

3. Design a synthesis for each of the following compounds, using any inorganic reagent of your choice and any hydrocarbon or alkyl halide of your choice:
   a. Octanal
   b. Cyclohexanone
   c. 2-Phenylethanoic acid
4. When alkenes react with ozone, O_3, the double bond is cleaved, and an aldehyde and/or a ketone is produced. The reaction, called *ozonolysis*, is shown in general as:

$$>C=C< + O_3 \longrightarrow >C=O + O=C<$$

   Predict the ozonolysis products that are formed when each of the following alkenes is reacted with ozone:
   a. 1-Butene
   b. 2-Hexene
   c. *cis*-3,6-Dimethyl-3-heptene
5. Lactose is the major sugar found in mammalian milk. It is a disaccharide composed of the monosaccharides glucose and galactose:

(Structure of lactose: CH_2OH, O, HO, H, OH, H, H, H, H, OH, O, CH_2OH, O, H, H, OH, OH, H, H, H, OH)

   Is lactose a hemiacetal or an acetal? Explain your choice.
6. The following are the keto and enol tautomers of phenol:

O—H ⇌ O H H

Enol form of phenol | Keto form of phenol

   We have seen that most simple aldehydes and ketones exist mainly in the keto form because it is more stable. Phenol is an exception, existing primarily in the enol form. Propose a hypothesis to explain this.

14

Carboxylic Acids and Carboxylic Acid Derivatives

ORGANIC CHEMISTRY

LEARNING GOALS

1. Write structures and describe the physical properties of carboxylic acids.
2. Determine the common and IUPAC names of carboxylic acids.
3. Describe the biological, medical, or environmental significance of several carboxylic acids.
4. Write equations that show the synthesis of a carboxylic acid.
5. Write equations representing acid-base reactions of carboxylic acids.
6. Write equations representing the preparation of an ester.
7. Write structures and describe the physical properties of esters.
8. Determine the common and IUPAC names of esters.
9. Write equations representing the hydrolysis of an ester.
10. Define the term *saponification* and describe how soap works in the emulsification of grease and oil.
11. Determine the common and IUPAC names of acid chlorides.
12. Determine the common and IUPAC names of acid anhydrides.
13. Write equations representing the synthesis of acid anhydrides.
14. Discuss the significance of thioesters and phosphoesters in biological systems.

The salad in this figure is part of a healthy diet. Using the Internet, make a list of the organic molecules found in these foods and their role in diet and health.

OUTLINE

Introduction 470

14.1 Carboxylic Acids 471

Chemistry at the Crime Scene: Carboxylic Acids and the Body Farm 476

Green Chemistry: Garbage Bags from Potato Peels? 478

14.2 Esters 484

A Human Perspective: The Chemistry of Flavor and Fragrance 488

A Human Perspective: Detergents 492

14.3 Acid Chlorides and Acid Anhydrides 494

14.4 Nature's High-Energy Compounds: Phosphoesters and Thioesters 498

A Human Perspective: Carboxylic Acid Derivatives of Special Interest 500

INTRODUCTION

Carboxylic acids and their derivatives the esters are a common part of our daily lives. You may encounter many of them in the chef's salad you have for lunch. The two-carbon carboxylic acid acetic acid in aqueous solution, or vinegar, adds that tartness to the Italian dressing on your salad. Propionic acid, with three carbons, gives that tangy flavor to the Swiss cheese on your salad.

Long-chain carboxylic acids are called fatty acids, and they form esters when they react with an alcohol, such as glycerol. The olive oil in your salad dressing and the solid fat in the meat and cheese on your salad are examples of such triglycerides.

Perhaps you had a fruit salad for breakfast. If so, you may have enjoyed a number of sweet, fruity-tasting esters, such as 2-methylbutyl ethanoate (bananas) or methyl thiobutanoate (strawberries).

Some carboxylic acids are key elements in exercise physiology and others are used in the treatment of diseases. For instance, lactic acid is a product of our metabolism that builds up in muscles and blood when we are exercising so strenuously that we cannot provide sufficient oxygen to working muscle. We will learn more about the lactate fermentation and its role in exercising muscle in Chapter 21. A four-carbon carboxylic acid, butanoic acid (butyric acid), is being used to treat sickle cell anemia. Although we don't yet understand how, this compound "turns on" the gene for fetal hemoglobin, protecting some patients from the harmful effects of this genetic disorder. To learn more about this therapy, see Chemistry Connection: Wake Up, Sleeping Gene, online at www.mhhe.com/denniston.

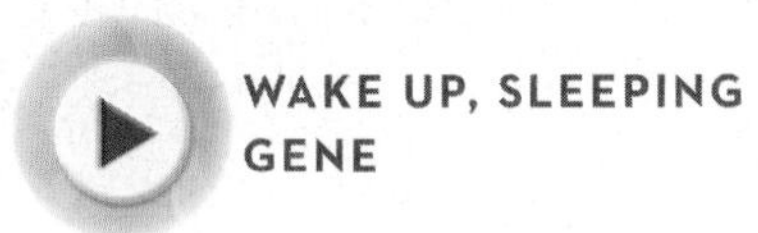

Carboxylic acids (Figure 14.1a) have the following general structure:

They are characterized by the carboxyl group, shown in red, which may also be written in condensed form as —COOH or —CO_2H. The name *carboxylic acid* describes this family of compounds quite well. The term *carboxylic* is taken from the terms *carbonyl* and *hydroxyl*, the two structural units that make up the carboxyl group. The word *acid* in the name tells us one of the more important properties of these molecules: they dissociate in water to release protons. Thus they are acids.

In fact, carboxylic acids are weak acids because they partially dissociate in water.

In this chapter we will also study the esters (Figure 14.1b), which have the following general structures:

R—C(=O)—O—R Ar—C(=O)—O—Ar Ar—C(=O)—O—R

Examples of aliphatic and aromatic esters

Amides are discussed in Chapter 15.

The group shown in red is called the acyl group. The acyl group is part of the functional group of the carboxylic acid derivatives, including the esters, acid chlorides, acid anhydrides, and amides.

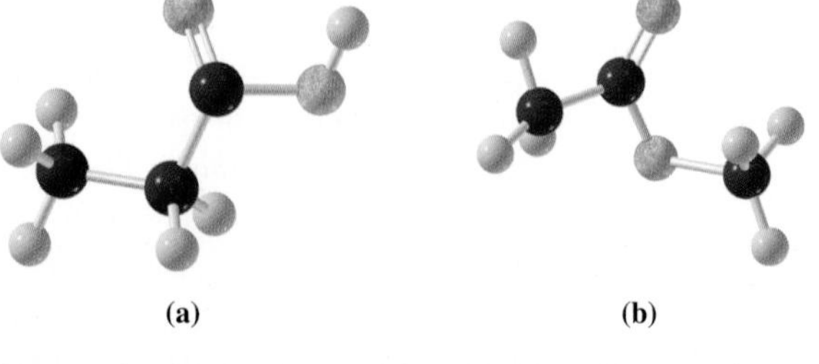

Figure 14.1 Ball-and-stick models of (a) a carboxylic acid, propanoic acid, and (b) an ester, methyl ethanoate.

14.1 Carboxylic Acids

Structure and Physical Properties

LEARNING GOAL

1 Write structures and describe the physical properties of carboxylic acids.

The **carboxyl group** consists of two very polar functional groups, the carbonyl group and the hydroxyl group. Thus **carboxylic acids** are very polar compounds. In addition, they can hydrogen bond to one another and to molecules of a polar solvent such as water. As a result of intermolecular hydrogen bonding, they boil at higher temperatures than aldehydes, ketones, or alcohols of comparable molar mass. A comparison of the boiling points of an alkane, alcohol, ether, aldehyde, ketone, and carboxylic acid of comparable molar mass is shown below:

$CH_3CH_2CH_2CH_3$	$CH_3—O—CH_2CH_3$	$CH_3CH_2CH_2—OH$
Butane (butane) M.M. = 58 b.p. −0.5°C	Methoxyethane (ethyl methyl ether) M.M. = 60 b.p. 7.0°C	1-Propanol (propyl alcohol) M.M. = 60 b.p. 97.2°C

$CH_3CH_2C(=O)—H$	$CH_3C(=O)—CH_3$	$CH_3C(=O)—OH$
Propanal (propionaldehyde) M.M. = 58 b.p. 49°C	Propanone (acetone) M.M. = 58 b.p. 56°C	Ethanoic acid (acetic acid) M.M. = 60 b.p. 118°C

Formic acid causes the burning sensation at the site of an ant bite. What is the IUPAC name for formic acid? Why does treating the bite with baking soda reduce the burning sensation?

As with alcohols, the smaller carboxylic acids are soluble in water (Figure 14.2). However, solubility falls off dramatically as the carbon content of the carboxylic acid increases because the molecules become more hydrocarbonlike and less polar. For example, acetic acid (the two-carbon carboxylic acid found in vinegar) is completely soluble in water, but hexadecanoic acid (a sixteen-carbon carboxylic acid found in palm oil) is insoluble in water.

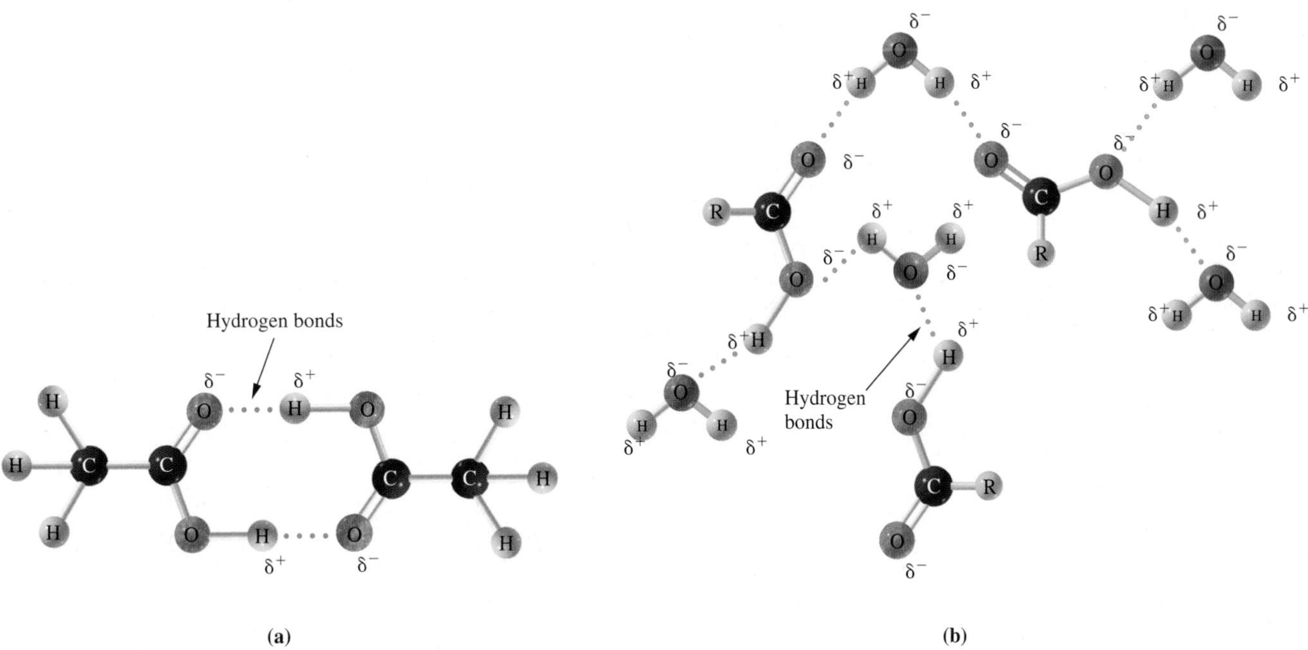

Figure 14.2 Hydrogen bonding (a) between carboxylic acid molecules and (b) between carboxylic acid molecules and water molecules.

The lower-molar-mass carboxylic acids have sharp, sour tastes and unpleasant aromas. Formic acid, HCOOH, is used as a chemical defense by ants and causes the burning sensation of the ant bite. Acetic acid, CH_3COOH, is found in vinegar; propionic acid, CH_3CH_2COOH, is responsible for the tangy flavor of Swiss cheese; and butyric acid, $CH_3CH_2CH_2COOH$, causes the stench associated with rancid butter and gas gangrene.

The longer-chain carboxylic acids are generally called **fatty acids** and are important components of biological membranes and triglycerides, the major lipid storage form in the body.

Question 14.1 Assuming that each of the following pairs of molecules has the same carbon chain length, which member of each of the following pairs has the lower boiling point?

a. a carboxylic acid or a ketone
b. a ketone or an alcohol
c. an alcohol or an alkane

Question 14.2 Assuming that each of the following pairs of molecules has the same carbon chain length, which member of each of the following pairs has the lower boiling point?

a. an ether or an aldehyde
b. an aldehyde or a carboxylic acid
c. an ether or an alcohol

Question 14.3 Why would you predict that a carboxylic acid would be more polar and have a higher boiling point than an aldehyde of comparable molar mass?

Question 14.4 Why would you predict that a carboxylic acid would be more polar and have a higher boiling point than an alcohol of comparable molar mass?

Nomenclature

LEARNING GOAL

2 Determine the common and IUPAC names of carboxylic acids.

In the IUPAC Nomenclature System, carboxylic acids are named according to the following set of rules:

- Determine the parent compound, the longest continuous carbon chain bearing the carboxyl group.
- Number the chain so that the carboxyl carbon is carbon-1.
- Replace the *-e* ending of the parent alkane with the suffix *-oic acid.* If there are two carboxyl groups, the suffix *-dioic acid* is used and the *-e* ending of the parent alkane is *not* dropped.
- Name and number substituents in the usual way. When a hydroxyl group (—OH) is one of the substituents, it is numbered and the term *hydroxy* is used in the prefix.

The following examples illustrate the naming of carboxylic acids with one carboxyl group:

$\overset{2}{C}H_3\overset{1}{C}(=O)—OH$ — Ethanoic acid (acetic acid)

$\overset{3}{C}H_3\overset{2}{C}H(OH)\overset{1}{C}(=O)—OH$ — 2-Hydroxypropanoic acid (α-Hydroxypropionic acid)

$\overset{4}{C}H_3\overset{3}{C}H(CH_3)\overset{2}{C}H_2\overset{1}{C}(=O)—OH$ — 3-Methylbutanoic acid (β-methylbutyric acid)

The following examples illustrate naming carboxylic acids with two carboxyl groups:

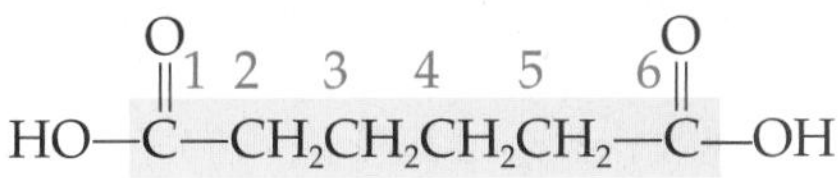

Hexanedioic acid
(adipic acid)

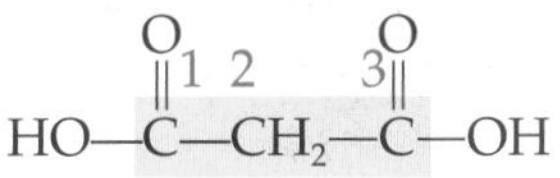

Propanedioic acid
(malonic acid)

EXAMPLE 14.1 Use the IUPAC Nomenclature System to Name a Carboxylic Acid

a. The following compound is one of the monomers from which a biodegradable plastic called Biopol is made (see Green Chemistry: Garbage Bags from Potato Peels? later in this chapter). Name this carboxylic acid using the IUPAC nomenclature system.

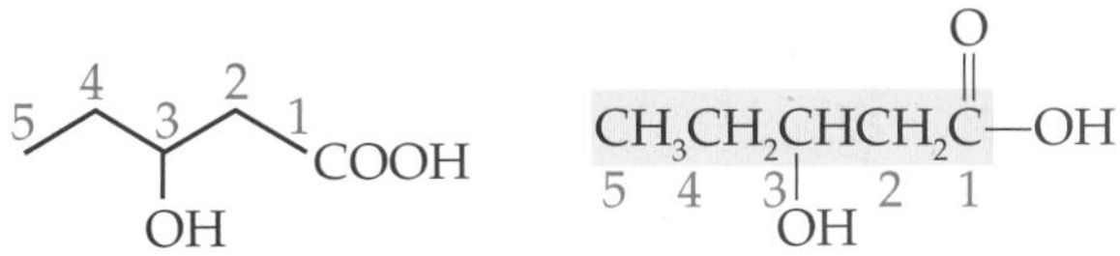

Solution

Parent compound: pentane (becomes pentanoic acid)
Position of —COOH: carbon-1 (must be!)
Substituent: 3-hydroxy
Name: 3-Hydroxypentanoic acid

b. Name the following carboxylic acid:

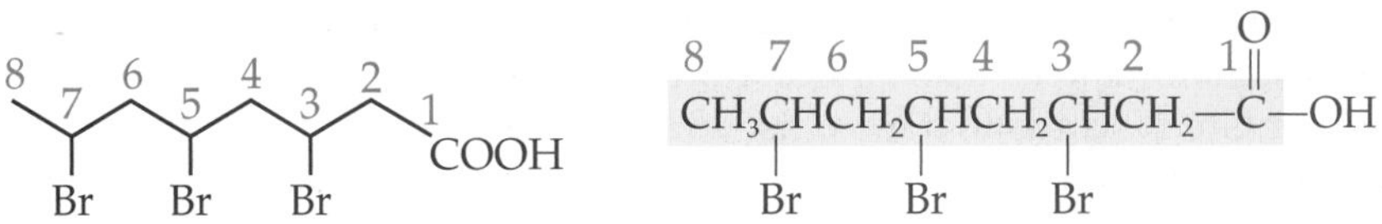

Solution

Parent compound: octane (becomes octanoic acid)
Position of —COOH: carbon-1 (must be!)
Substituents: 3,5,7-bromo
Name: 3,5,7-Tribromooctanoic acid

Practice Problem 14.1

Determine the IUPAC name for each of the following structures. Remember that —COOH is an alternative way to represent the carboxyl group.

a. 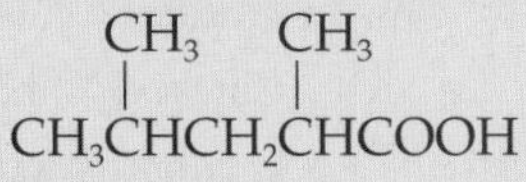

c. 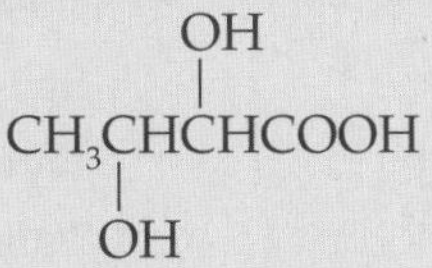

b. 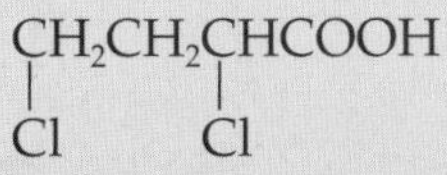

d. 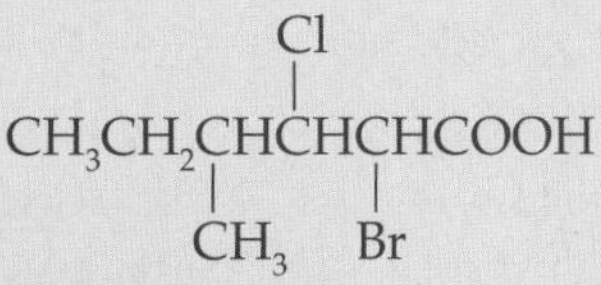

▸ For Further Practice: **Questions 14.32, 14.35, and 14.36.**

LEARNING GOAL

2 Determine the common and IUPAC names of carboxylic acids.

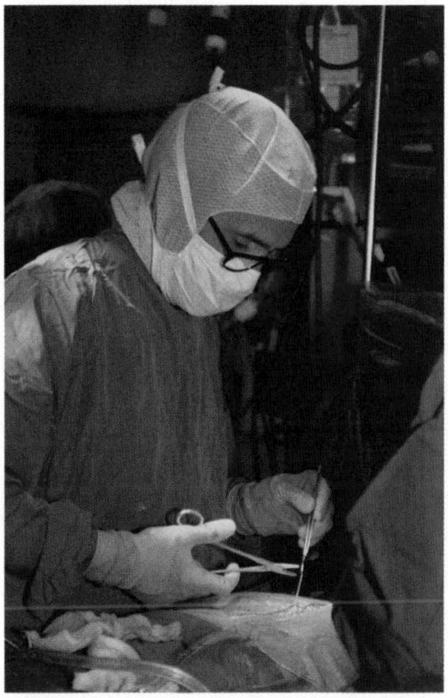

Polymers of lactic acid are used as biodegradable sutures. What is the IUPAC name of lactic acid, shown below?

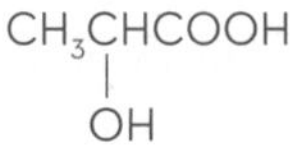

The carboxylic acid derivatives of cycloalkanes are named by adding the suffix *carboxylic acid* to the name of the cycloalkane or substituted cycloalkane. The carboxyl group is always on carbon-1 and other substituents are named and numbered as usual.

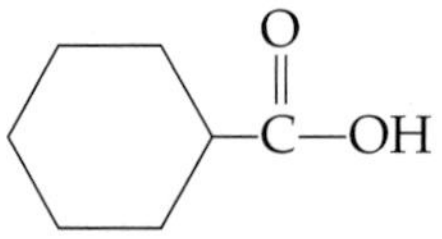

$$\text{C}_6\text{H}_{11}-\overset{\overset{\displaystyle O}{\|}}{C}-OH$$

Cyclohexanecarboxylic acid

Question 14.5 Determine the IUPAC name for each of the following structures.

a. 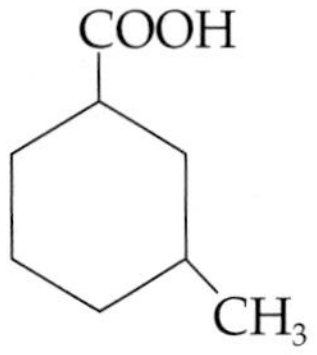 Cyclohexane ring with COOH and CH_3 substituents

b. 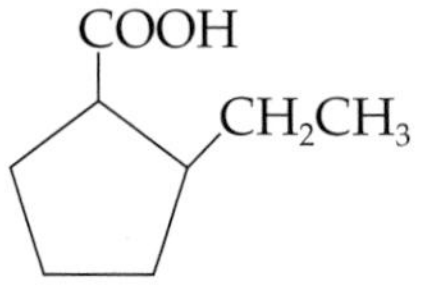 Cyclopentane ring with COOH and CH_2CH_3 substituents

Question 14.6 Write the structure for each of the following carboxylic acids.

a. 1,4-Cyclohexanedicarboxylic acid
b. 4-Hydroxycyclohexanecarboxylic acid

LEARNING GOAL

2 Determine the common and IUPAC names of carboxylic acids.

As we have seen so often, the use of common names, rather than systematic names, persists. Often these names have evolved from the source of a given compound. This is certainly true of the carboxylic acids. Table 14.1 shows the IUPAC and common names of several carboxylic acids, as well as their sources and the Latin or Greek words that gave rise to the common names. Not only are the prefixes different than those used in the IUPAC system, the suffix is different as well. Common names end in *-ic acid* rather than *-oic acid.*

In the common system of nomenclature, substituted carboxylic acids are named as derivatives of the parent compound (see Table 14.1). Greek letters are

TABLE 14.1 Names and Sources of Some Common Carboxylic Acids

Name	Structure	Source	Root
Formic acid (methanoic acid)	$HCOOH$	Ants	L: *formica,* ant
Acetic acid (ethanoic acid)	CH_3COOH	Vinegar	L: *acetum,* vinegar
Propionic acid (propanoic acid)	CH_3CH_2COOH	Swiss cheese	Gk: *protos,* first; *pion,* fat
Butyric acid (butanoic acid)	$CH_3(CH_2)_2COOH$	Rancid butter	L: *butyrum,* butter
Valeric acid (pentanoic acid)	$CH_3(CH_2)_3COOH$	Valerian root	
Caproic acid (hexanoic acid)	$CH_3(CH_2)_4COOH$	Goat fat	L: *caper,* goat
Caprylic acid (octanoic acid)	$CH_3(CH_2)_6COOH$	Goat fat	L: *caper,* goat
Capric acid (decanoic acid)	$CH_3(CH_2)_8COOH$	Goat fat	L: *caper,* goat
Palmitic acid (hexadecanoic acid)	$CH_3(CH_2)_{14}COOH$	Palm oil	
Stearic acid (octadecanoic acid)	$CH_3(CH_2)_{16}COOH$	Tallow (beef fat)	Gk: *stear,* tallow

Note: IUPAC names are shown in parentheses.

used to indicate the position of the substituent. The carbon atom bonded to the carboxyl group is the α-carbon, the next is the β-carbon, and so on.

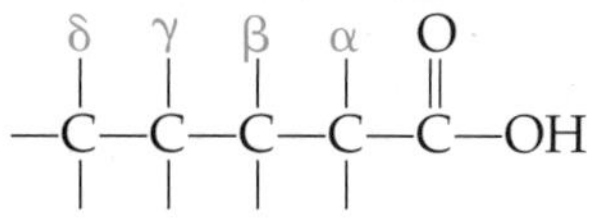

$$\overset{\delta}{-\text{C}}-\overset{\gamma}{\text{C}}-\overset{\beta}{\text{C}}-\overset{\alpha}{\text{C}}-\overset{\text{O}}{\overset{\|}{\text{C}}}-\text{OH}$$

Some examples of common names are

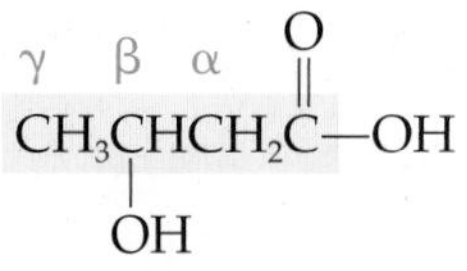

$$\overset{\gamma}{\text{CH}_3}\overset{\beta}{\underset{\underset{\text{OH}}{|}}{\text{CH}}}\overset{\alpha}{\text{CH}_2}\overset{\text{O}}{\overset{\|}{\text{C}}}-\text{OH} \qquad \overset{\beta}{\text{CH}_3}\overset{\alpha}{\underset{\underset{\text{OH}}{|}}{\text{CH}}}\overset{\text{O}}{\overset{\|}{\text{C}}}-\text{OH}$$

β-Hydroxybutyric acid 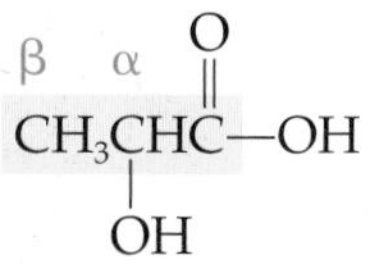 α-Hydroxypropionic acid

β-Hydroxybutyric acid is the other monomer used to make the biodegradable plastic Biopol (see Example 14.1).

EXAMPLE 14.2 Naming Carboxylic Acids Using the Common System of Nomenclature

LEARNING GOAL

2 Determine the common and IUPAC names of carboxylic acids.

Write the common name for each of the following carboxylic acids.

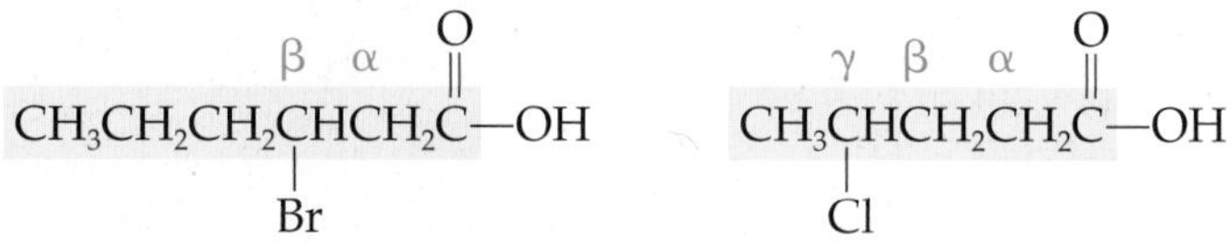

$$\overset{\beta}{\underset{\underset{\text{Br}}{|}}{\text{CH}_3\text{CH}_2\text{CH}_2\text{CH}}}\overset{\alpha}{\text{CH}_2}\overset{\text{O}}{\overset{\|}{\text{C}}}-\text{OH} \qquad \overset{\gamma}{\underset{\underset{\text{Cl}}{|}}{\text{CH}_3\text{CH}}}\overset{\beta}{\text{CH}_2}\overset{\alpha}{\text{CH}_2}\overset{\text{O}}{\overset{\|}{\text{C}}}-\text{OH}$$

Solution

Parent compound:	caproic acid	valeric acid
Substituents:	β-bromo	γ-chloro
Name:	β-Bromocaproic acid	γ-Chlorovaleric acid

Practice Problem 14.2

Provide the common name for each of the following molecules. Keep in mind that the carboxyl group can be represented as —COOH.

a. 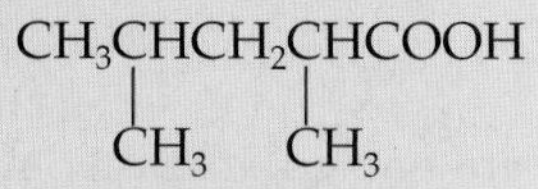 $\underset{\underset{\text{CH}_3}{|}}{\text{CH}_3\text{CH}}\text{CH}_2\underset{\underset{\text{CH}_3}{|}}{\text{CH}}\text{COOH}$

b. 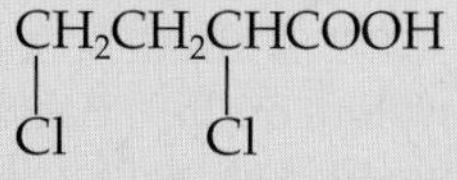 $\underset{\underset{\text{Cl}}{|}}{\text{CH}_2}\text{CH}_2\underset{\underset{\text{Cl}}{|}}{\text{CH}}\text{COOH}$

c. 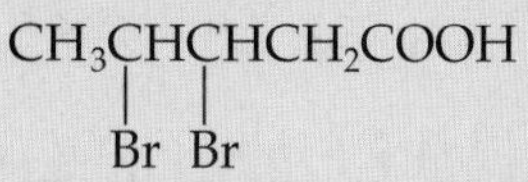 $\text{CH}_3\underset{\underset{\text{Br}}{|}}{\text{CH}}\underset{\underset{\text{Br}}{|}}{\text{CH}}\text{CH}_2\text{COOH}$

d. 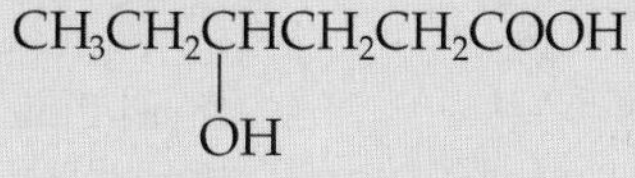 $\text{CH}_3\text{CH}_2\underset{\underset{\text{OH}}{|}}{\text{CH}}\text{CH}_2\text{CH}_2\text{COOH}$

► For Further Practice: **Questions 14.31, 14.37, and 14.38.**

Benzoic acid is the simplest aromatic carboxylic acid.

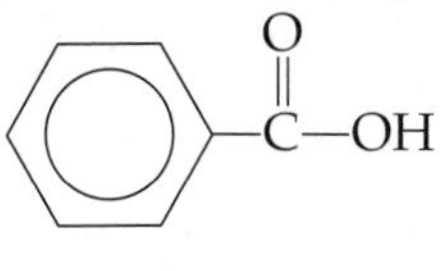

$$\text{C}_6\text{H}_5-\overset{\text{O}}{\overset{\|}{\text{C}}}-\text{OH}$$

Benzoic acid

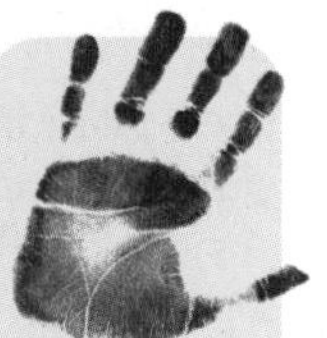

CHEMISTRY AT THE CRIME SCENE

Carboxylic Acids and the Body Farm

Dr. Arpad Vass of Oak Ridge National Laboratory explains his unusual vocation in the following way, "Each year there are about 90,000 homicides in this country and for every one, you need to know when the person died. Our research can help answer the where and when, and that should help law enforcement officials solve crimes." Time and location of death are key pieces of information in a criminal investigation. Whether a suspect is convicted or goes free may rest on an accurate estimate of the time since death (TSD). Dr. Vass and graduate student Jennifer Love study decomposing bodies on a research plot in Tennessee. Although its official name is University of Tennessee Anthropological Research Facility, it has been called the "Body Farm" since Patricia Cornwell published a novel of that name in 1994.

Vass and Love are trying to develop an instrument that can sample the air around a corpse to determine the concentrations of certain carboxylic acids, also referred to as volatile fatty acids. What they envision is a "tricorder"-like device that will sample the air for valeric acid, propionic acid, and the straight and branched types of butyric acid. Because the ratio of these carboxylic acids changes in a predictable way following death, measurement of their relative concentrations, from air or from the soil under the corpse, could provide an accurate TSD.

The research is done by taking daily measurements of the air around decomposing bodies at the "Body Farm." At death, the proteins and lipids of the body begin to break down. This decomposition produces, among other substances, the carboxylic acids being studied. The bodies may be placed in various environments so that the researchers can study the effects of different temperature and moisture levels on the process of decomposition. The more that is learned about the amounts and types of organic compounds produced during decomposition under different conditions, the more precise the TSD determinations will be. In fact, Vass considers that these processes are a chemical "clock" and is working to refine the accuracy of that clock so that, eventually, TSD may be measured accurately in hours, rather than days.

For Further Understanding

- Draw the structures of the carboxylic acids described in this article and write their IUPAC names.
- The bones of a murdered 9-year-old boy were found lying on his father's property. Immediately the father was suspected of having killed the child. A sample of the soil under the boy's bones was sent to Dr. Vass for analysis. No volatile fatty acids were found in the soil sample. What can you conclude from these data?

Nomenclature of aromatic compounds is described in Section 11.6.

In many cases the aromatic carboxylic acids are named, in either system, as derivatives of benzoic acid. Generally, the *-oic acid* suffix is used in the IUPAC system and the *-ic acid* suffix is used in the common system and is attached to the appropriate prefix. However, "common names" of substituted benzoic acids (for example, toluic acid and phthalic acid) are frequently used.

O
‖
C—OH
CH_3

m-Toluic acid

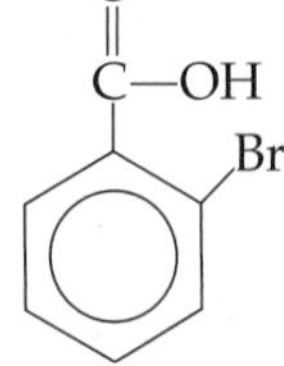

o-Bromobenzoic acid

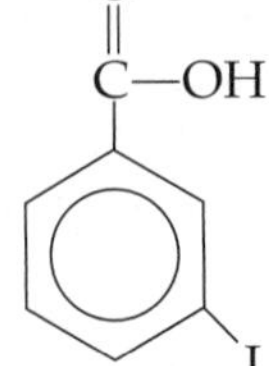

m-Iodobenzoic acid

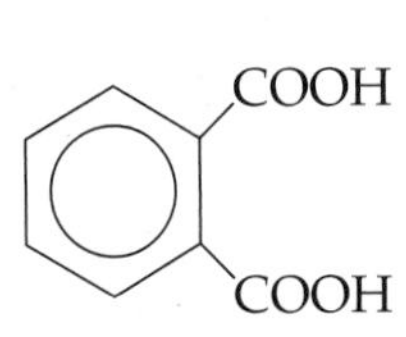

Phthalic acid

Often the phenyl group is treated as a substituent, and the name is derived from the appropriate alkanoic acid parent chain. For example:

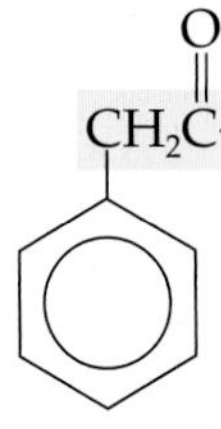

$C_6H_5CH_2COOH$ 2-Phenylethanoic acid (α-phenylacetic acid)

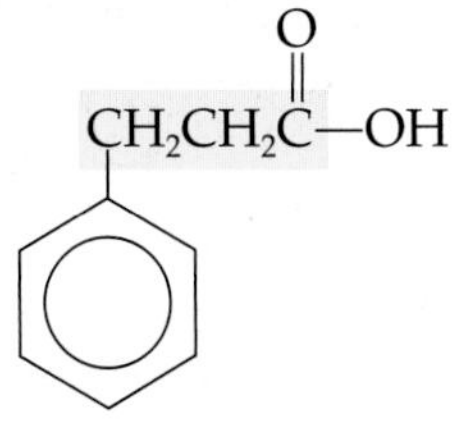

$C_6H_5CH_2CH_2COOH$ 3-Phenylpropanoic acid (β-phenylpropionic acid)

The phenyl group is benzene with one hydrogen removed.

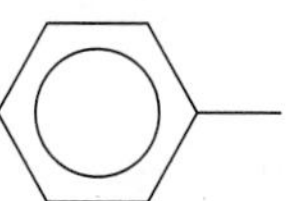

Phenyl group

The benzyl group is toluene with one hydrogen removed from the methyl group:

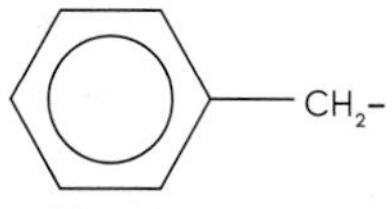

$C_6H_5CH_2-$

Benzyl group

EXAMPLE 14.3 Naming Aromatic Carboxylic Acids

LEARNING GOAL

2 Determine the common and IUPAC names of carboxylic acids.

a. Name the following aromatic carboxylic acid.

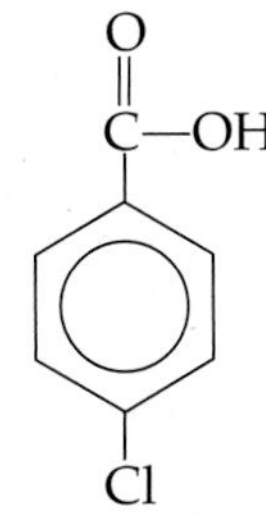

Solution

It is simplest to name the compound as a derivative of benzoic acid. The substituent, Cl, is attached to carbon-4 of the benzene ring. This compound is 4-chlorobenzoic acid or *p*-chlorobenzoic acid.

b. Name the following aromatic carboxylic acid.

$C_6H_5CH(CH_3)CH_2CH_2COOH$

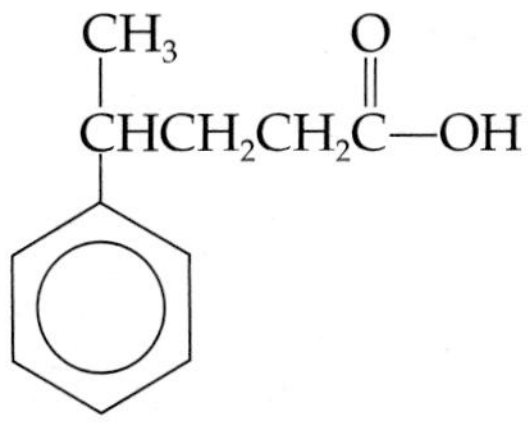

Solution

This compound is most easily named by treating the phenyl group as a substituent. The phenyl group is bonded to carbon-4 (or the γ-carbon, in the common system of nomenclature). The parent compound is pentanoic acid (valeric acid in the common system). Hence the name of this compound is 4-phenylpentanoic acid or γ-phenylvaleric acid.

Practice Problem 14.3

Draw structures for each of the following compounds.

a. *o*-Toluic acid
b. 2,4,6-Tribromobenzoic acid
c. 2,2,2-Triphenylethanoic acid
d. *p*-Toluic acid
e. 3-Phenylhexanoic acid
f. 3-Phenylcyclohexanecarboxylic acid

► For Further Practice: **Questions 14.39 and 14.40.**

GREEN CHEMISTRY

Garbage Bags from Potato Peels?

One problem facing society is its enormous accumulation of trash. To try to control the mountains of garbage that we produce, many institutions and towns practice recycling of aluminum, paper, and plastics. One problem that remains, however, is the plastic trash bag. We stuff the trash bag full of biodegradable garbage and bury it in a landfill; but soil bacteria can't break down the plastic to get to the biodegradable materials inside. Imagine a twenty-fourth century archeologist excavating one of these monuments to our society!

The good news is that laboratory research and products of bacterial metabolism are providing new materials that have the properties of plastics, but are readily biodegradable. For instance, sheets of plastic can be made by making polymers of lactic acid, which is a natural carboxylic acid produced by fermentation of sugars, particularly in milk and working muscle. Because many common soil bacteria can break down polylactic acid (PLA), trash bags made from this polymer would be quickly broken down in landfill soil.

Making plastic from lactic acid requires a huge supply of this carboxylic acid. As it turns out, we can produce an enormous quantity of lactic acid from garbage. When french fries are produced, nearly half of the potato is wasted. That amounts to about ten billion pounds (lb) of potato waste each year. When cheese is made, the curds are separated from the whey, and several billion gallons (gal) of whey are poured down the drain each year. Potato waste and whey can easily be broken down to produce glucose, which, in turn, can be converted into lactic acid used to make biodegradable plastics. PLA plastics have been available since the early 1990s and have been used successfully for sutures, medical implants, and drug delivery systems.

$$n\,H_3C{-}CH(OH){-}C({=}O){-}OH \longrightarrow \left[{-}O{-}CH(CH_3){-}C({=}O){-}O{-}CH(CH_3){-}C({=}O){-}O{-}\right]_n$$

Lactic acid — Polylactic acid (PLA)

Other researchers have experimented with heteropolymers, polymers composed of two or more different monomers. One such polymer with useful properties is a heteropolymer of β-hydroxybutyric acid and β-hydroxyvaleric acid, which has been given the name Biopol.

$$n\,H_3C{-}CH(OH){-}CH_2{-}C({=}O){-}OH + n\,H_3C{-}CH_2{-}CH(OH){-}CH_2{-}C({=}O){-}OH$$

β-Hydroxybutyric acid — β-Hydroxyvaleric acid

$$\downarrow$$

$$\left[{-}O{-}CH(CH_3){-}CH_2{-}C({=}O){-}O{-}CH(CH_2CH_3){-}CH_2{-}C({=}O){-}O{-}\right]_n$$

Biopol—a heteropolymer

Biopol has properties that make it commercially useful, and it is completely broken down into carbon dioxide and water by microorganisms in the soil. Thus, it is completely biodegradable. Because bacteria produced a low yield of Biopol, scientists produced transgenic plants in hopes that they would produce high yields of the polymer. This approach also encountered problems.

For the time being, biodegradable plastics cannot outcompete their nonbiodegradable counterparts. Future research and development will be required to reduce the cost of commercial production and fulfill the promise of an "environmentally friendly" garbage bag.

For Further Understanding

- Why are biodegradable plastics useful as sutures?
- Two hydrogen atoms are lost in each reaction that adds a carboxylic acid to the polymers described here. What type of chemical reaction is this?

LEARNING GOAL

3 Describe the biological, medical, or environmental significance of several carboxylic acids.

Some Important Carboxylic Acids

As Table 14.1 shows, many carboxylic acids occur in nature. The stinging sensation of an ant bite is caused by methanoic (formic) acid, and ethanoic (acetic) acid provides the acidic zip to vinegars. Propanoic (propionic) acid is the product of bacterial fermentation of milk products and is most notable as a tangy component in the characteristic flavor of Swiss cheese.

Several of the larger carboxylic acids have foul odors. For instance, butanoic (butyric) acid is the odor associated with rancid butter and is produced by the bacteria that cause gas gangrene, contributing to the characteristic smell of the necrotic tissue. Pentanoic (valeric) acid is associated with the valerian plant, which has long been known to have an aroma alternately described as over-ripe cheese or a wet dog. Nonetheless, extracts of valerian have been used for thousands of years as a natural sedative. Hexanoic (caproic) acid was first isolated from goats and, fittingly, is described as smelling like a goat. Heptanoic (enanthic) acid is also foul smelling and is associated with the odor of rancid oil.

These foul-smelling carboxylic acids have a far more pleasant potential, however. When carboxylic acids react with alcohols, the products are esters, which contribute to the lovely fragrance and flavor of many fruits.

To learn more about the fragrances and flavors of esters, see A Human Perspective: The Chemistry of Flavor and Fragrance later in this chapter.

Octanoic (caprylic) acid has an interesting function in the chemistry of human appetite. The hormone ghrelin, produced in the stomach, is sometimes called the "hunger hormone" because it stimulates the hypothalamus of the brain to signal that the body is hungry. However, the hormone alone does not have this effect. Ghrelin must be covalently bonded to a molecule of octanoic acid in order to have the hunger-stimulating effect on the hypothalamus.

Fatty acids are long-chain monocarboxylic acids and can be isolated from a variety of sources including palm oil, coconut oil, butter, milk, lard, and animal fat, including tallow (beef fat). These fatty acids, in the form of triglycerides, are the major energy storage form in mammals and many plants. When the fatty acids in the triglyceride are saturated, the result is solid fat, as in animal fats. When the fatty acids are unsaturated, the result is a liquid, as in olive oil and canola oil.

A triglyceride is a molecule of glycerol (Section 12.3) bonded to three fatty acid molecules by esterification (Sections 14.2 and 17.3).

Several common dicarboxylic acids are show in Table 14.2. Oxalic acid is a dicarboxylic acid found in spinach and rhubarb. Human kidney stones are often formed from the calcium salt of oxalic acid. In fact, it is toxic in high concentrations and foods with high levels of oxalic acid must be boiled before being eaten. While oxalic acid is used in industry as a bleaching agent and spot remover, the potassium salt is used in clinical laboratories to prevent blood samples from coagulating.

TABLE 14.2 Common Dicarboxylic Acids

Common Name	IUPAC Name	Condensed Formula	Line Formula
Oxalic acid	Ethanedioic acid	HOOCCOOH	
Malonic acid	Propanedioic acid	$HOOCCH_2COOH$	
Succinic acid	Butanedioic acid	$HOOC(CH_2)_2COOH$	
Glutaric acid	Pentanedioic acid	$HOOC(CH_2)_3COOH$	
Adipic acid	Hexanedioic acid	$HOOC(CH_2)_4COOH$	

Malonic acid is used in the synthesis of barbiturates. Succinic acid is one of the intermediates in the citric acid cycle, a metabolic pathway involved in the breakdown of carbohydrates, lipids, and proteins to harvest energy for cellular functions. The name comes from the Latin word for amber (L. *succinum*) because it was first isolated from crushed amber. Glutaric acid is used in the production of several types of condensation polymers, including polyester, polyols, and polyamides. It is useful because it has an odd number of carbons in the chain, which reduces the elasticity of the polymer. Adipic acid (hexanedioic acid) gives tartness to soft drinks and helps retard food spoilage. However, the greatest demand for adipic acid (2.5 billion kilograms (kg) per year) is for the synthesis of nylon and polyurethane, and of plasticizers that are particularly useful in the manufacture of polyvinyl chloride (PVC).

More complex carboxylic acids are found in a variety of foods. For example, citric acid is found in citrus fruits and is often used to give the sharp taste to sour candies. It is also added to foods as a preservative and antioxidant.

Bacteria in milk produce lactic acid as a product of fermentation of sugars. Lactic acid contributes a tangy flavor to yogurt and buttermilk. It is also used as a food preservative to lower the pH to a level that retards microbial growth that causes food spoilage. Lactic acid is produced in muscle cells when an individual is exercising strenuously. If the level of lactic acid in the muscle and bloodstream becomes high enough, the muscle can't continue to work.

Tartaric acid is used in baking powder because it will undergo a reaction with carbonates in the dough, producing CO_2 that will cause the bread or cake to rise. It has also been used as a laxative. Malic acid gives the sour taste to green apples. Since the amount of malic acid decreases as a fruit ripens, the fruit becomes sweeter and less tart as it ripens.

```
      COOH              COOH              COOH              COOH
       |                 |                 |                 |
     H—C—H             H—C—OH           HO—C—H             H—C—H
       |                 |                 |                 |
    HO—C—COOH           CH3             HO—C—H            HO—C—H
       |                                   |                 |
     H—C—H                               COOH              COOH
       |
      COOH

   Citric acid       Lactic acid      Tartaric acid      Malic acid
```

Several aromatic carboxylic acids are also of medical interest. The sodium salt of benzoic acid is used as a preservative in soft drinks, pickles, jellies, and many other foods and some cosmetics. It is of value as a preservative because it is colorless, odorless, and tasteless, and will kill bacteria at a concentration of only 0.1%.

Salicylic acid is used as a disinfectant and, in fact, is superior to phenol. It is also used in ointments to remove corns or warts because it causes the top layer of the skin to flake off, leaving the underlying living skin undamaged.

Acetylsalicylic acid is aspirin. As early as the fifth century BC, the revered physician Hippocrates described a bitter extract from willow bark that could reduce fevers and relieve pain. Ancient texts from the Middle East reveal that Egyptian and Sumerian physicians appreciated the medicinal value of willow bark, and Native Americans used it to treat headache, fever, and chills, as well as sore muscles. In 1828, Henri Leroux isolated crystals of the compound that came to be called salicin. Nearly 70 years later, in 1897, chemists at Bayer and Company chemically added an acetyl group to salicin, synthesizing acetylsalicylic acid, a derivative that did not produce the severe gastrointestinal side effects caused by salicin. Thus, aspirin became the first synthetic drug, launching the pharmaceutical industry. Today, aspirin is recommended in low daily doses by the American Heart Association as a preventive measure against heart attacks and strokes caused by blood clots.

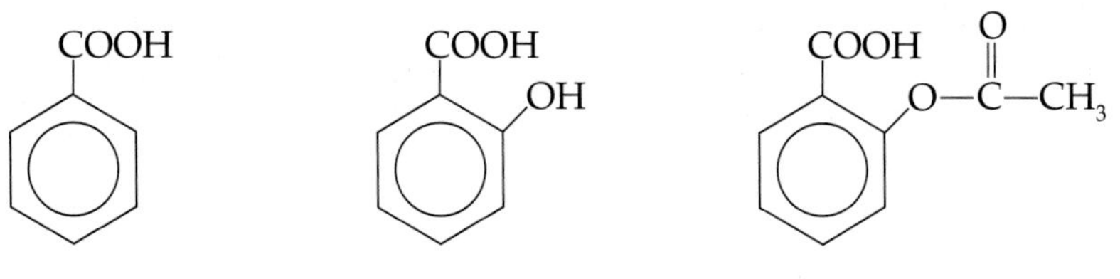

Benzoic acid (COOH on benzene ring) — Salicylic acid (COOH, OH on benzene ring) — Acetylsalicylic acid (COOH, $O-\overset{O}{\overset{\|}{C}}-CH_3$ on benzene ring)

Benzoic acid Salicylic acid Acetylsalicylic acid

As we will see in the next section, terephthalic acid is primarily used to synthesize polyethylene terephthalate (PETE). Because this polymer is so useful, in excess of 30 million tons (t) of terephthalic acid is needed each year.

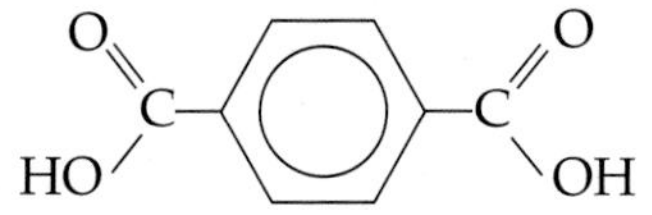

$$HO-\overset{O}{\overset{\|}{C}}-C_6H_4-\overset{O}{\overset{\|}{C}}-OH$$

Terephthalic acid

Reactions Involving Carboxylic Acids

Preparation of Carboxylic Acids

Many of the small carboxylic acids are prepared on a commercial scale. For example, ethanoic (acetic) acid, found in vinegar, is produced commercially by the **oxidation** of either ethanol or ethanal as shown here:

$$\underset{\text{Ethanol}}{CH_3CH_2OH} \quad \text{or} \quad \underset{\text{Ethanal}}{CH_3\overset{O}{\overset{\|}{C}}-H} \xrightarrow{\text{Oxidizing agent}} \underset{\text{Ethanoic acid}}{CH_3\overset{O}{\overset{\|}{C}}-OH}$$

LEARNING GOAL

4 Write equations that show the synthesis of a carboxylic acid.

A variety of oxidizing agents, including oxygen, can be used, and catalysts are often required to provide acceptable yields. Other simple carboxylic acids can be made by oxidation of the appropriate primary alcohol or aldehyde. The general reaction is

Oxidation reactions involving aldehydes and primary alcohols were discussed in Sections 12.4 and 13.4.

$$\underset{\text{Primary alcohol}}{R-CH_2OH} \xrightarrow{[O]} \underset{\text{Aldehyde}}{R-\overset{O}{\overset{\|}{C}}-H} \xrightarrow{[O]} \underset{\text{Carboxylic acid}}{R-\overset{O}{\overset{\|}{C}}-OH}$$

EXAMPLE 14.4 **Writing Equations for the Oxidation of a Primary Alcohol to a Carboxylic Acid**

LEARNING GOAL

4 Write equations that show the synthesis of a carboxylic acid.

Write an equation showing the oxidation of 1-propanol to propanoic acid.

Solution

$$\underset{\substack{\text{1-Propanol}\\\text{(propyl alcohol)}}}{CH_3CH_2\overset{H}{\underset{H}{C}}-OH} \xrightarrow{[O]} \underset{\substack{\text{Propanal}\\\text{(propionaldehyde)}}}{CH_3CH_2\overset{O}{\overset{\|}{C}}-H} \xrightarrow[\text{oxidation}]{\text{Continued}} \underset{\substack{\text{Propanoic acid}\\\text{(propionic acid)}}}{CH_3CH_2-\overset{O}{\overset{\|}{C}}-OH}$$

Practice Problem 14.4

Write equations showing the synthesis of (a) ethanoic acid, (b) butanoic acid, and (c) octanoic acid by oxidation of the corresponding primary alcohol.

► For Further Practice: **Questions 14.49 and 14.50.**

Acid-Base Reactions

LEARNING GOAL

5 Write equations representing acid-base reactions of carboxylic acids.

The carboxylic acids behave as acids because they are proton donors. They are weak acids that dissociate to form a carboxylate ion and a hydrogen ion, as shown in the following equation:

$$\underset{\text{Carboxylic acid}}{R{-}\overset{\overset{\displaystyle O}{\|}}{C}{-}OH} \rightleftharpoons \underset{\text{Carboxylate anion}}{R{-}\overset{\overset{\displaystyle O}{\|}}{C}{-}O^-} + \underset{\text{Hydrogen ion}}{H^+}$$

The properties of weak acids are described in Sections 8.1 and 8.2.

LeChatelier's principle is described in Section 7.4.

Carboxylic acids are weak acids because they dissociate only slightly in solution. The majority of the acid remains in solution in the undissociated form. Typically, less than 5% of the acid is ionized (approximately five carboxylate ions to every ninety-five carboxylic acid molecules).

When strong bases are added to a carboxylic acid, neutralization occurs. The acid protons are removed by the OH^- to form water and the carboxylate ion. The position of the equilibrium shown in the reaction above is shifted to the right, owing to removal of H^+. This is an illustration of LeChatelier's principle.

$$\underset{\text{Carboxylic acid}}{R{-}\overset{\overset{\displaystyle O}{\|}}{C}{-}OH} + \underset{\text{Strong base}}{NaOH} \longrightarrow \underset{\text{Carboxylic acid salt}}{R{-}\overset{\overset{\displaystyle O}{\|}}{C}{-}O^-Na^+} + \underset{\text{Water}}{H_2O}$$

The carboxylate anion and the cation of the base form the carboxylic acid salt.

The following examples show the neutralization of acetic acid and benzoic acid in solutions of the strong base NaOH.

$$\underset{\text{Acetic acid}}{CH_3\overset{\overset{\displaystyle O}{\|}}{C}{-}OH} + \underset{\text{Sodium hydroxide (strong base)}}{NaOH} \longrightarrow \underset{\text{Sodium acetate}}{CH_3\overset{\overset{\displaystyle O}{\|}}{C}{-}O^-Na^+} + \underset{\text{Water}}{H{-}O{-}H}$$

$$\underset{\text{Benzoic acid}}{C_6H_5{-}\overset{\overset{\displaystyle O}{\|}}{C}{-}OH} + \underset{\text{Sodium hydroxide (strong base)}}{NaOH} \longrightarrow \underset{\text{Sodium benzoate}}{C_6H_5{-}\overset{\overset{\displaystyle O}{\|}}{C}{-}O^-Na^+} + \underset{\text{Water}}{H{-}O{-}H}$$

Sodium benzoate is commonly used as a food preservative.

Note that the salt of a carboxylic acid is named by replacing the *-ic acid* suffix with *-ate.* Thus acetic acid becomes acetate, and benzoic acid becomes benzoate. This name is preceded by the name of the appropriate cation, sodium in the examples above.

EXAMPLE 14.5 Writing an Equation to Show the Neutralization of a Carboxylic Acid by a Strong Base

LEARNING GOAL

5 Write equations representing acid-base reactions of carboxylic acids.

Write an equation showing the neutralization of propanoic acid by sodium hydroxide.

Solution

The protons of the acid are removed by the OH^- of the base. This produces water. The cation of the base, in this case sodium ion, forms the salt of the carboxylic acid.

$$CH_3CH_2{-}\overset{\overset{\displaystyle O}{\|}}{C}{-}OH + NaOH \longrightarrow CH_3CH_2{-}\overset{\overset{\displaystyle O}{\|}}{C}{-}O^-Na^+ + H_2O$$

Propanoic acid | Sodium hydroxide | Sodium salt of propanoic acid | Water

Practice Problem 14.5

Write the formula of the organic product obtained through each of the following reactions.

a. $CH_3CH_2COOH + KOH \longrightarrow ?$
b. $CH_3CH_2CH_2COOH + Ba(OH)_2 \longrightarrow ?$
c. $CH_3CH_2CH_2CH_2CH_2COOH + KOH \longrightarrow ?$
d. Benzoic acid + sodium hydroxide $\longrightarrow ?$

► For Further Practice: **Questions 14.52a, b, and c, 14.55, and 14.56.**

EXAMPLE 14.6 Naming the Salt of a Carboxylic Acid

Write the common and IUPAC names of the salt produced in the reaction shown in Example 14.5.

Solution

$$CH_3CH_2{-}\overset{\overset{\displaystyle O}{\|}}{C}{-}O^-Na^+$$

IUPAC name of the parent carboxylic acid:	Propanoic acid
Replace the *-ic acid* ending with *-ate:*	Propanoate
Name of the cation of the base:	Sodium
Name of the carboxylic acid salt:	Sodium propanoate
Common name of the parent carboxylic acid:	Propionic acid
Replace the *-ic acid* ending with *-ate:*	Propionate
Name of the cation of the base:	Sodium
Name of the carboxylic acid salt:	Sodium propionate

Practice Problem 14.6

Name the products of the reactions in Practice Problem 14.5.

► For Further Practice: **Questions 14.57 and 14.58.**

Carboxylic acid salts are ionic substances. As a result, they are very soluble in water. The long-chain carboxylic acid salts (fatty acid salts) are called *soaps*.

Soaps are made by a process called saponification, which is the base-catalyzed hydrolysis of an ester. This is described in detail in Section 14.2.

LEARNING GOAL

6 Write equations representing the preparation of an ester.

Esterification

Carboxylic acids react with alcohols to form esters and water according to the general reaction:

$$R^1{-}\overset{\overset{\displaystyle O}{\|}}{C}{-}OH + R^2OH \underset{}{\overset{Acid}{\rightleftharpoons}} R^1{-}\overset{\overset{\displaystyle O}{\|}}{C}{-}OR^2 + H_2O$$

Carboxylic acid — Alcohol — Ester — Water

The details of these reactions will be examined in Section 14.2.

14.2 Esters

LEARNING GOAL

7 Write structures and describe the physical properties of esters.

Structure and Physical Properties

Esters are slightly polar and have pleasant aromas. Many esters are found in natural foodstuffs; banana oil (3-methylbutyl ethanoate; common name, isoamyl acetate), pineapples (ethyl butanoate; common name, ethyl butyrate), and raspberries (isobutyl methanoate; common name, isobutyl formate) are but a few examples.

See A Human Perspective: The Chemistry of Flavor and Fragrance later in this chapter.

Esters boil at approximately the same temperature as aldehydes or ketones of comparable molar mass. The simpler ones are somewhat soluble in water.

Nomenclature

LEARNING GOAL

8 Determine the common and IUPAC names of esters.

Esters are **carboxylic acid derivatives,** organic compounds derived from carboxylic acids. They are formed from the reaction of a carboxylic acid with an alcohol, and both of these reactants are reflected in the naming of the ester. They are named according to the following set of rules:

- Use the *alkyl* or *aryl* portion of the alcohol name as the first name.
- The *-ic acid* ending of the name of the carboxylic acid is replaced with *-ate* and follows the first name.

For example, in the following reaction, ethanoic acid reacts with methanol to produce methyl ethanoate:

$$CH_3\overset{\overset{\displaystyle O}{\|}}{C}{-}OH + CH_3OH \overset{H^+,\ heat}{\rightleftharpoons} CH_3\overset{\overset{\displaystyle O}{\|}}{C}{-}OCH_3 + H_2O$$

Ethano*ic acid* (acetic acid) — *Methanol* (methyl alcohol) — *Methyl* ethano*ate* (methyl acetate)

Similarly, acet*ic acid* and *ethanol* react to produce *ethyl* acet*ate,* and the product of the reaction between benzo*ic acid* and *isopropyl* alcohol is *isopropyl* benzo*ate.*

Naming esters is analogous to naming the salts of carboxylic acids. Consider the following comparison:

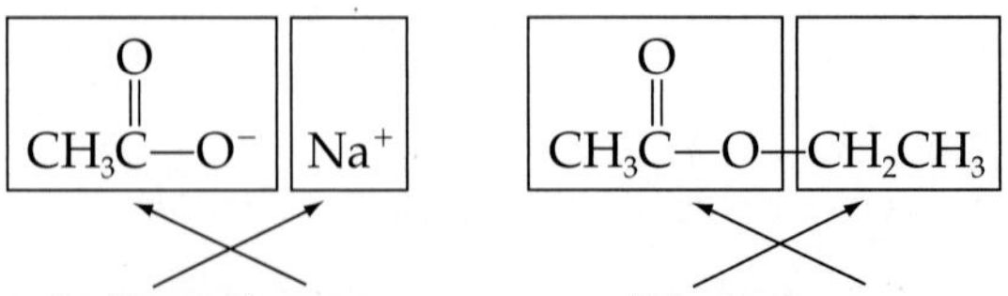

$$\boxed{CH_3\overset{\overset{\displaystyle O}{\|}}{C}{-}O^-}\ \boxed{Na^+} \qquad \boxed{CH_3\overset{\overset{\displaystyle O}{\|}}{C}{-}O}\boxed{CH_2CH_3}$$

Sodium ethanoate (sodium acetate) — Ethyl ethanoate (ethyl acetate)

As shown in this example, the alkyl group of the alcohol, rather than Na^+, has displaced the acidic hydrogen of the carboxylic acid.

EXAMPLE 14.7 Naming Esters Using the IUPAC and Common Nomenclature Systems

LEARNING GOAL

8 Determine the common and IUPAC names of esters.

a. The molecule shown below contributes to the flavor of pineapple. Write the IUPAC and common names for this ester.

$$CH_3CH_2CH_2\overset{\overset{\Large O}{\|}}{C}{-}OCH_2CH_3$$

Solution

	IUPAC	Common
IUPAC and common names of parent carboxylic acid:	butanoic acid	butyric acid
Replace the *-ic acid* ending of the carboxylic acid with *-ate:*	butanoate	butyrate
Name of the alkyl portion of the alcohol:	ethyl	ethyl
IUPAC and common names of the ester:	Ethyl butanoate	Ethyl butyrate

b. The molecule shown below is associated with the characteristic flavor of apricots. Write the common and IUPAC names of this ester.

$$CH_3CH_2CH_2\overset{\overset{\Large O}{\|}}{C}{-}OCH_2CH_2CH_2CH_2CH_3$$

Solution

	IUPAC	Common
IUPAC and common names of parent carboxylic acid:	butanoic acid	butyric acid
Replace the *-ic acid* ending of the carboxylic acid with *-ate:*	butanoate	butyrate
Name of the alkyl portion of the alcohol:	pentyl	pentyl
IUPAC and common names of the ester:	Pentyl butanoate	Pentyl butyrate

Practice Problem 14.7

Name each of the following esters using both the IUPAC and common nomenclature systems.

a. $$CH_3CH_2CH_2\overset{\overset{\Large O}{\|}}{C}{-}OCH_2CH_2CH_3$$

b. $$CH_3CH_2CH_2\overset{\overset{\Large O}{\|}}{C}{-}OCH_2CH_3$$

c. $$CH_3\overset{\overset{\Large O}{\|}}{C}{-}OCH_2CH_2CH_3$$

d. $$CH_3CH_2\overset{\overset{\Large O}{\|}}{C}{-}OCH_2CH_2CH_2CH_3$$

► For Further Practice: **Questions 14.63, 14.64, and 14.66.**

Reactions Involving Esters

Preparation of Esters

LEARNING GOAL

6 Write equations representing the preparation of an ester.

The conversion of a carboxylic acid to an ester requires heat and is catalyzed by a trace of acid (H^+). When esters are prepared directly from a carboxylic acid and an alcohol, a water molecule is lost, as in the reaction:

$$R^1{-}\overset{\displaystyle O}{\overset{\|}{C}}{-}OH + R^2OH \xrightleftharpoons{H^+,\ heat} R^1{-}\overset{\displaystyle O}{\overset{\|}{C}}{-}OR^2 + H_2O$$

Carboxylic acid — Alcohol — Ester — Water

$$CH_3CH_2\overset{\displaystyle O}{\overset{\|}{C}}{-}OH + CH_3OH \xrightleftharpoons{H^+,\ heat} CH_3CH_2\overset{\displaystyle O}{\overset{\|}{C}}{-}OCH_3 + H{-}O{-}H$$

Propanoic acid (propionic acid) — Methanol (methyl alcohol) — Methyl propanoate (methyl propionate)

Esterification is reversible. The direction of the reaction is determined by the conditions chosen. Excess alcohol favors ester formation. The carboxylic acid is favored when excess water is present.

Esterification is a *condensation* reaction, so called because a water molecule is removed during the reaction.

EXAMPLE 14.8 Writing Equations Representing Esterification Reactions

LEARNING GOAL

6 Write equations representing the preparation of an ester.

Write an equation showing the esterification reactions that would produce ethyl butanoate and propyl ethanoate.

Solution

The name, ethyl butanoate, tells us that the alcohol used in the reaction is ethanol and the carboxylic acid is butanoic acid. We must remember that a trace of acid and heat are required for the reaction and that the reaction is reversible. With this information, we can write the following equation representing the reaction:

$$CH_3CH_2CH_2\overset{\displaystyle O}{\overset{\|}{C}}{-}OH + CH_3CH_2OH \xrightleftharpoons{H^+,\ heat} CH_3CH_2CH_2\overset{\displaystyle O}{\overset{\|}{C}}{-}OCH_2CH_3 + H_2O$$

Butanoic acid (butyric acid) — Ethanol — Ethyl butanoate (ethyl butyrate)

Similarly, the name propyl ethanoate reveals that the alcohol used in this reaction is 1-propanol and the carboxylic acid must be ethanoic acid. Knowing that we must indicate that the reaction is reversible and that heat and a trace of acid are required, we can write the following equation:

$$CH_3\overset{\displaystyle O}{\overset{\|}{C}}{-}OH + CH_3CH_2CH_2OH \xrightleftharpoons{H^+,\ heat} CH_3\overset{\displaystyle O}{\overset{\|}{C}}{-}OCH_2CH_2CH_3 + H_2O$$

Ethanoic acid (acetic acid) — 1-Propanol (propyl alcohol) — Propyl ethanoate (propyl acetate)

Practice Problem 14.8

Write an equation showing the esterification reactions that would produce (a) butyl ethanoate and (b) ethyl propanoate.

▸ For Further Practice: **Questions 14.73 and 14.74.**

EXAMPLE 14.9 Designing the Synthesis of an Ester

LEARNING GOAL

6 Write equations representing the preparation of an ester.

Design the synthesis of ethyl propanoate from organic alcohols.

Solution

The ease with which alcohols are oxidized to aldehydes, ketones, or carboxylic acids (depending on the alcohol that you start with and the conditions that you employ), coupled with the ready availability of alcohols, provides the pathway necessary to many successful synthetic transformations. For example, let's develop a method for synthesizing ethyl propanoate, using an oxidizing agent and limiting yourself to organic alcohols that contain three or fewer carbon atoms:

$$CH_3CH_2\overset{\overset{\Large O}{\|}}{C}{-}O{-}CH_2CH_3$$

Ethyl propanoate
(ethyl propionate)

Ethyl propanoate can be made from propanoic acid and ethanol:

$$\underset{\text{Propanoic acid (propionic acid)}}{CH_3CH_2\overset{\overset{\Large O}{\|}}{C}{-}OH} + \underset{\text{Ethanol (ethyl alcohol)}}{CH_3CH_2OH} \xrightleftharpoons{H^+,\ heat} \underset{\text{Ethyl propanoate (ethyl propionate)}}{CH_3CH_2\overset{\overset{\Large O}{\|}}{C}{-}O{-}CH_2CH_3} + H_2O$$

Ethanol is a two-carbon alcohol that is an allowed starting material, but propanoic acid is not. Can we now make propanoic acid from an alcohol of three or fewer carbons? Yes!

$$\underset{\text{1-Propanol (propyl alcohol)}}{CH_3CH_2CH_2OH} \xrightarrow{[O]} \underset{\text{Propanal (propionaldehyde)}}{CH_3CH_2\overset{\overset{\Large O}{\|}}{C}{-}H} \xrightarrow{[O]} \underset{\text{Propanoic acid (propionic acid)}}{CH_3CH_2\overset{\overset{\Large O}{\|}}{C}{-}OH}$$

1-Propanol is a three-carbon alcohol, an allowed starting material. The synthesis is now complete. By beginning with ethanol and 1-propanol, ethyl propanoate can be synthesized easily by the reaction shown in the equation above.

Practice Problem 14.9

Design the synthesis of (a) methyl butanoate and (b) propyl methanoate from organic alcohols.

► For Further Practice: **Questions 14.75 and 14.76.**

Hydrolysis of Esters

LEARNING GOAL

9 Write equations representing the hydrolysis of an ester.

Hydrolysis refers to cleavage of any bond by the addition of a water molecule. Esters undergo hydrolysis reactions in water, as shown in the general reaction:

$$\underset{\text{Ester}}{R^1{-}\overset{\overset{\Large O}{\|}}{C}{-}OR^2} + \underset{\text{Water}}{H_2O} \xrightleftharpoons{H^+,\ heat} \underset{\text{Carboxylic acid}}{R^1{-}\overset{\overset{\Large O}{\|}}{C}{-}OH} + \underset{\text{Alcohol}}{R^2OH}$$

A HUMAN PERSPECTIVE

The Chemistry of Flavor and Fragrance

Carboxylic acids are often foul smelling. For instance, butyric acid is one of the worst smelling compounds imaginable—the smell of rancid butter.

$$CH_3CH_2CH_2\overset{\overset{\displaystyle O}{\|}}{C}{-}OH$$

Butanoic acid
(butyric acid)

Butyric acid is also a product of fermentation reactions carried out by *Clostridium perfringens*. This organism is the most common cause of gas gangrene. Butyric acid contributes to the notable foul smell accompanying this infection.

By forming esters of butyric acid, a chemist can generate compounds with pleasant smells. Ethyl butyrate is the essence of pineapple oil.

Pineapple

$$CH_3CH_2CH_2\overset{\overset{\displaystyle O}{\|}}{C}{-}OCH_2CH_3$$

Ethyl butanoate
(ethyl butyrate)

Volatile esters are often pleasant in both aroma and flavor. Natural fruit flavors are complex mixtures of many esters and other organic compounds. Chemists can isolate these mixtures and identify the chemical components. With this information they are able to synthesize artificial fruit flavors, using just a few of the esters found in the natural fruit. As a result, the artificial flavors rarely have the full-bodied flavor of nature's original blend.

Raspberries

$$H{-}\overset{\overset{\displaystyle O}{\|}}{C}{-}OCH_2\underset{\underset{\displaystyle CH_3}{|}}{C}HCH_3$$

Isobutyl methanoate
(isobutyl formate)

Bananas

$$CH_3\overset{\overset{\displaystyle O}{\|}}{C}{-}OCH_2CH_2\overset{\overset{\displaystyle CH_3}{|}}{C}HCH_3$$

3-Methylbutyl ethanoate
(isoamyl acetate)

Oranges

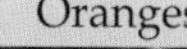

$$\mathrm{CH_3\overset{O}{\overset{\|}{C}}-OCH_2CH_2CH_2CH_2CH_2CH_2CH_2CH_3}$$

Octyl ethanoate
(octyl acetate)

Apples

$$\mathrm{CH_3CH_2CH_2\overset{O}{\overset{\|}{C}}-OCH_3}$$

Methyl butanoate
(methyl butyrate)

Apricots

$$\mathrm{CH_3CH_2CH_2\overset{O}{\overset{\|}{C}}-OCH_2CH_2CH_2CH_2CH_3}$$

Pentyl butanoate
(pentyl butyrate)

Strawberries

$$\mathrm{CH_3CH_2CH_2\overset{O}{\overset{\|}{C}}-SCH_3}$$

Methyl thiobutanoate
(methyl thiobutyrate)
(a thioester in which sulfur replaces oxygen)

For Further Understanding

- Draw the structure of methyl salicylate, which is found in oil of wintergreen.
- Write an equation for the synthesis of each of the esters shown in this Perspective.

This reaction requires heat. A small amount of acid (H^+) may be added to catalyze the reaction, as in the following example:

$$CH_3CH_2\overset{\overset{\large O}{\|}}{C}{-}OCH_2CH_2CH_3 + H_2O \xrightleftharpoons{H^+,\ heat} CH_3CH_2\overset{\overset{\large O}{\|}}{C}{-}OH + CH_3CH_2CH_2OH$$

Propyl propanoate (propyl propionate) — Propanoic acid (propionic acid) — 1-Propanol (propyl alcohol)

LEARNING GOAL

10 Define the term *saponification* and describe how soap works in the emulsification of grease and oil.

The base-catalyzed hydrolysis of an ester is called **saponification.**

$$R^1{-}\overset{\overset{\large O}{\|}}{C}{-}OR^2 + H_2O \xrightarrow{OH^-,\ heat} R^1{-}\overset{\overset{\large O}{\|}}{C}{-}O^- + R^2OH$$

Ester — Water — Carboxylic acid anion — Alcohol

Under basic conditions (NaOH or KOH) the acid cannot exist. Thus, the reaction yields the salt of the carboxylic acid having the cation of the basic catalyst.

$$CH_3\overset{\overset{\large O}{\|}}{C}{-}OCH_2CH_2CH_2CH_3 \xrightarrow{NaOH,\ heat} CH_3\overset{\overset{\large O}{\|}}{C}{-}O^-Na^+ + CH_3CH_2CH_2CH_2OH$$

Butyl ethanoate (butyl acetate) — Sodium ethanoate (sodium acetate) — 1-Butanol (butyl alcohol)

The carboxylic acid is formed when the reaction mixture is neutralized with an acid such as HCl.

$$CH_3\overset{\overset{\large O}{\|}}{C}{-}O^-Na^+ + HCl \longrightarrow CH_3\overset{\overset{\large O}{\|}}{C}{-}OH + NaCl$$

Sodium ethanoate (sodium acetate) — Ethanoic acid (acetic acid)

Question 14.7 Complete each of the following reactions by drawing the structure of the missing product(s).

a. $CH_3\overset{\overset{\large O}{\|}}{C}{-}OCH_2CH_2CH_3 + H_2O \xrightleftharpoons{H^+,\ heat} ?$

b. $CH_3CH_2CH_2CH_2CH_2\overset{\overset{\large O}{\|}}{C}{-}OCH_2CH_2CH_3 + H_2O \xrightarrow{KOH,\ heat} ?$

c. $CH_3CH_2CH_2CH_2\overset{\overset{\large O}{\|}}{C}{-}OCH_3 + H_2O \xrightarrow{NaOH,\ heat} ?$

d. $CH_3CH_2CH_2CH_2CH_2\overset{\overset{\large O}{\|}}{C}{-}O\underset{\underset{\large CH_3}{|}}{C}HCH_2CH_2CH_3 + H_2O \xrightleftharpoons{H^+,\ heat} ?$

Question 14.8 Use the IUPAC Nomenclature System to name each of the products in Question 14.7.

Triesters of glycerol are more commonly referred to as triglycerides. We know them as solid fats, generally from animal sources, and liquid oils, typically from plants. We will study triglycerides in detail in Section 17.3.

Fats and oils are triesters of the alcohol glycerol. When they are hydrolyzed by saponification, the products are **soaps,** which are the salts of long-chain carboxylic acids (fatty acid salts). According to Roman legend, soap was discovered by washerwomen, following a heavy rain on Mons Sapo ("Mount Soap"). An important

$$\begin{array}{l} CH_2-O-\overset{O}{\overset{\|}{C}}-R^1 \\ CH-O-\overset{O}{\overset{\|}{C}}-R^2 \\ CH_2-O-\overset{O}{\overset{\|}{C}}-R^3 \end{array} \xrightarrow[\text{heat, } H_2O]{M^+OH^-} \begin{array}{l} CH_2-OH \\ CH-OH \\ CH_2-OH \end{array} + \underbrace{R^1-\overset{O}{\overset{\|}{C}}-O^-M^+ + R^2-\overset{O}{\overset{\|}{C}}-O^-M^+ + R^3-\overset{O}{\overset{\|}{C}}-O^-M^+}$$

Fat or oil (triglyceride) — Glycerol — Soap (Mixture of carboxylic acid salts)

where $M^+ = Na^+$ or K^+

Figure 14.3 Saponification is the base-catalyzed hydrolysis of a glycerol triester.

sacrificial altar was located on the mountain. The rain mixed with the remains of previous animal sacrifices—wood ash and animal fat—at the base of the altar. Thus, the three substances required to make soap accidentally came together—water, fat, and alkali (potassium carbonate and potassium hydroxide, called *potash,* leached from the wood ash). The soap mixture flowed down the mountain and into the Tiber River, where the washerwomen quickly realized its value.

We still use the old Roman recipe to make soap from water, a strong base, and natural fats and oils obtained from animals or plants. The carbon chain length of the fatty acid salts governs the solubility of a soap. The lower-molar-mass carboxylic acid salts (up to twelve carbons) have greater solubility in water and give a lather containing large bubbles. The higher-molar-mass carboxylic acid salts (fourteen to twenty carbons) are much less soluble in water and produce a lather with fine bubbles. The nature of the cation also affects the solubility of the soap. In general, the potassium salts of carboxylic acids are more soluble in water than the sodium salts. The synthesis of a soap is shown in Figure 14.3.

The role of soap in the removal of soil and grease is best understood by considering the functional groups in soap molecules and studying the way in which they interact with oil and water. The long, continuous hydrocarbon side chains of soap molecules resemble alkanes, and they dissolve other nonpolar compounds such as oils and greases ("like dissolves like"). The large nonpolar hydrocarbon part of the molecule is described as *hydrophobic,* which means "water-fearing." This part of the molecule is repelled by water. The highly polar carboxylate end of the molecule is called *hydrophilic,* which means "water-loving."

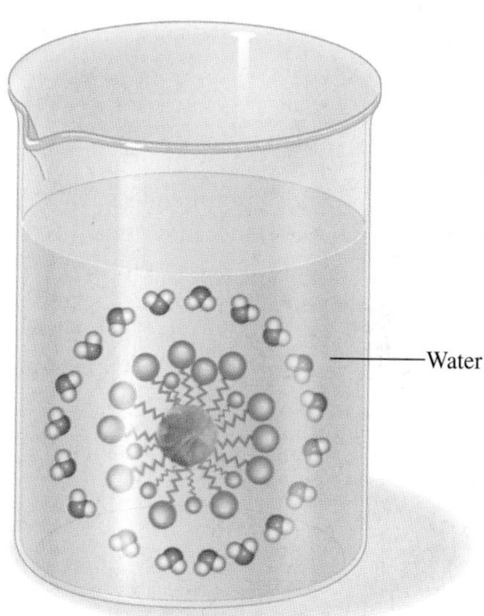

Figure 14.4 Simplified view of the action of a soap. The wiggly lines represent the long, continuous carbon chains of each soap molecule. Particles of oil and grease are surrounded by soap molecules to form a micelle.

When soap is dissolved in water, the carboxylate end actually dissolves. When soap solution comes in contact with oil or grease, the hydrocarbon part dissolves in the oil or grease, but the polar carboxylate group remains dissolved in water. When particles of oil or grease are surrounded by soap molecules, the resulting "units" formed are called *micelles.* A simplified view of this phenomenon is shown in Figure 14.4.

Micelles repel one another because they are surrounded on the surface by the negatively charged carboxylate ions. Mechanical action (for example, scrubbing or tumbling in a washing machine) causes oil or grease to be surrounded by soap molecules and broken into small droplets so that relatively small micelles are formed. These small micelles are then washed away. Careful examination of this solution shows that it is an *emulsion* containing suspended micelles.

An emulsion is a suspension of very fine droplets of one liquid in another. In this case it is oil in water.

Condensation Polymers

As we saw in Chapter 11, *polymers* are macromolecules, very large molecules. They result from the combination of many smaller molecules, usually in a repeating pattern, to give molecules whose molar mass may be 10,000 grams/mole (g/mol) or greater. The small molecules that make up the polymer are called *monomers.*

ANIMATION
- Natural and Synthetic Polymers

A polymer may be made from a single type of monomer (A). Such a polymer, called a homopolymer, would have the following general structure:

chain continues~A-A-A-A-A-A-A-A-A-A-A-A-A-A-A-A-A-A-A-A-A-A~chain continues

A HUMAN PERSPECTIVE

Detergents

Although soaps have served us for centuries as excellent cleansers, they do have some drawbacks. One of these is that they are salts of weak acids and thus may be converted into free fatty acids in the presence of weak acid:

$$CH_3(CH_2)_{16}\overset{O}{\overset{\|}{C}}\text{-}O^-Na^+ + HCl \longrightarrow CH_3(CH_2)_{16}\overset{O}{\overset{\|}{C}}\text{-}OH + Na^+ + Cl^-$$

Soap → Free fatty acid

Free fatty acids are much less water-soluble than the sodium or potassium salts and they tend to precipitate as soap scum. In short, they are no longer effective as soaps because the precipitate cannot emulsify the grease and dirt. Soaps are also ineffective in "hard" water, which is water having relatively high levels of calcium, magnesium, or iron, causing the following reaction:

$$2CH_3(CH_2)_{16}\overset{O}{\overset{\|}{C}}\text{-}O^-Na^+ + Ca^{2+} \longrightarrow [CH_3(CH_2)_{16}\overset{O}{\overset{\|}{C}}\text{-}O^-]Ca^{2+} + 2Na^+$$

Soap (sodium salt) (water-soluble) → Soap (calcium salt) (water-insoluble)

The calcium and magnesium salts of the carboxylic acids are much less water-soluble than the sodium salts and as a result precipitate, leaving rings in bathtubs and sinks. The precipitated soaps also leave a film on hair that can make it dull and may cause laundry to become gray. The solution to these problems with soap has been the detergent.

Detergents were not developed in response to the soap scum problems, but rather in response to a shortage of the natural fats (animal and plant) during World Wars I and II. Without these fats, soaps could not be made and an effective alternative cleaning agent was needed. The answer was detergents.

While soaps clean through emulsifying action, detergents are surfactants. Surfactants lower the surface tension of water so that the molecules are more likely to interact with grease and oil and less likely to interact with other water molecules. The structure of a detergent is very similar to that of a soap: there is a long hydrocarbon chain that is hydrophobic and a highly polar or charged end of the molecule. There are three common types of detergents: anionic, cationic, and nonionic. As the names suggest, these differ in the nature of the polar or charged ends of the molecules.

Anionic detergents have a negatively charged terminus, as you see in the structures of sodium dodecylsulfate (SDS) and sodium dodecylbenzenesulfonate shown here. SDS is primarily used in laundry detergents, but is also found in shampoo, bubble bath, toothpaste, and shaving foams. In higher concentrations it is used in floor cleaners, engine degreasers, and car wash soaps. Like SDS, sodium dodecylbenzenesulfonate is largely used in laundry detergents.

Anionic Detergents

O^-Na^+ | O=S=O (attached to benzene ring with dodecyl chain)

Sodium dodecylbenzensesulfonate

The addition polymers of alkenes that we studied in Chapter 11 are examples of this type of polymer. Alternatively, two different monomers (A and B) may be copolymerized, producing a heteropolymer with the following structure:

chain continues~A-B-A-B-A-B-A-B-A-B-A-B-A-B-A-B~chain continues

Polyesters are heteropolymers. They are also known as condensation polymers. **Condensation polymers** are formed by the polymerization of monomers in a reaction that forms a small molecule such as water or an alcohol. Polyesters are synthesized by reacting a dicarboxylic acid and a dialcohol (diol). Notice that each of the combining molecules has two reactive functional groups, highlighted in red here:

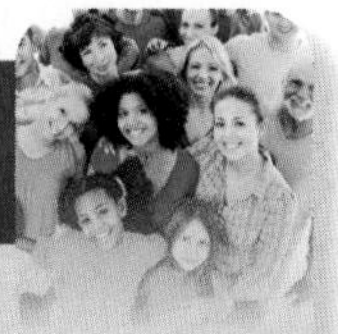

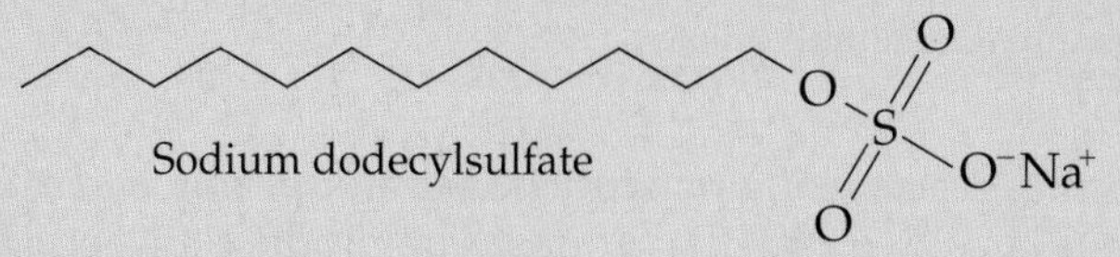

Sodium dodecylsulfate

Cationic detergents have a positively charged head group. In addition to being effective cleansing agents, cationic detergents have also been found to be effective antiseptics. Trimethylhexadecyl ammonium bromide is a cationic detergent found in topical antiseptics because it has been shown to be an effective agent against both bacteria and fungi.

Cationic Detergent

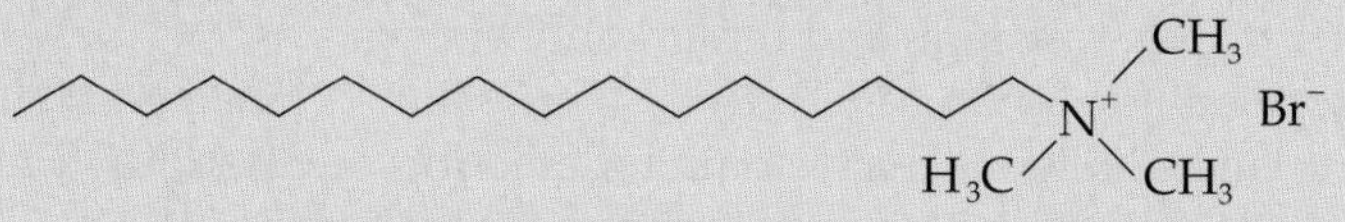

Trimethylhexadecylammonium bromide

Cationic detergents are most often found in shampoos, but are also used as fabric softeners. When added following the wash cycle, the cationic detergent neutralizes the residual charge of the anionic detergent, thereby reducing static cling.

Nonionic detergents have no charge at all on the molecule. As a result, they do not react with hard water ions, making them an excellent choice for toilet bowl cleaners to avoid unsightly buildup and to ensure that the detergent is fully active. Nonionic detergents are also very good at breaking up grease and oils and tend to foam less than ionic detergents. These properties make them very useful as dishwashing detergents. They are also used in a mixture with anionic detergents in formulations of laundry detergents.

Nonionic Detergent

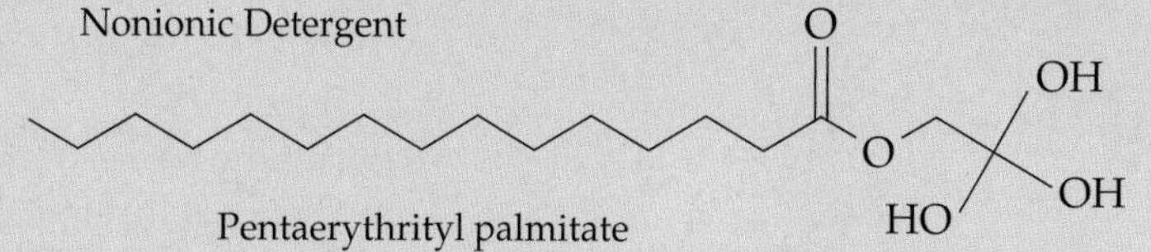

Pentaerythrityl palmitate

Whether brushing our teeth, shampooing our hair, washing the car, or doing the laundry, we find ourselves relying on the action of detergents many times through the course of the day. Our quality of life is much improved by this discovery born of wartime shortages of animal and plant fats!

For Further Understanding

- Compare and contrast the ways in which soaps and detergents work in the removal of dirt and grease. What is the role of agitation in the process?
- Below is one possible structure of an alkyl polyglucoside, the newest generation of environmentally friendly or "green" surfactants. They are synthesized in a reaction between glucose from corn and fatty alcohols from coconut or palm oil. Is this an anionic, cationic, or nonionic detergent? Explain your answer.

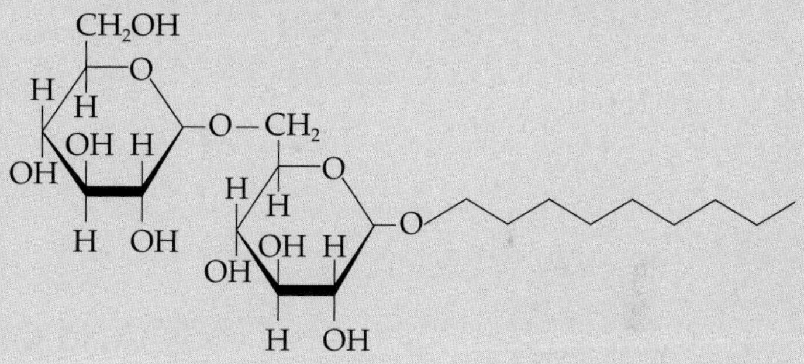

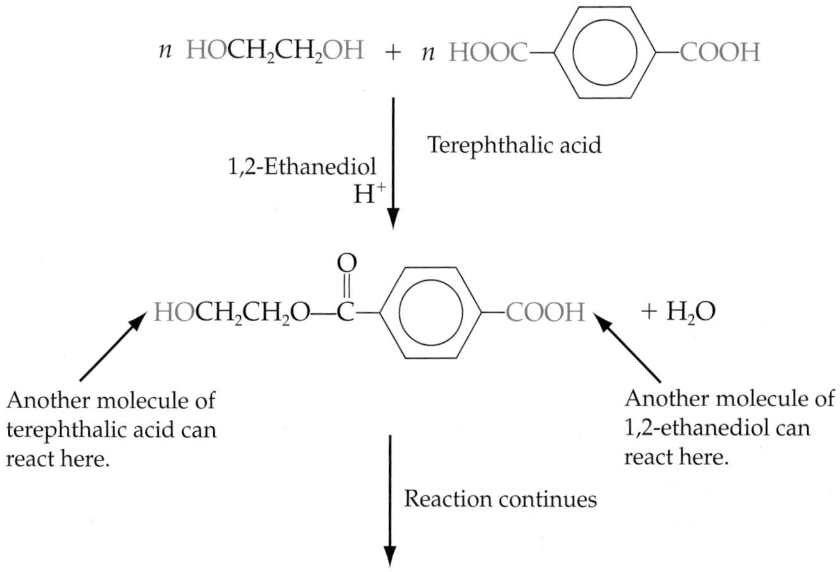

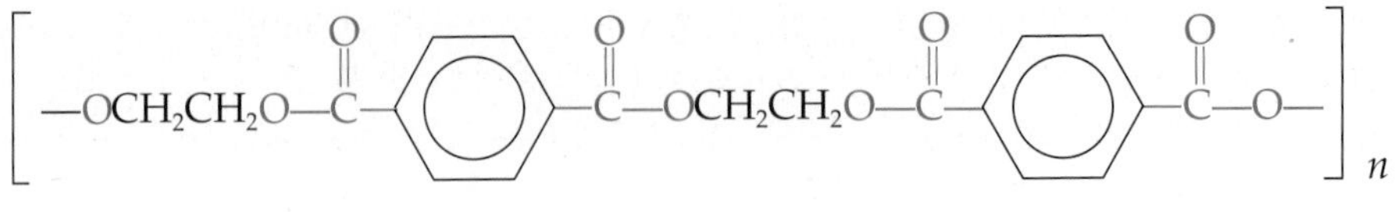

$$\left[-OCH_2CH_2O-\overset{O}{\overset{\|}{C}}-C_6H_4-\overset{O}{\overset{\|}{C}}-OCH_2CH_2O-\overset{O}{\overset{\|}{C}}-C_6H_4-\overset{O}{\overset{\|}{C}}-O-\right]_n$$

Polyethylene terephthalate
PETE

Each time a pair of molecules reacts using one functional group from each, a new molecule is formed that still has two reactive groups. The product formed in this reaction is polyethylene terephthalate, or PETE.

When formed as fibers, polyesters are used to make fabric for clothing. These polyesters were trendy in the 1970s, during the "disco" period, but lost their popularity soon thereafter. Polyester fabrics, and a number of other synthetic polymers used in clothing, have become even more fashionable since the introduction of microfiber technology. The synthetic polymers are extruded into fibers that are only half the diameter of fine silk fibers. When these fibers are used to create fabrics, the result is a fabric that drapes freely yet retains its shape. These fabrics are generally lightweight, wrinkle resistant, and remarkably strong.

Polyester can be formed into a film called Mylar. These films, coated with aluminum foil, are used to make balloons that remain inflated for long periods. They are also used as the base for recording tapes and photographic film.

Biodegradable plastics made of both homopolymers and heteropolymers are discussed in Green Chemistry: Garbage Bags from Potato Peels? found on page 478.

PETE can be used to make shatterproof plastic bottles, such as those used for soft drinks. However, these bottles cannot be recycled and reused directly because they cannot withstand the high temperatures required to sterilize them. PETE can't be used for any foods, such as jellies, that must be packaged at high temperatures. For these uses, a new plastic, PEN, or polyethylene naphthalate, is used.

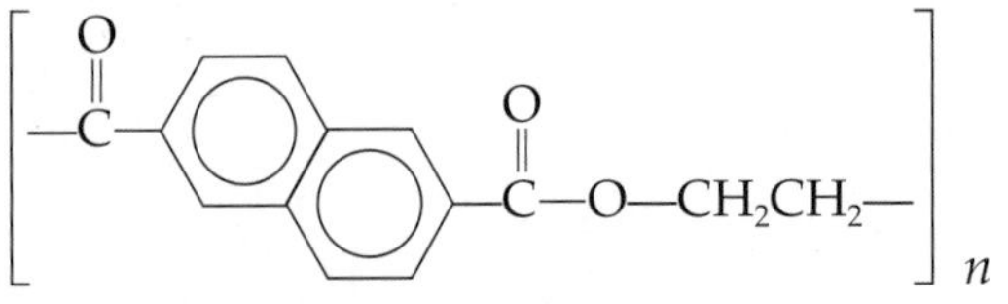

$$\left[-\overset{O}{\overset{\|}{C}}-C_{10}H_6-\overset{O}{\overset{\|}{C}}-O-CH_2CH_2-\right]_n$$

Naphthalate group   Ethylene group

LEARNING GOAL

11 Determine the common and IUPAC names of acid chlorides.

14.3 Acid Chlorides and Acid Anhydrides

Acid Chlorides

Acid chlorides are carboxylic acid derivatives having the general formula

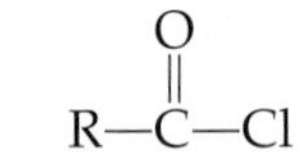

$$R-\overset{O}{\overset{\|}{C}}-Cl$$

They are named by replacing the *-ic acid* ending of the common name with *-yl chloride*, or the *-oic acid* ending of the IUPAC name of the carboxylic acid with *-oyl chloride*. For example,

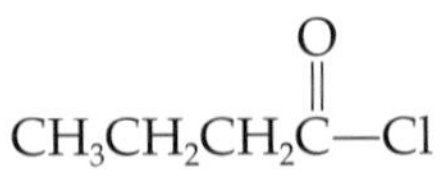

$$CH_3CH_2CH_2\overset{O}{\overset{\|}{C}}-Cl$$

Butanoyl chloride
(butyryl chloride)

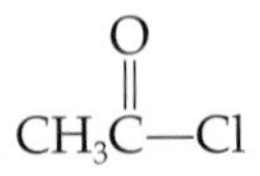

$$CH_3\overset{O}{\overset{\|}{C}}-Cl$$

Ethanoyl chloride
(acetyl chloride)

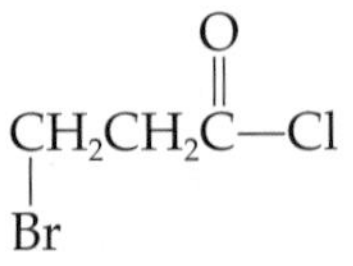

$$\underset{Br}{\underset{|}{C}}H_2CH_2\overset{O}{\overset{\|}{C}}-Cl$$

3-Bromopropanoyl chloride
(β-bromopropionyl chloride)

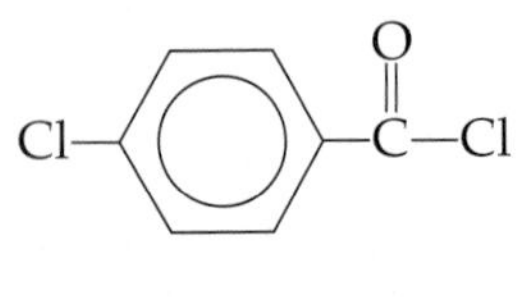

$$Cl-C_6H_4-\overset{O}{\overset{\|}{C}}-Cl$$

4-Chlorobenzoyl chloride
(*p*-chlorobenzoyl chloride)

Acid chlorides are noxious, irritating chemicals and must be handled with great care. They are slightly polar and boil at approximately the same temperature as the corresponding aldehyde or ketone of comparable molar mass. They react violently with water and therefore cannot be dissolved in that solvent. Acid chlorides have little commercial value other than their utility in the synthesis of esters and amides, two of the other carboxylic acid derivatives.

Acid Anhydrides

Acid anhydrides are molecules with the following general formula:

$$R^1-\overset{\overset{\displaystyle O}{\|}}{C}-O-\overset{\overset{\displaystyle O}{\|}}{C}-R^2$$

The name of the family is really quite fitting. The structure above reveals that acid anhydrides are actually two carboxylic acid molecules with a water molecule removed. The word *anhydride* means "without water."

$$R^1-\overset{\overset{\displaystyle O}{\|}}{C}-O-H + HO-\overset{\overset{\displaystyle O}{\|}}{C}-R^2$$

$$\downarrow$$

$$H-OH + R^1-\overset{\overset{\displaystyle O}{\|}}{C}-O-\overset{\overset{\displaystyle O}{\|}}{C}-R^2$$

Acid anhydrides are classified as *symmetrical* if both acyl groups are the same. Symmetrical acid anhydrides are named by replacing the *acid* ending of the carboxylic acid with the word *anhydride.* For example,

$$CH_3\overset{\overset{\displaystyle O}{\|}}{C}-O-\overset{\overset{\displaystyle O}{\|}}{C}CH_3$$

Ethanoic anhydride
(acetic anhydride)

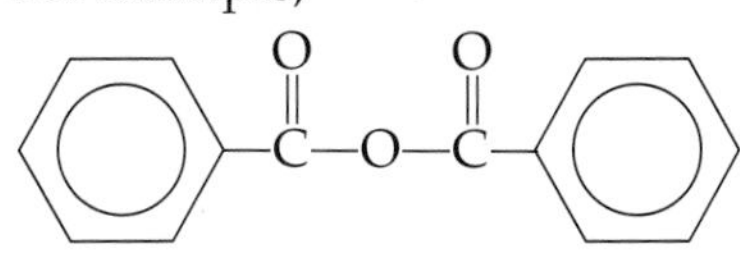

Benzoic anhydride

LEARNING GOAL

12 Determine the common and IUPAC names of acid anhydrides.

Unsymmetrical anhydrides are those having two different acyl groups. They are named by arranging the names of the two parent carboxylic acids and following them with the word *anhydride.* The names of the carboxylic acids may be arranged by size or alphabetically. For example:

$$CH_3\overset{\overset{\displaystyle O}{\|}}{C}-O-\overset{\overset{\displaystyle O}{\|}}{C}CH_2CH_3$$

Ethanoic propanoic anhydride
(acetic propionic anhydride)

$$CH_3\overset{\overset{\displaystyle O}{\|}}{C}-O-\overset{\overset{\displaystyle O}{\|}}{C}CH_2CH_2CH_2CH_3$$

Ethanoic pentanoic anhydride
(acetic valeric anhydride)

LEARNING GOAL

13 Write equations representing the synthesis of acid anhydrides.

Most acid anhydrides cannot be formed in a reaction between the parent carboxylic acids. One typical pathway for the synthesis of an acid anhydride is the reaction between an acid chloride and a carboxylate anion. This general reaction is seen in the equation below:

$$\underset{\text{Acid chloride}}{R^1-\overset{\overset{\displaystyle O}{\|}}{C}-Cl} \xrightarrow[\text{Carboxylate ion}]{R^2-\overset{\overset{\displaystyle O}{\|}}{C}-O^-} \underset{\text{Acid anhydride}}{R^1-\overset{\overset{\displaystyle O}{\|}}{C}-O-\overset{\overset{\displaystyle O}{\|}}{C}-R^2} + \underset{\text{Chloride ion}}{Cl^-}$$

The following equation shows the synthesis of ethanoic anhydride from ethanoic acid:

$$\underset{\substack{\text{Ethanoic acid}\\\text{(acetic acid)}}}{CH_3\overset{\overset{\displaystyle O}{\|}}{C}-OH} \xrightarrow{SOCl_2} \underset{\substack{\text{Ethanoyl chloride}\\\text{(acetyl chloride)}}}{CH_3\overset{\overset{\displaystyle O}{\|}}{C}-Cl} \xrightarrow{CH_3\overset{\overset{\displaystyle O}{\|}}{C}-O^-} \underset{\substack{\text{Ethanoic anhydride}\\\text{(acetic anhydride)}}}{CH_3\overset{\overset{\displaystyle O}{\|}}{C}-O-\overset{\overset{\displaystyle O}{\|}}{C}CH_3}$$

Acid anhydrides readily undergo hydrolysis. The rate of the hydrolysis reaction may be increased by the addition of a trace of acid or hydroxide base to the solution.

$$\underset{\text{Propanoic anhydride (propionic anhydride)}}{CH_3CH_2\overset{O}{\overset{\|}{C}}—O—\overset{O}{\overset{\|}{C}}CH_2CH_3} + H_2O \xrightarrow{\text{Heat}} \underset{\text{Propanoic acid (propionic acid)}}{2CH_3CH_2\overset{O}{\overset{\|}{C}}—OH}$$

EXAMPLE 14.10 Writing Equations Representing the Synthesis of Acid Anhydrides

LEARNING GOAL

13 Write equations representing the synthesis of acid anhydrides.

Write an equation representing the synthesis of propanoic anhydride.

Solution

Propanoic anhydride can be synthesized in a reaction between propanoyl chloride and the propanoate anion. This gives us the following equation:

$$\underset{\text{Propanoyl chloride}}{CH_3CH_2\overset{O}{\overset{\|}{C}}—Cl} \xrightarrow[\text{Propanoate ion}]{CH_3CH_2\overset{O}{\overset{\|}{C}}—O^-} \underset{\text{Propanoic anhydride}}{CH_3CH_2\overset{O}{\overset{\|}{C}}—O—\overset{O}{\overset{\|}{C}}CH_2CH_3} + \underset{\text{Chloride ion}}{Cl^-}$$

Practice Problem 14.10

Write equations representing the synthesis of (a) butanoic anhydride and (b) hexanoic anhydride.

► For Further Practice: **Questions 14.93 and 14.94.**

EXAMPLE 14.11 Naming Acid Anhydrides

LEARNING GOAL

12 Determine the common and IUPAC names of acid anhydrides.

Write the IUPAC and common names for each of the following acid anhydrides.

$$CH_3CH_2CH_2\overset{O}{\overset{\|}{C}}—O—\overset{O}{\overset{\|}{C}}CH_2CH_2CH_3$$

Solution

This is a symmetrical acid anhydride. The IUPAC name of the four-carbon parent carboxylic acid is butanoic acid (common name butyric acid). To name the anhydride, simply replace the word *acid* with the word *anhydride.* The IUPAC name of this compound is butanoic anhydride (common name butyric anhydride).

$$CH_3\overset{O}{\overset{\|}{C}}—O—\overset{O}{\overset{\|}{C}}CH_2CH_2CH_2CH_2CH_3$$

Solution

This is an unsymmetrical anhydride. The IUPAC names of the two parent carboxylic acids are ethanoic acid (two-carbon) and hexanoic acid (six-carbon). To name an unsymmetrical anhydride, the term *anhydride* is preceded by the names of the two parent acids. The IUPAC name of this compound is ethanoic hexanoic anhydride. The common names of the two parent carboxylic acids are acetic acid and caproic acid. Thus, the common name of this compound is acetic caproic anhydride.

Practice Problem 14.11

Write the common and IUPAC names for each of the following acid anhydrides.

a. $CH_3CH_2CH_2\overset{O}{\overset{\|}{C}}—O—\overset{O}{\overset{\|}{C}}CH_2CH_2CH_2CH_2CH_3$

b. $CH_3\overset{O}{\overset{\|}{C}}—O—\overset{O}{\overset{\|}{C}}CH_2CH_2CH_2CH_3$

c. $CH_3CH_2CH_2CH_2\overset{O}{\overset{\|}{C}}—O—\overset{O}{\overset{\|}{C}}CH_2CH_3$

d. $CH_3CH_2\overset{O}{\overset{\|}{C}}—O—\overset{O}{\overset{\|}{C}}CH_3$

► For Further Practice: **Questions 14.89 and 14.90.**

Acid anhydrides can also react with an alcohol. This reaction produces an ester and a carboxylic acid. This is an example of an acyl group transfer reaction. The **acyl group** of a carboxylic acid derivative has the following structure:

$$R—\overset{O}{\overset{\|}{C}}—$$

The following general equation represents the acyl group transfer reaction between an alcohol and an acid anhydride.

$$\underset{\text{Alcohol}}{R—OH} + \underset{\text{Acid anhydride}}{R—\overset{O}{\overset{\|}{C}}—O—\overset{O}{\overset{\|}{C}}—R} \longrightarrow \underset{\text{Ester}}{R—\overset{O}{\overset{\|}{C}}—OR} + \underset{\text{Carboxylic acid}}{R—\overset{O}{\overset{\|}{C}}—OH}$$

The acyl group of the acid anhydride is transferred to the oxygen of the alcohol in this reaction. The alcohol and anhydride reactants and ester product are described below. The carboxylic acid product is omitted.

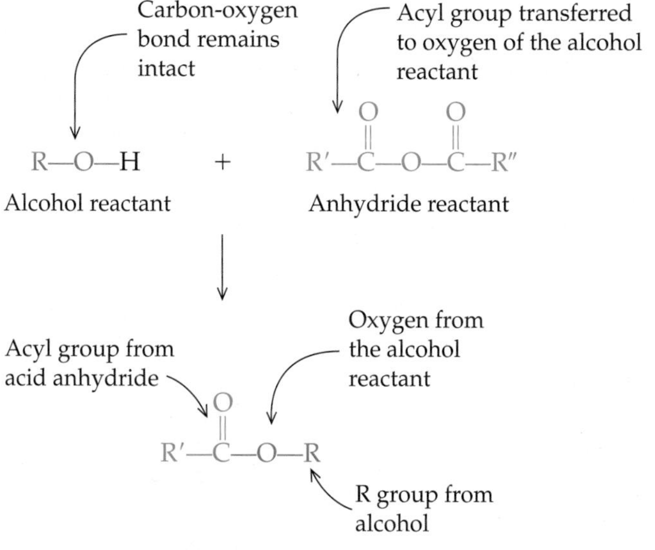

Other acyl group donors include thioesters and esters. As we will see in the final section of this chapter, acyl group transfer reactions are very important in nature, particularly in the pathways responsible for breakdown of food molecules and harvesting cellular energy.

Question 14.9 Write an equation showing the synthesis of each of the following acid anhydrides. Provide the IUPAC names of the acid chloride and carboxylate anion reactants and the acid anhydride product.

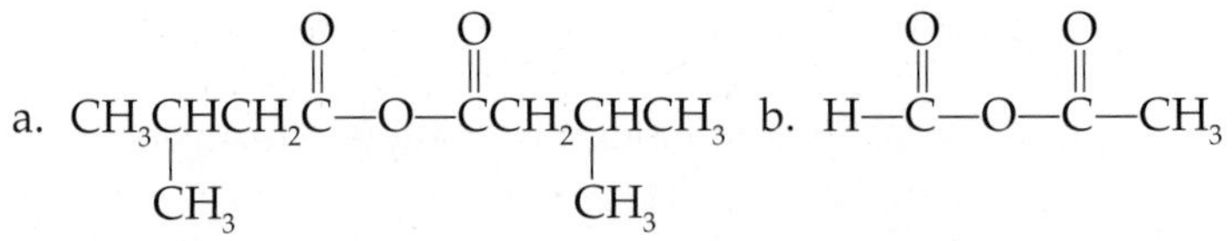

a. $CH_3CH(CH_3)CH_2C(=O)—O—C(=O)CH_2CH(CH_3)CH_3$ b. $H—C(=O)—O—C(=O)—CH_3$

Question 14.10 Write an equation showing the synthesis of each of the following acid anhydrides. Provide the common names of the acid chloride and carboxylate anion reactants and the acid anhydride products.

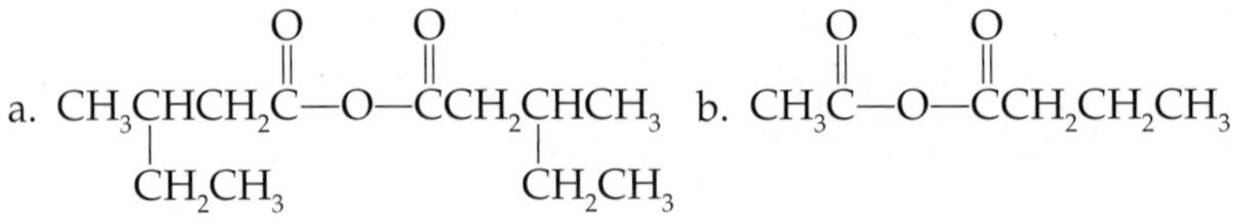

a. $CH_3CH(CH_2CH_3)CH_2C(=O)—O—C(=O)CH_2CH(CH_2CH_3)CH_3$ b. $CH_3C(=O)—O—C(=O)CH_2CH_2CH_3$

14.4 Nature's High-Energy Compounds: Phosphoesters and Thioesters

LEARNING GOAL

14 Discuss the significance of thioesters and phosphoesters in biological systems.

An alcohol can react with phosphoric acid to produce a phosphate ester, or **phosphoester,** as in

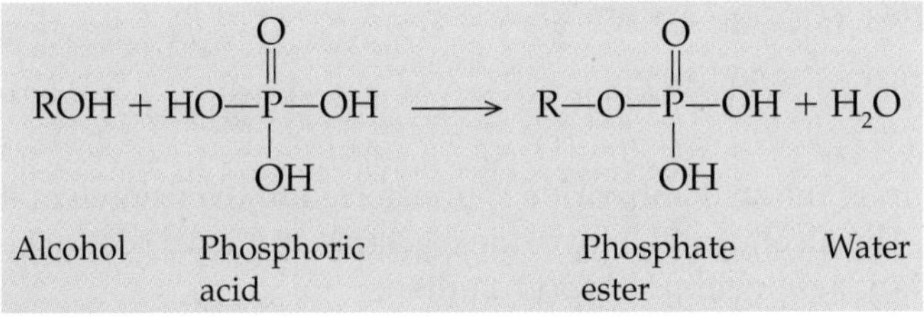

$$ROH + HO—P(=O)(OH)—OH \longrightarrow R—O—P(=O)(OH)—OH + H_2O$$

Alcohol — Phosphoric acid — Phosphate ester — Water

The many phosphorylated intermediates in the metabolism of sugars will be discussed in Chapter 21.

Phosphoesters of simple sugars or monosaccharides are very important in the energy-harvesting biochemical pathways that provide energy for all life functions. One such pathway is *glycolysis*. This pathway is the first stage in the breakdown of sugars. The first reaction in this pathway is the formation of a phosphoester of the six-carbon sugar, glucose. The phosphorylation of glucose to produce glucose-6-phosphate is represented in the following equation:

In fact the word *glycolysis* comes from two Greek words that mean "splitting sugars" (*glykos*, "sweet," and *lysis*, "to split"). In this pathway, the six-carbon sugar glucose is split, and then oxidized, to produce two three-carbon molecules, called *pyruvate*.

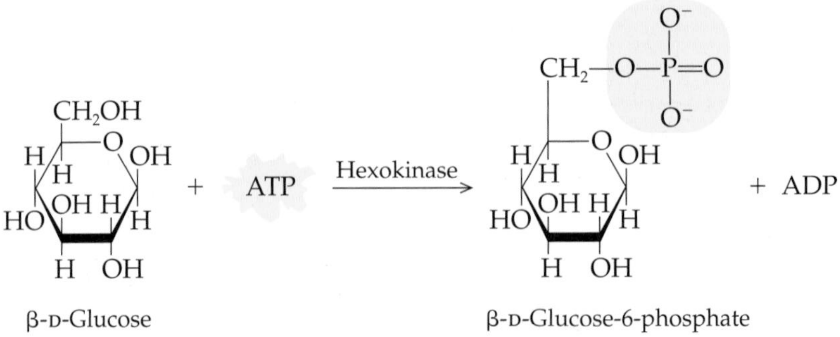

$$\beta\text{-D-Glucose} + ATP \xrightarrow{\text{Hexokinase}} \beta\text{-D-Glucose-6-phosphate} + ADP$$

β-D-Glucose β-D-Glucose-6-phosphate

In this reaction the source of the phosphoryl group is **adenosine triphosphate (ATP),** which is the universal energy currency for all living organisms. As such, ATP is used to store energy released in cellular metabolic reactions and to provide the energy required for most of the reactions that occur in the cell. The transfer of a phosphoryl group from ATP to glucose "energizes" the glucose molecule in preparation for other reactions of the pathway.

ATP consists of a nitrogenous base (adenine) and a phosphate ester of the five-carbon sugar ribose (Figure 14.5). The triphosphate group attached to ribose is made up of three phosphate groups bonded to one another by phosphoanhydride bonds. When two phosphate groups react with one another, a water molecule is lost. Because water is lost, the resulting bond is called a **phosphoanhydride** bond.

Phosphoryl is the term used to describe the functional group derived from phosphoric acid that is part of another molecule.

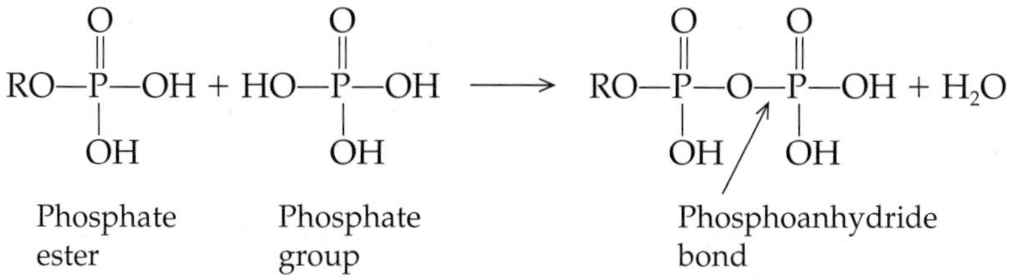

$$\underset{\text{Phosphate ester}}{RO-\overset{\overset{O}{\|}}{\underset{\underset{OH}{|}}{P}}-OH} + \underset{\text{Phosphate group}}{HO-\overset{\overset{O}{\|}}{\underset{\underset{OH}{|}}{P}}-OH} \longrightarrow RO-\overset{\overset{O}{\|}}{\underset{\underset{OH}{|}}{P}}-\underset{\text{Phosphoanhydride bond}}{O}-\overset{\overset{O}{\|}}{\underset{\underset{OH}{|}}{P}}-OH + H_2O$$

The energy of ATP is made available through hydrolysis of either of the two phosphoanhydride bonds, as shown in Figure 14.5. This is an exothermic process; that is, energy is given off. When the phosphoryl group is transferred to another molecule—for instance, glucose—some of that energy resides in the phosphorylated sugar, thereby "energizing" it. The importance of ATP as an energy source becomes apparent when we realize that we synthesize and break down an amount of ATP equivalent to our body weight each day.

The functions and properties of ATP in energy metabolism are discussed in Section 21.1.

Cellular enzymes can carry out a reaction between a thiol and a carboxylic acid to produce a **thioester:**

Thiols are described in Section 12.8.

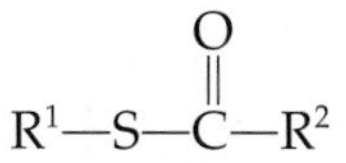

$$R^1-S-\overset{\overset{O}{\|}}{C}-R^2$$

Thioester

The reactions that produce thioesters are essential in energy-harvesting pathways as a means of "activating" acyl groups for subsequent breakdown reactions. The complex thiol coenzyme A is the most important acyl group activator in the cell. The detailed structure of coenzyme A appears in Section 12.8, but it is generally abbreviated CoA—SH to emphasize the importance of the sulfhydryl group. The most common thioester is the acetyl ester, called **acetyl coenzyme A** (acetyl CoA).

Acetyl CoA carries the acetyl group from glycolysis or β-oxidation of a fatty acid to an intermediate of the citric acid cycle. This reaction is an example of an acyl group transfer reaction. In this case, the acyl group donor is a thioester—acetyl

β-Oxidation is the pathway for the breakdown of fatty acids. Like glycolysis, it is an energy-harvesting pathway.

ATP: $^-O-P(=O)(O^-)-O-P(=O)(O^-)-O-P(=O)(O^-)-O-CH_2$–ribose (H, H, H, H; OH OH)–adenine (NH_2)

Bond cleaved on hydrolysis

$\downarrow H_2O$

ADP: $^-O-P(=O)(O^-)-O-P(=O)(O^-)-O-CH_2$–ribose (H, H, H, H; OH OH)–adenine (NH_2)

$+ \mathbf{H_2PO_4^-} + \textbf{energy}$

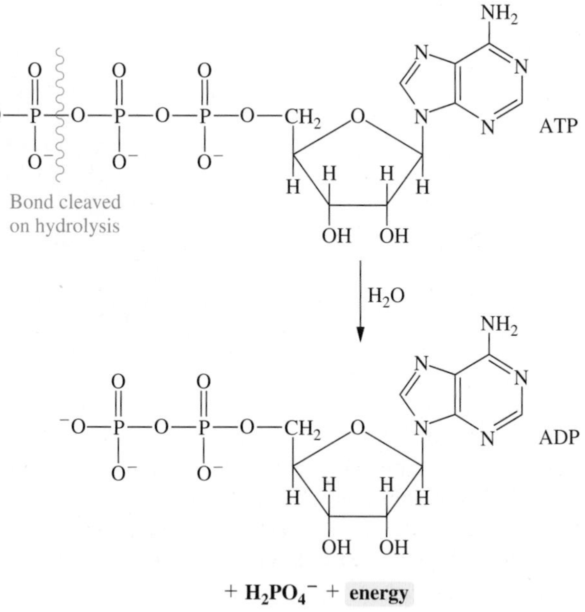

Figure 14.5 The hydrolysis of the phosphoanhydride bond of ATP is accompanied by the release of energy that is used for biochemical reactions in the cell.

A HUMAN PERSPECTIVE

Carboxylic Acid Derivatives of Special Interest

Analgesics (pain killers) and antipyretics (fever reducers)

Aspirin (*acetylsalicylic acid*), derived from the bark of the willow tree, is the most widely used drug in the world. Hundreds of millions of dollars are spent annually on this compound. It is used primarily as a pain reliever (analgesic) and in the reduction of fever (antipyretic). Aspirin is among the drugs often referred to as NSAIDs, or nonsteroidal anti-inflammatory drugs. These drugs inhibit the inflammatory response by inhibiting an enzyme called cyclooxygenase, which is the first enzyme in the pathway for the synthesis of prostaglandins. Prostaglandins are responsible, in part, for pain and fever. Thus, aspirin and other NSAIDs reduce pain and fever by decreasing prostaglandin synthesis. Aspirin's side effects are a problem for some individuals. Because aspirin inhibits clotting, its use is not recommended during pregnancy, nor should it be used by individuals with ulcers. In those instances, *acetaminophen,* found in the over-the-counter pain-reliever Tylenol, is often prescribed.

The search for NSAIDs that are more effective and yet gentler on the stomach has provided two new analgesics for the over-the-counter market. These are ibuprofen (sold as Motrin, Advil, Nuprin) and naproxen (sold as Naprosyn, Naprelan, Anaprox, and Aleve).

$$CH_3\underset{\displaystyle CH_3}{\underset{|}{C}}HCH_2-C_6H_4-\underset{\displaystyle CH_3}{\underset{|}{C}}H-\overset{\displaystyle O}{\overset{\|}{C}}-OH$$

Ibuprofen

$$CH_3O-C_{10}H_6-\underset{\displaystyle CH_3}{\underset{|}{C}}H-\overset{\displaystyle O}{\overset{\|}{C}}-OH$$

Naproxen

$$C_6H_4(\overset{\displaystyle O}{\overset{\|}{C}}-OH)(O-\overset{\displaystyle O}{\overset{\|}{C}}-CH_3) \qquad HO-C_6H_4-NH-\overset{\displaystyle O}{\overset{\|}{C}}-CH_3$$

Acetylsalicylic acid Acetaminophen

Some common analgesics.

Pheromones

Pheromones, chemicals secreted by animals, influence the behavior of other members of the same species. They often represent the major means of communication among simpler animals. The term *pheromone* literally means "to carry" and "to excite" (Greek, *pherein,* to carry; Greek, *horman,* to excite). They are chemicals carried or shed by one member of the species and used to alert other members of the species.

Pheromones may be involved in sexual attraction, trail marking, aggregation or recruitment, territorial marking, or signaling alarm. Others may be involved in defense or in species socialization—for example, designating various classes within the species as a whole. Among all of the pheromones, insect pheromones have been the most intensely studied. Many of the insect pheromones are carboxylic acids or acid derivatives, as seen here:

$$CH_3CH_2CH{=}CH(CH_2)_9CH_2O\overset{\displaystyle O}{\overset{\|}{C}}CH_3$$

Tetradecenyl acetate
(European corn borer sex pheromone)

$$CH_3\overset{\displaystyle O}{\overset{\|}{C}}CH_2CH_2CH_2CH_2CH_2\underset{H}{C}{=}\overset{H}{C}COOH$$

9-Keto-*trans*-2-decenoic acid
(queen bee socializing/royalty pheromone)

$$CH_3(CH_2)_3\overset{H}{C}{=}\overset{H}{C}(CH_2)_5CH_2O\overset{\displaystyle O}{\overset{\|}{C}}CH_3$$

cis-7-Dodecenyl acetate
(cabbage looper sex pheromone)

For Further Understanding

- A nonsteroidal anti-inflammatory drug can cause side effects if used over a long period. Do some research on the physiological roles of prostaglandins to develop hypotheses concerning these side effects.
- How might you make use of pheromones to control pests such as the corn borer?

- The boiling points and melting points of esters are comparable to those of aldehydes and ketones.
- Esters are formed from the reaction between a carboxylic acid and an alcohol.
- Esters can undergo **hydrolysis** back to the parent carboxylic acid and alcohol.
- The base-catalyzed hydrolysis of an ester is called **saponification.**
- **Condensation polymers** are large molecules formed by combination of many small molecules (monomers) that result from joining of monomers in a reaction that also forms a small molecule, such as water or an alcohol.

14.3 Acid Chlorides and Acid Anhydrides

- **Acid chlorides** are noxious chemicals and are useful in the synthesis of a variety of carboxylic acid derivatives.
- **Acid anhydrides** are formed by the combination of an acid chloride and a carboxylate anion.
- Acid anhydrides can react with an alcohol to produce an ester and a carboxylic acid. This is an example of an acyl group transfer.
- The **acyl group** in carboxylic acid derivatives contains the carbonyl group attached to one alkyl or one aryl group.

14.4 Nature's High-Energy Compounds: Phosphoesters and Thioesters

- An alcohol can react with phosphoric acid to produce a phosphate ester (**phosphoester**).
- When two phosphate groups are joined, the resulting bond is a **phosphoanhydride** bond.
- The phosphoester and phosphoanhydride bonds are important in the structure of **adenosine triphosphate (ATP),** the universal energy currency of all cells.
- Cellular enzymes carry out a reaction between a thiol and a carboxylic acid to produce a **thioester.** This reaction is essential for the activation of acyl groups in carbohydrate and fatty acid metabolism.
- Coenzyme A is the important thiol involved in these pathways, forming **acetyl coenzyme A.**

ANSWERS TO PRACTICE PROBLEMS

14.1 a. 2,4-Dimethylpentanoic acid
b. 2,4-Dichlorobutanoic acid
c. 2,3-Dihydroxybutanoic acid
d. 2-Bromo-3-chloro-4-methylhexanoic acid

14.2 a. α,γ-Dimethylvaleric acid
b. α,γ-Dichlorobutyric acid
c. β,γ-Dibromovaleric acid
d. γ-Hydroxycaproic acid

14.3 a. *o*-Toluic acid:

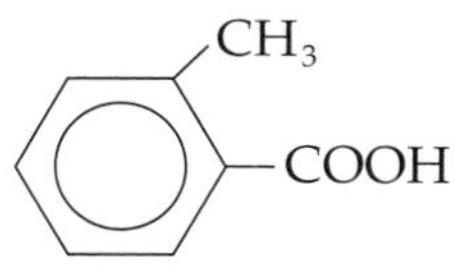

CH_3, COOH (ortho-substituted benzene ring)

b. 2,4,6-Tribromobenzoic acid:

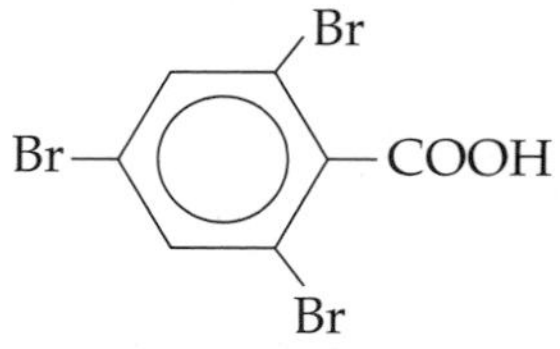

Br, Br, COOH, Br (benzene ring)

c. 2,2,2-Triphenylethanoic acid:

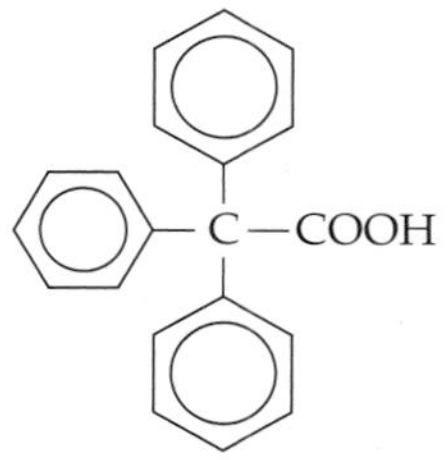

C—COOH (with three phenyl rings)

d. *p*-Toluic acid:

H_3C—(benzene ring)—C(=O)—OH

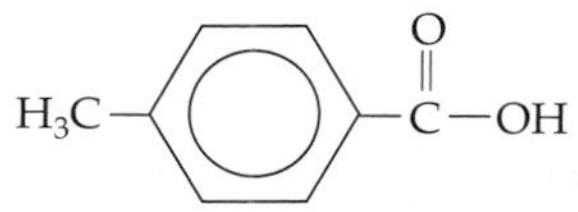

e. 3-Phenylhexanoic acid:

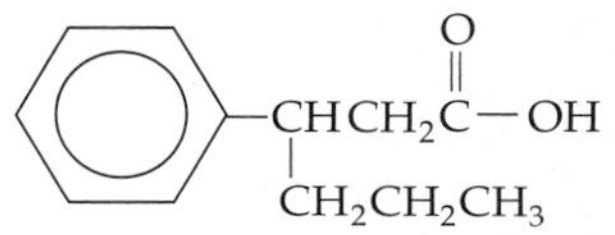

(benzene ring)—$CHCH_2C(=O)—OH$ with $CH_2CH_2CH_3$

f. 3-Phenylcyclohexanecarboxylic acid:

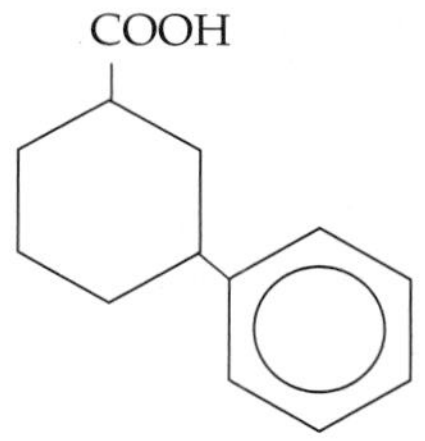

COOH (cyclohexane ring with phenyl)

14.4 a. The following equation represents the synthesis of ethanoic acid from ethanol.

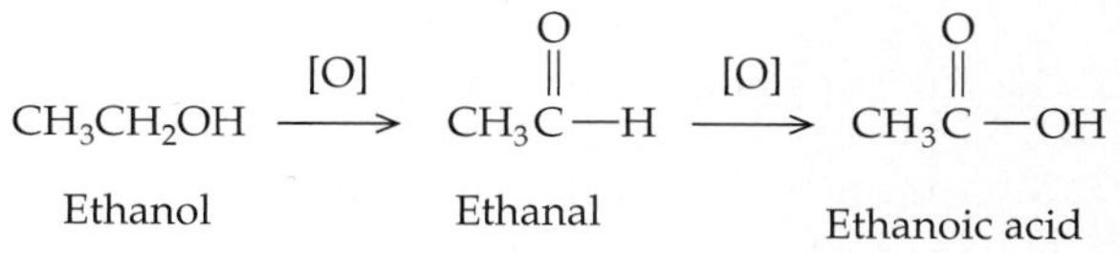

$$\underset{\text{Ethanol}}{CH_3CH_2OH} \xrightarrow{[O]} \underset{\text{Ethanal}}{CH_3C(=O)—H} \xrightarrow{[O]} \underset{\text{Ethanoic acid}}{CH_3C(=O)—OH}$$

b. The following equation represents the synthesis of butanoic acid from 1-butanol.

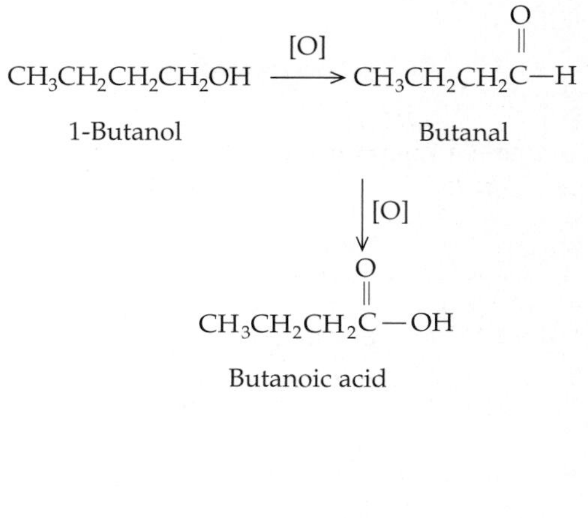

$$\underset{\text{1-Butanol}}{CH_3CH_2CH_2CH_2OH} \xrightarrow{[O]} \underset{\text{Butanal}}{CH_3CH_2CH_2C(=O)—H} \xrightarrow{[O]} \underset{\text{Butanoic acid}}{CH_3CH_2CH_2C(=O)—OH}$$

c. The following equation represents the synthesis of octanoic acid from 1-octanol.

$$\underset{\text{1-Octanol}}{CH_3(CH_2)_6CH_2OH} \xrightarrow{[O]} \underset{\text{Octanal}}{CH_3(CH_2)_6\overset{O}{\overset{\|}{C}}-H}$$

$$\downarrow [O]$$

$$\underset{\text{Octanoic acid}}{CH_3(CH_2)_6\overset{O}{\overset{\|}{C}}-OH}$$

14.5 a. $CH_3CH_2COO^-K^+$
b. $[CH_3CH_2CH_2COO^-]_2Ba^{2+}$
c. $CH_3CH_2CH_2CH_2CH_2COO^-K^+$
d. 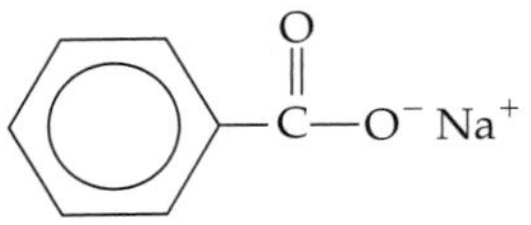 $C_6H_5-\overset{O}{\overset{\|}{C}}-O^-\ Na^+$

14.6 a. Potassium propanoate c. Potassium hexanoate
b. Barium butanoate d. Sodium benzoate

14.7 a. Propyl butanoate (propyl butyrate)
b. Ethyl butanoate (ethyl butyrate)
c. Propyl ethanoate (propyl acetate)
d. Butyl propanoate (butyl propionate)

14.8 a. The following reaction between 1-butanol and ethanoic acid produces butyl ethanoate. It requires a trace of acid and heat. It is also reversible.

$$CH_3CH_2CH_2CH_2OH + CH_3COOH$$

$$\updownarrow$$

$$CH_3\overset{O}{\overset{\|}{C}}-OCH_2CH_2CH_2CH_3$$

b. The following reaction between ethanol and propanoic acid produces ethyl propanoate. It requires a trace of acid and heat. It is also reversible.

$$CH_3CH_2OH + CH_3CH_2COOH$$

$$\updownarrow$$

$$CH_3CH_2\overset{O}{\overset{\|}{C}}-OCH_2CH_3$$

14.9 a. Methyl butanoate is made from methanol and butanoic acid.

$$\underset{\text{Methanol}}{CH_3OH} + \underset{\text{Butanoic acid}}{CH_3CH_2CH_2COOH} \longrightarrow \underset{\text{Methyl butanoate}}{CH_3CH_2CH_2\overset{O}{\overset{\|}{C}}OCH_3}$$

Methanol is an allowed starting material, but butanoic acid is not. However, it can easily be produced by the oxidation of its corresponding alcohol, 1-butanol:

$$\underset{\text{1-Butanol}}{CH_3CH_2CH_2CH_2OH} \xrightarrow{[O]} \underset{\text{Butanal}}{CH_3CH_2CH_2CHO}$$

$$\downarrow [O]$$

$$\underset{\text{Butanoic acid}}{CH_3CH_2CH_2COOH}$$

b. Propyl methanoate is made from 1-propanol and methanoic acid.

$$\underset{\text{1-Propanol}}{CH_3CH_2CH_2OH} + \underset{\text{Methanoic acid}}{HCOOH}$$

$$\downarrow$$

$$\underset{\text{Propyl methanoate}}{H\overset{O}{\overset{\|}{C}}OCH_2CH_2CH_3}$$

1-Propanol is an allowed starting material, but methanoic acid is not. However, it can easily be produced by the oxidation of its corresponding alcohol, methanol:

$$\underset{\text{Methanol}}{CH_3OH} \xrightarrow{[O]} \underset{\text{Methanal}}{HCHO} \xrightarrow{[O]} \underset{\text{Methanoic acid}}{HCOOH}$$

14.10 a. The following equation represents the synthesis of butanoic anhydride:

$$\underset{\text{Butanoate anion}}{CH_3CH_2CH_2\overset{O}{\overset{\|}{C}}O^-} + \underset{\text{Butanoyl chloride}}{CH_3CH_2CH_2\overset{O}{\overset{\|}{C}}-Cl}$$

$$\downarrow$$

$$\underset{\text{Butanoic anhydride}}{CH_3CH_2CH_2\overset{O}{\overset{\|}{C}}-O-\overset{O}{\overset{\|}{C}}CH_2CH_2CH_3}$$

b. The following equation represents the synthesis of hexanoic anhydride:

$$\underset{\text{Hexanoate anion}}{CH_3(CH_2)_4\overset{O}{\overset{\|}{C}}O^-} + \underset{\text{Hexanoyl chloride}}{CH_3(CH_2)_4\overset{O}{\overset{\|}{C}}-Cl}$$

$$\downarrow$$

$$\underset{\text{Hexanoic anhydride}}{CH_3(CH_2)_4\overset{O}{\overset{\|}{C}}-O-\overset{O}{\overset{\|}{C}}(CH_2)_4CH_3}$$

14.11 a. IUPAC name: Butanoic hexanoic anhydride
Common name: Butyric caproic anhydride
b. IUPAC name: Ethanoic pentanoic anhydride
Common name: Acetic valeric anhydride
c. IUPAC name: Propanoic pentanoic anhydride
Common name: Propionic valeric anhydride
d. IUPAC name: Ethanoic propanoic anhydride
Common name: Acetic propionic anhydride

QUESTIONS AND PROBLEMS

Carboxylic Acids: Structure and Properties

Foundations

14.11 The functional group is largely responsible for the physical and chemical properties of the various chemical families. Explain why a carboxylic acid is more polar and has a higher boiling point than an alcohol or an aldehyde of comparable molar mass.

14.12 Explain why carboxylic acids are weak acids.

Applications

14.13 Which member of the following pairs has the higher boiling point?
a. Pentanoic acid or pentanal
b. 3-Pentanone or 2-pentanol
c. 2-Pentanol or pentane

14.14 Which member of the following pairs has the higher boiling point?
a. Ethyl propyl ether or pentanal
b. 3-Pentanone or pentanoic acid
c. Methanol or methanoic acid

14.15 Arrange the following from highest to lowest melting points:

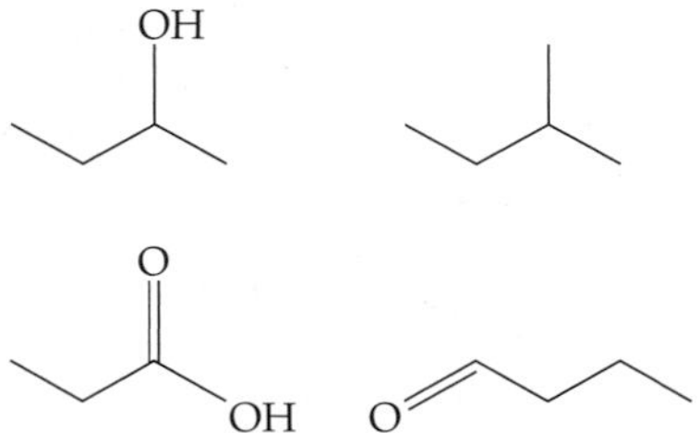

OH

O

OH O

14.16 Draw the condensed formula for each of the line formulas in Question 14.15 and provide the IUPAC name for each.

14.17 Which member in each of the following pairs has the higher boiling point?
a. Heptanoic acid or 1-heptanol
b. Propanal or 1-propanol
c. Methyl pentanoate or pentanoic acid
d. 1-Butanol or butanoic acid

14.18 Which member in each of the following pairs is more soluble in water?
a. $CH_3CH_2CH_2CH_2CH_2\overset{O}{\overset{\|}{C}}-OH$ or
$CH_3CH_2CH_2CH_2CH_2\overset{O}{\overset{\|}{C}}-O^-Na^+$
b. $CH_3CH_2CH_2CH_2CH_2CH_2CH_2CH_2CH_3$ or
$CH_3CH_2CH_2CH_2CH_2CH_2CH_2CH_2OH$
c. $CH_3CH_2-O-CH_2CH_3$ or $CH_3CH_2\overset{O}{\overset{\|}{C}}-OCH_3$
d. $CH_3CH_2-O-CH_2CH_3$ or $CH_3CH_2CH_2CH_2CH_2CH_3$
e. Decanoic acid or ethanoic acid

14.19 Describe the properties of low-molar-mass carboxylic acids.

14.20 What are some of the biological functions of the long-chain carboxylic acids called fatty acids?

14.21 Why is citric acid added to some food products?

14.22 What is the function of lactic acid in food products? Of what significance is lactic acid in muscle metabolism?

14.23 Why is glutaric acid particularly useful in the synthesis of condensation polymers?

14.24 What is the role of octanoic acid in the control of appetite?

Carboxylic Acids: Structure and Nomenclature

Foundations

14.25 Summarize the IUPAC nomenclature rules for naming carboxylic acids.

14.26 Describe the rules for determining the common names of carboxylic acids.

Applications

14.27 Adipic acid occurs naturally in beets and is used as a food additive. What is the IUPAC name for adipic acid? Why do you think that adipic acid is used as a food additive?

$$HOOCCH_2CH_2CH_2CH_2COOH$$

14.28 Propionic acid is a liquid fatty acid found in sweat and milk products. It is a bacterial fermentation product that gives the tangy flavor to Swiss cheese. What is the IUPAC name of propionic acid?

$$CH_3CH_2COOH$$

14.29 Write the condensed formula and the line formula for each of the following carboxylic acids:
a. 3-Methylhexanoic acid
b. 2-Ethyl-2-methylpentanoic acid
c. 3-Methylcyclopentanecarboxylic acid

14.30 Write the condensed formula and the line formula for each of the following carboxylic acids:
a. 2,3-Dibromocycloheptanecarboxylic acid
b. 2-Butenoic acid
c. 2,4,5-Trimethyloctanoic acid

14.31 Name each of the following carboxylic acids, using both the common and the IUPAC Nomenclature Systems:

a. $H-\overset{O}{\overset{\|}{C}}-OH$

b. $CH_3\overset{CH_3}{\overset{|}{C}}HCH_2\overset{O}{\overset{\|}{C}}-OH$

c. $\overset{O}{\overset{\|}{C}}-OH$

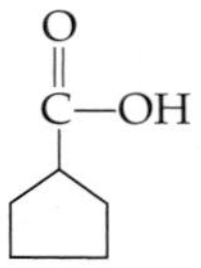

14.32 Name each of the following carboxylic acids, using both the common and IUPAC Nomenclature Systems:

a. 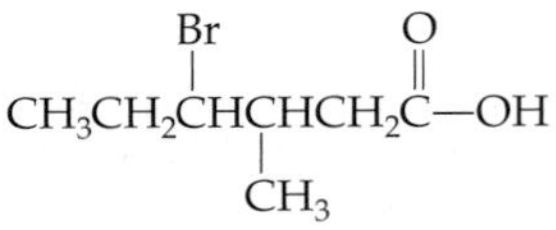 $CH_3CH_2CH(Br)CH(CH_3)CH_2C(=O)—OH$

b. 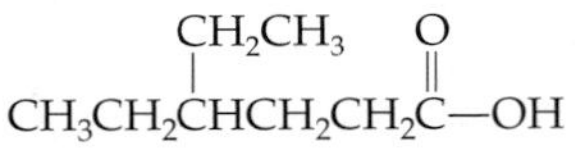 $CH_3CH_2CH(CH_2CH_3)CH_2CH_2C(=O)—OH$

c. 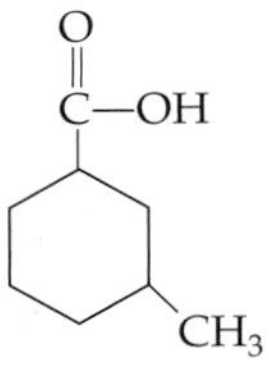 3-methylcyclohexane ring bearing $C(=O)—OH$ (with CH_3 substituent)

14.33 Write a complete structural formula and determine the IUPAC name for each of the carboxylic acids of molecular formula $C_4H_8O_2$.

14.34 Write the general structure of an aldehyde, a ketone, a carboxylic acid, and an ester. What similarities exist among these structures?

14.35 Write the condensed structure of each of the following carboxylic acids:

a. 4,4-Dimethylhexanoic acid
b. 3-Bromo-4-methylpentanoic acid
c. 2,3-Dinitrobenzoic acid
d. 3-Methylcyclohexanecarboxylic acid

14.36 Use IUPAC nomenclature to write the names for each of the following carboxylic acids:

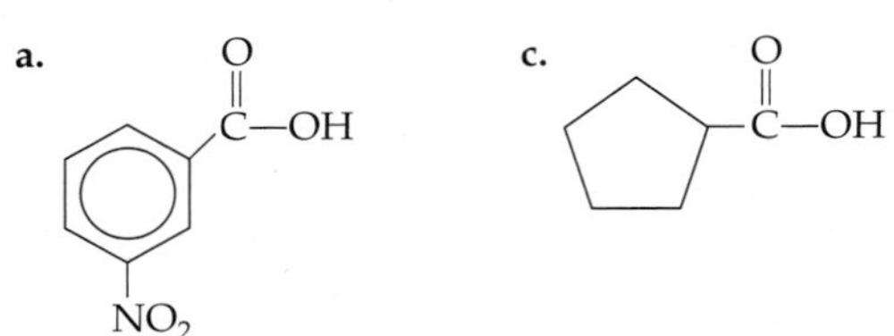

b. 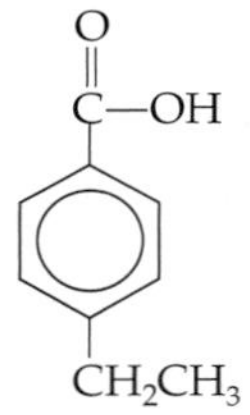 benzene ring bearing $C(=O)—OH$ and, para, CH_2CH_3

14.37 Provide the common and IUPAC names for each of the following compounds:

a. 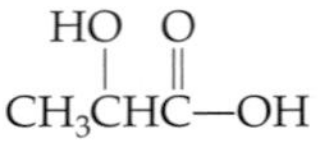 $CH_3CH(OH)C(=O)—OH$

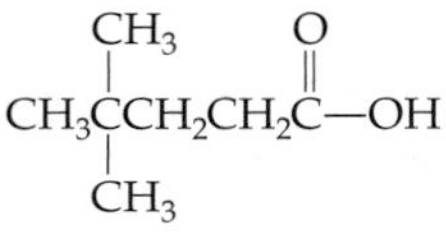

b. 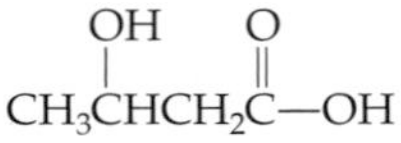 $CH_3CH(OH)CH_2C(=O)—OH$

c. $CH_3C(CH_3)_2CH_2CH_2C(=O)—OH$

d. 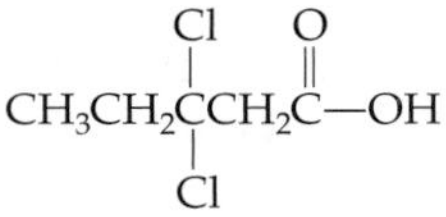 $CH_3CH_2CCl_2CH_2C(=O)—OH$

14.38 Draw the structure of each of the following carboxylic acids:

a. β-Chlorobutyric acid
b. α,β-Dibromovaleric acid
c. β,γ-Dihydroxybutyric acid
d. δ-Bromo-γ-chloro-β-methylcaproic acid

14.39 Provide the IUPAC name for each of the following aromatic carboxylic acids.

a. 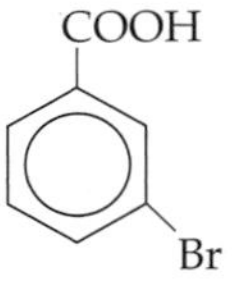 benzene ring bearing COOH and, meta, Br

b. 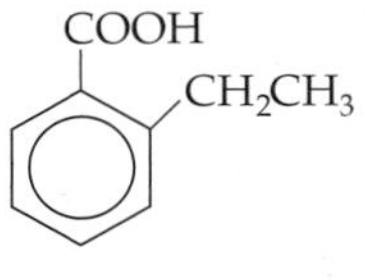 benzene ring bearing COOH and, ortho, CH_2CH_3

c. benzene ring bearing COOH and, para, OH

14.40 Provide the IUPAC name for each of the following aromatic carboxylic acids.

a. 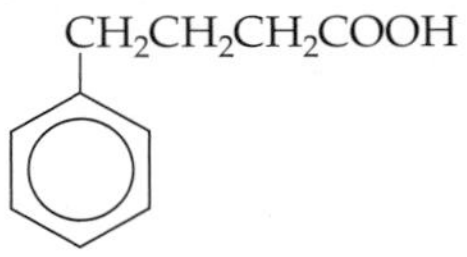 $CH_2CH_2CH_2COOH$ with benzene ring on the first carbon ($C_6H_5CH_2CH_2CH_2COOH$)

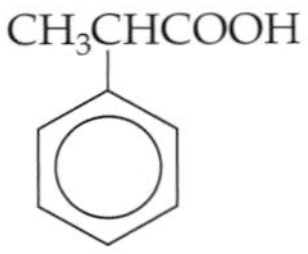

b. 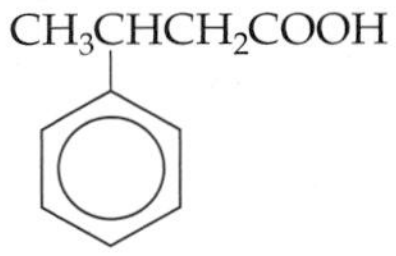 $CH_3CH(C_6H_5)CH_2COOH$

c. $CH_3CH(C_6H_5)COOH$

Carboxylic Acids: Reactions

Foundations

14.41 Explain what is meant by oxidation in organic molecules and provide an example of an oxidation reaction involving an aldehyde or an alcohol.

14.42 Write a general equation showing the preparation of a carboxylic acid from an alcohol.

14.43 Write a general equation showing the dissociation of a carboxylic acid in water.

14.44 Carboxylic acids are described as weak acids. To what extent do carboxylic acids generally dissociate?

14.45 What reaction occurs when a strong base is added to a carboxylic acid?

14.46 Write a general equation showing the reaction of a strong base with a carboxylic acid.

14.47 How is a soap prepared?

14.48 How do soaps assist in the removal of oil and grease from clothing?

Applications

14.49 Write an equation representing the oxidation of each of the following compounds:

a. 1-Pentanol
b. Butanal
c. Butanone

14.50 Write an equation representing the oxidation of each of the following compounds:

a. 3-Hexanol
b. 2-Methylpentanal
c. 3-Pentanone

14.51 Complete each of the following reactions by supplying the missing portion indicated by a question mark:

a. $CH_3\overset{\overset{\displaystyle O}{\|}}{C}-H \xrightarrow{[O]} ?$

b. $CH_3CH_2CH_2\overset{\overset{\displaystyle O}{\|}}{C}-OH + CH_3OH \xrightarrow{H^+,\ heat} ?$

c. 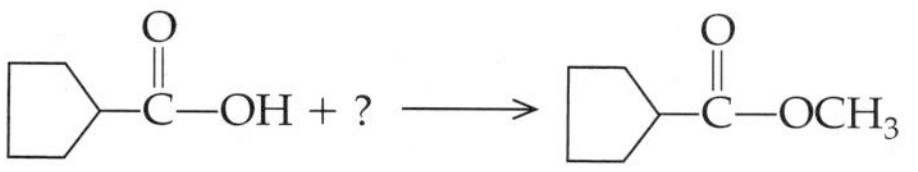 $\text{(cyclopentyl)}-\overset{\overset{\displaystyle O}{\|}}{C}-OH + ? \longrightarrow \text{(cyclopentyl)}-\overset{\overset{\displaystyle O}{\|}}{C}-OCH_3$

14.52 Complete each of the following reactions by supplying the missing part(s) indicated by the question mark(s):

a. 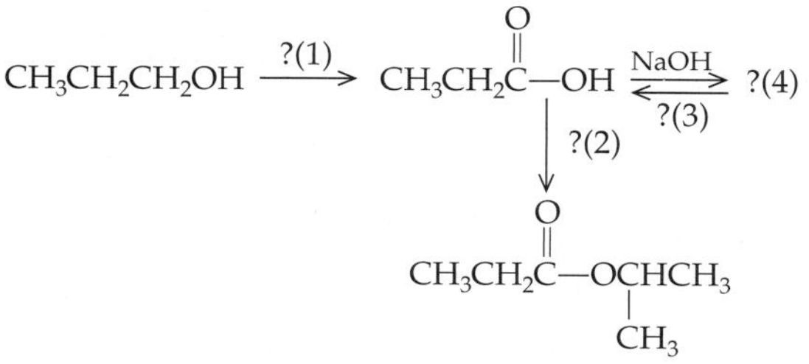 $CH_3CH_2CH_2OH \xrightarrow{?(1)} CH_3CH_2\overset{\overset{\displaystyle O}{\|}}{C}-OH \underset{?(3)}{\overset{NaOH}{\rightleftharpoons}} ?(4)$

$CH_3CH_2\overset{\overset{\displaystyle O}{\|}}{C}-OH \xrightarrow{?(2)} CH_3CH_2\overset{\overset{\displaystyle O}{\|}}{C}-O\underset{\underset{\displaystyle CH_3}{|}}{C}HCH_3$

b. $CH_3COOH + NaOH \longrightarrow ?$

c. $CH_3CH_2CH_2CH_2CH_2COOH + NaOH \longrightarrow ?$

d. $? + CH_3CH_2\overset{\overset{\displaystyle CH_3}{|}}{C}HOH \xrightarrow{H^+} CH_3\overset{\overset{\displaystyle O}{\|}}{C}-O\underset{\underset{\displaystyle CH_3}{|}}{C}HCH_2CH_3$

14.53 How might $CH_3CH_2CH_2CH_2CH_2OH$ be converted to each of the following products?

a. $CH_3CH_2CH_2CH_2CHO$
b. $CH_3CH_2CH_2CH_2COOH$

14.54 Which of the following alcohols can be oxidized to a carboxylic acid? Name the carboxylic acid produced. For those alcohols that cannot be oxidized to a carboxylic acid, name the final product.

a. Ethanol
b. 2-Propanol
c. 1-Propanol
d. 3-Pentanol

14.55 Write an equation representing the neutralization of pentanoic acid with each of the following bases:

a. NaOH
b. KOH
c. $Ca(OH)_2$

14.56 Write an equation representing the neutralization of each of the following carboxylic acids with KOH:

a. 3-Chlorohexanoic acid
b. Cyclohexanecarboxylic acid
c. 3,4-Dimethylpentanoic acid

14.57 The calcium salt of propionic acid is added to breads as a preservative that prevents mold growth. Draw the structure of the calcium salt of propionic acid. What are the common and IUPAC names of this carboxylic acid salt?

14.58 Oxalic acid is found in the leaves of rhubarb, primarily in the form of the calcium salt. Since high levels of oxalic acid are toxic, only rhubarb stalks are used to make strawberry rhubarb pie. What is the IUPAC name of oxalic acid? Write the structure of the calcium salt of oxalic acid.

Esters: Structure, Physical Properties, and Nomenclature

Foundations

14.59 Explain why esters are described as slightly polar.

14.60 Compare the boiling points of esters to those of aldehydes or ketones of similar molar mass.

14.61 Briefly summarize the IUPAC rules for naming esters.

14.62 How are the common names of esters derived?

Applications

14.63 Draw condensed formulas for each of the following compounds:

a. Methyl benzoate
b. Butyl decanoate
c. Methyl propionate
d. Ethyl propionate

14.64 Draw condensed formulas for each of the following compounds:

a. Ethyl *m*-nitrobenzoate
b. Isopropyl acetate
c. Methyl butyrate

14.65 Use the IUPAC Nomenclature System to name each of the following esters:

a. $CH_3\overset{\overset{\displaystyle O}{\|}}{C}-OCH_2CH_3$

b. $CH_3CH_2\overset{\overset{\displaystyle O}{\|}}{C}-OCH_3$

c. $CH_3\overset{\overset{\displaystyle CH_3}{|}}{C}HCH_2\overset{\overset{\displaystyle O}{\|}}{C}-OCH_3$

d. 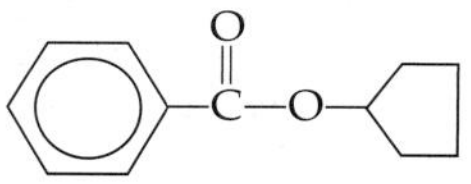 $\text{(phenyl)}-\overset{\overset{\displaystyle O}{\|}}{C}-O-\text{(cyclopentyl)}$

14.66 Use the IUPAC Nomenclature System to name each of the following:

a. 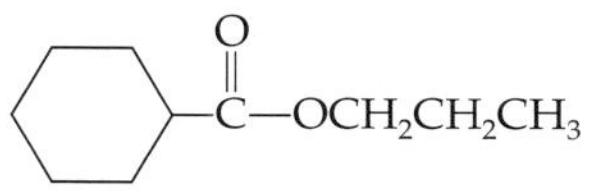 $\text{(cyclohexyl)}-\overset{\overset{\displaystyle O}{\|}}{C}-OCH_2CH_2CH_3$

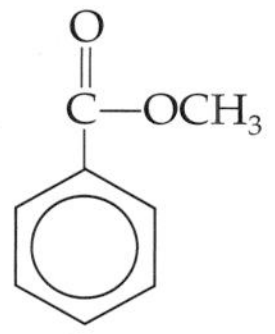

b. $\text{(phenyl)}-\overset{\overset{\displaystyle O}{\|}}{C}-OCH_3$

c. $\underset{\underset{\displaystyle Br}{|}}{C}H_2\underset{\underset{\displaystyle Br}{|}}{C}HCH_2CH_2\overset{\overset{\displaystyle O}{\|}}{C}-OCH_2CH_3$

Esters: Reactions

Foundations

14.67 Write a general reaction showing the preparation of an ester.

14.68 Why is preparation of an ester referred to as a condensation reaction?

14.69 Write a general reaction showing the hydrolysis of an ester using an acid catalyst.

14.70 Write a general reaction showing the base-catalyzed hydrolysis of an ester.

14.71 What is meant by a hydrolysis reaction?

14.72 Why is the salt of a carboxylic acid produced in a base-catalyzed hydrolysis of an ester?

Applications

14.73 Complete each of the following reactions by supplying the missing portion indicated with a question mark:

a. 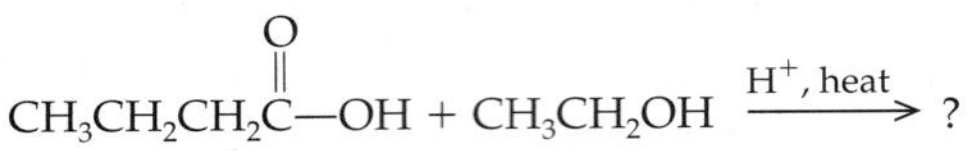 $CH_3CH_2CH_2\overset{O}{\overset{\|}{C}}{-}OH + CH_3CH_2OH \xrightarrow{H^+,\ heat} ?$

b. $CH_3CH_2\overset{O}{\overset{\|}{C}}{-}OCH_2CH_3 + H_2O \xrightarrow{H^+,\ heat} ?$

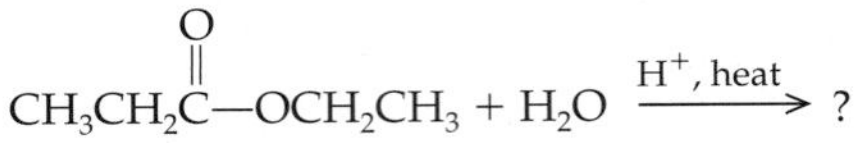

c. $CH_3\overset{CH_3}{\overset{|}{C}}HCH_2CH_2\overset{O}{\overset{\|}{C}}{-}OH + ? \xrightarrow{H^+,\ heat}$ $CH_3\overset{CH_3}{\overset{|}{C}}HCH_2CH_2\overset{O}{\overset{\|}{C}}{-}OCH_2CH_2CH_3$

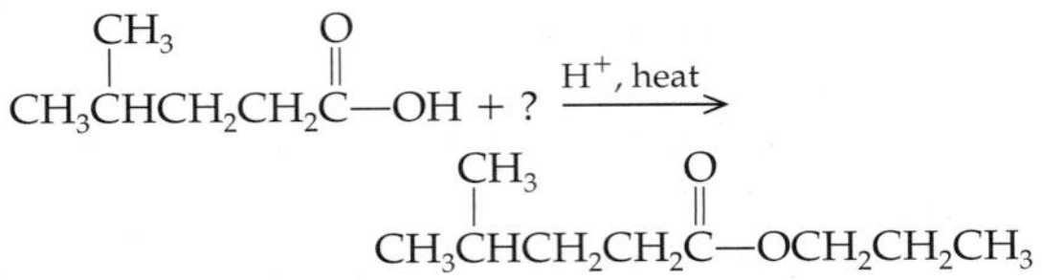

d.  $CH_3CH_2\overset{Br}{\overset{|}{C}}HCH_2\overset{O}{\overset{\|}{C}}{-}OCH_2CH_3 + H_2O \xrightarrow{OH^-,\ heat} ?$

14.74 Complete each of the following reactions by supplying the missing portion indicated with a question mark:

a. 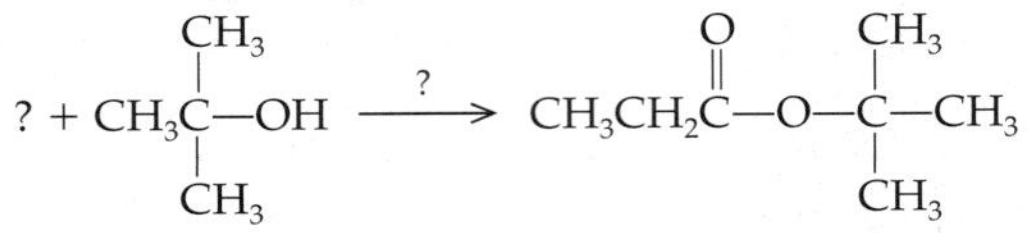 $? + CH_3\underset{CH_3}{\underset{|}{\overset{CH_3}{\overset{|}{C}}}}{-}OH \xrightarrow{?} CH_3CH_2\overset{O}{\overset{\|}{C}}{-}O{-}\underset{CH_3}{\underset{|}{\overset{CH_3}{\overset{|}{C}}}}{-}CH_3$

b. $CH_3CH_2CH_2CH_2COOH + CH_3CH_2CH_2CH_2OH \xrightarrow{H^+,\ heat} ?$

c. 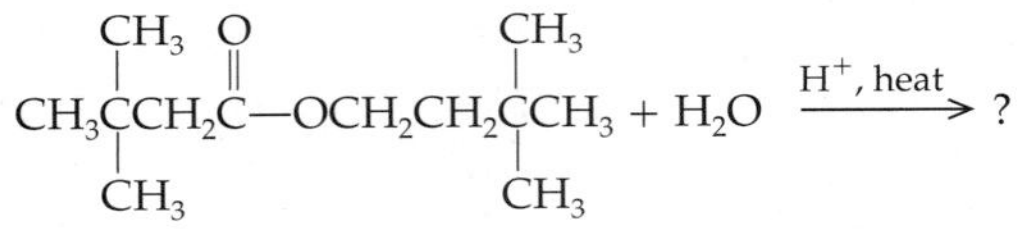 $CH_3\underset{CH_3}{\underset{|}{\overset{CH_3}{\overset{|}{C}}}}CH_2\overset{O}{\overset{\|}{C}}{-}OCH_2CH_2\underset{CH_3}{\underset{|}{\overset{CH_3}{\overset{|}{C}}}}CH_3 + H_2O \xrightarrow{H^+,\ heat} ?$

d. 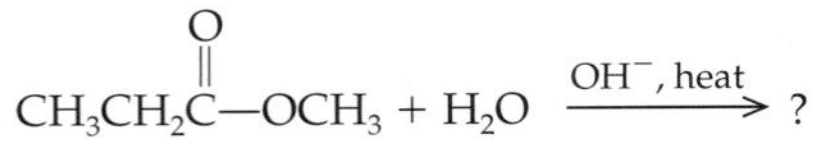 $CH_3CH_2\overset{O}{\overset{\|}{C}}{-}OCH_3 + H_2O \xrightarrow{OH^-,\ heat} ?$

14.75 Design the synthesis of each of the following esters from organic alcohols.
a. Isobutyl methanoate (raspberries)
b. Pentyl butanoate (apricot)

14.76 Design the synthesis of each of the following esters from organic alcohols.
a. Methyl butanoate (apples)
b. Octyl ethanoate (oranges)

14.77 What is saponification? Give an example using specific molecules.

14.78 When the methyl ester of hexanoic acid is hydrolyzed in aqueous sodium hydroxide in the presence of heat, a homogeneous solution results. When the solution is acidified with dilute aqueous hydrochloric acid, a new product forms. What is the new product? Draw its structure.

14.79 The structure of salicylic acid is shown. If this acid reacts with methanol, the product is an ester, methyl salicylate. Methyl salicylate is known as oil of wintergreen and is often used as a flavoring agent. Draw the structure of the product of this reaction.

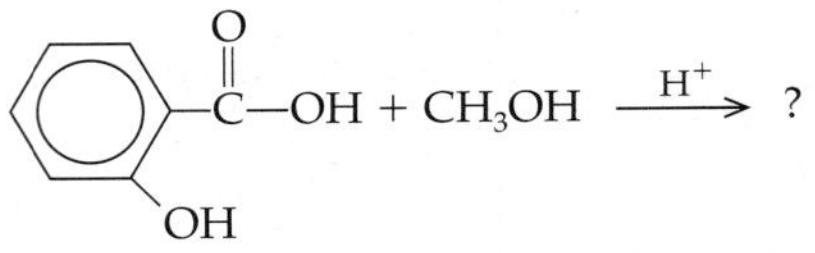

$(o\text{-}HOC_6H_4){-}\overset{O}{\overset{\|}{C}}{-}OH + CH_3OH \xrightarrow{H^+} ?$

14.80 When salicylic acid reacts with acetic anhydride, one of the products is an ester, acetylsalicylic acid. Acetylsalicylic acid is the active ingredient in aspirin. Complete the following equation by drawing the structure of acetylsalicylic acid. (*Hint:* Acid anhydrides are hydrolyzed by water.)

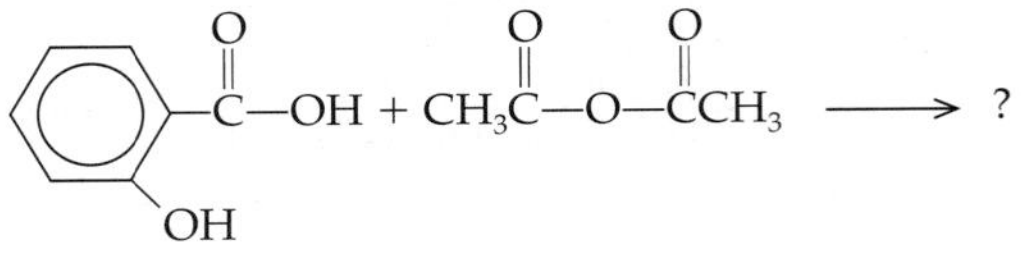

$(o\text{-}HOC_6H_4){-}\overset{O}{\overset{\|}{C}}{-}OH + CH_3\overset{O}{\overset{\|}{C}}{-}O{-}\overset{O}{\overset{\|}{C}}CH_3 \longrightarrow ?$

14.81 Compound A ($C_6H_{12}O_2$) reacts with water, acid, and heat to yield compound B ($C_5H_{10}O_2$) and compound C (CH_4O). Compound B is acidic. Deduce possible structures of compounds A, B, and C.

14.82 What products are formed when methyl *o*-bromobenzoate reacts with each of the following?
a. Aqueous acid and heat
b. Aqueous base and heat

14.83 Write an equation for the acid-catalyzed hydrolysis of each of the following esters:
a. Propyl propanoate
b. Butyl methanoate
c. Ethyl methanoate
d. Methyl pentanoate

14.84 Write an equation for the base-catalyzed hydrolysis of each of the following esters:
a. Pentyl methanoate
b. Hexyl propanoate
c. Butyl hexanoate
d. Methyl benzoate

Acid Chlorides and Acid Anhydrides

Foundations

14.85 Describe the physical properties of acid chlorides.

14.86 Describe the chemical properties of acid chlorides.

14.87 Describe the physical properties of acid anhydrides.

14.88 Write a general equation for the formation of acid anhydrides.

Applications

14.89 Write the condensed formula for each of the following compounds:
a. Decanoic anhydride
b. Acetic anhydride

14.90 Write the condensed formula for each of the following compounds:
a. Valeric anhydride
b. Benzoyl chloride

14.91 Write a condensed formula and a line formula for each of the following compounds:
a. Octanoyl chloride
b. Butanoyl chloride
c. Nonanoyl chloride

14.92 Write a condensed formula and a line formula for each of the following compounds:
a. Decanoyl chloride **c.** Ethanoyl chloride
b. Heptanoyl chloride

14.93 Write an equation representing the synthesis of methanoic anhydride.

14.94 Write an equation representing the synthesis of octanoic anhydride.

14.95 Write an equation for the reaction of each of the following acid anhydrides with ethanol.
a. Propanoic anhydride **c.** Methanoic anhydride
b. Ethanoic anhydride

14.96 Write an equation for the reaction of each of the following acid anhydrides with propanol. Name each of the products using the IUPAC Nomenclature System.
a. Butanoic anhydride **c.** Methanoic anhydride
b. Pentanoic anhydride

Phosphoesters and Thioesters

14.97 By reacting phosphoric acid with an excess of ethanol, it is possible to obtain the mono-, di-, and triesters of phosphoric acid. Draw all three of these products.

14.98 What is meant by a phosphoanhydride bond?

14.99 We have described the molecule ATP as the body's energy storehouse. What do we mean by this designation? How does ATP actually store energy and provide it to the body as needed?

14.100 Write an equation for each of the following reactions:
a. Ribose + phosphoric acid
b. Methanol + phosphoric acid
c. Adenosine diphosphate + phosphoric acid

14.101 Draw the thioester bond between the acetyl group and coenzyme A.

14.102 Explain the significance of thioester formation in the metabolic pathways involved in fatty acid and carbohydrate breakdown.

14.103 It is also possible to form esters of other inorganic acids such as sulfuric acid and nitric acid. One particularly noteworthy product is nitroglycerine, which is both highly unstable (explosive) and widely used in the treatment of the heart condition known as angina, a constricting pain in the chest usually resulting from coronary heart disease. In the latter case, its function is to alleviate the pain associated with angina. Nitroglycerine may be administered as a tablet (usually placed just beneath the tongue when needed) or as a salve or paste that can be applied to and absorbed through the skin. Nitroglycerine is the trinitroester of glycerol. Draw the structure of nitroglycerine, using the structure of glycerol.

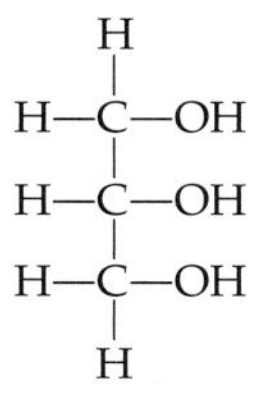

$$\begin{array}{c} \text{H} \\ | \\ \text{H—C—OH} \\ | \\ \text{H—C—OH} \\ | \\ \text{H—C—OH} \\ | \\ \text{H} \end{array}$$

Glycerol

14.104 Show the structure of the thioester that would be formed between coenzyme A and stearic acid.

CRITICAL THINKING PROBLEMS

1. Radioactive isotopes of an element behave chemically in exactly the same manner as the nonradioactive isotopes. As a result, they can be used as tracers to investigate the details of chemical reactions. A scientist is curious about the origin of the bridging oxygen atom in an ester molecule. She has chosen to use the radioactive isotope oxygen-18 to study the following reaction:

$$CH_3CH_2OH + CH_3\overset{\overset{\displaystyle O}{\|}}{C}—OH \xrightarrow{H^+,\ heat} CH_3\overset{\overset{\displaystyle O}{\|}}{C}—O—CH_2CH_3 + H_2O$$

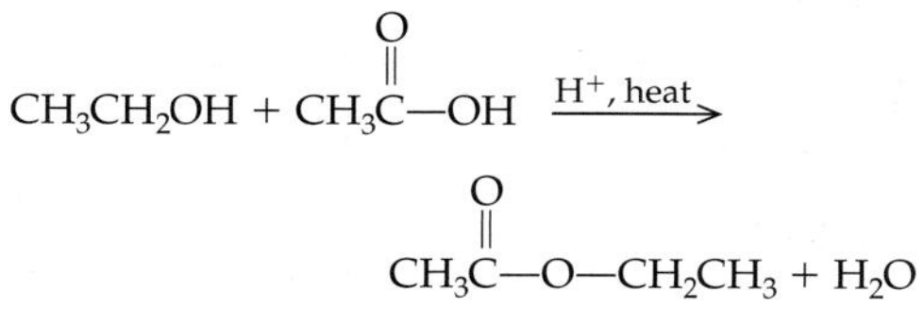

Design experiments using oxygen-18 that will demonstrate whether the oxygen in the water molecule came from the —OH of the alcohol or the —OH of the carboxylic acid.

2. Triglycerides are the major lipid storage form in the human body. They are formed in an esterification reaction between glycerol (1,2,3-propanetriol) and three fatty acids (long-chain carboxylic acids). Write a balanced equation for the formation of a triglyceride formed in a reaction between glycerol and three molecules of decanoic acid.

3. Chloramphenicol is a very potent, broad-spectrum antibiotic. It is reserved for life-threatening bacterial infections because it is quite toxic. It is also a very bitter-tasting chemical. As a result, children had great difficulty taking the antibiotic. A clever chemist found that the taste could be improved considerably by producing the palmitate ester. Intestinal enzymes hydrolyze the ester, producing chloramphenicol, which can then be absorbed. The following structure is the palmitate ester of chloramphenicol. Draw the structure of chloramphenicol.

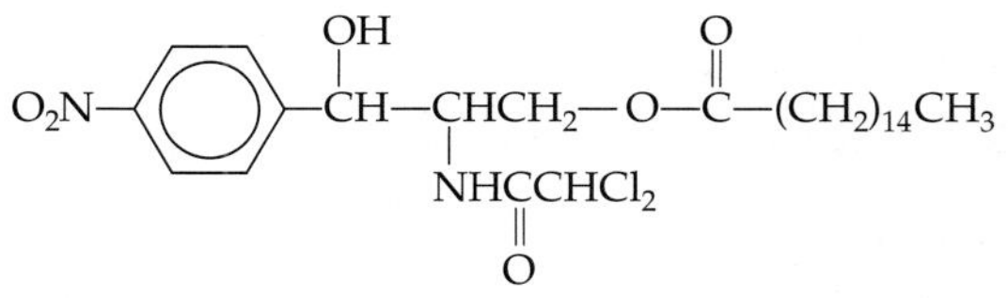

$$O_2N—C_6H_4—\underset{}{\overset{\overset{\displaystyle OH}{|}}{C}}H—\underset{\underset{\displaystyle NH\underset{\underset{\displaystyle O}{\|}}{C}CHCl_2}{|}}{C}HCH_2—O—\overset{\overset{\displaystyle O}{\|}}{C}—(CH_2)_{14}CH_3$$

Chloramphenicol palmitate

4. Acetyl coenzyme A (acetyl CoA) can serve as a donor of acetyl groups in biochemical reactions. One such reaction is the formation of acetylcholine, an important neurotransmitter involved in nerve signal transmission at neuromuscular junctions. The structure of choline is shown below. Draw the structure of acetylcholine.

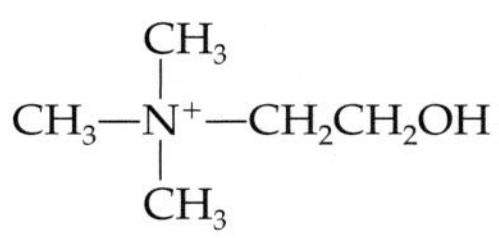

$$CH_3—\underset{\underset{\displaystyle CH_3}{|}}{\overset{\overset{\displaystyle CH_3}{|}}{N^+}}—CH_2CH_2OH$$

Choline

5. Hormones are chemical messengers that are produced in a specialized tissue of the body and travel through the bloodstream to reach receptors on cells of their target tissues. This specific binding to target tissues often stimulates a cascade of enzymatic reactions in the target cells. The work of Earl Sutherland and others led to the realization that there is a *second messenger* within the target cells. Binding of the hormone to the hormone receptor in the cell membrane triggers the enzyme adenyl cyclase to produce adenosine-3′,5′-monophosphate, which is also called *cyclic AMP,* from ATP. The reaction is summarized as follows:

$$\text{ATP} \xrightarrow{Mg^{2+}\text{, adenyl cyclase}} \text{cyclic AMP} + PP_i + H^+$$

PP_i is the abbreviation for a pyrophosphate group, shown here:

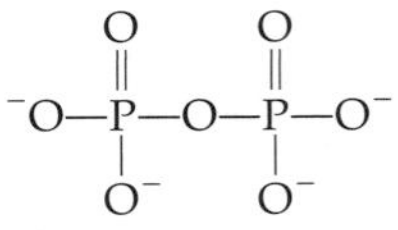

$$^{-}O-\overset{\overset{O}{\|}}{\underset{\underset{O^-}{|}}{P}}-O-\overset{\overset{O}{\|}}{\underset{\underset{O^-}{|}}{P}}-O^-$$

The structure of ATP is shown here with the carbon atoms of the sugar ribose numbered according to the convention used for nucleotides:

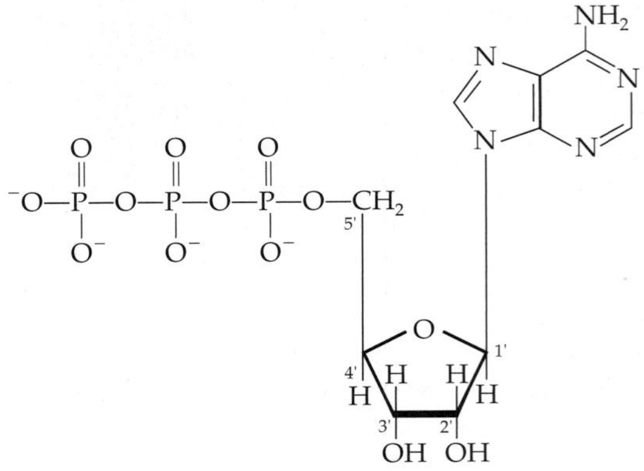

$$^{-}O-\overset{\overset{O}{\|}}{\underset{\underset{O^-}{|}}{P}}-O-\overset{\overset{O}{\|}}{\underset{\underset{O^-}{|}}{P}}-O-\overset{\overset{O}{\|}}{\underset{\underset{O^-}{|}}{P}}-O-CH_2$$

Adenosine-5′-triphosphate

Draw the structure of adenosine-3′,5′-monophosphate.

15

Amines and Amides

Ethnobotanists continue to search for medically active compounds from the rain forest.

LEARNING GOALS

1. Classify amines as primary, secondary, or tertiary.
2. Describe the physical properties of amines.
3. Draw and name simple amines using systematic and common nomenclature systems.
4. Write equations representing the synthesis of amines.
5. Write equations showing the basicity and neutralization of amines.
6. Describe the structure of quaternary ammonium salts and discuss their use as antiseptics and disinfectants.
7. Discuss the biological significance of heterocyclic amines.
8. Describe the physical properties of amides.
9. Draw the structure and write the common and IUPAC names of amides.
10. Write equations representing the preparation of amides.
11. Write equations showing the hydrolysis of amides.
12. Draw the general structure of an amino acid.
13. Draw and discuss the structure of a peptide bond.
14. Describe the function of neurotransmitters.

OUTLINE

Introduction 512
15.1 Amines 513
Chemistry at the Crime Scene: Methamphetamine 523
15.2 Heterocyclic Amines 525
15.3 Amides 527
Kitchen Chemistry: Browning Reactions and Flavor: The Maillard Reaction 528
A Medical Perspective: Semisynthetic Penicillins 532
15.4 A Preview of Amino Acids, Proteins, and Protein Synthesis 534
15.5 Neurotransmitters 535
A Medical Perspective: Opiate Biosynthesis and the Mutant Poppy 536

INTRODUCTION

In this chapter we introduce an additional element into the structure of organic molecules. That element is nitrogen, the fourth most common atom in living systems. It is an important component of the structure of the nucleic acids DNA and RNA, which are the molecules that carry the genetic information for living systems. It is also essential to the structure and function of proteins, molecules that carry out the majority of the work in biological systems. Some proteins serve as enzymes that catalyze the chemical reactions that allow life to exist. Other proteins, the antibodies, protect us against infection by a variety of infectious agents. Proteins are also structural components of the cell and of the body.

One class of organic molecules containing nitrogen is the amines. Amines are characterized by the presence of an amino group (—NH_2).

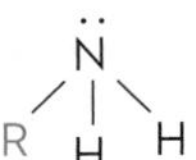

General structure of an amine

The nitrogen atom of the amino group may have one or more of its hydrogen atoms replaced by an organic group. General structures of these types of amines are shown below:

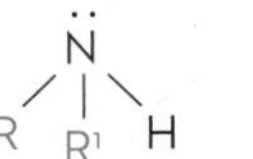

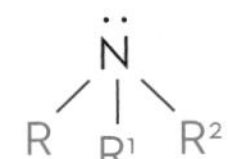

ANIMATIONS
- Valence-Shell Electron-Pair Repulsion Theory
- VSEPR and Molecular Geometry
- The Geometry of NH_3

Amines are very common in biological systems and exhibit important physiological activity. Consider histamine. Histamine contributes to the inflammatory response that causes the symptoms of colds and allergies, including swollen mucous membranes, congestion, and excessive nasal secretions. We take antihistamines to help relieve these symptoms. Ephedrine is an antihistamine that has been extracted from the leaves of the ma-huang plant in China for over 2000 years. Found in over-the-counter cold medications, this antihistamine helps to shrink swollen mucous membranes and reduce nasal secretions. The structures of histamine and ephedrine are shown below.

$CH_2CH_2NH_2$ HN N^+H

Histamine

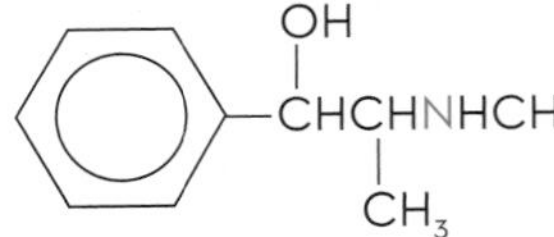

Ephedrine

The other group of nitrogen-containing organic compounds we will investigate in this chapter is the amides. Amides are the products of a reaction between an amine and a carboxylic acid derivative. They have the following general structure:

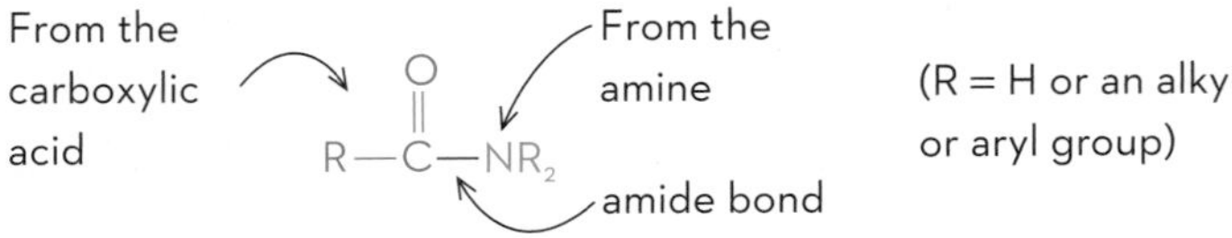

General structure of an amide

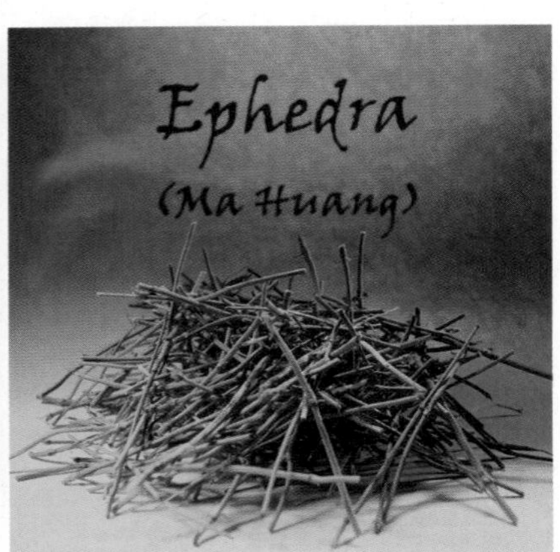

Ephedra, from the ma-huang plant, has been sold to promote weight loss and boost energy. What antihistamines are found in ephedra?

Amino acids are the subunits from which proteins are built. They are characterized by the presence of both an amino group and a carboxyl group. When amino acids are bonded to one another to produce a protein chain, the amino group of one amino acid reacts with the carboxyl group of another amino acid. The amide bond that results is called a *peptide bond.*

In this chapter we will explore the chemistry of the organic molecules that contain nitrogen. In upcoming chapters we will investigate the structure and properties of the nitrogen-containing biological molecules.

The general structure of an amino acid is

$$\mathrm{H{-}N(H){-}C(H)(R){-}C({=}O){-}OH}$$

The amino group is highlighted in red and the carboxyl group in blue. Amino acids are the basic subunits of all proteins.

15.1 Amines

Structure and Physical Properties

LEARNING GOAL

1 Classify amines as primary, secondary, or tertiary.

Amines are organic derivatives of ammonia and, like ammonia, they are basic. In fact, amines are the most important type of organic base found in nature. We can think of them as substituted ammonia molecules in which one, two, or three of the ammonia hydrogens have been replaced by an organic group:

$$\underset{\text{Ammonia}}{\ddot{N}H_3} \xrightarrow[\text{for H}]{\text{R substitutes}} \underset{\text{An amine}}{\ddot{N}H_2R}$$

The structures drawn above and in Figure 15.1 reveal that like ammonia, amines are pyramidal. The nitrogen atom has three groups bonded to it and has a nonbonding pair of electrons.

The geometry of ammonia is described in Section 3.4.

Amines are classified according to the number of alkyl or aryl groups attached to the nitrogen. In a **primary (1°) amine,** one of the hydrogens is replaced by an organic group. In a **secondary (2°) amine,** two hydrogens are replaced. In a **tertiary (3°) amine,** three organic groups replace the hydrogens:

H—N(H)—H	R—N(H)—H	R—N(H)—R	R—N(R)—R
Ammonia	1° amine (primary amine)	2° amine (secondary amine)	3° amine (tertiary amine)

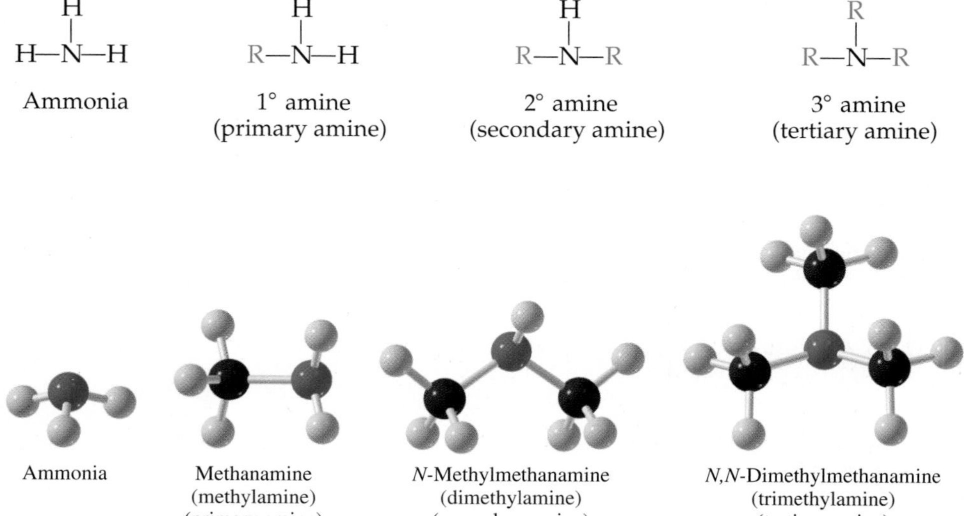

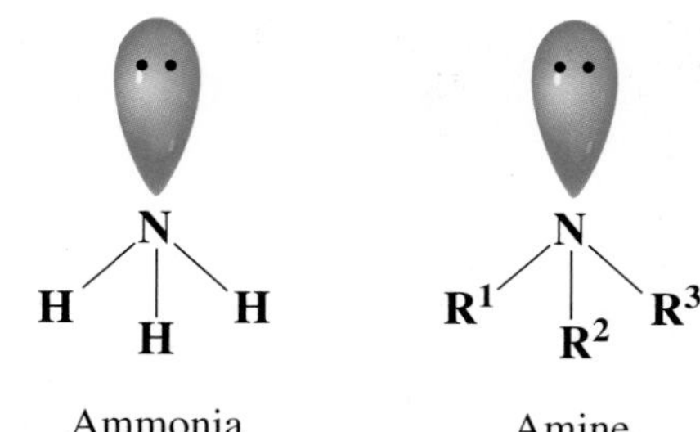

Figure 15.1 The trigonal pyramidal structure of amines. Note the similarities in structure between an amine and the ammonia molecule.

The nitrogen atom is more electronegative than the hydrogen atoms in amines. As a result, the N—H bond is polar, and hydrogen bonding between amine molecules or between amine molecules and water can occur (Figure 15.2).

Hydrogen bonding is described in Section 5.2.

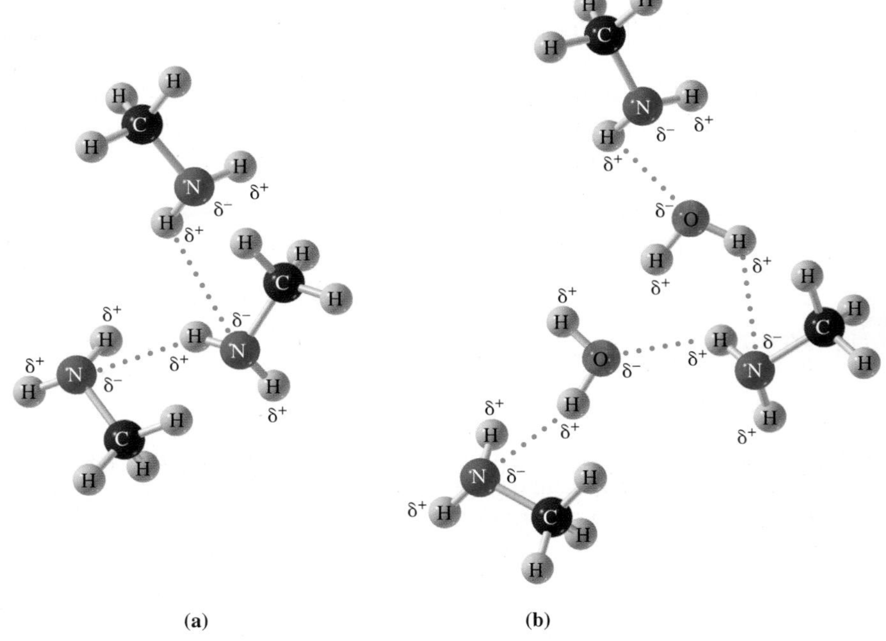

Figure 15.2 Hydrogen bonding (a) in methylamine and (b) between methylamine and water. Dotted lines represent hydrogen bonds.

EXAMPLE 15.1 Classifying Amines as Primary, Secondary, or Tertiary

LEARNING GOAL

1 Classify amines as primary, secondary, or tertiary.

Classify each of the following compounds as a primary, secondary, or tertiary amine.

Solution

Compare the structure of the amine with that of ammonia.

$H{-}\overset{CH_3}{\overset{\mid}{N}}{-}H$	$H{-}\overset{H}{\overset{\mid}{N}}{-}H$	1° amine: one hydrogen replaced
$CH_3{-}\overset{CH_3}{\overset{\mid}{N}}{-}H$	$H{-}\overset{H}{\overset{\mid}{N}}{-}H$	2° amine: two hydrogens replaced
$CH_3{-}\overset{CH_3}{\overset{\mid}{N}}{-}CH_3$	$H{-}\overset{H}{\overset{\mid}{N}}{-}H$	3° amine: three hydrogens replaced

Practice Problem 15.1

Determine whether each of the following amines is primary, secondary, or tertiary.

a. $CH_3CH_2\overset{CH_2CH_3}{\overset{\mid}{N}}CH_3$ b. $CH_3CH_2CH_2NH_2$ c. $CH_3\overset{H}{\overset{\mid}{N}}CH_3$

► For Further Practice: **Questions 15.29 and 15.30.**

Question 15.1 Refer to Figure 15.2 and draw a similar figure showing the hydrogen bonding that occurs between water and a 2° amine.

Question 15.2 Refer to Figure 15.2 and draw hydrogen bonding between two primary amines.

TABLE 15.1 Boiling Points of Amines

Systematic Name	Common Name	Structure	Boiling Point (°C)
	Ammonia	NH_3	−33.4
Methanamine	Methylamine	CH_3NH_2	−6.3
N-Methylmethanamine	Dimethylamine	$(CH_3)_2NH$	7.4
N,N-Dimethylmethanamine	Trimethylamine	$(CH_3)_3N$	2.9
Ethanamine	Ethylamine	$CH_3CH_2NH_2$	16.6
Propanamine	Propylamine	$CH_3CH_2CH_2NH_2$	48.7
Butanamine	Butylamine	$CH_3CH_2CH_2CH_2NH_2$	77.8

The ability of primary and secondary amines to form N—H···N hydrogen bonds is reflected in their boiling points (Table 15.1). Primary amines have boiling points well above those of alkanes of similar molar mass but considerably lower than those of comparable alcohols. Consider the following examples:

LEARNING GOAL

2 Describe the physical properties of amines.

$CH_3CH_2CH_3$	$CH_3CH_2NH_2$	CH_3CH_2OH
Propane	Ethanamine	Ethanol
M.M. = 44 g/mol	M.M. = 45 g/mol	M.M. = 46 g/mol
b.p. = −42.2°C	b.p. = 16.6°C	b.p. = 78.5°C

Tertiary amines do not have an N—H bond. As a result they cannot form intermolecular hydrogen bonds with other tertiary amines. Consequently, their boiling points are lower than those of primary or secondary amines of comparable molar mass. This is seen in a comparison of the boiling points of propanamine (propylamine; M.M. = 59) and *N,N*-dimethylmethanamine (trimethylamine; M.M. = 59). Trimethylamine, the tertiary amine, has a boiling point of 2.9°C, whereas propylamine, the primary amine, has a boiling point of 48.7°C. Clearly the inability of trimethylamine molecules to form intermolecular hydrogen bonds results in a much lower boiling point.

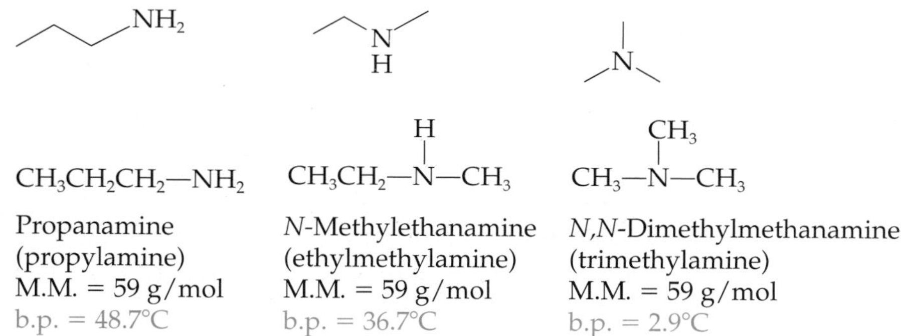

Propanamine (propylamine)	*N*-Methylethanamine (ethylmethylamine)	*N,N*-Dimethylmethanamine (trimethylamine)
M.M. = 59 g/mol	M.M. = 59 g/mol	M.M. = 59 g/mol
b.p. = 48.7°C	b.p. = 36.7°C	b.p. = 2.9°C

The intermolecular hydrogen bonds formed by primary and secondary amines are not as strong as the hydrogen bonds formed by alcohols because nitrogen is not as electronegative as oxygen. For this reason primary and secondary amines have lower boiling points than alcohols (Table 15.2).

All amines can form intermolecular hydrogen bonds with water (O—H···N). As a result, small amines (six or fewer carbons) are soluble in water. As we have noted for other families of organic molecules, water solubility decreases as the length of the hydrocarbon (hydrophobic) portion of the molecule increases.

TABLE 15.2 Comparison of the Boiling Points of Selected Alcohols and Amines

Name	Molar Mass (g/mol)	Boiling Point (°C)
Methanol	32	64.5
Methanamine	31	−6.3
Ethanol	46	78.5
Ethanamine	45	16.6
Propanol	60	97.2
Propanamine	59	48.7

EXAMPLE 15.2 Predicting the Physical Properties of Amines

LEARNING GOAL

2 Describe the physical properties of amines.

Which member of each of the following pairs of molecules has the higher boiling point?

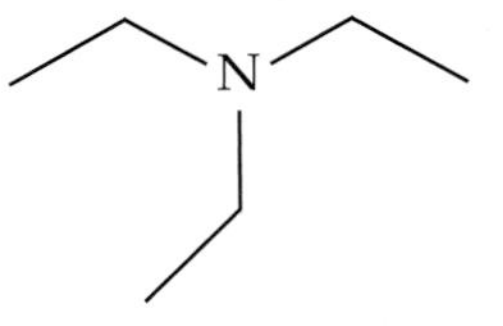

or

NH_2

Solution

The molecule on the right, hexanamine, has a higher boiling point than the molecule on the left, *N,N*-diethylethanamine (triethylamine). Triethylamine is a tertiary amine; therefore, it has no N—H bond and cannot form intermolecular hydrogen bonds with other triethylamine molecules.

or

Solution

The molecule on the left, 1-butanol, has a higher boiling point than the molecule on the right, 1-butanamine. Nitrogen is not as electronegative as oxygen, thus the hydroxyl group is more polar than the amino group and forms stronger hydrogen bonds.

Practice Problem 15.2

Which compound in each of the following pairs would you predict to have a higher boiling point? Explain your reasoning.

a. Methanol or methylamine
b. Dimethylamine or water
c. Methylamine or ethylamine
d. Propylamine or butane

► For Further Practice: **Questions 15.17 and 15.18.**

Nomenclature

LEARNING GOAL

3 Draw and name simple amines using systematic and common nomenclature systems.

In systematic nomenclature, primary amines are named according to the following rules:

- Determine the name of the *parent compound,* the longest continuous carbon chain containing the amine group.
- Replace the *-e* ending of the alkane chain with *-amine.* Following this pattern, the alkane becomes an alkan*amine;* for instance, ethan*e* becomes ethan*amine.*

- Number the parent chain to give the carbon bearing the amine group the lowest possible number.
- Name and number all substituents, and add them as prefixes to the "alkanamine" name.

For instance,

$CH_3—NH_2$ — Methanamine

$CH_3CH_2CH_2—NH_2$ — 1-Propanamine

$CH_3CH_2CH_2CH(NH_2)CH_3$ — 2-Pentanamine

For secondary or tertiary amines the prefix *N*-alkyl is added to the name of the parent compound. For example,

$CH_3—NH—CH_2CH_3$ — *N*-Methylethanamine

$CH_3—N(CH_3)—CH_3$ — *N,N*-Dimethylmethanamine

Several aromatic amines have special names that have also been approved for use by IUPAC. For example, the amine of benzene is given the name *aniline.* The systematic name for aniline is *benzenamine.*

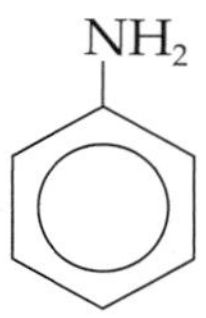

Aniline or benzenamine

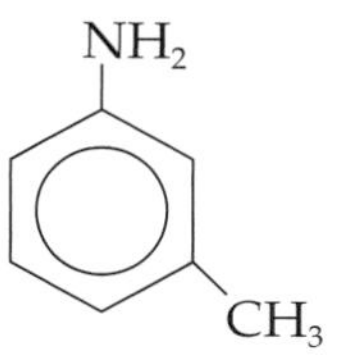

m-Toluidine or *meta*-toluidine

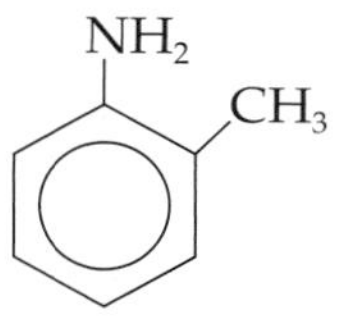

o-Toluidine or *ortho*-toluidine

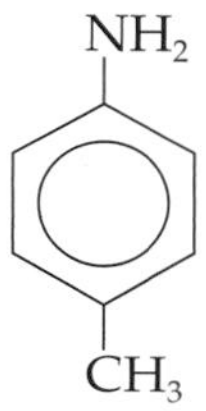

p-Toluidine or *para*-toluidine

If additional groups are attached to the nitrogen of an aromatic amine, they are indicated with the letter *N*- followed by the name of the group.

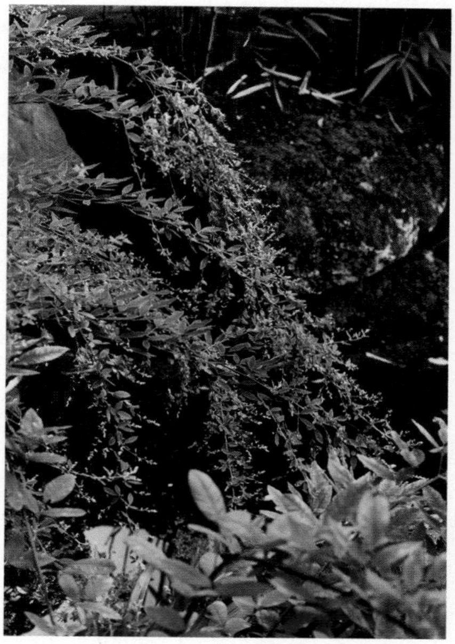

Aniline was first isolated from the blue dye indigo, a product of the indigo plant. It is the starting material in the synthesis of hundreds of dyes. Is aniline a primary, secondary, or tertiary amine?

EXAMPLE 15.3 Writing the Systematic Name for an Amine

a. Determine the systematic name for the following amine, which is used by the German cockroach as a pheromone.

$$CH_3—NH—CH_3$$

Solution

Parent compound: methane (becomes methanamine)
Additional group on N: methyl (becomes *N*-methyl)
Name: *N*-Methylmethanamine

b. Name the following amine.

$$CH_3CH_2CH_2—NH—CH_3$$

Continued...

LEARNING GOAL

3 Draw and name simple amines using systematic and common nomenclature systems.

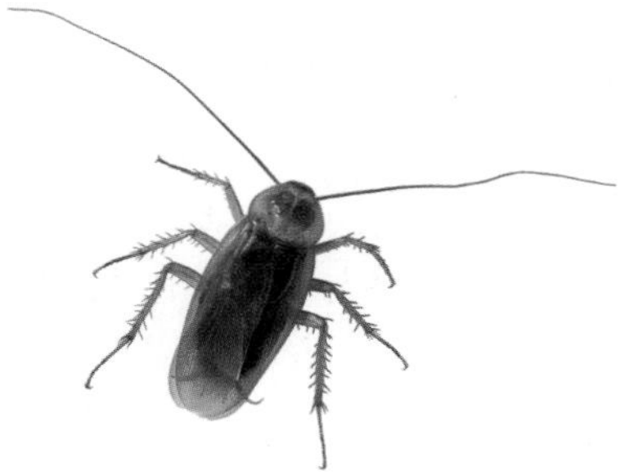

N-methylmethanamine is used by the German cockroach as a communication pheromone. What is the common name of this amine?

Solution

Parent compound: propane (becomes propanamine)
Additional group on N: methyl (becomes *N*-methyl)
Name: *N*-Methyl-1-propanamine

Practice Problem 15.3

What is the systematic name for each of the following amines?

a. 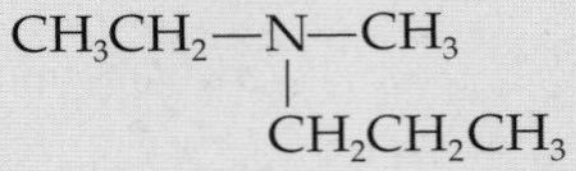 $CH_3CH_2—N(CH_2CH_2CH_3)—CH_3$

b. 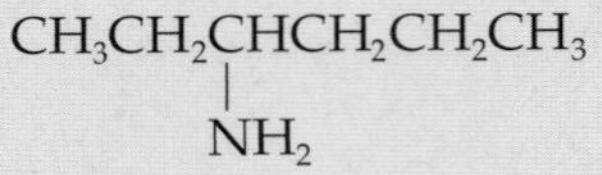 $CH_3CH_2CH(NH_2)CH_2CH_2CH_3$

c. 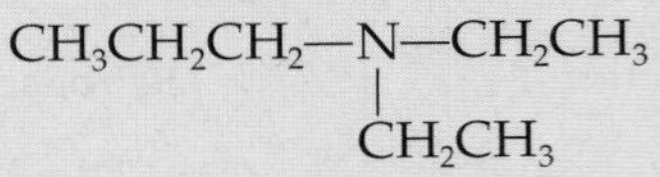 $CH_3CH_2CH_2—N(CH_2CH_3)—CH_2CH_3$

► For Further Practice: **Questions 15.21, 15.27, and 15.28.**

Common names are often used for the simple amines. The common names of the alkyl groups bonded to the amine nitrogen are followed by the ending *-amine.* Each group is listed alphabetically in one continuous word followed by the suffix *-amine:*

$CH_3—NH_2$
Methylamine

$CH_3—NH—CH_3$
Dimethylamine

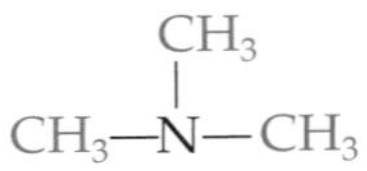

$CH_3—N(CH_3)—CH_3$
Trimethylamine

$CH_3CH_2—NH_2$
Ethylamine

$CH_3CH_2—NH—CH_3$
Ethylmethylamine

Table 15.3 compares these systems of nomenclature for a number of simple amines.

Question 15.3 Use the structure of aniline provided and draw the condensed formula for each of the following amines.

a. *N*-Methylaniline
b. *N,N*-Dimethylaniline
c. *N*-Ethylaniline
d. *N*-Isopropylaniline

TABLE 15.3 Systematic and Common Names of Amines

Compound	Systematic Name	Common Name
$R—NH_2$	Alkan*amine*	Alkyl*amine*
$CH_3—NH_2$	Methanamine	Methylamine
$CH_3CH_2—NH_2$	Ethanamine	Ethylamine
$CH_3CH_2CH_2—NH_2$	1-Propanamine	Propylamine
$CH_3—NH—CH_3$	*N*-Methylmethanamine	Dimethylamine
$CH_3—NH—CH_2CH_3$	*N*-Methylethanamine	Ethylmethylamine
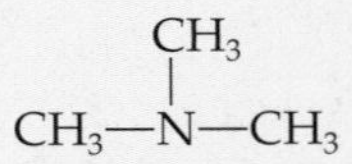 $CH_3—N(CH_3)—CH_3$	*N,N*-Dimethylmethanamine	Trimethylamine

Question 15.4 Name each of the following amines using the systematic and common nomenclature systems.

a.  $CH_3CH(NH_2)CH_2CH_3$

b. 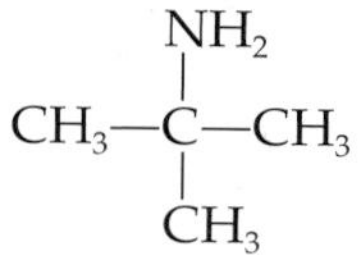 $CH_3—C(NH_2)(CH_3)—CH_3$

c. $CH_3CH(NHCH_3)CH_2CH_3$

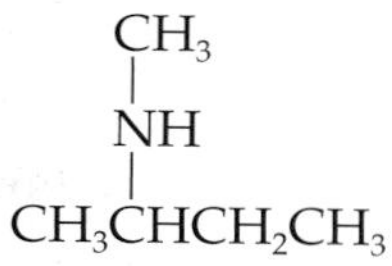

d. 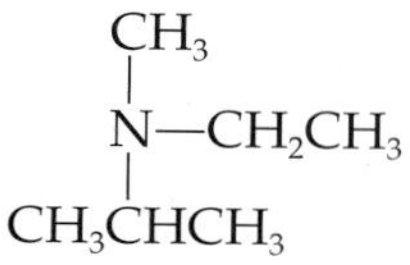 $CH_3CH(N(CH_3)—CH_2CH_3)CH_3$

Question 15.5 Draw the condensed formula for each of the following compounds.

a. 2-Propanamine
b. 3-Octanamine
c. *N*-Ethyl-2-heptanamine
d. 2-Methyl-2-pentanamine
e. 4-Chloro-5-iodo-1-nonanamine
f. *N,N*-Diethyl-1-pentanamine

Question 15.6 Draw the condensed formula for each of the following compounds.

a. Diethylmethylamine
b. 4-Methylpentylamine
c. *N*-Methylaniline
d. Triisopropylamine
e. Methyl-*t*-butylamine
f. Ethylhexylamine

Medically Important Amines

Although amines play many different roles in our day-to-day lives, one important use is in medicine. A host of drugs derived from amines is responsible for improving the quality of life, whereas others, such as cocaine and heroin, are highly addictive.

Amphetamines, such as benzedrine and methedrine, stimulate the central nervous system. They elevate blood pressure and pulse rate and are often used to decrease fatigue. Medically, they have been used to treat depression and epilepsy. Amphetamines have also been prescribed as diet pills because they decrease the appetite. Their use is controlled by federal law because excess use of amphetamines can cause paranoia and mental illness.

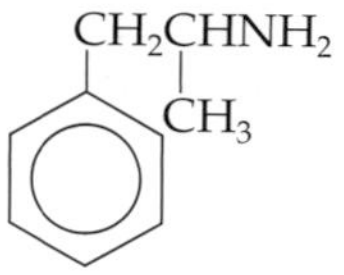

$C_6H_5—CH_2CH(CH_3)NH_2$

1-Phenyl-2-propanamine
(Amphetamine)

Benzedrine

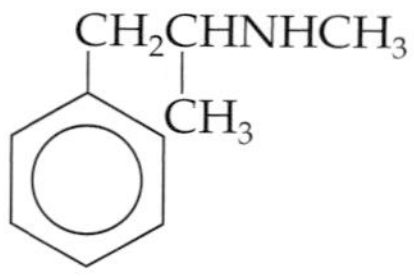

$C_6H_5—CH_2CH(CH_3)NHCH_3$

N-Methyl-1-phenyl-2-propanamine
(Methamphetamine)

Methedrine

Many of the medicinal amines are *analgesics* (pain relievers) or *anesthetics* (pain blockers). Novocaine and related compounds, for example, are used as local anesthetics. Demerol is a very strong pain reliever.

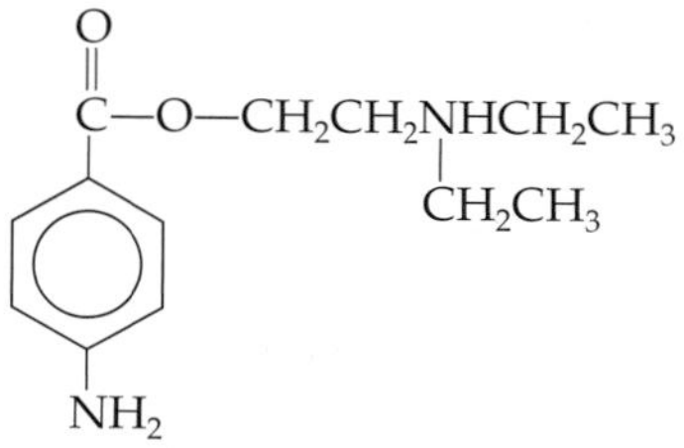

$H_2N—C_6H_4—C(=O)—O—CH_2CH_2N(CH_2CH_3)CH_2CH_3$

Novocaine

(4-phenyl-1-methylpiperidine-4-yl) $C(=O)—O—CH_2CH_3$; N—CH_3

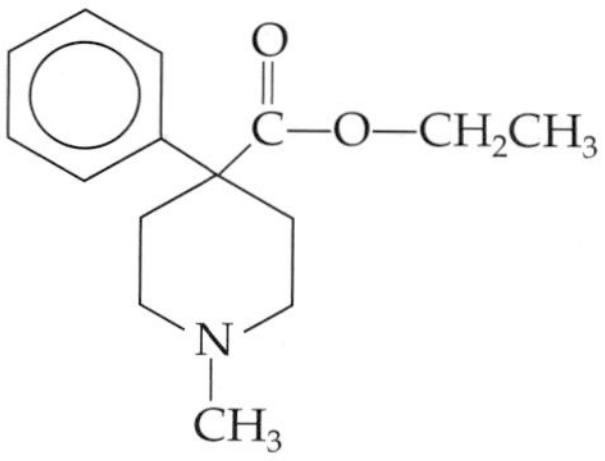

Demerol

Ephedrine, its stereoisomer pseudoephedrine, and phenylephrine (also called neosynephrine) are used as decongestants in cough syrups and nasal sprays.

L-Dopa, dopamine, and other key neurotransmitters are described in detail in Section 15.5.

By shrinking the membranes that line the nasal passages, they relieve the symptoms of congestion and stuffy nose. These compounds are very closely related to L-dopa and dopamine, which are key compounds in the function of the central nervous system.

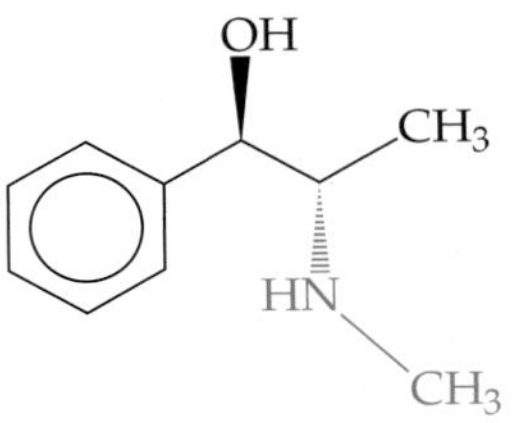

Ephedrine 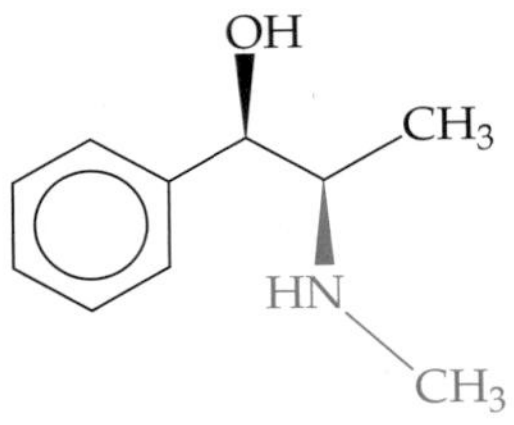 Pseudoephedrine 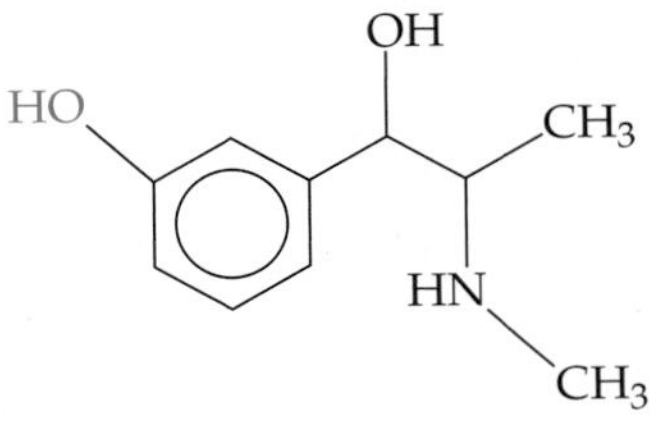 Phenylephrine (neosynephrine)

Methamphetamine use and abuse are discussed in Chemistry at the Crime Scene: Methamphetamine, found on page 523.

Recently, many states have restricted the sales of products containing ephedrine and pseudoephedrine, and many drugstore chains have moved these products behind the counter. The reason for these precautions is that either ephedrine or pseudoephedrine can be used as the starting material in the synthesis of methamphetamines. In response to this problem, pharmaceutical companies are replacing ephedrine and pseudoephedrine in these decongestants with phenylephrine, which cannot be used as a reactant in the synthesis of methamphetamine.

Ephedrine and pseudoephedrine are also the primary active ingredients in ephedra, a plant found in the deserts of central Asia. Ephedra is used as a stimulant in a variety of products that are sold over-the-counter as aids to boost energy, promote weight loss, and enhance athletic performance. In 2004, the Food and Drug Administration (FDA) banned the use of ephedra in these over-the-counter formulations after reviewing 16,000 reports of adverse side effects including nervousness, heart irregularities, seizures, heart attacks, and 80 deaths, including that of Baltimore Orioles pitcher Steve Bechler, age 23. However, in April 2005, a Federal judge in Texas ruled that the FDA had failed to prove that ephedra is dangerous at doses of 10 milligrams (mg) or lower, opening the way for the sale of ephedra-containing herbal remedies.

The *sulfa drugs,* the first chemicals used to fight bacterial infections, are synthesized from amines.

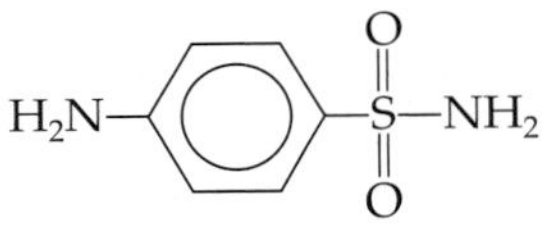

$H_2N-C_6H_4-SO_2-NH_2$

Sulfanilamide—a sulfa drug

Reactions Involving Amines

Preparation of Amines

LEARNING GOAL

4 Write equations representing the synthesis of amines.

In the laboratory, amines are prepared by the reduction of amides and nitro compounds.

$R-C(=O)-NH_2$ $Ar-C(=O)-NH_2$ $Ar-NO_2$

Examples of amides A nitro compound

As we will see in Section 15.3, amides are neutral nitrogen compounds that produce an amine and a carboxylic acid when hydrolyzed. Nitro compounds are prepared by the nitration of an aromatic compound.

Primary amines are readily produced by reduction of a nitro compound, as in the following reaction:

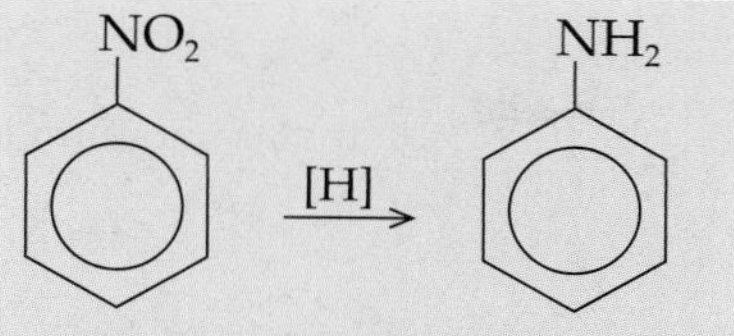

We are using the general symbol [H] to represent any reducing agent just as we used [O] to represent an oxidizing agent in previous chapters. Several different reducing agents may be used to effect the changes shown here; for example, metallic iron and acid may be used to reduce aromatic nitro compounds and $LiAlH_4$ in ether reduces amides.

$$C_6H_5NO_2 \xrightarrow{[H]} C_6H_5NH_2$$

A nitro compound — An aromatic primary amine

In this reaction the nitro compound is nitrobenzene and the product is aniline.

Amides may also be reduced to produce primary, secondary, or tertiary amines.

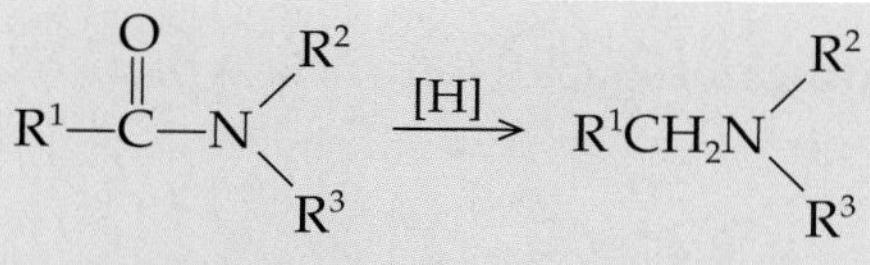

$$R^1{-}\overset{O}{\overset{\|}{C}}{-}N(R^2)(R^3) \xrightarrow{[H]} R^1CH_2N(R^2)(R^3)$$

Amide — Amine

(R^2 and R^3 may be a hydrogen atom or an organic group.)

If R^2 and R^3 are hydrogen atoms, the product will be a primary amine:

$$CH_3\overset{O}{\overset{\|}{C}}NH_2 \xrightarrow{[H]} CH_3CH_2NH_2$$

Ethanamide — Ethanamine (ethylamine)

If either R^2 or R^3 is an organic group, the product will be a secondary amine:

$$CH_3CH_2\overset{O}{\overset{\|}{C}}NHCH_3 \xrightarrow{[H]} CH_3CH_2CH_2NHCH_3$$

N-Methylpropanamide — *N*-Methyl-1-propanamine (methylpropylamine)

If both R^2 and R^3 are organic groups, the product will be a tertiary amine:

$$CH_3\overset{O}{\overset{\|}{C}}{-}N(CH_3)CH_3 \xrightarrow{[H]} CH_3CH_2N(CH_3)CH_3$$

N,*N*-Dimethylethanamide — *N*,*N*-Dimethylethanamine

Basicity

LEARNING GOAL

5 Write equations showing the basicity and neutralization of amines.

Amines behave as weak bases, accepting H^+ when dissolved in water. The nonbonding pair (lone pair) of electrons of the nitrogen atom can be shared with a proton (H^+) from a water molecule, producing an **alkylammonium ion.** Hydroxide ions are also formed, so the resulting solution is basic.

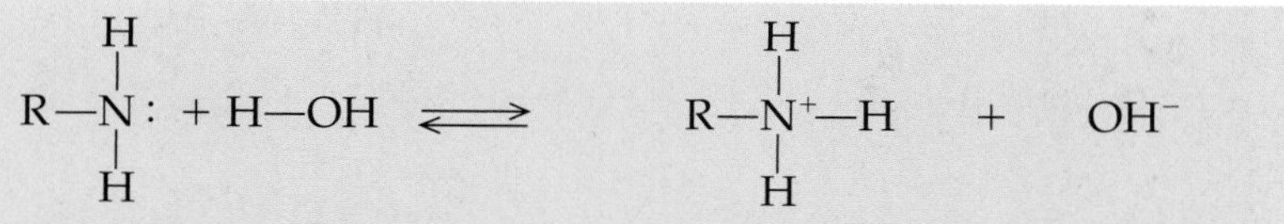

$$R{-}\ddot{N}H_2 + H{-}OH \rightleftharpoons R{-}NH_3^+ + OH^-$$

Amine — Water — Alkylammonium ion — Hydroxide ion

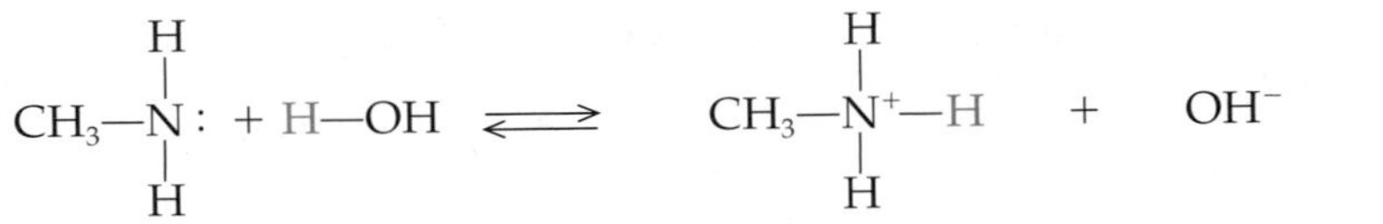

$$\mathrm{CH_3{-}\overset{\displaystyle H}{\underset{\displaystyle H}{N}}{:}} + \mathrm{H{-}OH} \rightleftharpoons \mathrm{CH_3{-}\overset{\displaystyle H}{\underset{\displaystyle H}{N^+}}{-}H} + \mathrm{OH^-}$$

Methylamine Water Methylammonium ion Hydroxide ion

Neutralization

Because amines are bases, they react with acids to form alkylammonium salts.

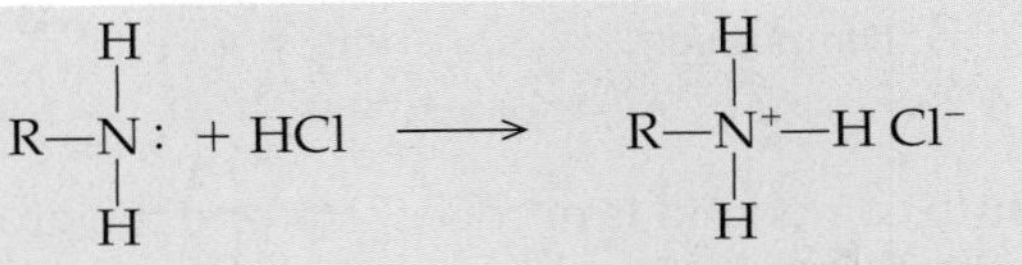

$$\mathrm{R{-}\overset{\displaystyle H}{\underset{\displaystyle H}{N}}{:}} + \mathrm{HCl} \longrightarrow \mathrm{R{-}\overset{\displaystyle H}{\underset{\displaystyle H}{N^+}}{-}H\;Cl^-}$$

Amine Acid Alkylammonium salt

Recall that the reaction of an acid and a base gives a salt (Section 8.3).

The reaction of methylamine with hydrochloric acid shown is typical of these reactions.

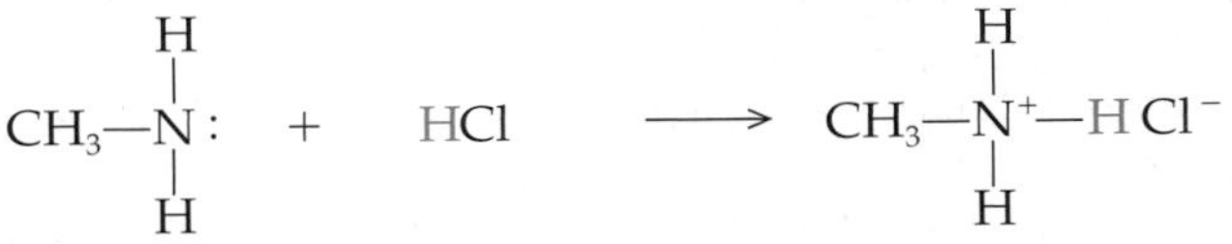

$$\mathrm{CH_3{-}\overset{\displaystyle H}{\underset{\displaystyle H}{N}}{:}} + \mathrm{HCl} \longrightarrow \mathrm{CH_3{-}\overset{\displaystyle H}{\underset{\displaystyle H}{N^+}}{-}H\;Cl^-}$$

Methylamine Hydrochloric acid Methylammonium chloride

Alkylammonium salts are named by replacing the suffix *-amine* with *ammonium.* This is then followed by the name of the anion. The salts are ionic and hence are quite soluble in water.

A variety of important drugs are amines. They are usually administered as alkylammonium salts because the salts are much more soluble in aqueous solutions and in body fluids.

Question 15.7 Complete each of the following reactions by supplying the missing product(s).

a. 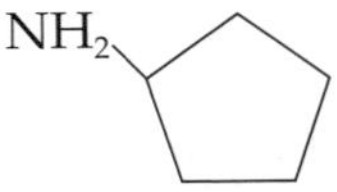 NH_2–(cyclopentane) $+ HBr \longrightarrow ?$

b. $CH_3CH_2NHCH_3 + H_2O \longrightarrow ?$

c. $CH_3NH_2 + H_2O \longrightarrow ?$

Question 15.8 Complete each of the following reactions by supplying the missing product(s).

a. $CH_3NH_2 + HI \longrightarrow ?$

b. $CH_3CH_2NH_2 + HBr \longrightarrow ?$

c. $(CH_3CH_2)_2NH + HCl \longrightarrow ?$

Alkylammonium salts can neutralize hydroxide ions. In this reaction, water is formed and the protonated amine cation is converted into an amine.

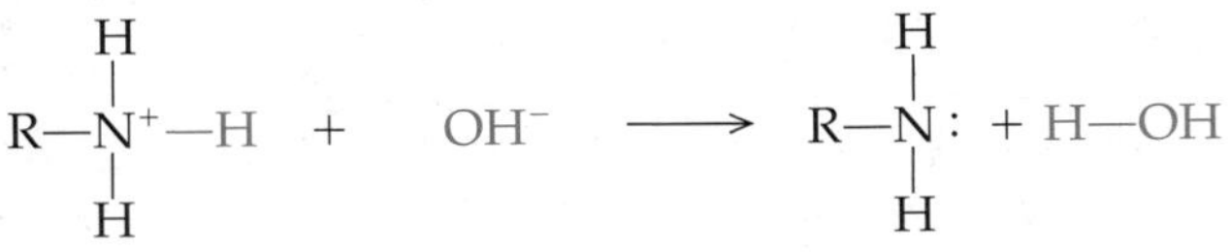

$$\mathrm{R{-}\overset{\displaystyle H}{\underset{\displaystyle H}{N^+}}{-}H} + \mathrm{OH^-} \longrightarrow \mathrm{R{-}\overset{\displaystyle H}{\underset{\displaystyle H}{N}}{:}} + \mathrm{H{-}OH}$$

Alkylammonium salt Hydroxide ion Amine Water

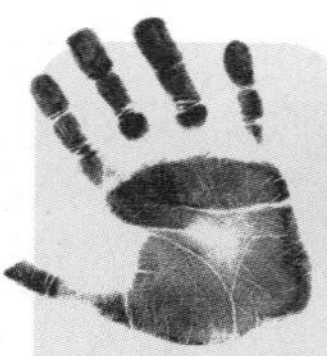

CHEMISTRY AT THE CRIME SCENE

Methamphetamine

Methamphetamine is an addictive drug known by many names, including "speed," "crystal," "crank," "ice," and "glass." A bitter-tasting, odorless, crystalline powder, it is easily dissolved in either water or alcohol. Methamphetamine was developed early in the twentieth century and used as a decongestant in nasal and bronchial inhalers. Now it is rarely used for medical purposes.

A 2002 Health and Human Services survey revealed that twelve million Americans age twelve and older had used methamphetamine. Use of methamphetamine was once associated with white, male, blue-collar workers; but a much more diverse group now uses the drug. Although it is still used by people in jobs such as long-distance trucking that require long hours and mental and physical alertness, it is disturbing that use of methamphetamine is becoming increasingly associated with sexual activity, teenagers attending "raves," homeless people, and runaway youths.

Methamphetamine can be smoked, taken orally, snorted, or injected, depending on the form of the drug; and it alters the user's mood differently depending on how it is taken. Smoking or injecting intravenously results in a "flash" or intense rush that lasts only a few minutes (min). This may be followed by a high that lasts several hours (h). Snorting and oral ingestion result in a euphoria lasting 3 to 5 min in the case of snorting and up to 20 min in the case of oral ingestion. Because the pleasurable effects are so short-lived, methamphetamine users tend to binge to try to sustain the high.

Both the intense rush and the longer-lasting euphoria are thought to result from a release of dopamine and norepinephrine into regions of the brain that control feelings of pleasure. Once inside nerve cells (neurons), methamphetamine causes the release of dopamine and norepinephrine. At the same time, it inhibits enzymes that would normally destroy these two neurotransmitters and the excess is transported out of neurons, causing the sensations of pleasure and euphoria. The excess norepinephrine may be responsible for the increased attention and decreased fatigue associated with methamphetamine use.

Symptoms of long-term use include addiction, anxiety, violent behavior, confusion, as well as psychotic symptoms of paranoia, hallucinations, and delusions. In severe cases, paranoia causes homicidal and/or suicidal feelings. Methamphetamine also increases heart rate and blood pressure. It can cause strokes, which result from irreversible damage to blood vessels in the brain, as well as respiratory problems, irregular heartbeat, and extreme anorexia. In extreme situations, it can cause cardiovascular collapse and death.

No physical symptoms accompany withdrawal from the drug, but psychological symptoms such as depression, anxiety, aggression, and intense craving are common. Of greatest concern is the brain damage that occurs in long-term users.

Dopamine release may be the cause of the drug's long-term toxic effects. Compare the structure of the neurotransmitter dopamine (Figure 15.7) with that of methamphetamine shown below. Research in humans has shown that even 3 years after chronic methamphetamine use, the former user continues to have a reduced ability to transport dopamine back into nerve cells. Parkinson's disease is characterized by a decrease in the dopamine-producing neurons in the brain; so it was logical to look for similarities between methamphetamine users and those suffering from Parkinson's. In fact, the brains of methamphetamine users showed damage similar to, but not as severe as, that in Parkinson's disease. Research in animals demonstrated that up to 50% of the dopamine-producing cells in parts of the brain may be destroyed by prolonged exposure, and that serotonin-containing neurons may sustain even worse damage.

Methamphetamine use continues to rise, in part, because it is easily synthesized, or "cooked," using "recipes" that are available from many sources, including the Internet. Ephedrine, an over-the-counter decongestant drug, is the starting material. (Pseudoephedrine, a stereoisomer of ephedrine, can also be used.) As shown in the equation below, ephedrine is simply reduced to produce methamphetamine.

$$C_6H_5\text{–}CH(OH)\text{–}CH(CH_3)\text{–}NH\text{–}CH_3 \xrightarrow{[H]} C_6H_5\text{–}CH_2\text{–}CH(CH_3)\text{–}NH\text{–}CH_3$$

Ephedrine Methamphetamine

While the synthesis involves a variety of dangerous chemicals, including anhydrous ammonia, anhydrous hydrochloric acid, sodium, and sodium hydroxide, most "meth cooks" do not have formal laboratory training. "Meth lab" fires are common, and the synthesis produces toxic wastes. The cleanup that followed the seizure of a major "meth lab" in 2003 took 8 days and required fifty people. Over four million pounds (lb) of toxic soil and 133 drums of hazardous waste were removed from the site, at a cost of $226,000.

For Further Understanding

- Compare the structures of methamphetamine and dopamine. Develop a hypothesis to explain why dopamine receptors also bind to and transport methamphetamine into neurons. (*Hint:* Receptors are proteins in cell membranes that have a pocket into which a specific molecule can fit.)
- Explain why methamphetamine is soluble in alcohols and in water.

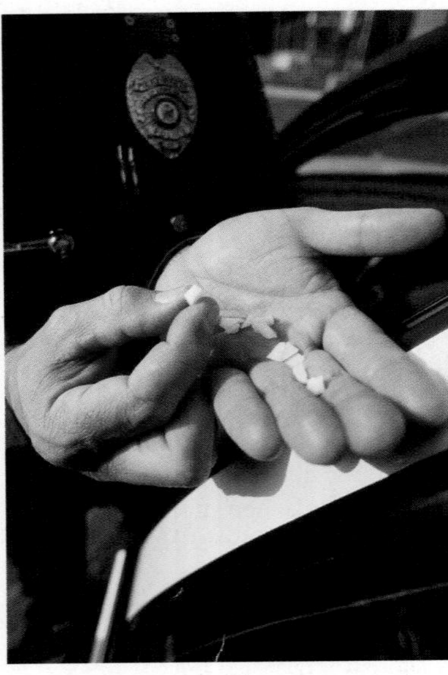

(a)

(b)

(c)

Figure 15.3 (a) Crack cocaine is a non-water-soluble base with a low melting point and a crystalline structure. (b) Powdered cocaine is a water-soluble salt of cocaine base. (c) Cocaine is extracted from the leaves of the coca plant.

The local anesthetic novocaine, which is often used in dentistry and for minor surgery, is injected as an amine salt. See Medically Important Amines earlier in this section.

Thus, by adding a strong acid to a water-insoluble amine, a water-soluble alkylammonium salt can be formed. The salt can just as easily be converted back to an amine by the addition of a strong base. The ability to manipulate the solubility of physiologically active amines through interconversion of the amine and its corresponding salt is extremely important in the development, manufacture, and administration of many important drugs.

"Crack" cocaine is an amine and a base (see Figure 15.4 and structure below) and is generally found in the form of relatively large crystals (Figure 15.3a) that may vary in color from white to dark brown or black. As we have just seen, when an amine reacts with an acid, an alkylammonium salt is formed. When cocaine reacts with HCl, the product is cocaine hydrochloride:

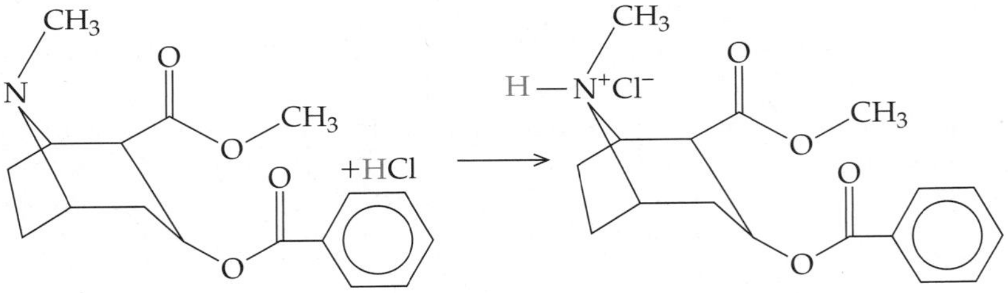

"Crack" cocaine (a base) $+ HCl \longrightarrow$ Cocaine hydrochloride (a salt)

The salt of cocaine is a powder (Figure 15.3b) and is soluble in water. Since it is a powder, it can be snorted, and because it is water-soluble, it dissolves in the fluids of the nasal mucous membranes and is absorbed into the bloodstream. This is a common form of cocaine because it is the direct product of the preparation from coca leaves (Figure 15.3c). A coca paste is made from the leaves and is mixed with HCl and water. After additional processing, the product is the salt of cocaine.

Cocaine hydrochloride salt can be converted into its base form by a process called "free basing." Although the chemistry is simple, the process is dangerous because it requires highly flammable solvents. This pure cocaine is not soluble in water. It has a relatively low melting point, however, and can be smoked. Crack, so called because of the crackling noise it makes when smoked, is absorbed into the body more quickly than the snorted powder and results in a more immediate high.

Quaternary Ammonium Salts

Quaternary ammonium salts are ammonium salts that have four organic groups bonded to the nitrogen. They have the following general structure:

$$R_4N^+X^- \quad (R = \text{any alkyl or aryl group; } X^- = \text{a halide anion, most commonly } Cl^-)$$

LEARNING GOAL

6 Describe the structure of quaternary ammonium salts and discuss their use as antiseptics and disinfectants.

Quaternary ammonium salts that have a very long carbon chain, sometimes called "quats," are used as disinfectants and antiseptics because they have detergent activity. Two popular quats are benzalkonium chloride (Zephiran) and cetylpyridinium chloride, found in the mouthwash Scope.

$$\left[C_6H_5{-}CH_2{-}\overset{CH_3}{\underset{CH_3}{N^+}}{-}C_{18}H_{37} \right] Cl^-$$

Benzalkonium chloride

$$\left[C_5H_5N^+{-}(CH_2)_{15}CH_3 \right] Cl^-$$

Cetylpyridinium chloride

Choline is an important quaternary ammonium salt in the body. It is part of the hydrophilic "head" of the membrane phospholipid lecithin. Choline is also a precursor for the synthesis of the neurotransmitter acetylcholine.

Phospholipids and biological membranes are discussed in Sections 17.3 and 17.6.

The function of acetylcholine is described in greater detail in Section 15.5.

$$\left[CH_3{-}\overset{CH_3}{\underset{CH_3}{N^+}}{-}CH_2CH_2OH \right] Cl^-$$

Choline

15.2 Heterocyclic Amines

LEARNING GOAL

7 Discuss the biological significance of heterocyclic amines.

Heterocyclic amines are cyclic compounds that have at least one nitrogen atom in the ring structure. The structures and common names of several heterocyclic amines important in nature are shown here. They are represented by their structural formulas and by abbreviated line formulas.

Imidazole

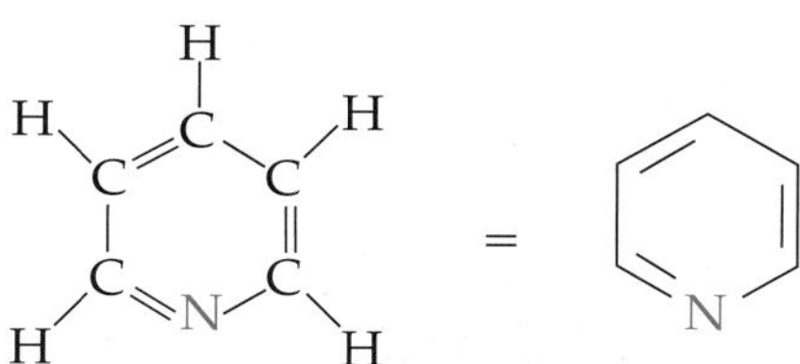

Pyridine

Pyrrole

Pyrimidine

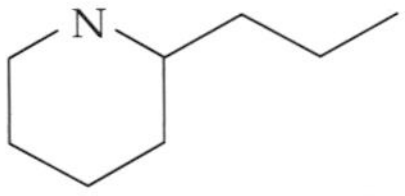

Coniine is produced by the poison hemlock plant. It is a neurotoxin that causes respiratory paralysis. It is the poison that was used to kill the Greek philosopher Socrates in 399 BC. To what class of molecules does coniine belong?

The heterocyclic amines shown below are examples of fused ring structures. Each ring pair shares two carbon atoms in common. Thus, two fused rings share one or more common bonds as part of their ring backbones. The fused ring structures of purine, indole, and porphyrin, are shown as structural formulas and as line diagrams:

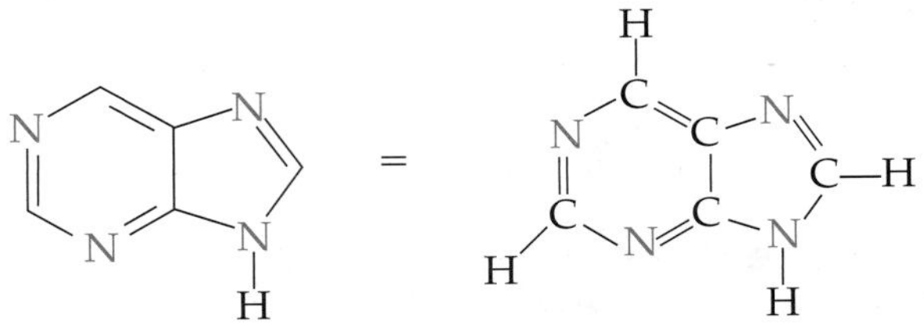

Purine

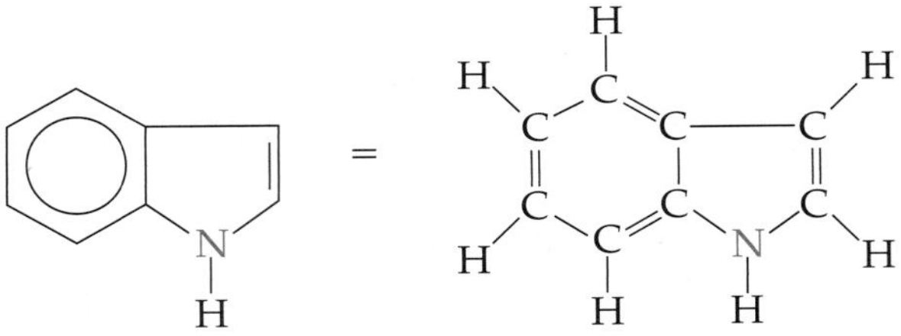

Indole

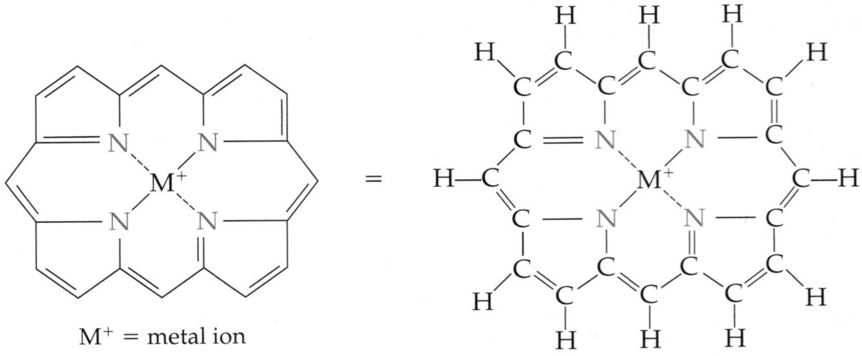

M^+ = metal ion

Porphyrin

The structures of purines and pyrimidines are presented in Section 20.1.

The structure of the heme group found in hemoglobin and myoglobin is presented in Section 18.8.

The pyrimidine and purine rings are found in DNA and RNA. The porphyrin ring structure is found in hemoglobin (an oxygen-carrying blood protein), myoglobin (an oxygen-carrying protein found in muscle tissue), and chlorophyll (a photosynthetic plant pigment). The indole and pyridine rings are found in many **alkaloids,** which are naturally occurring compounds with one or more nitrogen-containing heterocyclic rings. Alkaloids include cocaine, nicotine, quinine, morphine, heroin, and LSD (Figure 15.4).

Lysergic acid diethylamide (LSD) is a hallucinogenic compound that may cause severe mental disorders. Cocaine is produced by the coca plant. In small doses it is used as an anesthetic for the sinuses and eyes. An **anesthetic** is a drug that causes a lack of sensation in any part of the body (local anesthetic) or causes unconsciousness (general anesthetic). In higher doses, cocaine causes an intense feeling of euphoria followed by a deep depression. Cocaine is addictive because the user needs larger and larger amounts to overcome the depression. Nicotine is one of the simplest heterocyclic amines and appears to be the addictive component of cigarette smoke.

Morphine was the first alkaloid to be isolated from the sap of the opium poppy. Morphine is a strong **analgesic,** a drug that acts as a pain killer. However, it is a powerful and addictive narcotic. Codeine, also produced by the opium poppy, is

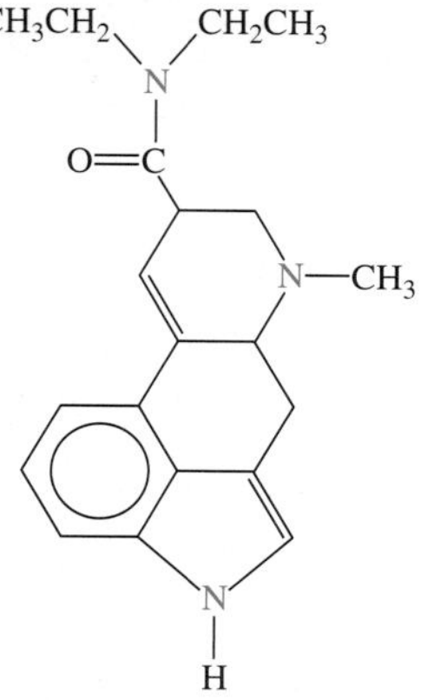

Lysergic acid diethylamide
(LSD)
(indole ring skeleton)

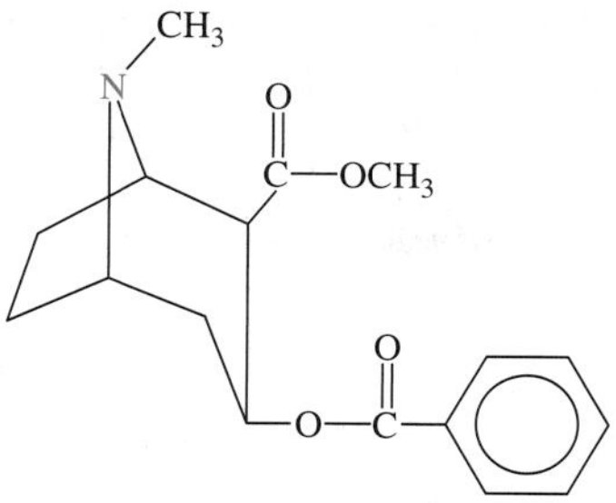

Cocaine
(tropane ring skeleton)

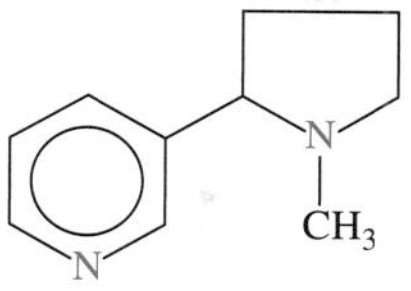

Nicotine
(pyridine and pyrrolidine ring skeleton)

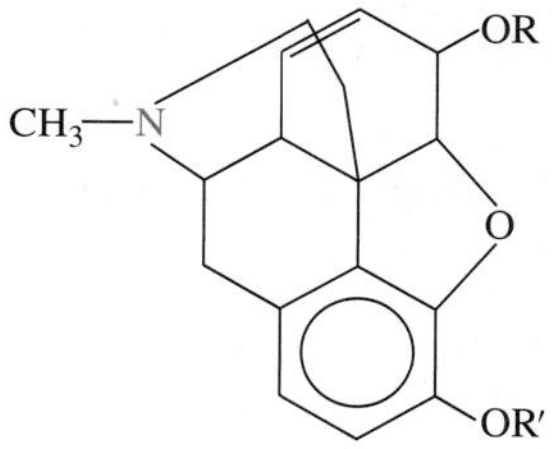

R=H R′=H Morphine
R=H R′=CH_3 Codeine
R=Ac R′=Ac Heroin
(piperidine ring skeleton)

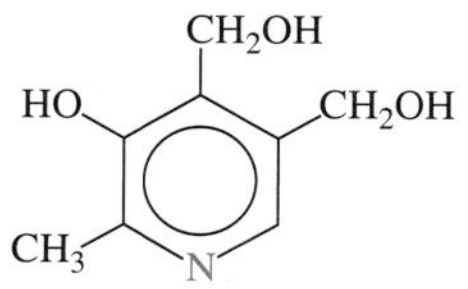

Vitamin B_6
(pyridine ring skeleton)

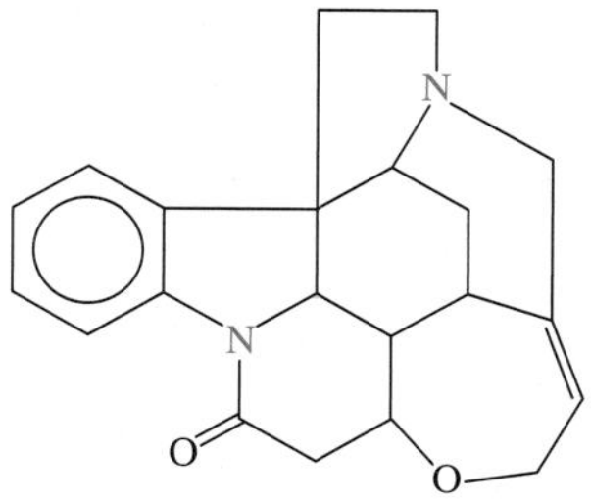

Strychnine
(indole and piperidine skeleton)

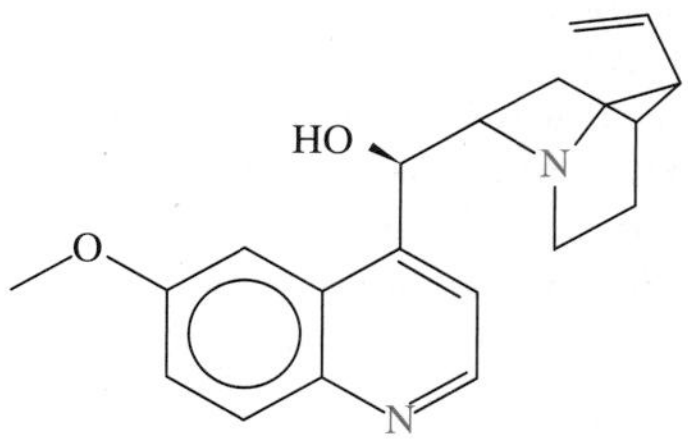

Quinine
(quinoline ring skeleton)

Figure 15.4 Structures of several heterocyclic amines with biological activity.

a less powerful analgesic than morphine, but it is one of the most effective cough suppressants known. Heroin is produced in the laboratory by adding two acetyl groups to morphine. It was initially made in the hopes of producing a compound with the benefits of morphine but lacking the addictive qualities. However, heroin is even more addictive than morphine.

Strychnine is found in the seeds of an Asiatic tree. It is extremely toxic and was commonly used as a rat poison at one time. Quinine, isolated from the bark of South American trees, was the first effective treatment for malaria. Vitamin B_6 is one of the water-soluble vitamins required by the body.

15.3 Amides

Amides are the products formed in a reaction between a carboxylic acid derivative and ammonia or an amine. The general structure of an amide is shown here.

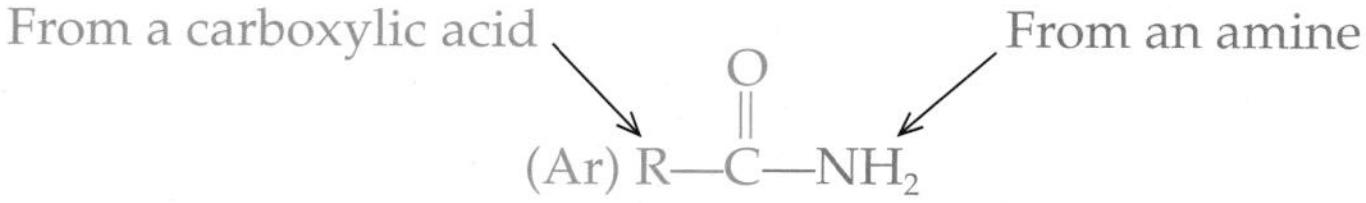

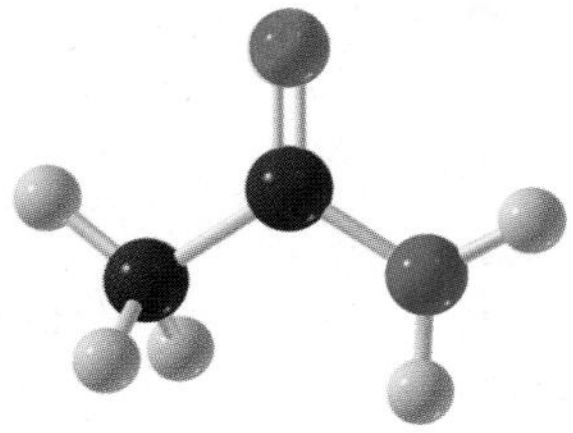

From a carboxylic acid → (Ar) R—C(=O)—NH_2 ← From an amine

Ethanamide

KITCHEN CHEMISTRY

Browning Reactions and Flavor: The Maillard Reaction

Since earliest times humans have enjoyed the delightful flavors and aromas of meat roasted over a hot fire or seared in a hot pan. The same chemical reaction that produces the aroma of roasted meat is also the reason that bread crust is brown and more flavorful than the inside of the bread, and is responsible for the wonderful smell of roasted coffee and chocolate. The reaction is called the Maillard reaction in honor of Louis Camille Maillard, a French physician who first described it in 1910.

The reaction begins with a carbohydrate molecule, generally glucose or fructose, which binds to an amino acid in a protein chain. This reaction involves a carbonyl group of the sugar and the amino group of the amino acid. The initial product is unstable and is converted into an intermediate that further reacts with other compounds in the food to create a wide variety of aromatic heterocyclic compounds, including heterocyclic amines. Several of the simpler products of the reactions are shown here:

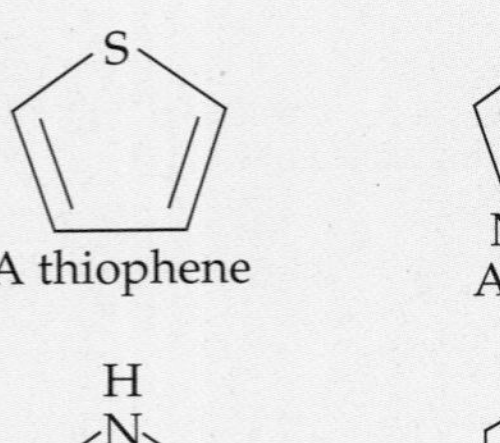

A thiophene

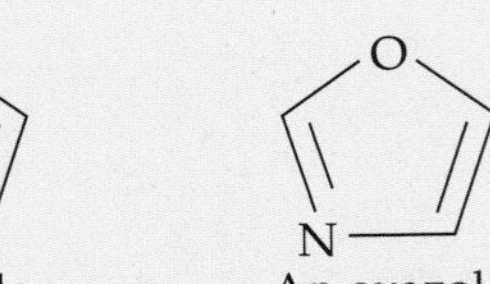

A thiazole

An oxazole

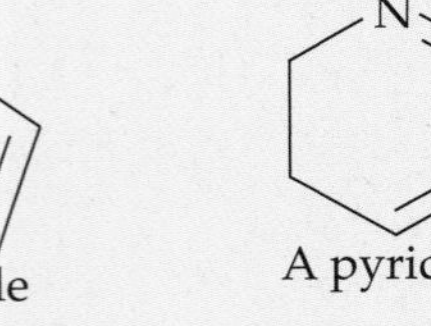

A pyrrole

A pyridine

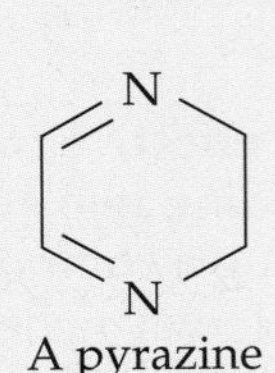

A pyrazine

The savory flavors are attributed to the peptides and amino acids in the food. Oxazoles lend a floral note to the flavor. Thiophenes and thiazoles are distinctive meaty and onion flavors. Pyrazines are in part responsible for the aroma of chocolate and pyridines and pyrazines are associated with the flavors of green vegetables.

The Maillard reaction only occurs at approximately 250°F, which is the reason that meats cooked by boiling or steaming are typically pale and don't have the flavor profile of meats that are seared on a hot surface like a sauté pan or on a grill. Meats that are cooked in oil or in a hot oven also undergo the browning reactions because the surface of the meat quickly dehydrates and rises to the temperature of the oven.

Because foods are chemically complex, we may never fully understand the products of the Maillard reaction, but that will not keep us from enjoying the flavors and aromas that they produce.

For Further Understanding

- Many stew recipes begin by browning the meat, vegetables, and flour before adding any water. How will this influence the characteristics of the stew?
- Microwave ovens are very useful for heating leftovers or steaming vegetables, but are generally not used to prepare hamburgers or roasts. Explain the reason for this in terms of what you have just learned of the Maillard reaction.

The amide group is composed of two portions: the carbonyl group from a carboxylic acid and the amino group from ammonia or an amine. The bond between the carbonyl carbon and the nitrogen of the amine or ammonia is called the **amide bond.**

Structure and Physical Properties

LEARNING GOAL

8 Describe the physical properties of amides.

Most amides are solids at room temperature. They have very high boiling points, and the simpler ones are quite soluble in water. Both of these properties are a result of strong intermolecular hydrogen bonding between the N—H bond of one amide and the C=O group of a second amide, as shown in Figure 15.5.

Unlike amines, amides are not bases (proton acceptors). The reason is that the highly electronegative oxygen atom of the carbonyl group causes a very strong attraction between the lone pair of nitrogen electrons and the carbonyl group. As a result, the unshared pair of electrons cannot "hold" a proton.

Resonance hybrids are discussed in Section 3.4.

Because of the attraction of the carbonyl group for the lone pair of nitrogen electrons, the structure of the C—N bond of an amide is a *resonance hybrid.* In the structures below lines are used to represent pairs of electrons.

Nomenclature

The common and IUPAC names of the amides are derived from the common and IUPAC names of the carboxylic acids from which they were made. Remove the *-ic acid* ending of the common name or the *-oic acid* ending of the IUPAC name of the carboxylic acid, and replace it with the ending *-amide.* Several examples of the common and IUPAC nomenclature are provided in Table 15.4 and in the following structures:

$$CH_3\overset{O}{\overset{\|}{C}}-NH_2 \qquad\qquad CH_3CH_2\overset{O}{\overset{\|}{C}}-NH_2$$

Ethan*oic acid* → Ethan*amide*
or
Acet*ic acid* → Acet*amide*

Propan*oic acid* → Propan*amide*
or
Propion*ic acid* → Propion*amide*

Substituents on the nitrogen are placed as prefixes and are indicated by *N*- followed by the name of the substituent. There are no spaces between the prefix and the amide name. For example:

$$CH_3CH_2\overset{O}{\overset{\|}{C}}-NH-CH_3$$

N-Methylpropanamide

$$CH_3CH_2CH_2CH_2CH_2\overset{O}{\overset{\|}{C}}-NH-CH_2CH_2CH_3$$

N-Propylhexanamide

Medically Important Amides

Barbiturates, often called "downers," are derived from amides and are used as sedatives. They are also used as anticonvulsants for epileptics and for people suffering from a variety of brain disorders that manifest themselves in neurosis, anxiety, and tension.

LEARNING GOAL

9 Draw the structure and write the common and IUPAC names of amides.

Nomenclature of carboxylic acids is described in Section 14.1.

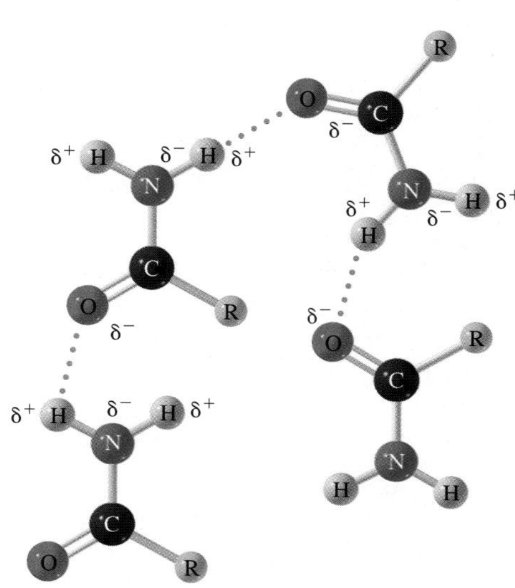

Figure 15.5 Hydrogen bonding in amides.

TABLE 15.4 **IUPAC and Common Names of Simple Amides**

Compound	IUPAC Name	Common Name
$R-\overset{O}{\overset{\|}{C}}-NH_2$	Alkan*amide* (-*amide* replaces the *-oic acid* ending of the IUPAC name of carboxylic acid)	Alkan*amide* (-*amide* replaces the *-ic acid* ending of the common name of carboxylic acid)
$H-\overset{O}{\overset{\|}{C}}-NH_2$	Methanamide	Formamide
$CH_3-\overset{O}{\overset{\|}{C}}-NH_2$	Ethanamide	Acetamide
$CH_3CH_2-\overset{O}{\overset{\|}{C}}-NH_2$	Propanamide	Propionamide
$H-\overset{O}{\overset{\|}{C}}-NHCH_3$	*N*-Methylmethanamide	*N*-Methylformamide
$CH_3-\overset{O}{\overset{\|}{C}}-NHCH_3$	*N*-Methylethanamide	*N*-Methylacetamide

LEARNING GOAL

9 Draw the structure and write the common and IUPAC names of amides.

EXAMPLE 15.4 Naming Amides Using Common and IUPAC Nomenclature Systems

a. Name the following amide using both the IUPAC and common systems.

$$CH_3CH_2CH_2\overset{\overset{\displaystyle O}{\|}}{C}{-}NH{-}CH_2CH_2CH_3$$

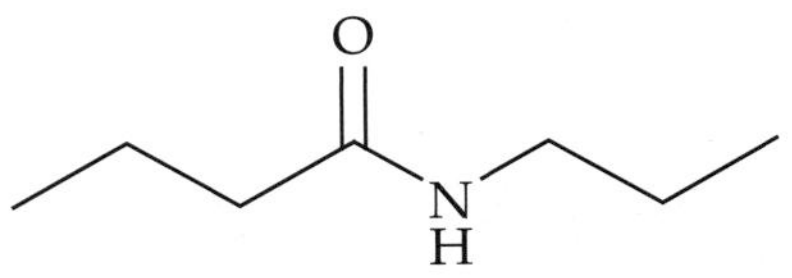

Solution

The names of amides are derived from the common and IUPAC names of the carboxylic acids from which they were made.

	IUPAC	**Common**
Parent carboxylic acid:	Butanoic acid (becomes butanamide)	Butyric acid (becomes butyramide)
Group on N:	propyl	propyl
Name:	*N*-Propylbutanamide	*N*-Propylbutyramide

b. Name the following amide using the IUPAC and common systems.

$$CH_3CH_2\overset{\overset{\displaystyle O}{\|}}{C}{-}NH{-}CH_2CH_2CH_2CH_2CH_3$$

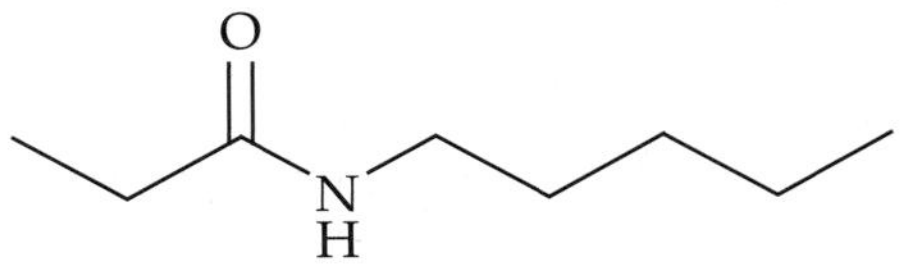

Solution

Parent carboxylic acid:	Propanoic acid (becomes propanamide)	Propionic acid (becomes propionamide)
Group on N:	pentyl	pentyl
Name:	*N*-Pentylpropanamide	*N*-Pentylpropionamide

Practice Problem 15.4

Provide the common and IUPAC names for each of the following amides.

a. $CH_3CH_2CH_2CH_2\overset{\overset{\displaystyle O}{\|}}{C}{-}NH{-}CH_2CH_2CH_2CH_2CH_3$

b. $CH_3CH_2CH_2CH_2CH_2\overset{\overset{\displaystyle O}{\|}}{C}{-}NH{-}CH_2CH_2CH_2CH_3$

► For Further Practice: **Questions 15.53, 15.54, and 15.57.**

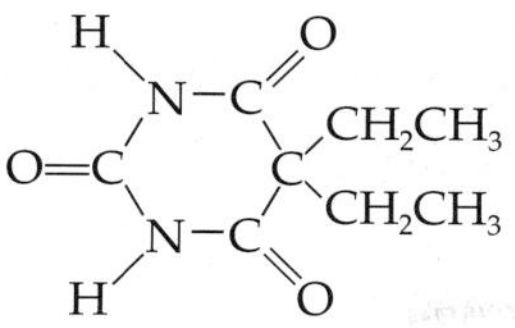

$$\text{Barbital structure: cyclic } (H)N-C(=O)-C(CH_2CH_3)_2-C(=O)-N(H)-C(=O)$$

Barbital—a barbiturate

Phenacetin and acetaminophen are also amides. Acetaminophen is an aromatic amide that is commonly used in place of aspirin, particularly by people who are allergic to aspirin or who suffer stomach bleeding from the use of aspirin. It was first synthesized in 1893 and is the active ingredient in Tylenol and Datril. Like aspirin, acetaminophen relieves pain and reduces fever. However, unlike aspirin, it is not an anti-inflammatory drug.

Phenacetin was synthesized in 1887 and used as an analgesic for almost a century. Its structure and properties are similar to those of acetaminophen. However, it was banned by the U.S. Food and Drug Administration (FDA) in 1983 because of the kidney damage and blood disorders that it causes.

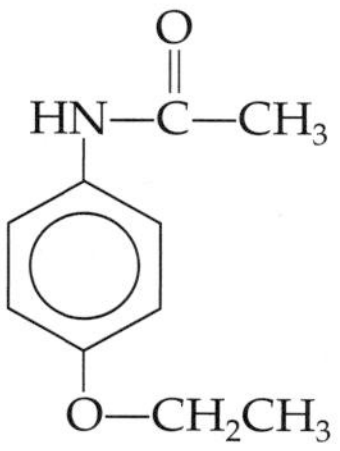

$$CH_3CH_2O-C_6H_4-NH-\overset{\displaystyle O}{\overset{\|}{C}}-CH_3 \qquad HO-C_6H_4-NH-\overset{\displaystyle O}{\overset{\|}{C}}-CH_3$$

Phenacetin 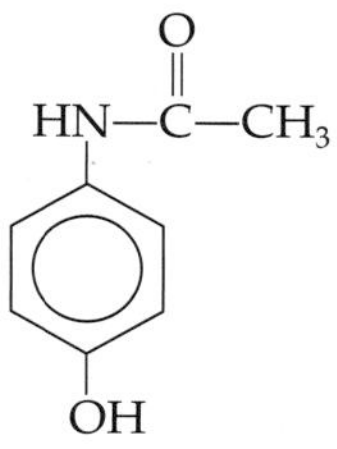 | Acetaminophen

Reactions Involving Amides

Preparation of Amides

Amides are prepared from carboxylic acid derivatives, either acid chlorides or acid anhydrides. Acid chlorides rapidly react with either ammonia or amines, as in:

LEARNING GOAL

10 Write equations representing the preparation of amides.

$$R-\overset{\displaystyle O}{\overset{\|}{C}}-Cl + 2NH_3 \longrightarrow R-\overset{\displaystyle O}{\overset{\|}{C}}-NH_2 + \overset{+}{N}H_4Cl^-$$

Acid chloride; Ammonia or amine; Amide; Ammonium chloride or alkylammonium chloride

Note that two molar equivalents of ammonia or amine are required in this reaction and that this is an acyl group transfer reaction. The **acyl group**

$$R-\overset{\displaystyle O}{\overset{\|}{C}}-$$

of the acid chloride is transferred from the Cl atom to the N atom of one of the ammonia or amine molecules. The second ammonia (or amine) reacts with the HCl formed in the transfer reaction to produce ammonium chloride or alkylammonium chloride.

The reaction between butanoyl chloride and methanamine to produce *N*-methylbutanamide is an example of an acyl group transfer reaction.

$$CH_3CH_2CH_2\overset{\displaystyle O}{\overset{\|}{C}}-Cl + 2CH_3NH_2 \longrightarrow CH_3CH_2CH_2\overset{\displaystyle O}{\overset{\|}{C}}-NH-CH_3 + CH_3\overset{+}{N}H_3Cl^-$$

Butanoyl chloride; Methanamine; *N*-Methylbutanamide; Methylammonium chloride

A MEDICAL PERSPECTIVE

Semisynthetic Penicillins

The antibacterial properties of penicillin were discovered by Alexander Fleming in 1929. These natural penicillins produced by several species of the mold *Penicillium* had a number of drawbacks. They were effective only against a type of bacteria referred to as Gram positive because of a staining reaction based on their cell wall structure. They were also very susceptible to destruction by bacterial enzymes called β-lactamases, and some were destroyed by stomach acid and had to be administered by injection.

To overcome these problems, chemists have produced semisynthetic penicillins by modifying the core structure. The core of penicillins is 6-aminopenicillanic acid, which consists of a thiazolidine ring fused to a β-lactam ring. In addition, there is an R group bonded via an amide bond to the core structure.

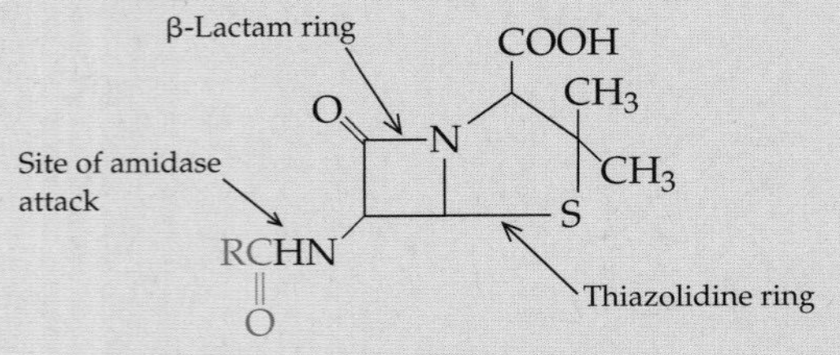

β-Lactam ring
Site of amidase attack
Thiazolidine ring

6-Aminopenicillanic acid

The β-lactam ring confers the antimicrobial properties. However, the R group determines the degree of antibacterial activity, the pharmacological properties, including the types of bacteria against which it is active, and the degree of resistance to the β-lactamases exhibited by any particular penicillin antibiotic. These are the properties that must be modified to produce penicillins that are acid resistant, effective with a broad spectrum of bacteria, and β-lactamase resistant.

Chemists simply remove the natural R group by cleaving the amide bond with an enzyme called an amidase. They then replace the R group and test the properties of the "new" antibiotic. Among the resulting semisynthetic penicillins are ampicillin, methicillin, and oxacillin.

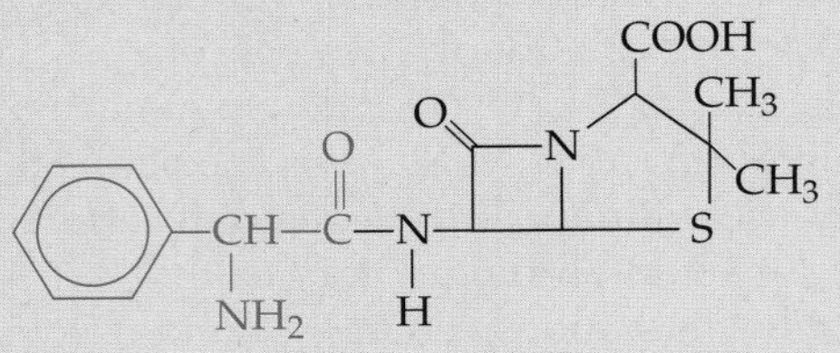

Ampicillin

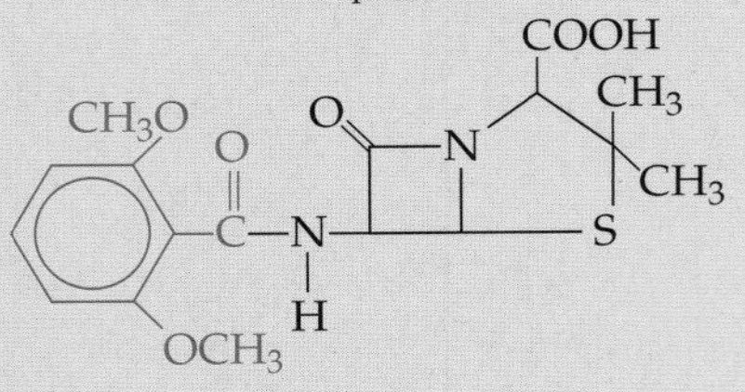

Methicillin

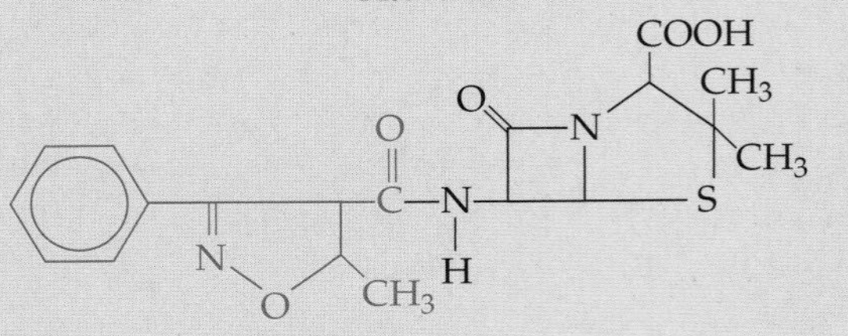

Oxacillin

For Further Understanding

- Using the Internet and other resources, investigate and describe the properties of some new penicillins and the bacteria against which they are effective.
- Why does changing the R group of a penicillin result in altered chemical and physiological properties?

The reaction between an amine and an acid anhydride is also an acyl group transfer. The general equation for the synthesis of an amide in the reaction between an acid anhydride and ammonia or an amine is

$$\underset{\text{Acid anhydride}}{R-\overset{O}{\overset{\|}{C}}-O-\overset{O}{\overset{\|}{C}}-R} + \underset{\text{Ammonia or amine}}{2NH_3} \longrightarrow \underset{\text{Amide}}{R-\overset{O}{\overset{\|}{C}}-NH_2} + \underset{\text{Carboxylic acid salt}}{R-\overset{O}{\overset{\|}{C}}-O^-\overset{+}{N}H_4}$$

When subjected to heat, the carboxylic acid salt loses a water molecule to produce a second amide molecule.

A well-known commercial amide is the artificial sweetener aspartame or NutraSweet. Although the name suggests that it is a sugar, it is not a sugar at all.

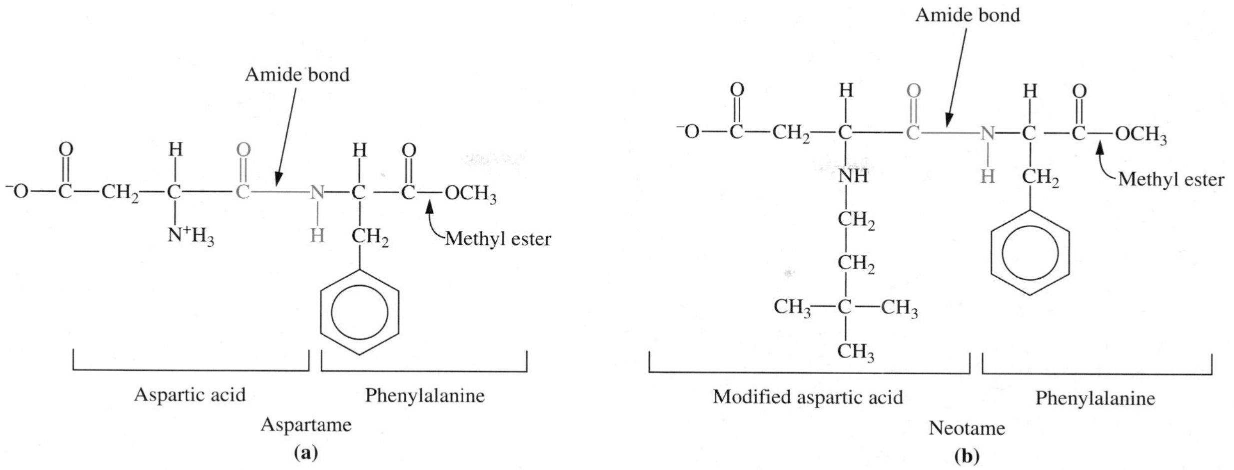

Amide bond

$^{-}O-\overset{O}{\overset{\|}{C}}-CH_2-\underset{N^+H_3}{\overset{H}{C}}-\overset{O}{\overset{\|}{C}}-\underset{H}{N}-\underset{CH_2-C_6H_5}{\overset{H}{C}}-\overset{O}{\overset{\|}{C}}-OCH_3$

Methyl ester

Aspartic acid Phenylalanine

Aspartame

(a)

Amide bond

$^{-}O-\overset{O}{\overset{\|}{C}}-CH_2-\underset{NH-CH_2-CH_2-C(CH_3)_3}{\overset{H}{C}}-\overset{O}{\overset{\|}{C}}-\underset{H}{N}-\underset{CH_2-C_6H_5}{\overset{H}{C}}-\overset{O}{\overset{\|}{C}}-OCH_3$

Methyl ester

Modified aspartic acid Phenylalanine

Neotame

(b)

Figure 15.6 The amide bond. (a) NutraSweet, the dipeptide aspartame, is a molecule composed of two amino acids joined by an amide (peptide) bond. (b) The sweetener Neotame, is also a dipeptide. One of the amino acids has been modified so that neotame is safe for use by phenylketonurics.

In fact, it is the methyl ester of a molecule composed of two amino acids, aspartic acid and phenylalanine, joined by an amide bond (Figure 15.6a).

Amino acids have both a carboxyl group and an amino group and are discussed in detail in Sections 15.4 and 18.1.

Packages of aspartame carry the warning: "Phenylketonurics: Contains Phenylalanine." Digestion of aspartame and heating to high temperatures during cooking break both the ester bond and the amide bond, which releases the amino acid phenylalanine. People with the genetic disorder phenylketonuria (PKU) cannot metabolize this amino acid. As a result, it builds up to toxic levels that can cause mental retardation in an infant born with the condition. This no longer occurs because every child is tested for PKU at the time of birth and each child with the disorder is treated with a diet that limits the amount of phenylalanine to only the amount required for normal growth.

In July 2002 the FDA approved a new artificial sweetener that is related to aspartame. Called neotame, it has the same core structure as aspartame, but a 3,3-dimethylbutyl group has been added to the aspartic acid (Figure 15.6b). Digestion and heating still cause breakage of the ester bond, but the bulky 3,3-dimethylbutyl group blocks the breakage of the amide bond. Neotame can be used without risk by people with PKU and also retains its sweetness during cooking.

Question 15.9 What is the structure of the amine that, on reaction with the acid chlorides shown, will give each of the following products?

a. $? + CH_3\overset{O}{\overset{\|}{C}}-Cl \longrightarrow CH_3\overset{O}{\overset{\|}{C}}NHCH_3 + CH_3\overset{+}{N}H_3\ Cl^-$

b. $? + CH_3CH_2CH_2CH_2\underset{CH_2CH_3}{\underset{|}{C}H}\overset{O}{\overset{\|}{C}}-Cl \longrightarrow (CH_3)_2N\overset{O}{\overset{\|}{C}}\underset{CH_2CH_3}{\underset{|}{C}H}CH_2CH_2CH_2CH_3 + (CH_3)_2\overset{+}{N}H_2\ Cl^-$

Question 15.10 What are the structures of the acid chlorides and the amines that will react to give each of the following products?

a. *N*-Ethylhexanamide

b. *N*-Propylbutanamide

LEARNING GOAL

11 Write equations showing the hydrolysis of amides.

Hydrolysis of Amides

Hydrolysis of an amide results in breaking the amide bond to produce a carboxylic acid and ammonia or an amine. It is very difficult to hydrolyze the amide bond. In fact, the reaction requires heating the amide in the presence of a strong acid or base.

$$R{-}\overset{\overset{\displaystyle O}{\|}}{C}{-}NH{-}R^1 + H_3O^+ \longrightarrow R{-}\overset{\overset{\displaystyle O}{\|}}{C}{-}OH + R^1{-}\overset{+}{N}H_3$$

Amide; Strong acid; Carboxylic acid; Alkylammonium ion or ammonium ion

$$CH_3CH_2CH_2\overset{\overset{\displaystyle O}{\|}}{C}{-}NH_2 + H_3O^+ \longrightarrow CH_3CH_2CH_2\overset{\overset{\displaystyle O}{\|}}{C}{-}OH + \overset{+}{N}H_4$$

Butanamide (butyramide); Butanoic acid (butyric acid)

If a strong base is used, the products are the amine and the salt of the carboxylic acid:

$$R{-}\overset{\overset{\displaystyle O}{\|}}{C}{-}NH{-}R^1 + NaOH \longrightarrow R{-}\overset{\overset{\displaystyle O}{\|}}{C}{-}O^-Na^+ + R^1{-}NH_2$$

Amide; Strong base; Carboxylic acid salt; Amine or ammonia

$$CH_3CH_2\overset{\overset{\displaystyle O}{\|}}{C}{-}NHCH_3 + NaOH \longrightarrow CH_3CH_2\overset{\overset{\displaystyle O}{\|}}{C}{-}O^-Na^+ + CH_3NH_2$$

N-Methylpropanamide (*N*-methylpropionamide); Sodium propanoate (sodium propionate); Methanamine (methylamine)

LEARNING GOAL

12 Draw the general structure of an amino acid.

LEARNING GOAL

13 Draw and discuss the structure of a peptide bond.

15.4 A Preview of Amino Acids, Proteins, and Protein Synthesis

In Chapter 18 we will describe the structure of proteins, the molecules that carry out the majority of the biological processes essential to life. Proteins are polymers of **amino acids.** As the name suggests, amino acids have two essential functional groups, an amino group ($-NH_2$) and a carboxyl group ($-COOH$). Typically amino acids have the following general structure:

$$H_2N{-}\underset{\underset{\displaystyle R}{|}}{\overset{\overset{\displaystyle H}{|}}{C}}{-}COOH$$

(R may be a hydrogen atom or an organic group.)

In the cell the amino group is usually protonated and the carboxyl group is usually ionized to the carboxylate anion. In the future we will represent an amino acid in the following way:

$$H_3\overset{+}{N}{-}\underset{\underset{\displaystyle R}{|}}{\overset{\overset{\displaystyle H}{|}}{C}}{-}COO^-$$

The amide bond that forms between the carboxyl group of one amino acid and the amino group of another is called the **peptide bond.**

The peptide bond is an amide bond.

$$H_3\overset{+}{N}{-}\underset{\underset{\displaystyle R}{|}}{\overset{\overset{\displaystyle H}{|}}{C}}{-}\overset{\overset{\displaystyle O}{\|}}{C}{-}\underset{\underset{\displaystyle H}{|}}{N}{-}\underset{\underset{\displaystyle R}{|}}{\overset{\overset{\displaystyle H}{|}}{C}}{-}\overset{\overset{\displaystyle O}{\|}}{C}{-}O^-$$

The joining of amino acids by amide bonds produces small *peptides* and larger *proteins.* Because protein structure and function are essential for life processes, it is fortunate indeed that the amide bonds that hold them together are not easily hydrolyzed at physiological pH and temperature.

The process of protein synthesis in the cell mimics amide formation in the laboratory; it involves acyl group transfer. There are several important differences between the chemistry in the laboratory and the chemistry in the cell. During protein synthesis, the **aminoacyl group** of the amino acid is transferred, rather than the acyl group of a carboxylic acid. In addition, the aminoacyl group is not transferred from a carboxylic acid derivative; it is transferred from a special carrier molecule called a **transfer RNA (tRNA).** When the aminoacyl group is covalently bonded to a tRNA, the resulting structure is called an *aminoacyl tRNA:*

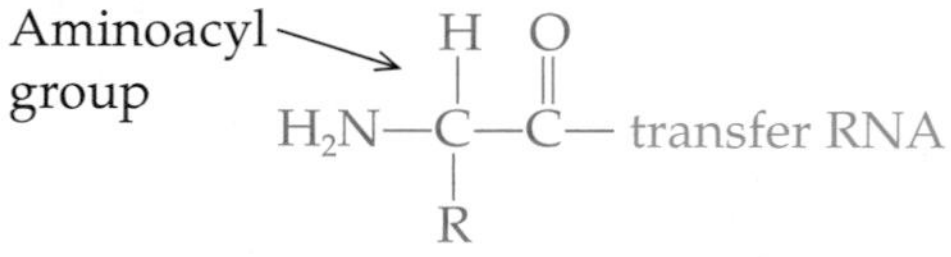

Aminoacyl group → $H_2N-\overset{\overset{\large H}{|}}{\underset{\underset{\large R}{|}}{C}}-\overset{\overset{\large O}{\|}}{C}-$ transfer RNA

The aminoacyl group of the aminoacyl tRNA is transferred to the amino group nitrogen to form a peptide bond. The transfer RNA is recycled by binding to another of the same kind of aminoacyl group.

More than 100 kinds of proteins, nucleotides, and RNA molecules participate in the incredibly intricate process of protein synthesis. In Chapter 18 we will study protein structure and learn about the many functions of proteins in the life of the cell. In Chapter 20 we will study the details of protein synthesis to see how these aminoacyl transfer reactions make us the individuals that we are.

15.5 Neurotransmitters

LEARNING GOAL

14 Describe the function of neurotransmitters.

Neurotransmitters are chemicals that carry messages, or signals, from a nerve cell to a target cell, which may be another nerve cell or a muscle cell. Neurotransmitters are classified as being *excitatory,* stimulating their target cell, or *inhibitory,* decreasing activity of the target cell. One feature shared by the neurotransmitters is that they are all nitrogen-containing compounds. Some of them have rather complex structures and one, nitric oxide (NO), consists of only two atoms. Several important neurotransmitters are discussed in the following sections.

Catecholamines

All of the catecholamine neurotransmitters, including dopamine, epinephrine, and norepinephrine, are synthesized from the amino acid tyrosine (Figure 15.7). *Dopamine* is critical to good health. A deficiency in this neurotransmitter, for example, results in Parkinson's disease, a disorder characterized by tremors, monotonous speech, loss of memory and problem-solving ability, and loss of motor function. It would seem logical to treat Parkinson's disease with dopamine. Unfortunately, dopamine cannot cross the blood-brain barrier to enter brain cells. As a result, L-dopa, which is converted to dopamine in brain cells, is used to treat this disorder.

Just as too little dopamine causes Parkinson's disease, an excess is associated with schizophrenia. Dopamine also appears to play a role in addictive behavior. In proper amounts, it causes a pleasant, satisfied feeling. The greater the amount of dopamine, the more intense the sensation, the "high." Several drugs have been shown to increase the levels of dopamine. Among these are cocaine, heroin, amphetamines, alcohol, and nicotine. Marijuana also causes an increase in brain dopamine, raising the possibility that it, too, has the potential to produce addiction.

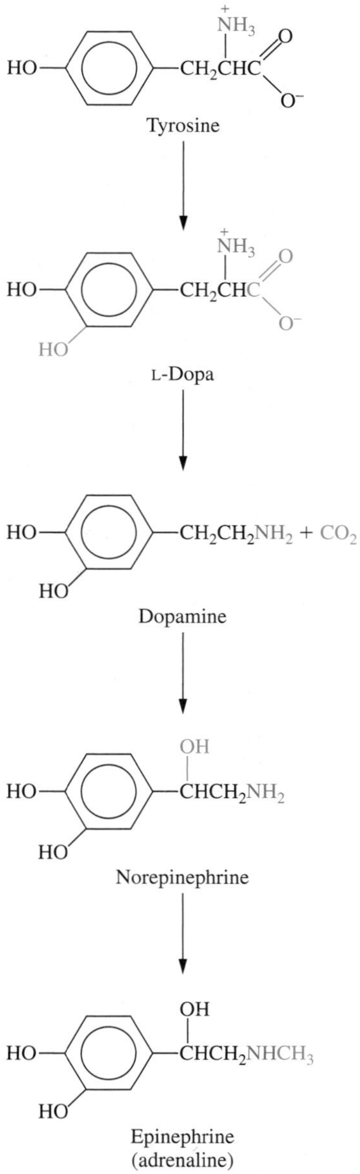

HO–(benzene ring)–$CH_2CH(\overset{+}{N}H_3)CO_2^-$
Tyrosine
↓
HO, HO–(benzene ring)–$CH_2CH(\overset{+}{N}H_3)CO_2^-$
L-Dopa
↓
HO, HO–(benzene ring)–$CH_2CH_2NH_2 + CO_2$
Dopamine
↓
HO, HO–(benzene ring)–$CH(OH)CH_2NH_2$
Norepinephrine
↓
HO, HO–(benzene ring)–$CH(OH)CH_2NHCH_3$
Epinephrine (adrenaline)

Figure 15.7 The pathway for synthesis of dopamine, epinephrine, and norepinephrine.

A MEDICAL PERSPECTIVE

Opiate Biosynthesis and the Mutant Poppy

Hippocrates, the "father of medicine," left us the first record of the therapeutic use of opium (460 BC). Although not recorded, it is probably true that the addictive properties of opium were recognized soon thereafter!

The opium poppy (*Papaver somniferum*) is cultivated, legally and illegally, in many parts of the world. The flowers vary in color from white to deep red, but it is the seed pod that is sought after. In the seed pod is a milky fluid that contains morphine and codeine, and a small amount of an opioid called thebaine. The juice is extracted from the unripe seed pods and dried, and the opium alkaloids are extracted and purified.

In the legal pharmaceutical world, morphine and codeine are used to ease pain and spasmodic coughing. Thebaine is used as a reactant in pharmaceutical synthesis to produce a number of synthetic opioid compounds with a variety of biological effects. These include the analgesics oxycodone (brand name OxyContin), oxymorphone, and nalbuphine; naloxone, which is used to treat opioid overdosage; naltrexone, which is useful in helping people with narcotic or alcohol addictions to remain drug free; and buprenorphine, which is useful in the treatment of opiate addiction because it prevents withdrawal symptoms.

Approximately 40% of the world's legal opium poppies are grown on the Australian island state of Tasmania. This is big business, and the industry has developed an active research program to study the biochemical pathway for the synthesis of morphine and codeine. That pathway begins with the amino acid tyrosine, the same amino acid that is the initial reactant for the synthesis of dopamine and epinephrine (Section 15.5).

$$\text{Tyrosine} \xrightarrow{\text{7 steps}} \text{Reticuline} \xrightarrow{\text{6 steps}} \text{Thebaine} \xrightarrow{\text{3 steps}} \text{Codeine} \xrightarrow{\text{1 step}} \text{Morphine}$$

Through seven chemical reactions, tyrosine is converted to reticuline. Another six reactions convert reticuline to thebaine. Three chemical modifications convert thebaine to codeine, which undergoes an ester hydrolysis to produce morphine.

(a) (b)

(a) Opium poppies are the source of morphine and codeine.
(b) The sap of an opium poppy is white. The sap of the no-morphine mutant poppy is red.

In the course of their studies, researchers produced a mutant strain of poppy that cannot make morphine or codeine, but does produce high levels of thebaine. "Norman," for "No Morphine," has been the most common strain of poppy grown in Tasmania since 1997. The mutation that causes Norman to produce high levels of thebaine is an alteration in one of the enzymes that catalyzes the conversion of thebaine to codeine. Since it can't be converted into codeine, large amounts of thebaine accumulate in the seed pods.

Synthetic opioids, such as naloxone and buprenorphine and the others mentioned above, have become much more important commercially than codeine and morphine. The economic value of Norman is that it produces large amounts of the starting material for the synthesis of these synthetic opioids, as well as the experimental synthesis of new drugs with unknown potential.

Consider the drug formulation Suboxone, a combination of buprenorphine and naloxone, approved for use in the United States in 2003 and produced by the British company Reckitt Benckiser. This combination of synthetic opiates calms the addict's craving for opiates and yet poses little risk of being abused.

Buprenorphine or "bupe" works by binding to the same receptors in the brain to which heroin binds; but the drug is only a partial heroin agonist, so there is no high. As a result,

Both *epinephrine* (adrenaline) and *norepinephrine* are involved in the "fight or flight" response. Epinephrine stimulates the breakdown of glycogen to produce glucose, which is then metabolized to provide energy for the body. Norepinephrine is involved with the central nervous system in the stimulation of other glands and the constriction of blood vessels. All of these responses prepare the body to meet the stressful situation.

Serotonin

Serotonin is synthesized from the amino acid tryptophan (Figure 15.8). A deficiency of serotonin has been associated with depression. It is also thought to be involved in bulimia and anorexia nervosa, as well as the carbohydrate-cravings that characterize seasonal affective disorder (SAD), a depression caused by a decrease in daylight during autumn and winter.

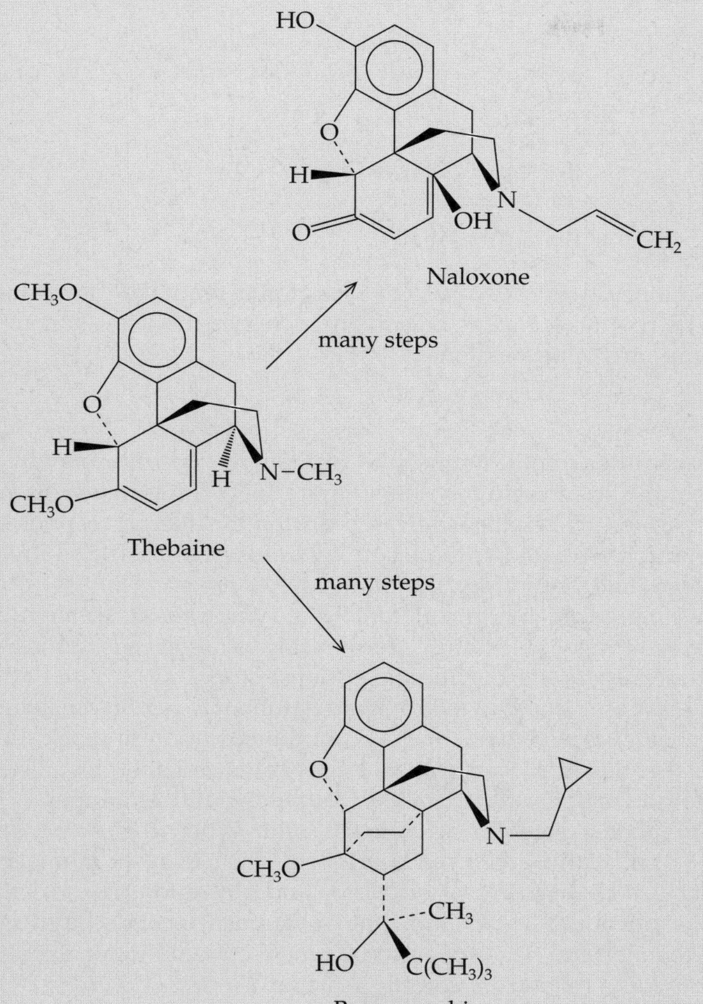

HO
O
H
O
OH
N
CH_2
Naloxone

CH_3O
O
H
CH_3O
H
N–CH_3
Thebaine

many steps

many steps

O
CH_3O
N
CH_3
HO
$C(CH_3)_3$
Buprenorphine

buprenorphine is much less addictive than drugs such as methadone, leaves patients much more clearheaded, and makes it easier for them to withdraw from the drug after a few months.

Because addicts don't get high from Suboxone, it is much less likely than methadone to be stolen and sold illegally. It has the added advantage that its effects are longer lasting than those of methadone; so addicts need only one pill every 2 or 3 days. In addition, because naloxone is an opioid antagonist, it causes instant withdrawal symptoms if an addict tries to inject Suboxone for a high. As a result, Suboxone can be given to addicts to be taken at home, rather than being dispensed only at clinics, as methadone is. With all of these features, Suboxone begins to sound like a miracle drug; but as with any addiction treatment, it will only help those who want to quit and are willing to work with counselors and support groups to resolve the underlying problems that caused the addiction in the first place.

For Further Understanding

- In 1998 researchers in England reported that some individuals who had eaten poppy seed rolls or cake tested positive in an opiate drug screen. Using Internet or other resources, investigate the "poppy seed defense" and suggest guidelines for opiate testing that would protect the innocent.
- OxyContin is the brand name for a formulation of oxycodone in a timed-release tablet. It is prescribed to provide up to 12 h of relief from chronic pain. Recently, OxyContin has become a commonly abused drug and is thought to be responsible for a number of deaths. Abusers crush the timed-release tablets and ingest or snort the drug, which results in a rapid and powerful high often compared to the euphoria experienced from taking heroin. Use the Internet or other resources to explain why abuse of this prescription medication has overshadowed heroin use in some areas. Consider ways to prevent such abuse.

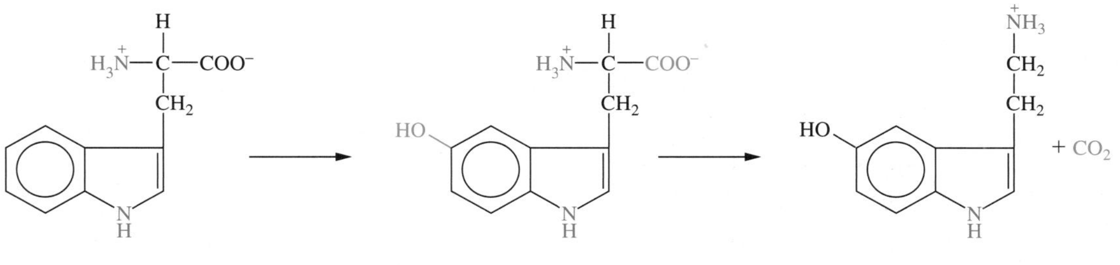

H
$H_3\overset{+}{N}$—C—COO^-
CH_2
N
H
Tryptophan

H
$H_3\overset{+}{N}$—C—COO^-
CH_2
HO
N
H

$\overset{+}{N}H_3$
CH_2
CH_2
HO
N
H
Serotonin
$+ CO_2$

Figure 15.8 Synthesis of serotonin from the amino acid tryptophan.

Serotonin also affects the perception of pain, thermoregulation, and sleep. There are those who believe that a glass of warm milk will help you fall asleep. We have all noticed how sleepy we become after that big Thanksgiving turkey dinner.

Histidine

$\rightarrow$

Histamine $+ CO_2$

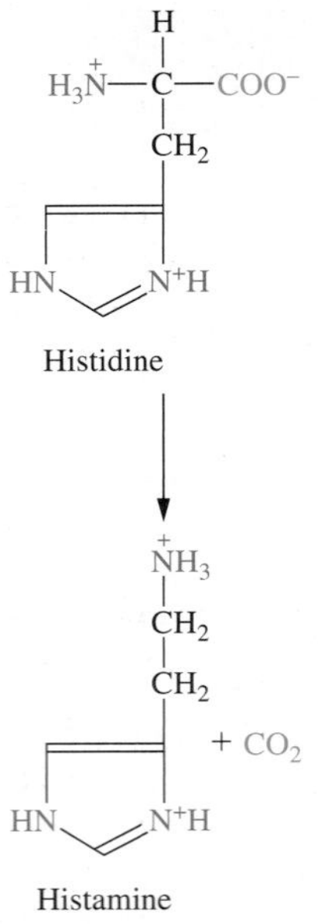

Figure 15.9 Synthesis of histamine from the amino acid histidine.

Both milk protein and turkey are exceptionally high in tryptophan, the precursor of serotonin!

Prozac (fluoxetine), one of the antidepressant drugs, is one of the most widely prescribed drugs in the United States.

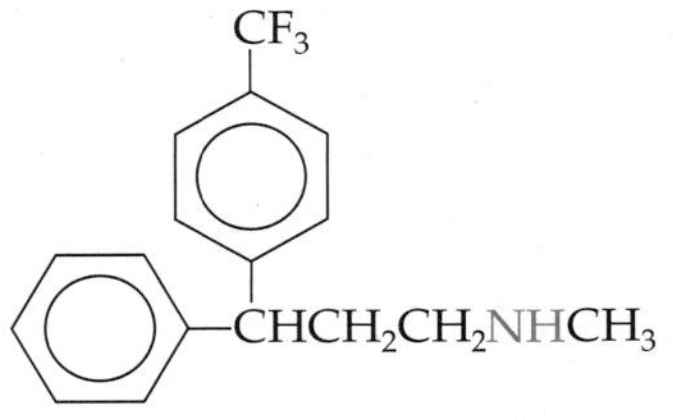

CF_3 / $CHCH_2CH_2NHCH_3$

Prozac (fluoxetine)

It is a member of a class of drugs called selective serotonin reuptake inhibitors (SSRI). By inhibiting the reuptake, Prozac effectively increases the level of serotonin, relieving the symptoms of depression.

Histamine

Histamine is a neurotransmitter that is synthesized in many tissues by removing the carboxyl group from the amino acid histidine (Figure 15.9). It has many, often annoying, physiological roles. Histamine is released during the allergic response. It causes the itchy skin rash associated with poison ivy or insect bites. It also promotes the red, watery eyes and respiratory symptoms of hay fever.

Many antihistamines are available to counteract the symptoms of histamine release. These act by competing with histamine for binding to target cells. If histamine cannot bind to these target cells, the allergic response stops.

Benadryl is an antihistamine that is available as an ointment to inhibit the itchy rash response to allergens. It is also available as an oral medication to block the symptoms of systemic allergies. You need only visit the "colds and allergies" aisle of your grocery store to find dozens of medications containing antihistamines.

Histamine also stimulates secretion of stomach acid. When this response occurs frequently, the result can be chronic heartburn. The reflux of stomach acid into the esophagus can result in erosion of tissue and ulceration. The excess stomach acid may also contribute to development of stomach ulcers. The drug marketed as Tagamet (cimetidine) has proven to be an effective inhibitor of this histamine response, providing relief from chronic heartburn.

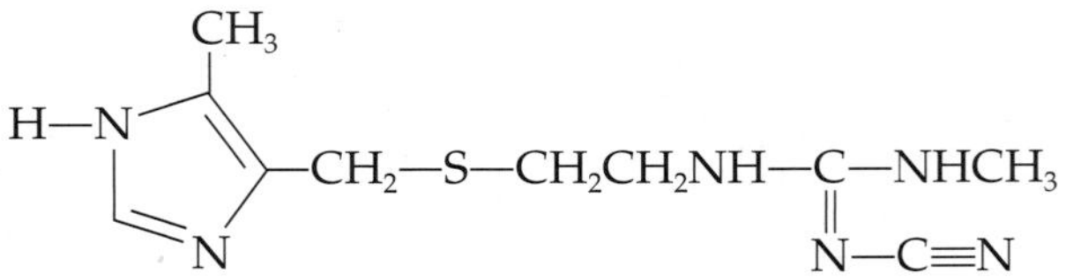

$-CH_2-S-CH_2CH_2NH-C(=N-C\equiv N)-NHCH_3$

Tagamet (cimetidine)

γ-Aminobutyric Acid and Glycine

γ-*Aminobutyric acid* (GABA) is produced by removal of a carboxyl group from the amino acid glutamate (Figure 15.10). Both GABA and the amino acid *glycine*

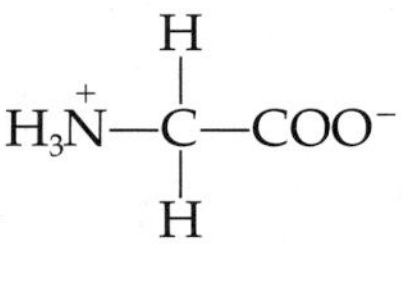

$H_3\overset{+}{N}-CH_2-COO^-$

Glycine

$H_3\overset{+}{N}-CH(COO^-)-CH_2-CH_2-COO^- \longrightarrow H_3\overset{+}{N}-CH_2-CH_2-CH_2-COO^- + CO_2$

Glutamate γ-Aminobutyric acid

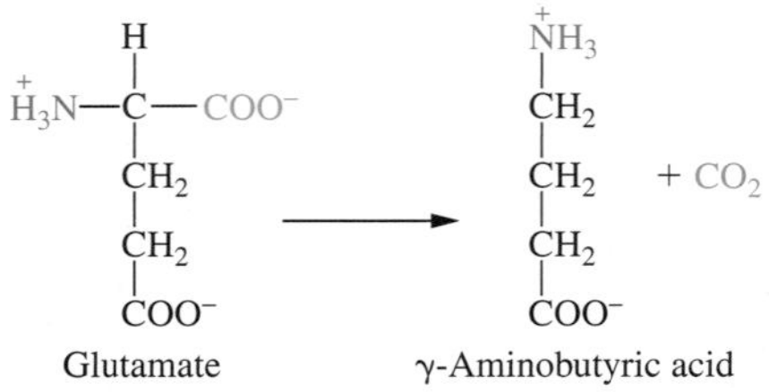

Figure 15.10 Synthesis of GABA from the amino acid glutamate.

are inhibitory neurotransmitters acting in the central nervous system. One class of tranquilizers, the benzodiazopines, relieves aggressive behavior and anxiety. These drugs have been shown to enhance the inhibitory activity of GABA, suggesting one of the roles played by this neurotransmitter.

Acetylcholine

Acetylcholine is a neurotransmitter that functions at the neuromuscular junction, carrying signals from the nerve to the muscle. It is synthesized in a reaction between the quaternary ammonium ion choline and acetyl coenzyme A (Figure 15.11). When it is released from the nerve cell, acetylcholine binds to receptors on the surface of muscle cells. This binding stimulates the muscle cell to contract. Acetylcholine is then broken down to choline and acetate ion.

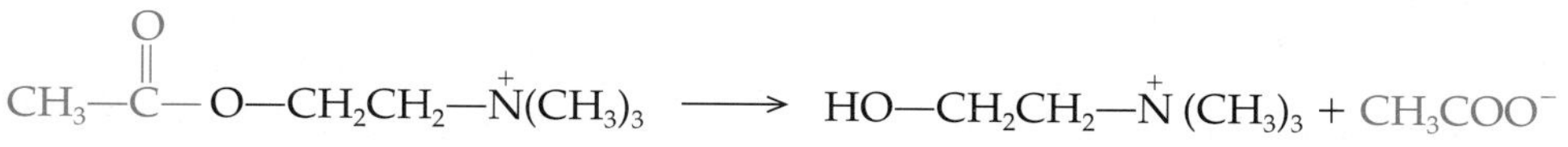

$$CH_3-\overset{\overset{O}{\|}}{C}-O-CH_2CH_2-\overset{+}{N}(CH_3)_3 \longrightarrow HO-CH_2CH_2-\overset{+}{N}(CH_3)_3 + CH_3COO^-$$

Acetylcholine — Choline — Acetate

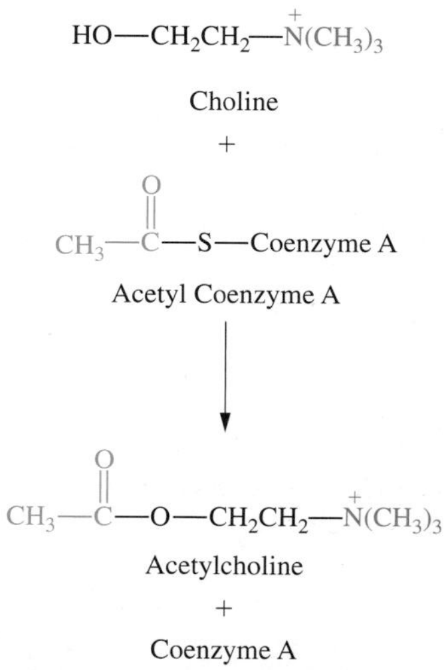

These molecules are essentially recycled. They are taken up by the nerve cell where they are used to resynthesize acetylcholine, which is stored in the nerve cell until it is needed.

Nicotine is an agonist of acetylcholine. An agonist is a compound that binds to the receptor for another compound and causes or enhances the biological response. By binding to acetylcholine receptors, nicotine causes the sense of alertness and calm many smokers experience. Nerve cells that respond to nicotine may also signal nerve cells that produce dopamine. As noted above, the dopamine may be responsible for the addictive property of nicotine.

Inhibitors of acetylcholinesterase, the enzyme that catalyzes the breakdown of acetylcholine, are used both as poisons and as drugs. Among the most important poisons of acetylcholinesterase are a class of compounds known as organophosphates. One of these is *diisopropyl fluorophosphate* (DIFP). This molecule forms a covalently bonded intermediate with the enzyme, irreversibly inhibiting its activity.

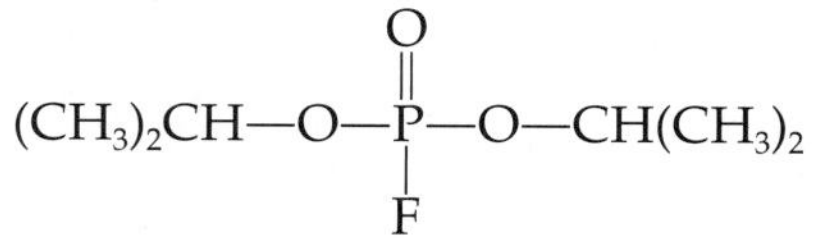

$$HO-CH_2CH_2-\overset{+}{N}(CH_3)_3$$

Choline

+

$$CH_3-\overset{\overset{O}{\|}}{C}-S-\text{Coenzyme A}$$

Acetyl Coenzyme A

$$\downarrow$$

$$CH_3-\overset{\overset{O}{\|}}{C}-O-CH_2CH_2-\overset{+}{N}(CH_3)_3$$

Acetylcholine

+

Coenzyme A

Figure 15.11 Synthesis of acetylcholine.

$$(CH_3)_2CH-O-\underset{\underset{F}{|}}{\overset{\overset{O}{\|}}{P}}-O-CH(CH_3)_2$$

Diisopropyl fluorophosphate (DIFP)

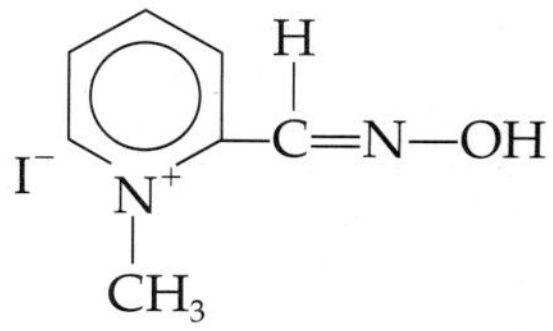

$$I^- \quad \text{(pyridinium ring, } N^+-CH_3\text{)}-\overset{\overset{H}{|}}{C}=N-OH$$

Pyridine aldoxime methiodide

Thus, it is unable to break down the acetylcholine, and nerve transmission continues, resulting in muscle spasm. Death may occur as a result of laryngeal spasm. Antidotes for poisoning by organophosphates, which include many insecticides and nerve gases, have been developed. The antidotes work by reversing the effects of the inhibitor. One of these antidotes is *pyridine aldoxime methiodide* (PAM). This molecule displaces the organophosphate group from the active site of the enzyme, alleviating the effects of the poison.

Succinylcholine is a competitive inhibitor of acetylcholine that is used as a muscle relaxant in surgical procedures. Competitive inhibition occurs because the two molecules have structures so similar that both can bind to the acetylcholine receptor (compare the structures on the next page). When administered to a patient, there is more succinylcholine than acetylcholine in the synapse, and thus more succinylcholine binding to the receptor. Because it cannot stimulate muscle contraction, succinylcholine causes muscles to relax. Normal muscle contraction resumes when the drug is no longer administered.

$$CH_3\overset{O}{\overset{\|}{C}}-O-CH_2CH_2-\overset{+}{N}(CH_3)_3$$

Acetylcholine

$$(CH_3)_3\overset{+}{N}-CH_2CH_2-O-\overset{O}{\overset{\|}{C}}CH_2CH_2\overset{O}{\overset{\|}{C}}-O-CH_2CH_2-\overset{+}{N}(CH_3)_3$$

Succinylcholine

Acetylcholine nerve transmission is discussed in further detail in Chemistry at the Crime Scene: Enzymes, Nerve Agents, and Poisoning in Chapter 19.

Nitric Oxide and Glutamate

Nitric oxide (NO) is an amazing little molecule that has been shown to have many physiological functions. Among these is its ability to act as a neurotransmitter. NO is synthesized in many areas of the brain from the amino acid arginine. Research has suggested that NO works in conjunction with another neurotransmitter, the amino acid glutamate (see the structure of glutamate in Figure 15.10). Glutamate released from one nerve cell binds to receptors on its target cell. This triggers the target cell to produce NO, which then diffuses back to the original nerve cell. The NO signals the cell to release more glutamate, thus stimulating this neural pathway even further. This is a kind of positive feedback loop. It is thought that this NO-glutamate mechanism is involved in learning and the formation of memories.

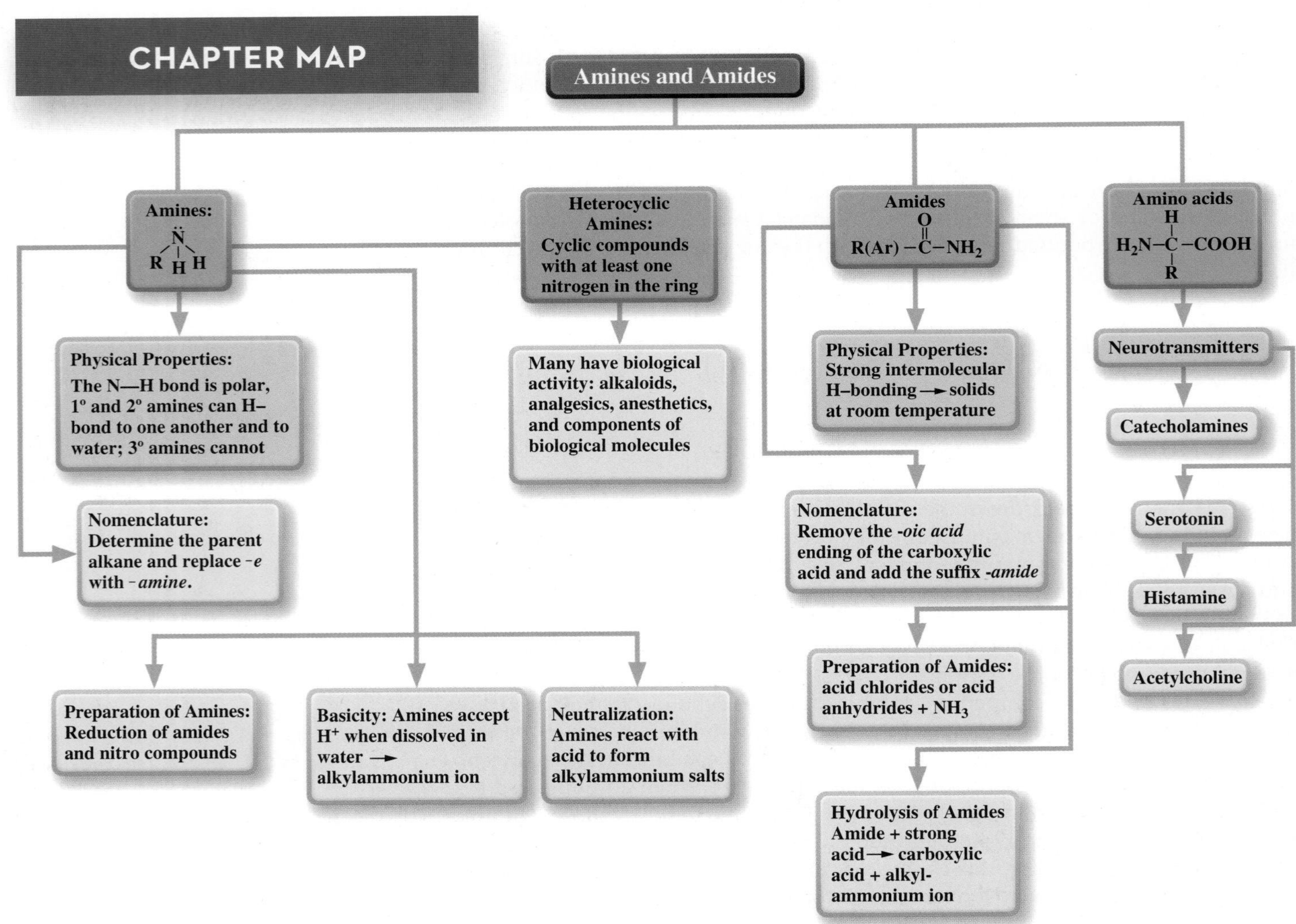

SUMMARY OF REACTIONS

Preparation of Amines

$$\text{C}_6\text{H}_5\text{NO}_2 \xrightarrow{[H]} \text{C}_6\text{H}_5\text{NH}_2$$

A nitro compound → An aromatic primary amine

$$R^1{-}\overset{O}{\overset{\|}{C}}{-}NR^2R^3 \xrightarrow{[H]} R^1CH_2NR^2R^3$$

Amide → Amine

Basicity of Amines

$$R{-}NH_2 + H{-}OH \rightleftharpoons R{-}NH_3^+ + OH^-$$

Amine, Water, Alkylammonium ion, Hydroxide ion

Neutralization of Amines

$$R{-}NH_2 + HCl \longrightarrow R{-}NH_3^+\,Cl^-$$

Amine, Acid, Alkylammonium salt

Preparation of Amides

$$R{-}\overset{O}{\overset{\|}{C}}{-}Cl + 2NH_3 \longrightarrow R{-}\overset{O}{\overset{\|}{C}}{-}NH_2 + \overset{+}{N}H_4Cl^-$$

Acid chloride, Ammonia or amine → Amide, Ammonium chloride or alkylammonium chloride

$$R{-}\overset{O}{\overset{\|}{C}}{-}O{-}\overset{O}{\overset{\|}{C}}{-}R + 2NH_3 \longrightarrow R{-}\overset{O}{\overset{\|}{C}}{-}NH_2 + R{-}\overset{O}{\overset{\|}{C}}{-}O^-\overset{+}{N}H_4$$

Acid anhydride, Ammonia or amine → Amide, Carboxylic acid salt

Hydrolysis of Amides

$$R{-}\overset{O}{\overset{\|}{C}}{-}NH{-}R^1 + H_3O^+ \longrightarrow R{-}\overset{O}{\overset{\|}{C}}{-}OH + R^1{-}\overset{+}{N}H_3$$

Amide, Strong acid → Carboxylic acid, Alkylammonium ion

$$R{-}\overset{O}{\overset{\|}{C}}{-}NH{-}R^1 + NaOH \longrightarrow R{-}\overset{O}{\overset{\|}{C}}{-}O^-Na^+ + R^1{-}NH_2$$

Amide, Strong base → Carboxylic acid salt, Amine or ammonia

SUMMARY

15.1 Amines

- **Amines** are a family of organic compounds that contain an amino group or substituted amino group.
- A **primary amine** has the general formula RNH_2; a **secondary amine** has the general formula R_2NH; and a **tertiary amine** has the general formula R_3N.
- In the systematic nomenclature system, amines are named as *alkanamines.*
- In the common system, they are named as *alkylamines.*
- Amines behave as weak bases, forming **alkylammonium ions** in water and alkylammonium salts when they react with acids.
- **Quaternary ammonium salts** are ammonium salts that have four organic groups bonded to the nitrogen atom.

15.2 Heterocyclic Amines

- **Heterocyclic amines** are cyclic compounds having at least one nitrogen atom in the ring structure.
- **Alkaloids** are natural plant products that contain at least one heterocyclic ring.
- Many alkaloids have powerful biological effects.
- Cocaine is an example of an **anesthetic,** which is a drug that causes a lack of sensation in any part of the body or which causes unconsciousness.
- Morphine is a strong **analgesic,** a drug that acts as a painkiller.

15.3 Amides

- **Amides** are formed in a reaction between a carboxylic acid derivative and an amine (or ammonia).
- The **amide bond** is the bond between the carbonyl carbon of the **acyl group** and the nitrogen of the amine.
- In the IUPAC Nomenclature System, amides are named by replacing the *-oic acid* ending of the carboxylic acid with the *-amide* ending.
- In the common system of nomenclature, the *-ic acid* ending of the carboxylic acid is replaced by the *-amide* ending.
- Hydrolysis of an amide produces a carboxylic acid and an amine (or ammonia).

15.4 A Preview of Amino Acids, Proteins, and Protein Synthesis

- Proteins are polymers of **amino acids** joined to one another by amide bonds called **peptide bonds.**
- During protein synthesis, the **aminoacyl group** of one amino acid is transferred from a carrier molecule called **transfer RNA (tRNA)** to the amino group nitrogen of another amino acid.

15.5 Neurotransmitters

- **Neurotransmitters** are chemicals that carry messages, or signals, from a nerve cell to a target cell, which may be another nerve cell or a muscle cell.
- Neurotransmitters may be inhibitory or excitatory and all are nitrogen-containing compounds.
- The catecholamines include dopamine, norepinephrine, and epinephrine.
    - Too little dopamine results in Parkinson's disease. Too much is associated with schizophrenia.
    - Dopamine is also associated with addictive behavior.
- A deficiency of serotonin is associated with depression and eating disorders. Serotonin is involved in pain perception, regulation of body temperature, and sleep.
- Histamine contributes to allergy symptoms.
    - Antihistamines block histamine and provide relief from allergies.
- γ-Aminobutyric acid (GABA) and glycine are inhibitory neurotransmitters.
    - It is believed that GABA is involved in control of aggressive behavior.
- Acetylcholine is a neurotransmitter that functions at the neuromuscular junction, carrying signals from the nerve to the muscle.
- Nitric oxide and glutamate function in a positive feedback loop that is thought to be involved in learning and the formation of memories.

ANSWERS TO PRACTICE PROBLEMS

15.1 a. Tertiary amine
b. Primary amine
c. Secondary amine

15.2 a. Methanol would have a higher boiling point than methylamine. The intermolecular hydrogen bonds between alcohol molecules will be stronger than those between two amines because oxygen is more electronegative than nitrogen.
b. Water would have a higher boiling point than dimethylamine. The intermolecular hydrogen bonds between water molecules will be stronger than those between two amines because oxygen is more electronegative than nitrogen.
c. Ethylamine will have a higher boiling point than methylamine because it has a higher molar mass.
d. Propylamine will have a higher boiling point than butane because propylamine molecules can form intermolecular hydrogen bonds, and the nonpolar butane cannot do so.

15.3 a. *N*-Ethyl-*N*-methyl-1-propanamine
b. 3-Hexanamine
c. *N,N*-Diethyl-1-propanamine

15.4 a. IUPAC name: *N*-Pentylpentanamide
Common name: *N*-Pentylvaleramide
b. IUPAC name: *N*-Butylhexanamide
Common name: *N*-Butylcaproamide

QUESTIONS AND PROBLEMS

Amines

Foundations

15.11 Compare the boiling points of amines, alkanes, and alcohols of the same molar mass. Explain these differences in boiling points.

15.12 Describe the water solubility of amines in relation to their carbon chain length.

15.13 Describe the systematic rules for naming amines.

15.14 How are the common names of amines derived?

15.15 Describe the physiological effects of amphetamines.

15.16 Define the terms *analgesic* and *anesthetic* and list some amines that have these activities.

Applications

15.17 For each pair of compounds predict which would have greater solubility in water. Explain your reasoning.
- **a.** Hexane or 1-pentanamine
- **b.** Cyclopentane or 2-butanamine

15.18 For each pair of compounds predict which would have the higher boiling point. Explain your reasoning.
- **a.** Propanamine or propanol
- **b.** Propane or ethanamine
- **c.** Methanamine or water
- **d.** Propylmethylamine or pentane

15.19 Explain why a tertiary amine such as triethylamine has a significantly lower boiling point than its primary amine isomer, 1-hexanamine.

15.20 Draw a diagram to illustrate your answer to Question 15.19.

15.21 Use systematic nomenclature to name each of the following amines:

a. $CH_3CH_2CHNH_2$ (with CH_3 on the CH)

b. $CH_3CH_2CH_2CHCH_2CH_3$ (with NH_2 on the CH)

c. cyclopentane ring–NH_2

d. $(CH_3)_3C{-}NH_2$

15.22 Use systematic and common nomenclature to name each of the following amines:

a. $CH_3CH_2CH_2CH_2CH_2CH_2CH_2CH_2NH_2$

b. Cl–benzene ring–NH_2 (para)

c. $CH_3CHCH_2CH_3$ (with NH_2 on the CH)

d. $CH_3NCH_2CH_3$ (with CH_3 on the N)

15.23 Draw the condensed formula and line formula of each of the following compounds:
- **a.** Diethylamine
- **b.** Butylamine
- **c.** 3-Decanamine
- **d.** 3-Bromo-2-pentanamine
- **e.** Triphenylamine

15.24 Draw the condensed formula and line formula of each of the following compounds:
- **a.** *N,N*-Dipropylaniline
- **b.** Cyclohexanamine
- **c.** 2-Bromocyclopentanamine
- **d.** Tetraethylammonium iodide
- **e.** 3-Bromobenzenamine

15.25 Draw the condensed formula for each of the following compounds:
- **a.** 3-Hexanamine
- **b.** Hexylpentylamine
- **c.** Cyclobutanamine
- **d.** 2-Methylcyclopentanamine
- **e.** Triethylammonium chloride

15.26 Draw the condensed formula for each of the following compounds:
- **a.** 2,3-Dibromoaniline
- **b.** 2-Octanamine
- **c.** 2-Chloro-2-pentanamine
- **d.** *N,N*-Diethylpentanamine
- **e.** Diisopropylamine

15.27 Draw condensed formulas for the eight isomeric amines that have the molecular formula $C_4H_{11}N$. Name each of the isomers using the systematic names and determine whether each isomer is a 1°, 2°, or 3° amine.

15.28 Draw all of the isomeric amines of molecular formula C_3H_9N. Name each of the isomers using the systematic names and determine whether each isomer is a primary, secondary, or tertiary amine.

15.29 Classify each of the following amines as 1°, 2°, or 3°:
- **a.** Cyclohexanamine
- **b.** Dibutylamine
- **c.** 2-Methyl-2-heptanamine
- **d.** Tripentylamine

15.30 Classify each of the following amines as primary, secondary, or tertiary:
- **a.** Benzenamine
- **b.** *N*-Ethyl-2-pentanamine
- **c.** Ethylmethylamine
- **d.** Tripropylamine
- **e.** *m*-Chloroaniline

15.31 Write an equation to show a reaction that would produce each of the following products:

a. NH_2 (top) on benzene ring, CH_3 (bottom)

b. NH_2 on benzene ring, OH (ortho)

c. NH_2 on benzene ring

d. NH_2–CH_2–cyclohexane ring

15.32 Write an equation to show a reaction that would produce each of the following amines:
- **a.** 1-Pentanamine
- **b.** *N,N*-Dimethylethanamine
- **c.** *N*-Ethylpropanamine

15.33 Complete each of the following equations by supplying the missing reactant or product indicated by a question mark:

a. CH_3NH (with CH_3 on N) $+\ ? \longrightarrow CH_3N^+H$ (with CH_3 and H on N) $+\ OH^-$

b. CH_3CH_2N (with CH_3 and CH_2CH_3 on N) $+\ ? \longrightarrow CH_3CH_2N^+H\ Br^-$ (with CH_3 and CH_2CH_3 on N)

c. $CH_3CH_2CH_2NH_2 + H_2O \longrightarrow\ ? + OH^-$

d. CH_3CH_2NH (with CH_2CH_3 on N) $+\ HCl \longrightarrow\ ?$

15.34 Complete each of the following equations by supplying the missing reactant or product indicated by a question mark:

a. $CH_3CH_2NH_2 + H_2O \longrightarrow ? + OH^-$

b. $? + HCl \longrightarrow CH_3CH_2CH_2\underset{\underset{H}{|}}{\overset{\overset{CH_2CH_2CH_3}{|}}{N^+}}H\ Cl^-$

c. $CH_3\underset{\underset{CH_3}{|}}{C}H\overset{\overset{CH_3}{|}}{N}H + H_2O \longrightarrow ? + ?$

d. $NH_3 + HBr \longrightarrow ?$

15.35 Using condensed formulas, write an equation for the reaction that would produce each of the following amines:
a. Hexanamine
b. *N*-Methylbutanamine
c. *N,N*-Dimethylpropanamine

15.36 Write an equation for the reaction that would produce each of the following amines:
a. Octanamine
b. *N*-Methylpropanamine
c. *N,N*-Diethylpentanamine

15.37 Briefly explain why the lower-molar-mass amines (fewer than five carbons) exhibit appreciable solubility in water.

15.38 Why is the salt of an amine appreciably more soluble in water than the amine from which it was formed?

15.39 Most drugs containing amine groups are not administered as the amine but rather as the ammonium salt. Can you suggest a reason why?

15.40 Why does aspirin upset the stomach, whereas acetaminophen (Tylenol) does not?

15.41 Putrescine and cadaverine are two odoriferous amines that are produced by decaying flesh. Putrescine is 1,4-butanediamine, and cadaverine is 1,5-pentanediamine. Draw the structures of these two compounds.

15.42 How would you quickly convert an alkylammonium salt into a water-insoluble amine? Explain the rationale for your answer.

Heterocyclic Amines

15.43 Indole and pyridine rings are found in alkaloids.
a. Sketch each ring.
b. Name one compound containing each of the ring structures and indicate its use.

15.44 What is an alkaloid?

15.45 List some heterocyclic amines that are used in medicine.

15.46 Distinguish between the terms *analgesic* and *anesthetic.*

Amides

Foundations

15.47 Why do amides have very high boiling points?

15.48 Describe the water solubility of amides in relation to their carbon chain length.

15.49 Explain the IUPAC nomenclature rules for naming amides.

15.50 How are the common names of amides derived?

15.51 Describe the physiological effects of barbiturates.

15.52 Why is acetaminophen often recommended in place of aspirin?

Applications

15.53 Use the IUPAC and common systems of nomenclature to name the following amides:

a. $CH_3CH_2\overset{\overset{O}{\|}}{C}NH_2$

b. $CH_3CH_2CH_2CH_2\overset{\overset{O}{\|}}{C}NH_2$

c. $CH_3\overset{\overset{O}{\|}}{C}N(CH_3)_2$

15.54 Use the IUPAC Nomenclature System to name each of the following amides:

a. $CH_3CH_2\underset{\underset{Br}{|}}{C}HCH_2\overset{\overset{O}{\|}}{C}NH_2$

b. $Br\text{-}C_6H_4\text{-}\overset{\overset{O}{\|}}{C}NH_2$ (Br in the *meta* position of the benzene ring)

c. $CH_3\underset{\underset{CH_3}{|}}{C}H\overset{\overset{O}{\|}}{C}NH_2$

15.55 Draw the condensed formula for each of the following amides:
a. Propanamide
b. *N,N*-Diethylbutanamide
c. 2,3-Diethylpentanamide
d. *N*-Methylhexanamide

15.56 Draw the condensed formula for each of the following amides:
a. *N*-Propylbutanamide
b. *N*-Butyloctanamide
c. *N*-Methylpropanamide
d. *N*-Isopropylhexanamide

15.57 Draw the condensed formula and line formula of each of the following amides:
a. Ethanamide
b. *N*-Methylpropanamide
c. *N,N*-Diethylbenzenamide
d. 3-Bromo-4-methylhexanamide
e. *N,N*-Dimethylacetamide

15.58 Draw the condensed formula and line formula of each of the following amides:
a. Acetamide
b. 4-Methylpentanamide
c. *N,N*-Dimethylpropanamide
d. Formamide
e. *N*-Ethylpropionamide

15.59 The active ingredient in many insect repellents is *N,N*-diethyl-*m*-toluamide (DEET). Draw the structure of this compound. Which carboxylic acid and amine would be released by hydrolysis of this compound?

15.60 When an acid anhydride and an amine are combined, an amide is formed. This approach may be used to synthesize acetaminophen, the active ingredient in Tylenol. Complete the following equation to determine the structure of acetaminophen:

$$CH_3\overset{\overset{O}{\|}}{C}-O-\overset{\overset{O}{\|}}{C}CH_3 + H_2N-C_6H_4-OH \longrightarrow ? + CH_3COOH$$

15.61 Explain why amides are neutral in the acid-base sense.

15.62 The amide bond is stabilized by resonance. Draw the contributing resonance forms of the amide bond.

15.63 Lidocaine is often used as a local anesthetic. For medicinal purposes it is often used in the form of its hydrochloride salt because the salt is water-soluble. In the structure of lidocaine hydrochloride shown, locate the amide functional group.

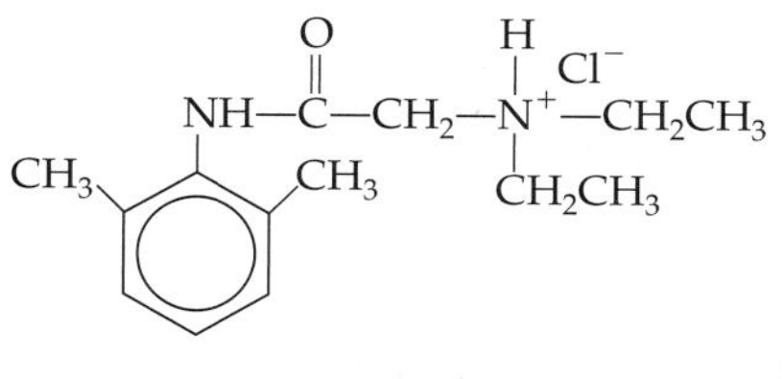

$$\text{2,6-}(CH_3)_2C_6H_3\text{—}NH\text{—}\overset{O}{\overset{\|}{C}}\text{—}CH_2\text{—}\overset{H}{\underset{CH_2CH_3}{N^+}}\text{—}CH_2CH_3 \quad Cl^-$$

Lidocaine hydrochloride

15.64 Locate the amine functional group in the structure of lidocaine. Is lidocaine a primary, secondary, or tertiary amine?

15.65 The antibiotic penicillin BT contains functional groups discussed in this chapter. In the structure of penicillin BT shown, locate and name as many functional groups as you can.

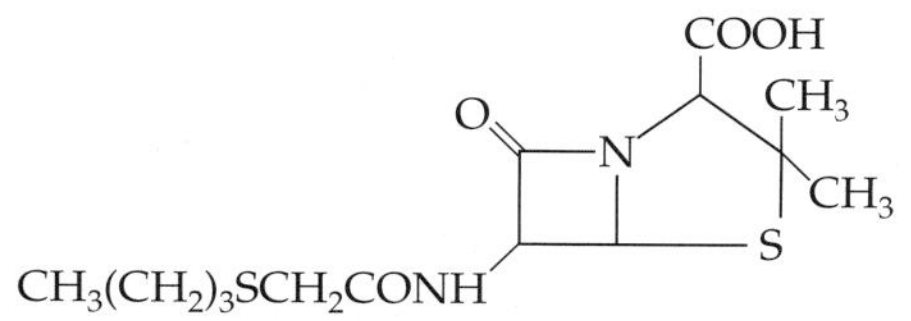

$CH_3(CH_2)_3SCH_2CONH$ (β-lactam ring with C=O and N, fused to thiazolidine ring bearing COOH, CH_3, CH_3, S)

Penicillin BT

15.66 The structure of saccharin, an artificial sweetener, is shown. Circle the amide group.

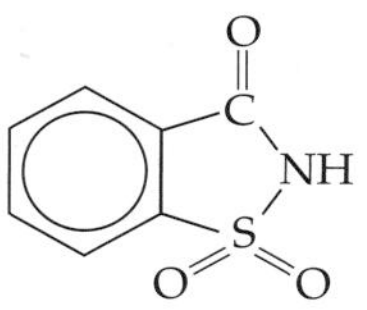

Saccharin

15.67 Complete each of the following equations by supplying the missing reactant(s) or product(s) indicated by a question mark. Provide the systematic name for all the reactants and products.

a. 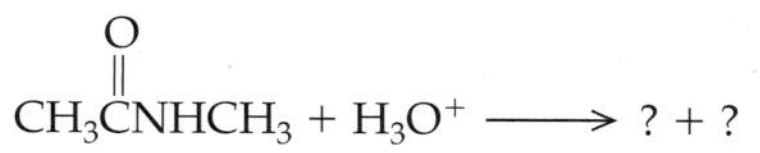 $CH_3\overset{O}{\overset{\|}{C}}NHCH_3 + H_3O^+ \longrightarrow ? + ?$

b. $? + H_3O^+ \longrightarrow CH_3CH_2CH_2\overset{O}{\overset{\|}{C}}\text{—}OH + CH_3\overset{+}{N}H_3$

c. $CH_3\underset{CH_3}{\underset{|}{C}}HCH_2\overset{O}{\overset{\|}{C}}NHCH_2CH_3 + ? \longrightarrow CH_3\underset{CH_3}{\underset{|}{C}}HCH_2\overset{O}{\overset{\|}{C}}\text{—}OH + ?$

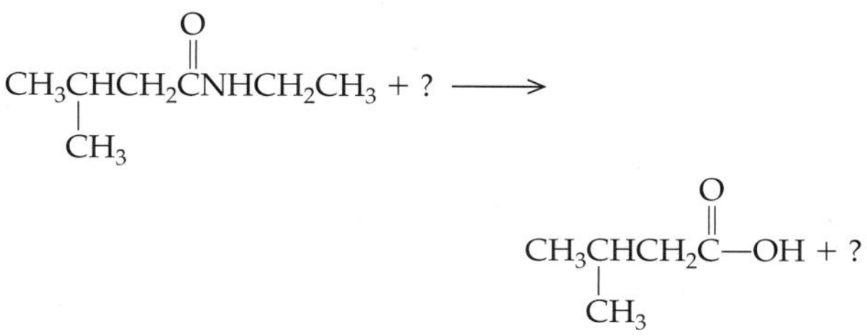

15.68 Complete each of the following by supplying the missing reagents. Draw the structures of each of the reactants and products.

a. *N*-Methylpropanamide + ? $\longrightarrow$ propanoic acid + ?

b. *N*,*N*-Dimethylacetamide + strong acid $\longrightarrow$? + ?

c. Formamide + strong acid $\longrightarrow$? + ?

15.69 Complete each of the following equations by supplying the missing reactant(s) or product(s) indicated by a question mark.

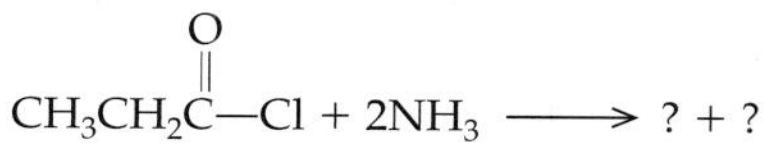

a. 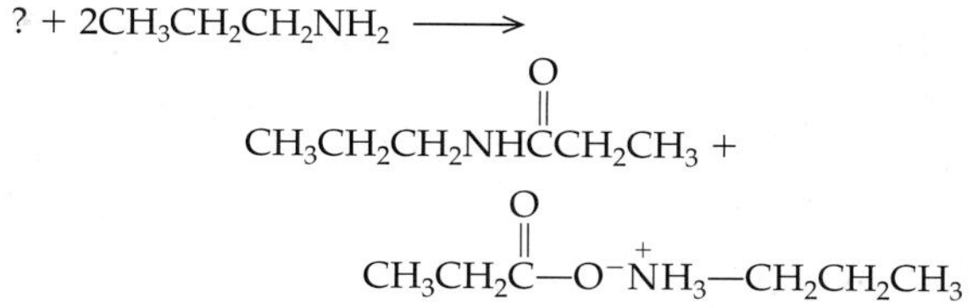 $? + 2CH_3CH_2CH_2NH_2 \longrightarrow CH_3CH_2CH_2NH\overset{O}{\overset{\|}{C}}CH_2CH_3 + CH_3CH_2\overset{O}{\overset{\|}{C}}\text{—}O^-\overset{+}{N}H_3\text{—}CH_2CH_2CH_3$

b. $CH_3CH_2\overset{O}{\overset{\|}{C}}\text{—}Cl + 2NH_3 \longrightarrow ? + ?$

c. $? + ? \longrightarrow CH_3CH_2CH_2\overset{O}{\overset{\|}{C}}NHCH_2CH_3 + CH_3CH_2\text{—}\overset{+}{N}H_3Cl^-$

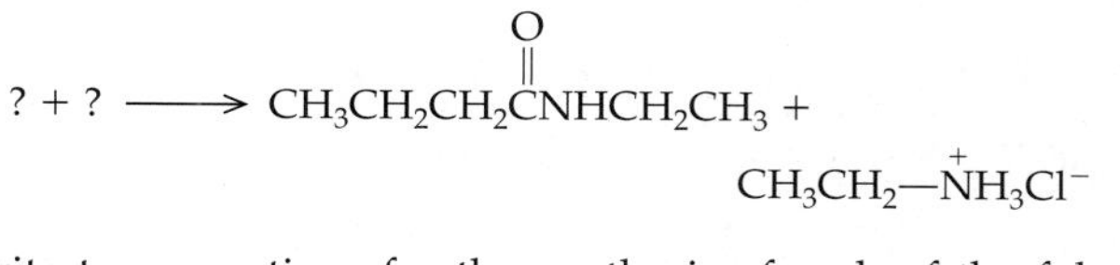

15.70 Write two equations for the synthesis of each of the following amides. In one equation use an acid chloride as a reactant. In the second equation use an acid anhydride.

a. Ethanamide

b. *N*-Propylpentanamide

c. Propionamide

A Preview of Amino Acids, Proteins, and Protein Synthesis

Foundations

15.71 Draw the general structure of an amino acid.

15.72 What is the name of the amide bond formed between two amino acids?

Applications

15.73 The amino acid glycine has a hydrogen atom as its R group, and the amino acid alanine has a methyl group. Draw these two amino acids.

15.74 Draw a dipeptide composed of glycine and alanine. Begin by drawing glycine with its amino group on the left. Circle the amide bond.

15.75 Draw the amino acid alanine (see Question 15.73). Place a star by the chiral carbon. (*Hint:* A chiral carbon is one that is bonded to four different groups or atoms.)

15.76 Does glycine have a chiral carbon? Explain your reasoning.

15.77 Describe acyl group transfer.

15.78 Describe the relationship between acyl group transfer and the process of protein synthesis.

Neurotransmitter

Foundations

15.79 Define the term *neurotransmitter.*

15.80 What are the two general classes of neurotransmitters? What distinguishes them from one another?

Applications

15.81 a. What symptoms result from a deficiency of dopamine?

b. What is the name of this condition?

c. What symptoms result from an excess of dopamine?

15.82 What is the starting material in the synthesis of dopamine, epinephrine, and norepinephrine?

15.83 Explain the connection between addictive behavior and dopamine.

15.84 Why is L-dopa used to treat Parkinson's disease rather than dopamine?

15.85 What is the function of epinephrine?

15.86 What is the function of norepinephrine?

15.87 What is the starting material from which serotonin is made?

15.88 What symptoms are associated with a deficiency of serotonin?

15.89 What physiological processes are affected by serotonin?

15.90 How does Prozac relieve the symptoms of depression?

15.91 What are the physiological roles of histamine?

15.92 How do antihistamines function to control the allergic response?

15.93 What type of neurotransmitters are γ-aminobutyric acid and glycine?

15.94 Explain the evidence for a relationship between γ-aminobutyric acid and aggressive behavior.

15.95 Explain the function of acetylcholine at the neuromuscular junction.

15.96 Explain why organophosphates are considered to be poisons.

15.97 How does pyridine aldoxime methiodide function as an antidote for organophosphate poisoning?

15.98 Explain the mechanism by which glutamate and NO may function to promote development of memories and learning.

CRITICAL THINKING PROBLEMS

1. Histamine is made and stored in blood cells called *mast cells.* Mast cells are involved in the allergic response. Release of histamine in response to an allergen causes dilation of capillaries. This, in turn, allows fluid to leak out of the capillary, resulting in local swelling. It also causes an increase in the volume of the vascular system. If this increase is great enough, a severe drop in blood pressure may cause shock. Histamine is produced by decarboxylation (removal of the carboxylate group as CO_2) of the amino acid histidine shown below. Draw the structure of histamine.

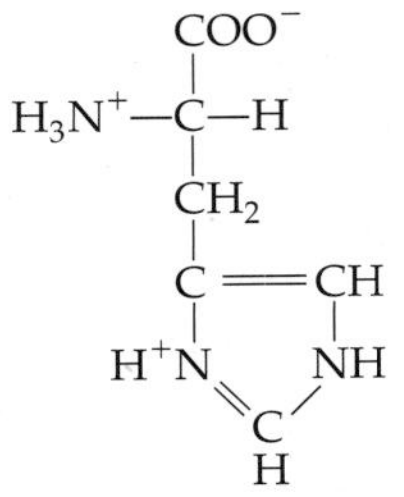

COO^-
$H_3N^+—C—H$
CH_2
$C═CH$
H^+N NH
C
H

2. Carnitine tablets are sold in health food stores. It is claimed that carnitine will enhance the breakdown of body fat. Carnitine is a tertiary amine found in mitochondria, cell organelles in which food molecules are completely oxidized and ATP is produced. Carnitine is involved in transporting the acyl groups of fatty acids from the cytoplasm into the mitochondria. The fatty acyl group is transferred from a fatty acyl CoA molecule and esterified to carnitine. Inside the mitochondria the reaction is reversed and the fatty acid is completely oxidized. The structure of carnitine is shown here:

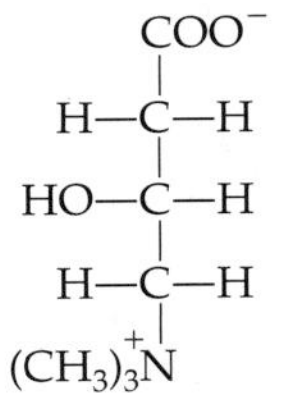

COO^-
$H—C—H$
$HO—C—H$
$H—C—H$
$(CH_3)_3\overset{+}{N}$

Draw the acyl carnitine molecule that is formed by esterification of palmitic acid with carnitine.

3. The amino acid proline has a structure that is unusual among amino acids. Compare the general structure of an amino acid with that of proline, shown here:

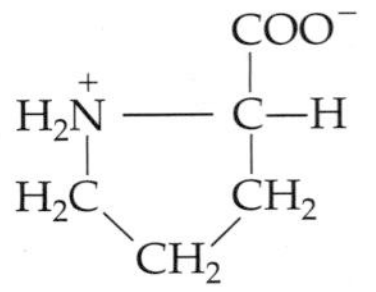

COO^-
$H_2\overset{+}{N}$ — $C—H$
H_2C CH_2
CH_2

What is the major difference between proline and the other amino acids? Draw the structure of a dipeptide in which the amino group of proline forms a peptide bond with the carboxyl group of alanine.

4. Bulletproof vests are made of the polymer called Kevlar. It is produced by the copolymerization of the following two monomers:

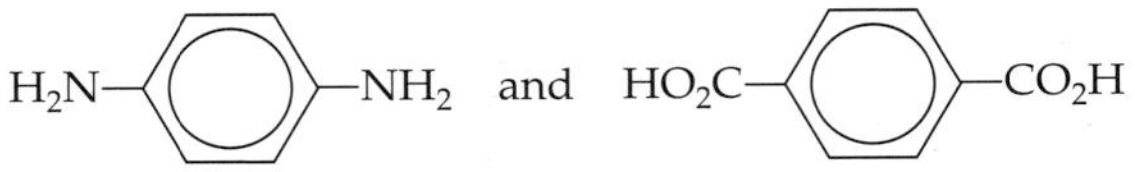

$H_2N—C_6H_4—NH_2$ and $HO_2C—C_6H_4—CO_2H$

Draw the structure of a portion of Kevlar polymer.

16

Carbohydrates

LEARNING GOALS

1. Explain the difference between complex and simple carbohydrates and know the amounts of each recommended in the daily diet.
2. Apply the systems of classifying and naming monosaccharides according to the functional group and number of carbons in the chain.
3. Determine whether a molecule has a chiral center.
4. Explain stereoisomerism.
5. Identify monosaccharides as either D- or L-.
6. Draw and name the common monosaccharides using structural formulas.
7. Given the linear structure of a monosaccharide, draw the Haworth projection of its α- and β-cyclic forms and vice versa.
8. By inspection of the structure, predict whether a sugar is a reducing or a nonreducing sugar.
9. Discuss the use of the Benedict's reagent to measure the level of glucose in urine.
10. Draw and name the common disaccharides and discuss their significance in biological systems.
11. Describe the difference between galactosemia and lactose intolerance.
12. Discuss the structural, chemical, and biochemical properties of starch, glycogen, and cellulose.

Would "looking-glass milk" be nutritious?

OUTLINE

Introduction 548
16.1 Types of Carbohydrates 548
16.2 Monosaccharides 550
A Medical Perspective: Tooth Decay and Simple Sugars 551
16.3 Stereoisomers and Stereochemistry 552
16.4 Biologically Important Monosaccharides 559
Kitchen Chemistry: The Chemistry of Caramels 566
16.5 Biologically Important Disaccharides 567
Chemistry at the Crime Scene: Blood Group Antigens 570
16.6 Polysaccharides 571
A Medical Perspective: Monosaccharide Derivatives and Heteropolysaccharides of Medical Interest 573

INTRODUCTION

In his children's story *Through the Looking Glass*, Lewis Carroll's heroine Alice wonders whether "looking-glass milk" would be good to drink. As we will see in this chapter, many biological molecules, such as the sugars, exist as two stereoisomers, *enantiomers*, that are mirror images of one another. Because two mirror-image forms occur, it is rather remarkable that in our bodies, and in most of the biological world, only one of the two is found. For instance, the common sugars are members of the D-family, whereas all the common amino acids that make up our proteins are members of the L-family. It is not too surprising, then, that the enzymes in our bodies that break down the sugars and proteins we eat are *stereospecific*, that is, they recognize only one mirror-image isomer. Knowing this, we can make an educated guess that "looking-glass milk" could not be digested by our enzymes and therefore would not be a good source of food for us. It is even possible that it might be toxic to us!

Pharmaceutical chemists are becoming more and more concerned with the stereochemical purity of the drugs that we take. Consider a few examples. In 1960, the drug thalidomide was commonly prescribed in Europe as a sedative. However, during that year, hundreds of women who took thalidomide during pregnancy gave birth to babies with severe birth defects. Thalidomide, it turned out, was a mixture of two enantiomers. One is a sedative; the other is a teratogen, a chemical that causes birth defects.

One of the common side effects of taking antihistamines for colds or allergies is drowsiness. Again, this is the result of the fact that antihistamines are mixtures of enantiomers. One causes drowsiness; the other is a good decongestant.

One enantiomer of the compound carvone is associated with the smell of spearmint; the other produces the aroma of caraway seeds or dill. One mirror-image form of limonene smells like lemons; the other has the aroma of oranges.

The pain reliever ibuprofen is currently sold as a mixture of enantiomers, but one is a much more effective analgesic than the other.

Taste, smell, and the biological effects of drugs in the body all depend on the stereochemical form of compounds and their interactions with cellular enzymes or receptors. As a result, chemists are actively working to devise methods of separating the isomers in pure form. Alternatively, methods of conducting stereospecific syntheses that produce only one stereoisomer are being sought. By preparing pure stereoisomers, the biological activity of a compound can be much more carefully controlled. This will lead to safer medications.

In this chapter we will begin our study of stereochemistry, the spatial arrangement of atoms in molecules, with the carbohydrates. Later, we will examine the stereochemistry of the amino acids that make up our proteins and consider the stereochemical specificity of the metabolic reactions that are essential to life.

16.1 Types of Carbohydrates

LEARNING GOAL

1 Explain the difference between complex and simple carbohydrates and know the amounts of each recommended in the daily diet.

We begin our study of biochemistry with the carbohydrates. Carbohydrates are produced in plants by photosynthesis (Figure 16.1). Natural carbohydrate sources such as grains and cereals, breads, sugarcane, fruits, milk, and honey are an important source of energy for animals. **Carbohydrates** include simple sugars as well as long polymers of these simple sugars, for instance potato starch, and a variety of molecules of intermediate size. The simple sugar glucose, $C_6H_{12}O_6$, is the primary energy source for the brain and nervous system and can be used by many other tissues. When "burned" by cells for energy, each gram (g) of carbohydrate releases approximately 4 kilocalories (kcal) of energy.

A kilocalorie is the same as the calorie (Cal) referred to in the "count-your-calories" books and on nutrition labels.

A healthy diet contains both complex carbohydrates, such as starches and cellulose, and simple sugars, such as fructose and sucrose (Figure 16.2). However, the quantity of simple sugars, especially sucrose, should be minimized because large quantities of sucrose in the diet promote obesity and tooth decay.

Complex carbohydrates are better for us than the simple sugars. Starch, found in rice, potatoes, breads, and cereals, is an excellent energy source. In addition, the complex carbohydrates, such as cellulose, provide us with an important supply of dietary fiber.

See A Medical Perspective: Tooth Decay and Simple Sugars on page 551.

It is hard to determine exactly what percentage of the daily diet *should* consist of carbohydrates. The *actual* percentage varies widely throughout the world, from 80% in the Far East, where rice is the main component of the diet, to 40–50% in the United States. Currently, it is recommended that 45–65% of the calories in the diet should come from carbohydrates and that no more than 10% of the daily caloric intake should be sucrose.

Question 16.1 What is the current recommendation for the amount of carbohydrates that should be included in the diet? Of the daily intake of carbohydrates, what percentage should be simple sugar?

Question 16.2 Distinguish between simple and complex carbohydrates. What are some sources of complex carbohydrates?

Monosaccharides such as glucose and fructose are the simplest carbohydrates because they contain a single (*mono-*) sugar **(*saccharide*)** unit. **Disaccharides,** including sucrose and lactose, consist of two monosaccharide units joined through bridging oxygen atoms. Such a bond is called a **glycosidic bond. Oligosaccharides** consist of three to ten monosaccharide units joined by glycosidic bonds. The largest and most complex carbohydrates are the **polysaccharides,** which are long, often highly branched, chains of monosaccharides. Starch, glycogen, and cellulose are all examples of polysaccharides.

Figure 16.1 Carbohydrates are produced by plants such as this potato in the process of photosynthesis, which uses the energy of sunlight to produce hexoses from CO_2 and H_2O.

Figure 16.2 Carbohydrates from a variety of foods are an essential component of the diet.

16.2 Monosaccharides

The importance of phosphorylated sugars in metabolic reactions is discussed in Sections 14.4 and 21.3.

LEARNING GOAL

2 Apply the systems of classifying and naming monosaccharides according to the functional group and number of carbons in the chain.

Monosaccharides are composed of carbon, hydrogen, and oxygen. They can be classified on the basis of the functional groups they contain. A monosaccharide with a ketone (carbonyl) group is a **ketose.** If an aldehyde (carbonyl) group is present, it is called an **aldose.** Sometimes monosaccharides are called *polyhydroxyaldehydes* or *polyhydroxyketones* because they also contain many hydroxyl groups.

Aldehyde functional group

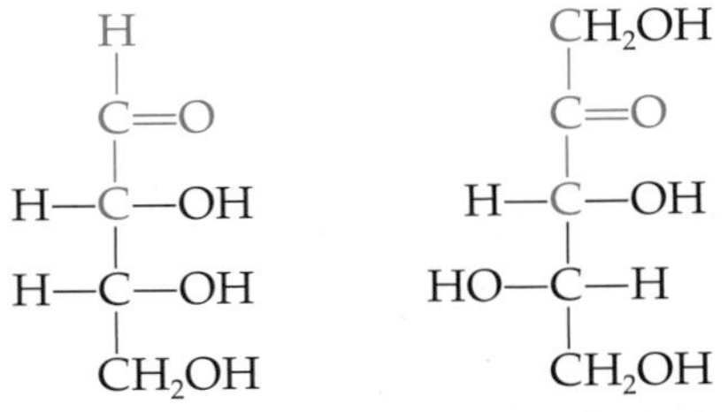

H–C=O
H–C–OH
H–C–OH
CH_2OH

An aldose

CH_2OH
C=O
H–C–OH
HO–C–H
CH_2OH

A ketose

Ketone functional group

The simplest aldose is D-glyceraldehyde:

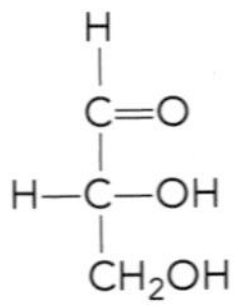

H–C=O
H–C–OH
CH_2OH

The simplest ketose is dihydroxyacetone:

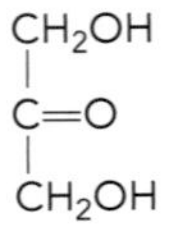

CH_2OH
C=O
CH_2OH

Stereoisomers are described in detail in the next section.

Another system of classification tells us the number of carbon atoms in the main skeleton. A three-carbon monosaccharide is a ***triose,*** a four-carbon sugar is a ***tetrose,*** a five-carbon sugar is a ***pentose,*** a six-carbon sugar is a ***hexose,*** and so on. Combining the two classification systems gives even more information about the structure and composition of a sugar. For example, an aldotetrose is a four-carbon sugar that is also an aldehyde.

In addition to these general classification schemes, each monosaccharide has a unique name. These names are shown in blue for the following structures. Because the monosaccharides can exist in several different stereoisomers, it is important to provide the complete name. Thus the complete names of the following structures are D-glyceraldehyde, D-glucose, and D-fructose. These names tell us that the structure represents one particular sugar and also identifies the sugar as one of two possible stereoisomers (D- or L-).

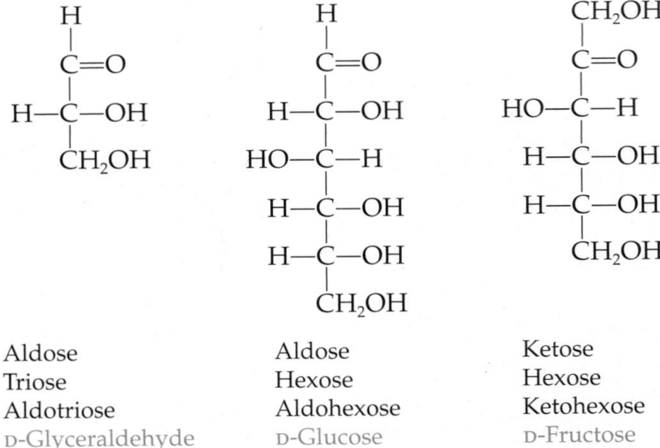

Question 16.3 What is the structural difference between an aldose and a ketose?

Question 16.4 Explain the difference between:

a. A ketohexose and an aldohexose
b. A triose and a pentose

A MEDICAL PERSPECTIVE

Tooth Decay and Simple Sugars

How many times have you heard the lecture from parents or your dentist about brushing your teeth after a sugary snack? Annoying as this lecture might be, it is based on sound scientific data that demonstrate that the cause of tooth decay is plaque and acid formed by the bacterium *Streptococcus mutans* using sucrose as its substrate.

Saliva is teeming with bacteria in concentrations up to 100 million (10^8) per milliliter (mL) of saliva! Within minutes after you brush your teeth, sticky glycoproteins in the saliva adhere to tooth surfaces. Then millions of oral bacteria immediately bind to this surface.

Although many oral bacteria stick to the tooth surface, as the diagram shows, only *S. mutans* causes cavities. The reason for this is that this organism alone can make the enzyme *glucosyl transferase.* This enzyme acts only on the disaccharide sucrose, breaking it down into glucose and fructose. The glucose is immediately added to a growing polysaccharide called *dextran,* the glue that allows the bacteria to adhere to the tooth surface, contributing to the formation of plaque.

Now the bacteria embedded in the dextran take in the fructose and use it in the lactic acid fermentation. The lactic acid that is produced lowers the pH on the tooth surface and begins to dissolve calcium from the tooth enamel. Even though we produce about 1 liter (L) of saliva each day, the acid cannot be washed away from the tooth surface because the dextran plaque is not permeable to saliva.

So what can we do to prevent tooth decay? Of course, brushing after each meal and flossing regularly reduce plaque buildup. Eating a diet rich in calcium also helps build strong tooth enamel. Foods rich in complex carbohydrates, such as fruits and vegetables, help prevent cavities in two ways. Glucosyl transferase can't use complex carbohydrates in its cavity-causing chemistry, and eating fruits and vegetables helps to mechanically remove plaque.

Perhaps the most effective way to prevent tooth decay is to avoid sucrose-containing snacks between meals. Studies have shown that eating sucrose-rich foods doesn't cause much tooth decay if followed immediately by brushing. However, even small amounts of sugar eaten between meals actively promote cavity formation.

For Further Understanding

- It has been suggested that tooth decay could be prevented by a vaccine that would rid the mouth of *Streptococcus mutans.* Explain this from the point of view of the chemical reactions that are described above.
- What steps could you take following a sugary snack to help prevent tooth decay, even when it is not possible to brush your teeth?

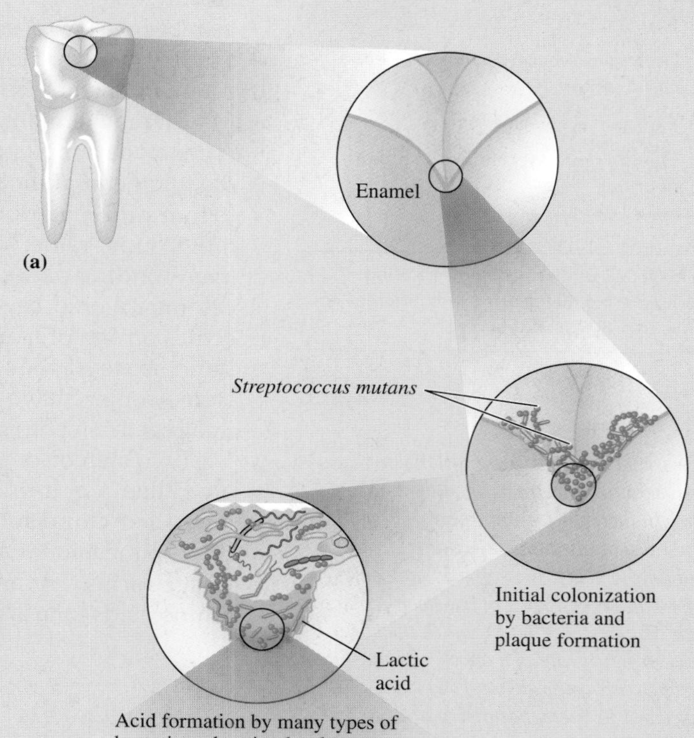

(a) The complex process of tooth decay. (b) Electron micrograph of dental plaque.

16.3 Stereoisomers and Stereochemistry

Stereoisomers

LEARNING GOALS

3 Determine whether a molecule has a chiral center.

4 Explain stereoisomerism.

5 Identify monosaccharides as either D- or L-.

The prefixes D- and L- found in the complete name of a monosaccharide are used to identify one of two possible isomeric forms called **stereoisomers.** By definition, each member of a pair of stereoisomers must have the same molecular formula and the same bonding pattern. How then do stereoisomers of the D-family differ from those of the L-family? D- and L-isomers differ in the spatial arrangements of atoms in the molecule.

Stereochemistry is the study of the different spatial arrangements of atoms. A general example of a pair of stereoisomers is shown in Figure 16.3. In this example, the general molecule C-abcd is formed from the bonding of a central carbon to four different groups: a, b, c, and d. This results in two possible ways to arrange the groups, rather than one. Each isomer is bonded together through the exact *same* bonding pattern, yet the two molecules are *not* identical. If they were identical, they would be superimposable. This means that you can place the two molecules on top of one another and every atom and every bond of the two lie in the same space. If they cannot be superimposed, they are stereoisomers. These two stereoisomers have a mirror-image relationship that is analogous to the mirror-image relationship of the left and right hands (see Figure 16.3b).

Build models of these compounds using toothpicks and gumdrops of five different colors to prove this to yourself.

Two stereoisomers that are nonsuperimposable mirror images of one another are called a pair of **enantiomers.** Molecules that can exist in enantiomeric forms are called **chiral molecules.** The term simply means that as a result of different three-dimensional arrangements of atoms, the molecule can exist in two mirror-image forms. For any pair of nonsuperimposable mirror-image carbohydrates or amino acids, one is always designated D- and the other L-.

The structures and designations of D- and L-glyceraldehyde are defined by convention. In fact, the D- and L-terminology is generally applied only to carbohydrates and amino acids. For organic molecules, the D- and L-convention has been replaced by a new system that provides the absolute configuration of a chiral carbon. This system, called the (R) and (S) system, is described in Stereochemistry and Stereoisomers Revisited.

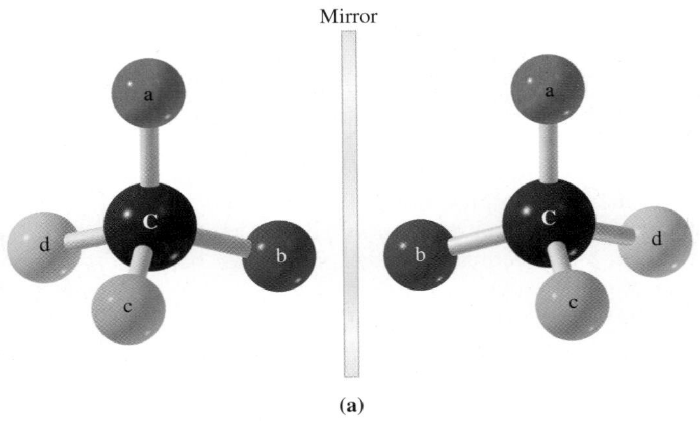

(a)

Nonsuperimposable mirror images: enantiomers

Mirror

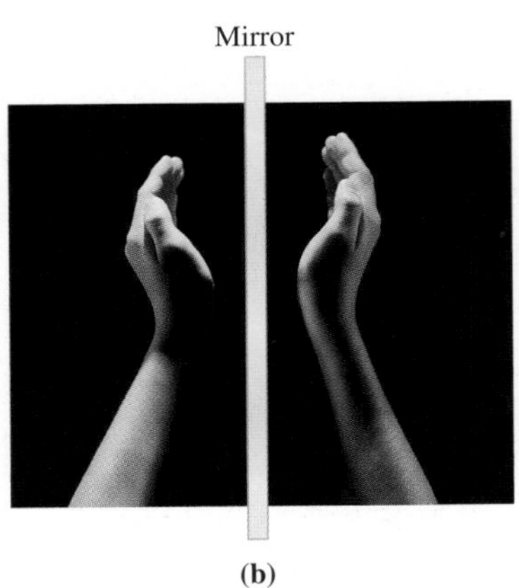

(b)

Figure 16.3 (a) A pair of enantiomers for the general molecule C-abcd.
(b) Mirror-image right and left hands.

Figure 16.4 (a) Structural formulas of D- and L-glyceraldehyde. The end of the molecule with the carbonyl group is the most oxidized end. The D- or L-configuration of a monosaccharide is determined by the orientation of the functional groups attached to the chiral carbon farthest from the oxidized end. In the D-enantiomer, the —OH is to the right. In the L-enantiomer, the —OH is to the left. (b) A three-dimensional representation of D- and L-glyceraldehyde.

A carbon atom that has four different groups bonded to it is called a **chiral carbon** atom. Any molecule containing a chiral carbon is a chiral molecule and will exist as a pair of enantiomers. Consider the simplest chiral carbohydrate, **glyceraldehyde,** which is shown in Figure 16.4. Note that the second carbon is bonded to four different groups. It is therefore a chiral carbon. As a result, we can draw two enantiomers of glyceraldehyde that are nonsuperimposable mirror images of one another. Larger biological molecules typically have more than one chiral carbon.

ANIMATIONS
- Chiral Molecules
- Chiral Molecules (B)

Rotation of Plane-Polarized Light

Stereoisomers can be distinguished from one another by their different optical properties. Each member of a pair of stereoisomers will rotate plane-polarized light in a different direction.

As we learned in Chapter 2, white light is a form of electromagnetic radiation that consists of many different wavelengths (colors) vibrating in *planes* that are all perpendicular to the direction of the light beam. To measure optical properties of enantiomers, scientists use special light sources to produce *monochromatic light,* that is, light of a single wavelength. The monochromatic light is passed through a polarizing material, like a Polaroid lens, so that only waves in one plane can pass through. The light that emerges from the lens is *plane-polarized light* (Figure 16.5).

The polarimeter, measurement of the rotation of plane-polarized light, and the calculation of specific rotation are discussed in detail online in Stereochemistry and Stereoisomers Revisited.

STEREOCHEMISTRY AND STEREOISOMERS REVISITED

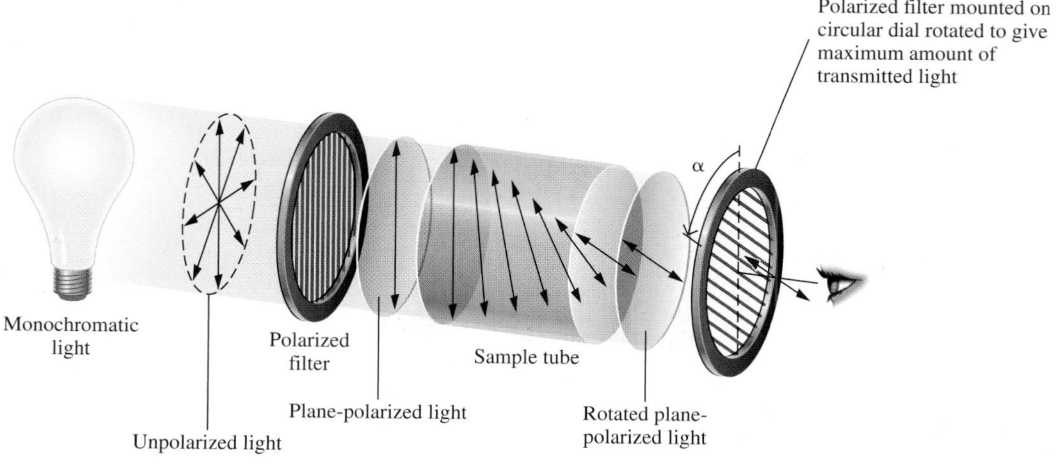

Figure 16.5 Schematic drawing of a polarimeter.

Applying these principles, scientists have developed the *polarimeter* to measure the ability of a compound to change the angle of the plane of plane-polarized light (see Figure 16.5). The polarimeter allows the determination of the specific rotation of a compound, that is, the measure of its ability to rotate plane-polarized light.

Some compounds rotate light in a clockwise direction. These are said to be *dextrorotatory* and are designated by a plus sign (+) before the specific rotation value. Other substances rotate light in a counterclockwise direction. These are called *levorotatory* and are indicated by a minus sign (−) before the specific rotation value.

The Relationship Between Molecular Structure and Optical Activity

In 1848, Louis Pasteur was the first to see a relationship between the structure of a compound and the effect of that compound on plane-polarized light. In his studies of winemaking, Pasteur noticed that salts of tartaric acid were formed as a by-product. It is a tribute to his extraordinary powers of observation that he noticed that two types of crystals were formed and that they were mirror images of one another. Using a magnifying glass and forceps, Pasteur separated the left-handed and right-handed crystals into separate piles. When he measured the optical activity of each of the mirror-image forms and of the original mixed sample, he obtained the following results:

- A solution of the original mixture of crystals was optically inactive.
- But both of the mirror-image crystals were optically active. In fact, the specific rotation produced by each was identical in magnitude but was of opposite sign.

Although Pasteur's work opened the door to understanding the relationship between structure and optical activity, it was not until 1874 that the Dutch chemist van't Hoff and the French chemist LeBel independently came up with a basis for the observed optical activity: tetrahedral carbon atoms bonded to four different atoms or groups of atoms. Thus, two enantiomers, which are identical to one another in all other chemical and physical properties, will rotate plane-polarized light to the same degree, but in opposite directions.

Fischer Projection Formulas

Emil Fischer devised a simple way to represent the structure of stereoisomers. The **Fischer Projection** is a two-dimensional drawing of a molecule that shows a chiral carbon at the intersection of two lines. The horizontal lines represent bonds projecting out of the page, and the vertical lines represent bonds that project into the page. Figure 16.6 demonstrates how to draw the Fischer Projections for the

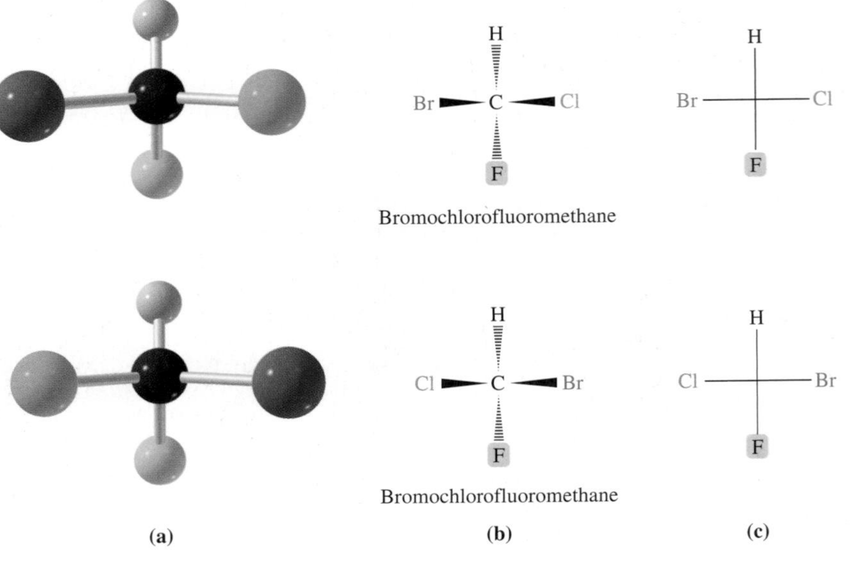

Figure 16.6 Drawing a Fischer Projection. (a) The ball-and-stick models for the stereoisomers of bromochlorofluoromethane. (b) The wedge-and-dash and (c) Fischer Projections of these molecules.

stereoisomers of bromochlorofluoromethane. In Figure 16.6a, the two isomers are represented using ball-and-stick models. The molecules are reinterpreted using the wedge-and-dash representations in Figure 16.6b. In the Fischer Projections shown in Figure 16.6c, the point at which two lines cross represents the chiral carbon. Horizontal lines replace the solid wedges indicating that the bonds are projecting toward the reader. Vertical lines replace the dashed wedges, indicating that the bonds are projecting away from the reader. For sugars, the aldehyde or ketone group, the most oxidized carbon, is always represented at the "top."

EXAMPLE 16.1 Drawing Fischer Projections for a Sugar

LEARNING GOAL

5 Identify monosaccharides as either D- or L-.

Draw the Fischer Projections for the stereoisomers of glyceraldehyde.

Solution

Review the structures of the two stereoisomers of glyceraldehyde (Figure 16.4b). The ball-and-stick models can be represented using three-dimensional wedge drawings. Remember that for sugars the most oxidized carbon (the aldehyde or ketone group) is always drawn at the top of the structure. Here we show the aldehyde in a condensed form, —CHO.

CHO
H—C—OH
CH_2OH
D-Glyceraldehyde

CHO
HO—C—H
CH_2OH
L-Glyceraldehyde

Remember that in the wedge diagram, the solid wedges represent bonds directed toward the reader. The dashed wedges represent bonds directed away from the reader and into the page. In these molecules, the center carbon is the only chiral carbon in the structure. To convert these wedge representations to a Fischer Projection, simply use a horizontal line in place of each solid wedge and use a vertical line to represent each dashed wedge. The chiral carbon is represented by the point at which the vertical and horizontal lines cross, as shown below.

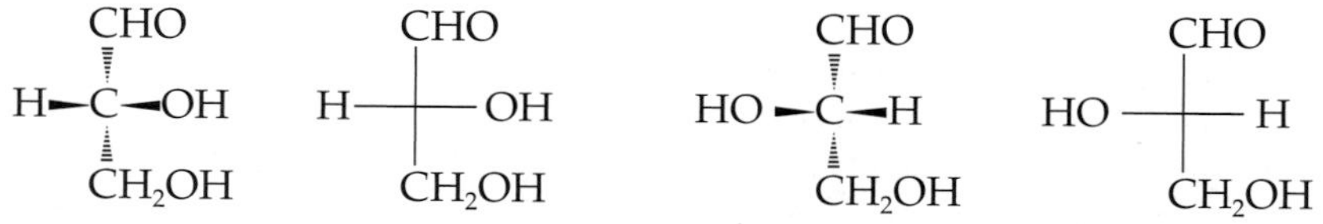

CHO
H—C—OH
CH_2OH

CHO
H—+—OH
CH_2OH

D-Glyceraldehyde

CHO
HO—C—H
CH_2OH

CHO
HO—+—H
CH_2OH

L-Glyceraldehyde

Practice Problem 16.1

Draw Fischer Projections for each of the following molecules and for their mirror images.

a. 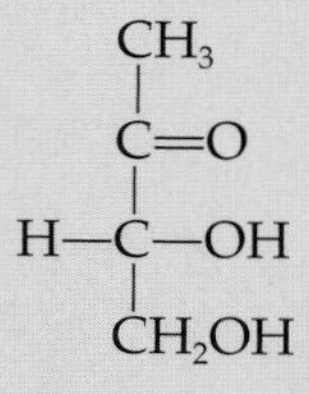
CH_3
C=O
H—C—OH
CH_2OH

b.
H
C=O
H—C—OH
H—C—OH
HO—C—H
CH_2OH

c.
CH_2OH
C=O
HO—C—H
H—C—OH
H—C—OH
CH_2OH

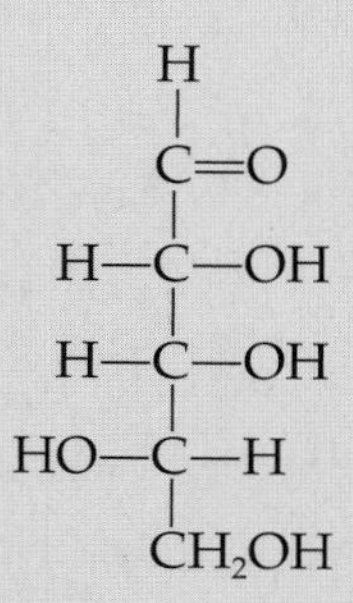

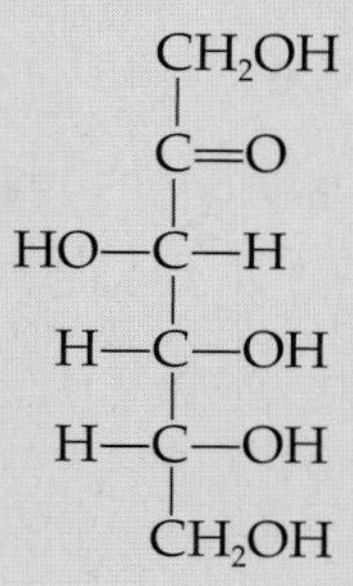

► For Further Practice: **Questions 16.45 and 16.46.**

Racemic Mixtures

When Louis Pasteur measured the specific rotation of the mixture of tartaric acid salt crystals, he observed that it was optically inactive. The reason was that the mixture contained equal amounts of the (+) enantiomer and the (−) enantiomer. A mixture of equal amounts of a pair of enantiomers is called a *racemic mixture,* or simply a *racemate.* The prefix (±) is used to designate a racemic mixture. In this situation the specific rotation is zero because the rotation caused by one enantiomer is canceled by the opposite rotation caused by the mirror-image enantiomer.

Diastereomers

So far, we have looked only at molecules containing a single chiral carbon. In this case only two enantiomers are possible. However, it is quite common to find molecules with two or more chiral carbons. For a molecule of n chiral carbons the maximum possible number of different configurations is 2^n. Note that this formula predicts the *maximum* number of configurations. As we will see, there may actually be fewer.

EXAMPLE 16.2 Drawing Stereoisomers for Compounds with More Than One Chiral Carbon

LEARNING GOALS

3 Determine whether a molecule has a chiral center.

4 Explain stereoisomerism.

Draw all the possible stereoisomers of 2,3,4-trichlorobutanal.

Solution

1. There are two chiral carbons in this molecule, C-2 and C-3. Thus there are 2^2 or 4 possible stereoisomers.
2. There are two possible configurations for each of the chiral carbons (Cl on the left or on the right). Begin by drawing an isomer with both Cl atoms on the right (a). Now draw the mirror image (b). You have now generated the first pair of enantiomers, (a) and (b).

(a):
- CHO
- H—C—Cl
- H—C—Cl
- CH_2Cl

(b):
- CHO
- Cl—C—H
- Cl—C—H
- CH_2Cl

Enantiomers

3. Next, change the location of one of the two Cl atoms bonded to a chiral carbon to produce another possible isomer (c). Finally, draw the mirror image of (c) to produce the second set of enantiomers, (c) and (d).

(c):
- CHO
- H—C—Cl
- Cl—C—H
- CH_2Cl

(d):
- CHO
- Cl—C—H
- H—C—Cl
- CH_2Cl

Enantiomers

4. By this systematic procedure we have drawn the four possible isomers of 2,3,4-trichlorobutanal.

Practice Problem 16.2

Draw all of the possible stereoisomers of each of the compounds listed below. Indicate which are enantiomers.

a. 2-Bromo-3-chlorobutane b. 2-Chloro-3-fluoropentane c. 2,3,4-Tribromopentanal

▶ For Further Practice: **Questions 16.47 and 16.48.**

In Example 16.2, structures (a) and (b) are clearly enantiomers, as are (c) and (d). But how do we describe the relationship between structures (a) and (c) or any of the pairs of stereoisomers that are *not* enantiomers? The term **diastereomers** is used to describe a pair of stereoisomers having two or more chiral centers and that are not enantiomers.

Although enantiomers differ from one another only in the direction of rotation of plane-polarized light, diastereomers are different in their chemical and physical properties.

Meso Compounds

As mentioned previously, the maximum number of configurations for a molecule with two chiral carbons is 2^2, or 4. However, if each of the two chiral carbons is bonded to the same four nonidentical groups, fewer than four stereoisomers exist. Such compounds are called **meso compounds.** The example of tartaric acid, studied by Pasteur, helps to explain this phenomenon.

EXAMPLE 16.3 Drawing Stereoisomers of Compounds with More Than One Chiral Carbon

LEARNING GOALS

3 Determine whether a molecule has a chiral center.

4 Explain stereoisomerism.

Draw all the possible stereoisomers of tartaric acid,:

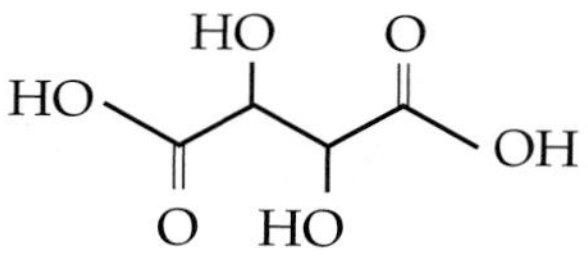

HO O
HO OH
O HO

Solution

1. Proceeding as in Example 16.2, you will generate the following four structures:

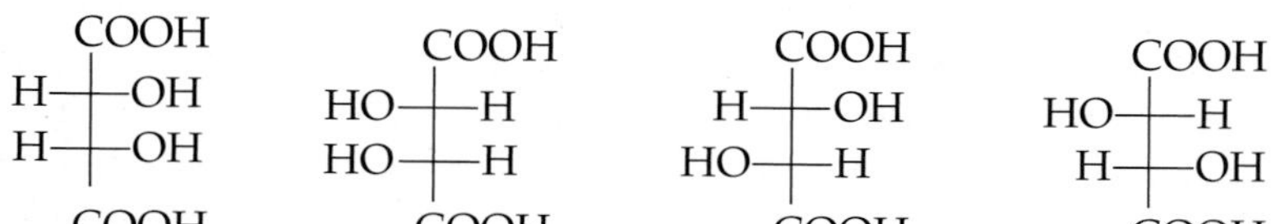

COOH H—OH H—OH COOH (a)	COOH HO—H HO—H COOH (b)	COOH H—OH HO—H COOH (c)	COOH HO—H H—OH COOH (d)

Identical ((a) and (b)) Enantiomers ((c) and (d))

2. Careful examination of pair (c) and (d) reveals that these molecules are nonsuperimposable mirror images. Thus they are enantiomers.
3. Similar inspection of structures (a) and (b) reveals that, although they are mirror images, they are identical. Structure (b) can simply be rotated 180° to produce structure (a); therefore they are identical.

Practice Problem 16.3

Draw all of the possible stereoisomers of each of the compounds listed below. Indicate which are enantiomers and which will have a meso compound.

a. 2,3-Dichlorobutane b. 1,2-Dibromocyclopentane c. 3,4-Difluorohexane

► For Further Practice: **Questions 16.49 and 16.50.**

Note that if you draw a line between chiral carbon-2 and chiral carbon-3 of the meso compound represented in (a) and (b) in Example 16.3, the top half of the molecule is the mirror image of the bottom half. There is a plane of symmetry within the molecule:

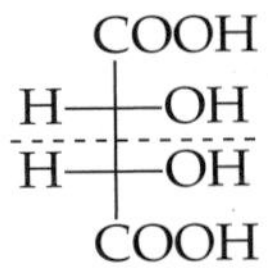

COOH
H—|—OH
- - - - - - - -
H—|—OH
COOH

As a result, structure (a) is optically inactive. Even though there are two chiral carbons, the rotation of plane-polarized light by chiral carbon-2 is canceled by the opposite rotation of plane-polarized light caused by chiral carbon-3. This molecule is *achiral* and is termed meso-tartaric acid. Any compound with an internal plane of symmetry (that is, that can be superimposed on its mirror image) is optically inactive and is termed a meso compound.

The D- and L- System of Nomenclature

In 1891 Emil Fischer devised a nomenclature system that would allow scientists to distinguish between enantiomers. Fischer knew that the two enantiomers of glyceraldehyde rotated plane-polarized light in opposite directions, but he did not have the sophisticated tools needed to make an absolute connection between the structure and the direction of rotation of plane-polarized light. He simply decided that the (+) enantiomer would be the one with the hydroxyl group of the chiral carbon on the right. He called this D-glyceraldehyde. The enantiomer that rotated plane-polarized light in the (−) or levorotatory direction, he called L-glyceraldehyde (see Figure 16.4).

It was not until 1952 that researchers were able to demonstrate that Fischer had guessed correctly when he proposed the structures of the (+) and (−) enantiomers of glyceraldehyde.

While specific rotation is an experimental value that must be measured, the D- and L-designations of all other monosaccharides are determined by comparison of their structures with D- and L-glyceraldehyde. Sugars with more than three carbons will have more than one chiral carbon. *By convention,* it is the position of the hydroxyl group on the chiral carbon farthest from the carbonyl group (the most oxidized end of the molecule) that determines whether a monosaccharide is in the D- or L-configuration. One way to be sure you are considering the correct chiral carbon is to number the carbon chain, giving the carbonyl group the lowest possible number. It is the chiral carbon with the highest number that is used to determine the D- or L-configuration. If the —OH group is on the right, the molecule is in the D-configuration. If the —OH group is on the left, the molecule is in the L-configuration. Almost all carbohydrates in living systems are members of the D-family.

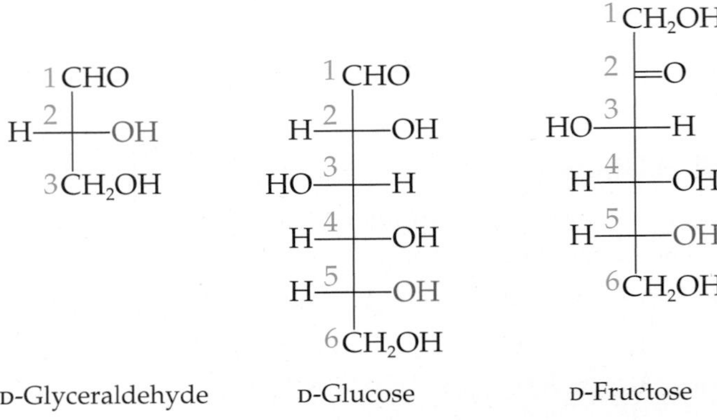

Question 16.5 Place an asterisk beside each chiral carbon in the Fischer Projections you drew for Practice Problem 16.1 at the end of Example 16.1.

Question 16.6 In the Fischer Projections you drew for Practice Problem 16.1 at the end of Example 16.1, indicate which bonds project toward you and which project into the page.

Question 16.7 Determine the configuration (D- or L-) for each of the molecules in Practice Problem 16.1 at the end of Example 16.1.

Question 16.8 Explain the difference between the D- and L-designation and the (+) and (−) designation.

16.4 Biologically Important Monosaccharides

Monosaccharides, the simplest carbohydrates, have backbones of from three to seven carbons. There are many monosaccharides, but we will focus on those that are most common in biological systems. These include the five- and six-carbon sugars: glucose, fructose, galactose, ribose, and deoxyribose.

LEARNING GOAL

6 Draw and name the common monosaccharides using structural formulas.

Glucose

Glucose is the most important sugar in the human body. It is found in numerous foods and has several common names, including dextrose, grape sugar, and blood sugar. Glucose is broken down in glycolysis and other pathways to release energy for body functions.

The concentration of glucose in the blood is critical to normal body function. As a result, it is carefully controlled by the hormones insulin and glucagon. Normal blood glucose levels are 100–120 mg glucose/100 mL blood, with the highest concentrations appearing after a meal. Insulin stimulates the uptake of the excess glucose by most cells of the body, and after 1 to 2 hours (h), levels return to normal. If blood glucose concentrations drop too low, the individual feels lightheaded and shaky. When this happens, glucagon stimulates the liver to release glucose into the blood, reestablishing normal levels. We will take a closer look at this delicate balancing act in Section 23.6.

The molecular formula of glucose, an aldohexose, is $C_6H_{12}O_6$. The structure of glucose is shown in Figure 16.7, and the method used to draw this structure is described in Example 16.4.

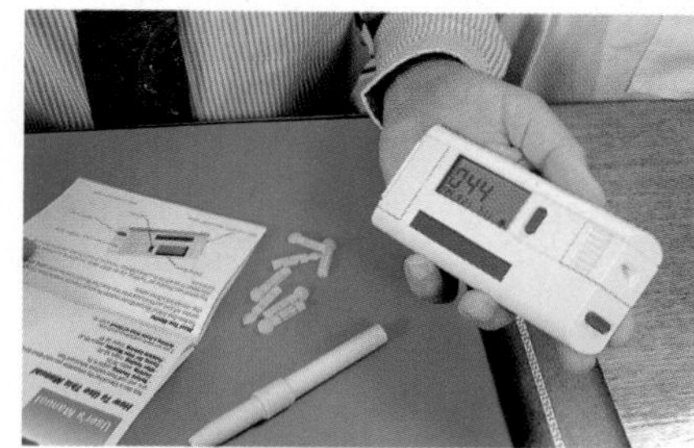

Why do diabetics need to use a blood glucose monitor like the one shown here?

EXAMPLE 16.4 **Drawing the Structure of a Monosaccharide**

LEARNING GOAL

6 Draw and name the common monosaccharides using structural formulas.

Draw the structure and Fischer Projection for D-glucose.

Solution

Glucose is an aldohexose.

Step 1. Draw six carbons in a straight vertical line; each carbon is separated from the ones above and below it by a bond:

Continued...

Step 2. The most highly oxidized carbon is, by convention, drawn as the uppermost carbon (carbon-1). In this case, carbon-1 is an aldehyde carbon:

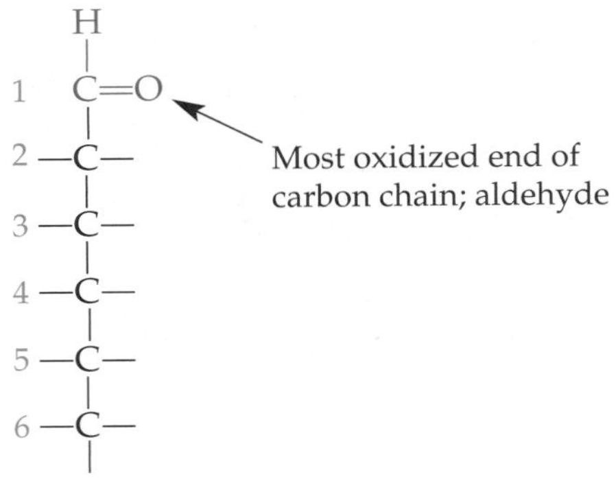

```
        H
        |
  1     C=O  <--- Most oxidized end of
        |         carbon chain; aldehyde
  2   —C—
        |
  3   —C—
        |
  4   —C—
        |
  5   —C—
        |
  6   —C—
        |
```

Step 3. The atoms are added to the next to the last carbon atom, at the bottom of the chain, to give either the D- or L-configuration as desired. Remember, when the —OH group is to the right, you have D-glucose. When in doubt, compare your structure to D-glyceraldehyde!

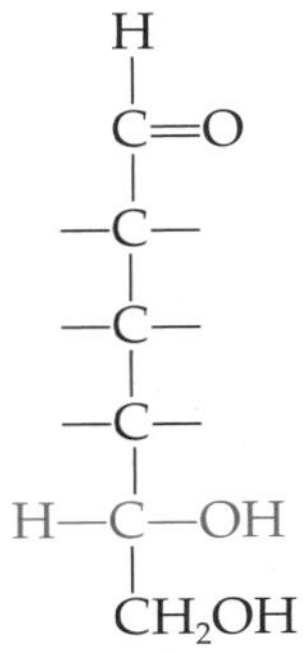

```
       H
       |
       C=O
       |
     —C—
       |
     —C—                 H
       |                 |
     —C—                 C=O
       |                 |
   H—C—OH            H—C—OH
       |                 |
      CH2OH             CH2OH

   D-Isomer         D-Glyceraldehyde
```

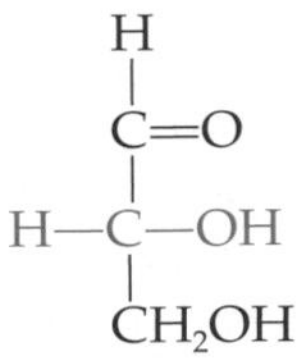

Compare chiral carbons farthest from the carbonyl group

Step 4. All the remaining atoms are then added to give the desired carbohydrate. For example, you would draw the following structure for D-glucose.

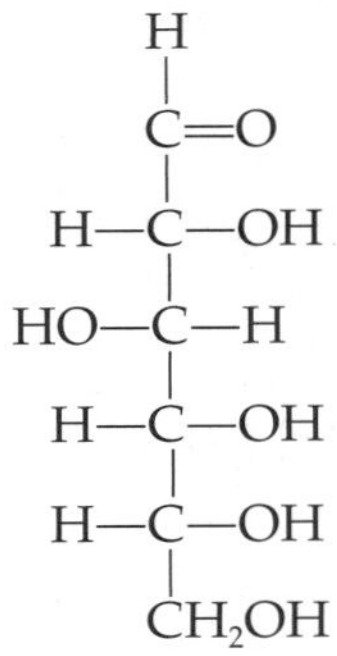

```
        H                    H    O
        |                     \  //
        C=O                     C
        |                   H --+-- OH
    H—C—OH                HO --+-- H
        |                   H --+-- OH
   HO—C—H                  H --+-- OH
        |                       CH2OH
    H—C—OH
        |
    H—C—OH
        |
       CH2OH

     D-Glucose             D-Glucose
                       (Fischer Projection)
```

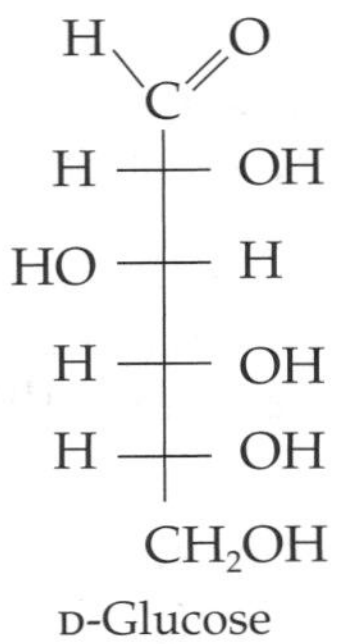

The positions for the hydrogen atoms and the hydroxyl groups on the remaining carbons must be learned for each sugar.

Practice Problem 16.4

Draw the structures of D-ribose and L-ribose. (Information on the structure of D-ribose is found later in this chapter.)

▸ For Further Practice: **Questions 16.9 and 16.10.**

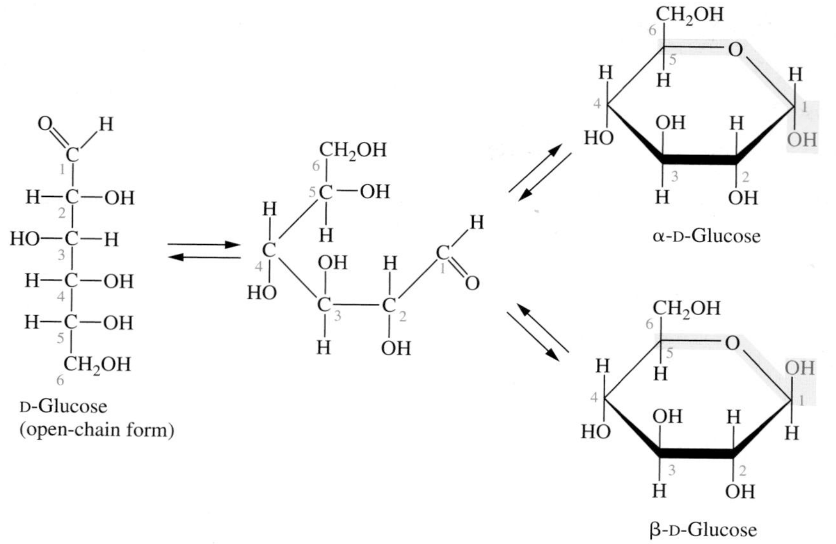

Figure 16.7 Cyclization of glucose to give α- and β-D-glucose. Note that the carbonyl carbon (C-1) becomes chiral in this process, yielding the α- and β-forms of glucose. The hemiacetal is highlighted in yellow.

In actuality the open-chain form of glucose is present in very small concentrations in cells. It exists in cyclic form under physiological conditions because the carbonyl group at C-1 of glucose reacts with the hydroxyl group at C-5 to give a six-member ring. In the discussion of aldehydes, we noted that the reaction between an aldehyde and an alcohol yields a **hemiacetal.** When the aldehyde portion of the glucose molecule reacts with the C-5 hydroxyl group, the product is a cyclic *intramolecular hemiacetal.* For D-glucose, two isomers can be formed in this reaction (see Figure 16.7). These isomers are called α- and β-D-glucose. The two isomers formed differ from one another in the location of the —OH attached to the hemiacetal carbon, C-1. Such isomers, differing in the arrangement of bonds around the hemiacetal carbon, are called **anomers.** In the α-anomers, the C-1 (*anomeric carbon*) hydroxyl group is below the ring, and in the β-anomers, the C-1 hydroxyl group is above the ring. Like the stereoisomers discussed previously, the α and β forms can be distinguished from one another because they rotate plane-polarized light differently.

Hemiacetal structure,

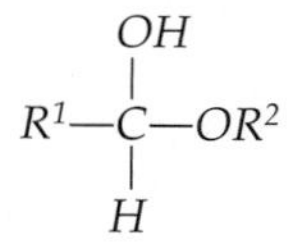

$$R^1{-}\underset{\displaystyle H}{\overset{\displaystyle OH}{\underset{|}{\overset{|}{C}}}}{-}OR^2$$

and formation are described in Section 13.4.

Question 16.9 Draw the structure of D-galactose. (Information on the structure of D-galactose is found later in this chapter.)

Question 16.10 Draw the structure of L-galactose.

In Figure 16.7 a new type of structural formula, called a **Haworth projection,** is presented. Although on first inspection it appears complicated, it is quite simple to derive a Haworth projection from a structural formula, as Example 16.5 shows.

EXAMPLE 16.5 Drawing the Haworth Projection of a Monosaccharide from the Structural Formula

LEARNING GOAL

7 Given the linear structure of a monosaccharide, draw the Haworth projection of its α- and β-cyclic forms and vice versa.

Draw the Haworth projections of α- and β-D-glucose.

Solution

1. Before attempting to draw a Haworth projection, look at the first steps of ring formation shown here:

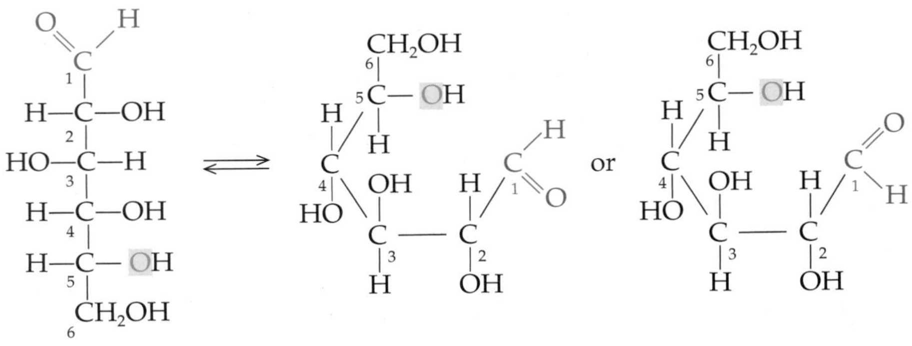

Glucose (open chain)

Glucose (intermediates in ring formation)

Try to imagine that you are seeing the molecules shown above in three dimensions. Some of the substituent groups on the molecule will be above the ring, and some will be beneath it. The question then becomes: How do you determine which groups to place above the ring and which to place beneath the ring?

2. Look at the two-dimensional structural formula. Note the groups (drawn in blue) to the left of the carbon chain. These are placed above the ring in the Haworth projection.

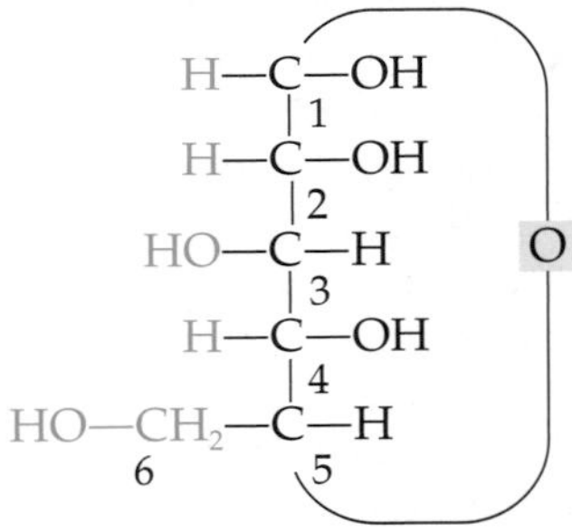

α-D-Glucose 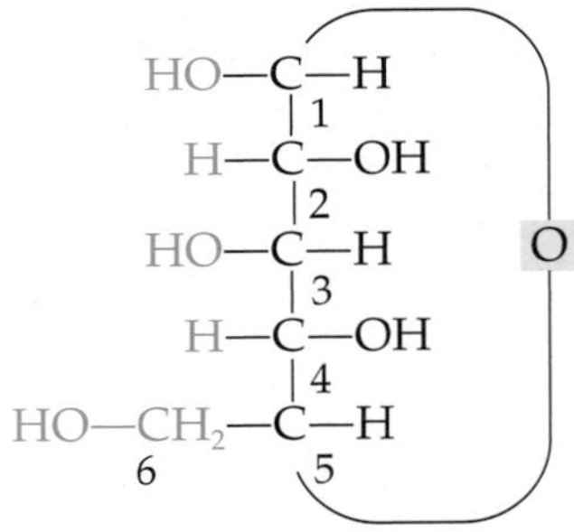 β-D-Glucose

3. Now note the groups (drawn in red) to the right of the carbon chain. These will be located beneath the carbon ring in the Haworth projection.

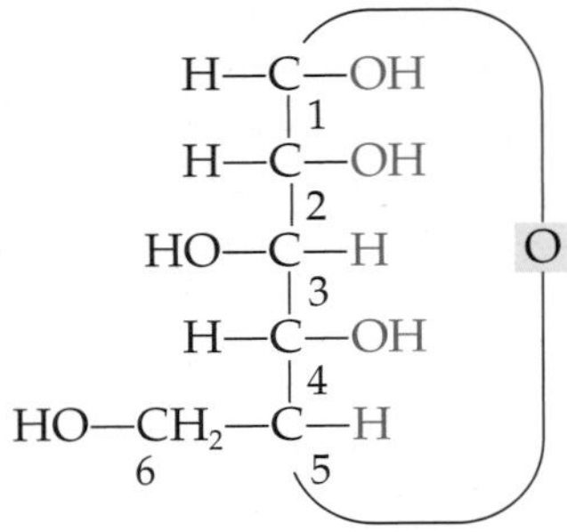

α-D-Glucose 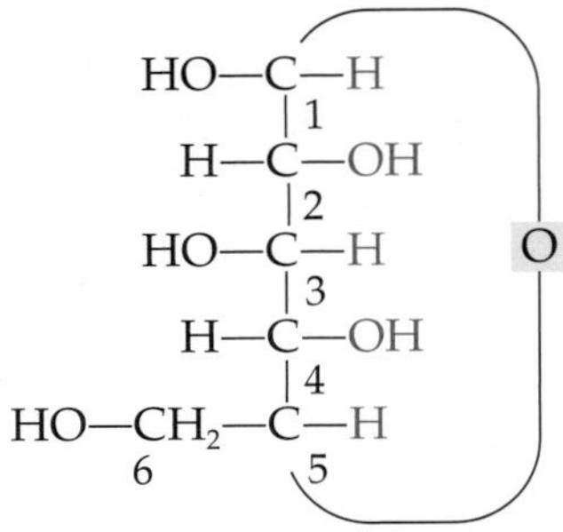 β-D-Glucose

4. Thus in the Haworth projection of the cyclic form of any D-sugar the —CH_2OH group is always "up." When the —OH group at C-1 is also "up," *cis* to the —CH_2OH group, the sugar is β-D-glucose. When the —OH group at C-1 is "down," *trans* to the —CH_2OH group, the sugar is α-D-glucose.

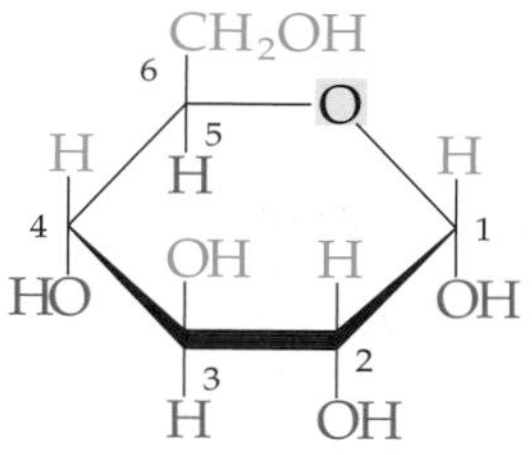

Haworth projection
α-D-Glucose

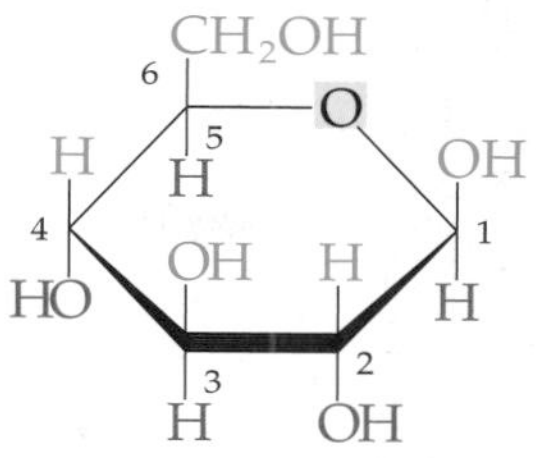

Haworth projection
β-D-Glucose

Practice Problem 16.5

Refer to the linear structures of D-galactose and D-ribose. Draw the Haworth projections of (a) α- and β-D-galactose and of (b) α- and β-D-ribose. Note that D-ribose is a pentose.

► For Further Practice: **Questions 16.55 and 16.56.**

Fructose

Fructose, also called levulose and fruit sugar, is the sweetest of all sugars. It is found in large amounts in honey, corn syrup, and sweet fruits. The structure of fructose is similar to that of glucose. When there is a —CH_2OH group instead of a —CHO group at carbon-1 and a —C=O group instead of CHOH at carbon-2, the sugar is a ketose. In this case it is D-fructose.

Cyclization of fructose produces α- and β-D-fructose:

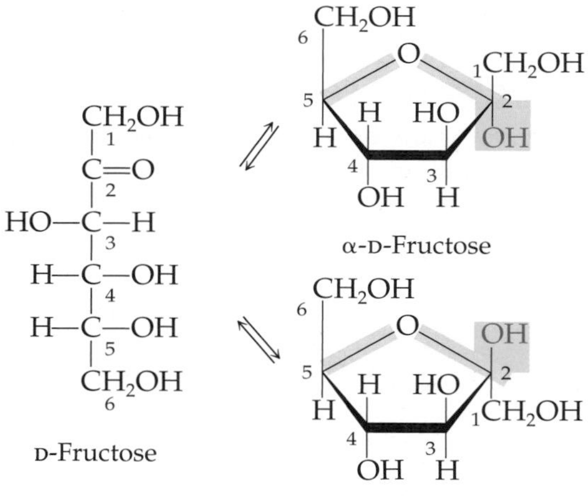

D-Fructose

α-D-Fructose

β-D-Fructose

In the equation above, the hemiacetal is highlighted. Fructose forms a five-member ring structure.

Fructose is often called fruit sugar because it contributes sweetness to ripe fruits, such as these peaches. Is fructose an aldose or a ketose?

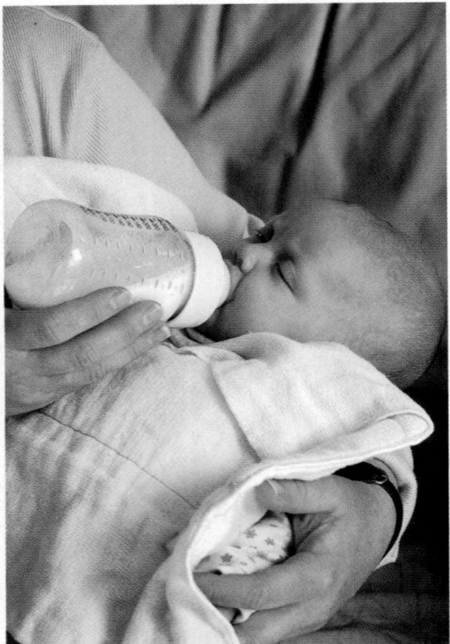

Galactose is one of the components of lactose, or milk sugar. Read about galactosemia in Section 16.5 and describe the symptoms and treatment for this genetic disorder.

Galactose

Another important hexose is **galactose.** The linear structure of D-galactose and the Haworth projections of α-D-galactose and β-D-galactose are shown here:

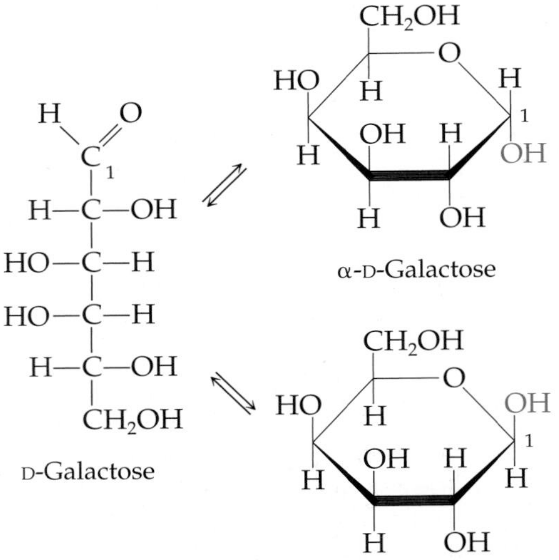

D-Galactose

α-D-Galactose

β-D-Galactose

Galactose is found in biological systems as a component of the disaccharide lactose, or milk sugar. This is the principal sugar found in the milk of most mammals. β-D-Galactose and a modified form, β-D-*N*-acetylgalactosamine, are also components of the blood group antigens.

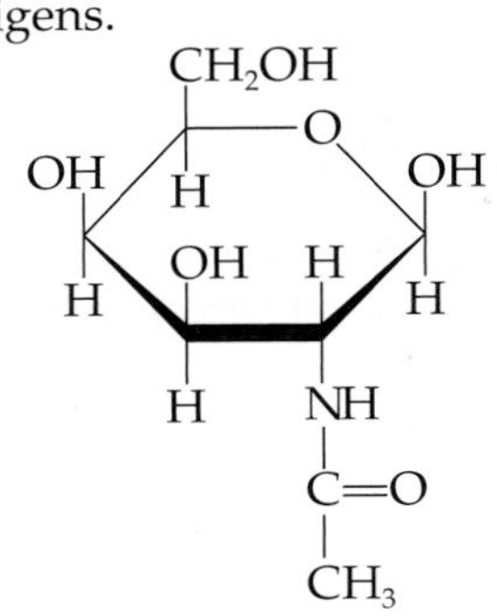

β-D-*N*-Acetylgalactosamine

Ribose and Deoxyribose, Five-Carbon Sugars

Ribose is a component of many biologically important molecules, including RNA and various coenzymes that are required by many of the enzymes that carry out biochemical reactions in the body. The structure of the five-carbon sugar D-ribose is shown in its open-chain form and in the α- and β-cyclic forms.

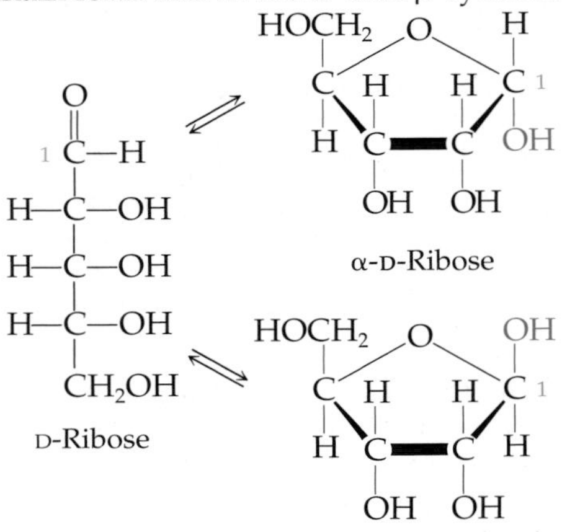

D-Ribose

α-D-Ribose

β-D-Ribose

β-D-2-Deoxyribose is one of the components of the sugar-phosphate backbone of the DNA molecule. How does this molecule differ from β-D-ribose?

DNA, the molecule that carries the genetic information of the cell, contains 2-deoxyribose. In this molecule the —OH group at C-2 has been replaced by a hydrogen, hence the designation "2-deoxy," indicating the absence of an oxygen.

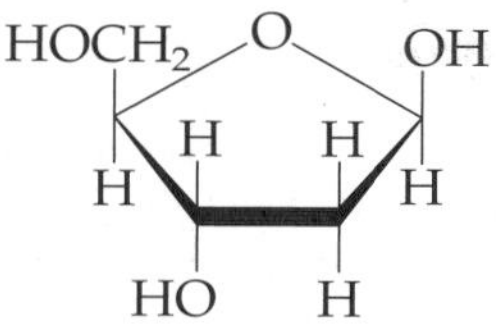

β-D-2-Deoxyribose

Reducing Sugars

LEARNING GOALS

8 By inspection of the structure, predict whether a sugar is a reducing or a nonreducing sugar.

9 Discuss the use of the Benedict's reagent to measure the level of glucose in urine.

The aldehyde group of aldoses is readily oxidized by the Benedict's reagent. Recall that the **Benedict's reagent** is a basic buffer solution that contains Cu^{2+} ions. The Cu^{2+} ions are reduced to Cu^{+} ions, which, in basic solution, precipitate as brick-red Cu_2O. The aldehyde group of the aldose is oxidized to a carboxylic acid, which undergoes an acid-base reaction to produce a carboxylate anion.

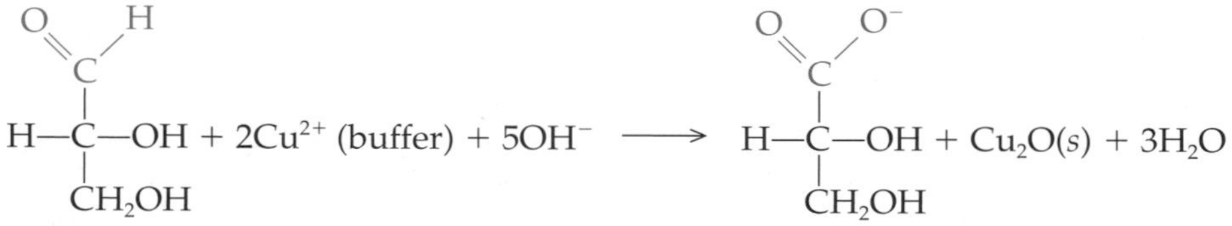

$$\text{H—C(OH)(CHO)—CH}_2\text{OH} + 2Cu^{2+}\text{ (buffer)} + 5OH^- \longrightarrow \text{H—C(OH)(COO}^-\text{)—CH}_2\text{OH} + Cu_2O(s) + 3H_2O$$

Although ketones generally are not easily oxidized, ketoses are an exception to that rule. Because of the —OH group on the carbon next to the carbonyl group, ketoses can be converted to aldoses, under basic conditions, via an *enediol reaction:*

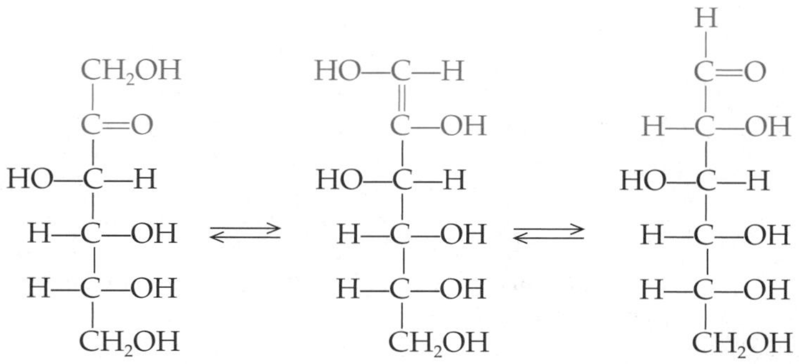

D-Fructose ⇌ Enediol ⇌ D-Glucose

The name of the enediol reaction is derived from the structure of the intermediate through which the ketose is converted to the aldose: It has a double bond (ene), and it has two hydroxyl groups (diol). Because of this enediol reaction, ketoses are also able to react with Benedict's reagent, which is basic. Because the metal ions in the solution are reduced, the sugars are serving as reducing agents and are called **reducing sugars.** All monosaccharides and all the common disaccharides, except sucrose, are reducing sugars.

For many years the Benedict's reagent was used to test for *glucosuria,* the presence of excess glucose in the urine. Individuals suffering from *Type I insulin-dependent diabetes mellitus* do not produce the hormone insulin, which controls the uptake of glucose from the blood. When the blood glucose level rises above 160 mg/100 mL, the kidney is unable to reabsorb the excess, and glucose is found

See A Medical Perspective: Diabetes Mellitus and Ketone Bodies in Chapter 23.

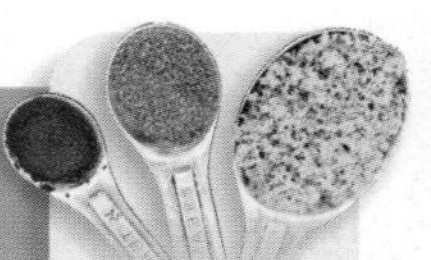

KITCHEN CHEMISTRY

The Chemistry of Caramels

Of all the treats at the holidays, my grandmother's caramels were my favorite. Unwrapped from their waxed paper, they melted in your mouth. It seemed mystical that she could mix sugar, corn syrup, butter, and cream into a very pale and unappetizing liquid and heat it to 248°F (120°C), watching it very carefully for the color change that indicated that the chemical reactions were occurring exactly as they should. I know that she never thought of herself as a chemist when she made the many holiday candies that delighted the family. But a chemist she was, carrying out reactions that are still poorly understood.

When sucrose is heated, its molecules begin to break apart into glucose and fructose. This destruction begins a series of reactions that convert the liquid sucrose, which itself is odorless, colorless, and cloyingly sweet, into literally hundreds of compounds. Some of these products are small molecules that enhance the flavor and aroma of the candy; others are little understood polymers, caramelans, caramelens, and caramelins, that give the creamy, soft texture.

Sucrose → Ethanol, Ethanoic acid, Butanedione, Ethanal, Ethyl ethanoate, Furan, Maltol

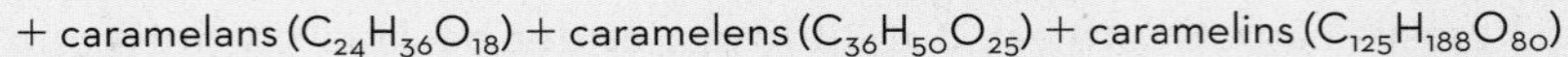

$+$ caramelans ($C_{24}H_{36}O_{18}$) $+$ caramelens ($C_{36}H_{50}O_{25}$) $+$ caramelins ($C_{125}H_{188}O_{80}$)

Of course, the sweet flavor is due to the sucrose and other sugars in the caramels. But notice that there are even slightly acidic and bitter notes that round out the flavor. As you can see in the diagram, the sour flavor is contributed by the acids produced, including acetic acid in the "equation" above. The fruity flavors are added by esters, and there is a sherry-like flavor that ethanol brings to the party. Butanedione adds a butterscotch flavor and aroma and furans add a nutty accent. Maltol brings the aroma that we associate with caramels.

While these products have been identified, many others have not. In fact, the reactions that cause this amazing change are poorly understood. Nonetheless, we can be grateful for the delightful treats that are the result.

For Further Understanding

- The temperature must be very carefully controlled during candy making. Explain this in terms of chemical reactions.
- List some other foods and beverages that owe their color and flavor to caramelization.

in the urine. Although the level of blood glucose could be controlled by the injection of insulin, urine glucose levels were monitored to ensure that the amount of insulin injected was correct. The Benedict's reagent was a useful tool because the amount of Cu_2O formed, and hence the degree of color change in the reaction, is directly proportional to the amount of reducing sugar in the urine. A brick-red color indicates a very high concentration of glucose in the urine. Yellow, green, and blue-green solutions indicate decreasing amounts of glucose in the urine, and a blue solution indicates an insignificant concentration.

Use of Benedict's reagent to test urine glucose levels has largely been replaced by chemical tests that provide more accurate results. The most common technology is based on a test strip that is impregnated with the enzyme glucose oxidase and other agents that will cause a measurable color change. In one such kit, the compounds that result in color development include the enzyme peroxidase, a compound called orthotolidine, and a yellow dye. When a drop of urine is placed on the strip, the glucose oxidase catalyzes the conversion of glucose into gluconic acid and hydrogen peroxide.

$$
\underset{\text{D-Glucose}}{\begin{array}{c} \text{O} \\ \| \\ \text{C—H} \\ | \\ \text{H—C—OH} \\ | \\ \text{HO—C—H} \\ | \\ \text{H—C—OH} \\ | \\ \text{H—C—OH} \\ | \\ \text{CH}_2\text{OH} \end{array}} + O_2 \xrightarrow[\text{oxidase}]{\text{Glucose}} \underset{\text{D-Gluconic acid}}{\begin{array}{c} \text{O} \\ \| \\ \text{C—OH} \\ | \\ \text{H—C—OH} \\ | \\ \text{HO—C—H} \\ | \\ \text{H—C—OH} \\ | \\ \text{H—C—OH} \\ | \\ \text{CH}_2\text{OH} \end{array}} + H_2O_2
$$

The enzyme peroxidase catalyzes a reaction between the hydrogen peroxide and orthotolidine. This produces a blue product. The yellow dye on the test strip simply serves to "dilute" the blue end product, thereby allowing greater accuracy of the test over a wider range of glucose concentrations. The test strip remains yellow if there is no glucose in the sample. It will vary from a pale green to a dark blue, depending on the concentration of glucose in the urine sample.

Frequently, doctors recommend that diabetics monitor their *blood* glucose levels multiple times each day because this provides a more accurate indication of how well the diabetic is controlling his or her diet. Many small, inexpensive glucose meters are available that couple the oxidation of glucose by glucose oxidase with an appropriate color change system. As with the urine test, the intensity of the color change is proportional to the amount of glucose in the blood. A photometer within the device reads the color change and displays the glucose concentration. An even newer technology uses a device that detects the electrical charge generated by the oxidation of glucose. In this case, it is the amount of electrical charge that is proportional to the glucose concentration.

Actually, glucose oxidase can only oxidize β-D-glucose. However, in the blood there is an equilibrium mixture of the α and β anomers of glucose. Fortunately, α-D-glucose is very quickly converted to β-D-glucose.

16.5 Biologically Important Disaccharides

LEARNING GOAL

10 Draw and name the common disaccharides and discuss their significance in biological systems.

Recall that disaccharides consist of two monosaccharides joined through an "oxygen bridge." In biological systems, monosaccharides exist in the cyclic form and, as we have seen, they are actually hemiacetals. Recall that when a hemiacetal reacts with an alcohol, the product is an *acetal.* In the case of disaccharides, the alcohol comes from a second monosaccharide. The acetals formed are given the general name *glycosides,* and the carbon-oxygen bonds are called *glycosidic bonds.*

Glycosidic bond formation is nonspecific; that is, it can occur between a hemiacetal and any of the hydroxyl groups on the second monosaccharide. However, in biological systems, we commonly see only particular disaccharides, such as maltose (Figure 16.8), lactose (Figure 16.10), or sucrose (Figure 16.11). These specific disaccharides are produced in cells because the reactions are catalyzed by enzymes. Each enzyme catalyzes the synthesis of one specific disaccharide, ensuring that one particular pair of hydroxyl groups on the reacting monosaccharides participates in glycosidic bond formation.

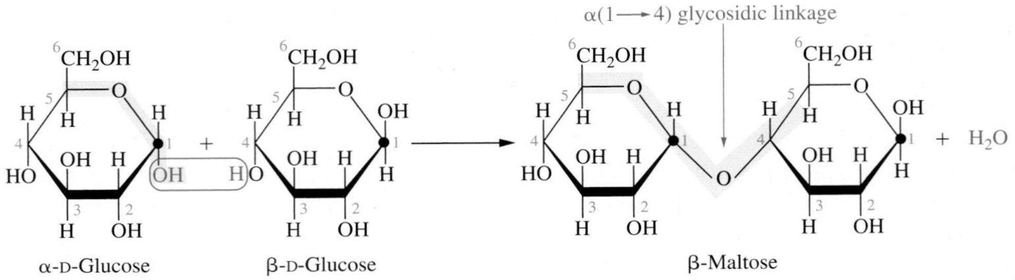

Figure 16.8 Glycosidic bond formed between the C-1 hemiacetal hydroxyl group of α-D-glucose and the C-4 alcohol hydroxyl group of β-D-glucose. The disaccharide is called β-maltose because the hydroxyl group at the reducing end of the disaccharide has the β-configuration. The hemiacetal of α-D-glucose and the acetal in β-maltose are highlighted in β yellow.

Maltose

If an α-D-glucose and a second glucose are linked, as shown in Figure 16.8, the disaccharide is **maltose,** or malt sugar. This is one of the intermediates in the hydrolysis of starch. Because the C-1 hydroxyl group of α-D-glucose is attached to C-4 of another glucose molecule, the disaccharide is linked by an α(1 → 4) glycosidic bond.

Maltose is a reducing sugar. Any disaccharide that has a hemiacetal hydroxyl group (a free —OH group at C-1) is a reducing sugar. This is because the cyclic structure can open at this position to form a free aldehyde. Disaccharides that do not contain a hemiacetal group on C-1 do not react with the Benedict's reagent and are called **nonreducing sugars.**

Lactose

LEARNING GOAL

11 Describe the difference between galactosemia and lactose intolerance.

Glycolysis is discussed in Chapter 21.

Milk sugar, or **lactose,** is a disaccharide made up of one molecule of β-D-galactose and one of either α- or β-D-glucose. Galactose differs from glucose only in the configuration of the hydroxyl group at C-4 (Figure 16.9). In the cyclic form of glucose, the C-4 hydroxyl group is "down," and in galactose it is "up." In lactose the C-1 hydroxyl group of β-D-galactose is bonded to the C-4 hydroxyl group of either an α- or β-D-glucose. The bond between the two monosaccharides is therefore a β(1 → 4) glycosidic bond (Figure 16.10).

Lactose is the principal sugar in the milk of most mammals. To be used by the body as an energy source, lactose must be hydrolyzed to produce glucose and galactose. Note that this is simply the reverse of the reaction shown in Figure 16.10. Glucose liberated by the hydrolysis of lactose is used directly in the energy-harvesting reactions of glycolysis. However, a series of reactions is necessary to convert galactose into a phosphorylated form of glucose that can be used in cellular metabolic reactions. In humans the genetic disease **galactosemia** is caused by the absence of one or more of the enzymes needed for this conversion. A toxic compound formed from galactose accumulates in people who suffer from galactosemia. If the condition is not treated, galactosemia leads to severe mental disabilities, cataracts, and early death. However, the effects of this disease can be avoided entirely by providing galactosemic infants with a diet that does not contain galactose. Such a diet, of course, cannot contain lactose and therefore must contain no milk or milk products.

Many adults, and some children, are unable to hydrolyze lactose because they do not make the enzyme *lactase.* This condition, which affects 20% of the population of the United States, is known as **lactose intolerance.** Undigested lactose remains in the intestinal tract and causes cramping and diarrhea that can eventually lead to dehydration. Some of the lactose is metabolized by intestinal bacteria that release organic acids and CO_2 gas into the intestines, causing further discomfort. Lactose intolerance is unpleasant, but its effects can be avoided by a diet that excludes milk and milk products. Alternatively, the enzyme that hydrolyzes lactose is available in tablet form. When ingested with dairy products, it breaks down the lactose, preventing symptoms.

Sucrose

Sucrose is also called table sugar, cane sugar, or beet sugar. Sucrose is an important carbohydrate in plants. It is water-soluble and can easily be transported

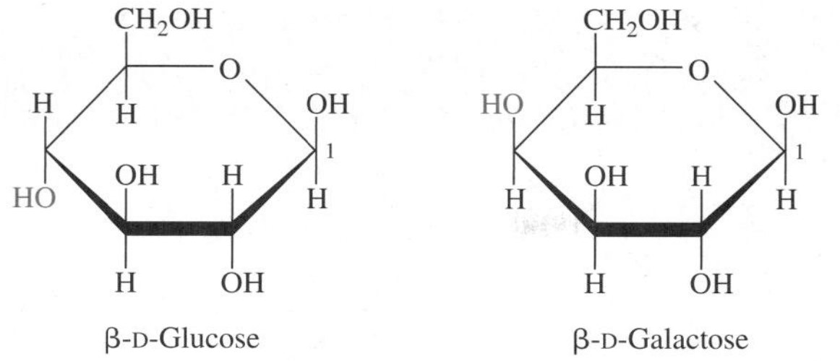

β-D-Glucose β-D-Galactose

Figure 16.9 Comparison of the cyclic forms of glucose and galactose. Note that galactose is identical to glucose except in the position of the C-4 hydroxyl group.

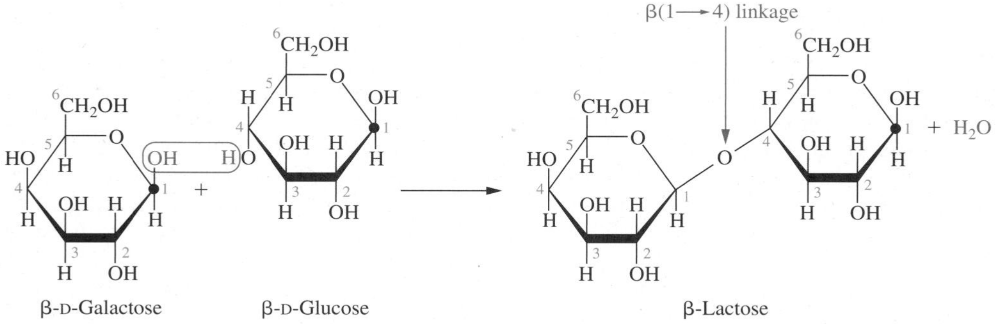

β(1⟶4) linkage

β-D-Galactose + β-D-Glucose ⟶ β-Lactose + H_2O

Figure 16.10 Glycosidic bond formed between the C-1 hydroxyl group of β-D-galactose and the C-4 hydroxyl group of β-D-glucose. The disaccharide is called β-lactose because the hydroxyl group at the reducing end of the disaccharide has the β-configuration.

through the circulatory system of the plant. It cannot be synthesized by animals. High concentrations of sucrose produce a high osmotic pressure, which inhibits the growth of microorganisms, so it is used as a preservative. Of course, it is also widely used as a sweetener. In fact, it is estimated that the average American consumes 100–125 pounds (lb) of sucrose each year. It has been suggested that sucrose in the diet is undesirable because it represents a source of empty calories; that is, it contains no vitamins or minerals. However, the only negative association that has been scientifically verified is the link between sucrose in the diet and dental caries, or cavities (see A Medical Perspective: Tooth Decay and Simple Sugars on p. 551).

Both galactosemia and lactose intolerance are treated by removing milk and milk products from the diet. Explain the difference between these two conditions.

Sucrose is a disaccharide of α-D-glucose joined to β-D-fructose (Figure 16.11). The glycosidic linkage between α-D-glucose and β-D-fructose is quite different from those that we have examined for lactose and maltose. This bond involves the anomeric carbons of *both* sugars! This bond is called an (α1 → β2) glycosidic linkage, since it involves the C-1 anomeric carbon of glucose and the C-2 anomeric carbon of fructose (noted in red in Figure 16.11). Because the (α1 → β2) glycosidic bond joins both anomeric carbons, there is no hemiacetal group. As a result, the ring cannot open to the linear form and sucrose will not react with Benedict's reagent. Thus, sucrose is not a reducing sugar.

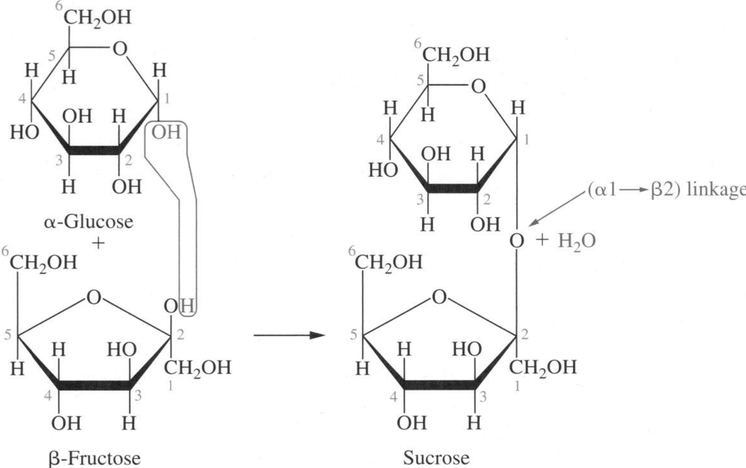

Figure 16.11 Glycosidic bond formed between the C-1 hydroxyl of α-D-glucose and the C-2 hydroxyl of β-D-fructose. This bond is called an (α1 → β2) glycosidic linkage. The disaccharide formed in this reaction is sucrose.

CHEMISTRY AT THE CRIME SCENE

Blood Group Antigens

Before DNA fingerprinting was available, blood typing was often used to analyze blood from a crime scene. Such evidence could exonerate a suspect or provide further evidence of guilt. But with only four human blood types, you can imagine how inexact conclusions could be drawn from this evidence!

In 1904, Dr. Karl Landsteiner performed a series of experiments on the blood of workers in his laboratory. He separated the blood cells from the serum, the liquid component of the blood, and mixed these samples in test tubes. When he mixed serum from one individual with blood cells of another, Landsteiner observed that, in some instances, the serum samples caused clumping, or *agglutination,* of red blood cells (RBC). (See figure below.) As a result of many such experiments, Landsteiner showed that there are four human blood groups, designated A, B, AB, and O.

We now know that differences among blood groups reflect differences among oligosaccharides attached to the proteins and lipids of the RBC membranes. The oligosaccharides on the RBC surface have a common core, consisting of β-D-*N*-acetylgalactosamine, galactose, *N*-acetylneuraminic acid (sialic acid), and L-fucose. It is the terminal monosaccharide of this oligosaccharide that distinguishes the cells and governs the compatibility of the blood types.

The A blood group antigen has β-D-*N*-acetylgalactosamine at its end, whereas the B blood group antigen has α-D-galactose. In type O blood, neither of these sugars is found on the cell surface; only the core oligosaccharide is present. Some oligosaccharides on type AB blood cells have a terminal β-D-*N*-acetylgalactosamine, whereas others have a terminal α-D-galactose.

Why does agglutination occur? The clumping reaction that occurs when incompatible bloods are mixed is an antigen-antibody reaction. Antigens are large molecules, often portions of bacteria or viruses, that stimulate the immune defenses of the body to produce protective antibodies. Antibodies bind to the foreign antigens and help to destroy them.

People with type A blood also have antibodies against type B blood (anti-B antibodies) in the blood serum. If the person with type A blood receives a transfusion of type B blood, the anti-B antibodies bind to the type B blood cells, causing clumping and destruction of those cells that can result in death. Individuals with type B blood also produce anti-A antibodies and therefore cannot receive a transfusion from a type A individual. Those with type AB blood have neither anti-A nor anti-B antibodies in their blood. (If they did, they would destroy their own red blood cells!) Type O blood has no A or B antigens on the RBC but has both anti-A and anti-B antibodies. Because of the presence of both types of antibodies, type O individuals can receive transfusions only from a person who is also type O.

In the forensic laboratory, this same agglutination reaction can be used to determine the blood type of a sample from a crime scene for comparison with the blood of the victim and that of a suspect. The results may clear the suspect or further incriminate him or her. Because there are only four human blood types, significant additional evidence is needed to prove the guilt of a suspect. In fact, DNA fingerprinting is currently being used to reevaluate guilty verdicts obtained with this less reliable evidence.

Type A

Type B

Type AB

Type O

ABO blood typing kit. When antibodies bind to antigens on the cell surface, clumping occurs.

For Further Understanding

- People with type AB blood are referred to as universal recipients. Explain why these people can receive blood of any of the four ABO types.
- Why is blood typing insufficient to prove the guilt of a suspect?

16.6 Polysaccharides

LEARNING GOAL

12 Discuss the structural, chemical, and biochemical properties of starch, glycogen, and cellulose.

Starch

Many carbohydrates that are found in nature are large polymers of glucose. Thus a polysaccharide is a large polymer composed of many monosaccharide units (the monomers) joined in one or more chains. **Homopolysaccharides** are those

α (1⟶4) linkage

(a)

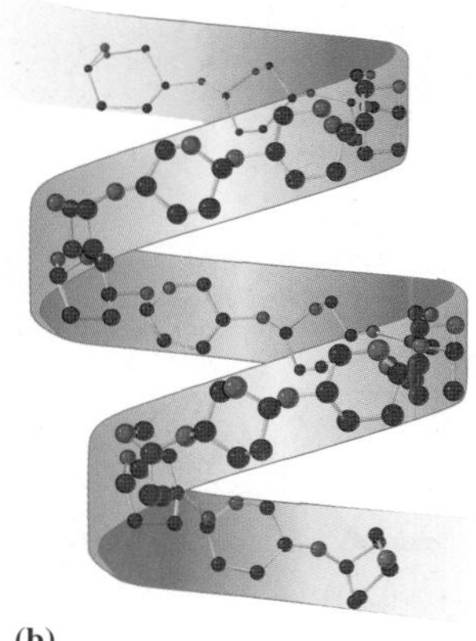

(b)

Figure 16.12 Structure of amylose. (a) A linear chain of α-D-glucose joined in α(1 ⟶ 4) glycosidic linkage makes up the primary structure of amylose. (b) Owing to hydrogen bonding, the amylose chain forms a left-handed helix that contains six glucose units per turn.

composed of a single monosaccharide. **Heteropolysaccharides** are those made up of two or more different monosaccharides. (See A Medical Perspective: Monosaccharide Derivatives and Heteropolysaccharides of Medical Interest on page 573.)

Plants have the ability to use the energy of sunlight to produce monosaccharides, principally glucose, from CO_2 and H_2O. Although sucrose is the major transport form of sugar in the plant, starch (a homopolysaccharide) is the principal storage form in most plants. These plants store glucose in starch granules. Nearly all plant cells contain some starch granules, but in some seeds, such as corn, as much as 80% of the cell's dry weight is starch.

A polymer (Section 11.5) is a large molecule made up of many small units, the monomers, held together by chemical bonds.

Starch is a heterogeneous material composed of the glucose polymers **amylose** and **amylopectin.** Amylose, which accounts for about 20% of the starch of a plant cell, is a linear polymer of α-D-glucose molecules connected by glycosidic bonds between C-1 of one glucose molecule and C-4 of a second glucose. Thus the glucose units in amylose are joined by α(1 ⟶ 4) glycosidic bonds. A single chain can contain up to 4000 glucose units. Amylose coils up into a helix that repeats every six glucose units. The structure of amylose is shown in Figure 16.12.

ANIMATION

- Natural and Synthetic Polymers

Amylose is degraded by two types of enzymes. They are produced in the pancreas, from which they are secreted into the small intestine, and the salivary glands, from which they are secreted into the saliva. α-*Amylase* cleaves the glycosidic bonds of amylose chains at random along the chain, producing shorter polysaccharide chains. The enzyme β-*amylase* sequentially cleaves the disaccharide maltose from the reducing end of the amylose chain. The maltose is hydrolyzed into glucose by the enzyme *maltase.* The glucose is quickly absorbed by intestinal cells and used by the cells of the body as a source of energy.

Enzymes are proteins that serve as biological catalysts. They speed up biochemical reactions so that life processes can function. α- and β-Amylases are called α(1 ⟶ 4) glycosidases because they cleave α(1 ⟶ 4) glycosidic bonds.

Amylopectin is a highly branched amylose in which the branches are attached to the C-6 hydroxyl groups by α(1 ⟶ 6) glycosidic bonds (Figure 16.13). The main chains consist of α(1 ⟶ 4) glycosidic bonds. Each branch contains 20–25 glucose units, and there are so many branches that the main chain can scarcely be distinguished.

Potatoes contain large amounts of starch. Describe the composition of this starch.

Glycogen

Glycogen is the major glucose storage molecule in animals. The structure of glycogen is similar to that of amylopectin. The "main chain" is linked by α(1 ⟶ 4) glycosidic bonds, and it has numerous α(1 ⟶ 6) glycosidic bonds, which provide many branch points along the chain. Glycogen differs from amylopectin only by having more and shorter branches. Otherwise, the two molecules are virtually identical. The structure of glycogen is shown in Figure 16.13.

Glycogen is stored in the liver and skeletal muscle. Glycogen synthesis and degradation in the liver are carefully regulated. As we will see in Section 21.7, these two processes are intimately involved in keeping blood glucose levels constant.

(a)

(b)

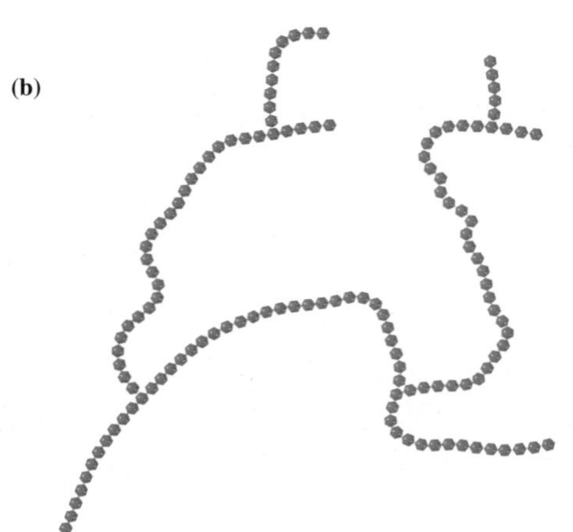

(c)

Figure 16.13 Structure of amylopectin and glycogen. (a) Both amylopectin and glycogen consist of chains of α-D-glucose molecules joined in α(1 → 4) glycosidic linkages. Branching from these chains are other chains of the same structure. Branching occurs by formation of α(1 → 6) glycosidic bonds between glucose units. (b) A representation of the branched-chain structure of amylopectin. (c) A representation of the branched-chain structure of glycogen. Glycogen differs from amylopectin only in that the branches are shorter and there are more of them.

Cellulose

The most abundant polysaccharide, indeed the most abundant organic molecule in the world, is **cellulose,** a polymer of β-D-glucose units linked by β(1 → 4) glycosidic bonds (Figure 16.14). A molecule of cellulose typically contains about 3000 glucose units, but the largest known cellulose, produced by the alga *Valonia,* contains 26,000 glucose molecules.

Cellulose is a structural component of the plant cell wall. The unbranched structure of the cellulose polymer and the β(1 → 4) glycosidic linkages allow cellulose molecules to form long, straight chains of parallel cellulose molecules called *fibrils.* These fibrils are quite rigid and are held together tightly by hydrogen bonds; thus it is not surprising that cellulose is a cell wall structural element.

In contrast to glycogen, amylose, and amylopectin, cellulose *cannot* be digested by humans. The reason is that we cannot synthesize the enzyme *cellulase,* which can hydrolyze the β(1 → 4) glycosidic linkages of the cellulose polymer. Indeed, only a few animals, such as termites, cows, and goats, are able to digest cellulose. These animals have, within their digestive tracts, microorganisms that produce the enzyme cellulase. The sugars released by this microbial digestion can then be absorbed and used by these animals. In humans, cellulose from fruits and vegetables serves as fiber in the diet.

Vegetables contribute fiber to our diet. What carbohydrate provides this fiber?

Figure 16.14 The structure of cellulose.

A MEDICAL PERSPECTIVE

Monosaccharide Derivatives and Heteropolysaccharides of Medical Interest

Many of the carbohydrates with important functions in the human body are either derivatives of simple monosaccharides or are complex polymers of monosaccharide derivatives. One type of monosaccharide derivatives, the uronates, is formed when the terminal —CH_2OH group of a monosaccharide is oxidized to a carboxylate group. α-D-Glucuronate is a uronate of glucose (see right).

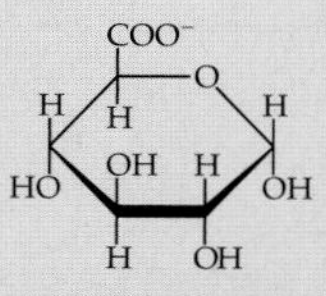

α-D-Glucuronate

In liver cells, α-D-glucuronate is bonded to hydrophobic molecules, such as steroids, to increase their solubility in water. When bonded to the modified sugar, steroids are more readily removed from the body.

Amino sugars are a second important group of monosaccharide derivatives. In amino sugars one of the hydroxyl groups (usually on carbon-2) is replaced by an amino group. Often these are found in complex oligosaccharides that are attached to cellular proteins and lipids. The most common amino sugars, D-glucosamine and D-galactosamine, are often found in the *N*-acetyl form. *N*-acetylglucosamine is a component of bacterial cell walls and *N*-acetylgalactosamine is a component of the ABO blood group antigens (see preceding, Chemistry at the Crime Scene: Blood Group Antigens).

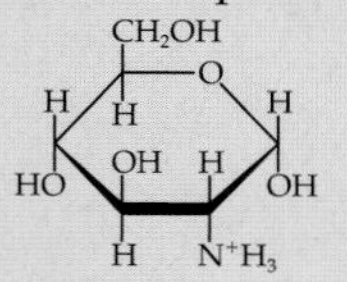

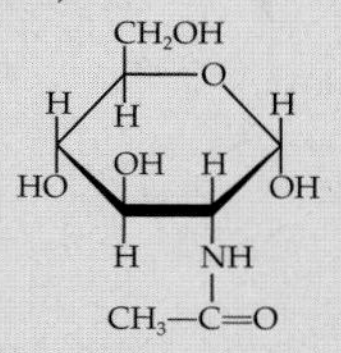

α-D-Glucosamine α-D-*N*-Acetylglucosamine

Heteropolysaccharides are long-chain polymers that contain more than one type of monosaccharide, many of which are amino sugars. These *glycosaminoglycans* include chondroitin sulfate, hyaluronic acid, and heparin. Hyaluronic acid is abundant in the fluid of joints and in the vitreous humor of the eye. Chondroitin sulfate is an important component of cartilage; and heparin has anticoagulant function. The structures of the repeat units of these polymers are shown below.

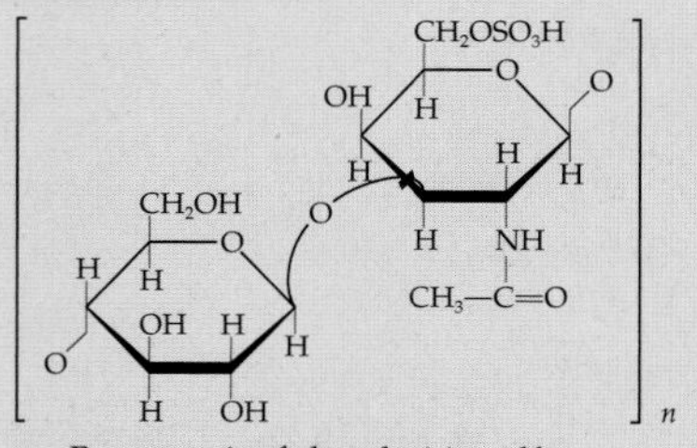

Repeat unit of chondroitin sulfate

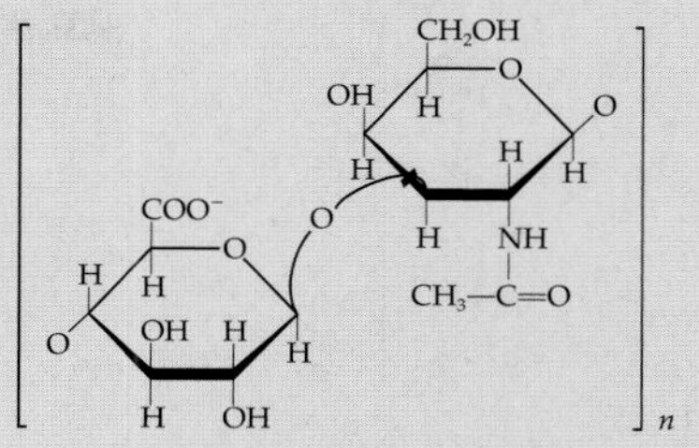

Repeat unit of hyaluronic acid

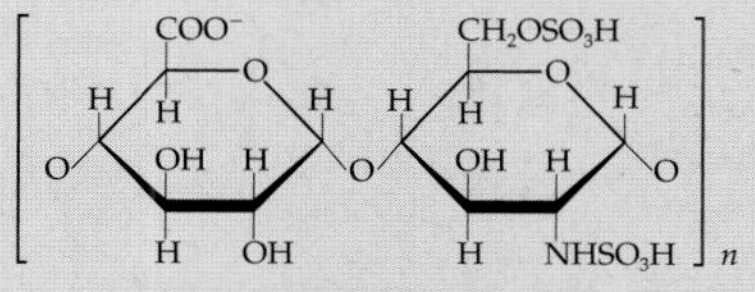

Repeat unit of heparin

Two of these molecules have been studied as potential treatments for osteoarthritis, a painful, degenerative disease of the joints. The amino sugar D-glucosamine is thought to stimulate the production of collagen. Collagen is one of the main components of articular cartilage, which is the shock-absorbing cushion within the joints. With aging, some of the D-glucosamine is lost, leading to a reduced cartilage layer and to the onset and progression of arthritis. It has been suggested that ingestion of D-glucosamine can actually "jump-start" production of cartilage and help repair eroded cartilage in arthritic joints.

It has also been suggested that chondroitin sulfate can protect existing cartilage from premature breakdown. It absorbs large amounts of water, which is thought to facilitate diffusion of nutrients into the cartilage, providing precursors for the synthesis of new cartilage. The increased fluid also acts as a shock absorber.

Capsules containing D-glucosamine and chondroitin sulfate are available over the counter, and many sufferers of osteoarthritis prefer to take this nutritional supplement as an alternative to any nonsteroidal anti-inflammatory drug (NSAID), such as ibuprofen. Although NSAIDs can reduce inflammation and pain, long-term use of NSAIDs can result in stomach ulcers, damage to auditory nerves, and kidney damage.

For Further Understanding

- In Chapter 15 we learned that nonsteroidal anti-inflammatory drugs (NSAIDs), such as ibuprofen, are analgesics used to treat pain, such as that associated with osteoarthritis. Why do many people prefer to treat osteoarthritis with D-glucosamine and chondroitin sulfate rather than NSAIDs?
- Explain why attaching a molecule such as α-D-glucuronate to a steroid molecule would increase its water solubility.

Question 16.11 What chemical reactions are catalyzed by α-amylase and β-amylase?

Question 16.12 What is the function of cellulose in the human diet? How does this relate to the structure of cellulose?

CHAPTER MAP

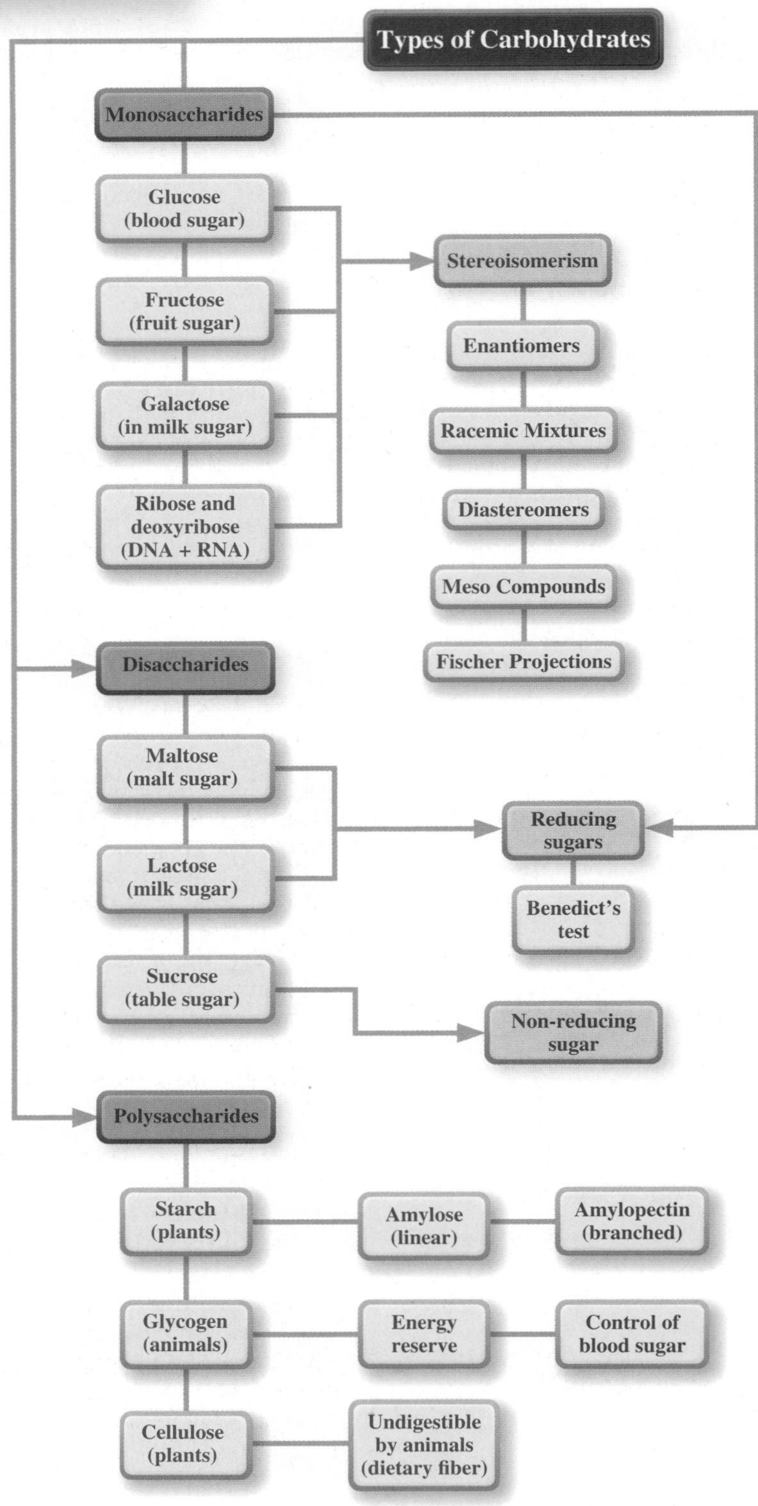
Types of Carbohydrates
Monosaccharides
Glucose (blood sugar)
Fructose (fruit sugar)
Galactose (in milk sugar)
Ribose and deoxyribose (DNA + RNA)
Stereoisomerism
Enantiomers
Racemic Mixtures
Diastereomers
Meso Compounds
Fischer Projections
Disaccharides
Maltose (malt sugar)
Lactose (milk sugar)
Sucrose (table sugar)
Reducing sugars
Benedict's test
Non-reducing sugar
Polysaccharides
Starch (plants)
Amylose (linear)
Amylopectin (branched)
Glycogen (animals)
Energy reserve
Control of blood sugar
Cellulose (plants)
Undigestible by animals (dietary fiber)

SUMMARY

16.1 Types of Carbohydrates

- **Carbohydrates** are found in a wide variety of naturally occurring substances and serve as principal energy sources for the body.
- Dietary carbohydrates include complex carbohydrates, such as starch in potatoes, and simple carbohydrates, such as sucrose.
- Carbohydrates are classified as **monosaccharides** (one **saccharide** or sugar unit), **disaccharides** (two sugar units), **oligosaccharides** (three to ten sugar units), and **polysaccharides** (many sugar units).
- Individual monosaccharides are joined to others through **glycosidic bonds.**

16.2 Monosaccharides

- Monosaccharides that have an aldehyde as their most oxidized functional group are **aldoses** and those having a ketone group as their most oxidized functional group are **ketoses.**
- Monosaccharides are classified as **trioses, tetroses, pentoses, hexoses,** and so forth, depending on the number of carbon atoms in the molecule.

16.3 Stereoisomers and Stereochemistry

- **Stereochemistry** is the study of the different spatial arrangements of atoms.
- **Stereoisomers** of monosaccharides exist because of the presence of **chiral carbon** atoms. They are nonsuperimposable mirror images of one another or **enantiomers.** Molecules that exist as enantiomers are **chiral molecules.**
  - Stereoisomers of monosaccharides are classified as D- or L- based on the arrangement of atoms on the chiral carbon farthest from the aldehyde or ketone group.
  - If this —OH is on the right of the molecule, the stereoisomer is of the D-family.
  - If this —OH is on the left of the molecule, the stereoisomer is of the L-family.
- Each pair of stereoisomers rotates plane-polarized light in opposite directions.
  - A polarimeter is used to measure the direction of rotation of plane-polarized light.
  - Compounds that rotate light in a clockwise direction are termed *dextrorotatory* and are designated (+).
  - Compounds that rotate light in a counterclockwise direction are termed *levorotatory* and are designated (−).
- **Diastereomers** are stereoisomers with more than one chiral center that are not mirror images of one another.
- **Meso compounds** have two chiral carbons and each carbon is bonded to identical substituents. As a result, they are achiral.
- A **Fischer Projection** is a two-dimensional drawing of a molecule that shows a chiral carbon at the intersection of two lines.
  - Horizontal lines represent bonds projecting out of the page.
  - Vertical lines represent bonds that project into the page.

16.4 Biologically Important Monosaccharides

- Important monosaccharides include **glyceraldehyde, glucose, galactose, fructose,** and **ribose.**
- Monosaccharides containing five or six carbon atoms can exist as five- or six-member rings. These are **hemiacetals.**
  - Ring formation produces a new chiral carbon at the original carbonyl carbon, which is designated either α or β depending on the orientation of the groups.
  - Isomers differing in the arrangement of bonds around the hemiacetal carbon are called **anomers.**
  - The **Haworth projection** is used to represent the orientation of substituents around a cyclic sugar molecule.
- **Reducing sugars** are oxidized by the **Benedict's reagent.** All monosaccharides and all common disaccharides, except sucrose, are reducing sugars.

16.5 Biologically Important Disaccharides

- **Maltose** is a disaccharide formed from α-D-glucose and a second glucose molecule.
  - It is formed in the hydrolysis of starch.
- **Lactose** is a disaccharide of β-D-galactose bonded β(1 → 4) with D-glucose.
  - In **galactosemia,** defective metabolism of galactose leads to accumulation of a toxic by-product. Symptoms can be avoided by exclusion of milk from the diet.
  - About 20% of the U.S. population has **lactose intolerance.** Caused by the inability to digest lactose, the symptoms can be avoided by exclusion of milk from the diet.
- **Sucrose** is a dimer composed of α-D-glucose bonded (α1 → β2) with β-D-fructose.
- Sucrose is a **nonreducing sugar.**

16.6 Polysaccharides

- **Homopolysaccharides** are made up of a single monosaccharide.
- Starch, the storage polysaccharide of many plants, is a homopolysaccharide of glucose. Starch is 20% **amylose** and 80% **amylopectin.**
  - Amylose is a polymer of α-D-glucose **monomers** bonded α(1 → 4).
  - Amylopectin has a main chain like amylose and has branches that are joined α(1 → 6) to the main chain.
- **Glycogen** is the major storage polysaccharide of animal cells and resembles amylopectin. It differs by having more and shorter branches.
  - Liver glycogen is a reserve that is used to regulate blood glucose levels.
- **Cellulose** is a major structural molecule of plants. It is a β(1 → 4) polymer of D-glucose that may contain thousands of glucose monomers.
  - Cellulose cannot be digested by animals.
- A **heteropolysaccharide** is a polysaccharide composed of two or more different monosaccharides.

ANSWERS TO PRACTICE PROBLEMS

16.1 a.

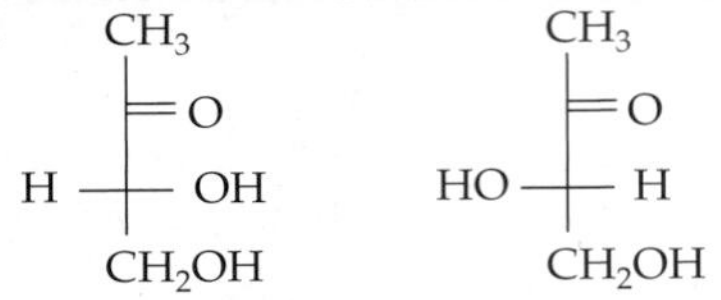

CH_3	CH_3
=O	=O
H — OH	HO — H
CH_2OH	CH_2OH

b.

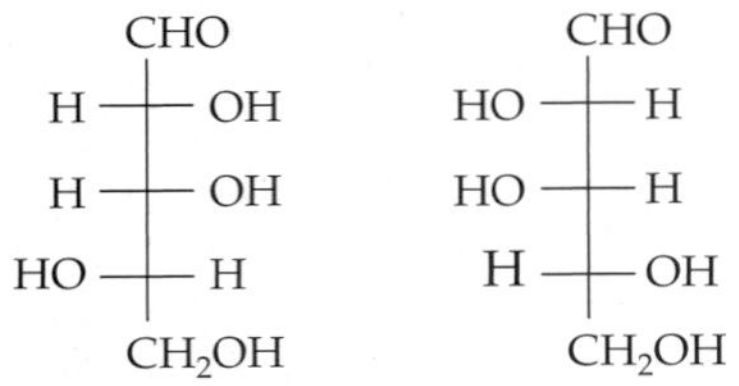

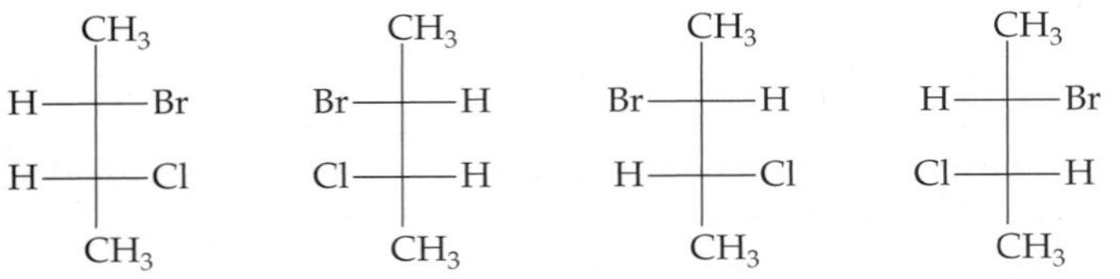

CHO	CHO
H — OH	HO — H
H — OH	HO — H
HO — H	H — OH
CH_2OH	CH_2OH

c.

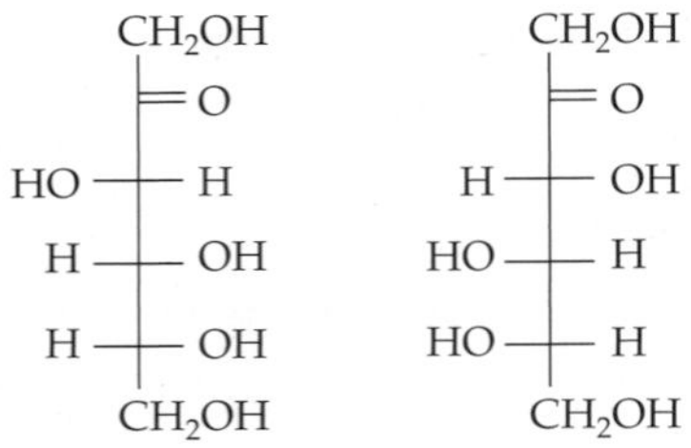

CH_2OH	CH_2OH
=O	=O
HO — H	H — OH
H — OH	HO — H
H — OH	HO — H
CH_2OH	CH_2OH

16.2 a.

A	B	C	D
CH_3	CH_3	CH_3	CH_3
H — Br	Br — H	Br — H	H — Br
H — Cl	Cl — H	H — Cl	Cl — H
CH_3	CH_3	CH_3	CH_3

There are two chiral carbons in this molecule. Thus there are four possible stereoisomers. There are two possible configurations for each chiral carbon. Compounds A and B are mirror images. Compounds C and D are also mirror images.

b.

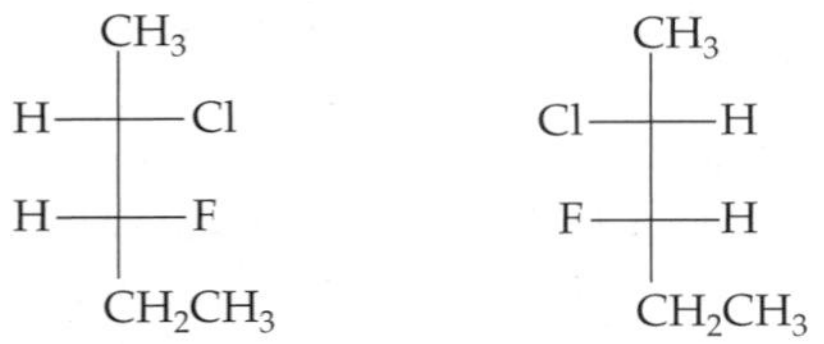

A	B
CH_3	CH_3
H — Cl	Cl — H
H — F	F — H
CH_2CH_3	CH_2CH_3

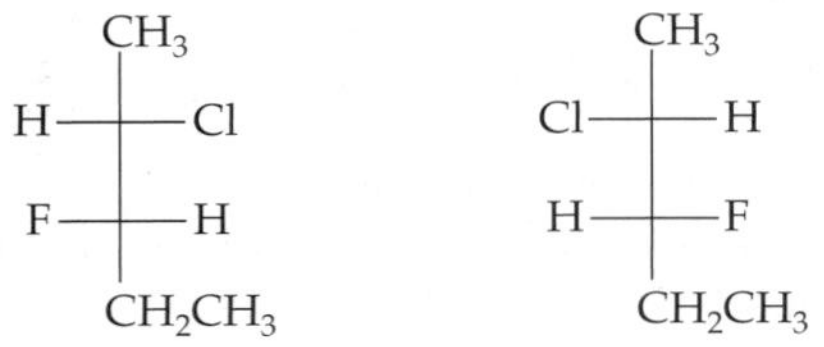

C	D
CH_3	CH_3
H — Cl	Cl — H
F — H	H — F
CH_2CH_3	CH_2CH_3

There are two chiral carbons in this molecule. Thus there are four possible stereoisomers. There are two possible configurations for each chiral carbon. Compounds A and B are mirror images. Compounds C and D are also mirror images.

c.

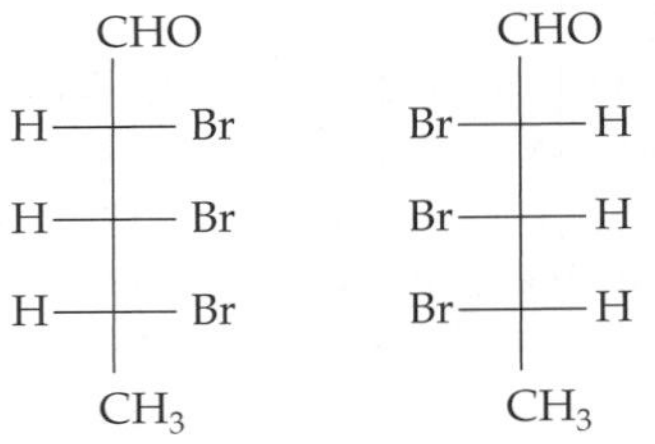

A	B
CHO	CHO
H — Br	Br — H
H — Br	Br — H
H — Br	Br — H
CH_3	CH_3

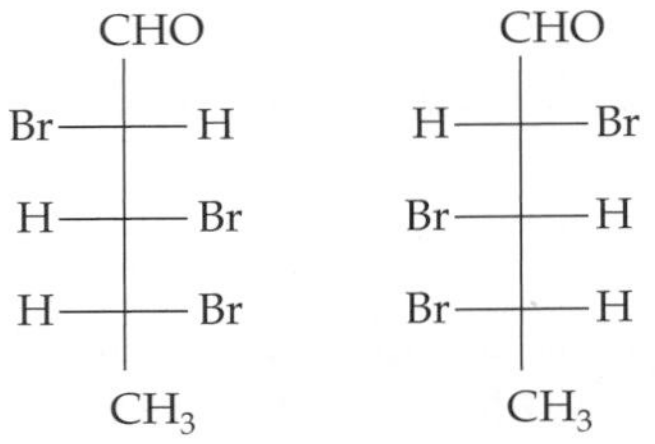

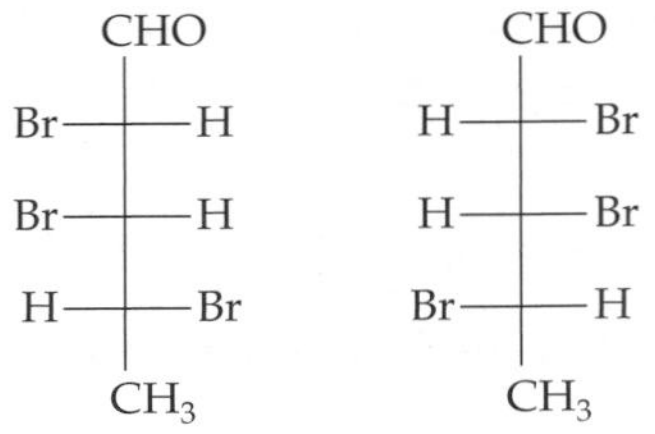

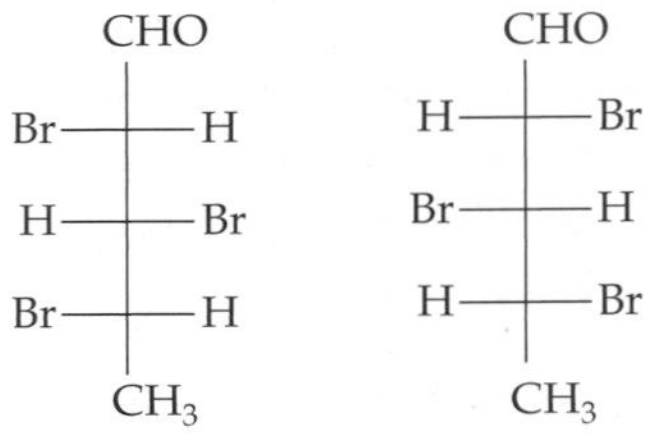

C	D
CHO	CHO
Br — H	H — Br
H — Br	Br — H
H — Br	Br — H
CH_3	CH_3

E	F
CHO	CHO
Br — H	H — Br
Br — H	H — Br
H — Br	Br — H
CH_3	CH_3

G	H
CHO	CHO
Br — H	H — Br
H — Br	Br — H
Br — H	H — Br
CH_3	CH_3

There are three chiral carbons in this molecule. Thus there are eight possible stereoisomers. There are two possible configurations for each chiral carbon. Pairs of enantiomers include: A and B, C and F, and G and H.

16.3 a.

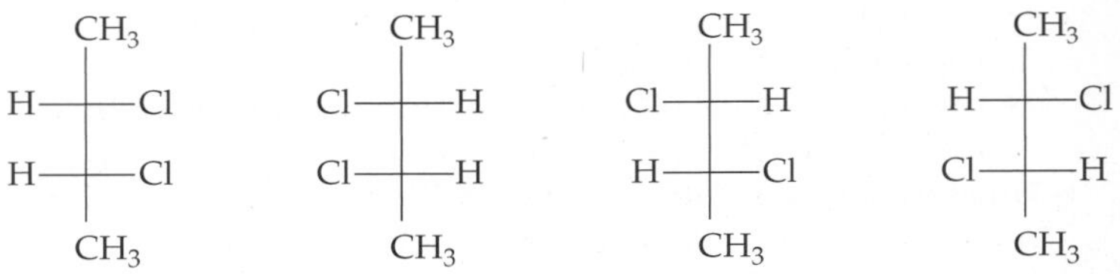

A	B	C	D
CH_3	CH_3	CH_3	CH_3
H — Cl	Cl — H	Cl — H	H — Cl
H — Cl	Cl — H	H — Cl	Cl — H
CH_3	CH_3	CH_3	CH_3

There are two chiral carbons in this molecule. But, each of the two chiral carbons is bonded to the same four nonidentical groups. Therefore, there are only three possible stereoisomers. Compounds A and B are identical and they are meso. Compounds C and D are enantiomers.

b.

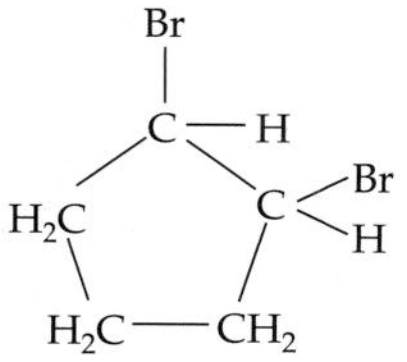

A 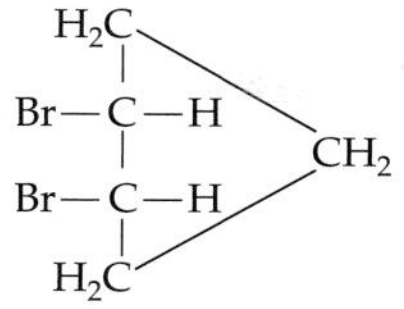 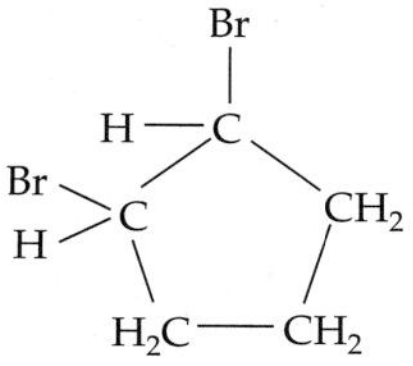 B 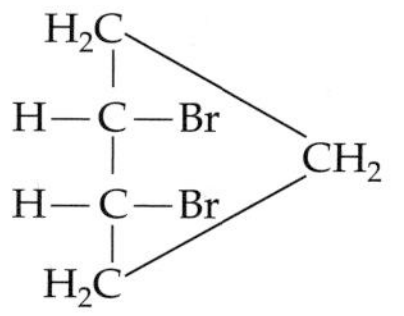 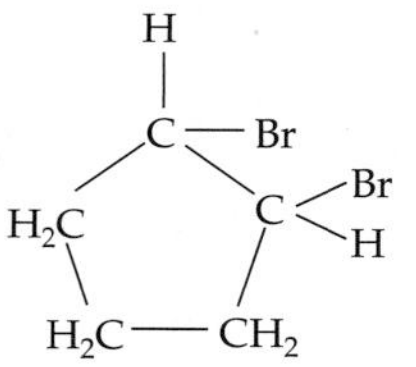 C 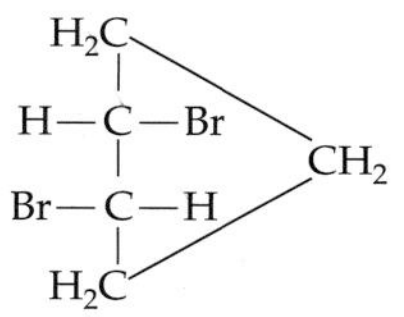 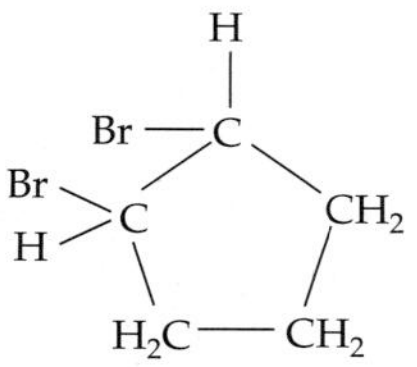 D

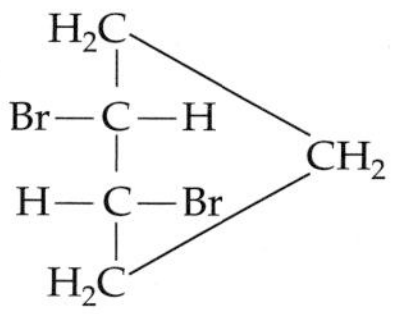

When 1.2-dibromocyclopentane is drawn as shown in the four structures on the left, it is shown that there are two chiral carbons in this molecule. The set of structures on the right is provided to help you see the stereochemistry around those chiral carbons. Here it should be noted that there is a plane of symmetry within the molecule. Each of the two chiral carbons is bonded to the same four nonidentical groups. Therefore, there are only three possible stereoisomers. Compounds A and B are identical and they are meso. Compounds C and D are enantiomers.

c.

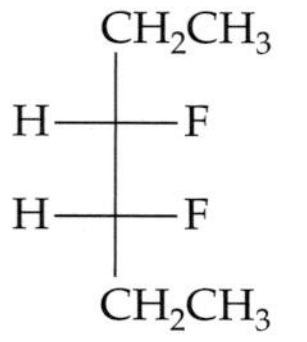

A: CH_2CH_3; H—F; H—F; CH_2CH_3

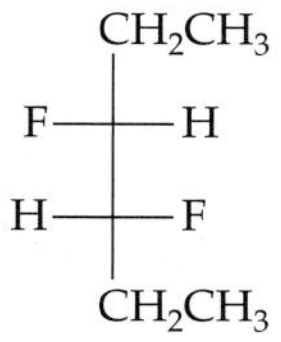

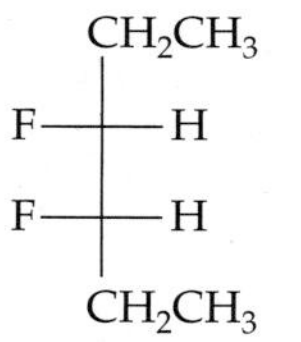

C: CH_2CH_3; F—H; H—F; CH_2CH_3

B: CH_2CH_3; F—H; F—H; CH_2CH_3

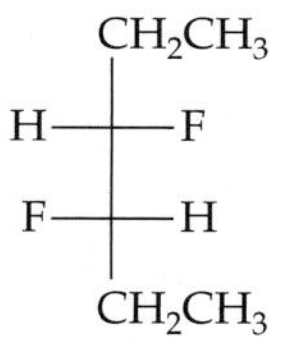

D: CH_2CH_3; H—F; F—H; CH_2CH_3

There are two chiral carbons in this molecule. But, each of the two chiral carbons is bonded to the same four nonidentical groups. Therefore, there are only three possible stereoisomers. Compounds A and B are identical and they are meso. Compounds C and D are enantiomers.

16.4

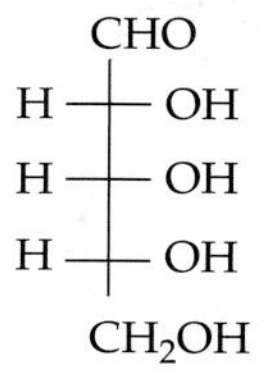

D-Ribose: CHO; H—OH; H—OH; H—OH; CH_2OH

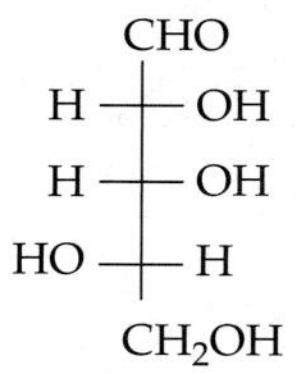

L-Ribose: CHO; H—OH; H—OH; HO—H; CH_2OH

16.5 **a.**

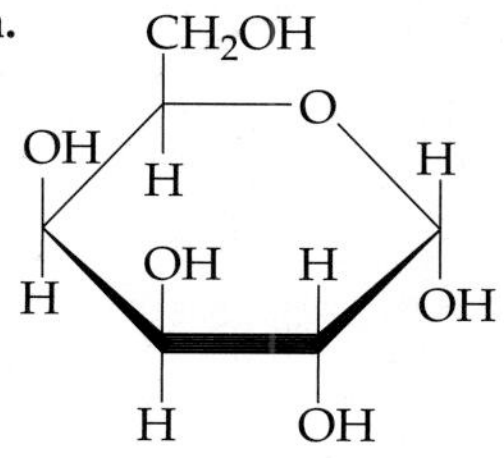

α-D-Galactose 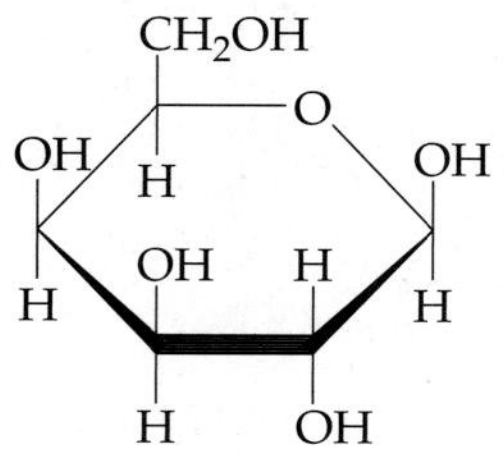 β-D-Galactose

b.

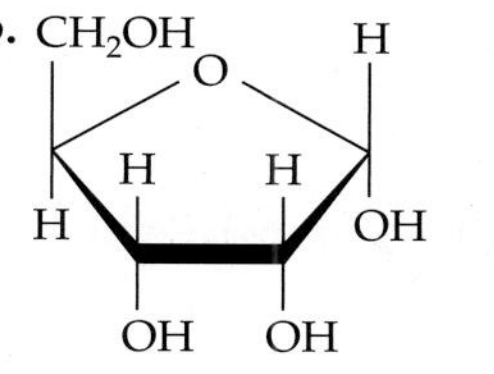

α-D-Ribose 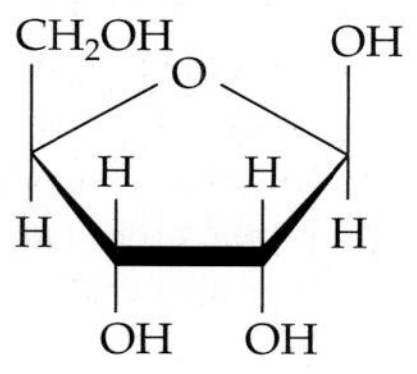 β-D-Ribose

QUESTIONS AND PROBLEMS

Types of Carbohydrates

Foundations

16.13 What is the difference between a monosaccharide and a disaccharide?

16.14 What is a polysaccharide?

Applications

16.15 Read the labels on some of the foods in your kitchen, and see how many products you can find that list one or more carbohydrates among the ingredients in the package. Make a list of these compounds, and attempt to classify them as monosaccharides, disaccharides, or polysaccharides.

16.16 Some disaccharides are often referred to by their common names. What are the chemical names of (a) milk sugar, (b) beet sugar, and (c) cane sugar?

16.17 How many kcal of energy are released when 1 g of carbohydrate is "burned" or oxidized?

16.18 List some natural sources of carbohydrates.

16.19 Draw and provide the names of an aldohexose and a ketohexose.

16.20 Draw and provide the name of an aldotriose.

Monosaccharides

Foundations

16.21 Define the term *aldose.*

16.22 Define the term *ketose.*

16.23 What is a tetrose?

16.24 What is a hexose?

16.25 What is a ketopentose?

16.26 What is an aldotriose?

Applications

16.27 Identify each of the following sugars.

a. CH_2OH / O / H, H, OH, HO, OH, H, H, H, OH

c. CH_2OH / O / HO, H, H, H, OH, H, OH, H, OH

b. $HOCH_2$ / O / OH / H, HO, H, CH_2OH, OH, H

16.28 Draw the open-chain form of the sugars in Question 16.27.

16.29 Draw all of the different possible aldotrioses of molecular formula $C_3H_6O_3$.

16.30 Draw all of the different possible aldotetroses of molecular formula $C_4H_8O_4$.

Stereoisomers and Stereochemistry

Foundations

16.31 Define the term *stereoisomer.*

16.32 Define the term *enantiomer.*

16.33 Define the term *chiral carbon.*

16.34 Draw an aldotetrose. Note each chiral carbon with an asterisk (*).

16.35 Explain how a polarimeter works.

16.36 What is plane-polarized light?

16.37 What is a Fischer Projection?

16.38 How would you produce a Fischer Projection beginning with a three-dimensional model of a sugar?

16.39 Define the term *diastereomer.*

16.40 Define the term *meso compound.*

Applications

16.41 Is there any difference between dextrose and D-glucose?

16.42 The linear structure of D-glucose is shown in Figure 16.7. Draw its mirror image.

16.43 How are D- and L-glyceraldehyde related?

16.44 Determine whether each of the following is a D- or L-sugar:

a.
```
     O
     ‖
     CH
H────OH
H────OH
     CH2OH
```

b.
```
     O
     ‖
     CH
H────OH
H────OH
HO───H
     CH2OH
```

c.
```
     O
     ‖
     CH
H────OH
HO───H
     CH2OH
```

16.45 Draw a Fischer Projection formula for each of the following compounds. Indicate each of the chiral carbons with an asterisk (*).

a.
```
      O
      ‖
      C—H
HO—C—H
 H—C—OH
HO—C—H
HO—C—H
      CH2OH
```

b.
```
      O
      ‖
      C—H
 H—C—OH
 H—C—OH
      CH2OH
```

c.
```
      O
      ‖
      C—H
HO—C—H
 H—C—OH
HO—C—H
 H—C—OH
HO—C—H
      CH2OH
```

16.46 Draw a Fischer Projection formula for each of the following compounds. Indicate each of the chiral carbons with an asterisk (*).

a.
```
      O
      ‖
      C—H
 H—C—H
HO—C—H
HO—C—H
HO—C—H
      CH2OH
```

b.
```
      O
      ‖
      C—H
 H—C—H
 H—C—OH
      CH2OH
```

c.
```
      O
      ‖
      C—H
HO—C—H
HO—C—H
HO—C—H
 H—C—OH
HO—C—H
      CH2OH
```

16.47 Draw all the possible stereoisomers of each of the following compounds and indicate which are enantiomers, diastereomers, or meso compounds.

a.
```
   CHO
H──┼──OH
H──┼──OH
   CHO
```

b.
```
   CH2OH
H──┼──Br
H──┼──CH3
   CH2OH
```

16.48 Draw all the possible stereoisomers of each of the following compounds and indicate which are enantiomers, diastereomers, or meso compounds.

a.
```
   COOH
H──┼──H
H──┼──Br
H──┼──Cl
H──┼──H
   COOH
```

b.
```
   CHO
H──┼──OH
H──┼──Br
   CHO
```

16.49 Draw all the possible stereoisomers of each of the following compounds and indicate which are enantiomers, diastereomers, or meso compounds.

a. $CH_3CH_2CHOHCHOHCH_2CH_3$

b. $CH_2OH\overset{O}{\overset{\|}{C}}CHFCHCl\overset{O}{\overset{\|}{C}}CH_2OH$

16.50 Draw all the possible stereoisomers of each of the following compounds and indicate which are enantiomers, diastereomers, or meso compounds.

a. $CH_3\overset{O}{\overset{\|}{C}}CHOHCHOH\overset{O}{\overset{\|}{C}}CH_3$

b. $CH_2OHCHOHCHClCH_2OH$

Biologically Important Monosaccharides

Foundations

16.51 Define the term *anomer.*
16.52 What is a Haworth projection?
16.53 What is a hemiacetal?
16.54 Explain why the cyclization of D-glucose forms a hemiacetal.

Applications

16.55 Why does cyclization of D-glucose give two isomers, α- and β-D-glucose?
16.56 Draw the structure of the open-chain form of D-fructose, and show how it cyclizes to form α- and β-D-fructose.
16.57 Which of the following would give a positive Benedict's test?
a. Sucrose
b. Glycogen
c. β-Maltose
d. α-Lactose
16.58 Why was the Benedict's reagent useful for determining the amount of glucose in the urine?
16.59 Describe what is meant by a pair of enantiomers. Draw an example of a pair of enantiomers.
16.60 What is a chiral carbon atom?
16.61 When discussing sugars, what do we mean by an intramolecular hemiacetal?
16.62 Explain why ketoses can be oxidized in the Benedict's test in contrast to ketones, which cannot.

Biologically Important Disaccharides

Foundations

16.63 Define the term *disaccharide.*
16.64 What is an acetal?
16.65 What is a glycosidic bond?
16.66 Why are glycosidic bonds acetals?

Applications

16.67 Maltose is a disaccharide isolated from amylose that consists of two glucose units linked by an $\alpha(1 \rightarrow 4)$ bond. Draw the structure of this molecule.
16.68 Sucrose is a disaccharide formed by linking α-D-glucose and β-D-fructose by an $(\alpha 1 \rightarrow \beta 2)$ bond. Draw the structure of this disaccharide.
16.69 What is the major biological source of lactose?
16.70 What metabolic defect causes galactosemia?
16.71 What simple treatment prevents most of the ill effects of galactosemia?
16.72 What are the major physiological effects of galactosemia?
16.73 What is lactose intolerance?
16.74 What is the difference between lactose intolerance and galactosemia?

Polysaccharides

Foundations

16.75 What is a polymer?
16.76 What form of sugar is used as the major transport sugar in a plant?
16.77 What is the major storage form of sugar in a plant?
16.78 What is the major structural form of sugar in a plant?
16.79 What is a homopolysaccharide?
16.80 What is a heteropolysaccharide?
16.81 List some examples of homopolysaccharides.
16.82 List some examples of heteropolysaccharides. (*Hint:* Refer to A Medical Perspective: Monosaccharide Derivatives and Heteropolysaccharides of Medical Interest.)

Applications

16.83 What is the difference between the structure of cellulose and the structure of amylose?
16.84 How does the structure of amylose differ from that of amylopectin and glycogen?
16.85 What is the major physiological purpose of glycogen?
16.86 Where in the body do you find glycogen stored?
16.87 Where are α-amylase and β-amylase produced?
16.88 Where do α-amylase and β-amylase carry out their enzymatic functions?

CRITICAL THINKING PROBLEMS

1. The six-member glucose ring structure is not a flat ring. Like cyclohexane, it can exist in the chair conformation. Build models of the chair conformation of α- and β-D-glucose. Draw each of these structures. Which would you predict to be the more stable isomer? Explain your reasoning.
2. The following is the structure of salicin, a bitter-tasting compound found in the bark of willow trees:

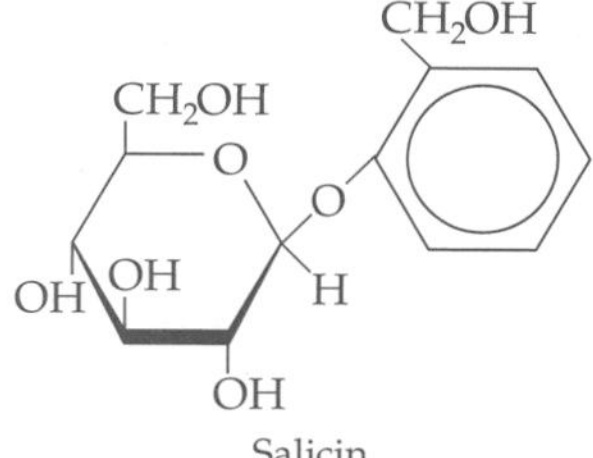

Salicin

The aromatic ring portion of this structure is quite insoluble in water. How would forming a glycosidic bond between the aromatic ring and β-D-glucose alter the solubility? Explain your answer.

3. Ancient peoples used salicin to reduce fevers. Write an equation for the acid-catalyzed hydrolysis of the glycosidic bond of salicin. Compare the aromatic product with the structure of acetylsalicylic acid (aspirin). Use this information to develop a hypothesis explaining why ancient peoples used salicin to reduce fevers.

4. Chitin is a modified cellulose in which the C-2 hydroxyl group of each glucose is replaced by

$$\mathrm{-NH\overset{\overset{\displaystyle O}{\|}}{C}CH_3}$$

This nitrogen-containing polysaccharide makes up the shells of lobsters, crabs, and the exoskeletons of insects. Draw a portion of a chitin polymer consisting of four monomers.

5. Pectins are polysaccharides obtained from fruits and berries and used to thicken jellies and jams. Pectins are $\alpha(1 \rightarrow 4)$ linked D-galacturonic acid. D-Galacturonic acid is D-galactose in which the C-6 hydroxyl group has been oxidized to a carboxyl group. Draw a portion of a pectin polymer consisting of four monomers.

6. Peonin is a red pigment found in the petals of peony flowers. Consider the structure of peonin:

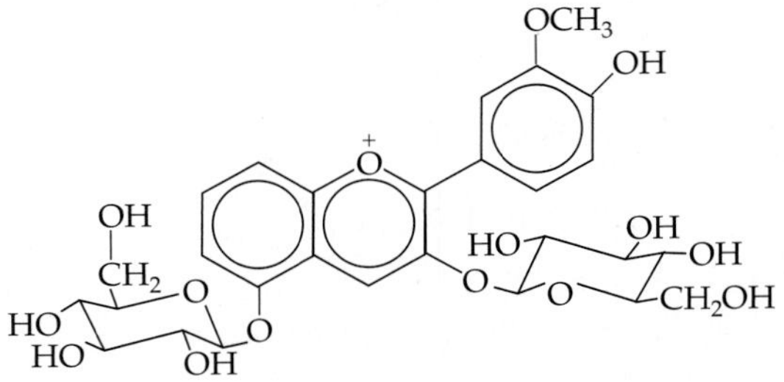

Why do you think peonin is bonded to two hexoses? What monosaccharide(s) would be produced by acid-catalyzed hydrolysis of peonin?

17

Lipids and Their Functions in Biochemical Systems

LEARNING GOALS

1 Discuss the physical and chemical properties and biological functions of each of the types of lipids.
2 Write the structures of saturated and unsaturated fatty acids.
3 Compare and contrast the structures and properties of saturated and unsaturated fatty acids.
4 Describe the functions of prostaglandins.
5 Discuss the mechanism by which aspirin reduces pain.
6 Write equations representing the reactions that fatty acids and glycerides undergo.
7 Draw the structure of a phospholipid and discuss its amphipathic nature.
8 Discuss the general classes of sphingolipids and their functions.
9 Draw the structure of the steroid nucleus and discuss the functions of steroid hormones.
10 Describe the function of lipoproteins in triglyceride and cholesterol transport in the body.
11 Draw the structure of the cell membrane and discuss its functions.

The foxglove plant is a source of digitoxin and other cardiotonic steroids. Read A Medical Perspective: Steroids and the Treatment of Heart Disease in this chapter and explain why the ingestion of foxglove can have deadly consequences.

OUTLINE

Introduction 582
17.1 Biological Functions of Lipids 582
A Medical Perspective: Lifesaving Lipids 583
17.2 Fatty Acids 584
17.3 Glycerides 590
Chemistry at the Crime Scene: Adipocere and Mummies of Soap 597
17.4 Nonglyceride Lipids 598
A Medical Perspective: Disorders of Sphingolipid Metabolism 601
A Medical Perspective: Steroids and the Treatment of Heart Disease 602
17.5 Complex Lipids 605
17.6 The Structure of Biological Membranes 608
A Medical Perspective: Liposome Delivery Systems 610

INTRODUCTION

Lipids seem to be the most controversial group of biological molecules, particularly in the fields of medicine and nutrition. We are concerned about the use of anabolic steroids by athletes. Although these hormones increase muscle mass and enhance performance, we are just beginning to understand the damage they cause to the body.

We worry about what types of dietary fat we should consume. We hear frequently about the amounts of saturated fats and cholesterol in our diets because a strong correlation has been found between these lipids and heart disease. Large quantities of dietary saturated fats may also predispose an individual to colon, esophageal, stomach, and breast cancers. As a result, we are advised to reduce our intake of cholesterol and saturated fats.

In this chapter we will study the diverse collection of molecules referred to as lipids. We will see that triglycerides are both a dietary source of energy and a (sometimes unwanted) storage form of energy. Other lipids serve as structural components of the cell; for instance, phospholipids and cholesterol are components of the membranes around each of our cells. Some of the chemical messengers of our bodies are lipids. These include the steroid hormones and the hormonelike prostaglandins. Even some of the vitamins that are required in our diet are lipids and any diet that is completely fat-free will result in deficiencies of these vitamins.

This quick tour through a few of the potential hazards of lipids and their essential roles in our bodies makes it easy to understand why lipids are so controversial and why so much literature has been published about the lipids in our diets. But, in fact, standards of fat intake have not been experimentally determined. The most recent U.S. Dietary Guidelines recommend that our daily fat intake be 20–35% of our daily caloric intake. Fewer than 10% of the calories we consume should be saturated fats, and cholesterol intake should be less than 300 milligrams/day. Overall, the intake of fats and oils that are high in saturated fats or in *trans*-fatty acids should be limited.

17.1 Biological Functions of Lipids

LEARNING GOAL

1 Discuss the physical and chemical properties and biological functions of each of the types of lipids.

The term **lipids** actually refers to a collection of organic molecules of varying chemical composition. They are grouped together on the basis of their solubility in nonpolar solvents. Lipids may be subdivided into four main types:

1. *Fatty acids* (saturated and unsaturated)
2. *Glycerides* (glycerol-containing lipids)
3. *Nonglyceride lipids* (sphingolipids, steroids, waxes)
4. *Complex lipids* (lipoproteins)

In this chapter we examine the structure, properties, chemical reactions, and biological functions of each of the lipid groups shown in Figure 17.1.

As a result of differences in their structures, lipids serve many different functions in the human body. The following brief list will give you an idea of the importance of lipids in biological processes:

- *Energy source.* Like carbohydrates, lipids are an excellent source of energy for the body. When oxidized, each gram of fat releases 9 kilocalories (kcal) of energy, or more than twice the energy released by oxidation of a gram of carbohydrate.
- *Energy storage.* Most of the energy stored in the body is in the form of lipids (triglycerides). Stored in fat cells called *adipocytes,* these fats are a particularly rich source of energy for the body.
- *Cell membrane structural components.* Phosphoglycerides, sphingolipids, and steroids make up the basic structure of all cell membranes. These membranes control the flow of molecules into and out of cells and allow cell-to-cell communication.

A MEDICAL PERSPECTIVE

Lifesaving Lipids

In the intensive-care nursery the premature infant struggles for life. Born three and a half months early, the baby weighs only 1.6 pounds (lb), and the lungs labor to provide enough oxygen to keep the tiny body alive. Premature infants often have respiratory difficulties because they have not yet begun to produce *pulmonary surfactant.*

Pulmonary surfactant is a combination of phospholipids and proteins that reduces surface tension in the alveoli of the lungs. (Alveoli are the small, thin-walled air sacs in the lungs.) This allows efficient gas exchange across the membranes of the alveolar cells; oxygen can more easily diffuse from the air into the tissues and carbon dioxide can easily diffuse from the tissues into the air. Without pulmonary surfactant, gas exchange in the lungs is very poor.

Pulmonary surfactant is not produced until early in the sixth month of pregnancy. Premature babies born before they have begun secretion of natural surfactant suffer from *respiratory distress syndrome* (*RDS*), which is caused by the severe difficulty they have obtaining enough oxygen from the air that they breathe.

Until recently, RDS was a major cause of death among premature infants, but now a lifesaving treatment is available. A fine aerosol of an artificial surfactant is administered directly into the trachea. The Glaxo-Wellcome Company product EXOSURF Neonatal contains the phospholipid lecithin to reduce surface tension; 1-hexadecanol, which spreads the lecithin; and a polymer called *tyloxapol,* which disperses both the lecithin and the 1-hexadecanol.

Artificial pulmonary surfactant therapy has dramatically reduced premature infant death caused by RDS and appears to have reduced overall mortality for all babies born weighing less than 700 grams (g) (about 1.5 lb). Advances such as this have come about as a result of research on the makeup of body tissues and secretions in both healthy and diseased individuals. Often, such basic research provides the information needed to develop effective therapies.

For Further Understanding

- Draw the structure of 1-hexadecanol.
- Draw the structure of lecithin. Explain how lecithin reduces surface tension.

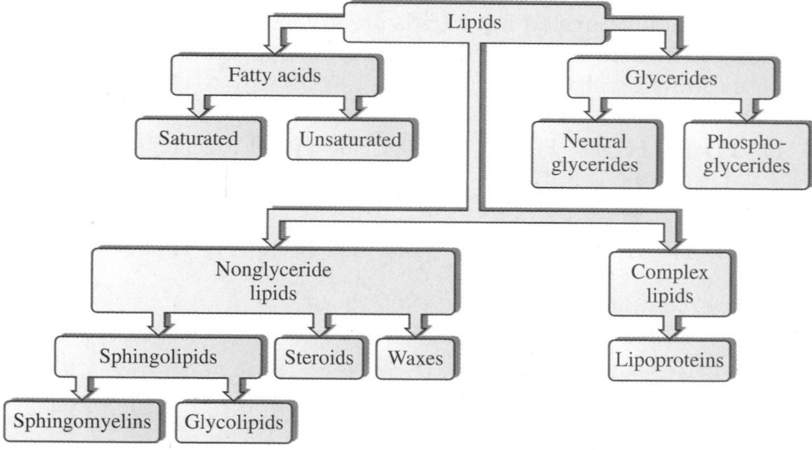

Figure 17.1 Types of lipids.

- *Hormones.* The steroid hormones are critical chemical messengers that allow tissues of the body to communicate with one another. The hormonelike prostaglandins exert strong biological effects on both the cells that produce them and other cells of the body.
- *Vitamins.* The lipid-soluble vitamins, A, D, E, and K, play a major role in the regulation of several critical biological processes, including blood clotting and vision.
- *Vitamin absorption.* Dietary fat serves as a carrier of the lipid-soluble vitamins. All are transported into cells of the small intestine in association with fat molecules. Therefore a diet that is too low in fat (less than 20% of calories) can result in a deficiency of these four vitamins.

- *Protection.* Fats serve as a shock absorber, or protective layer, for the vital organs. About 4% of the total body fat is reserved for this critical function.
- *Insulation.* Fat stored beneath the skin (subcutaneous fat) serves to insulate the body from extremes of cold temperatures.

17.2 Fatty Acids

Structure and Properties

LEARNING GOAL

2 Write the structures of saturated and unsaturated fatty acids.

Fatty acids are long-chain monocarboxylic acids. As a consequence of their biosynthesis, fatty acids generally contain an *even number* of carbon atoms. The general formula for a **saturated fatty acid** is $CH_3(CH_2)_nCOOH$, in which n in biological systems is an even integer. Recall that —COOH is a representation of the carboxyl group. If $n = 16$, the result is an 18-carbon saturated fatty acid, stearic acid, having the following structural formula:

```
    H  H  H  H  H  H  H  H  H  H  H  H  H  H  H  H  H  O
    |  |  |  |  |  |  |  |  |  |  |  |  |  |  |  |  |  ||
H—C—C—C—C—C—C—C—C—C—C—C—C—C—C—C—C—C—C—OH
    |  |  |  |  |  |  |  |  |  |  |  |  |  |  |  |  |
    H  H  H  H  H  H  H  H  H  H  H  H  H  H  H  H  H
```

```
                                              O
                                              ||
/\/\/\/\/\/\/\/\/\/\/\/\/\/\/\/\/\/\/\/\/\/\/\C
                                               \OH
```

The saturated fatty acids may be thought of as derivatives of alkanes, the saturated hydrocarbons described in Chapter 10.

Note that each of the carbons in the chain is bonded to the maximum number of hydrogen atoms. To help remember the structure of a saturated fatty acid, you might think of each carbon in the chain being "saturated" with hydrogen atoms. Examples of common saturated fatty acids are given in Table 17.1. An example of an **unsaturated fatty acid** is the eighteen-carbon unsaturated fatty acid oleic acid, which has the following structural formula:

```
    H  H  H  H  H  H  H  H              H  H  H  H  H  H  H  O
    |  |  |  |  |  |  |  |              |  |  |  |  |  |  |  ||
H—C—C—C—C—C—C—C—C              C—C—C—C—C—C—C—C—OH
    |  |  |  |  |  |  |  |  \          /  |  |  |  |  |  |  |
    H  H  H  H  H  H  H  H   C=C    H  H  H  H  H  H  H
                           /     \
                          H       H
```

```
                                               O
                                              //
/\/\/\/\/\/\/\=\/\/\/\/\/\/\/\/\C
                                              \OH
```

The unsaturated fatty acids may be thought of as derivatives of the alkenes, the unsaturated hydrocarbons discussed in Chapter 11.

A discussion of trans-fatty acids is found in Section 11.3.

In the case of unsaturated fatty acids, there is at least one carbon-to-carbon double bond. Because of the double bonds, the carbon atoms involved in these bonds are not "saturated" with hydrogen atoms. The double bonds found in almost all naturally occurring unsaturated fatty acids are in the *cis* configuration. In addition, the double bonds are not randomly located in the hydrocarbon chain. Both the placement and the geometric configuration of the double bonds are dictated by the enzymes that catalyze the biosynthesis of unsaturated fatty acids. Examples of common unsaturated fatty acids are also given in Table 17.1. The similarities and differences between saturated and unsaturated fatty acids are described in Table 17.2.

Examination of Table 17.1 and Figure 17.2 reveals several interesting and important points about the physical properties of fatty acids.

EXAMPLE 17.1 Writing the Structural Formula of an Unsaturated Fatty Acid

Draw the structural formula for palmitoleic acid.

Solution

The IUPAC name of palmitoleic acid is *cis*-9-hexadecenoic acid. The name tells us that this is a 16-carbon fatty acid having a carbon-to-carbon double bond between carbons 9 and 10. The name also reveals that this is the *cis* isomer.

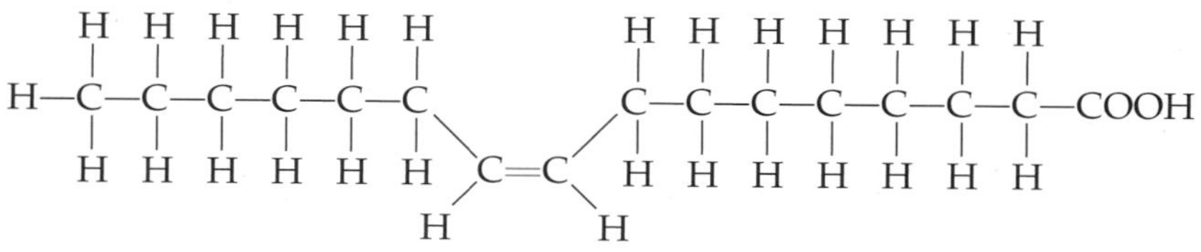

```
     H  H  H  H  H  H           H  H  H  H  H  H  H
     |  |  |  |  |  |           |  |  |  |  |  |  |
  H—C—C—C—C—C—C           C—C—C—C—C—C—C—COOH
     |  |  |  |  |  | \        / |  |  |  |  |  |  |
     H  H  H  H  H  H  C=C   H  H  H  H  H  H  H
                      /    \
                     H      H

    16 15 14 13 12 11 10  9  8  7  6  5  4  3  2  1
```

Practice Problem 17.1

Draw the line formulas for (a) oleic acid and (b) linoleic acid.

► For Further Practice: **Questions 17.27 and 17.28.**

LEARNING GOAL

2 Write the structures of saturated and unsaturated fatty acids.

TABLE 17.1 Common Saturated and Unsaturated Fatty Acids

Common Saturated Fatty Acids

Common Name	IUPAC Name	Melting Point (°C)	Molar Mass	Condensed Formula
Capric	Decanoic	32	172.26	$CH_3(CH_2)_8COOH$
Lauric	Dodecanoic	44	200.32	$CH_3(CH_2)_{10}COOH$
Myristic	Tetradecanoic	54	228.37	$CH_3(CH_2)_{12}COOH$
Palmitic	Hexadecanoic	63	256.42	$CH_3(CH_2)_{14}COOH$
Stearic	Octadecanoic	70	284.48	$CH_3(CH_2)_{16}COOH$
Arachidic	Eicosanoic	77	312.53	$CH_3(CH_2)_{18}COOH$

Common Unsaturated Fatty Acids

Common Name	IUPAC Name	Melting Point (°C)	Molar Mass	Number of Double Bonds	Position of Double Bond(s)
Palmitoleic	*cis*-9-Hexadecenoic	0	254.41	1	9
Oleic	*cis*-9-Octadecenoic	16	282.46	1	9
Linoleic	*cis,cis*-9,12-Octadecadienoic	5	280.45	2	9, 12
Linolenic	All *cis*-9,12,15-Octadecatrienoic	−11	278.43	3	9, 12, 15
Arachidonic	All *cis*-5,8,11,14-Eicosatetraenoic	−50	304.47	4	5, 8, 11, 14

Condensed Formula

Common Name	Condensed Formula
Palmitoleic	$CH_3(CH_2)_5CH{=}CH(CH_2)_7COOH$
Oleic	$CH_3(CH_2)_7CH{=}CH(CH_2)_7COOH$
Linoleic	$CH_3(CH_2)_4CH{=}CH{-}CH_2{-}CH{=}CH(CH_2)_7COOH$
Linolenic	$CH_3CH_2CH{=}CH{-}CH_2{-}CH{=}CH{-}CH_2{-}CH{=}CH(CH_2)_7COOH$
Arachidonic	$CH_3(CH_2)_4CH{=}CH{-}CH_2{-}CH{=}CH{-}CH_2{-}CH{=}CH{-}CH_2{-}CH{=}CH{-}(CH_2)_3COOH$

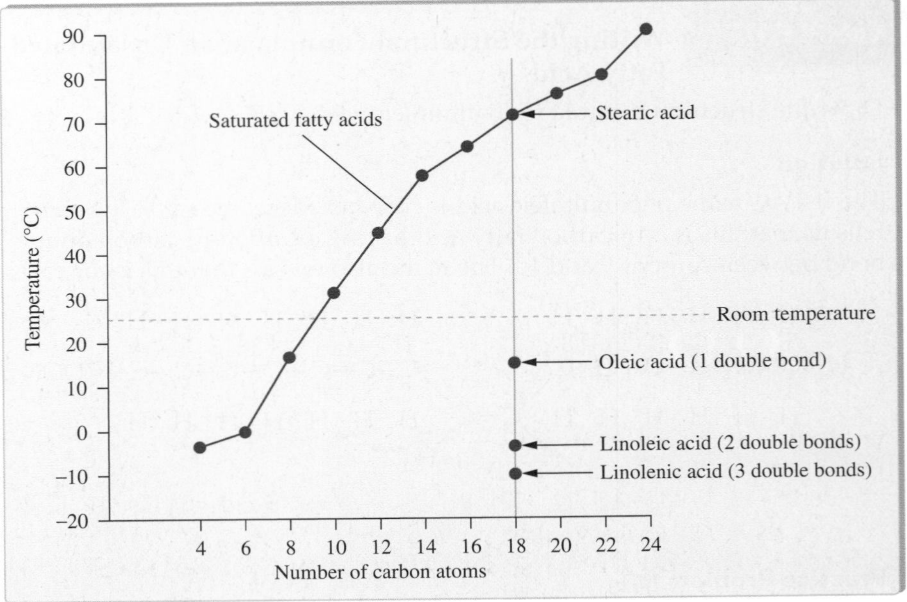

Figure 17.2 The melting points of fatty acids. Melting points of both saturated and unsaturated fatty acids increase as the number of carbon atoms in the chain increases. The melting points of unsaturated fatty acids are lower than those of the corresponding saturated fatty acid with the same number of carbon atoms. Also, as the number of double bonds in the chain increases, the melting points decrease.

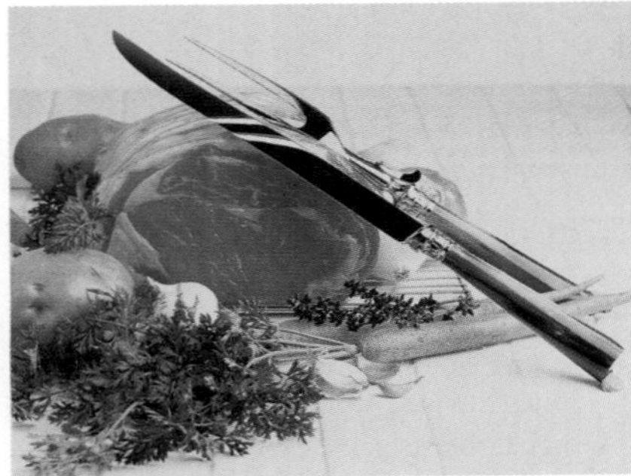

Explain why the olive oil in the photo above is liquid at room temperature but the beef fat is solid.

TABLE 17.2 Similarities and Differences Between Saturated and Unsaturated Fatty Acids

Property	Saturated Fatty Acid	Unsaturated Fatty Acid
Chemical composition	Carbon, hydrogen, oxygen	Carbon, hydrogen, oxygen
Chemical structure	Hydrocarbon chain with a terminal carboxyl group	Hydrocarbon chain with a terminal carboxyl group
Carbon-carbon bonds within the hydrocarbon chain	Only C—C single bonds	At least one C—C double bond
Hydrocarbon chains are characteristic of what group of hydrocarbons	Alkanes	Alkenes
"Shape" of hydrocarbon chain	Linear, fully extended	Bend in carbon chain at site of C—C double bond
Physical state at room temperature	Solid	Liquid
Melting point for two fatty acids of the same hydrocarbon chain length	Higher	Lower
Relationship between melting point and chain length	Longer chain length, higher melting point	Longer chain length, higher melting point

LEARNING GOAL

3 Compare and contrast the structures and properties of saturated and unsaturated fatty acids.

The relationship between alkane chain length and melting point is described in Section 10.2.

- The melting points of saturated fatty acids increase with increasing carbon number, as is the case with alkanes. Saturated fatty acids containing ten or more carbons are solids at room temperature.
- The melting point of a saturated fatty acid is greater than that of an unsaturated fatty acid of the same chain length. The reason is that saturated fatty acid chains tend to be fully extended and to stack in a regular structure, thereby causing increased intermolecular London dispersion force attraction. Introduction of a *cis* double bond into the hydrocarbon chain produces a rigid 30° bend. Such "kinked" molecules cannot stack in an organized

arrangement and thus have lower intermolecular attractions and lower melting points.
- As in the case for saturated fatty acids, the melting points of unsaturated fatty acids increase with increasing hydrocarbon chain length.

The relationship between alkene chain length and melting point is described in Section 11.1.

Question 17.1 Draw formulas for each of the following fatty acids:

a. Oleic acid
b. Lauric acid
c. Linoleic acid
d. Stearic acid

Question 17.2 What is the IUPAC name for each of the fatty acids in Question 17.1? (*Hint:* Review the naming of carboxylic acids in Section 14.1, and Table 17.1.)

Eicosanoids: Prostaglandins, Leukotrienes, and Thromboxanes

Some of the unsaturated fatty acids containing more than one double bond cannot be synthesized by the body. For many years it has been known that linolenic acid, also called α-linolenic acid to distinguish it from isomeric forms, and linoleic acid, called the **essential fatty acids,** are necessary for specific biochemical functions and must be supplied in the diet (see Table 17.1). The function of linoleic acid became clear in the 1960s when it was discovered that linoleic acid is required for the biosynthesis of **arachidonic acid,** the precursor of a class of hormonelike molecules known as **eicosanoids.** The name is derived from the Greek word *eikos,* meaning "twenty," because they are all derivatives of twenty-carbon fatty acids. The eicosanoids include three groups of structurally related compounds: the prostaglandins, the leukotrienes, and the thromboxanes.

LEARNING GOAL

4 Describe the functions of prostaglandins.

Prostaglandins are extremely potent biological molecules with hormonelike activity. They got their name because they were originally isolated from seminal fluid produced in the prostate gland. More recently they also have been isolated from most animal tissues. Prostaglandins are unsaturated carboxylic acids consisting of a twenty-carbon skeleton that contains a five-carbon ring.

Several general classes of prostaglandins are grouped under the designations A, B, E, and F, among others. The nomenclature of prostaglandins is based on the arrangement of the carbon skeleton and the number and orientation of double bonds, hydroxyl groups, and ketone groups. For example, in the name PGF_2, PG stands for prostaglandin, F indicates a particular group of prostaglandins with a hydroxyl group bonded to carbon-9, and 2 indicates that there are two carbon-carbon double bonds in the compound. The examples in Figure 17.3 illustrate the general structure of prostaglandins and the current nomenclature system.

Prostaglandins are made in most tissues, and exert their biological effects on the cells that produce them and on other cells in the immediate vicinity. Because the prostaglandins and the closely related leukotrienes and thromboxanes affect so many body processes and because they often cause opposing effects in different tissues, it can be difficult to keep track of their many regulatory functions. The following is a brief summary of some of the biological processes that are thought to be regulated by the prostaglandins, leukotrienes, and thromboxanes.

1. **Blood clotting.** Blood clots form when a blood vessel is damaged, yet such clotting along the walls of undamaged vessels could result in heart attack or stroke. *Thromboxane* A_2 (Figure 17.4) is produced by platelets in the blood and stimulates constriction of the blood vessels and aggregation of the platelets. Conversely, PGI_2 (prostacyclin) is produced by the cells lining the blood vessels and has precisely the opposite effect of thromboxane A_2. Prostacyclin inhibits platelet aggregation and causes dilation of blood vessels and thus prevents the untimely production of blood clots.
2. **The inflammatory response.** The inflammatory response is another of the body's protective mechanisms. When tissue is damaged by mechanical injury, burns, or invasion by microorganisms, a variety of white blood cells descend on the

Prostaglandin E_1

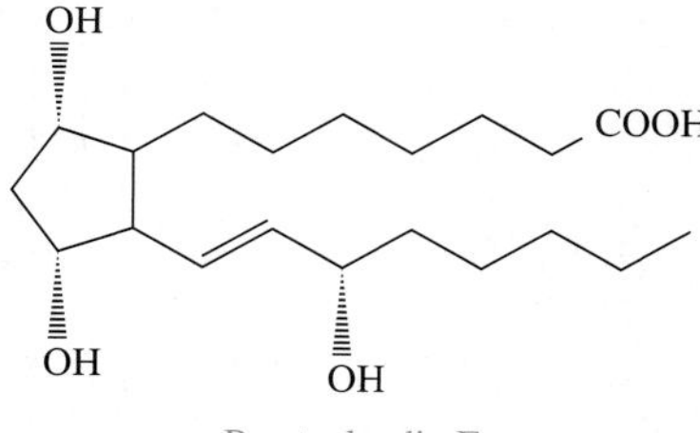

Prostaglandin F_1

Prostaglandin E_2

Prostaglandin F_2

Figure 17.3 The structures of four prostaglandins.

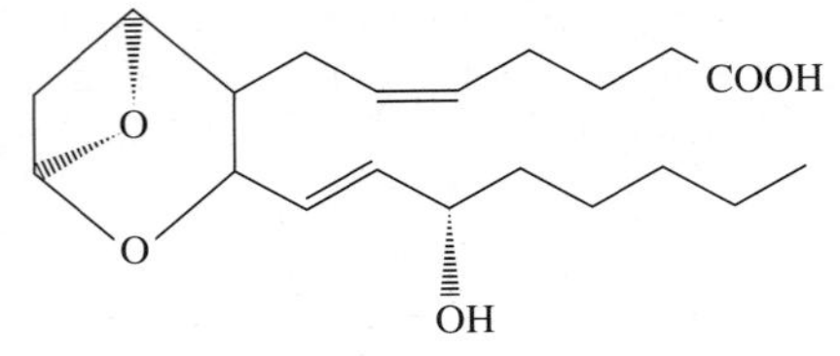

Figure 17.4 The structures of thromboxane A_2 and leukotriene B_4.

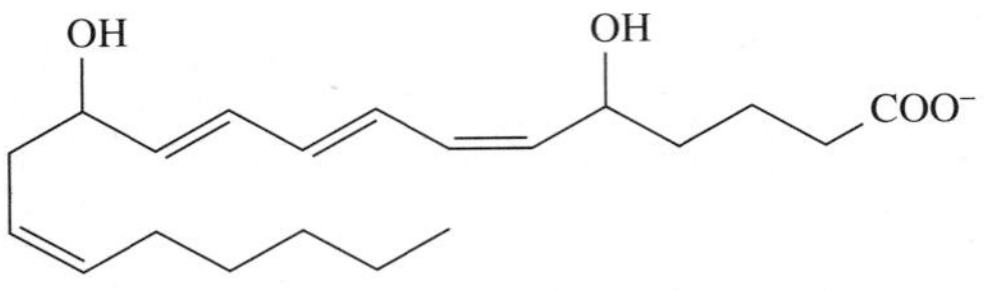

damaged site to try to minimize the tissue destruction. The result of this response is swelling, redness, fever, and pain. Prostaglandins are thought to promote certain aspects of the inflammatory response, especially pain and fever. Drugs such as aspirin block prostaglandin synthesis and help to relieve the symptoms. We will examine the mechanism of action of these drugs later in this section.

3. **Reproductive system.** PGE_2 stimulates smooth muscle contraction, particularly uterine contractions. An increase in the level of prostaglandins has been noted immediately before the onset of labor. PGE_2 has also been used to induce second trimester abortions. There is strong evidence that dysmenorrhea (painful menstruation) suffered by many women may be the result of an excess of two prostaglandins. Indeed, drugs such as ibuprofen that inhibit prostaglandin synthesis have been approved by the Food and Drug Administration (FDA) and are found to provide relief from these symptoms.
4. **Gastrointestinal tract.** Prostaglandins have been shown to both inhibit the secretion of acid and increase the secretion of a protective mucus layer into the stomach. In this way, prostaglandins help to protect the stomach lining. Consider for a moment the possible side effect that prolonged use of a drug such as aspirin might have on the stomach—ulceration of the stomach lining. Because aspirin inhibits prostaglandin synthesis, it may actually encourage stomach ulcers by inhibiting the formation of the normal protective mucus layer, while simultaneously allowing increased secretion of stomach acid.
5. **Kidneys.** Prostaglandins produced in the kidneys cause the renal blood vessels to dilate. The greater flow of blood through the kidney results in increased water and electrolyte excretion.
6. **Respiratory tract.** Eicosanoids produced by certain white blood cells, the *leukotrienes* (see Figure 17.4), promote the constriction of the bronchi associated with asthma. Other prostaglandins promote bronchodilation.

A hormone is a chemical signal that is produced by a specialized tissue and is carried by the bloodstream to send a message to target tissues. Eicosanoids are referred to as hormonelike because they affect the cells that produce them, as well as other target tissues.

As this brief survey suggests, the prostaglandins have numerous, often antagonistic effects. Although they do not fit the formal definition of a hormone (a substance produced in a specialized tissue and transported by the circulatory system to target tissues *elsewhere* in the body), the prostaglandins are clearly strong biological regulators with far-reaching effects.

As mentioned, prostaglandins stimulate the inflammatory response and, as a result, are partially responsible for the cascade of events that cause pain. Aspirin has long been known to alleviate such pain, and we now know that it does so by inhibiting the synthesis of prostaglandins (Figure 17.5).

LEARNING GOAL

5 Discuss the mechanism by which aspirin reduces pain.

The first two steps of prostaglandin synthesis (Figure 17.6), the release of arachidonic acid from the membrane and its conversion to PGH_2 by the enzyme cyclooxygenase, occur in all tissues that are able to produce prostaglandins. The conversion of PGH_2 into the other biologically active forms is tissue-specific and requires the appropriate enzymes, which are found only in certain tissues.

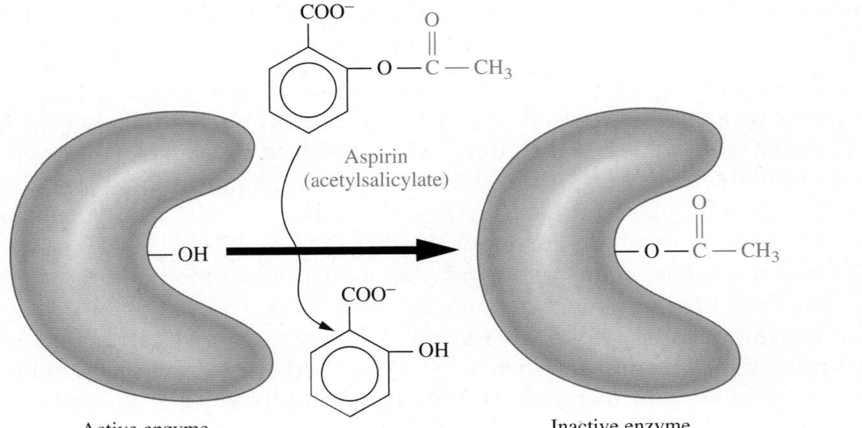

Figure 17.5 Aspirin inhibits the synthesis of prostaglandins by acetylating the enzyme cyclooxygenase. The acetylated enzyme is no longer functional.

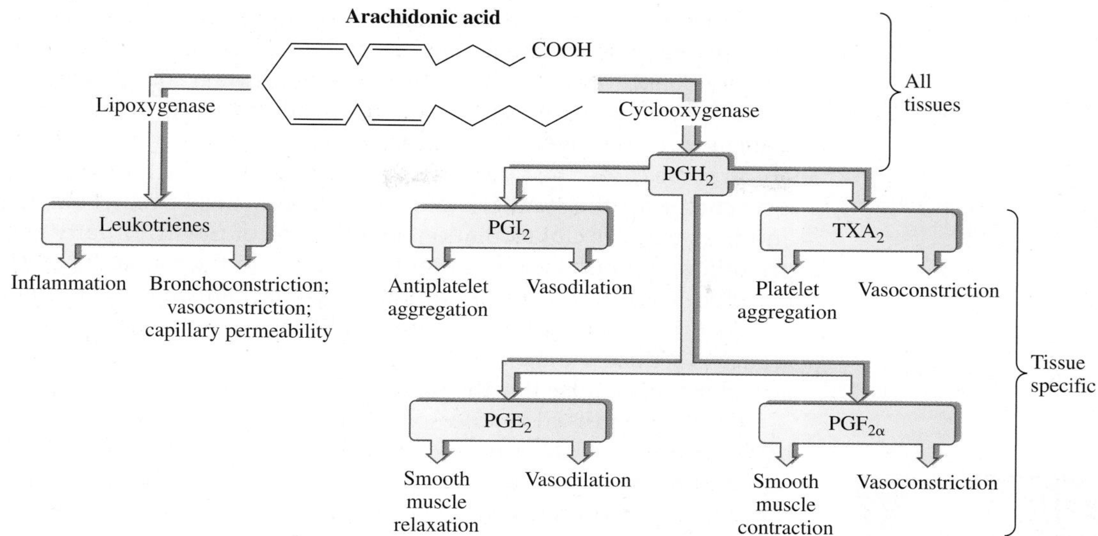

Figure 17.6 A summary of the synthesis of several prostaglandins from arachidonic acid.

Aspirin works by inhibiting the cyclooxygenase, which catalyzes the first step in the pathway leading from arachidonic acid to PGH_2. The acetyl group of aspirin becomes covalently bound to the enzyme, thereby inactivating it (Figure 17.5). Because the reaction catalyzed by cyclooxygenase occurs in all cells, aspirin effectively inhibits synthesis of all of the prostaglandins.

Omega-3 Fatty Acids

In 2002, the American Heart Association (AHA) issued dietary guidelines that recommend that we include at least two servings of "oily" fish in our diet each week. Among the fish recommended are salmon, albacore tuna, sardines, lake trout, and mackerel. The reason for this recommendation is that these fish contain high levels of two omega-3 fatty acids called eicosapentaenoic acid (EPA) and docosahexaenoic acid (DHA). The AHA further recommended a third omega-3 fatty acid, α-linolenic acid, which is found in flax seed, soybeans, and canola, as well as in oil made from these plants.

The name of this group of fatty acids arises from the position of the double bond nearest the terminal *methyl group* of the molecule. In these fatty acids, it is the third carbon from the end, designated omega (ω), which is the location of the double bond.

All *cis*-9,12,15-Octadecatrienoic acid
(α-Linolenic acid or ALA)

All *cis*-5,8,11,14,17-Eicosapentaenoic acid
(EPA)

All *cis*-4,7,10,13,16,19-Docosahexaenoic acid
(DHA)

The reason for this dietary recommendation was research that supported the idea that omega-3 fatty acids reduce the risk of cardiovascular disease by decreasing blood clot formation, blood triglyceride levels, and growth of atherosclerotic plaque. Because of these effects, arterial health improved and blood pressure decreased, as did the risk of sudden death and heart arrhythmias.

In some cases, the reason for the effect can be understood. For instance, EPA is a precursor for the synthesis of prostacyclin, which inhibits clumping of platelets and thus reduces clot formation. DHA is one of the major fatty acids in the phospholipids of sperm and brain cells, as well as in the retina. It has also been shown to reduce triglyceride levels, although the mechanism is not understood.

As we learned earlier, linolenic acid is an essential fatty acid. Although it, too, seems to reduce the incidence of cardiovascular disease, it is not clear whether it acts alone or because it is the precursor of DHA and EPA.

Linoleic acid is also an essential fatty acid, required for the synthesis of arachidonic acid, the precursor for many prostaglandins. These two fatty acids are termed omega-6 fatty acids because the first double bond in the molecule is six carbon atoms from the methyl (ω) end of the molecule.

cis,cis-9,12-Octadecadienoic acid
(Linoleic acid)

All *cis*-5,8,11,14-Eicosatetraenoic acid
(Arachidonic acid)

The American Heart Association recommends that we include two meals of fish, such as salmon, in our diets each week. However, there is concern about the amount of heavy metals and other environmental contaminants in wild-caught fish. Go online to investigate the reasons that these contaminants accumulate in these fish.

It is intriguing to note that the omega-3 fatty acids are precursors of prostaglandins that exhibit anti-inflammatory effects, and the omega-6 fatty acids are precursors to prostaglandins that have inflammatory effects. This has led researchers to suggest that the amount of omega-6 fatty acids in our diets should not exceed 4–5 times the amount of omega-3. In fact, in the United States, the diet often contains 10–30 times more omega-6 fatty acids than omega-3 fatty acids. Thus, changing the ratio of the two in the diet could increase the levels of anti-inflammatory prostaglandins and reduce the level of inflammatory prostaglandins. To encourage this dietary change, the National Institutes of Health have issued recommended daily intakes of four of these fatty acids: 650 mg/day of EPA and DHA, 2.22 g/day of α-linolenic acid, and 4.44 g/day of linoleic acid.

17.3 Glycerides

Neutral Glycerides

Glycerides are lipid esters that contain the glycerol molecule and fatty acids. They may be subdivided into two classes: neutral glycerides and phosphoglycerides. Neutral glycerides are nonionic and nonpolar. Phosphoglyceride molecules have a polar region, the phosphoryl group, in addition to the nonpolar fatty acid tails. The structures of each of these types of glycerides are critical to their function.

The esterification of glycerol with a fatty acid produces a **neutral glyceride.** Esterification may occur at one, two, or all three positions, producing **monoglycerides, diglycerides,** or **triglycerides.** You will also see these referred to as *mono-, di-,* or *triacylglycerols.*

EXAMPLE 17.2 Writing an Equation for the Synthesis of a Monoglyceride

Write a general equation for the esterification of glycerol and one fatty acid.

Solution

$$\begin{array}{c}\text{H}\\|\\\text{H—C—OH}\\|\\\text{H—C—OH}\\|\\\text{H—C—OH}\\|\\\text{H}\end{array} + \text{R—}\overset{\overset{\text{O}}{\|}}{\text{C}}\text{—OH} \rightleftharpoons \begin{array}{c}\text{H}\quad\quad\text{O}\\|\quad\quad\|\\\text{H—C—O—C—R}\\|\\\text{H—C—OH}\\|\\\text{H—C—OH}\\|\\\text{H}\end{array} + H_2O$$

Glycerol — Fatty acid — Monoglyceride — Water

LEARNING GOAL

6 Write equations representing the reactions that fatty acids and glycerides undergo.

Practice Problem 17.2

Write equations for the following esterification reactions.

a. Glycerol with two molecules of stearic acid
b. Glycerol with one molecule of myristic acid

► For Further Practice: **Questions 17.41 and 17.42.**

Although monoglycerides and diglycerides are present in nature, the most important neutral glycerides are the triglycerides, the major component of fat cells. The triglyceride consists of a glycerol backbone (shown in black) joined to three fatty acid units through ester bonds (shown in red). The formation of a triglyceride is shown in the following equation:

$$\begin{array}{c}\text{H}\\|\\\text{H—C—OH}\\|\\\text{H—C—OH}\\|\\\text{H—C—OH}\\|\\\text{H}\end{array} + 3\text{R—}\overset{\overset{\text{O}}{\|}}{\text{C}}\text{—OH} \rightleftharpoons \begin{array}{c}\text{H}\quad\quad\text{O}\\|\quad\quad\|\\\text{H—C—O—C—R}\\|\quad\quad\text{O}\\|\quad\quad\|\\\text{H—C—O—C—R}\\|\quad\quad\text{O}\\|\quad\quad\|\\\text{H—C—O—C—R}\\|\\\text{H}\end{array} + 3H_2O$$

Glycerol — Fatty acids — Triglyceride — Water

Because there are no charges (+ or −) on these molecules, they are called *neutral glycerides.* These long molecules readily stack with one another and constitute the majority of the lipids stored in the body's fat cells.

The principal function of triglycerides in biochemical systems is the storage of energy. If more energy-rich nutrients are consumed than are required for metabolic processes, much of the excess is converted to neutral glycerides and stored as triglycerides in fat cells of *adipose tissue.* When energy is needed, the triglycerides are metabolized by the body, and energy is released. For this reason, exercise, along with moderate reduction in caloric intake, is recommended for overweight individuals. Exercise, an energy-demanding process, increases the rate of metabolism of fats and results in weight loss.

Lipid metabolism is discussed in Chapter 23.

See A Human Perspective: Losing Those Unwanted Pounds of Adipose Tissue in Chapter 23.

Chemical Reactions of Fatty Acids and Glycerides

LEARNING GOAL

6 Write equations representing the reactions that fatty acids and glycerides undergo.

The reactions of fatty acids are identical to those of short-chain carboxylic acids. The major reactions that they undergo include esterification, saponification, and addition at the double bond of the carbon chain. Triglycerides can undergo acid hydrolysis and saponification.

Esterification

Esterification is described in Sections 14.1 and 14.2.

In **esterification,** fatty acids react with alcohols to form esters and water according to the following general equation:

$$\underset{\text{Fatty acid}}{R^1{-}\overset{\overset{\displaystyle O}{\|}}{C}{-}OH} + \underset{\text{Alcohol}}{R^2OH} \xrightarrow{H^+,\ \text{heat}} \underset{\text{Ester}}{R^1{-}\overset{\overset{\displaystyle O}{\|}}{C}{-}OR^2} + \underset{\text{Water}}{H{-}OH}$$

EXAMPLE 17.3 Writing Equations Representing the Esterification of Fatty Acids

LEARNING GOAL

6 Write equations representing the reactions that fatty acids and glycerides undergo.

Write an equation representing the esterification of capric acid with propyl alcohol and write the IUPAC name of each of the organic reactants and products.

Solution

$$\underset{\text{Decanoic acid}}{CH_3(CH_2)_8{-}\overset{\overset{\displaystyle O}{\|}}{C}{-}OH} + \underset{\text{1-Propanol}}{CH_3CH_2CH_2OH} \xrightarrow{H^+,\ \text{heat}}$$

$$\underset{\text{Propyl decanoate}}{CH_3(CH_2)_8{-}\overset{\overset{\displaystyle O}{\|}}{C}{-}O{-}CH_2CH_2CH_3} + H_2O$$

Practice Problem 17.3

Write an equation for the esterification of the following carboxylic acids and alcohols. Write the IUPAC names for all of the organic reactants and products.

a. Lauric acid and ethyl alcohol
b. Palmitic acid and 1-pentanol

▸ For Further Practice: **Questions 17.31 and 17.32.**

Acid Hydrolysis

Acid hydrolysis is discussed in Section 14.2.

Recall that hydrolysis is the reverse of esterification, producing fatty acids from esters:

$$\underset{\text{Ester}}{R^1{-}\overset{\overset{\displaystyle O}{\|}}{C}{-}OR^2} + \underset{\text{Water}}{HO{-}H} \xrightarrow{H^+,\ \text{heat}} \underset{\text{Fatty acid}}{R^1{-}\overset{\overset{\displaystyle O}{\|}}{C}{-}OH} + \underset{\text{Alcohol}}{R^2OH}$$

EXAMPLE 17.4 Writing Equations Representing the Acid Hydrolysis of a Monoglyceride

LEARNING GOAL

6 Write equations representing the reactions that fatty acids and glycerides undergo.

Write an equation representing the acid hydrolysis of a monoglyceride composed of one decanoic acid molecule esterified to glycerol.

Solution

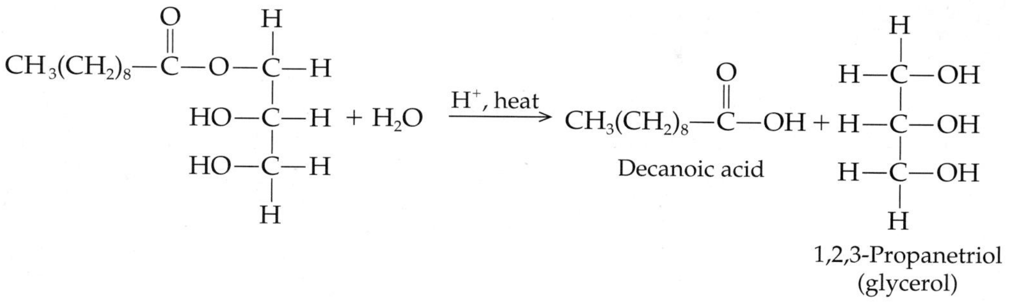

$$CH_3(CH_2)_8-\overset{\overset{O}{\|}}{C}-O-CH_2-CH(OH)-CH_2OH + H_2O \xrightarrow{H^+,\ heat} \underset{\text{Decanoic acid}}{CH_3(CH_2)_8-\overset{\overset{O}{\|}}{C}-OH} + \underset{\text{1,2,3-Propanetriol (glycerol)}}{HOCH_2-CH(OH)-CH_2OH}$$

Practice Problem 17.4

Write a complete equation for the acid hydrolysis of the following monoglycerides.

a. Tetradecanoic acid esterified to glycerol

b. Dodecanoic acid esterified to glycerol

► For Further Practice: **Questions 17.33 and 17.34.**

Saponification

Saponification is the base-catalyzed hydrolysis of an ester:

Saponification is described in Section 14.2.

$$\underset{\text{Ester}}{R^1-\overset{\overset{O}{\|}}{C}-OR^2} + \underset{\text{Base}}{NaOH} \longrightarrow \underset{\text{Salt}}{R^1-\overset{\overset{O}{\|}}{C}-O^-Na^+} + \underset{\text{Alcohol}}{R^2OH}$$

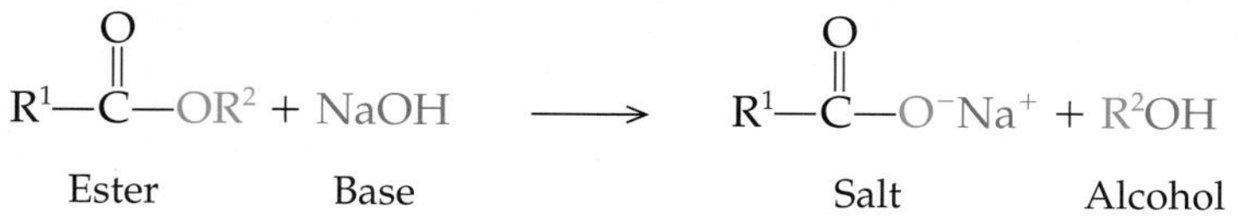

The product of this reaction, an ionized salt, is a soap. Because soaps have a long uncharged hydrocarbon tail and a negatively charged terminus (the carboxylate group), they form micelles that dissolve oil and dirt particles. Thus the dirt is emulsified and broken into small particles, and can be rinsed away.

The role of soaps in removal of dirt and grease is described in Section 14.2.

Examples of micelles are shown in Figures 14.4 and 23.1.

EXAMPLE 17.5 Writing Equations Representing the Base-Catalyzed Hydrolysis of a Monoglyceride

LEARNING GOAL

6 Write equations representing the reactions that fatty acids and glycerides undergo.

Write an equation representing the base-catalyzed hydrolysis of a monoglyceride composed of dodecanoic acid and glycerol.

Solution

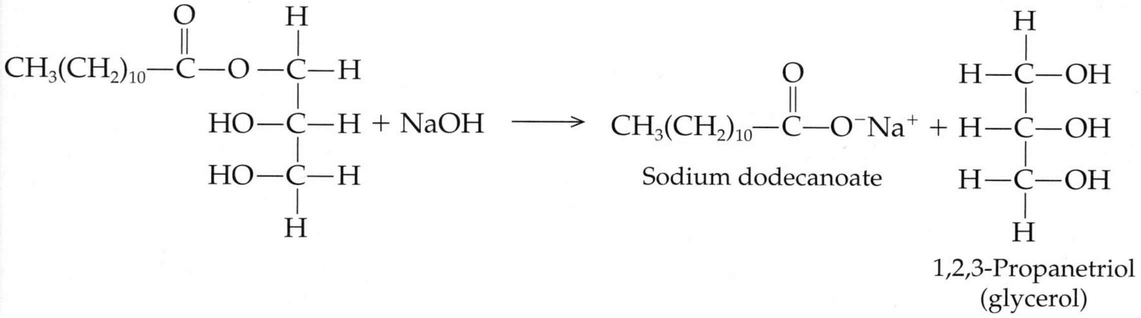

$$CH_3(CH_2)_{10}-\overset{\overset{O}{\|}}{C}-O-CH_2-CH(OH)-CH_2OH + NaOH \longrightarrow \underset{\text{Sodium dodecanoate}}{CH_3(CH_2)_{10}-\overset{\overset{O}{\|}}{C}-O^-Na^+} + \underset{\text{1,2,3-Propanetriol (glycerol)}}{HOCH_2-CH(OH)-CH_2OH}$$

Continued...

Practice Problem 17.5

Write a complete equation for the following reactions.

a. A monoglyceride composed of hexadecanoic acid and glycerol with KOH
b. A diglyceride composed of octanoic acid, decanoic acid, and glycerol with NaOH

▸ For Further Practice: **Questions 17.39 and 17.40.**

Problems can arise when "hard" water is used for cleaning because the high concentrations of Ca^{2+} and Mg^{2+} in such water cause fatty acid salts to precipitate. Not only does this interfere with the emulsifying action of the soap, it also leaves a hard scum on the surface of sinks and tubs.

$$2R{-}\overset{\overset{\large O}{\|}}{C}{-}O^- + Ca^{2+} \longrightarrow (R{-}\overset{\overset{\large O}{\|}}{C}{-}O^-)_2Ca^{2+}(s)$$

Hydrogenation is described in Section 11.5.

Reaction at the Double Bond (Unsaturated Fatty Acids)

Hydrogenation is an example of an addition reaction. The following is a typical example of the addition of hydrogen to the double bonds of a fatty acid:

$$\underset{\text{Linoleic acid}}{CH_3(CH_2)_4CH{=}CHCH_2CH{=}CH(CH_2)_7COOH} \xrightarrow{2H_2,\ Ni} \underset{\text{Stearic acid}}{CH_3(CH_2)_{16}COOH}$$

EXAMPLE 17.6 Writing Equations for the Hydrogenation of a Fatty Acid

LEARNING GOAL

6 Write equations representing the reactions that fatty acids and glycerides undergo.

Write an equation representing the hydrogenation of oleic acid and write the IUPAC name of each of the organic reactants and products.

Solution

$$\underset{\textit{cis}\text{-9-Octadecenoic acid}}{CH_3(CH_2)_7CH{=}CH(CH_2)_7{-}\overset{\overset{\large O}{\|}}{C}{-}OH} \xrightarrow{H_2,\ Ni} \underset{\text{Octadecanoic acid}}{CH_3(CH_2)_{16}{-}\overset{\overset{\large O}{\|}}{C}{-}OH}$$

Practice Problem 17.6

Write balanced equations showing the hydrogenation of (a) *cis*-9-hexadecenoic acid and (b) arachidonic acid.

▸ For Further Practice: **Questions 17.37 and 17.38.**

Hydrogenation of vegetable oils produces a mixture of *cis* and *trans* unsaturated fatty acids. The *trans* unsaturated fatty acids are thought to contribute to atherosclerosis (hardening of the arteries).

Hydrogenation is used in the food industry to convert polyunsaturated vegetable oils into saturated solid fats. *Partial hydrogenation* is carried out to add hydrogen to some, but not all, double bonds in polyunsaturated oils. In this way liquid vegetable oils are converted into solid form. Crisco is one example of a hydrogenated vegetable oil.

Margarine is also produced by partial hydrogenation of vegetable oils, such as corn oil or soybean oil. The extent of hydrogenation is carefully controlled so that the solid fat will be spreadable and have the consistency of butter when eaten. If too many double bonds were hydrogenated, the resulting product would have the undesirable consistency of animal fat. Artificial color is added to the product, and it may be mixed with milk to produce a butterlike appearance and flavor.

Question 17.3 Write the complete equation for the esterification of myristic acid and ethyl alcohol. Write the IUPAC name for each of the organic reactants and products.

Question 17.4 Write the complete equation for the esterification of arachidic acid and ethyl alcohol. Write the IUPAC name for each of the organic reactants and products.

Question 17.5 Write a complete equation for the acid hydrolysis of pentyl butyrate. Write the IUPAC name for each of the organic reactants and products.

Question 17.6 Write a complete equation for the acid hydrolysis of butyl acetate. Write the IUPAC name for each of the organic reactants and products.

Question 17.7 Write a complete equation for the reaction of butyl acetate and KOH. Write the IUPAC name for each of the organic reactants and products.

Question 17.8 Write a complete equation for the reaction of methyl butyrate and NaOH. Write the IUPAC name for each of the organic reactants and products.

Question 17.9 Write a balanced equation for the hydrogenation of linolenic acid.

Question 17.10 Write a balanced equation for the hydrogenation of 2-hexenoic acid.

Phosphoglycerides

LEARNING GOAL

7 Draw the structure of a phospholipid and discuss its amphipathic nature.

Phospholipids are a group of lipids that are phosphate esters. The presence of the phosphoryl group results in a molecule with a polar head (the phosphoryl group) and a nonpolar tail (the alkyl chain of the fatty acid). Because the phosphoryl group ionizes in solution, a charged lipid results.

The most abundant membrane lipids are derived from glycerol-3-phosphate and are known as **phosphoglycerides.** Phosphoglycerides contain acyl groups derived from long-chain fatty acids at C-1 and C-2 of glycerol-3-phosphate. At C-3 the phosphoryl group is joined to glycerol by a phosphoester bond. The simplest phosphoglyceride contains a free phosphoryl group and is known as a **phosphatidate** (Figure 17.7). When the phosphoryl group is attached to another hydrophilic molecule, a more complex phosphoglyceride is formed. For example, *phosphatidylcholine* (*lecithin*) and *phosphatidylethanolamine* (*cephalin*) are found in the membranes of most cells (Figure 17.7).

Phosphoesters are described in Section 14.4.

Lecithin possesses a polar "head" and a nonpolar "tail." Thus, it is an *amphipathic* molecule. This structure is similar to that of soap and detergent molecules, discussed earlier. The ionic "head" is hydrophilic and interacts with water molecules, whereas the nonpolar "tail" is hydrophobic and interacts with nonpolar molecules. This amphipathic nature is central to the structure and function of cell membranes.

In addition to being a component of cell membranes, lecithin is the major phospholipid in pulmonary surfactant. It is also found in egg yolks and soybeans and is used as an emulsifying agent in ice cream. An **emulsifying agent** aids in the suspension of triglycerides in water. The amphipathic lecithin serves as a bridge, holding together the highly polar water molecules and the nonpolar triglycerides. Emulsification occurs because the hydrophilic head of lecithin dissolves in water and its hydrophobic tail dissolves in the triglycerides.

See A Medical Perspective: Lifesaving Lipids, at the beginning of this chapter.

Cephalin is similar in general structure to lecithin; the amine group bonded to the phosphoryl group is the only difference.

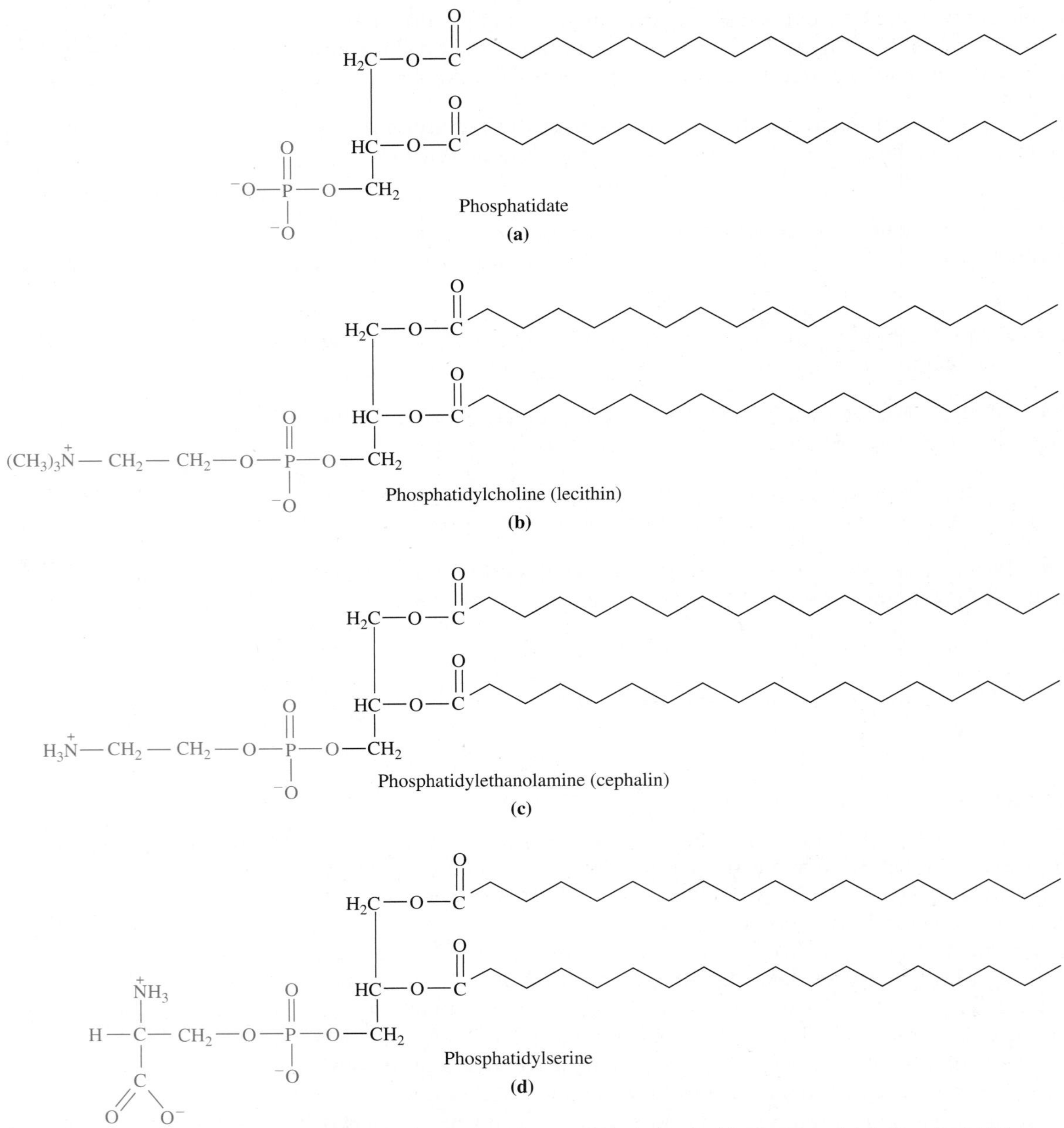

Phosphatidate
(a)

Phosphatidylcholine (lecithin)
(b)

Phosphatidylethanolamine (cephalin)
(c)

Phosphatidylserine
(d)

Figure 17.7 The structures of (a) phosphatidate and the common membrane phospholipids, (b) phosphatidylcholine (lecithin), (c) phosphatidylethanolamine (cephalin), and (d) phosphatidylserine.

Question 17.11 Using condensed formulas, draw the mono-, di-, and triglycerides that would result from the esterification of glycerol with each of the following fatty acids.

a. Oleic acid
b. Capric acid

Question 17.12 Using condensed formulas, draw the mono-, di-, and triglycerides that would result from the esterification of glycerol with each of the following fatty acids.

a. Palmitic acid
b. Lauric acid

CHEMISTRY AT THE CRIME SCENE

Adipocere and Mummies of Soap

One November evening in 1911, widower Patrick Higgins stepped into his local pub in Abercorn, Scotland. To the surprise of his drinking companions, he did not have his two young boys with him. Neighbors knew that the boys had been a great burden on Patrick since the death of his wife; so they believed Patrick's story that he left William, age 6, and John, age 4, with two women in Edinburgh who had offered to adopt the boys.

More than 18 months had passed when an object was seen floating in the Hopetoun Quarry, an unused, flooded quarry near town. When the object was fished out, it was obvious that it was the body of a young boy; the rescuers were stunned to find another small body tied to the first by a rope. How were these bodies preserved after such a long time and why did they float? The answer is that their bodies had almost completely turned into adipocere, or more simply, soap.

Forensic scientists are trying to understand the nature of the reaction that creates *adipocere,* the technical term for the yellowish-white, greasy, waxlike substance that results from the saponification of fatty tissue. Some researchers hope that this information may allow determination of the postmortem interval (length of time since death). Others simply value the process because it helps preserve the body so well that even after long periods, it can be easily recognized and any wounds or injuries can be observed.

It is known that adipocere is produced when body fat is hydrolyzed (water is needed) to release fatty acids. Because the fatty acids lower the pH in the tissues, they inhibit many of the bacteria that would begin the process of decay. Certain other bacteria, particularly *Clostridium welchii,* an organism that cannot grow in the presence of oxygen, is known to speed up the formation of adipocere in moist, warm, anaerobic (oxygenless) environments. Adipocere forms first in subcutaneous tissues, including the cheeks, breasts, and buttocks. Given appropriate warmth and damp conditions, it may be seen as early as 3 to 4 weeks after death; but more commonly it is not observed until 5 to 6 months after death.

Adipocere formation in John and William Higgins was so extensive that their former neighbors had no trouble recognizing them. At the postmortem, another advantage of adipocere formation became obvious—it had preserved the stomach contents of the boys! From this, the coroner learned that the boys had eaten Scotch broth about an hour before they died. Investigators were able to find the woman who had given the broth to the boys and, from her testimony, learned that she had fed them on the last day they were seen in the village. Clearly their father had lied about the adoption by two Edinburgh women! In under one and one-half hours, a jury convicted the father of murdering his sons and he was hanged in October 1913.

For Further Understanding

- Adipocere is the technical term for "soap mummification." It comes from the Latin words *adipis* or fat, as in adipose tissue, and *cera,* which means wax. Draw a triglyceride composed of the fatty acids myristic acid, stearic acid, and oleic acid. Write a balanced equation showing a possible reaction that would lead to the formation of adipocere.
- Forensic scientists are studying adipocere formation as a possible source of information to determine postmortem interval (length of time since death) of bodies of murder or accident victims. Among the factors being studied are the type of soil, including pH, moisture, temperature, and presence or absence of lime. How might each of these factors influence the rate of adipocere formation and hence the determination of the postmortem interval?

17.4 Nonglyceride Lipids

LEARNING GOAL

8 Discuss the general classes of sphingolipids and their functions.

Sphingolipids

Sphingolipids are lipids that are not derived from glycerol. Like phospholipids, sphingolipids are amphipathic, having a polar head group and two nonpolar fatty acid tails, and are structural components of cellular membranes. They are derived from sphingosine, a long-chain, nitrogen-containing (amino) alcohol:

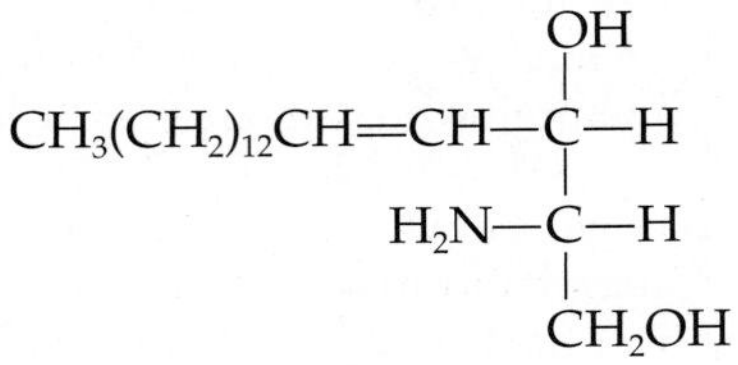

$$CH_3(CH_2)_{12}CH{=}CH{-}\underset{\underset{\underset{\displaystyle CH_2OH}{|}}{H_2N-C-H}}{\overset{\overset{\displaystyle OH}{|}}{C}}{-}H$$

Sphingosine

The sphingolipids include the sphingomyelins and the glycosphingolipids. The **sphingomyelins** are the only class of sphingolipids that are also phospholipids:

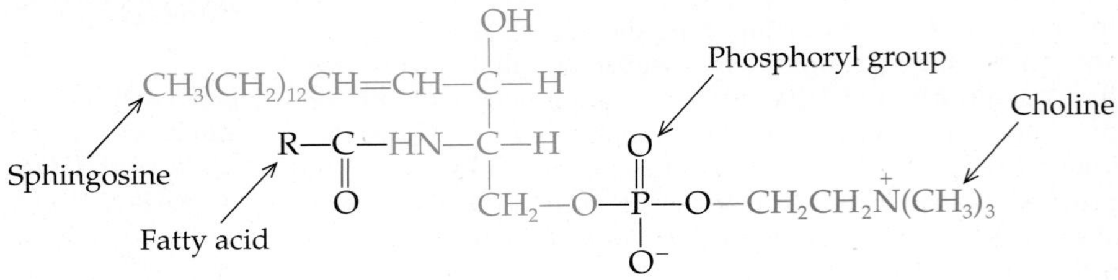

$$CH_3(CH_2)_{12}CH{=}CH{-}\overset{\overset{\displaystyle OH}{|}}{C}{-}H \\ R{-}\underset{\displaystyle O}{\overset{\|}{C}}{-}HN{-}C{-}H \\ CH_2{-}O{-}\overset{\overset{\displaystyle O}{\|}}{\underset{\underset{\displaystyle O^-}{|}}{P}}{-}O{-}CH_2CH_2\overset{+}{N}(CH_3)_3$$

Sphingosine; Fatty acid; Phosphoryl group; Choline

Sphingomyelin

Sphingomyelins are located throughout the body, but are particularly important structural lipid components of nerve cell membranes. They are found in abundance in the myelin sheath that surrounds and insulates cells of the central nervous system. In humans, about 25% of the lipids of the myelin sheath are sphingomyelins. Their role is essential to proper cerebral function and nerve transmission.

Glycosphingolipids, or *glycolipids*, include the cerebrosides, sulfatides, and gangliosides and are built on a ceramide backbone structure, which is a fatty acid amide derivative of sphingosine:

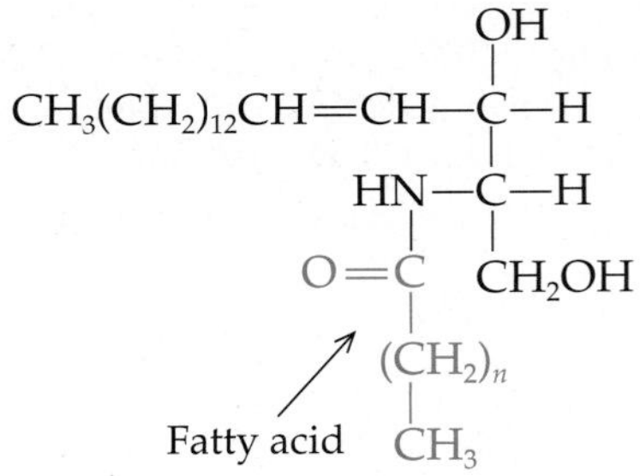

$$CH_3(CH_2)_{12}CH{=}CH{-}\overset{\overset{\displaystyle OH}{|}}{C}{-}H \\ HN{-}C{-}H \\ O{=}C \quad CH_2OH \\ (CH_2)_n \\ CH_3$$

Fatty acid

Ceramide

The *cerebrosides* are characterized by the presence of a single monosaccharide head group. Two common cerebrosides are glucocerebroside, found in the membranes of macrophages (cells that protect the body by ingesting and destroying foreign microorganisms) and galactocerebroside, found almost exclusively in the membranes of brain cells. Glucocerebroside consists of ceramide bonded to the hexose glucose; galactocerebroside consists of ceramide joined to the monosaccharide galactose.

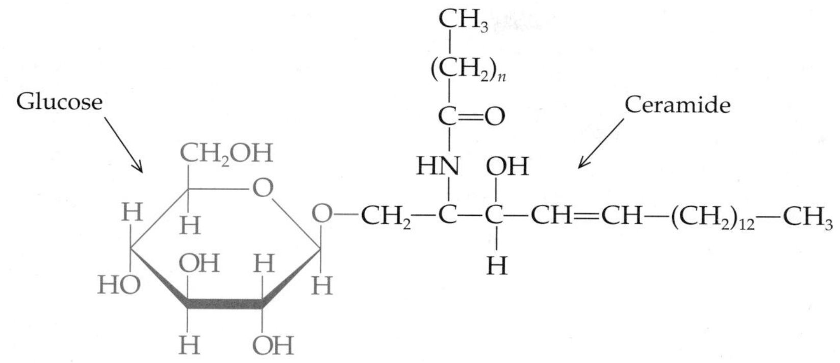

Glucose

Ceramide

$$\text{Glucose–O–CH}_2\text{–CH(NH–C(=O)–(CH}_2)_n\text{–CH}_3\text{)–CH(OH)–CH=CH–(CH}_2)_{12}\text{–CH}_3$$

Glucocerebroside

Galactose

Ceramide

$$\text{Galactose–O–CH}_2\text{–CH(NH–C(=O)–(CH}_2)_n\text{–CH}_3\text{)–CH(OH)–CH=CH–(CH}_2)_{12}\text{–CH}_3$$

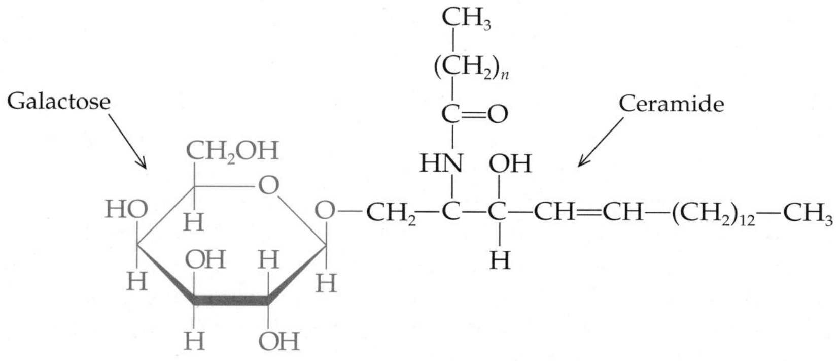

Galactocerebroside

Sulfatides are derivatives of galactocerebroside that contain a sulfate group. Notice that they carry a negative charge at physiological pH.

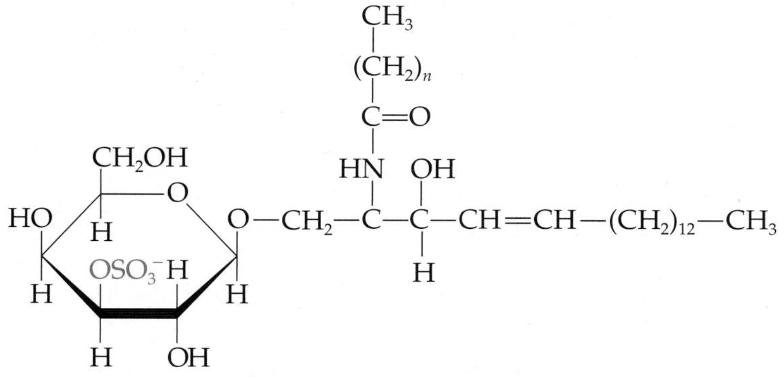

$$\text{Galactose(3-}OSO_3^-\text{)–O–CH}_2\text{–CH(NH–C(=O)–(CH}_2)_n\text{–CH}_3\text{)–CH(OH)–CH=CH–(CH}_2)_{12}\text{–CH}_3$$

A sulfatide of galactocerebroside

Gangliosides are glycolipids that possess oligosaccharide groups, including one or more molecules of *N*-acetylneuraminic acid (sialic acid). First isolated from membranes of nerve tissue, gangliosides are found in most tissues of the body.

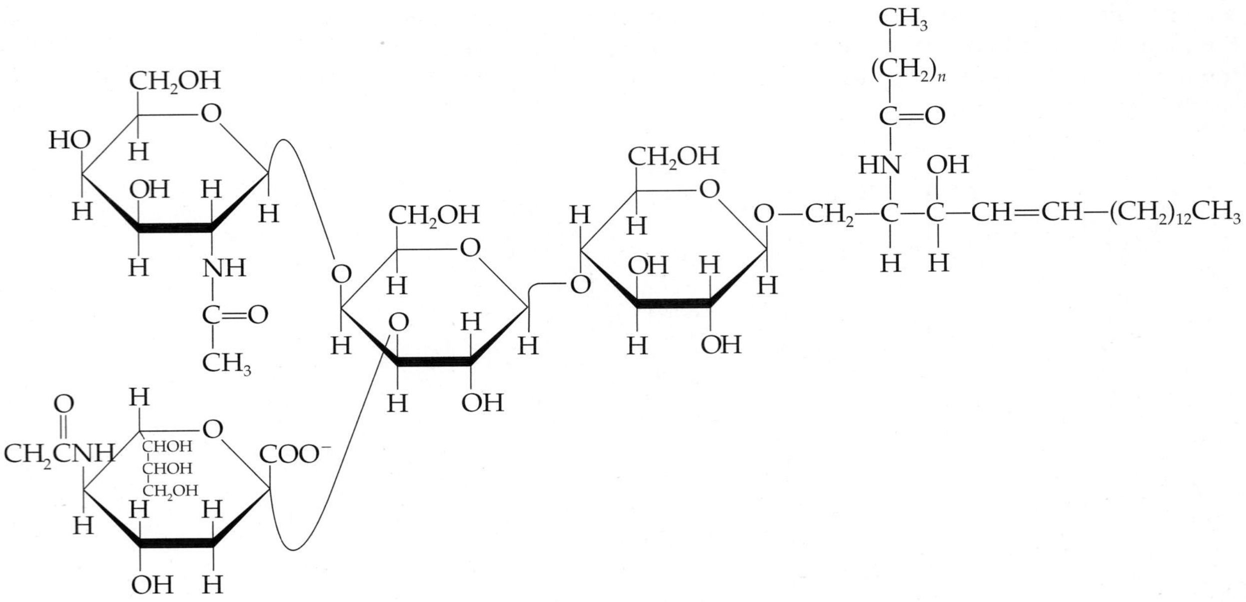

A ganglioside associated with Tay-Sachs disease

Steroids

LEARNING GOAL

9 Draw the structure of the steroid nucleus and discuss the functions of steroid hormones.

Steroids are a naturally occurring family of organic molecules of biochemical and medical interest. A great deal of controversy has surrounded various steroids. We worry about the amount of cholesterol in the diet and the possible health effects. We are concerned about the use of anabolic steroids by athletes wishing to build muscle mass and improve their performance. However, members of this family of molecules derived from cholesterol have many important functions in the body. The bile salts that aid in the emulsification and digestion of lipids are steroid molecules, as are the sex hormones testosterone and estrone.

Lipid digestion is described in Section 23.1.

The steroids are members of a large, diverse collection of lipids called the *isoprenoids.* All of these compounds are built from one or more five-carbon units called *isoprene.*

$CH_2{=}C(CH_3){-}CH{=}CH_2$

Isoprene

Terpene is the general term for lipids that are synthesized from isoprene units. Examples of terpenes include the steroids and bile salts, the lipid-soluble vitamins, chlorophyll, and certain plant hormones.

All steroids contain the steroid nucleus (steroid carbon skeleton) as shown here:

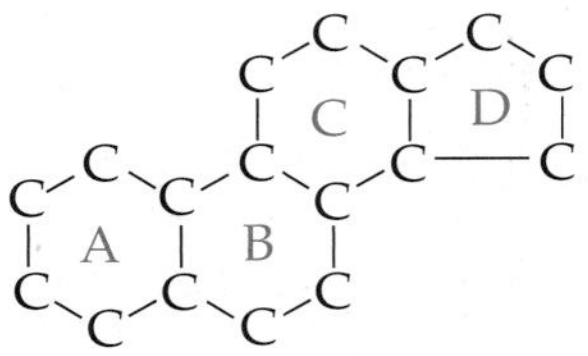

Carbon skeleton of the steroid nucleus

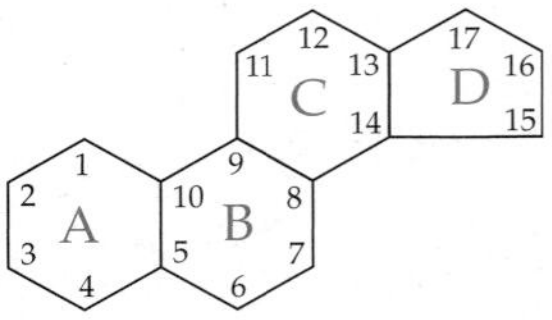

Steroid nucleus

The steroid carbon skeleton consists of four fused rings. Each ring pair has two carbons in common. Thus two fused rings share one or more common bonds as part of their ring backbones. For example, rings A and B, B and C, and C and D are all fused in the preceding structure. Many steroids have methyl groups attached to carbons 10 and 13, as well as an alkyl, alcohol, or ketone group attached to carbon-17.

Cholesterol, a common steroid, is found in the membranes of most animal cells. It is an amphipathic molecule and is readily soluble in the hydrophobic region of membranes. It is involved in regulation of the fluidity of the membrane as a result of the nonpolar fused ring. However, the hydroxyl group is polar and

A MEDICAL PERSPECTIVE

Disorders of Sphingolipid Metabolism

There are a number of human genetic disorders that are caused by a deficiency in one of the enzymes responsible for the breakdown of sphingolipids. In general, the symptoms are caused by the accumulation of abnormally large amounts of these lipids within particular cells. It is interesting to note that three of these diseases, Niemann-Pick disease, Gaucher's disease, and Tay-Sachs disease are found much more frequently among Ashkenazi Jews of Northern European heritage than among other ethnic groups.

Of the four subtypes of Niemann-Pick disease, type A is the most severe. It is inherited as a recessive disorder (that is, a defective copy of the gene must be inherited from each parent) that results in an absence of the enzyme sphingomyelinase. The absence of this enzyme causes the storage of large amounts of sphingomyelin and cholesterol in the brain, bone marrow, liver, and spleen.

Symptoms may begin when a baby is only a few months old. The parents may notice a delay in motor development and/or problems with feeding. Although the infants may develop some motor skills, they quickly begin to regress as they lose muscle strength and tone, as well as vision and hearing. The disease progresses rapidly and the children typically die within the first few years of life.

Tay-Sachs disease is a lipid storage disease caused by an absence of the enzyme hexosaminidase, which functions in ganglioside metabolism. As a result of the enzyme deficiency, the ganglioside, shown on page 600, accumulates in the cells of the brain, causing neurological deterioration. Like Niemann-Pick disease, it is an autosomal recessive genetic trait that becomes apparent in the first few months of the life of an infant and rapidly progresses to death within a few years. Symptoms include listlessness, irritability, seizures, paralysis, loss of muscle tone and function, blindness, deafness, and delayed mental and social skills.

Gaucher's disease is an autosomal recessive genetic disorder resulting in a deficiency of the enzyme glucocerebrosidase. In the normal situation, this enzyme breaks down glucocerebroside, which is an intermediate in the synthesis and degradation of complex glycosphingolipids found in cellular membranes. In Gaucher's disease, glucocerebroside builds up in macrophages found in the liver, spleen, and bone marrow. These cells become engorged with excess lipid and displace healthy, normal cells in bone marrow. The symptoms of Gaucher's disease include severe anemia, thrombocytopenia (reduction in the number of platelets), and hepatosplenomegaly (enlargement of the spleen and liver). There can also be skeletal problems including bone deterioration and secondary fractures.

Fabry's disease is an X-linked inherited disorder caused by the deficiency of the enzyme α-galactosidase A. This disease afflicts as many as 50,000 people worldwide. Typically, symptoms, including pain in the fingers and toes and a red rash around the waist, begin to appear when individuals reach their early twenties. A preliminary diagnosis can be confirmed by determining the concentration of the enzyme α-galactosidase A. Patients with Fabry's disease have an increased risk of kidney and heart disease, and a reduced life expectancy. Because this is an X-linked disorder, it is more common among males than females.

For Further Understanding

- A defect in the enzyme sphingomyelinase is the cause of Niemann-Pick disease. Write a chemical equation to represent the reaction catalyzed by the enzyme sphingomyelinase, the cleavage of sphingomyelin to produce phosphorylcholine and ceramide. Show the structural formulas for the reactant and products of this reaction.
- A defect in the enzyme glucocerebrosidase is the cause of Gaucher's disease. Write a chemical equation to represent the reaction catalyzed by the enzyme glucocerebrosidase, the cleavage of glucocerebroside to produce glucose and ceramide. Show the structural formulas for the reactant and products of this reaction.

functions like the polar heads of sphingolipids and phospholipids. There is a strong correlation between the concentration of cholesterol found in the blood plasma and heart disease, particularly **atherosclerosis** (hardening of the arteries). Cholesterol, in combination with other substances, contributes to a narrowing of the artery passageway. As narrowing increases, more pressure is necessary to ensure adequate blood flow, and high blood pressure (*hypertension*) develops. Hypertension is also linked to heart disease.

Cholesterol

This breakfast is high in cholesterol and saturated fats. Why do nutritionists recommend that we limit the amount of such foods in our diets?

A MEDICAL PERSPECTIVE

Steroids and the Treatment of Heart Disease

The foxglove plant (*Digitalis purpurea*) is an herb that produces one of the most powerful known stimulants of heart muscle. The active ingredients of the foxglove plant (digitalis) are the so-called cardiac glycosides, or *cardiotonic steroids,* which include digitoxin, digosin, and gitalin.

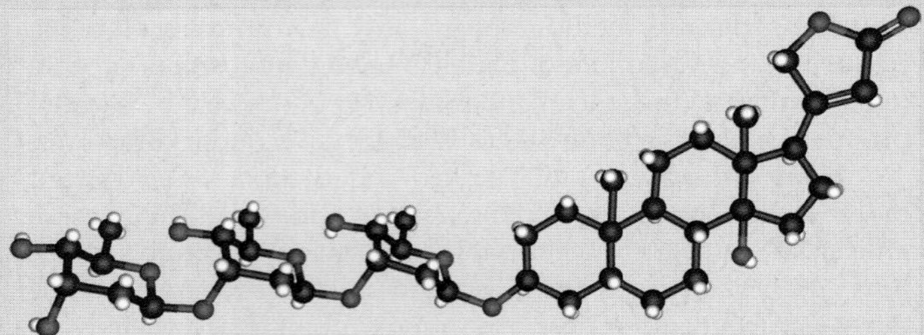

The structure of digitoxin, one of the cardiotonic steroids produced by the foxglove plant.

Digitalis purpurea, the foxglove plant.

These drugs are used clinically in the treatment of congestive heart failure, which results when the heart is not beating with strong, efficient strokes. When the blood is not propelled through the cardiovascular system efficiently, fluid builds up in the lungs and lower extremities (edema). The major symptoms of congestive heart failure are an enlarged heart, weakness, edema, shortness of breath, and fluid accumulation in the lungs.

This condition was originally described in 1785 by a physician, William Withering, who found a peasant woman whose folk medicine was famous as a treatment for chronic heart problems. Her potion contained a mixture of more than twenty herbs, but Dr. Withering, a botanist as well as physician, quickly discovered that foxglove was the active ingredient in the mixture. Withering used *Digitalis purpurea* successfully to treat congestive heart failure and even described some cautions in its use.

The cardiotonic steroids are extremely strong heart stimulants. A dose as low as 1 milligram (mg) increases the stroke volume of the heart (volume of blood per contraction), increases the strength of the contraction, and reduces the heart rate. When the heart is pumping more efficiently because of stimulation by digitalis, the edema disappears.

Digitalis can be used to control congestive heart failure, but the dose must be carefully determined and monitored because the therapeutic dose is close to the dose that causes toxicity. The symptoms that result from high body levels of cardiotonic steroids include vomiting, blurred vision and lightheadedness, increased water loss, convulsions, and death. Only a physician can determine the initial dose and maintenance schedule for an individual to control congestive heart failure and yet avoid the toxic side effects.

For Further Understanding

- Foxglove is a perennial plant, that is, a plant that will grow back each year for at least 3 years. Occasionally, foxglove first-year growth has been mistaken for comfrey, another plant with medical applications. Greeks and Romans used comfrey to treat wounds and to stop heavy bleeding, as well as for bronchial problems. Explain why the use of foxglove in place of comfrey might have fatal consequences.
- Drugs such as digitalis are referred to as *cardiac glycosides* and as *cardiotonic steroids.* Explain why both these names are valid.

Egg yolks contain a high concentration of cholesterol, as do many dairy products and animal fats. As a result, it has been recommended that the amounts of these products in the diet be regulated to moderate the dietary intake of cholesterol.

Bile salts are described in greater detail in Section 23.1.

Bile salts are amphipathic derivatives of cholesterol that are synthesized in the liver and stored in the gallbladder. The principal bile salts in humans are cholate and chenodeoxycholate.

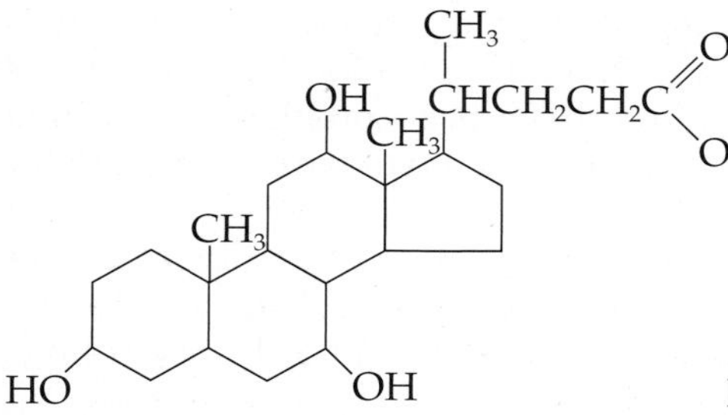

Cholate

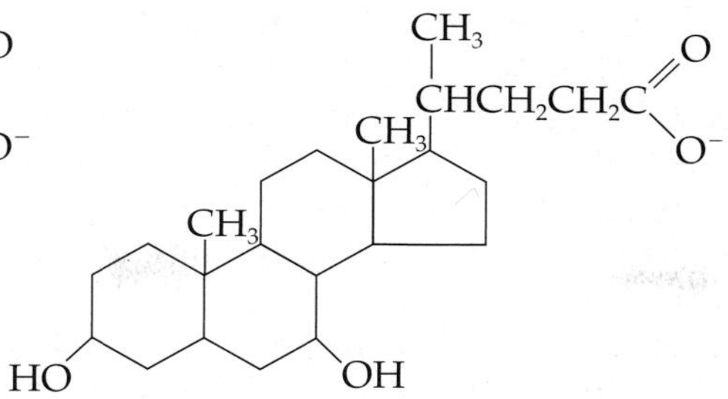

Chenodeoxycholate

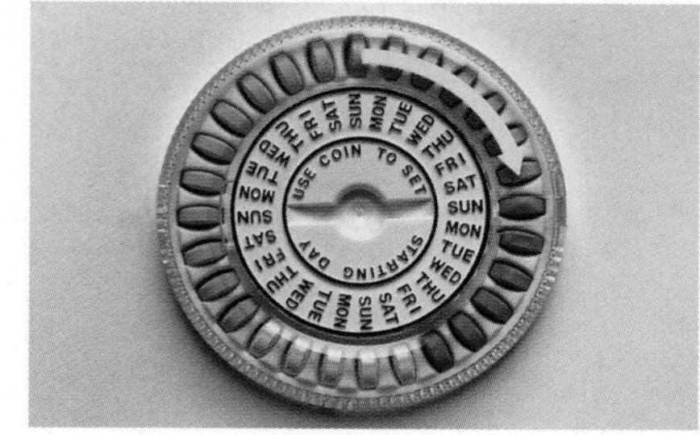

Newer birth control pill formulations include both a progesterone and an estrogen. How do these steroids prevent pregnancy?

Bile salts are emulsifying agents whose polar hydroxyl groups interact with water and whose hydrophobic regions bind to lipids. Following a meal, bile flows from the gallbladder to the duodenum (the uppermost region of the small intestine). Here the bile salts emulsify dietary fats into small droplets that can be more readily digested by lipases (lipid digesting enzymes) also found in the small intestine.

Steroids play a role in the reproductive cycle. In a series of chemical reactions, cholesterol is converted to the steroid *progesterone,* the most important hormone associated with pregnancy. Produced in the ovaries and in the placenta, progesterone is responsible for both the successful initiation and the successful completion of pregnancy. It prepares the lining of the uterus to accept the fertilized egg. Once the egg is attached, progesterone is involved in the development of the fetus and plays a role in the suppression of further ovulation during pregnancy.

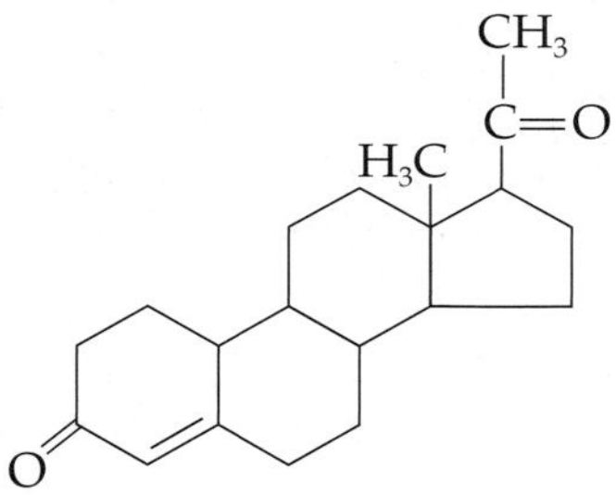

19-Norprogesterone

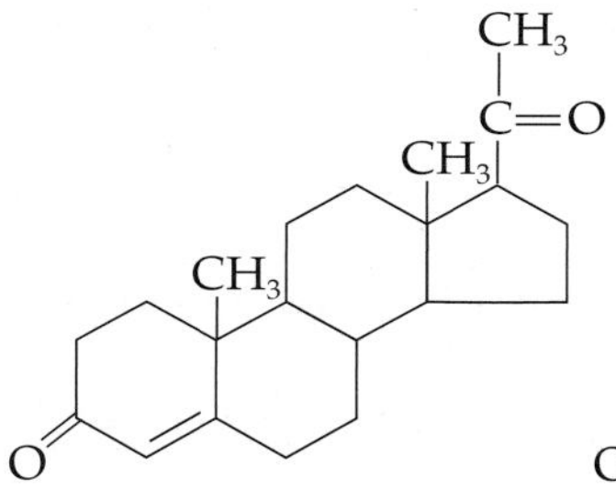

Progesterone

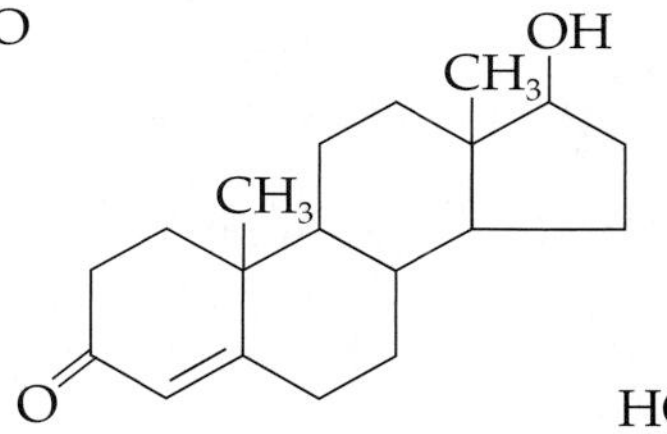

Testosterone

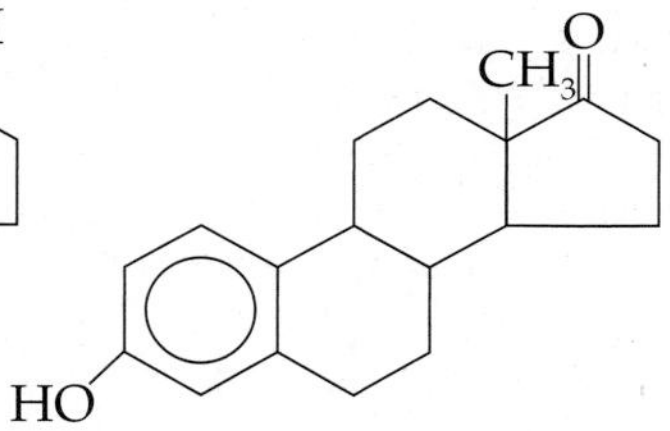

Estrone

Testosterone, a male sex hormone found in the testes, and *estrone,* a female sex hormone, are both produced by the chemical modification of progesterone. These hormones are involved in the development of male and female sex characteristics.

Many steroids, including progesterone, have played important roles in the development of birth control agents. 19-Norprogesterone was one of the first synthetic birth control agents. It is approximately ten times as effective as progesterone in providing birth control. However, its utility was severely limited because this compound could not be administered orally and had to be taken by injection. A related compound, norlutin (chemical name: 17-α-ethynyl-19-nortestosterone), was found to provide both the strength and the effectiveness of 19-norprogesterone and could be taken orally.

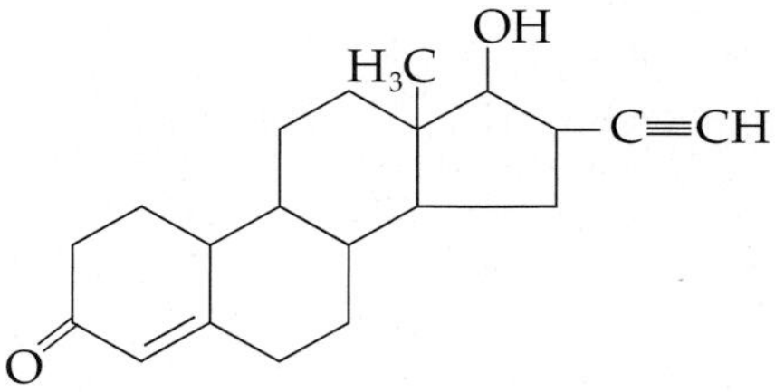

Norlutin

Currently "combination" oral contraceptives are prescribed most frequently. These include a progesterone and an estrogen. These newer products confer better contraceptive protection than either agent administered individually. They are also used to regulate menstruation in patients with heavy menstrual bleeding. First investigated in the late 1950s and approved by the FDA in 1961, there are at least thirty combination pills currently available. In addition, a transdermal patch for the treatment of postmenopausal osteoporosis is being investigated.

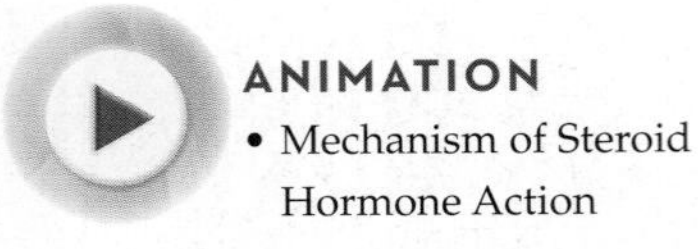

ANIMATION

- Mechanism of Steroid Hormone Action

All of these compounds act by inducing a false pregnancy, which prevents ovulation. When oral contraception is discontinued, ovulation usually returns within three menstrual cycles. Although there have been problems associated with "the pill," it appears to be an effective and safe method of family planning for much of the population.

Cortisone is a steroid important to the proper regulation of a number of biochemical processes. For example, it is involved in the metabolism of carbohydrates. Cortisone is also used in the treatment of rheumatoid arthritis, asthma, gastrointestinal disorders, many skin conditions, and a variety of other diseases. However, treatment with cortisone is not without risk. Some of the possible side effects of cortisone therapy include fluid retention, sodium retention, and potassium loss that can lead to congestive heart failure. Other side effects include muscle weakness, osteoporosis, gastrointestinal upsets including peptic ulcers, and neurological symptoms, including vertigo, headaches, and convulsions.

Cortisone

Aldosterone is a steroid hormone produced by the adrenal cortex and secreted into the bloodstream when blood sodium ion levels are too low. Upon reaching its target tissues in the kidney, aldosterone activates a set of reactions that cause sodium ions and water to be returned to the blood. If sodium levels are elevated, aldosterone is not secreted from the adrenal cortex and the sodium ions filtered out of the blood by the kidney will be excreted.

Aldosterone

Question 17.13 Draw the structure of the steroid nucleus. Note the locations of the A, B, C, and D steroid rings.

Question 17.14 What is meant by the term *fused ring?*

Waxes

Waxes are derived from many different sources and have a variety of chemical compositions, depending on the source. Paraffin wax, for example, is composed of a mixture of solid hydrocarbons (usually straight-chain compounds). The natural waxes generally are composed of a long-chain fatty acid esterified to a long-chain alcohol. Because the long hydrocarbon tails are extremely hydrophobic, waxes are completely insoluble in water. Waxes are also solid at room temperature, owing to their high molar masses. Two examples of waxes are myricyl palmitate, a major component of beeswax, and whale oil (spermaceti wax), from the head of the sperm whale, which is composed of cetyl palmitate.

Naturally occurring waxes have a variety of uses. Lanolin, which serves as a protective coating for hair and skin, is used in skin creams and ointments. Carnauba wax is used in automobile polish. Whale oil was once used as a fuel, in ointments, and in candles. However, synthetic waxes have replaced whale oil to a large extent, because of efforts to ban the hunting of whales.

$$CH_3(CH_2)_{14}-\overset{\overset{\displaystyle O}{\|}}{C}-O-(CH_2)_{29}CH_3$$

Myricyl palmitate (beeswax)

$$CH_3(CH_2)_{14}-\overset{\overset{\displaystyle O}{\|}}{C}-O-(CH_2)_{15}CH_3$$

Cetyl palmitate (whale oil)

17.5 Complex Lipids

LEARNING GOAL

10 Describe the function of lipoproteins in triglyceride and cholesterol transport in the body.

Complex lipids are lipids that are bonded to other types of molecules. The most common and important complex lipids are plasma lipoproteins, which are responsible for the transport of other lipids in the body.

Lipids are only sparingly soluble in water, and the movement of lipids from one organ to another through the bloodstream requires a transport system that uses **plasma lipoproteins.** Lipoprotein particles consist of a core of hydrophobic lipids surrounded by amphipathic proteins, phospholipids, and cholesterol (Figure 17.8).

There are four major classes of human plasma lipoproteins:

- **Chylomicrons,** which have a density of less than 0.95 g/mL, carry dietary triglycerides from the intestine to other tissues. The remaining lipoproteins are classified by their densities.
- **Very low density lipoproteins (VLDL)** have a density of 0.95–1.019 g/mL. They bind triglycerides synthesized in the liver and carry them to adipose and other tissues for storage.
- **Low-density lipoproteins (LDL)** are characterized by a density of 1.019–1.063 g/mL. They carry cholesterol to peripheral tissues and help regulate cholesterol levels in those tissues. These are richest in cholesterol, frequently carrying 40% of the plasma cholesterol.
- **High-density lipoproteins (HDL)** have a density of 1.063–1.210 g/mL. They are bound to plasma cholesterol; however, they transport cholesterol from peripheral tissues to the liver.

A summary of the composition of each of the plasma lipoproteins is presented in Figure 17.9.

Chylomicrons are aggregates of triglycerides and protein that transport dietary triglycerides to cells throughout the body. Not all lipids in the blood are derived directly from the diet. Triglycerides and cholesterol are also synthesized in the liver and also are transported through the blood in lipoprotein packages. Triglycerides are assembled into VLDL particles that carry the energy-rich lipid molecules either to tissues requiring an energy source or to adipose tissue for storage. Similarly, cholesterol is assembled into LDL particles for transport from the liver to peripheral tissues.

Entry of LDL particles into the cell is dependent on a specific recognition event and binding between the LDL particle and a protein receptor embedded within the membrane. Low-density lipoprotein receptors (LDL receptors) are found in the membranes of cells outside the liver and are responsible for the uptake of cholesterol by the cells of various tissues. LDL (lipoprotein bound to cholesterol) binds specifically to the LDL receptor, and the complex is taken into the cell by a process called *receptor-mediated endocytosis* (Figure 17.10). The membrane begins to be pulled into the cell at the site of the LDL receptor complexes. This draws the entire LDL particle into the cell. Eventually, the portion of the membrane

Phospholipid
Cholesterol
Protein
Cholesterol esters
Triglycerides
(a)

Cholesterol
Cholesterol esters
Protein
Phospholipid
(b)

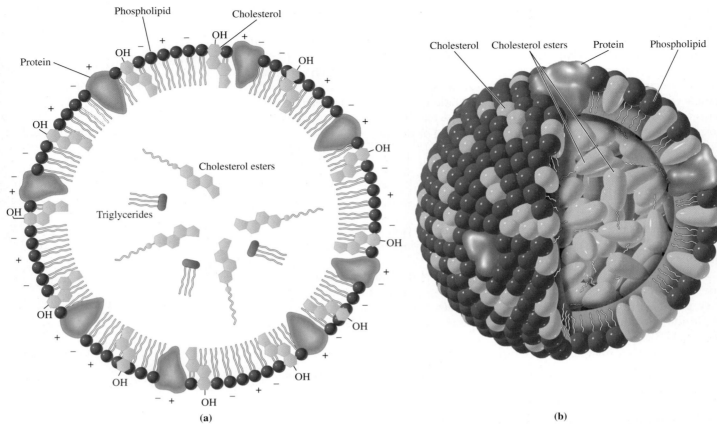

Figure 17.8 A model for the structure of a plasma lipoprotein. The various lipoproteins are composed of a shell of protein, cholesterol, and phospholipids surrounding more hydrophobic molecules such as triglycerides or cholesterol esters (cholesterol esterified to fatty acids). (a) Cross section, (b) three-dimensional view.

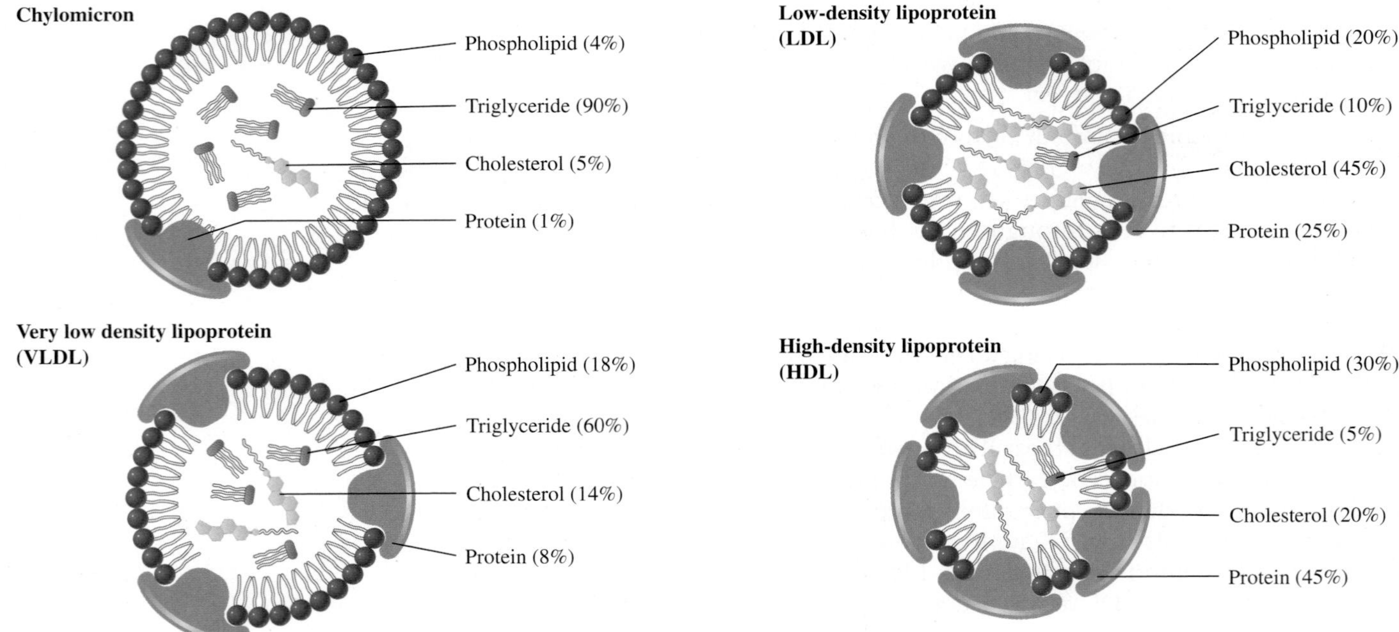

Figure 17.9 A summary of the relative amounts of cholesterol, phospholipid, protein, and triglycerides in the four classes of lipoproteins.

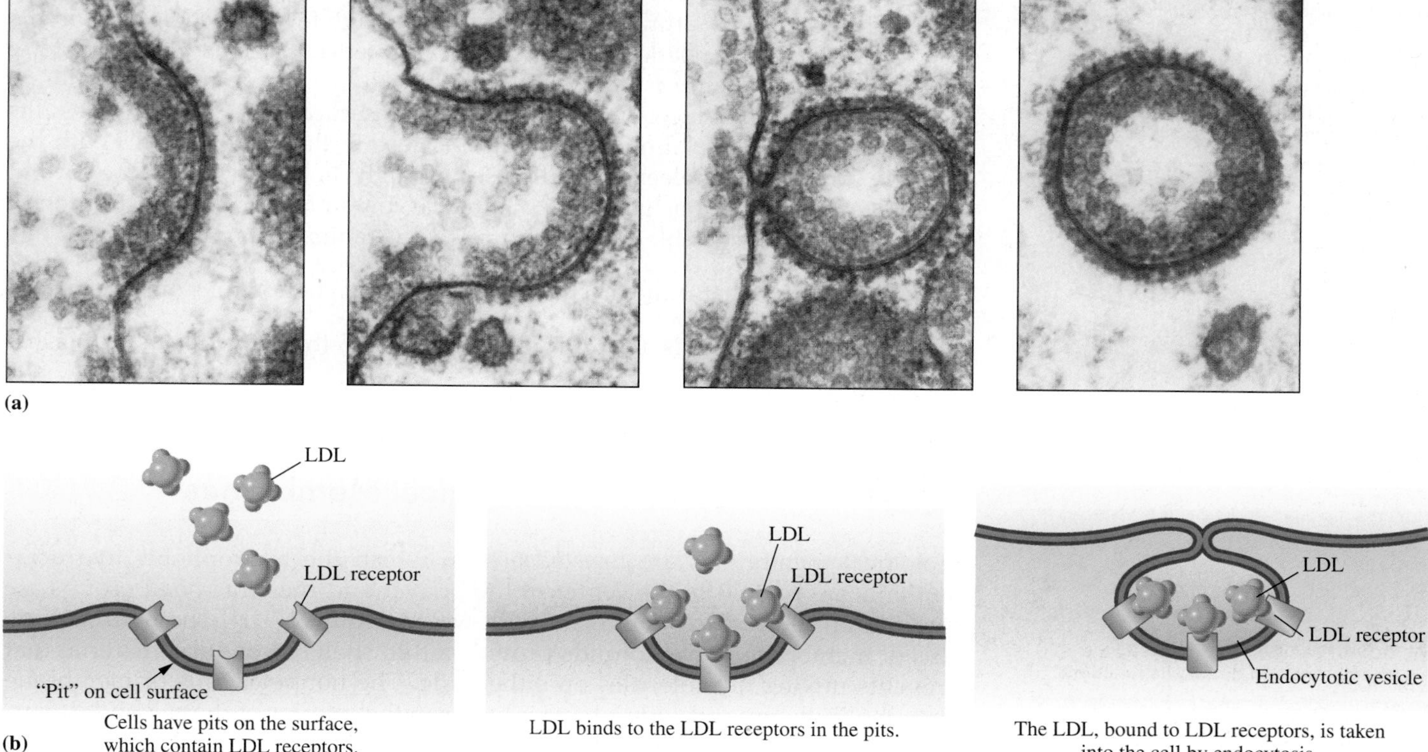

Figure 17.10 Receptor-mediated endocytosis. (a) Electron micrographs of the process of receptor-mediated endocytosis. (b) Summary of the events of receptor-mediated endocytosis of LDL.

surrounding the LDL particles pinches away from the cell membrane and forms a membrane around the LDL particles. As we will see in Section 17.6, membranes are fluid and readily flow. Thus, they can form a vesicle or endosome containing the LDL particles.

Cellular digestive organelles known as *lysosomes* fuse with the endosomes. This fusion is accomplished when the membranes of the endosome and the lysosome flow together to create one larger membrane-bound body or vesicle. Hydrolytic enzymes from the lysosome then digest the entire complex to release cholesterol into the cytoplasm of the cell. There, cholesterol inhibits its own biosynthesis and activates an enzyme that stores cholesterol in cholesterol ester droplets. High concentrations of cholesterol inside the cell also inhibit the synthesis of LDL receptors to ensure that the cell will not take up too much cholesterol. People who have a genetic defect in the gene coding for the LDL receptor do not take up as much cholesterol. As a result they accumulate LDL cholesterol in the plasma. This excess plasma cholesterol is then deposited on the artery walls, causing atherosclerosis. This disease is called *hypercholesterolemia.*

Liver lipoprotein receptors enable large amounts of cholesterol to be removed from the blood, thus ensuring low concentrations of cholesterol in the blood plasma. Other factors being equal, the person with the most lipoprotein receptors will be the least vulnerable to a high-cholesterol diet and have the least likelihood of developing atherosclerosis.

There is also evidence that high levels of HDL in the blood help reduce the incidence of atherosclerosis, perhaps because HDL carries cholesterol from the peripheral tissues back to the liver. In the liver, some of the cholesterol is used for bile synthesis and secreted into the intestines, from which it is excreted.

Recently an inflammatory protein, the C-reactive protein (CRP), has been implicated in atherosclerosis. A test for the level of this protein in the blood is being suggested as a way to predict the risk of heart attack. A high sensitivity CRP test is now widely available.

A final correlation has been made between diet and atherosclerosis. People whose diet is high in saturated fats tend to have high levels of cholesterol in the blood. Although the relationship between saturated fatty acids and cholesterol metabolism is unclear, it is known that a diet rich in unsaturated fats results in decreased cholesterol levels. In fact, the use of unsaturated fat in the diet results in a decrease in the level of LDL and an increase in the level of HDL. With the positive correlation between heart disease and high cholesterol levels, the current dietary recommendations include a diet that is low in fat and the substitution of unsaturated fats (vegetable oils) for saturated fats (animal fats).

Question 17.15 What is the mechanism of uptake of cholesterol from plasma?

Question 17.16 What is the role of lysosomes in the metabolism of plasma lipoproteins?

17.6 The Structure of Biological Membranes

LEARNING GOAL

11 Draw the structure of the cell membrane and discuss its functions.

Biological membranes are *lipid bilayers* in which the hydrophobic hydrocarbon tails are packed in the center of the bilayer and the ionic head groups are exposed on the surface to interact with water (Figure 17.11). The hydrocarbon tails of membrane phospholipids provide a thin shell of nonpolar material that prevents mixing of molecules on either side. The nonpolar tails of membrane phospholipids thus provide a barrier between the interior of the cell and its surroundings. The polar heads of lipids are exposed to water, and they are highly solvated.

The two layers of the phospholipid bilayer membrane are not identical in composition. For instance, in human red blood cells, approximately 80% of the phospholipids in the outer layer of the membrane are phosphatidylcholine and sphingomyelin; whereas phosphatidylethanolamine and phosphatidylserine make up approximately 80% of the inner layer. In addition, carbohydrate groups are found attached only to those phospholipids found on the outer layer of a membrane. Here they participate in receptor and recognition functions.

Fluid Mosaic Structure of Biological Membranes

As we have just noted, membranes are not static; they are composed of molecules in motion. The fluidity of biological membranes is determined by the proportions of saturated and unsaturated fatty acid groups in the membrane phospholipids. About half of the fatty acids that are isolated from membrane lipids from all sources are unsaturated.

The bacteria growing in this hot spring in Yellowstone National Park are called thermophiles because they live at temperatures approaching the boiling point of water. What type of fatty acids do you think will be found in their membrane phospholipids?

The unsaturated fatty acid tails of the phospholipids contribute to membrane fluidity because of the bends introduced into the hydrocarbon chain by the double bonds. Because of these "kinks," the fatty acid tails do not pack together tightly.

We also find that the percentage of unsaturated fatty acid groups in membrane lipids is inversely proportional to the temperature of the environment. Bacteria, for example, have different ratios of saturated and unsaturated fatty acids in their membrane lipids, depending on the temperatures of their surroundings. For instance, the membranes of bacteria that grow in the Arctic Ocean have high levels of unsaturated fatty acids so that their membranes remain fluid even at these frigid temperatures. Conversely, the organisms that live in the hot springs of Yellowstone National Park, with temperatures near the boiling point of water, have membranes with high levels of saturated fatty acids. This flexibility in fatty acid content enables the bacteria to maintain the same membrane fluidity over a temperature range of almost 100°C.

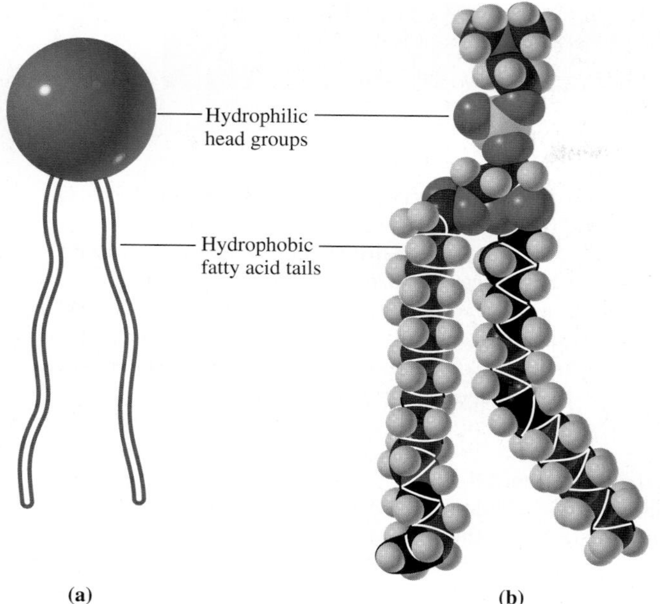

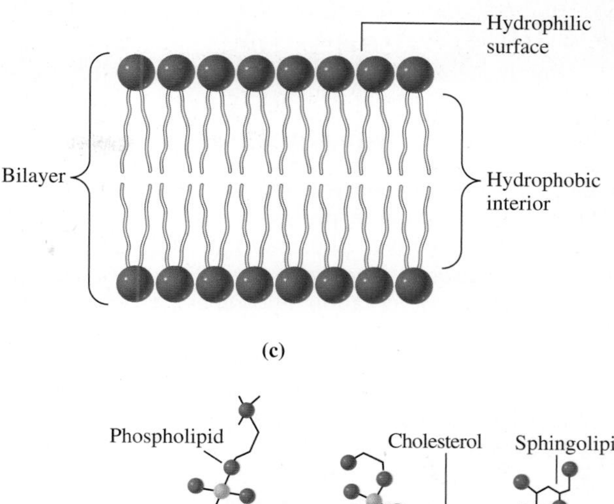

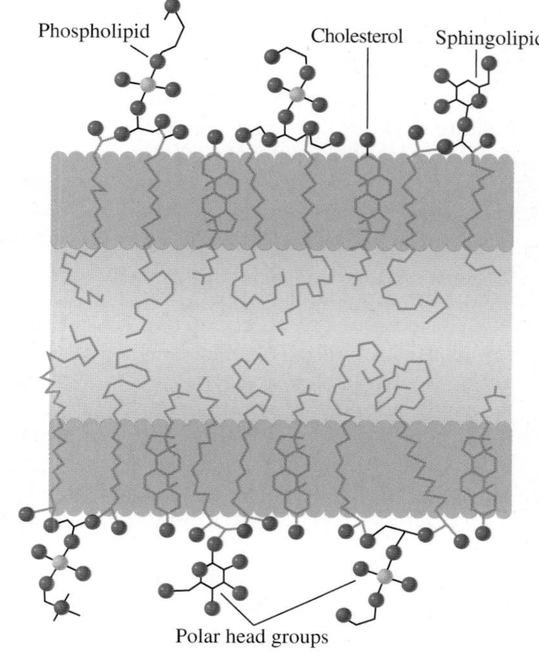

Figure 17.11 (a) Representation of a phospholipid. (b) Space-filling model of a phospholipid. (c) Representation of a phospholipid bilayer membrane. (d) Line formula structure of a bilayer membrane composed of phospholipids, cholesterol, and sphingolipids.

Generally, the body temperatures of mammals are quite constant, and the fatty acid composition of their membrane lipids is therefore usually very uniform. One interesting exception is the reindeer. Much of the year the reindeer must travel through ice and snow. Thus the hooves and lower legs must function at much colder temperatures than the rest of the body. Because of this, the percentage of unsaturation in the membranes varies along the length of the reindeer leg. We find that the proportion of unsaturated fatty acids increases closer to the hoof, permitting the membranes to function in the low temperatures of ice and snow to which the lower leg is exposed.

Thus, membranes are fluid, regardless of the environmental temperature conditions. In fact, it has been estimated that membranes have the consistency of olive oil.

Although the hydrophobic barrier created by the fluid lipid bilayer is an important feature of membranes, the proteins embedded within the lipid bilayer are equally important and are responsible for critical cellular functions. The presence of these membrane proteins was revealed by an electron microscopic technique called *freeze-fracture.* Cells are frozen to very cold temperatures and then fractured with a very fine diamond knife. Some of the cells are fractured between the two layers of the lipid bilayer. When viewed with the electron microscope, the membrane appeared to be a mosaic, studded with proteins. Because of the fluidity of membranes and the appearance of the proteins seen by electron microscopy, our concept of membrane structure is called the **fluid mosaic model** (Figure 17.12).

Some of the observed proteins, called **peripheral membrane proteins,** are bound only to one of the surfaces of the membrane by interactions between ionic head groups of the membrane lipids and ionic amino acids on the surface of the peripheral protein. Other membrane proteins, called **transmembrane proteins,** are embedded within the membrane and extend completely through it, being exposed both inside and outside the cell.

Just as the phospholipid composition of the membrane is asymmetric, so too is the orientation of transmembrane proteins. Each transmembrane protein has

A MEDICAL PERSPECTIVE

Liposome Delivery Systems

Liposomes were discovered by Dr. Alec Bangham in 1961. During his studies on phospholipids and blood clotting, he found that if he mixed phospholipids and water, tiny phospholipid bilayer sacs, called liposomes, would form spontaneously. Since that first observation, liposomes have been developed as efficient delivery systems for everything from antitumor and antiviral drugs, to the hair-loss therapy minoxidil!

If a drug is included in the solution during formation of liposomes, the phospholipids will form a sac around the solution. In this way the drug becomes encapsulated within the phospholipid sphere. These liposomes can be injected intravenously or applied to body surfaces. Sometimes scientists include hydrophilic molecules in the surface of the liposome. This increases the length of time that they will remain in circulation in the bloodstream. These so-called stealth liposomes are being used to carry anticancer drugs, such as doxorubicin and mitoxantrone. Liposomes are also being used as carriers for the antiviral drugs, such as AZT and ddC, that are used to treat human immunodeficiency virus (HIV) infection.

A clever trick to help target the drug-carrying liposome is to include an antibody on the surface of the liposome. These antibodies are proteins designed to bind specifically to the surface of a tumor cell. Upon attaching to the surface of the tumor cell, the liposome "membrane" fuses with the cell membrane. In this way the deadly chemicals are delivered only to those cells targeted for destruction. This helps to avoid many of the unpleasant side effects of chemotherapy treatment that occur when normal healthy cells are killed by the drug.

Another application of liposomes is in the cosmetics industry. Liposomes can be formed that encapsulate a vitamin, herbal agent, or other nutritional element. When applied to the skin, the liposomes pass easily through the outer layer of dead skin, delivering their contents to the living skin cells beneath. As with the pharmaceutical liposomes, these liposomes, sometimes called *cosmeceuticals,* fuse with skin cells. Thus, they directly deliver the beneficial cosmetic agent directly to the cells that can benefit the most.

Since their accidental discovery 50 years ago, much has been learned about the formation of liposomes and ways to engineer them for more efficient delivery of their contents. This is another example of the marriage of serendipity, an accidental discovery, with scientific research and technological application. As the development of new types of liposomes continues, we can expect that even more ways will be found to improve the human condition.

For Further Understanding

- From what you know of the structure of phospholipids, explain the molecular interactions that cause liposomes to form.
- Could you use liposome technology to deliver a hydrophobic drug? Explain your answer.

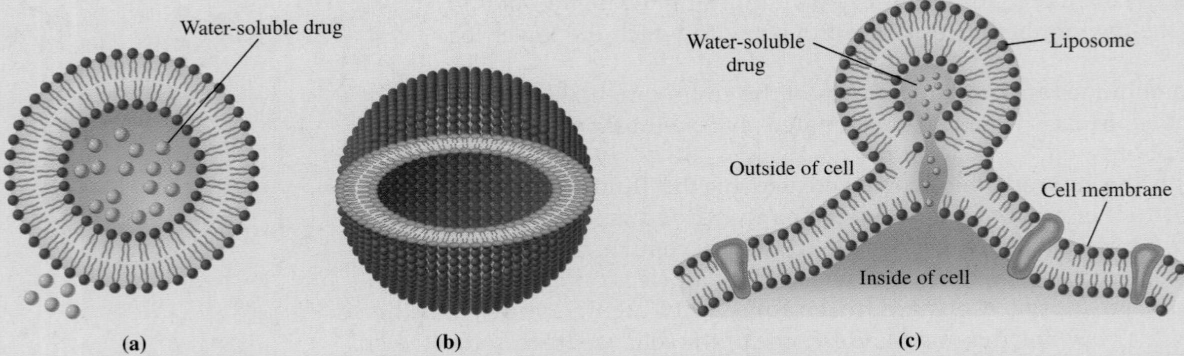

(a) Cross section of a liposome, (b) three-dimensional view of a liposome, and (c) liposome fusing with cell membrane.

hydrophobic regions that associate with the fatty acid tails of membrane phospholipids. Each also has a unique hydrophilic domain that is always found associated with the outer layer of the membrane and is located on the outside of the cell. This region of the protein typically has oligosaccharides covalently attached. Hence these proteins are *glycoproteins.* Similarly, each transmembrane protein has a second hydrophilic domain that is always found associated with the inner layer of the membrane and projects into the cytoplasm of the cell. Typically this region of the transmembrane protein is attached to filaments of the cytoplasmic skeleton.

Membranes are dynamic structures. The mobility of proteins embedded in biological membranes was studied by labeling certain proteins in human and mouse cell membranes with red and green fluorescent dyes. The human and

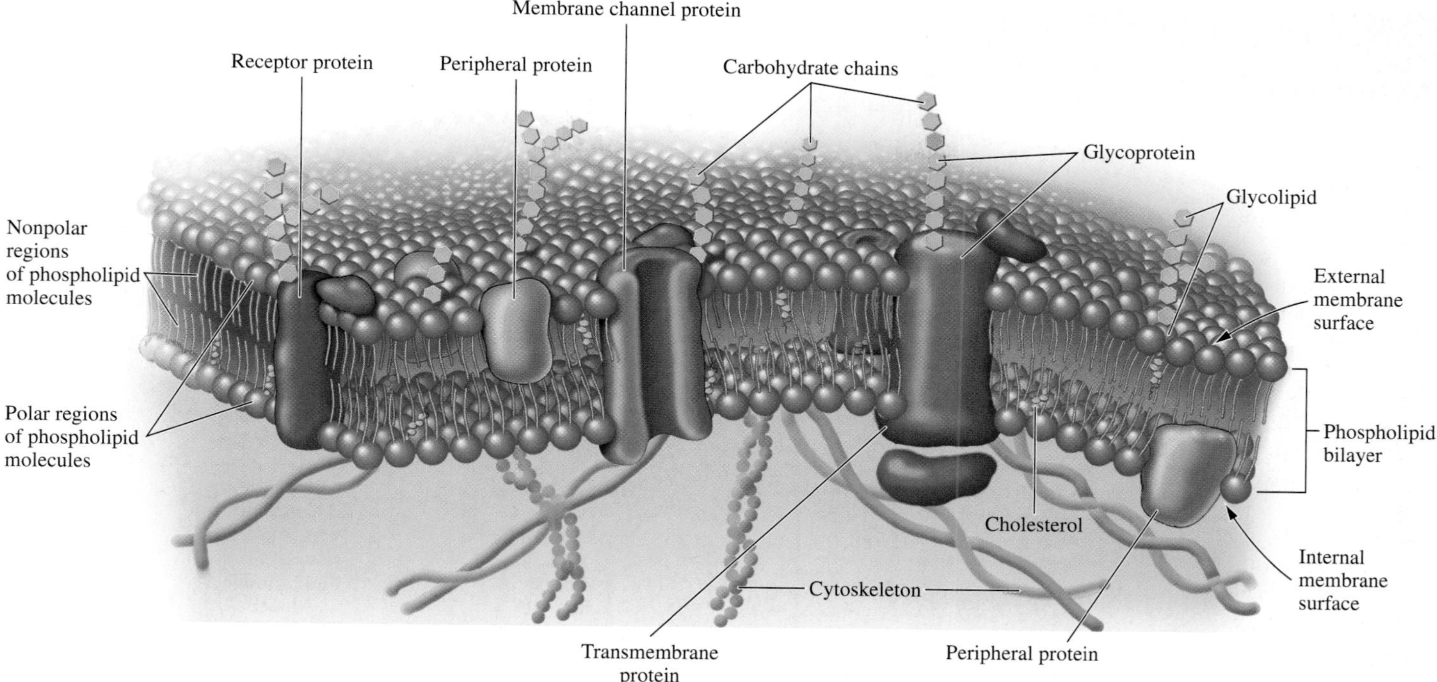

Figure 17.12 The fluid mosaic model of membrane structure.

mouse cells were fused; in other words, special techniques were used to cause the membranes of the mouse and human cells to flow together to create a single cell. The new cell was observed through a special ultraviolet or fluorescence microscope. The red and green patches were localized within regions of their original cell membranes when the experiment began. Forty minutes later the color patches were uniformly distributed in the fused cellular membrane (Figure 17.13). This experiment suggests that we can think of the fluid mosaic membrane as an ocean filled with mobile, floating icebergs.

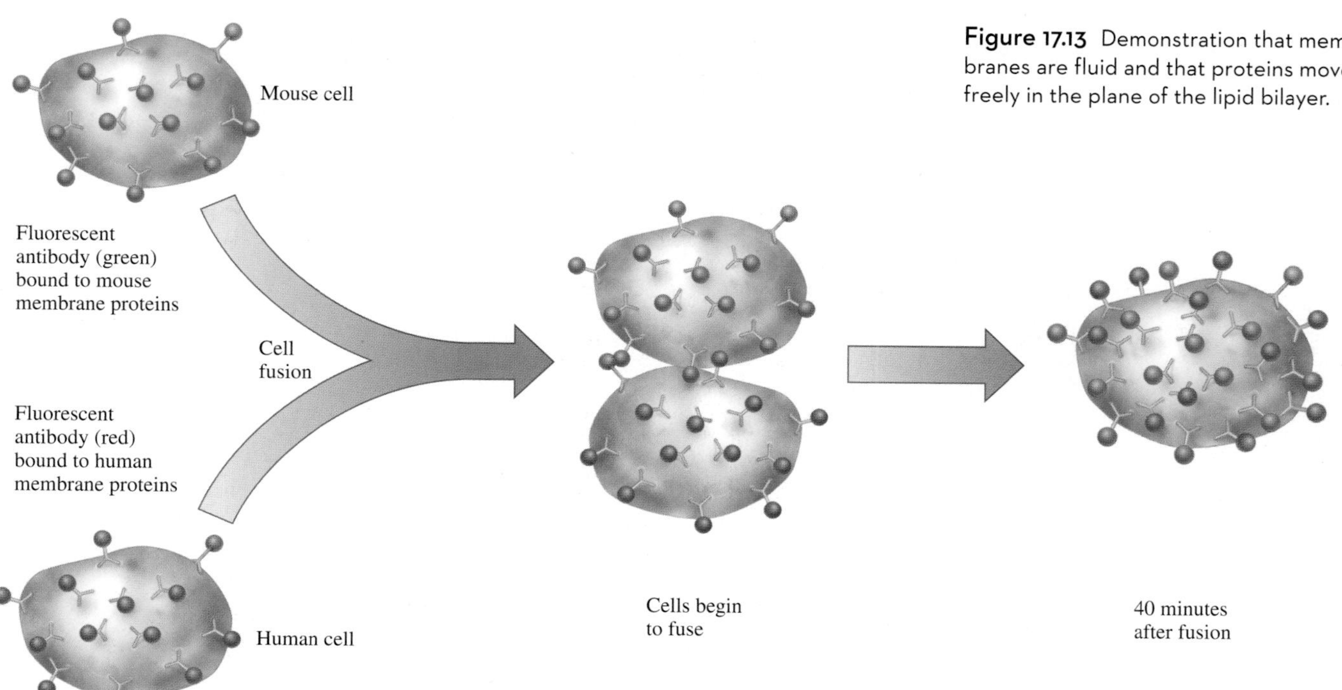

Figure 17.13 Demonstration that membranes are fluid and that proteins move freely in the plane of the lipid bilayer.

CHAPTER MAP

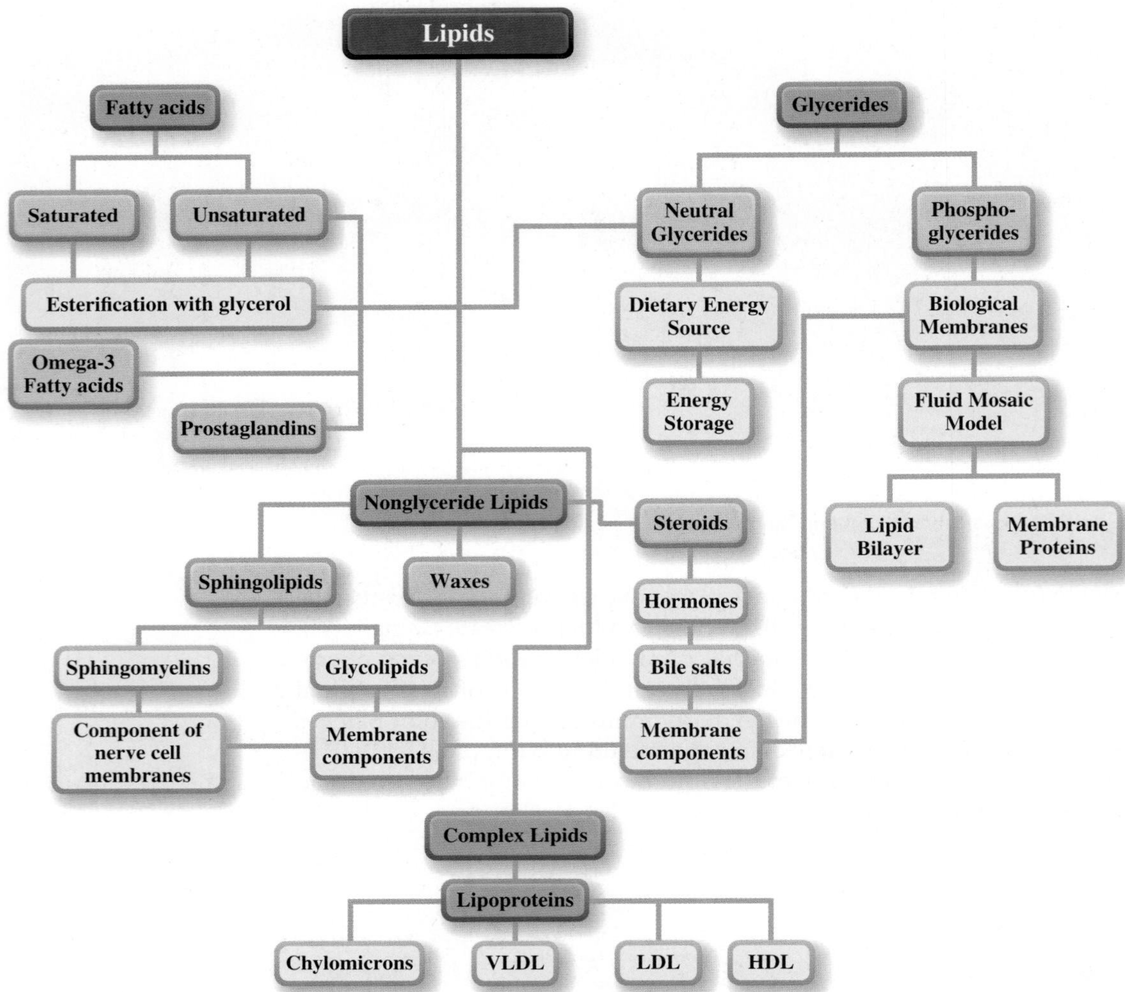
Lipids
Fatty acids
Saturated
Unsaturated
Esterification with glycerol
Omega-3 Fatty acids
Prostaglandins
Glycerides
Neutral Glycerides
Phospho-glycerides
Dietary Energy Source
Energy Storage
Biological Membranes
Fluid Mosaic Model
Lipid Bilayer
Membrane Proteins
Nonglyceride Lipids
Sphingolipids
Waxes
Steroids
Hormones
Bile salts
Membrane components
Sphingomyelins
Glycolipids
Component of nerve cell membranes
Membrane components
Complex Lipids
Lipoproteins
Chylomicrons
VLDL
LDL
HDL

SUMMARY

17.1 Biological Functions of Lipids

- **Lipids** are organic molecules characterized by their solubility in nonpolar solvents.
- Lipids serve many functions in the body including: energy storage, protection of organs, insulation, absorption of vitamins, energy sources, and hormones.

17.2 Fatty Acids

- **Fatty acids** may be **saturated** or **unsaturated** carboxylic acids containing 12–24 carbon atoms.
- Fatty acids with even numbers of carbon atoms occur most frequently in nature.
- **Essential fatty acids** are those that must be provided in the diet. Linoleic and linolenic acids are essential fatty acids.
- Linoleic acid is needed for the synthesis of **arachidonic acid,** which is the precursor of the **eicosanoids.**
- Among the eicosanoids are the **prostaglandins,** thromboxanes, and leukotrienes, all of which have important physiological effects.
- Omega-3 fatty acids are important components of a healthy diet.

17.3 Glycerides

- **Glycerides** are the most abundant lipids. The **neutral glycerides** are esters of one **(monoglycerides),** two **(diglycerides),** or three **(triglycerides)** fatty acids and glycerol.
- The reactions of fatty acids are identical to those of carboxylic acids: **esterification, hydrogenation,** and production by acid hydrolysis of esters. The base-catalyzed hydrolysis of a glyceride is **saponification.**
- **Phospholipids** are important components of biological membranes.
- **Phosphoglycerides** are esters derived from glycerol-3-phosphate and two fatty acids.
- The simplest phosphoglyceride is **phosphatidate.**
- Because of their amphipathic nature, phospholipids are excellent **emulsifying agents.**

17.4 Nonglyceride Lipids

- Nonglyceride lipids include the **sphingolipids, steroids,** and **waxes.**
- **Sphingomyelin** is a component of the myelin sheath around cells of the central nervous system.
- **Steroids** are important for many biochemical functions. They are **terpenes** because they are synthesized from isoprene units.
    - **Cholesterol** is a membrane component. However, high concentrations in the blood can contribute to **atherosclerosis.**
    - Testosterone, progesterone, and estrone are sex hormones.
    - Cortisone is an anti-inflammatory steroid that is important in the regulation of biological pathways.

17.5 Complex Lipids

- **Plasma lipoproteins** are **complex lipids** that transport other lipids through the bloodstream.
- **Chylomicrons** carry dietary triglycerides from the intestine to other tissues.
- **Very low density lipoproteins** carry triglycerides synthesized in the liver to other tissues for storage.
- **Low-density lipoproteins** carry cholesterol to peripheral tissues and help regulate cholesterol levels.
- **High-density lipoproteins** transport cholesterol from peripheral tissues to the liver.

17.6 The Structure of Biological Membranes

- The **fluid mosaic model** of membrane structure pictures biological membranes that are composed of lipid bilayers in which proteins are embedded.
- Membrane lipids contain polar head groups and nonpolar hydrocarbon tails.
- Membrane proteins may be embedded within the membrane **(transmembrane proteins)** or may lie on one surface of the membrane **(peripheral membrane proteins).**

ANSWERS TO PRACTICE PROBLEMS

17.1 a. Oleic acid: $CH_3(CH_2)_7CH{=}CH(CH_2)_7COOH$

H

H

O

oleic acid

OH

b. Linoleic acid: $CH_3(CH_2)_4CH{=}CH{-}CH_2{-}CH{=}CH(CH_2)_7COOH$

O

OH

linoleic acid

17.2 a.

$$\begin{array}{c} \text{H} \\ | \\ \text{H}-\text{C}-\text{OH} \\ | \\ \text{H}-\text{C}-\text{OH} \\ | \\ \text{H}-\text{C}-\text{OH} \\ | \\ \text{H} \\ \text{Glycerol} \end{array} + \begin{array}{c} 2CH_3(CH_2)_{16}COOH \\ \text{Stearic acid} \end{array} \longrightarrow \begin{array}{l} \quad\text{H} \qquad\quad \text{O} \\ \quad | \qquad\quad \| \\ \text{H}-\text{C}-\text{O}-\text{C}-(CH_2)_{16}CH_3 \\ \quad | \\ \text{H}-\text{C}-\text{O}-\text{C}-(CH_2)_{16}CH_3 \\ \quad | \qquad\quad \| \\ \text{H}-\text{C}-\text{OH}\ \ \text{O} \\ \quad | \\ \quad\text{H} \end{array}$$

b.

$$\begin{array}{c} \text{H} \\ | \\ \text{H}-\text{C}-\text{OH} \\ | \\ \text{H}-\text{C}-\text{OH} \\ | \\ \text{H}-\text{C}-\text{OH} \\ | \\ \text{H} \\ \text{Glycerol} \end{array} + \begin{array}{c} CH_3(CH_2)_{12}COOH \\ \text{Myristic acid} \end{array} \longrightarrow \begin{array}{l} \quad\text{H} \qquad\quad \text{O} \\ \quad | \qquad\quad \| \\ \text{H}-\text{C}-\text{O}-\text{C}-(CH_2)_{12}CH_3 \\ \quad | \\ \text{H}-\text{C}-\text{OH} \\ \quad | \\ \text{H}-\text{C}-\text{OH} \\ \quad | \\ \quad\text{H} \end{array}$$

17.3 a. $CH_3(CH_2)_{10}COOH + CH_3CH_2OH \xrightarrow{H^+,\ \text{heat}}$

Dodecanoic acid / Lauric acid; Ethanol

$$\begin{array}{c} \text{O} \\ \| \\ CH_3(CH_2)_{10}COCH_2CH_3 \end{array}$$

Ethyl dodecanoate

b. $CH_3(CH_2)_{14}COOH + CH_3(CH_2)OH \xrightarrow{H^+,\ \text{heat}}$

Hexadecanoic acid / Palmitic acid; 1-Pentanol

$$\begin{array}{c} \text{O} \\ \| \\ CH_3(CH_2)_{14}CO(CH_2)_4CH_3 \end{array}$$

Pentyl hexadecanoate

17.4 a.

$$\begin{array}{l} \quad\text{H} \qquad\quad \text{O} \\ \quad | \qquad\quad \| \\ \text{H}-\text{C}-\text{O}-\text{C}-(CH_2)_{12}CH_3 \\ \quad | \\ \text{H}-\text{C}-\text{OH} \\ \quad | \\ \text{H}-\text{C}-\text{OH} \\ \quad | \\ \quad\text{H} \end{array} \xrightarrow{H^+,\ \text{heat}} \begin{array}{c} \text{H} \\ | \\ \text{H}-\text{C}-\text{OH} \\ | \\ \text{H}-\text{C}-\text{OH} \\ | \\ \text{H}-\text{C}-\text{OH} \\ | \\ \text{H} \\ \text{1,2,3-Propanetriol} \end{array} + \begin{array}{c} CH_3(CH_2)_{12}COOH \\ \text{Tetradecanoic acid} \end{array}$$

b.

$$\begin{array}{l} \quad\text{H} \qquad\quad \text{O} \\ \quad | \qquad\quad \| \\ \text{H}-\text{C}-\text{O}-\text{C}-(CH_2)_{10}CH_3 \\ \quad | \\ \text{H}-\text{C}-\text{OH} \\ \quad | \\ \text{H}-\text{C}-\text{OH} \\ \quad | \\ \quad\text{H} \end{array} \xrightarrow{H^+,\ \text{heat}} \begin{array}{c} \text{H} \\ | \\ \text{H}-\text{C}-\text{OH} \\ | \\ \text{H}-\text{C}-\text{OH} \\ | \\ \text{H}-\text{C}-\text{OH} \\ | \\ \text{H} \\ \text{1,2,3-Propanetriol} \end{array} + \begin{array}{c} CH_3(CH_2)_{10}COOH \\ \text{Dodecanoic acid} \end{array}$$

17.5 a.

$$\begin{array}{l} \quad\text{H} \qquad\quad \text{O} \\ \quad | \qquad\quad \| \\ \text{H}-\text{C}-\text{O}-\text{C}-(CH_2)_{14}CH_3 \\ \quad | \\ \text{H}-\text{C}-\text{OH} \\ \quad | \\ \text{H}-\text{C}-\text{OH} \\ \quad | \\ \quad\text{H} \end{array} + \text{KOH} \longrightarrow \begin{array}{c} \text{H} \\ | \\ \text{H}-\text{C}-\text{OH} \\ | \\ \text{H}-\text{C}-\text{OH} \\ | \\ \text{H}-\text{C}-\text{OH} \\ | \\ \text{H} \\ \text{1,2,3-Propanetriol} \end{array} + \begin{array}{c} CH_3(CH_2)_{14}COOH \\ \text{Potassium} \\ \text{hexadecanoate} \end{array}$$

b.

$$\begin{array}{l} \quad\text{H} \qquad\quad \text{O} \\ \quad | \qquad\quad \| \\ \text{H}-\text{C}-\text{O}-\text{C}-(CH_2)_6CH_3 \\ \quad | \qquad\quad \text{O} \\ \quad | \qquad\quad \| \\ \text{H}-\text{C}-\text{O}-\text{C}-(CH_2)_8CH_3 \\ \quad | \\ \text{H}-\text{C}-\text{OH} \\ \quad | \\ \quad\text{H} \end{array} + 2\ \text{NaOH} \longrightarrow \begin{array}{c} \text{H} \\ | \\ \text{H}-\text{C}-\text{OH} \\ | \\ \text{H}-\text{C}-\text{OH} \\ | \\ \text{H}-\text{C}-\text{OH} \\ | \\ \text{H} \\ \text{1,2,3-Propanetriol} \end{array} \begin{array}{l} \qquad\qquad\qquad\quad \text{O} \\ \qquad\qquad\qquad\quad \| \\ + CH_3(CH_2)_6CO^-Na^+ \\ \quad \text{Sodium octanoate} \\ \qquad\qquad\qquad\quad \text{O} \\ \qquad\qquad\qquad\quad \| \\ + CH_3(CH_2)_8CO^-Na^+ \\ \quad \text{Sodium decanoate} \end{array}$$

17.6 a. $CH_3(CH_2)_5CH{=}CH(CH_2)_7COOH + H_2$

cis-9-Hexadecenoic acid

$$\downarrow \text{Ni}$$

$CH_3(CH_2)_{14}COOH$

Hexadecanoic acid

b. $CH_3(CH_2)_4CH{=}CH{-}CH_2{-}CH{=}CH{-}CH_2{-}CH{=}$
$CH{-}CH_2{-}CH{=}CH{-}(CH_2)_3COOH + 4H_2$

$$\downarrow \text{Ni}$$

$CH_3(CH_2)_{18}COOH$

QUESTIONS AND PROBLEMS

Biological Functions of Lipids

Foundations

17.17 List the four main groups of lipids.
17.18 List the biological functions of lipids.

Applications

17.19 In terms of solubility, explain why a diet that contains no lipids can lead to a deficiency of the lipid-soluble vitamins.
17.20 Why are lipids (triglycerides) such an efficient molecule for the storage of energy in the body?

Fatty Acids

Foundations

17.21 What is the difference between a saturated and an unsaturated fatty acid?
17.22 Write the structures for a saturated and an unsaturated fatty acid.
17.23 As the length of the hydrocarbon chain of saturated fatty acids increases, what is the effect on the melting point?
17.24 As the number of carbon-carbon double bonds in fatty acids increases, what is the effect on the melting point?

Applications

17.25 Explain the relationship between fatty acid chain length and melting points that you described in answer to Question 17.23.
17.26 Explain the relationship that you described in answer to Question 17.24 for the effect of the number of carbon-carbon double bonds in fatty acids on their melting points.
17.27 Draw the structures of each of the following fatty acids:
a. Decanoic acid **b.** Stearic acid
17.28 Draw the structures of each of the following fatty acids:
a. *trans*-5-Decenoic acid **b.** *cis*-5-Decenoic acid
17.29 What are the common and IUPAC names of each of the following fatty acids?
a. $C_{15}H_{31}COOH$ **b.** $C_{11}H_{23}COOH$
17.30 What are the common and IUPAC names of each of the following fatty acids?
a. $CH_3(CH_2)_5CH{=}CH(CH_2)_7COOH$
b. $CH_3(CH_2)_7CH{=}CH(CH_2)_7COOH$
17.31 Write an equation for the esterification of glycerol with three molecules of myristic acid.
17.32 Write an equation for the esterification of glycerol with three molecules of palmitic acid.
17.33 Write an equation for the acid hydrolysis of a triglyceride containing three oleic acid molecules.
17.34 Write an equation for the acid hydrolysis of a triglyceride containing three capric acid molecules.
17.35 Write equations for the reactions of octanoic acid and stearic acid with KOH.
17.36 Write equations for the reactions of lauric acid and linoleic acid with KOH.
17.37 Using line formulas, write an equation for the hydrogenation of all *cis*-5,8,11,14,17-eicosapentaenoic acid.
17.38 Using line formulas, write an equation for the hydrogenation of all *cis*-4,7,10,13,16,19-docosahexaenoic acid.
17.39 Write an equation for the base-catalyzed hydrolysis of a triglyceride containing a molecule of lauric acid, a molecule of stearic acid, and a molecule of capric acid.
17.40 Write an equation for the base-catalyzed hydrolysis of a triglyceride containing a molecule of palmitoleic acid, a molecule of oleic acid, and a molecule of palmitic acid.
17.41 Write an equation for the esterification of glycerol with a molecule of hexadecanoic acid, a molecule of dodecanoic acid, and a molecule of decanoic acid.
17.42 Write an equation for the esterification of glycerol with a molecule of capric acid, a molecule of oleic acid, and a molecule of stearic acid.
17.43 What is the function of the essential fatty acids?
17.44 What molecules are formed from arachidonic acid?
17.45 What is the biochemical basis for the effectiveness of aspirin in decreasing the inflammatory response?
17.46 What is the role of prostaglandins in the inflammatory response?
17.47 List four effects of prostaglandins.
17.48 What are the functions of thromboxane A_2 and leukotrienes?
17.49 What do the terms *omega-3* and *omega-6* indicate about structures of the fatty acids in those classifications?
17.50 What foods are good sources of EPA and DHA?
17.51 Summarize the health benefits associated with omega-3 fatty acids.
17.52 List some foods that are good sources of α-linolenic acid.
17.53 Explain the relationship between increased levels of omega-3 fatty acids and a decreased risk of cardiovascular disease.
17.54 Do you think that a diet higher in omega-3 fatty acids would be an effective treatment for the symptoms of arthritis? Defend your answer.
17.55 Explain the logic behind decreasing the ratio of omega-6 to omega-3 fatty acids in the diet.
17.56 What is the recommendation of the National Institutes of Health for intake of DHA, EPA, linoleic acid, and linolenic acid?

Glycerides

Foundations

17.57 Define the term *glyceride.*
17.58 Define the term *phosphatidate.*
17.59 What are emulsifying agents and what are their practical uses?
17.60 Why are triglycerides also referred to as triacylglycerols?

Applications

17.61 What do you predict the physical state would be of a triglyceride with three saturated fatty acid tails? Explain your reasoning.
17.62 What do you predict the physical state would be of a triglyceride with three unsaturated fatty acid tails? Explain your reasoning.
17.63 Draw the structure of the triglyceride molecule formed by esterification at C-1, C-2, and C-3 with hexadecanoic acid, *trans*-9-hexadecenoic acid, and *cis*-9-hexadecenoic acid, respectively.
17.64 Draw one possible structure of a triglyceride that contains the three fatty acids capric acid, lauric acid, and arachidonic acid.

17.65 Draw the structure of the phosphatidate formed between glycerol-3-phosphate that is esterified at C-1 and C-2 with capric and lauric acids, respectively.

17.66 Draw the structure of a lecithin molecule in which the fatty acyl groups are derived from arachidic acid.

17.67 What are the structural differences between triglycerides (triacylglycerols) and phospholipids?

17.68 How are the structural differences between triglycerides and phospholipids reflected in their different biological functions?

Nonglyceride Lipids

Foundations

17.69 Define the term *sphingolipid.*

17.70 What are the two major types of sphingolipids?

17.71 Define the term *glycosphingolipid.*

17.72 Distinguish among the three types of glycosphingolipids, cerebrosides, sulfatides, and gangliosides.

Applications

17.73 What is the biological function of sphingomyelin?

17.74 Why are sphingomyelins amphipathic?

17.75 What is the role of cholesterol in biological membranes?

17.76 How does cholesterol contribute to atherosclerosis?

17.77 What are the biological functions of progesterone, testosterone, and estrone?

17.78 How has our understanding of the steroid sex hormones contributed to the development of oral contraceptives?

17.79 What is the medical application of cortisone?

17.80 What are the possible side effects of cortisone treatment?

17.81 A wax found in beeswax is myricyl palmitate. What fatty acid and what alcohol are used to form this compound?

17.82 A wax found in the head of sperm whales is cetyl palmitate. What fatty acid and what alcohol are used to form this compound?

17.83 What are isoprenoids?

17.84 What is a terpene?

17.85 List some important biological molecules that are terpenes.

17.86 Draw the five-carbon isoprene unit.

Complex Lipids

Foundations

17.87 What are the four major types of plasma lipoproteins?

17.88 What is the function of each of the four types of plasma lipoproteins?

Applications

17.89 There is a single, unique structure for the cholesterol molecule. What is meant by the terms *good* and *bad* cholesterol?

17.90 Distinguish among the four plasma lipoproteins in terms of their composition and their function.

17.91 What is the relationship between atherosclerosis and high blood pressure?

17.92 How is LDL taken into cells?

17.93 How does a genetic defect in the LDL receptor contribute to atherosclerosis?

17.94 What is the correlation between saturated fats in the diet and atherosclerosis?

The Structure of Biological Membranes

Foundations

17.95 What is the basic structure of a biological membrane?

17.96 Describe the fluid mosaic model of membrane structure.

17.97 Describe peripheral membrane proteins.

17.98 Describe transmembrane proteins and list some of their functions.

Applications

17.99 What is the major effect of cholesterol on the properties of biological membranes?

17.100 Why do the hydrocarbon tails of membrane phospholipids provide a barrier between the inside and outside of the cell?

17.101 What experimental observation shows that proteins diffuse within the lipid bilayers of biological membranes?

17.102 Why don't proteins turn around in biological membranes like revolving doors?

17.103 How will the properties of a biological membrane change if the fatty acid tails of the phospholipids are converted from saturated to unsaturated chains?

17.104 What is the function of unsaturation in the hydrocarbon tails of membrane lipids?

CRITICAL THINKING PROBLEMS

1. Olestra is a fat substitute that provides no calories, yet has all the properties of a naturally occurring fat. It has a creamy, tongue-pleasing consistency. Unlike other fat substitutes, olestra can withstand heating. Thus, it can be used to prepare foods such as potato chips and crackers. Olestra is a sucrose polyester and is produced by esterification of six, seven, or eight fatty acids to molecules of sucrose. Draw the structure of one such molecule having eight stearic acid acyl groups attached.
2. Liposomes can be made by vigorously mixing phospholipids (like phosphatidylcholine) in water. When the mixture is allowed to settle, spherical vesicles form that are surrounded by a phospholipid bilayer "membrane." Pharmaceutical chemists are trying to develop liposomes as a targeted drug delivery system. By adding the drug of choice to the mixture described above, liposomes form around the solution of drug. Specific proteins can be incorporated into the mixture that will end up within the phospholipid bilayers of the liposomes. These proteins are able to bind to targets on the surface of particular kinds of cells in the body. Explain why injection of liposome encapsulated pharmaceuticals might be a good drug delivery system.
3. "Cholesterol is bad and should be eliminated from the diet." Do you agree or disagree? Defend your answer.
4. Why would a phospholipid such as lecithin be a good emulsifying agent for ice cream?
5. When a plant becomes cold-adapted, the composition of the membranes changes. What changes in fatty acid and cholesterol composition would you predict? Explain your reasoning.

Protein Structure and Function

Silk fibers are harvested from the cocoons of silkworms.

LEARNING GOALS

1. List the functions of proteins.
2. Draw the general structure of an amino acid and classify amino acids based on their R groups.
3. Describe the primary structure of proteins and draw the structure of the peptide bond.
4. Draw the structures of small peptides and name them.
5. Describe the types of secondary structure of a protein.
6. Discuss the forces that maintain secondary structure.
7. Describe the structure and functions of fibrous proteins.
8. Describe the tertiary and quaternary structure of a protein.
9. List the R group interactions that maintain protein conformation.
10. List examples of proteins that require prosthetic groups and explain the way in which they function.
11. Discuss the importance of the three-dimensional structure of a protein to its function.
12. Describe the roles of hemoglobin and myoglobin.
13. Describe how extremes of pH and temperature cause denaturation of proteins.
14. Explain the difference between essential and nonessential amino acids.

OUTLINE

Introduction 618

18.1 Protein Building Blocks: The α-Amino Acids 618

18.2 The Peptide Bond 622

A Human Perspective: The Opium Poppy and Peptides in the Brain 625

18.3 The Primary Structure of Proteins 626

18.4 The Secondary Structure of Proteins 626

18.5 The Tertiary Structure of Proteins 629

A Medical Perspective: Collagen, Cosmetic Procedures, and Clinical Applications 631

18.6 The Quaternary Structure of Proteins 632

18.7 An Overview of Protein Structure and Function 633

18.8 Myoglobin and Hemoglobin 634

18.9 Proteins in the Blood 636

18.10 Denaturation of Proteins 637

Kitchen Chemistry: Egg Foams: Meringues and Soufflés 639

A Medical Perspective: Immunoglobulins: Proteins That Defend the Body 640

18.11 Dietary Protein and Protein Digestion 641

INTRODUCTION

LEARNING GOAL

1 List the functions of proteins.

In the 1800s, Johannes Mulder came up with the name **protein,** a term derived from a Greek word that means "of first importance." Indeed, proteins are a very important class of food molecules because they provide an organism not only with carbon and hydrogen, but also with nitrogen and sulfur. These latter two elements are unavailable from fats and carbohydrates, the other major classes of food molecules.

In addition to their dietary importance, the proteins are the most abundant macromolecules in the cell, and have a wide variety of biological functions. **Enzymes** are biological catalysts and most of them are proteins. Reactions that would take days or weeks or require extremely high temperatures without enzymes are completed in an instant. **Defense proteins** include **antibodies** (also called *immunoglobulins*), which are specific protein molecules produced by specialized cells of the immune system in response to foreign **antigens.** These foreign invaders include bacteria and viruses that infect the body. Each antibody has regions that precisely fit and bind to a single antigen, helping to destroy it or remove it from the body. **Transport proteins** carry materials from one place to another in the body. The protein *transferrin* transports iron from the liver to the bone marrow, where it is used to synthesize the heme group for hemoglobin. The proteins *hemoglobin* and *myoglobin* are responsible for transport and storage of oxygen in higher organisms, respectively. **Regulatory proteins** control many aspects of cell function, including metabolism and reproduction. We can function only within a limited set of conditions. For life to exist, body temperature, the pH of the blood, and blood glucose levels must be carefully regulated. Many of the hormones that regulate body function, such as *insulin* and *glucagon,* are proteins. **Structural proteins** provide mechanical support to large animals and provide them with their outer coverings. Our hair and fingernails are largely composed of the protein *keratin.* Other proteins provide mechanical strength for our bones, tendons, and skin. Without such support, large, multicellular organisms like ourselves could not exist. **Movement proteins** are necessary for all forms of movement. Our muscles, including that most important muscle, the heart, contract and expand through the interaction of *actin* and *myosin* proteins. Sperm can swim because they have long flagella made up of proteins. **Nutrient proteins** serve as sources of amino acids for embryos or infants. Egg *albumin* and *casein* in milk are examples of nutrient storage proteins.

18.1 Protein Building Blocks: The α-Amino Acids

Structure of Amino Acids

LEARNING GOAL

2 Draw the general structure of an amino acid and classify amino acids based on their R groups.

The proteins of the body are made up of some combination of twenty different subunits called **α-amino acids.** The general structure of an α-amino acid is shown in Figure 18.1. We find that nineteen of the twenty amino acids that are commonly isolated from proteins have this same general structure; they are primary amines on the α-carbon. The remaining amino acid, proline, is a secondary amine.

Notice that the α-carbon in the general structure is attached to a carboxylate group (a carboxyl group that has lost a proton, $—COO^-$) and a protonated amino group (an amino group that has gained a proton, $—N^+H_3$). At pH 7, a condition required for life functions, you will not find amino acids in which the carboxylate group is protonated ($—COOH$) and the amino group is unprotonated ($—NH_2$). Under these conditions, the carboxyl group is in the conjugate base form ($—COO^-$), and the amino group is in its conjugate acid form ($—N^+H_3$). Any neutral molecule with equal numbers of positive and negative charges is called a *zwitterion.* Thus, amino acids in water exist as dipolar ions called zwitterions.

Conjugate acids and bases are described in detail in Section 8.1.

The α-carbon of each amino acid is also bonded to a hydrogen atom and a side chain, or R group. In a protein, the R groups interact with one another through a variety of weak attractive forces. These interactions participate in folding the protein chain into a precise three-dimensional shape that determines its ultimate function. They also serve to maintain that three-dimensional conformation.

α-Carbon
α-Amino group
α-Carboxylate group
Side-chain R group

Figure 18.1 General structure of an α-amino acid. All amino acids isolated from proteins, with the exception of proline, have this general structure.

Stereoisomers of Amino Acids

The α-carbon is attached to four different groups in all amino acids except glycine. The α-carbon of most α-amino acids is therefore chiral, allowing mirror-image forms, enantiomers, to exist. Glycine has two hydrogen atoms attached to the α-carbon and is the only amino acid commonly found in proteins that is not chiral.

The L-configuration of α-amino acids is isolated from proteins. The D-L notation is very similar to that discussed for carbohydrates, but instead of the —OH group we use the —N^+H_3 group to determine which is D- and which is L- (Figure 18.2). In Figure 18.2a we see a comparison of D- and L-glyceraldehyde with D- and L-alanine. Notice that the most oxidized end of the molecule, the carbonyl group of glyceraldehyde or carboxyl group of alanine, is drawn at the top of the molecule. In the D-isomer of glyceraldehyde, the —OH group is on the right. Similarly, in the D-isomer of alanine, the —N^+H_3 is on the right. In the L-isomers of the two compounds, the —OH and —N^+H_3 groups are on the left. By this comparison with the enantiomers of glyceraldehyde, we can define the D- and L-enantiomers of the amino acids. Figure 18.2b shows ball-and-stick models of the D- and L-isomers of alanine.

Stereochemistry is discussed in Section 16.3.

Mirror plane

L-Isomers	D-Isomers	
L-Glyceraldehyde	D-Glyceraldehyde	Carbohydrate pair
L-Alanine	D-Alanine	Amino acid pair

(a)

L-Alanine D-Alanine

(b)

Figure 18.2 (a) Structures of D- and L-glyceraldehyde and their relationship to D- and L-alanine. (b) Ball-and-stick models of D- and L-alanine.

In Chapter 16 we learned that almost all of the monosaccharides found in nature are in the D-family. Just the opposite is true of the α-amino acids. Almost all of the α-amino acids isolated from proteins in nature are members of the L-family. In other words, the orientation of the four groups around the chiral carbon of these α-amino acids resembles the orientation of the four groups around the chiral carbon of L-glyceraldehyde.

Classes of Amino Acids

Because all amino acids have a carboxyl group and an amino group, all differences between amino acids depend upon their side-chain R groups. The amino acids are grouped in Figure 18.3 according to the polarity of their side chains.

The hydrophobic interaction between nonpolar R groups is one of the forces that helps maintain the proper three-dimensional shape of a protein.

The side chains of some amino acids are nonpolar. They prefer contact with one another over contact with water and are said to be **hydrophobic** ("water-fearing") **amino acids.** They are generally found buried in the interior of proteins, where they can associate with one another and remain isolated from water. Nine amino acids fall into this category: alanine, valine, leucine, isoleucine, proline, glycine, methionine, phenylalanine, and tryptophan. The R group of proline is unique; it is actually bonded to the α-amino group, forming a secondary amine.

The side chains of the remaining amino acids are polar. Because they are attracted to polar water molecules, they are said to be **hydrophilic** ("water-loving") **amino acids.** The hydrophilic side chains are often found on the surfaces of proteins. The polar amino acids can be subdivided into three classes.

Hydrogen bonding (Section 5.2) is another weak interaction that helps maintain the proper three-dimensional structure of a protein. The positively and negatively charged amino acids within a protein interact with one another to form ionic bridges that also help to keep the protein chain folded in a precise way.

- *Polar, neutral amino acids* have R groups that have a high affinity for water but are not ionic at pH 7. Serine, threonine, tyrosine, cysteine, asparagine, and glutamine fall into this category. Most of these amino acids associate with one another by hydrogen bonding; but cysteine molecules form disulfide bonds with one another, as we will discuss in Section 18.5.
- *Negatively charged amino acids* have ionized carboxyl groups in their side chains. At pH 7 these amino acids have a net charge of −1. Aspartate and glutamate are the two amino acids in this category. They are acidic amino acids because ionization of the carboxylic acid releases a proton.
- *Positively charged amino acids.* At pH 7, lysine, arginine, and histidine have a net positive charge because their side chains contain positive groups. These amino groups are basic because the side chain reacts with water, picking up a proton and releasing a hydroxide anion.

The names of the amino acids can be abbreviated by a three-letter and by a one-letter code. These abbreviations are shown in Table 18.1.

Question 18.1 Write the one-letter and three-letter abbreviations and draw the structure of each of the following amino acids.

a. Glycine
b. Proline
c. Threonine
d. Aspartate
e. Lysine

Question 18.2 Indicate whether the side chains of each of the amino acids listed in Question 18.1 is polar, nonpolar, basic, or acidic.

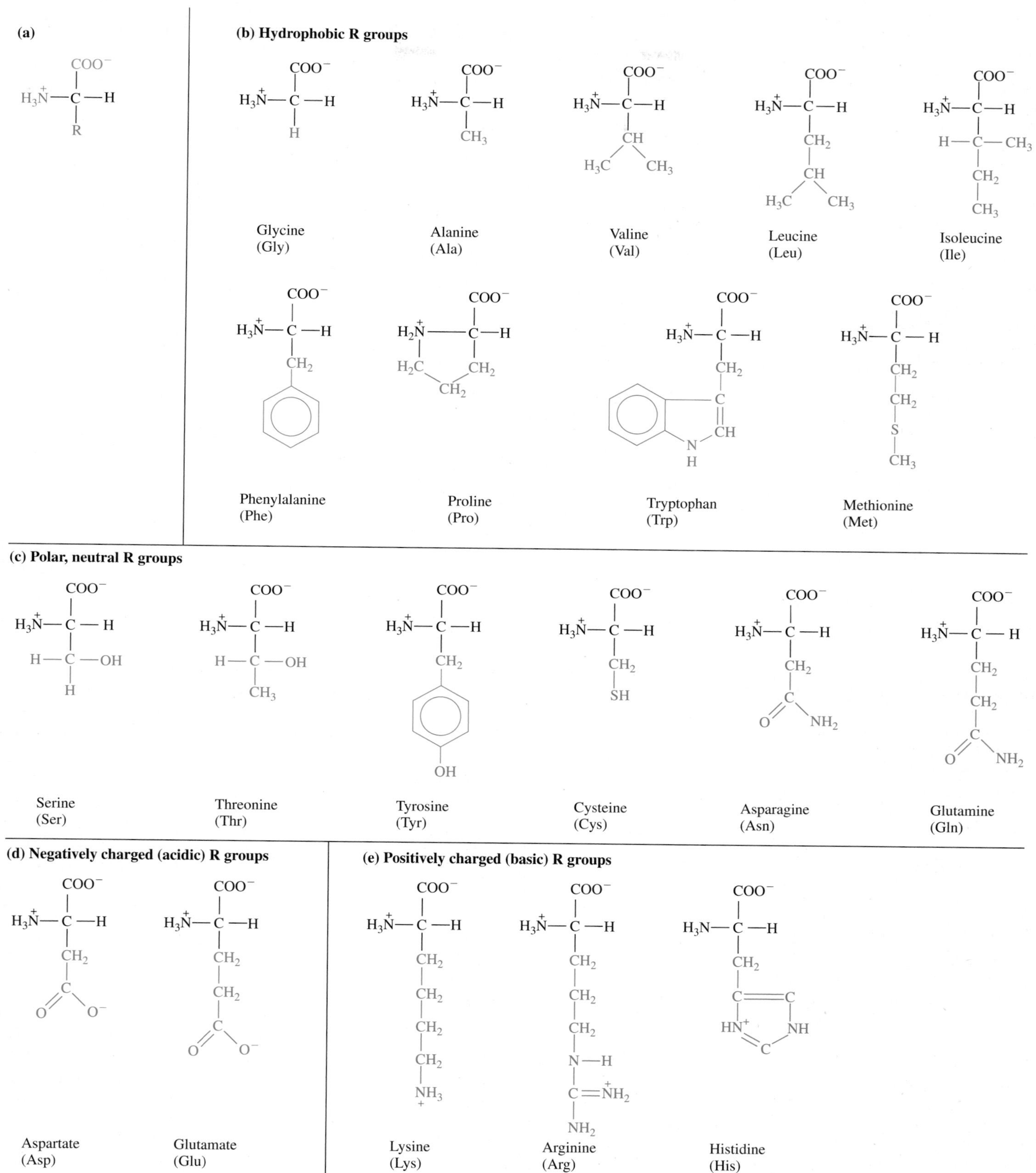

Figure 18.3 Structures of the amino acids at pH 7.0. (a) The general structure of an amino acid. Structures of the amino acids having (b) hydrophobic; (c) polar, neutral; (d) negatively charged; and (e) positively charged R groups.

TABLE 18.1 Names and the One- and Three-Letter Abbreviations of the α-Amino Acids

Amino Acid	Three-Letter Abbreviation	One-Letter Abbreviation
Alanine	ala	A
Arginine	arg	R
Asparagine	asn	N
Aspartate	asp	D
Cysteine	cys	C
Glutamate	glu	E
Glutamine	gln	Q
Glycine	gly	G
Histidine	his	H
Isoleucine	ile	I
Leucine	leu	L
Lysine	lys	K
Methionine	met	M
Phenylalanine	phe	F
Proline	pro	P
Serine	ser	S
Threonine	thr	T
Tryptophan	trp	W
Tyrosine	tyr	Y
Valine	val	V

18.2 The Peptide Bond

LEARNING GOAL

3 Describe the primary structure of proteins and draw the structure of the peptide bond.

Proteins are linear polymers of L-α-amino acids in which the carboxyl group of one amino acid is linked to the amino group of another amino acid. The **peptide bond** is an *amide bond* formed between the —COO^- group of one amino acid and the α-N^+H_3 group of another amino acid. The reaction, shown below for the amino acids glycine and alanine, is a condensation reaction, because a water molecule is lost as the amide bond is formed.

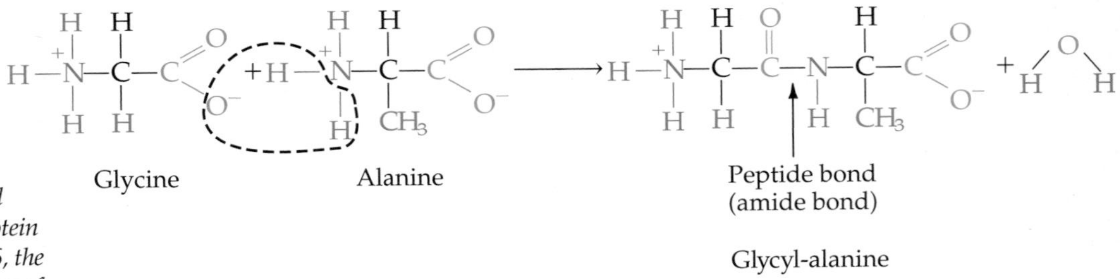

$$H_3N^+{-}CH_2{-}COO^- + H_3N^+{-}CH(CH_3){-}COO^- \longrightarrow H_3N^+{-}CH_2{-}CO{-}NH{-}CH(CH_3){-}COO^- + H_2O$$

Glycine Alanine Peptide bond (amide bond)

Glycyl-alanine

To understand why the N-terminus is placed first and the C-terminus is placed last, we need to look at the process of protein synthesis. As we will see in Section 20.6, the N-terminus is the first amino acid residue of the protein. It forms a peptide bond involving its carboxyl group and the amino group of the second amino acid residue in the protein. Thus, a free amino group literally projects from the "left" end of the protein. Similarly, the C-terminal amino acid is the last amino acid residue added to the protein during protein synthesis. Because the peptide bond is formed between the amino group of this amino acid residue and the carboxyl group of the previous amino acid residue, a free carboxyl group projects from the "right" end of the protein chain.

The molecule formed by condensing two amino acids is called a *dipeptide*. The amino acid with a free α-N^+H_3 group is known as the amino terminal, or simply the **N-terminal amino acid** residue or **N-terminus,** and the amino acid with a free —COO^- group is known as the carboxyl, or **C-terminal amino acid** residue or **C-terminus.** Structures of proteins are conventionally written with their N-terminal amino acid on the left.

The number of amino acids in small peptides is indicated by the prefixes *di-* (two units), *tri-* (three units), *tetra-* (four units), and so forth. Peptides are named as derivatives of the C-terminal amino acid, which receives its entire name. For all other amino acids, the ending *-ine* is changed to *-yl*. Thus, the dipeptide above has glycine as its *N*-terminal amino acid, as indicated by its full name, glycyl-alanine.

The dipeptide formed from alanine and glycine that has alanine as its *N*-terminal amino acid, alanyl-glycine, is shown to the right. These two dipeptides have the same amino acid composition, but different amino acid sequences.

$$H_3\overset{+}{N}-\underset{CH_3}{\overset{H}{C}}-\overset{O}{\overset{\|}{C}}-\underset{H}{N}-\underset{H}{\overset{H}{C}}-C\genfrac{}{}{0pt}{}{\nearrow O}{\searrow O^-}$$

Alanyl-glycine (ala-gly)

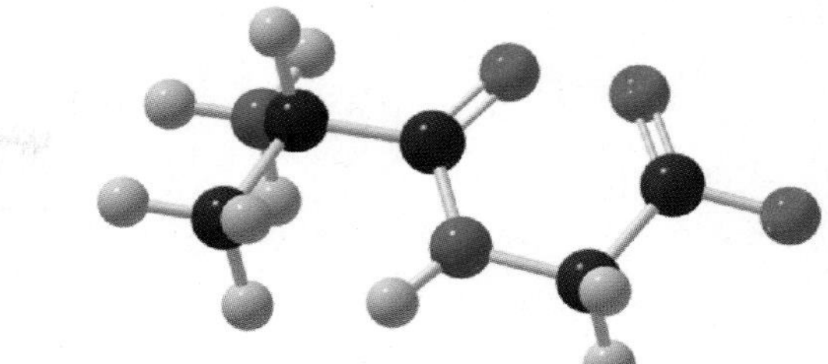

Alanyl-glycine

The structures of small peptides can easily be drawn with practice if certain rules are followed. First note that the backbone of the peptide contains the repeating sequence

$$N-\underset{2}{C}-\underset{1}{C}-N-\underset{2}{C}-\underset{1}{C}-N-\underset{2}{C}-\underset{1}{C}$$

in which N is the α-amino group, carbon-2 is the α-carbon, and carbon-1 is the carboxyl group. Carbon-2 is always bonded to a hydrogen atom and to the R group side chain that is unique to each amino acid. Continue drawing as outlined in Example 18.1.

EXAMPLE 18.1 Writing the Structure of a Tripeptide

LEARNING GOAL

4 Draw the structures of small peptides and name them.

Draw the structure of the tripeptide alanyl-glycyl-valine.

Solution

Step 1. Write the backbone for a tripeptide. It will contain three sets of three atoms, or nine atoms in all. Remember that the N-terminal amino acid is written to the left.

$$\underset{\text{Set 1}}{N-C-C} \qquad \underset{\text{Set 2}}{N-C-C} \qquad \underset{\text{Set 3}}{N-C-C}$$

Step 2. Add oxygens to the carboxyl carbons and hydrogens to the amino nitrogens:

$$H-\underset{H}{\overset{H}{N^+}}-C-\overset{O}{\overset{\|}{C}}-\underset{H}{N}-C-\overset{O}{\overset{\|}{C}}-\underset{H}{N}-C-\overset{O}{\overset{\|}{C}}-O^-$$

Step 3. Add hydrogens to the α-carbons:

$$H-\underset{H}{\overset{H}{N^+}}-\overset{H}{C}-\overset{O}{\overset{\|}{C}}-\underset{H}{N}-\overset{H}{C}-\overset{O}{\overset{\|}{C}}-\underset{H}{N}-\overset{H}{C}-\overset{O}{\overset{\|}{C}}-O^-$$

Step 4. Add the side chains. In this example (ala-gly-val) they are, from left to right, $—CH_3$, —H, and $—CH(CH_3)_2$:

$$H-\underset{H}{\overset{H}{N^+}}-\underset{CH_3}{\overset{H}{C}}-\overset{O}{\overset{\|}{C}}-\underset{H}{N}-\underset{H}{\overset{H}{C}}-\overset{O}{\overset{\|}{C}}-\underset{H}{N}-\underset{\underset{CH_3\;CH_3}{CH}}{\overset{H}{C}}-\overset{O}{\overset{\|}{C}}-O^-$$

Practice Problem 18.1

Write the structure of each of the following peptides at pH 7.

a. Methionyl-leucyl-cysteine b. Tyrosyl-seryl-histidine c. Arginyl-isoleucyl-glutamine

► For Further Practice: **Questions 18.37 and 18.38.**

At first it appears logical to think that a long polymer of amino acids would undergo constant change in conformation because of free rotation around the —N—C—C— single bonds of the peptide backbone. In reality, this is not the case. An explanation for this phenomenon resulted from the early X-ray diffraction studies of Linus Pauling. By interpreting the pattern formed when X-rays were diffracted by a crystal of pure protein, Pauling discovered that peptide bonds are both planar (flat) and rigid and that the N—C bonds are shorter than expected. What did all of this mean? Pauling concluded that the peptide bond has a partially double bond character because it exhibits resonance.

$$—C_\alpha—C(=O)—\ddot{N}(H)—C_\alpha— \longleftrightarrow —C_\alpha—C(—O^-)=\overset{+}{N}(H)—C_\alpha—$$

This means that there is free rotation around only two of the three single bonds of the peptide backbone (Figure 18.4a), which limits the number of possible conformations for any peptide. A second feature of the rigid peptide bond is that the R groups on adjacent amino acids are on opposite sides of the extended peptide chain (Figure 18.4b).

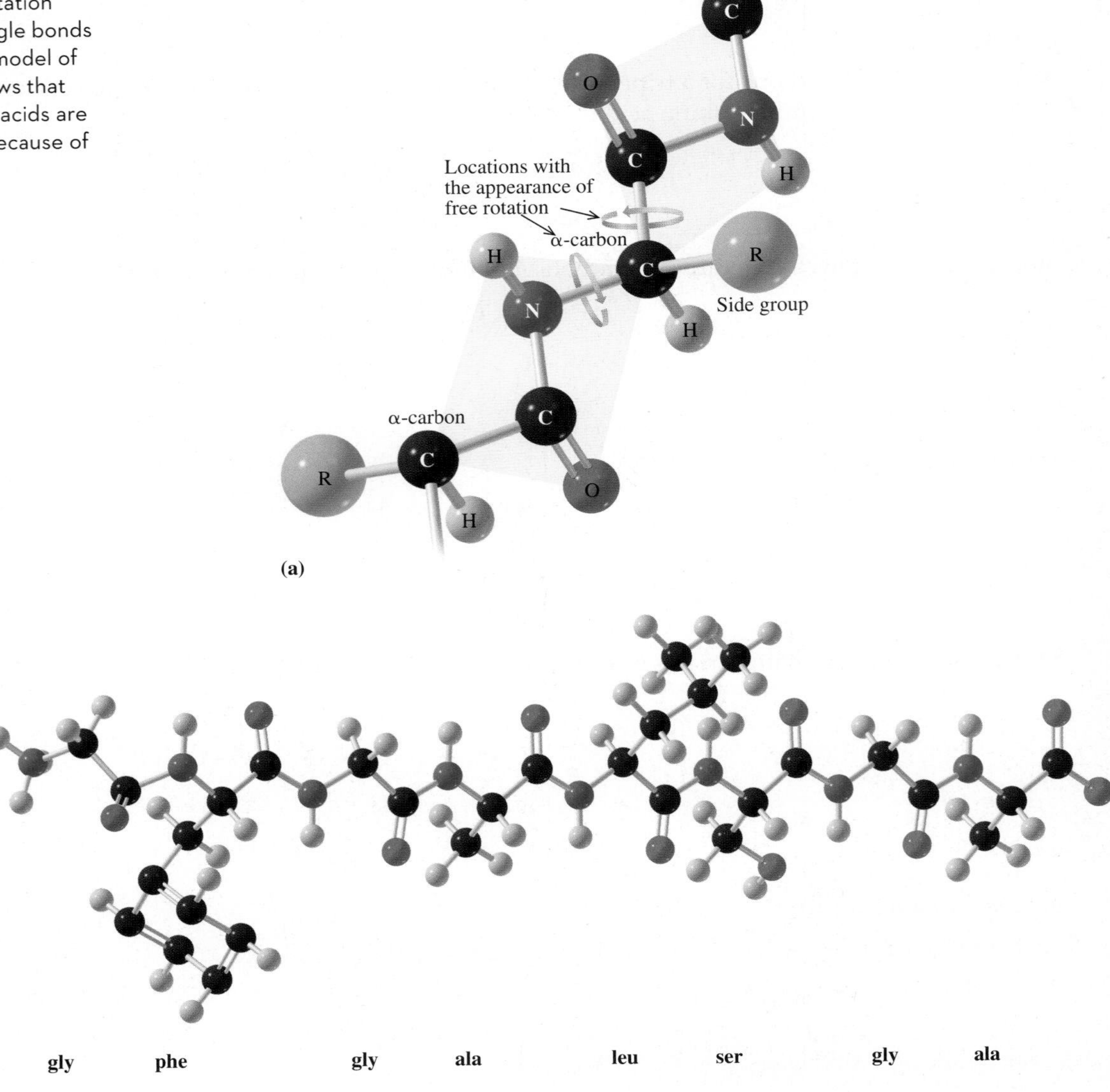

Figure 18.4 (a) There is free rotation around only two of the three single bonds of a peptide backbone. (b) This model of an eight amino acid peptide shows that the R groups on adjacent amino acids are on opposite sides of the chain because of the rigid peptide bond.

A HUMAN PERSPECTIVE

The Opium Poppy and Peptides in the Brain

The seed pods of the oriental poppy contain morphine. *Morphine* is a narcotic that has a variety of effects on the body and the brain, including drowsiness, euphoria, mental confusion, and chronic constipation. Although morphine was first isolated in 1805, not until the 1850s and the advent of the hypodermic was it effectively used as a painkiller. During the American Civil War, morphine was used extensively to relieve the pain of wounds and amputations. It was at this time that the addictive properties were noticed. By the end of the Civil War, over 100,000 soldiers were addicted to morphine.

As a result of the Harrison Act (1914), morphine came under government control and was made available only by prescription.

Why does morphine have such powerful effects on the brain? The drug has been found to bind to *receptors* on the surface of the cells of the brain. The function of these receptors is to bind specific chemical signals and to direct the brain cells to respond. Yet it seemed odd that the cells of our brain should have receptors for a plant chemical. This mystery was solved in 1975, when John Hughes discovered that the brain itself synthesizes small peptide hormones with a morphine-like structure. Two of these opiate peptides are called *methionine enkephalin,* or met-enkephalin, and *leucine enkephalin,* or leu-enkephalin.

These neuropeptide hormones have a variety of effects. They inhibit intestinal motility and blood flow to the gastrointestinal tract. This explains the chronic constipation of morphine users. In addition, it is thought that these *enkephalins* play a role in pain perception, perhaps serving as a pain blockade. This is supported by the observation that they are found in higher concentrations in the bloodstream following painful stimulation. It is further suspected that they may play a role in mood and mental health. The so-called runner's high is thought to be a euphoria brought about by an excessively long or strenuous run!

Morphine

The structure of morphine.

Unlike morphine, the action of enkephalins is short-lived. They bind to the cellular receptor and thereby induce the cells to respond. Then they are quickly destroyed by enzymes in the brain that hydrolyze the peptide bonds of the enkephalin. Once destroyed, they are no longer able to elicit a cellular response. Morphine binds to these same receptors and induces the cells to respond. However, it is not destroyed and therefore persists in the brain for long periods at concentrations high enough to continue to cause biological effects.

Many researchers are working to understand why drugs like morphine are addictive. Studies with cells in culture have suggested one mechanism for morphine tolerance and addiction. Normally, when the cell receptors bind to enkephalins, this signals the cell to decrease the production of a chemical messenger called *cyclic AMP,* or simply cAMP. (This compound is very closely related to the nucleotide adenosine-5′-monophosphate.) The decrease in cAMP level helps to block pain and elevate mood. When morphine is applied to these cells they initially respond by decreasing cAMP levels. However, with chronic use of morphine the cells become desensitized; that is, they do not decrease cAMP production and thus behave as though no morphine were present. However, a greater amount of morphine will once again cause the decrease in cAMP levels. Thus addiction and the progressive need for more of the drug seem to result from biochemical reactions in the cells.

Tyr-Gly-Gly-Phe-Met
Methionine enkephalin

Tyr-Gly-Gly-Phe-Leu
Leucine enkephalin

Structures of the peptide opiates leucine enkephalin and methionine enkephalin. These are the body's own opiates.

This logic can be extended to understand withdrawal symptoms. When an addict stops using the drug, he or she exhibits withdrawal symptoms that include excessive sweating, anxiety, and tremors. The cause may be that the high levels of morphine were keeping the cAMP levels low, thus reducing pain and causing euphoria. When morphine is removed

Continued...

The Opium Poppy and Peptides in the Brain (continued)

completely, the cells overreact and produce huge quantities of cAMP. The result is all of the unpleasant symptoms known collectively as the *withdrawal syndrome*.

Clearly, morphine has demonstrated the potential for misuse and is a problem for society in several respects. Nonetheless, morphine remains one of the most effective painkillers known. Certainly, for people suffering from cancer, painful burns, or serious injuries, the risk of addiction is far outweighed by the benefits of relief from excruciating pain.

For Further Understanding

- Compare the structures of leucine and methionine enkephalin with that of morphine. What similarities do you see that might cause them to bind to the same receptors on the surfaces of nerve cells?
- What characteristics might you look for in a nonaddictive drug that could be used both to combat morphine addiction and to treat the symptoms of withdrawal?

Question 18.3 Write the structure of each of the following peptides at pH 7:

a. Alanyl-phenylalanine
b. Lysyl-alanine
c. Phenylalanyl-tyrosyl-leucine

Question 18.4 Write the structure of each of the following peptides at pH 7:

a. Glycyl-valyl-serine
b. Threonyl-cysteine
c. Isoleucyl-methionyl-aspartate

18.3 The Primary Structure of Proteins

LEARNING GOAL

3 Describe the primary structure of proteins and draw the structure of the peptide bond.

The genetic code and the process of protein synthesis are described in Sections 20.5 and 20.6.

The **primary structure** of a protein is the amino acid sequence of the protein chain. It results from the covalent bonding between the amino acid residues in the chain (peptide bonds). The primary structures of proteins are translations of information contained in genes. Each protein has a different primary structure with different amino acid residues in different places along the chain. This sequence of amino acid residues is dictated by the sequence of the gene.

Ultimately, it is the primary structure of a protein that will determine its biologically active form. The interactions among the R groups of the amino acids in the protein chain depend on the location of those R groups along the chain. These interactions will govern how the protein chain folds, which, in turn, dictates its final three-dimensional structure and its biological function.

18.4 The Secondary Structure of Proteins

LEARNING GOAL

5 Describe the types of secondary structure of a protein.

The primary sequence of a protein, the chain of covalently linked amino acids, folds into regularly repeating structures that resemble designs in a tapestry. These repeating structures define the **secondary structure** of the protein. The secondary structure is the result of hydrogen bonding between the amide hydrogens and carbonyl oxygens of the peptide bonds. Many hydrogen bonds are needed to maintain the secondary structure and thereby the overall structure of the protein. Different regions of a protein chain may have different types of secondary structure. Some regions of a protein chain may have a random or nonregular structure; however, the two most common types of secondary structure are the α-helix and the β-pleated sheet because they maximize hydrogen bonding in the backbone.

LEARNING GOAL

6 Discuss the forces that maintain secondary structure.

In the photo above, some of the children have straight hair and some have curly hair. Knowing that the primary structure of a protein is dictated by the sequence of a gene, in this case a keratin gene, develop a hypothesis to explain hair curliness.

α-Helix

The most common type of secondary structure is a coiled, helical conformation known as the **α-helix** (Figure 18.5). The α-helix has several important features.

- Every amide hydrogen and carbonyl oxygen associated with the peptide backbone is involved in a hydrogen bond when the chain coils into an α-helix. These hydrogen bonds lock the α-helix into place.
- Every carbonyl oxygen is hydrogen-bonded to an amide hydrogen four amino acids away in the chain.
- The hydrogen bonds of the α-helix are parallel to the long axis of the helix (see Figure 18.5).

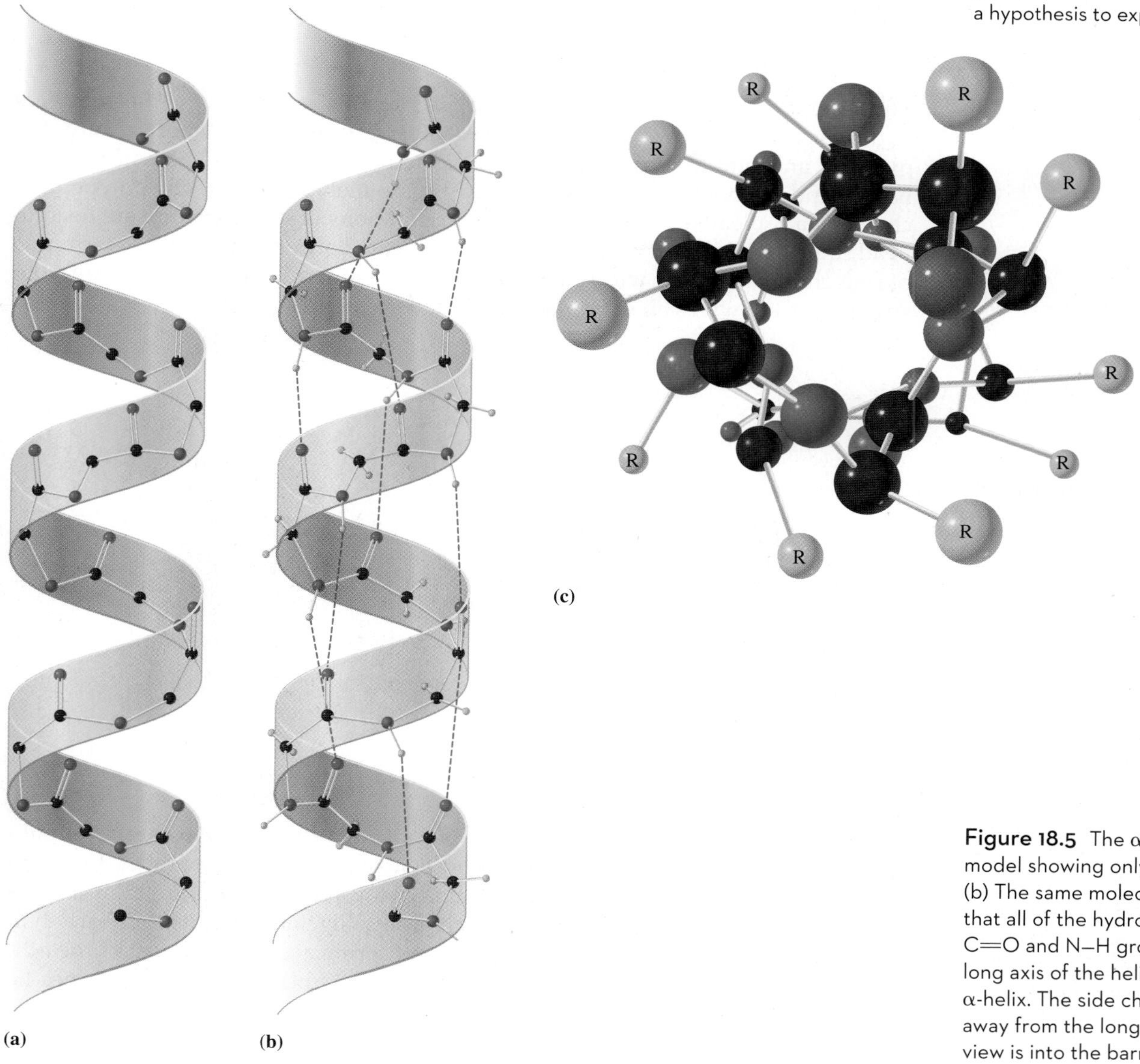

(a) (b) (c)

Figure 18.5 The α-helix. (a) Molecular model showing only the helical backbone. (b) The same molecular model showing that all of the hydrogen bonds between C=O and N—H groups are parallel to the long axis of the helix. (c) Top view of an α-helix. The side chains of the helix point away from the long axis of the helix. The view is into the barrel of the helix.

LEARNING GOAL

7 Describe the structure and functions of fibrous proteins.

- The polypeptide chain in an α-helix is right-handed. It is oriented like a normal screw. If you turn a screw clockwise it goes into the wall; turned counterclockwise, it comes out of the wall.
- The repeat distance of the helix, or its pitch, is 5.4 angstroms (Å), and there are 3.6 amino acids per turn of the helix.

Fibrous proteins are structural proteins arranged in fibers or sheets that have only one type of secondary structure. The **α-keratins** are fibrous proteins that form the covering (hair, wool, nails, hooves, and fur) of most land animals. Human hair provides a typical example of the structure of the α-keratins. The proteins of hair consist almost exclusively of polypeptide chains coiled up into α-helices. A single α-helix is coiled in a bundle with two other helices to give a three-stranded superstructure called a *protofibril* that is part of an array known as a *microfibril* (Figure 18.6). These structures, which resemble "molecular pigtails," possess great mechanical strength, and they are virtually insoluble in water.

The major structural property of a coiled coil superstructure of α-helices is its great mechanical strength. This property is applied very efficiently in both the fibrous proteins of skin and those of muscle. As you can imagine, these proteins must be very strong to carry out their functions of mechanical support and muscle contraction.

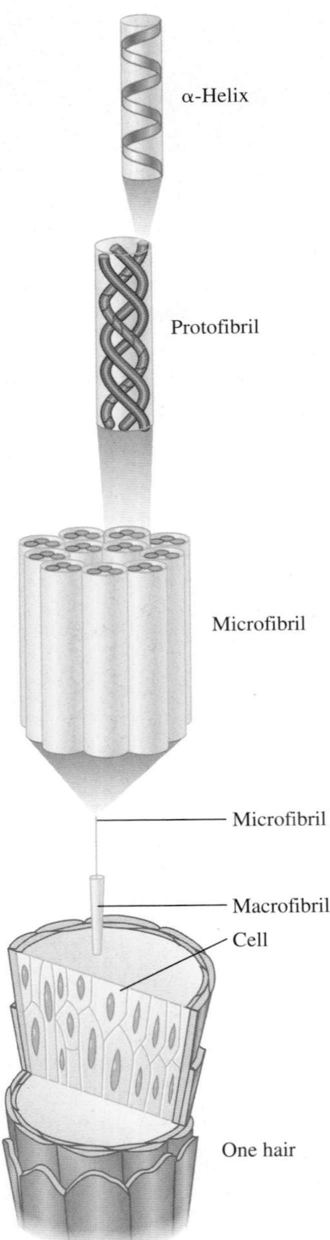

Figure 18.6 Structure of the α-keratins. These proteins are assemblies of triple-helical protofibrils that are assembled in an array known as a *microfibril*. These in turn are assembled into macrofibrils. Hair is a collection of macrofibrils and hair cells.

β-Pleated Sheet

The second common secondary structure in proteins resembles the pleated folds of drapery and is known as the **β-pleated sheet** (Figure 18.7a). All of the carbonyl oxygens and amide hydrogens in a β-pleated sheet are involved in hydrogen bonds, and the polypeptide chain is nearly completely extended. The polypeptide chains in a β-pleated sheet can have two orientations. If the N-termini are head to head, the structure is known as a *parallel* β-pleated sheet. And if the N-terminus of one chain is aligned with the C-terminus of a second chain (head to tail), the structure is known as an *antiparallel* β-pleated sheet.

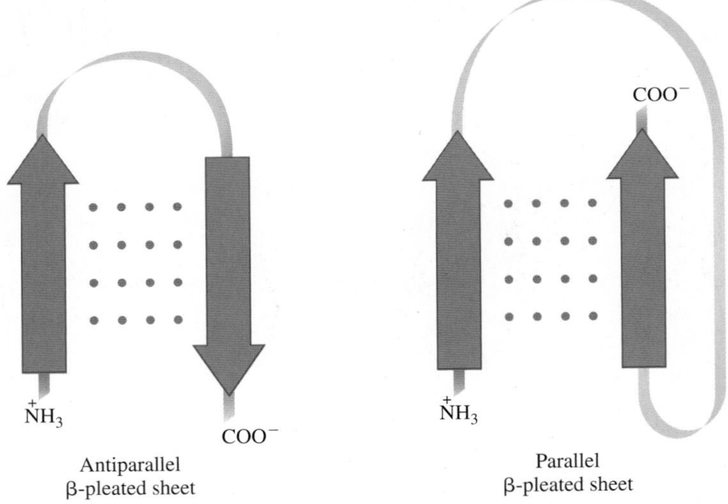

Some fibrous proteins are composed of β-pleated sheets. For example, the silkworm produces *silk fibroin*, a protein whose structure is an antiparallel β-pleated sheet (Figure 18.7). The polypeptide chains of a β-pleated sheet are almost completely extended, and silk does not stretch easily. Glycine accounts for nearly half of the amino acids of silk fibroin. Alanine and serine account for most of the others. The methyl groups of alanines and the hydroxymethyl groups of serines lie on opposite sides of the sheet. Thus the stacked sheets nestle comfortably, like sheets of corrugated cardboard, because the R groups are small enough to allow the stacked-sheet superstructure.

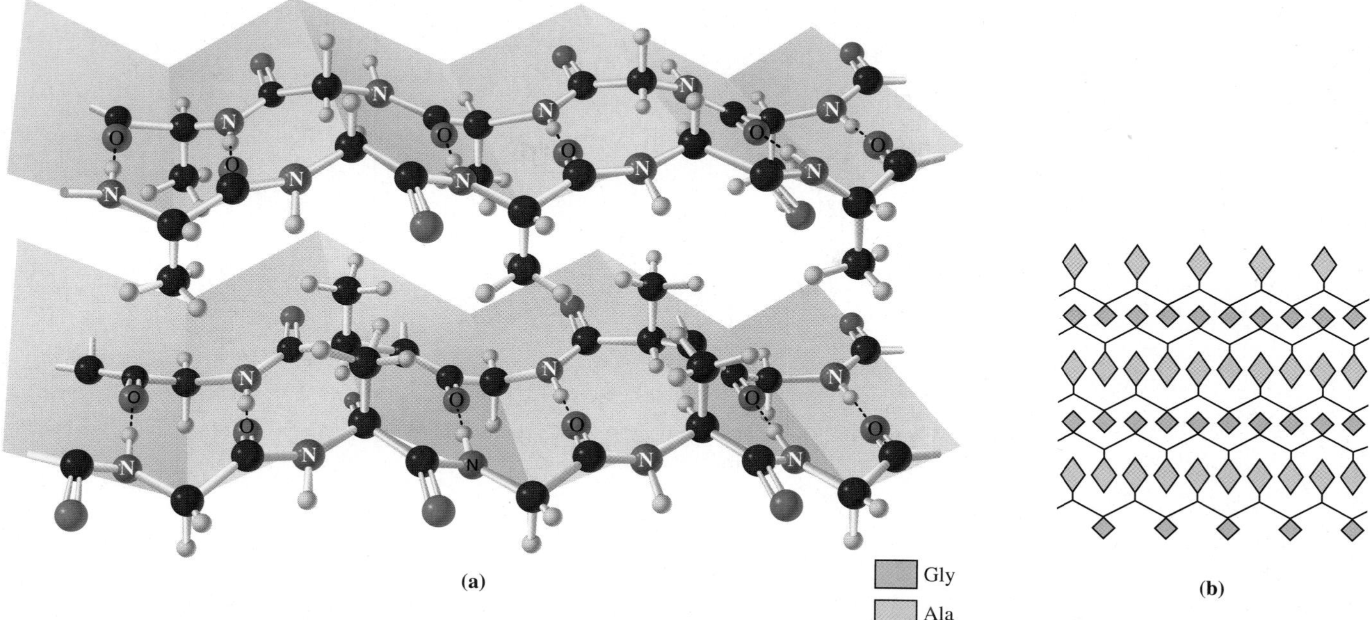

Figure 18.7 The structure of silk fibroin is almost entirely antiparallel β-pleated sheet. (a) The molecular structure of a portion of the silk fibroin protein. (b) A schematic representation of the antiparallel β-pleated sheet with the nestled R groups.

18.5 The Tertiary Structure of Proteins

Most fibrous proteins, such as silk, collagen, and the α-keratins, are almost completely insoluble in water. (Our skin would do us very little good if it dissolved in the rain.) The majority of cellular proteins, however, are soluble in the cell cytoplasm. Soluble proteins are usually **globular proteins.** Globular proteins have three-dimensional structures called the **tertiary structure** of the protein, which are distinct from their secondary structure. The polypeptide chain with its regions of secondary structure, α-helix and β-pleated sheet, further folds on itself to achieve the tertiary structure.

LEARNING GOAL

8 Describe the tertiary and quaternary structure of a protein.

We have seen that the forces that maintain the secondary structure of a protein are hydrogen bonds between the amide hydrogen and the carbonyl oxygen of the peptide bond. What are the forces that maintain the tertiary structure of a protein? The globular tertiary structure forms spontaneously and is maintained as a result of interactions among the side chains, the R groups, of the amino acids. The structure is maintained by the following molecular interactions:

- van der Waals forces (London dispersion and dipole-dipole attractions) between the hydrophobic R groups
- Hydrogen bonds between the polar R groups
- Ionic bonds (salt bridges) between the oppositely charged R groups
- Covalent bonds between the thiol-containing amino acid residues. Two of the polar cysteines can be oxidized to a dimeric amino acid called *cystine* (Figure 18.8). The disulfide bond of cystine can be a cross-link between different proteins, or it can tie two segments within a protein together.

LEARNING GOAL

9 List the R group interactions that maintain protein conformation.

Thiols were discussed in Section 12.8.

The bonds that maintain the tertiary structure of proteins are shown in Figure 18.9. The importance of these bonds becomes clear when we realize that it is the tertiary structure of the protein that defines its biological function. Most of

In the next section we will see that some proteins have an additional level of structure, quaternary structure, that also influences function.

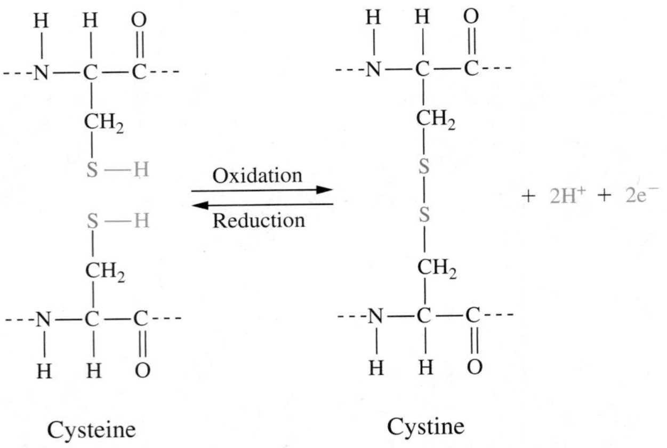

$$\text{2 Cysteine } (\text{---NH---CH(CH}_2\text{---SH)---CO---}) \underset{\text{Reduction}}{\overset{\text{Oxidation}}{\rightleftharpoons}} \text{Cystine } (\text{---NH---CH(CH}_2\text{---S---S---CH}_2\text{)CH---CO---}) + 2H^+ + 2e^-$$

Cysteine Cystine

Figure 18.8 Oxidation of two cysteines to give the dimer cystine. This reaction occurs in cells and is readily reversible.

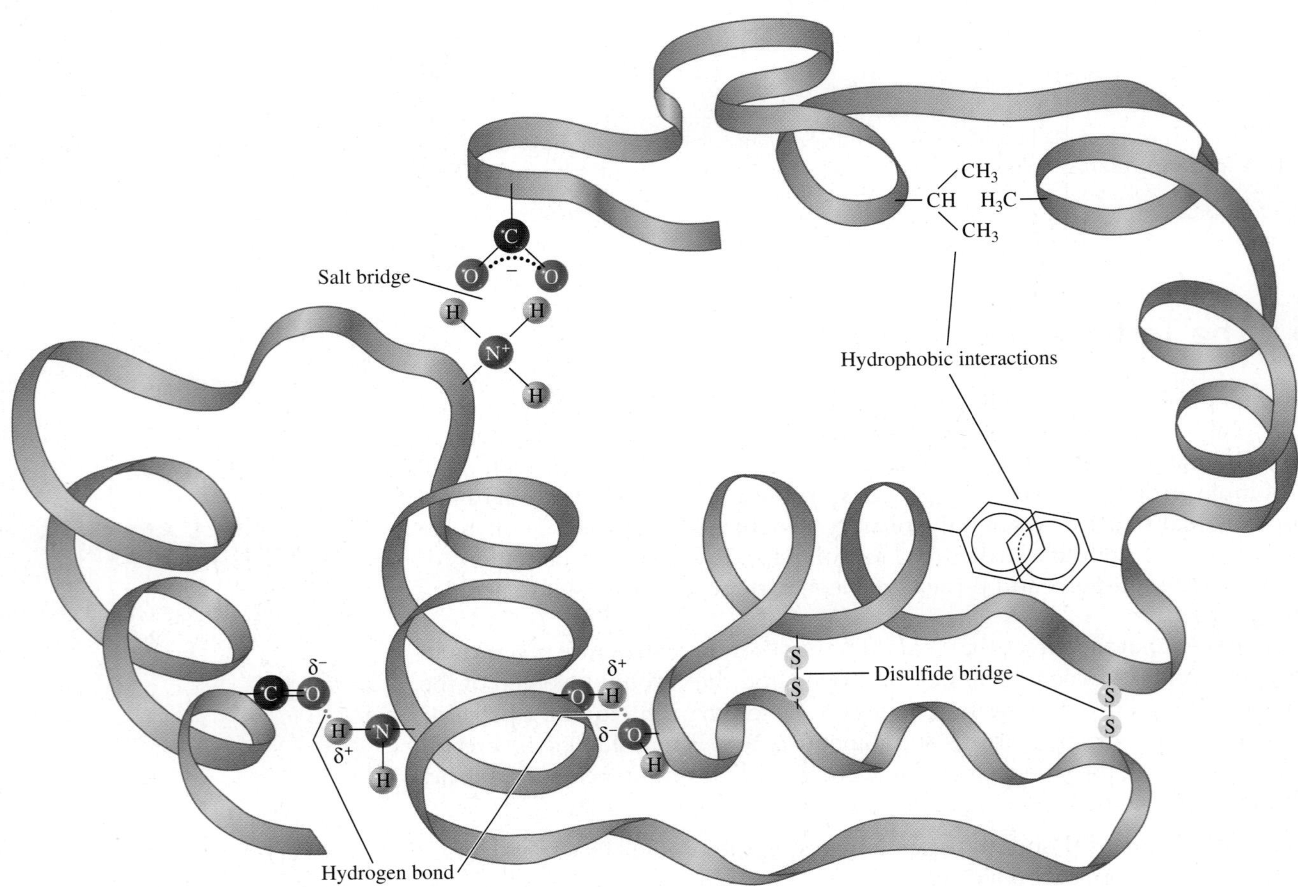

Figure 18.9 Summary of the weak interactions that help maintain the tertiary structure of a protein.

the time, nonpolar side chains of amino acid residues are buried, closely packed, in the interior of a globular protein, out of contact with water. Polar and charged side chain amino acid residues lie on the surfaces of globular proteins. Globular proteins are extremely compact. The tertiary structure can contain regions of α-helix and regions of β-pleated sheet. "Hinge" regions of random coil connect regions of α-helix and β-pleated sheet. Because of its cyclic structure, proline disrupts an α-helix. As a result, proline is often found in these hinge regions.

A MEDICAL PERSPECTIVE

Collagen, Cosmetic Procedures, and Clinical Applications

Collagen is the most abundant protein in the human body, making up about one-third of the total protein content. It provides mechanical strength to bone, tendon, skin, and blood vessels. Collagen fibers in bone provide a scaffolding around which *hydroxyapatite* (a calcium phosphate polymer) crystals are arranged. Skin contains loosely woven collagen fibers that can expand in all directions. The corneas of the eyes are composed of collagen. As we consider these tissues, we realize that they have quite different properties, ranging from tensile strength (tendons) and flexibility (blood vessels) to transparency (cornea).

How could such diverse structures be composed of a single protein? The answer lies in the fact that collagen is actually a family of twenty genetically distinct, but closely related proteins. Although the differences in the amino acid sequence of these different collagen proteins allow them to carry out a variety of functions in the body, they all have a similar three-dimensional structure. Collagen is composed of three left-handed polypeptide helices that are twisted around one another to form a "superhelix" called a *triple helix*. Each of the individual peptide chains of collagen is a left-handed helix, but they are wrapped around one another in the right-handed sense.

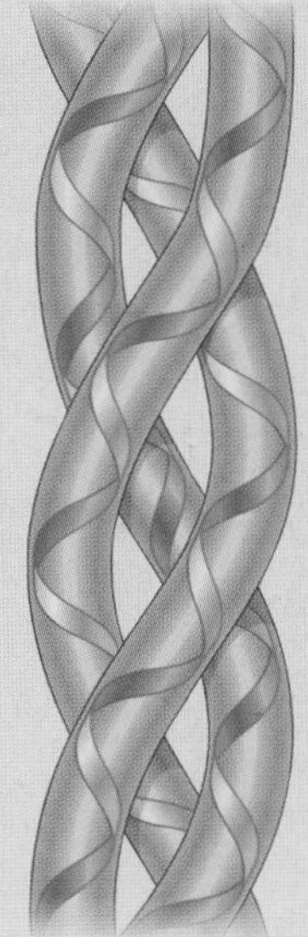

Structure of the collagen triple helix.

Every third amino acid in the collagen chain is glycine. It is important to the structure because the triple-stranded helix forms as a result of interchain hydrogen bonding involving glycine. Thus, every third amino acid on one strand is in very close contact with the other two strands. Glycine has another advantage; it is the only amino acid with an R group small enough for the space allowed by the triple-stranded structure.

Collagen injections have been used in cosmetic procedures to add fullness to lips or minimize the appearance of wrinkled or sunken facial skin. This procedure is no longer very common because of the relatively high frequency of allergic reactions to the bovine collagen used in the injections. Popular alternatives to collagen injections include the patient's own fat and hyaluronic acid (see also A Medical Perspective: Monosaccharide Derivatives and Heteropolysaccharides of Medical Interest in Chapter 16). Another alternative, although an expensive one, is the injection of recombinant human collagen. This reduces the incidence of allergic reactions.

Collagen is also used in the preparation of artificial skin for severe burn patients. The collagen is used in combination with silicones, glycosaminoglycans (such as hyaluronic acid), growth factors, and human fibroblasts, which are the most common type of cell in connective tissue and which promote wound healing.

Collagen even finds its way into our diet. When partially hydrolyzed, the three polypeptide strands separate from one another and then curl up into globular random coils. The product is gelatin, found most notably in gelatin desserts such as Jello. However, gelatin is found in many other foods, as well as in dietary supplements that claim to improve fingernail and skin condition.

Two unusual, hydroxylated amino acids account for nearly one-fourth of the amino acids in collagen. These amino acids are 4-hydroxyproline and 5-hydroxylysine.

4-Hydroxyproline   5-Hydroxylysine

Structures of 4-hydroxyproline and 5-hydroxylysine, two amino acids found only in collagen.

These amino acids are an important component of the structure of collagen because they form covalent cross-linkages between adjacent molecules within the triple strand. They can also participate in interstrand hydrogen bonding to further strengthen the structure.

Continued...

Collagen, Cosmetic Procedures, and Clinical Applications (continued)

When collagen is synthesized, the amino acids proline and lysine are incorporated into the chain of amino acids. These are later modified by two enzymes to form 4-hydroxyproline and 5-hydroxylysine. Both of these enzymes require vitamin C to carry out these reactions. In fact, this is the major known physiological function of vitamin C. Without hydroxylation, hydrogen bonds cannot form and the triple helix is weak, resulting in fragile blood vessels.

Vitamin C
(ascorbic acid)

People who are deprived of vitamin C, as were sailors on long voyages before the eighteenth century, develop *scurvy*, a disease of collagen metabolism. The symptoms of scurvy include skin lesions, fragile blood vessels, and bleeding gums. The British Navy provided the antidote to scurvy by including limes, which are rich in vitamin C, in the diets of its sailors. The epithet *limey*, a slang term for *British*, entered the English language as a result.

For Further Understanding

- What feature of glycine is responsible for its importance in the hydrogen bonding that maintains the helical structure of collagen?
- Collagen may have great tensile strength (as in tendons) and flexibility (as in skin and blood vessels), and may even be transparent (cornea of the eye). Propose a hypothesis to explain the biochemical differences between different forms of collagen that give rise to such different properties.

18.6 The Quaternary Structure of Proteins

LEARNING GOAL

8 Describe the tertiary and quaternary structure of a protein.

For many proteins the functional form is not composed of a single peptide but is rather an aggregate of smaller globular peptides. For instance, the protein hemoglobin is composed of four individual globular peptide subunits: two identical α-subunits and two identical β-subunits. Only when the four peptides are bound to one another is the protein molecule functional. The association of several polypeptides to produce a functional protein defines the **quaternary structure** of a protein.

The forces that hold the quaternary structure of a protein are the same as those that hold the tertiary structure. These include, van der Waals forces between hydrophobic R groups, hydrogen bonds between polar R groups, ionic bridges between oppositely charged R groups, and disulfide bridges.

LEARNING GOAL

10 List examples of proteins that require prosthetic groups and explain the way in which they function.

In some cases the quaternary structure of a functional protein involves binding to a nonprotein group. This additional group is called a **prosthetic group.** For example, many of the receptor proteins on cell surfaces are **glycoproteins.** These are proteins with sugar groups covalently attached. Each of the subunits of hemoglobin is bound to an iron-containing heme group. The heme group is a large, unsaturated organic cyclic amine with an iron ion coordinated within it. As in the case of hemoglobin, the prosthetic group often determines the function of a protein. For instance, in hemoglobin it is the iron-containing heme groups that have the ability to bind reversibly to oxygen.

Question 18.5 Describe the four levels of protein structure.

Question 18.6 What are the weak interactions that maintain the tertiary structure of a protein?

18.7 An Overview of Protein Structure and Function

LEARNING GOALS

3 Describe the primary structure of proteins and draw the structure of the peptide bond.

5 Describe the types of secondary structure of a protein.

6 Discuss the forces that maintain secondary structure.

7 Describe the structure and functions of fibrous proteins.

8 Describe the tertiary and quaternary structure of a protein.

9 List the R group interactions that maintain protein conformation.

Let's summarize the various types of protein structure and their relationship to one another (Figure 18.10).

- *Primary Structure:* The primary structure of the protein is the amino acid sequence of the protein. The primary structure results from the formation of covalent peptide bonds between amino acids. Peptide bonds are amide bonds formed between the carboxylate group of one amino acid and the amino group of another.
- *Secondary Structure:* As the protein chain grows, numerous opportunities for noncovalent interactions in the backbone of the polypeptide chain become available. These cause the chain to fold and orient itself in a variety of conformational arrangements. The secondary level of structure includes the α-helix and the β-pleated sheet, which are the result of hydrogen bonding between the amide hydrogens and carbonyl oxygens of the peptide bonds. Different portions of the chain may be involved in different types of secondary structure arrangements; some regions might be α-helix and others might be a β-pleated sheet.
- *Tertiary Structure:* When we discuss tertiary structure, we are interested in the overall folding of the entire chain. In other words, we are concerned with the further folding of the secondary structure. Are the two ends of the chain close together or far apart? What general shape is involved? Both noncovalent interactions between the R groups of the amino acids and covalent disulfide bridges play a role in determining the tertiary structure. The noncovalent interactions include hydrogen bonding, ionic bonding, and van der Waals forces (London dispersion forces and dipole-dipole attractions).
- *Quaternary Structure:* Like tertiary structure, quaternary structure is concerned with the topological, spatial arrangements of two or more peptide chains with respect to each other. How is one chain oriented with respect to another? What is the overall shape of the final functional protein?

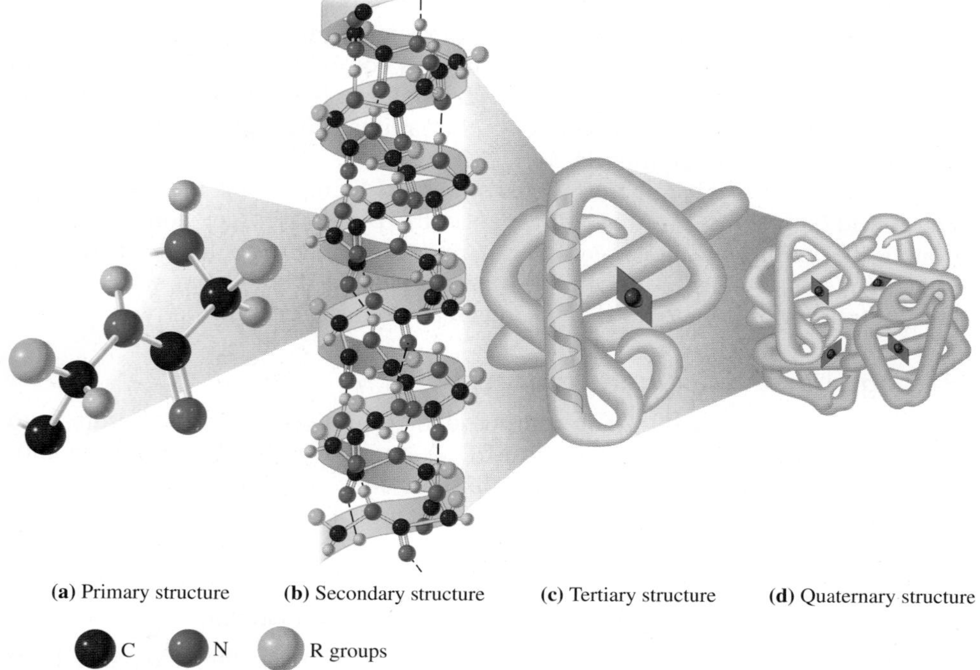

Figure 18.10 Summary of the four levels of protein structure, using hemoglobin as an example.

LEARNING GOAL

11 Discuss the importance of the three-dimensional structure of a protein to its function.

The three-dimensional structure of a protein is the feature that allows it to carry out its specific biological function. However, we must always remember that it is the primary structure, the order of the R groups, that determines how the protein will fold and what the ultimate shape will be.

The quaternary structure is maintained by the same forces that are responsible for the tertiary structure. It is the tertiary and quaternary structures of the protein that ultimately define its function. Some have a fibrous structure with great mechanical strength. These make up the major structural components of the cell and the organism. Often they are also responsible for the movement of the organism. Others fold into globular shapes. Most of the transport proteins, regulatory proteins, and enzymes are globular proteins. The very precise three-dimensional structure of the transport proteins allows them to recognize a particular molecule and facilitate its entry into the cell. Similarly, it is the specific three-dimensional shape of regulatory proteins that allows them to bind to their receptors on the surfaces of the target cell. In this way they can communicate with the cell, instructing it to take some course of action. In Chapter 19 we will see that the three-dimensional structure of enzyme active sites allows them to bind to their specific reactants and speed up biochemical reactions.

As we will see with the example of sickle cell hemoglobin in the next section, an alteration of just a single amino acid within the primary structure of a protein can have far-reaching implications. When an amino acid replaces another in a peptide, there is a change in the R group at that position in the protein chain. This leads to different tertiary and perhaps quaternary structure because the nature of the noncovalent interactions is altered by changing the R group that is available for that bonding. Similarly, replacement of another amino acid with proline can disrupt important regions of secondary structure. Thus changes in the primary amino acid sequence can change the three-dimensional structure of a protein in ways that cause it to be nonfunctional. In the case of sickle cell hemoglobin, this protein malfunction can lead to death.

18.8 Myoglobin and Hemoglobin

Myoglobin and Oxygen Storage

LEARNING GOAL

12 Describe the roles of hemoglobin and myoglobin.

Most of the cells of our bodies are buried in the interior of the body and cannot directly get food molecules or eliminate waste. The circulatory system solves this problem by delivering nutrients and oxygen to body cells and carrying away wastes. Our cells require a steady supply of oxygen, but oxygen is only slightly soluble in aqueous solutions. To overcome this solubility problem, we have an oxygen transport protein, **hemoglobin.** Hemoglobin is found in red blood cells and is the oxygen transport protein of higher animals. **Myoglobin** is the oxygen storage protein of skeletal muscle.

The structure of myoglobin (Mb) is shown in Figure 18.11. The **heme group** (Figure 18.12) is also an essential component of this protein. The Fe^{2+} ion in the heme group is the binding site for oxygen in both myoglobin and hemoglobin. Fortunately, myoglobin has a greater attraction for oxygen than does hemoglobin, which allows efficient transfer of oxygen from the bloodstream to the cells of the body.

Hemoglobin and Oxygen Transport

Hemoglobin (Hb) is a tetramer composed of four polypeptide subunits: two α-subunits and two β-subunits (Figure 18.13). Because each subunit of hemoglobin contains a heme group, a hemoglobin molecule can bind four molecules of oxygen:

$$\underset{\text{Deoxyhemoglobin}}{Hb} + 4O_2 \longrightarrow \underset{\text{Oxyhemoglobin}}{Hb(O_2)_4}$$

The oxygenation of hemoglobin in the lungs and the transfer of oxygen from hemoglobin to myoglobin in the tissues are very complex processes. We begin our investigation of these events with the inhalation of a breath of air.

The oxygenation of hemoglobin in the lungs is greatly favored by differences in the oxygen partial pressure (pO_2) in the lungs and in the blood. The pO_2 in the

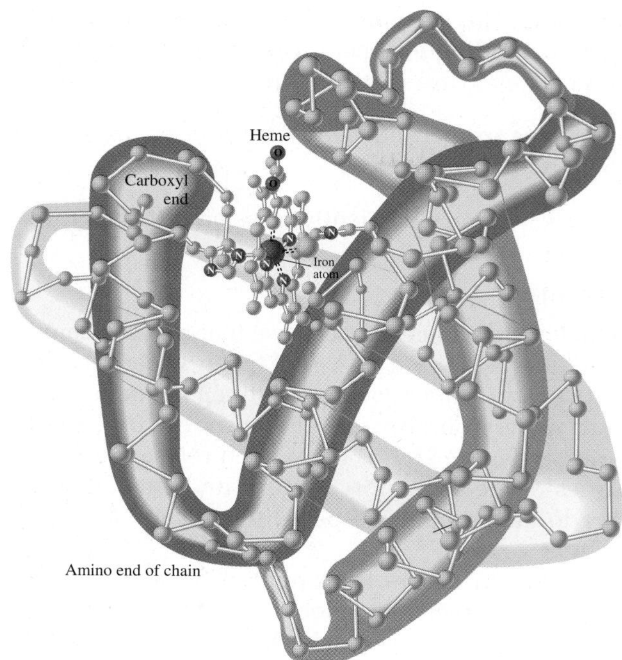

Figure 18.11 Myoglobin. The heme group has an iron atom to which oxygen binds.

```
                    CH3       CH=CH2
                    |         |
                    C ======= C
                    |         |
              HC—C           C=CH
              ||    \\     /     |
    CH3—C—C          N         C=C—CH3
        ||    \      |       /    |
        ||     N---Fe2+—N         |
        ||    //     |       \    |
    CH2—C—C          N         C=C—CH=CH2
    |       |      /   \       |
    CH2     HC=C           C=CH
    |           |         |
    COOH        C ======= C
                |         |
                CH2       CH3
                |
                CH2
                |
                COOH
```

Figure 18.12 Structure of the heme prosthetic group, which binds to myoglobin and hemoglobin.

air in the lungs is approximately 100 millimeters of mercury (mm Hg); the pO_2 in oxygen-depleted blood is only about 40 mm Hg. Oxygen diffuses from the region of high pO_2 in the lungs to the region of low pO_2 in the blood. There it enters red blood cells and binds to the Fe^{2+} ions of the heme groups of deoxyhemoglobin, forming oxyhemoglobin. This binding actually helps bring more O_2 into the blood.

Oxygen Transport from Mother to Fetus

A fetus receives its oxygen from its mother by simple diffusion across the placenta. If both the fetus and the mother had the same type of hemoglobin, this transfer process would not be efficient, because the hemoglobin of the fetus and the mother would have the same affinity for oxygen. The fetus, however, has a unique type of hemoglobin, called *fetal hemoglobin.* This unique hemoglobin molecule has a greater affinity for oxygen than does the mother's hemoglobin. Oxygen is therefore efficiently transported, via the circulatory system, from the lungs of

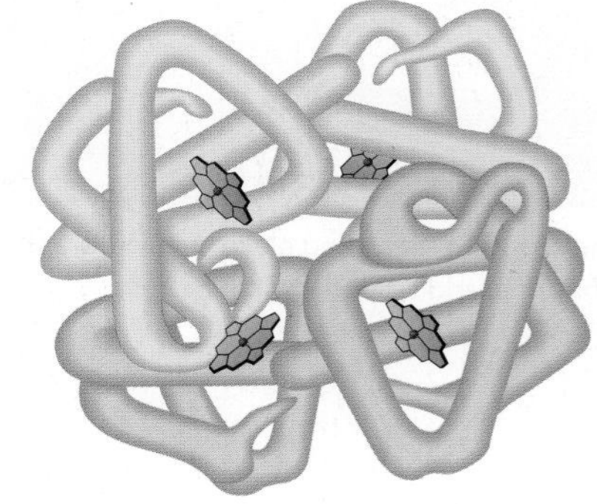

Hemoglobin
- α-chains
- β-chains
- Heme groups

Figure 18.13 Structure of hemoglobin. The protein contains four subunits, designated α and β. The α- and β-subunits face each other across a central cavity. Each subunit in the tetramer contains a heme group that binds oxygen.

the mother to the fetus. The biosynthesis of fetal hemoglobin stops shortly after birth when the genes encoding fetal hemoglobin are switched "off" and the genes coding for adult hemoglobin are switched "on."

Question 18.7 Why is oxygen efficiently transferred from hemoglobin in the blood to myoglobin in the muscles?

Question 18.8 How is oxygen efficiently transferred from mother to fetus?

Sickle Cell Anemia

The genetic basis of this alteration is discussed in Chapter 20.

Sickle cell anemia is a human genetic disease that first appeared in tropical west and central Africa. It afflicts about 0.4% of African Americans. These individuals produce a mutant hemoglobin known as sickle cell hemoglobin (Hb S). Sickle cell anemia receives its name from the sickled appearance of the red blood cells that form in this condition (Figure 18.14). The sickled cells are unable to pass through the small capillaries of the circulatory system, and circulation is hindered. This results in damage to many organs, especially bone and kidney, and can lead to death at an early age.

When hemoglobin is carrying O_2, it is called oxyhemoglobin. When it is not bound to O_2, it is called deoxyhemoglobin.

Sickle cell hemoglobin differs from normal hemoglobin by a single amino acid. In the β-chain of sickle cell hemoglobin, a valine (a hydrophobic amino acid) has replaced a glutamic acid (a negatively charged amino acid). This substitution provides a basis for the binding of hemoglobin S molecules to one another. When oxyhemoglobin S unloads its oxygen, individual deoxyhemoglobin S molecules bind to one another as long polymeric fibers. This occurs because the valine fits into a hydrophobic pocket on the surface of a second deoxyhemoglobin S molecule. The fibers generated in this way radically alter the shape of the red blood cell, resulting in the sickling effect.

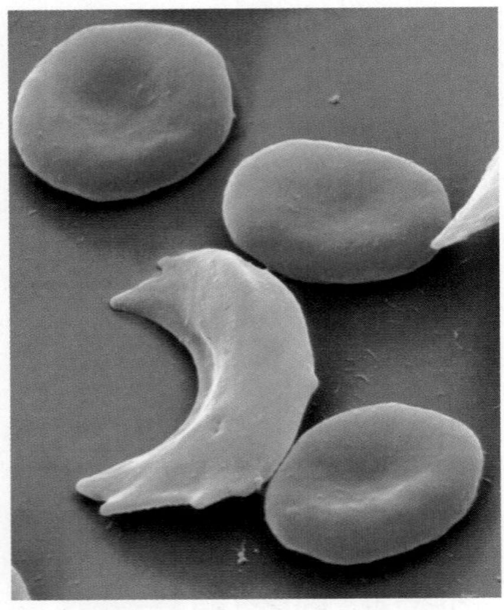

Figure 18.14 Scanning electron micrographs of normal and sickled red blood cells.

Sickle cell anemia occurs in individuals who have inherited the gene for sickle cell hemoglobin from both parents. Afflicted individuals produce 90–100% defective β-chains. Individuals who inherit one normal gene and one defective gene produce both normal and altered β-chains. About 10% of African Americans carry a single copy of the defective gene, a condition known as *sickle cell trait.* Although not severely affected, they have a 50% chance of passing the gene to each of their children.

An interesting relationship exists between sickle cell trait and resistance to malaria. In some parts of Africa, up to 20% of the population has sickle cell trait. In those same parts of Africa, one of the leading causes of death is malaria. The presence of sickle cell trait is linked to an increased resistance to malaria because the malarial parasite cannot feed efficiently on sickled red blood cells. People who have sickle cell disease die young; those without sickle cell trait have a high probability of succumbing to malaria. Occupying the middle ground, people who have sickle cell trait do not suffer much from sickle cell anemia and simultaneously resist deadly malaria. Because those with sickle cell trait have a greater chance of survival and reproduction, the sickle cell hemoglobin gene is maintained in the population.

18.9 Proteins in the Blood

The blood plasma of a healthy individual typically contains 60–80 grams per liter (g/L) of protein. This protein can be separated into five classes designated α through γ. The separation is based on the overall surface charge on each of the types of protein.

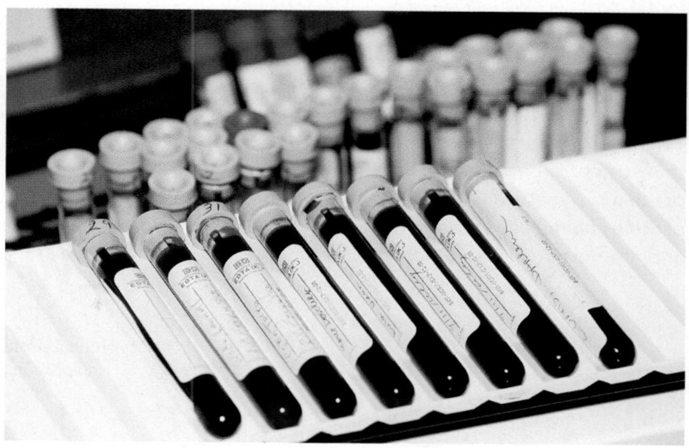

Blood samples drawn from patients.

The most abundant protein in the blood is albumin, making up about 55% of the blood protein. Albumin contributes to the osmotic pressure of the blood simply because it is a dissolved molecule. It also serves as a nonspecific transport molecule for important metabolites that are otherwise poorly soluble in water. Among the molecules transported through the blood by albumin are bilirubin (a waste product of the breakdown of hemoglobin), Ca^{2+}, and fatty acids (organic anions).

The α-globulins (α_1 and α_2) make up 13% of the plasma proteins. They include glycoproteins (proteins with sugar groups attached), high-density lipoproteins, haptoglobin (a transport protein for free hemoglobin), ceruloplasmin (a copper transport protein), prothrombin (a protein involved in blood clotting), and very low density lipoproteins. The most abundant is α_1-globulin α_1-antitrypsin. Although the name leads us to believe that this protein inhibits a digestive enzyme, trypsin, the primary function of α_1-antitrypsin is the inactivation of an enzyme that causes damage in the lungs (see also A Medical Perspective: α_1-Antitrypsin and Familial Emphysema in Chapter 19). α_1-Antichymotrypsin is another inhibitor found in the bloodstream. This protein, along with amyloid proteins, is found in the amyloid plaques characteristic of Alzheimer's disease (AD). As a result, it has been suggested that an overproduction of this protein may contribute to AD. In the blood, α_1-antichymotrypsin is also found complexed to prostate specific antigen (PSA), the protein antigen that is measured as an indicator of prostate cancer. Elevated PSA levels are observed in those with the disease. It is interesting to note that PSA is a chymotrypsin-like proteolytic enzyme.

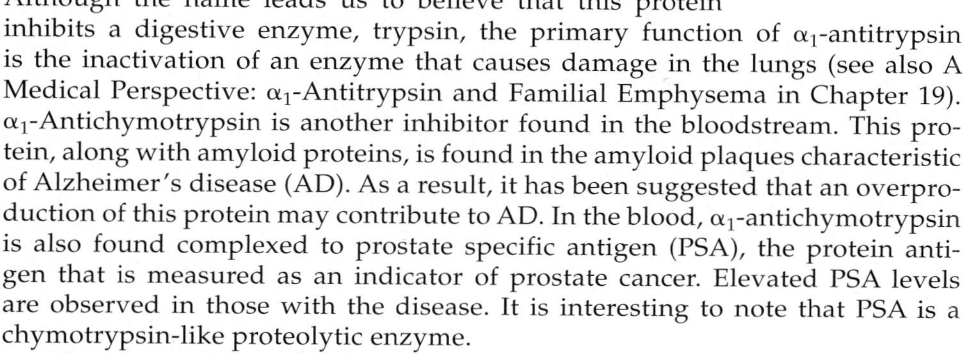

The β-globulins represent 13% of the blood plasma proteins and include transferrin (an iron transport protein) and low-density lipoprotein. Fibrinogen, a protein involved in coagulation of blood, comprises 7% of the plasma protein. Finally, the γ-globulins, IgG, IgM, IgA, IgD, and IgE, make up the remaining 11% of the plasma proteins. See A Medical Perspective: Immunoglobulins: Proteins that Defend the Body in this chapter. The γ-globulins are synthesized by B lymphocytes, but most of the remaining plasma proteins are synthesized in the liver. In fact, a frequent hallmark of liver disease is reduced amounts of one or more of the plasma proteins.

18.10 Denaturation of Proteins

LEARNING GOAL

13 Describe how extremes of pH and temperature cause denaturation of proteins.

We have shown that the shape of a protein is absolutely essential to its function. We have also mentioned that life can exist only within a rather narrow range of temperature and pH. How are these two concepts related? As we will see, extremes of pH or temperature have a drastic effect on protein conformation, causing the molecules to lose their characteristic three-dimensional shape. **Denaturation** occurs when the organized structures of a globular protein, the α-helix, the β-pleated sheet, and tertiary folds become completely disorganized. However, it does not alter the primary structure. Denaturation of an α-helical protein is shown in Figure 18.15.

Temperature

ANIMATION
- Protein Denaturation

Consider the effect of increasing temperature on a solution of proteins—for instance, egg white. At first, increasing the temperature simply increases the rate

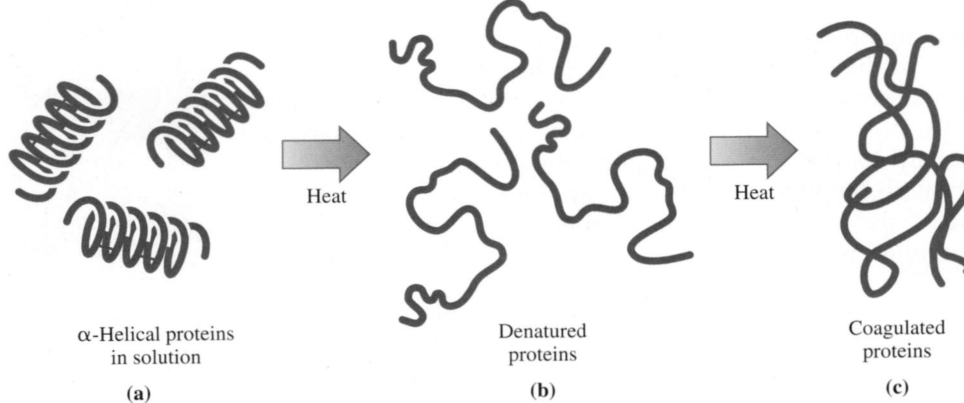

Figure 18.15 The denaturation of proteins by heat. (a) The α-helical proteins are in solution. (b) As heat is applied, the hydrogen bonds maintaining the secondary structure are disrupted, and the protein structure becomes disorganized. The protein is denatured. (c) The denatured proteins clump together, or coagulate, and are now in an insoluble form.

Proteins in each of the foods shown here have been denatured. What agent caused denaturation in each case?

Lactate fermentation is discussed in Section 21.4.

of molecular movement, the movement of the individual molecules within the solution. Then, as the temperature continues to increase, the bonds within the proteins begin to vibrate more violently. Eventually, the weak interactions, like hydrogen bonds and hydrophobic interactions, that maintain the protein structure are disrupted. The protein molecules are denatured as they lose their characteristic three-dimensional conformation and become completely disorganized. **Coagulation** occurs as the protein molecules then unfold and become entangled. At this point they are no longer in solution; they have aggregated to become a solid (see Figure 18.15). The egg white began as a viscous solution of egg albumins; but when it was cooked, the proteins were denatured and coagulated to become solid.

Many of the proteins of our cells, for instance, the enzymes, are in the same kind of viscous solution within the cytoplasm. To continue to function properly, they must remain in solution and maintain the correct three-dimensional configuration. If the body temperature becomes too high, or if local regions of the body are subjected to very high temperatures, as when you touch a hot cookie sheet, cellular proteins become denatured. They lose their function, and the cell or the organism dies.

pH

Because of the R groups of the amino acids, all proteins have a characteristic electrical charge. Because every protein has a different amino acid composition, each will have a characteristic net electrical charge on its surface. The positively and negatively charged R groups on the surface of the molecule interact with ions and water molecules, and these interactions keep the protein in solution within the cytoplasm.

When the pH of the solution is changed dramatically, the acid or base will change the charge of the protein, interfering with the salt bridges and hydrogen bonds that stabilize the tertiary structure.

This is a reaction that you have probably observed in your own kitchen. When milk sits in the refrigerator for a prolonged period, the bacteria in the milk begin to grow. They use the milk sugar, lactose, as an energy source in the process of fermentation and produce lactic acid as a by-product. As the bacteria continue to grow, the concentration of lactic acid increases. The additional acid results in the protonation of exposed carboxylate groups on the surface of the dissolved milk proteins. As a result, they lose their characteristic surface charge and can no longer associate with ions and water or repel one another. Under these conditions the proteins tend to clump together and precipitate out of solution, forming a solid curd.

KITCHEN CHEMISTRY

Egg Foams: Meringues and Soufflés

The transformation of an egg white into a bowl of snow-white fluff simply by whisking vigorously for a few minutes seems quite amazing. Somehow, the liquid egg white and the air whisked into it form a structure that appears solid and has the body to form lovely peaks. Chefs have been using this method for about 350 years to provide delightful meringues for pies and the base for sweet or savory soufflés and mousses.

This foam is really just a bowl of air bubbles, and each of the bubbles is encased in a thin film of denatured egg protein. Two physical stresses, brought about by whipping the egg whites, cause the proteins to denature. First, the drag of the whisk through the liquid creates a pulling force that unfolds and stretches out the normally globular proteins. The interface of the water and the air further causes unfolding because of the two very different environments. The denatured proteins tend to gather at the interface of the air and the water. Their hydrophilic regions remain in the water and their hydrophobic regions project into the air. In this way a layer of denatured protein forms around the bubbles, causing them to be stable.

With time, the foam will separate. So how can we stabilize the foam for the final dish? One common way is simply to bake it. The heat of baking causes the ovalbumin, which isn't denatured by the whipping, to denature. This further adds to the wall of protein surrounding the air bubbles. At the same time, much of the water evaporates from the foam. This further aids the transformation of the egg foam into a permanent solid form—a meringue.

French chefs in the eighteenth century noticed that the use of a copper bowl to create egg foams created a more stable foam. We now know that the reason for this is that copper forms an extremely tight bond to —SH groups. This prevents disulfide bond formation which, in turn, keeps the proteins from binding to one another too tightly. When these stronger disulfide bonds form, the protein meshwork around the bubbles tends to become heavy and to collapse the fragile structure. Of course, copper bowls are expensive and difficult to care for. It turns out that the addition of a bit of acid will do the same thing; the addition of 1/8 teaspoon (tsp) of cream of tartar or ½ tsp of lemon juice per egg at the beginning will also inhibit disulfide bond formation and promote a more stable foam.

Soufflés are simply a savory or sweet mixture or batter into which egg foam is folded. When placed in the oven, they puff up into delightfully light dishes that please both the eye and the palate. The principle governing the behavior of a soufflé is Charles' law. As you learned much earlier in this book, the volume of a gas is proportional to its temperature. When the soufflé is baked, the gas trapped within the bubbles expands as the temperature rises. Although the cooked mixture gives some stability to the risen soufflé, Charles's law determines the behavior of the soufflé when it is taken from the oven and served. The result—the soufflé will fall.

Both the rise and the fall of a soufflé depend on the ingredients in the mixture and the details of the way in which it is baked. Modern chefs sometimes use unusual apparatus to prepare their soufflés. The area of molecular gastronomy has combined the chemistry lab with the kitchen and the results are sometimes astounding. Hervé This, a French physical chemist and father of the molecular gastronomy movement, describes baking a soufflé in a vacuum to provide the highest, lightest soufflé yet served!

For Further Understanding

- Why does the use of a vacuum lead to a lighter soufflé?
- The presence of egg yolks or detergents makes it impossible to create an egg foam. Explain this observation.

Organic Solvents

Polar organic solvents, such as rubbing alcohol (2-propanol), denature proteins by disrupting hydrogen bonds within the protein, in addition to forming hydrogen bonds with the solvent, water. The nonpolar regions of these solvents interfere with hydrophobic interactions in the interior of the protein molecule, thereby disrupting the conformation. Traditionally, a 70% solution of rubbing alcohol was often used as a disinfectant or antiseptic. However, recent evidence suggests that it is not an effective agent in this capacity.

A MEDICAL PERSPECTIVE

Immunoglobulins: Proteins That Defend the Body

A living organism is subjected to a constant barrage of bacterial, viral, parasitic, and fungal diseases. Without a defense against such perils we would soon perish. All vertebrates possess an *immune system.* In humans the immune system is composed of about 10^{12} cells, about as many as the brain or liver, which protect us from foreign invaders. This immune system has three important characteristics.

1. **It is highly specific.** The immune response to each infection is specific to, or directed against, only one disease organism or similar, related organisms.
2. **It has a memory.** Once the immune system has responded to an infection, the body is protected against reinfection by the same organism.
3. **It can recognize "self" from "nonself."** When we are born, our immune system is already aware of all the antigens of our bodies. These it recognizes as "self" and will not attack. Every antigen that is not classified as "self" will be attacked by the immune system when it is encountered.

One facet of the immune response is the synthesis of *immunoglobulins,* or *antibodies,* that specifically bind a single macromolecule called an *antigen.* These antibodies are produced by specialized white blood cells called *B lymphocytes.* We are born with a variety of B lymphocytes that are capable of producing antibodies against perhaps a million different antigens. When a foreign antigen enters the body, it binds to the B lymphocyte that was preprogrammed to produce antibodies to destroy it. This stimulates the B cell to grow and divide. Then all of these new B cells produce antibodies that will bind to the disease agent and facilitate its destruction. Each B cell produces only one type of antibody with an absolute specificity for its target antigen. Many different B cells respond to each infection because the disease-causing agent is made up of many different antigens. Antibodies are made that bind to many of the antigens of the invader. This primary immune response is rather slow. It can take a week or two before there are enough B cells to produce a high enough level of antibodies in the blood to combat an infection.

Because the immune response has a memory, the second time we encounter a disease-causing agent the antibody response is immediate. This is why it is extremely rare to suffer from mumps, measles, or chickenpox a second time. We take advantage of this property of the immune system to protect ourselves against many diseases. In the process of *vaccination* a person can be immunized against an infectious disease by injection of a small amount of the antigens of the virus or microorganism (the vaccine). The B lymphocytes of the body then manufacture antibodies against the antigens of the infectious agent. If the individual comes into contact with the disease-causing microorganism at some later time, the sensitized B lymphocytes "remember" the antigen and very quickly produce a large amount of specific antibody to overwhelm the microorganism or virus before it can cause overt disease.

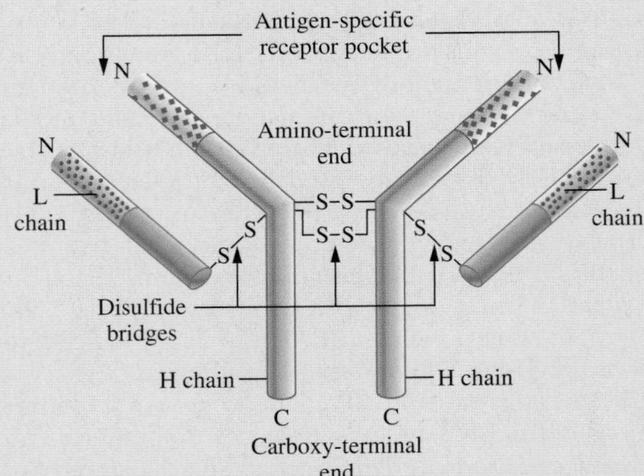

Schematic diagram of a Y-shaped immunoglobulin molecule. The binding sites for antigens are at the tips of the Y.

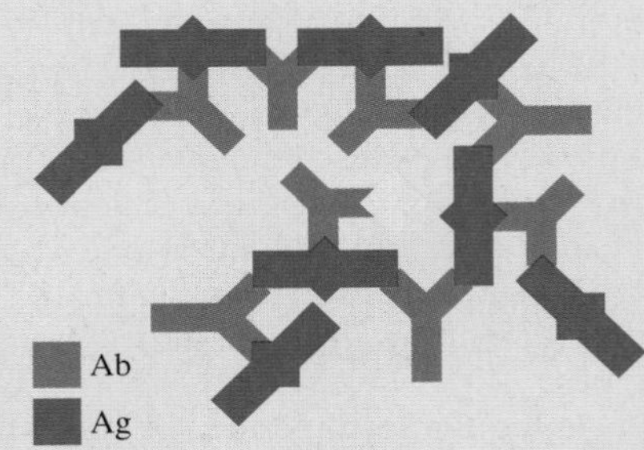

Schematic diagram of cross-linked antibody (Ab)–antigen (Ag) lattice.

Immunoglobulin molecules contain four peptide chains that are connected by disulfide bonds and arranged in a Y-shaped quaternary structure.

Each immunoglobulin has two identical antigen-binding sites located at the tips of the Y. Because most antigens have three or more antibody-binding sites, immunoglobulins can form large cross-linked antigen-antibody complexes that precipitate from solution.

Immunoglobulin G (IgG) is the major serum immunoglobulin. Some immunoglobulin G molecules can cross cell membranes and thus can pass between mother and fetus through the placenta, before birth. This is important because the immune system of a fetus is immature and cannot provide adequate protection from disease. Fortunately, the IgG acquired from the mother protects the fetus against most bacterial and viral infections that it might encounter before birth.

There are four additional types of antibody molecules that vary in their protein composition, but all have the same general Y shape. One of these is IgM, which is the first antibody produced in response to an infection. Secondarily, the B cell produces IgG molecules with the same antigen-binding region but a different protein composition in the rest of the molecule. IgA is the immunoglobulin responsible for protecting the body surfaces, such as the mucous membranes of the gut, the oral cavity, and the genitourinary tract. IgA is also found in mother's milk, protecting the newborn against diseases during the first few weeks of life. IgD is found in very small amounts and is thought to be involved in the regulation of antibody synthesis. The last type of immunoglobulin is IgE. For many years the function of IgE was unknown. When it was found in large quantities in the blood of people suffering from allergies, scientists realized that it is responsible for this "overblown" immunological reaction to dust particles and pollen grains.

For Further Understanding

- Develop a hypothesis to explain why we may suffer from dozens of cases of the common cold caused by rhinoviruses. (*Hint:* Think about the structure of the proteins at the surface of the virus that serve as antigens.)
- Describe the kinds of interactions that you would expect to find when an antibody binds to its cognate antigen.

Detergents

Detergents have both a hydrophobic region (the fatty acid tail) and a polar or hydrophilic region. When detergents interact with proteins, they disrupt hydrophobic interactions, causing the protein chain to unfold.

Heavy Metals

Heavy metals such as mercury (Hg^{2+}) or lead (Pb^{2+}) may form bonds with negatively charged side chain groups. This interferes with the salt bridges formed between amino acid R groups of the protein chain, resulting in loss of conformation. Heavy metals may also bind to sulfhydryl groups of a protein. This may cause a profound change in the three-dimensional structure of the protein, accompanied by loss of function.

Mechanical Stress

Stirring, whipping, or shaking can disrupt the weak interactions that maintain protein conformation. The drag of the whisk or beater creates a pulling force that unfolds and stretches the proteins. This is part of the reason that whipping egg whites produces a stiff meringue. For more information on the preparation of egg foams and their use in the kitchen, see Kitchen Chemistry: Egg Foams: Meringues and Soufflés.

Question 18.9 How does high temperature denature proteins?

Question 18.10 How does extremely low pH cause proteins to coagulate?

18.11 Dietary Protein and Protein Digestion

LEARNING GOAL

14 Explain the difference between essential and nonessential amino acids.

Proteins, as well as carbohydrates and fats, are an energy source in the diet. As do carbohydrates and fats, proteins serve several dietary purposes. They can be oxidized to provide energy. In addition, the amino acids liberated by the hydrolysis of proteins are used directly in biosynthesis. The protein synthetic machinery of the cell can incorporate amino acids, released by the digestion of dietary protein, directly into new cellular proteins. Amino acids are also used in the biosynthesis of a large number of important molecules called the *nitrogen compounds.* This group includes some hormones, the heme groups of hemoglobin and myoglobin, and the nitrogen-containing bases found in DNA and RNA.

Digestion of dietary protein begins in the stomach. The stomach enzyme *pepsin* begins the digestion by hydrolyzing some of the peptide bonds of the protein. This breaks the protein down into smaller peptides.

The inactive form of a proteolytic enzyme is called a proenzyme. These are discussed in Section 19.9.

Production of pepsin and other proteolytic digestive enzymes must be carefully controlled because the active enzymes would digest and destroy the cell that produces them. Thus, the stomach lining cells that make pepsin actually synthesize and secrete an inactive form called *pepsinogen.* Pepsinogen has an additional forty-two amino acids in its primary structure. These are removed in the stomach to produce active pepsin.

The specificity of proteolytic enzymes is described in Section 19.11.

See Section 19.11 and Figure 19.13 for a more detailed picture of the action of digestive proteases.

Protein digestion continues in the small intestine where the enzymes trypsin, chymotrypsin, elastase, and others catalyze the hydrolysis of peptide bonds at different sites in the protein. For instance, chymotrypsin cleaves peptide bonds on the carbonyl side of aromatic amino acids and trypsin cleaves peptide bonds on the carbonyl side of basic amino acids. Together these proteolytic enzymes degrade large dietary proteins into amino acids that can be absorbed by cells of the small intestine.

Amino acids can be divided into two major nutritional classes. **Essential amino acids** are those that cannot be synthesized by the body and are required in the diet. **Nonessential amino acids** are those amino acids that can be synthesized by the body and need not be included in the diet. Table 18.2 lists the essential and nonessential amino acids.

Proteins are also classified as *complete* or *incomplete.* Protein derived from animal sources is generally **complete protein.** That is, it provides all of the essential and nonessential amino acids in approximately the correct amounts for biosynthesis. In contrast, protein derived from vegetable sources is generally **incomplete protein** because it lacks a sufficient amount of one or more essential amino acids. People who want to maintain a strictly vegetarian diet or for whom animal protein is often not available have the problem that no single high-protein vegetable has all of the essential amino acids to ensure a sufficient daily intake.

TABLE 18.2 The Essential and Nonessential Amino Acids

Essential Amino Acids	Nonessential Amino Acids
Isoleucine	Alanine
Leucine	Arginine[1]
Lysine	Asparagine
Methionine	Aspartate
Phenylalanine	Cysteine[2]
Threonine	Glutamate
Tryptophan	Glutamine
Valine	Glycine
	Histidine[1]
	Proline
	Serine
	Tyrosine[2]

[1]Histidine and arginine are essential amino acids for infants but not for healthy adults.

[2]Cysteine and tyrosine are considered to be semiessential amino acids. They are required by premature infants and adults who are ill.

For example, the major protein of beans contains abundant lysine and tryptophan but very little methionine, whereas corn contains considerable methionine but very little tryptophan or lysine. A mixture of corn and beans, however, satisfies both requirements. This combination, called *succotash,* was a staple of the diet of Native Americans for centuries.

Eating a few vegetarian meals each week can provide all the required amino acids and simultaneously help reduce the amount of saturated fats in the diet. Many ethnic foods apply the principle of mixing protein sources. Mexican foods such as tortillas and refried beans, Cajun dishes of spicy beans and rice, Indian cuisine of rice and lentils, and even the traditional American peanut butter sandwich are examples of ways to mix foods to provide complete protein.

Question 18.11 Why must vegetable sources of protein be mixed to provide an adequate diet?

Question 18.12 What are some common sources of dietary protein?

CHAPTER MAP

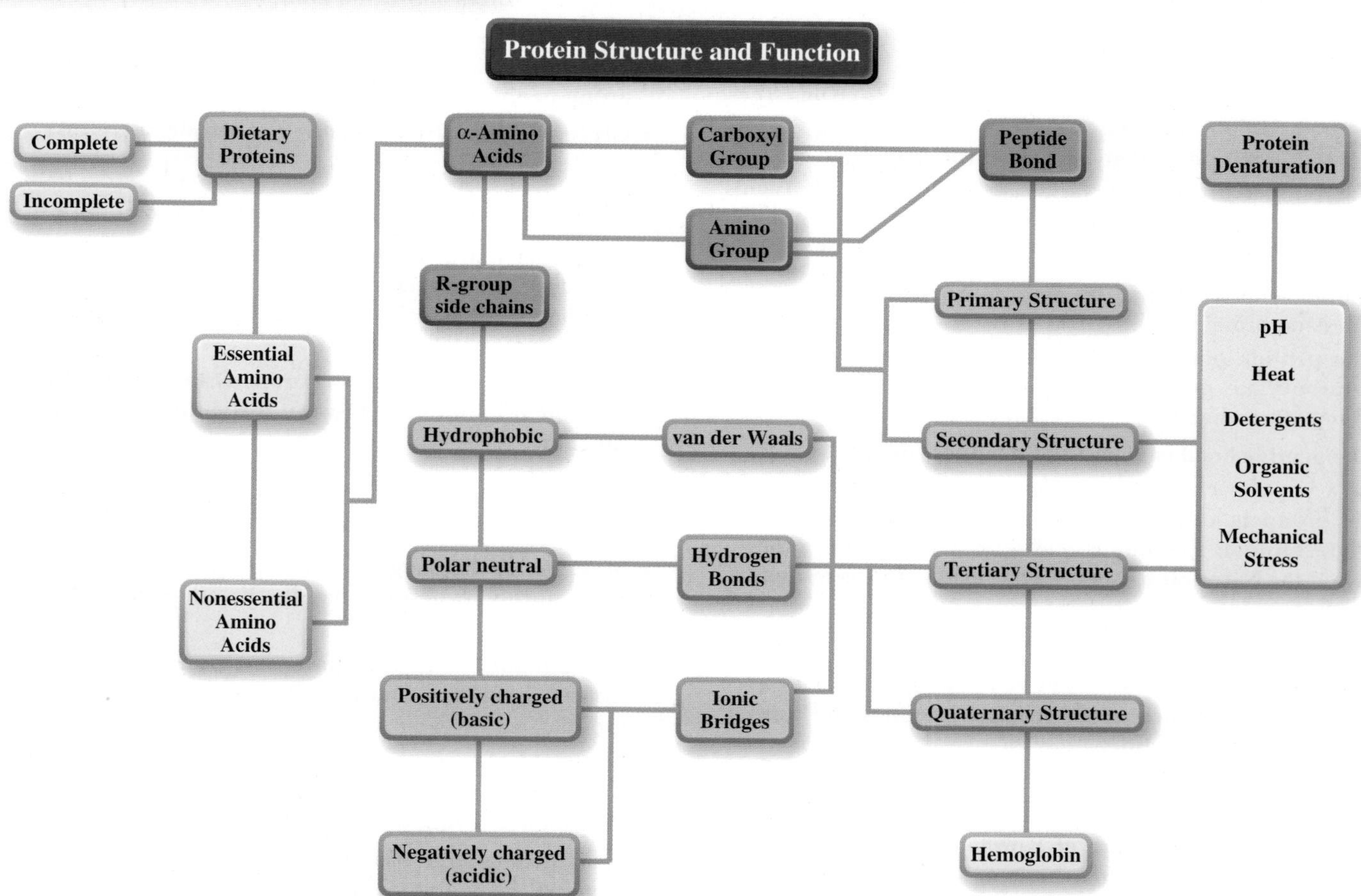

SUMMARY

Introduction

- **Proteins** have many functions in the body.
  - **Enzymes** are biological catalysts.
  - **Defense proteins,** including **antibodies** are produced in response to foreign **antigens.**
  - **Transport proteins** carry materials throughout the body.
  - **Regulatory proteins** control many aspects of cellular function.
  - **Movement proteins** such as actin and myosin in muscle cells are needed for all types of motion.
  - **Nutrient proteins** such as egg albumin and casein in milk, serve as amino acid sources for embryos or infants.
  - **Structural proteins** provide mechanical support.

18.1 Protein Building Blocks: The α-Amino Acids

- Proteins are made up of twenty different **α-amino acids,** each having an α-carboxylate group and an α-amino group.
- Amino acids differ from one another in their side-chain R groups. Differences in polarity distinguish different groups of amino acids.
  - Some amino acid side chains are nonpolar. These are **hydrophobic amino acids.**
  - Some amino acids have polar or charged side chains. These are **hydrophilic amino acids.**
- All amino acids except glycine are chiral molecules.
- Naturally occurring amino acids are generally L-amino acids.

18.2 The Peptide Bond

- Amino acids are joined by **peptide bonds** to produce peptides and proteins.
- The peptide bond is an amide bond formed between the α-carboxylate group of one amino acid and the α-amino group of another.
- The peptide bond is planar and relatively rigid.
- In a peptide chain, the amino acid with a free carboxylate group is called the **C-terminal amino acid** residue **(C-terminus);** the amino acid with a free amino group is called the **N-terminal amino acid** residue **(N-terminus).**

18.3 The Primary Structure of Proteins

- Proteins are linear polymers of amino acids.
- The linear sequence of amino acids defines the **primary structure** of the peptide.

18.4 The Secondary Structure of Proteins

- The **secondary structure** of a protein is the folding of the primary sequence into an **α-helix** or a **β-pleated sheet.**
- These two structures are maintained by hydrogen bonds between the amide nitrogen and the carbonyl oxygen of the peptide bond.
- Some structural proteins, such as the **α-keratins,** are entirely composed of α-helix.
- Some **fibrous proteins,** such as silk fibroin, are composed of β-pleated sheets.

18.5 The Tertiary Structure of Proteins

- **Globular proteins** have varying amounts of α-helix or β-pleated sheet folded into higher levels of structure called **tertiary structure.**
- The tertiary structure of a protein is maintained by attractive forces between the R groups of amino acids, including the following:
  - Hydrophobic interactions
  - Hydrogen bonds
  - Ionic bridges
  - Disulfide bonds

18.6 The Quaternary Structure of Proteins

- Proteins composed of more than one peptide are said to have **quaternary structure.**
- Attractive forces between R groups hold the peptide subunits together.
- Some proteins require an additional nonprotein **prosthetic group** in order to carry out their functions.
- **Glycoproteins** have covalently bonded sugar groups.

18.7 An Overview of Protein Structure and Function

- The primary structure of a protein dictates the way in which it folds into secondary and tertiary levels of structure and whether it will associate with other protein subunits, producing quaternary structure.
- An amino acid change in the protein can have drastic effects on protein folding and thus on the ability of the protein to function.

18.8 Myoglobin and Hemoglobin

- **Myoglobin,** the oxygen storage protein of skeletal muscle, has a prosthetic group called the **heme group,** which is the site of oxygen binding.
- **Hemoglobin,** which transports oxygen from the lungs to the tissues, consists of four peptides, each of which has a heme group.
- Myoglobin has a greater affinity for oxygen than hemoglobin; so oxygen is efficiently transferred from hemoglobin in the blood to myoglobin in the tissues.
- Fetal hemoglobin has a greater affinity for oxygen than maternal hemoglobin, allowing efficient transfer of oxygen across the placenta from mother to fetus.
- **Sickle cell anemia** is caused by a mutant hemoglobin gene.

18.9 Proteins in the Blood

- **Blood plasma contains 60–80 g/L of protein.**
- **These proteins can be separated into five classes designated α through γ.**
- **Albumin is the most abundant protein in the blood (55%).**
- **The α-globulins and β-globulins each make up 13% of the blood proteins.**
- **Fibrinogen comprises 7% of the blood proteins.**
- **The remaining proteins in the blood are the γ-globulins.**

18.10 Denaturation of Proteins

- **Heat disrupts the hydrogen bonds and hydrophobic interactions that maintain protein structure, causing the protein to unfold and lose its organized structure. This is denaturation.**
- **Coagulation, or clumping, occurs when the protein chains unfold and become entangled. When this happens, the protein is no longer water-soluble.**
- **Changes in pH interfere with ionic bridges and hydrogen bonds that stabilize and maintain tertiary structure.**

18.11 Dietary Protein and Protein Digestion

- **Essential amino acids must be acquired in the diet.**
- **Nonessential amino acids can be synthesized by the body.**
- **Complete proteins contain all the essential and nonessential amino acids.**
- **Incomplete proteins are missing one or more essential amino acids.**
- **Protein digestion begins in the stomach, where proteins are degraded by pepsin.**
- **Further digestion occurs in the small intestine by enzymes such as trypsin and chymotrypsin.**

ANSWERS TO PRACTICE PROBLEMS

18.1 a. Methionyl-leucyl-cysteine

```
        O  H       O  H       O
        ‖  |       ‖  |       ‖
H3+N—CH–C—N—CH–C—N—CH–C—O−
      |          |          |
     CH2        CH2        CH2
      |          |          |
     CH2       CH–CH3      SH
      |          |
      S         CH3
      |
     CH3
```

b. Tyrosyl-seryl-histidine

```
        O  H       O  H       O
        ‖  |       ‖  |       ‖
H3+N—CH–C—N—CH–C—N—CH–C—O−
      |          |          |
     CH2        CH2        CH2
      |          |          |
   (benzene)    OH     (imidazole: N, NH)
      |
     OH
```

c. Arginyl-isoleucyl-glutamine

```
       O  H        O  H       O
 +     ‖  |        ‖  |       ‖
H3N —CH–C—N—CH–C—N—CH–C—O−
      |          |          |
     CH2       CHCH3       CH2
      |          |          |
     CH2        CH2        CH2
      |          |          |
     CH2        CH3         C
      |                   //  \
     NH                  O    NH2
      |     +
     C = NH2
      |
     NH2
```

QUESTIONS AND PROBLEMS

Introduction to Protein Functions

Foundations

18.13 Define the term *enzyme.*
18.14 Define the term *antibody.*
18.15 What is a transport protein?
18.16 What are the functions of structural proteins?

Applications

18.17 Of what significance are enzymes in the cell?
18.18 How do antibodies protect us against infection?
18.19 List two transport proteins and describe their significance to the organism.
18.20 What is the function of regulatory proteins?
18.21 Provide two examples of nutrient proteins.
18.22 Provide two examples of proteins that are required for movement.

Protein Building Blocks: The α-Amino Acids

Foundations

18.23 Describe the basic general structure of an L-α-amino acid and draw its structure.
18.24 Draw the D- and L-isomers of valine. Which would you expect to find in nature?

18.25 What is a zwitterion?
18.26 Why are amino acids zwitterions at pH 7.0?

Applications

18.27 What is a chiral carbon?
18.28 Why are all of the α-amino acids except glycine chiral?
18.29 What is the importance of the R groups of the amino acids?
18.30 Describe the classification of the R groups of the amino acids, and provide an example of each class.
18.31 Write the structures of the six amino acids that have polar, neutral side chains.
18.32 Write the structures of the positively charged amino acids. Indicate whether you would expect to find each on the surface or buried in a globular protein.

The Peptide Bond

Foundations

18.33 Define the term *peptide bond*.
18.34 What type of bond is the peptide bond? Explain why the peptide bond is rigid.
18.35 What observations led Linus Pauling and his colleagues to hypothesize that the peptide bond exists as a resonance hybrid?
18.36 Draw the resonance hybrids that represent the peptide bond.

Applications

18.37 Write the structure of each of the following peptides:
- **a.** Phe-val-tyr
- **b.** Ala-glu-cys
- **c.** Asn-leu-gly

18.38 Write the structure of each of the following peptides:
- **a.** Lys-trp-pro
- **b.** Gln-ser-his
- **c.** Arg-met-asp

The Primary Structure of Proteins

Foundations

18.39 Define the *primary structure* of a protein.
18.40 What type of bond joins the amino acids to one another in the primary structure of a protein?

Applications

18.41 How does the primary structure of a protein determine its three-dimensional shape and biological function?
18.42 Explain the relationship between the primary structure of a protein and the gene for that protein.
18.43 Write a balanced equation showing peptide bond formation between leucine and arginine.
18.44 Write a balanced equation showing peptide bond formation between threonine and aspartate.

The Secondary Structure of Proteins

Foundations

18.45 Define the secondary structure of a protein.
18.46 What are the two most common types of secondary structure?

Applications

18.47 What type of secondary structure is characteristic of:
- **a.** The α-keratins?
- **b.** Silk fibroin?

18.48 Describe the forces that maintain the two types of secondary structure: α-helix and β-pleated sheet.
18.49 Define fibrous proteins.
18.50 What is the relationship between the structure of fibrous proteins and their functions?
18.51 Describe a parallel β-pleated sheet.
18.52 Compare a parallel β-pleated sheet to an antiparallel β-pleated sheet.

The Tertiary Structure of Proteins

Foundations

18.53 Define the tertiary structure of a protein.
18.54 Use examples of specific amino acids to show the variety of weak interactions that maintain tertiary protein structure.

Applications

18.55 Write the structure of the amino acid produced by the oxidation of cysteine.
18.56 What is the role of cystine in maintaining protein structure?
18.57 Explain the relationship between the secondary and tertiary protein structures.
18.58 Why is the amino acid proline often found in the random coil hinge regions of the tertiary structure?

The Quaternary Structure of Proteins

Foundations

18.59 Describe the quaternary structure of proteins.
18.60 What weak interactions are responsible for maintaining quaternary protein structure?

Applications

18.61 What is a glycoprotein?
18.62 What is a prosthetic group?

An Overview of Protein Structure and Function

Applications

18.63 Why is hydrogen bonding so important to protein structure?
18.64 Explain why α-keratins that have many disulfide bonds between adjacent polypeptide chains are much less elastic and much harder than those without disulfide bonds.
18.65 How does the structure of the peptide bond make the structure of proteins relatively rigid?
18.66 The primary structure of a protein known as histone H4, which tightly binds DNA, is identical in all mammals and differs by only one amino acid between the calf and pea seedlings. What does this extraordinary conservation of primary structure imply about the importance of that one amino acid?
18.67 What does it mean to say that the structure of proteins is genetically determined?
18.68 Explain why genetic mutations that result in the replacement of one amino acid with another can lead to the formation of a protein that cannot carry out its biological function.

Myoglobin and Hemoglobin

Foundations

18.69 What is the function of hemoglobin?
18.70 What is the function of myoglobin?
18.71 Describe the structure of hemoglobin.
18.72 Describe the structure of myoglobin.
18.73 What is the function of heme in hemoglobin and myoglobin?
18.74 Write an equation representing the binding to and release of oxygen from hemoglobin.

Applications

18.75 Carbon monoxide binds tightly to the heme groups of hemoglobin and myoglobin. How does this affinity reflect the toxicity of carbon monoxide?
18.76 The blood of the horseshoe crab is blue because of the presence of a protein called *hemocyanin.* What is the function of hemocyanin?
18.77 Why does replacement of glutamic acid with valine alter hemoglobin and ultimately result in sickle cell anemia?
18.78 How do sickled red blood cells hinder circulation?
18.79 What is the difference between sickle cell disease and sickle cell trait?
18.80 How is it possible for sickle cell trait to confer a survival benefit on the person who possesses it?

Proteins in the Blood

Foundations

18.81 What is the most abundant protein in the blood?
18.82 List the functions of several α-globulins.

Applications

18.83 Develop a hypothesis to explain why albumin in the blood can serve as a nonspecific carrier for such diverse substances as bilirubin, Ca^{2+}, and fatty acids. (*Hint:* Consider what you know about the structures of amino acid R groups.)
18.84 Fibrinogen and prothrombin are both involved in formation of blood clots when they are converted into proteolytic enzymes. However, they are normally found in the blood in an inactive form. Develop an explanation for this observation.

Denaturation of Proteins

Foundations

18.85 Define the term *denaturation.*
18.86 What is the difference between denaturation and coagulation?

Applications

18.87 Why is heat an effective means of sterilization?
18.88 As you increase the temperature of an enzyme-catalyzed reaction, the rate of the reaction initially increases. It then reaches a maximum rate and finally dramatically declines. Keeping in mind that enzymes are proteins, how do you explain these changes in reaction rate?
18.89 Yogurt is produced from milk by the action of dairy bacteria. These bacteria produce lactic acid as a by-product of their metabolism. The pH decrease causes the milk proteins to coagulate. Why are food preservatives not required to inhibit the growth of bacteria in yogurt?
18.90 Wine is made from the juice of grapes by varieties of yeast. The yeast cells produce ethanol as a by-product of their fermentation. However, when the ethanol concentration reaches 12–13%, all the yeast die. Explain this observation.

Dietary Protein and Protein Digestion

Foundations

18.91 Define the term *essential amino acid.*
18.92 Define the term *nonessential amino acid.*
18.93 Define the term *complete protein.*
18.94 Define the term *incomplete protein.*

Applications

18.95 Write an equation representing the action of the proteolytic enzyme chymotrypsin. (*Hint:* In order to write the structure of a dipeptide that would be an appropriate reactant, you must consider what is known about where chymotrypsin cleaves a protein chain.)
18.96 Write an equation representing the action of the proteolytic enzyme trypsin. (*Hint:* In order to write the structure of a dipeptide that would be an appropriate reactant, you must consider what is known about where trypsin cleaves a protein chain.)
18.97 Why is it necessary to mix vegetable proteins to provide an adequate vegetarian diet?
18.98 Name some ethnic foods that apply the principle of mixing vegetable proteins to provide all of the essential amino acids.
18.99 Why must synthesis of digestive enzymes be carefully controlled?
18.100 What is the relationship between pepsin and pepsinogen?

CRITICAL THINKING PROBLEMS

1. Calculate the length of an α-helical polypeptide that is twenty amino acids long. Calculate the length of a region of antiparallel β-pleated sheet that is forty amino acids long.
2. Proteins involved in transport of molecules or ions into or out of cells are found in the membranes of all cells. They are classified as transmembrane proteins because some regions are embedded within the lipid bilayer, whereas other regions protrude into the cytoplasm or outside the cell. Review the classification of amino acids based on the properties of their R groups. What type of amino acids would you expect

to find in the regions of the proteins embedded within the membrane? What type of amino acids would you expect to find on the surface of the regions in the cytoplasm or that protrude outside the cell?

3. A biochemist is trying to purify the enzyme hexokinase from a bacterium that normally grows in the Arctic Ocean at 5° C. In the next lab, a graduate student is trying to purify the same protein from a bacterium that grows in the vent of a volcano at 98° C. To maintain the structure of the protein from the Arctic bacterium, the first biochemist must carry out all her purification procedures at refrigerator temperatures. The second biochemist must perform all his experiments in a warm room incubator. In molecular terms, explain why the same kind of enzyme from organisms with different optimal temperatures for growth can have such different thermal properties.

4. The α-keratin of hair is rich in the amino acid cysteine. The location of these cysteines in the protein chain is genetically determined; as a result of the location of the cysteines in the protein, a person may have curly, wavy, or straight hair. How can the location of cysteines in α-keratin result in these different styles of hair? Propose a hypothesis to explain how a "perm" causes straight hair to become curly.

5. Calculate the number of different pentapeptides you can make in which the amino acids phenylalanine, glycine, serine, leucine, and histidine are each found. Imagine how many proteins could be made from the twenty amino acids commonly found in proteins.

19

Enzymes

LEARNING GOALS

1. Classify enzymes according to the type of reaction catalyzed and the type of specificity.
2. Give examples of the correlation between an enzyme's common name and its function.
3. Describe the effect that enzymes have on the activation energy of a reaction.
4. Explain the effect of substrate concentration on enzyme-catalyzed reactions.
5. Discuss the role of the active site and the importance of enzyme specificity.
6. Describe the difference between the lock-and-key model and the induced fit model of enzyme-substrate complex formation.
7. Discuss the roles of cofactors and coenzymes in enzyme activity.
8. Explain how pH and temperature affect the rate of an enzyme-catalyzed reaction.
9. Describe the mechanisms used by cells to regulate enzyme activity.
10. Discuss the mechanisms by which certain chemicals inhibit enzyme activity.
11. Discuss the role of the enzyme chymotrypsin and other serine proteases.
12. Provide examples of medical uses of enzymes.

A hot-spring-fed lake at Yellowstone National Park. Explain how bacteria can thrive at temperatures near the boiling point of water.

OUTLINE

Introduction 650
19.1 Nomenclature and Classification 650
Kitchen Chemistry: Transglutaminase: aka Meat Glue 655
19.2 The Effect of Enzymes on the Activation Energy of a Reaction 656
19.3 The Effect of Substrate Concentration on Enzyme-Catalyzed Reactions 657
19.4 The Enzyme-Substrate Complex 658
19.5 Specificity of the Enzyme-Substrate Complex 659
19.6 The Transition State and Product Formation 660
A Medical Perspective: HIV Protease Inhibitors and Pharmaceutical Drug Design 662
19.7 Cofactors and Coenzymes 663
19.8 Environmental Effects 666
A Medical Perspective: α_1-Antitrypsin and Familial Emphysema 667
19.9 Regulation of Enzyme Activity 668
19.10 Inhibition of Enzyme Activity 671
Chemistry at the Crime Scene: Enzymes, Nerve Agents, and Poisoning 672
19.11 Proteolytic Enzymes 675
19.12 Uses of Enzymes in Medicine 676

INTRODUCTION

Imagine the earth about four billion years ago: it was young then, not even a billion years old. Beginning as a red-hot molten sphere, slowly the earth's surface had cooled and become solid rock. But the interior, still extremely hot, erupted through the crust, spewing hot gases and lava. Eventually these eruptions produced craggy landmasses and an atmosphere composed of gases like hydrogen, carbon dioxide, ammonia, and water vapor. As the water vapor cooled, it condensed into liquid water, forming ponds and shallow seas.

At the dawn of biological life, the surface of the earth was still very hot and covered with rocky peaks and hot shallow oceans. The atmosphere was not very inviting either—filled with noxious gases and containing no molecular oxygen. Yet this is the environment where life on our planet began.

Some scientists think that they have found bacteria—living fossils—that may be very closely related to the first inhabitants of earth. These bacteria thrive at temperatures higher than the boiling point of water. Some need only H_2, CO_2, and H_2O for their metabolic processes and they quickly die in the presence of molecular oxygen.

But this lifestyle raises some uncomfortable questions. For instance, how do these bacteria survive at these extreme temperatures that would cook the life-forms with which we are more familiar? Researcher Mike Adams of the University of Georgia has found some of the answers. Adams and his students have studied the structure of an enzyme from one of these extraordinary bacteria. He found that the three-dimensional structure of the super-hot enzymes is held together by many more attractive forces than the structure of the low-temperature version of the same enzyme. Thus these proteins are stable and functional even at temperatures above the boiling point of water.

The enzymes discussed in this chapter are proteins; however, several ribonucleic acid (RNA) molecules have been demonstrated to have the ability to catalyze biological reactions. These are called *ribozymes.*

In Chapter 18 we studied the structure and properties of proteins. We are now going to apply that knowledge to the study of a group of proteins that do the majority of the work for the cell. These special proteins, the **enzymes,** catalyze the biochemical reactions that break down food molecules to allow the cell to harvest energy. They also catalyze the biosynthetic reactions that produce the molecules required for cellular life. In this chapter we will study the properties of this extraordinary group of proteins and learn how they dramatically speed up biochemical reactions.

19.1 Nomenclature and Classification

LEARNING GOAL

1 Classify enzymes according to the type of reaction catalyzed and the type of specificity.

Classification of Enzymes

Enzymes may be classified according to the type of reaction that they catalyze. The six classes are as follows.

Oxidoreductases

Oxidoreductases are enzymes that catalyze oxidation–reduction (redox) reactions. *Lactate dehydrogenase* is an oxidoreductase that removes hydrogen from a molecule of lactate. Other subclasses of the oxidoreductases include oxidases and reductases.

Recall that redox reactions involve electron transfer from one substance to another (Section 8.5).

$$\underset{\text{Lactate}}{HO-\overset{\displaystyle COO^-}{\underset{\displaystyle CH_3}{C}}-H} + NAD^+ \xrightleftharpoons{\text{Lactate dehydrogenase}} \underset{\text{Pyruvate}}{\overset{\displaystyle COO^-}{\underset{\displaystyle CH_3}{C}}=O} + NADH$$

Transferases

Transferases are enzymes that catalyze the transfer of functional groups from one molecule to another. For example, a *transaminase* catalyzes the transfer of an amino functional group, and a *kinase* catalyzes the transfer of a phosphate group. Kinases play a major role in energy-harvesting processes involving ATP. In the adrenal glands, norepinephrine is converted to epinephrine by the enzyme *phenylethanolamine-N-methyltransferase* (PNMT), a *transmethylase.*

The significance of phosphate group transfers in energy metabolism is discussed in Sections 21.1 and 21.3.

$$\text{Methyl group donor} + \text{HO}-\text{C}_6\text{H}_3(\text{HO})-\underset{\text{OH}}{\text{CHCH}_2\text{NH}_2} \xrightleftharpoons{\text{PNMT}} \text{HO}-\text{C}_6\text{H}_3(\text{HO})-\underset{\text{OH}}{\text{CHCH}_2\text{NH}}-\text{CH}_3$$

Norepinephrine   Epinephrine

Hydrolases

Hydrolases catalyze hydrolysis reactions, that is, the addition of a water molecule to a bond, resulting in bond breakage. These reactions are important in the digestive process. For example, lipases catalyze the hydrolysis of the ester bonds in triglycerides:

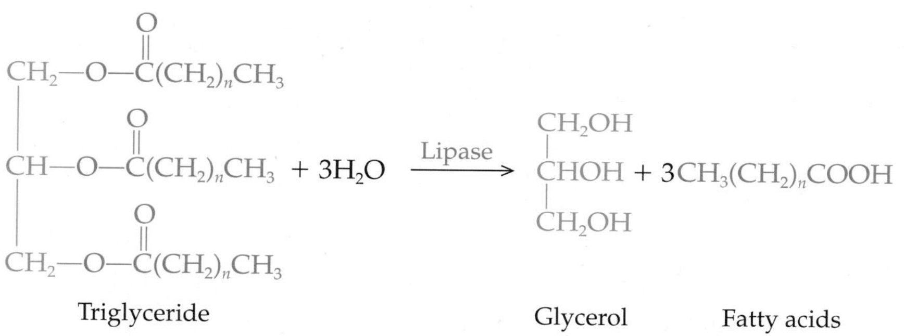

These kittens are adorable, but there is nothing lovely about the aroma of an untended kitty litter box. Urease, a hydrolase, catalyzes the reaction responsible for this smell. Write an equation representing the reaction catalyzed by urease and identify the offending molecule.

Hydrolysis of esters is described in Section 14.2. The action of lipases in digestion is discussed in Section 23.1.

Lyases

Lyases catalyze the addition of a group to a double bond or the removal of a group to form a double bond. *Fumarase* is an example of a lyase. In the citric acid cycle, fumarase catalyzes the addition of a water molecule to the double bond of the substrate fumarate. The product is malate.

$$\begin{array}{c} COO^- \\ | \\ C-H \\ \| \\ H-C \\ | \\ COO^- \end{array} + H_2O \xrightarrow{\text{Fumarase}} \begin{array}{c} COO^- \\ | \\ HO-C-H \\ | \\ H-C-H \\ | \\ COO^- \end{array}$$

Fumarate   Malate

The reactions of the citric acid cycle are described in Section 22.4.

Citrate lyase catalyzes a far more complicated reaction in which we see the removal of a group and formation of a double bond. Specifically, citrate lyase catalyzes the removal of an acetyl group from a molecule of citrate. The products of this reaction include oxaloacetate, acetyl CoA, ADP, and an inorganic phosphate group (P_i):

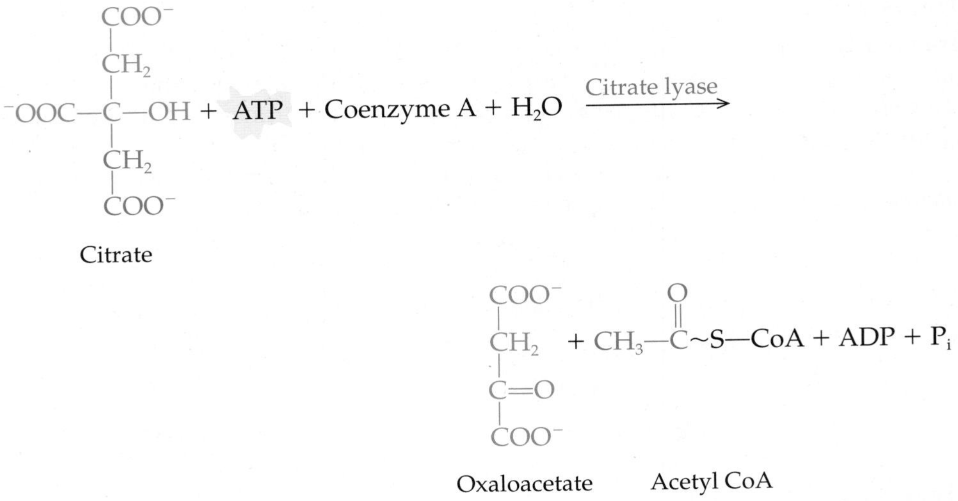

$$\begin{array}{c} COO^- \\ | \\ CH_2 \\ | \\ {}^-OOC-C-OH \\ | \\ CH_2 \\ | \\ COO^- \end{array} + \text{ATP} + \text{Coenzyme A} + H_2O \xrightarrow{\text{Citrate lyase}}$$

Citrate

$$\begin{array}{c} COO^- \\ | \\ CH_2 \\ | \\ C=O \\ | \\ COO^- \end{array} + CH_3-\overset{\overset{\large O}{\|}}{C}\sim S-\text{CoA} + \text{ADP} + P_i$$

Oxaloacetate Acetyl CoA

Recall that the squiggle (~) represents a high-energy bond.

This reaction is important in glycolysis, an energy-harvesting pathway described in Chapter 21.

Isomerases

Isomerases rearrange the functional groups within a molecule and catalyze the conversion of one isomer into another. For example, *phosphoglycerate mutase* converts one structural isomer, 3-phosphoglycerate, into another, 2-phosphoglycerate:

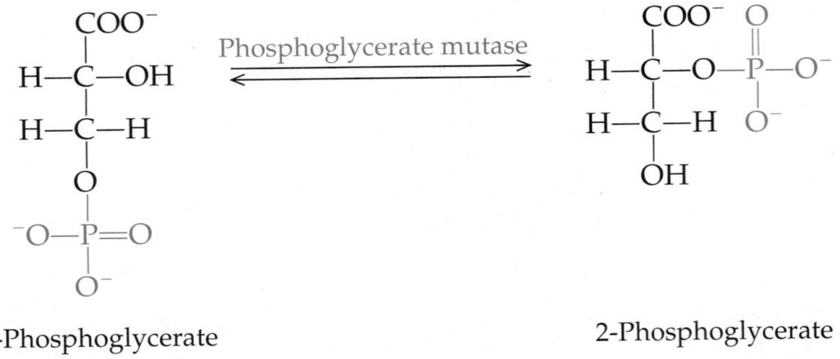

$$\begin{array}{c} COO^- \\ | \\ H-C-OH \\ | \\ H-C-H \\ | \\ O \\ | \\ {}^-O-P=O \\ | \\ O^- \end{array} \xrightleftharpoons{\text{Phosphoglycerate mutase}} \begin{array}{c} COO^- \quad O \\ | \qquad\quad \| \\ H-C-O-P-O^- \\ | \qquad\quad | \\ H-C-H \quad O^- \\ | \\ OH \end{array}$$

3-Phosphoglycerate 2-Phosphoglycerate

The use of DNA ligase in recombinant DNA studies is detailed in Section 20.8.

Ligases

Ligases are enzymes that catalyze a reaction in which a C—C, C—S, C—O, or C—N bond is made or broken. This is accompanied by an ATP-ADP interconversion. For example, *DNA ligase* catalyzes the joining of the hydroxyl group of a nucleotide in a DNA strand with the phosphoryl group of the adjacent nucleotide to form a phosphoester bond:

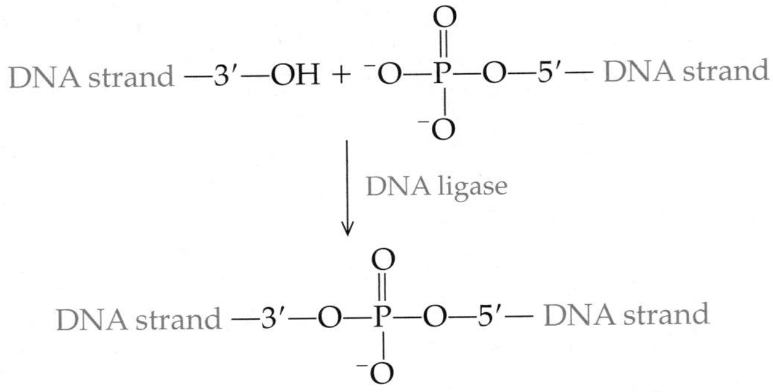

$$\text{DNA strand}-3'-OH + {}^-O-\overset{\overset{\large O}{\|}}{\underset{\underset{\large {}^-O}{|}}{P}}-O-5'-\text{DNA strand}$$

$$\Big\downarrow \text{DNA ligase}$$

$$\text{DNA strand}-3'-O-\overset{\overset{\large O}{\|}}{\underset{\underset{\large {}^-O}{|}}{P}}-O-5'-\text{DNA strand}$$

LEARNING GOAL

2 Give examples of the correlation between an enzyme's common name and its function.

Nomenclature of Enzymes

The common names for some enzymes are derived from the name of the **substrate,** the reactant that binds to the enzyme and is converted into product. In many cases, the name of the enzyme is simply derived by adding the suffix *-ase* to the name of the substrate. For instance, *urease* catalyzes the hydrolysis of urea and *lactase* catalyzes the hydrolysis of the disaccharide lactose.

EXAMPLE 19.1 Classifying Enzymes According to the Type of Reaction That They Catalyze

LEARNING GOAL

1 Classify enzymes according to the type of reaction catalyzed and the type of specificity.

Classify the enzyme that catalyzes each of the following reactions, and explain your reasoning.

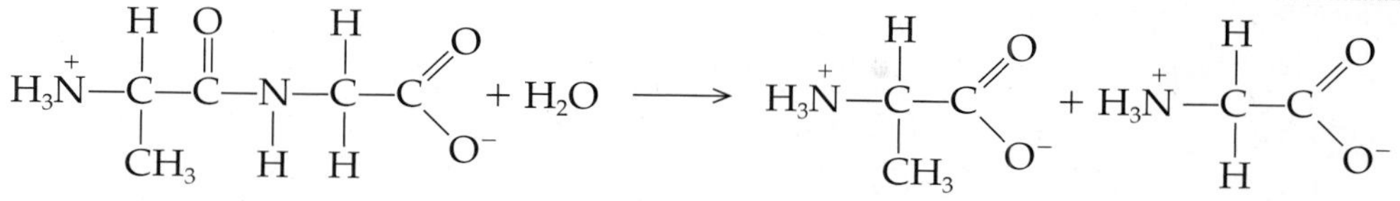

$$H_3\overset{+}{N}-CH(CH_3)-C(=O)-NH-CH_2-COO^- + H_2O \longrightarrow H_3\overset{+}{N}-CH(CH_3)-COO^- + H_3\overset{+}{N}-CH_2-COO^-$$

Alanyl-glycine Alanine Glycine

Solution

The reaction occurring here involves breaking a bond, in this case a peptide bond, by adding a water molecule. The enzyme is classified as a *hydrolase,* specifically a *peptidase.*

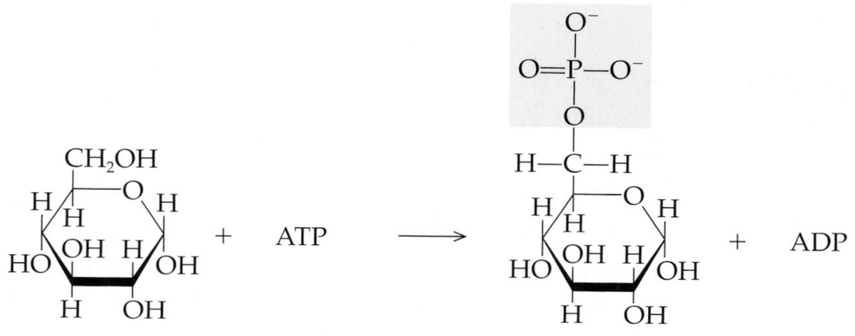

Glucose + ATP ⟶ Glucose-6-phosphate + ADP

Glucose Adenosine triphosphate Glucose-6-phosphate Adenosine diphosphate

Solution

This is the first reaction in the biochemical pathway called *glycolysis.* A phosphoryl group is transferred from a donor molecule, adenosine triphosphate, to the recipient molecule, glucose. The products are glucose-6-phosphate and adenosine diphosphate. This enzyme, called *hexokinase,* is an example of a *transferase.*

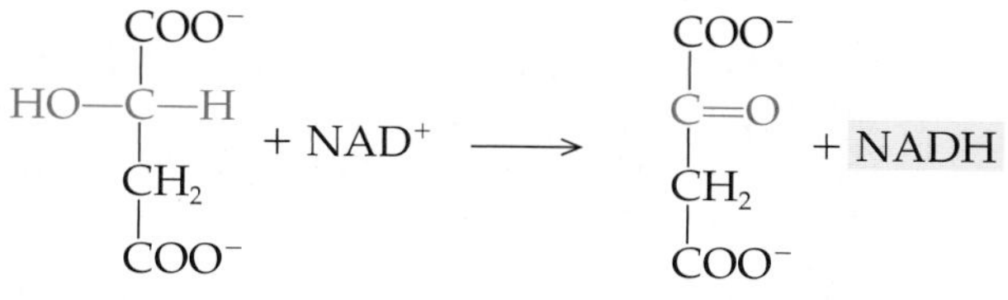

$$^-OOC-CH(OH)-CH_2-COO^- + NAD^+ \longrightarrow {}^-OOC-C(=O)-CH_2-COO^- + NADH$$

Malate Oxaloacetate

Solution

In this reaction, the reactant malate is oxidized and the coenzyme NAD^+ is reduced. The enzyme that catalyzes this reaction, *malate dehydrogenase,* is an *oxidoreductase.*

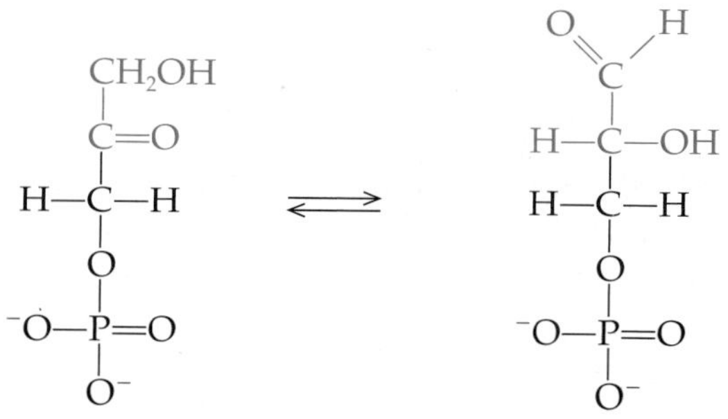

$$HOCH_2-C(=O)-CH_2-O-PO_3^{2-} \rightleftharpoons OHC-CH(OH)-CH_2-O-PO_3^{2-}$$

Dihydroxyacetone phosphate Glyceraldehyde-3-phosphate

Continued…

Solution

Careful inspection of the structure of the reactant and the product reveals that they each have the same number of carbon, hydrogen, oxygen, and phosphorus atoms; thus, they must be structural isomers. The enzyme must be an *isomerase.* Its name is *triose phosphate isomerase.*

Practice Problem 19.1

To which class of enzymes does each of the following belong?

a. Pyruvate kinase
b. Alanine transaminase
c. Triose phosphate isomerase
d. Pyruvate dehydrogenase
e. Lactase
f. Phosphofructokinase
g. Lipase
h. Acetoacetate decarboxylase
i. Succinate dehydrogenase

► For Further Practice: **Questions 19.23 and 19.25.**

Names of other enzymes reflect the type of reaction that they catalyze. *Dehydrogenases* catalyze the removal of hydrogen atoms from a substrate, while *decarboxylases* catalyze the removal of carboxyl groups. *Hydrogenases* and *carboxylases* carry out the opposite reaction, adding hydrogen atoms or carboxyl groups to their substrates.

Thus, the common name of an enzyme often tells us a great deal about the function of an enzyme. Yet other enzymes have historical names that have no relationship to either the substrates or the reactions that they catalyze. A few examples include catalase, trypsin, pepsin, and chymotrypsin. In these cases, the names of the enzymes and the reactions that they catalyze must simply be memorized.

Coenzymes are molecules required by some enzymes to serve as donors or acceptors of electrons, hydrogen atoms, or other functional groups during a chemical reaction. Coenzymes are discussed in Section 19.7.

The systematic names for enzymes tell us the substrate, the type of reaction that is catalyzed, and the name of any coenzyme that is required. For instance, the systematic name of the oxidoreductase lactate dehydrogenase is lactate: NAD oxidoreductase.

Question 19.1 Write an equation representing the reaction catalyzed by each of the enzymes listed in Practice Problem 19.1a through d at the end of Example 19.1. (*Hint:* You may need to refer to the index of this book to learn more about the substrates and the reactions that are catalyzed.)

Question 19.2 Write an equation representing the reaction catalyzed by each of the enzymes listed in Practice Problem 19.1e through i at the end of Example 19.1. (*Hint:* You may need to refer to the index of this book to learn more about the substrates and the reactions that are catalyzed.)

Question 19.3 What is the substrate for each of the following enzymes?

a. Sucrase
b. Pyruvate decarboxylase
c. Succinate dehydrogenase

Question 19.4 What chemical reaction is mediated by each of the enzymes in Question 19.3?

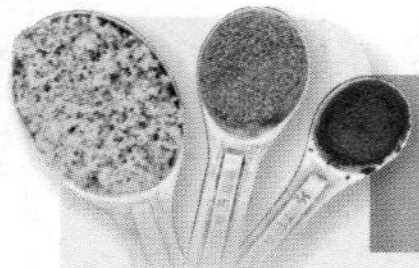

KITCHEN CHEMISTRY

Transglutaminase: aka Meat Glue

Transglutaminases belong to a family of enzymes that catalyze a reaction between a glutamine residue in a protein and a lysine residue in the same or another protein, as shown in the following schematic diagram:

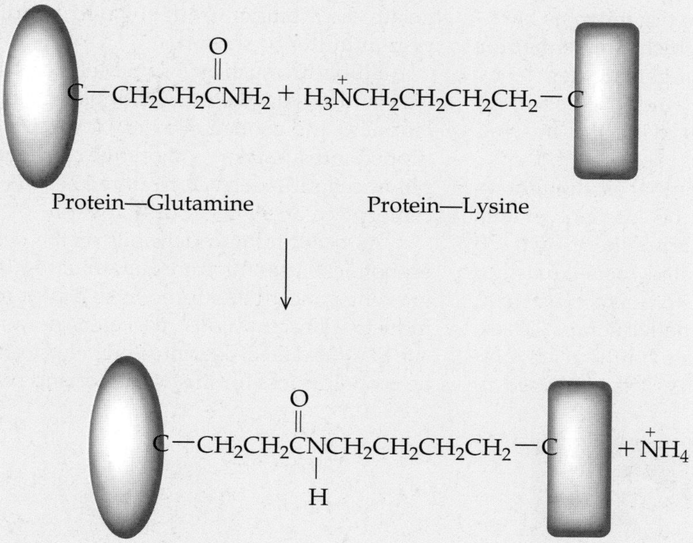

$$\text{C}-\text{CH}_2\text{CH}_2\overset{\text{O}}{\overset{\|}{\text{C}}}\text{NH}_2 + \text{H}_3\overset{+}{\text{N}}\text{CH}_2\text{CH}_2\text{CH}_2\text{CH}_2-\text{C}$$

Protein—Glutamine Protein—Lysine

$$\downarrow$$

$$\text{C}-\text{CH}_2\text{CH}_2\overset{\text{O}}{\overset{\|}{\text{C}}}\underset{\text{H}}{\underset{|}{\text{N}}}\text{CH}_2\text{CH}_2\text{CH}_2\text{CH}_2-\text{C} + \overset{+}{\text{N}}\text{H}_4$$

Cross-linked Proteins

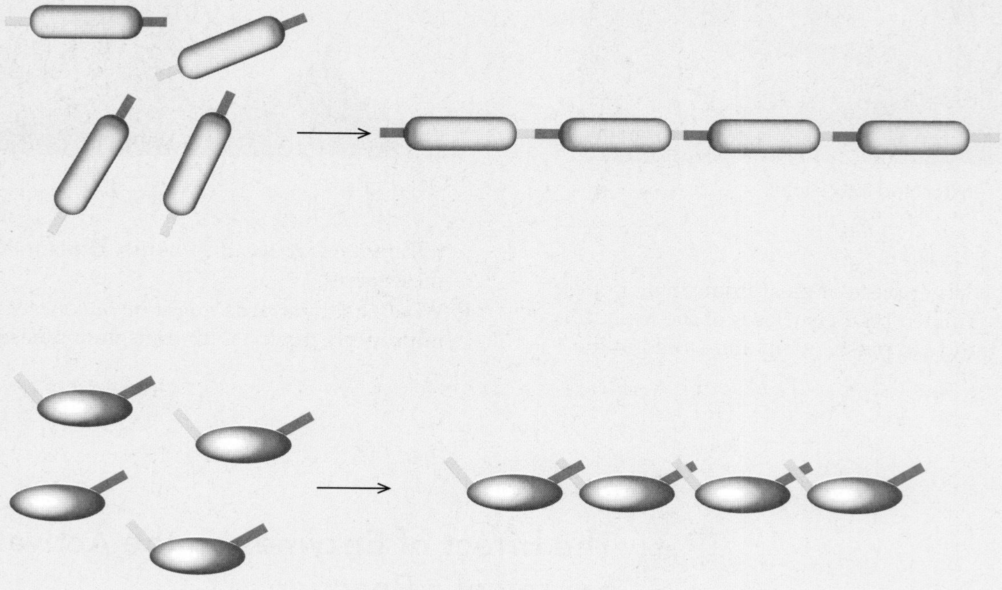

Possible Cross-linking Reactions

Continued...

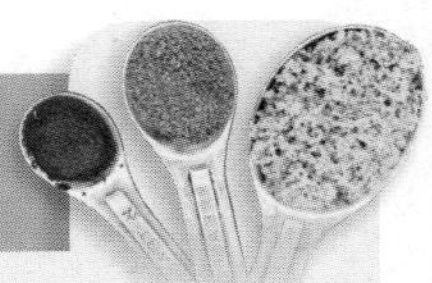

Transglutaminase: aka Meat Glue (continued)

The result of these reactions is the formation of large polymers of protein that are very tightly linked to one another. In the body, transglutaminases form large, generally insoluble protein polymers that are important to the organism as barriers. One transglutaminase is factor XIII, which is essential for the formation of blood clots. Those with a genetic deficiency of factor XIII are prone to hemorrhage, and the condition can be treated by providing the patient with the missing transglutaminase.

The great British chef Heston Blumenthal is thought to have introduced transglutaminases into the kitchen. In this country, Wylie Dufresne, executive chef and owner of wd~50 in New York City, has brought the so-called meat glue into American cuisine. Meat glue can be used to make consistent, uniform portions of meat or fish from smaller scraps. These portions will cook more evenly, be attractive on the plate, and reduce the waste of such unproductive bits. It is also used to prepare sausages without casings and to prepare unusual meat combinations, such as a chicken and beef loaf. But the creative ideas for the use of this enzyme are much more fanciful. Using gelatin as a binder, protein-based noodles can be made from peanut butter or shrimp.

Edible art, such as Adam Melonas's octopop, combines artistry and savory flavors. Octopus legs are fused with transglutaminase and cooked at a very low temperature. They are then dipped into a saffron and orange carrageenan (a linear, sulfated polysaccharide derived from red seaweed) gel and placed as a centerpiece on stalks of dill flowers.

As beautiful and delicious as the octopop is, and as many economical uses of transglutaminases there may be, there is growing concern about the misuse of transaminases in the food industry. Unscrupulous marketers now have the tools to form sub-standard meat cuts into "higher priced" cuts. The result could be economic loss for the consumer and potential health hazards.

Chicken and beef transformed into a loaf.

Octopops.

For Further Understanding

- When forming a larger piece of meat from smaller ones, the enzyme is sprinkled on the surfaces of the meat. It is then wrapped tightly in plastic wrap and stored in the refrigerator for about 24 hours. Explain the logic of each of these steps.
- What health hazards might be of concern if meat is improperly treated with transglutaminase?

19.2 The Effect of Enzymes on the Activation Energy of a Reaction

LEARNING GOAL

3 Describe the effect that enzymes have on the activation energy of a reaction.

How does an enzyme speed up a chemical reaction? It changes the path by which the reaction occurs, providing a lower energy route for the conversion of the substrate into the **product,** the substance that results from the enzyme-catalyzed reaction. Thus enzymes speed up reactions by lowering the activation energy of the reaction.

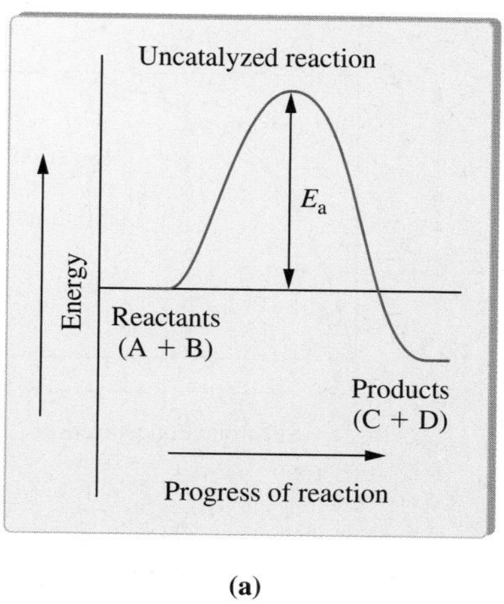

(a)

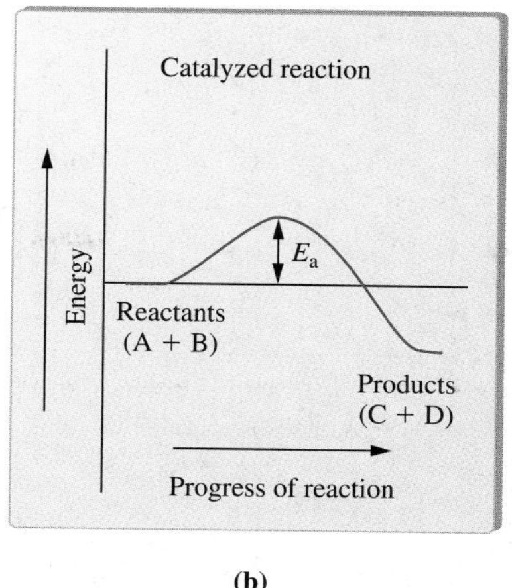

(b)

Figure 19.1 Diagram of the difference in energy between the reactants (*A* and *B*) and products (*C* and *D*) for a reaction. Enzymes cannot change this energy difference but act by lowering the activation energy (E_a) for the reaction, thereby speeding up the reaction.

Recall that every chemical reaction is characterized by an equilibrium constant. Consider, for example, the simple equilibrium

Equilibrium constants are described in Section 7.4.

$$aA \rightleftharpoons bB$$

The equilibrium constant for this reaction, K_{eq}, is defined as

Energy, rate, and equilibrium are described in Chapter 7.

$$K_{eq} = \frac{[B]^b}{[A]^a} = \frac{[\text{product}]^b}{[\text{reactant}]^a}$$

This equilibrium constant is actually a reflection of the difference in energy between reactants and products. It is a measure of the relative stabilities of the reactants and products. No matter how the chemical reaction occurs (which path it follows), the difference in energy between the reactants and the products is always the same. **For this reason, an enzyme cannot alter the equilibrium constant for the reaction that it catalyzes.** An enzyme does, however, change the path by which the process occurs, providing a lower energy route for the conversion of the substrate into the product. An enzyme increases the rate of a chemical reaction by lowering the activation energy for the reaction (Figure 19.1). An enzyme thus increases the rate at which the reaction it catalyzes reaches equilibrium.

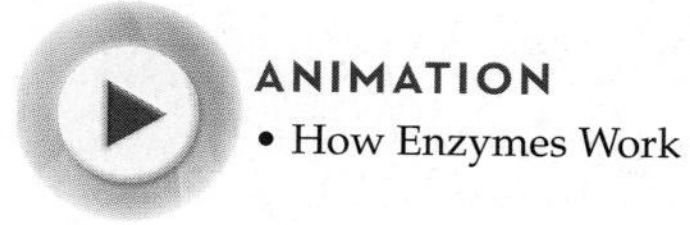

The activation energy (Section 7.3) of a reaction is the threshold energy that must be overcome to produce a chemical reaction.

19.3 The Effect of Substrate Concentration on Enzyme-Catalyzed Reactions

LEARNING GOAL

4 Explain the effect of substrate concentration on enzyme-catalyzed reactions.

The rates of uncatalyzed chemical reactions often double every time the substrate concentration is doubled (Figure 19.2a). Therefore as long as the substrate concentration increases, there is a direct increase in the rate of the reaction. For enzyme-catalyzed reactions, however, this is not the case. Although the rate of the reaction is initially responsive to the substrate concentration, at a certain concentration of substrate the rate of the reaction reaches a maximum value. A graph of the rate of reaction, *V*, versus the substrate concentration, [*S*], is shown in Figure 19.2b. We see that the rate of the reaction initially increases rapidly as the substrate concentration is increased but that the rate levels off at a maximum value. At its maximum rate, the active sites of all the enzyme molecules are occupied by a substrate molecule. The active site is the region of the enzyme that specifically binds the substrate and catalyzes the reaction. A new molecule of substrate cannot bind to the enzyme molecule until the substrate molecule already held in the active site is converted to product and released. Thus, it appears that the enzyme-catalyzed reaction occurs in two stages. The first, rapid step is the formation of the *enzyme-substrate complex.*

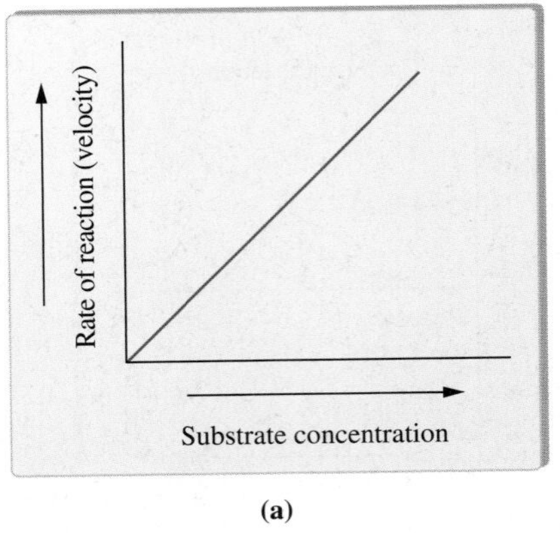

(a)

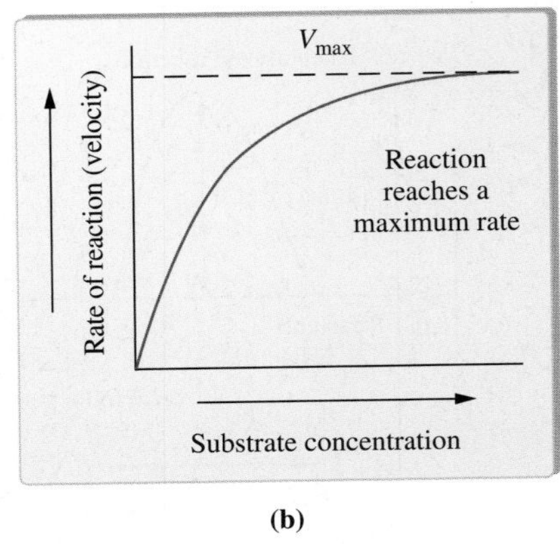

(b)

Figure 19.2 Plot of the rate or velocity, *V*, of a reaction versus the concentration of substrate, [*S*], for (a) an uncatalyzed reaction and (b) an enzyme-catalyzed reaction. For an enzyme-catalyzed reaction, the rate is at a maximum when all of the enzyme molecules are bound to the substrate. Beyond this concentration of substrate, further increases in substrate concentration have no effect on the rate of the reaction.

The second step is slower and involves conversion of the substrate to product and the release of the product and enzyme from the resulting enzyme-product complex. It is called the *rate-limiting step* because the rate of the reaction is limited by the speed with which the substrate is converted into product and the product is released. Thus, the reaction rate is dependent on the amount of enzyme available.

19.4 The Enzyme-Substrate Complex

LEARNING GOAL

5 Discuss the role of the active site and the importance of enzyme specificity.

The following series of reversible reactions represents the steps in an enzyme-catalyzed reaction. The first step (highlighted in blue) involves the encounter of the enzyme with its substrate and the formation of an **enzyme-substrate complex.**

$$\underset{\text{Enzyme + substrate}}{E + S} \xrightleftharpoons{\text{Step I}} \underset{\text{Enzyme–substrate complex}}{ES} \xrightleftharpoons{\text{Step II}} \underset{\text{Transition state}}{ES^*} \xrightleftharpoons{\text{Step III}} \underset{\text{Enzyme–product complex}}{EP} \xrightleftharpoons{\text{Step IV}} \underset{\text{Enzyme + product}}{E + P}$$

The part of the enzyme that binds with the substrate is called the **active site.** The characteristics of the active site that are crucial to enzyme function include the following:

- Enzyme active sites are pockets or clefts in the surface of the enzyme. The R groups in the active site that are involved in catalysis are called *catalytic groups.*
- The shape of the active site is complementary to the shape of the substrate. That is, the substrate fits neatly into the active site of the enzyme.
- An enzyme attracts and holds its substrate by weak, noncovalent interactions. The R groups involved in substrate binding, and not necessarily catalysis, make up the *binding site.*
- The conformation of the active site determines the specificity of the enzyme because only the substrate that fits into the active site will be used in a reaction.

LEARNING GOAL

6 Describe the difference between the lock-and-key model and the induced fit model of enzyme-substrate complex formation.

The **lock-and-key model** of enzyme activity, shown in Figure 19.3a, was devised by Emil Fischer in 1894. At that time it was thought that the substrate simply snapped into place like a piece of a jigsaw puzzle or a key into a lock.

Today we know that proteins are flexible molecules. This led Daniel E. Koshland, Jr., to propose a more sophisticated model of the way enzymes and substrates interact. This model, proposed in 1958, is called the **induced fit model** (Figure 19.3b). In this model, the active site of the enzyme is not a rigid pocket into which the substrate fits precisely; rather, it is a flexible pocket that *approximates* the shape of the substrate. When the substrate enters the pocket, the active site "molds" itself around the substrate. This produces the perfect enzyme-substrate "fit."

The overall shape of a protein is maintained by many weak interactions. At any time a few of these weak interactions may be broken by heat energy or a local change in pH. If only a few bonds are broken, they will re-form very quickly. The overall result is that there is a brief change in the shape of the enzyme. Thus the protein or enzyme can be viewed as a flexible molecule, changing shape slightly in response to minor local changes.

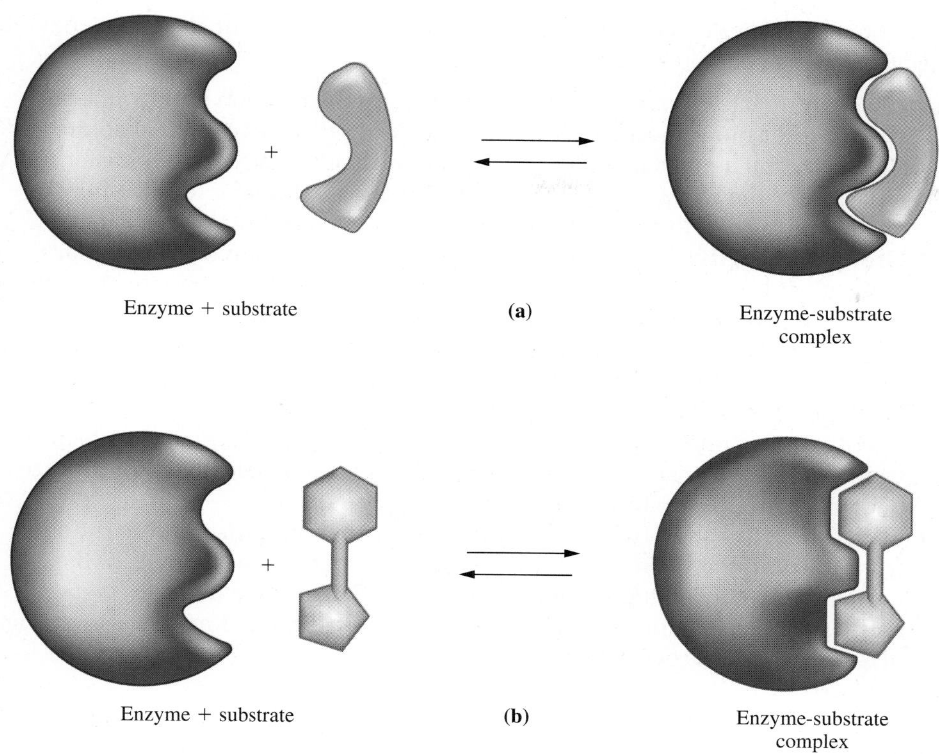

Figure 19.3 (a) The lock-and-key model of enzyme-substrate binding assumes that the enzyme active site has a rigid structure that is precisely complementary in shape and charge distribution to the substrate. (b) The induced fit model of enzyme-substrate binding. As the enzyme binds to the substrate, the shape of the active site conforms precisely to the shape of the substrate. The shape of the substrate may also change.

Question 19.5 Compare the lock-and-key and induced fit models of enzyme-substrate binding.

Question 19.6 What is the relationship between an enzyme active site and its substrate?

19.5 Specificity of the Enzyme-Substrate Complex

LEARNING GOAL

5 Discuss the role of the active site and the importance of enzyme specificity.

For an enzyme-substrate interaction to occur, the surfaces of the enzyme and substrate must be complementary. It is this requirement for a specific fit that determines whether an enzyme will bind to a particular substrate and carry out a chemical reaction.

Enzyme specificity is the ability of an enzyme to bind only one, or a very few, substrates and thus catalyze only a single reaction. To illustrate the specificity of enzymes, consider the following reactions.

The enzyme urease catalyzes the hydrolysis of urea to carbon dioxide and ammonia as follows:

$$H_2N-\overset{\overset{\Large O}{\|}}{C}-NH_2 + H_2O \xrightarrow{\text{Urease}} CO_2 + 2NH_3$$

Urea

Methylurea, in contrast, though structurally similar to urea, is not affected by urease:

$$H_2N-\overset{\overset{\Large O}{\|}}{C}-NHCH_3 + H_2O \xrightarrow{\text{Urease}} \text{no reaction}$$

Methylurea

Not all enzymes exhibit the same degree of specificity. Four classes of enzyme specificity have been observed.

Aminoacyl tRNA synthetases are discussed in Section 20.6. Aminoacyl group transfer reactions were described in Section 15.4.

Hexokinase activity is described in Section 21.3.

Proteolytic enzymes are discussed in Section 19.11.

- **Absolute specificity:** An enzyme that catalyzes the reaction of only one substrate has absolute specificity. *Aminoacyl tRNA synthetases* exhibit absolute specificity. Each must attach the correct amino acid to the correct transfer RNA molecule. If the wrong amino acid is attached to the transfer RNA, it may be mistakenly added to a peptide chain, producing a nonfunctional protein.
- **Group specificity:** An enzyme that catalyzes processes involving similar molecules containing the same functional group has group specificity. *Hexokinase* is a group-specific enzyme that catalyzes the addition of a phosphoryl group to the hexose sugar glucose in the first step of glycolysis. Hexokinase can also add a phosphoryl group to several other six-carbon sugars.
- **Linkage specificity:** An enzyme that catalyzes the formation or breakage of only certain bonds in a molecule has linkage specificity. *Proteases,* such as trypsin, chymotrypsin, and elastase, are enzymes that selectively hydrolyze peptide bonds. Thus, these enzymes are linkage specific.
- **Stereochemical specificity:** An enzyme that can distinguish one enantiomer from the other has stereochemical specificity. Most of the enzymes of the human body show stereochemical specificity. Because we use only D-sugars and L-amino acids, the enzymes involved in digestion and metabolism recognize only those particular stereoisomers.

19.6 The Transition State and Product Formation

How does enzyme-substrate binding result in a faster chemical reaction? To answer this question, we must once again look at the steps of an enzyme-catalyzed reaction, focusing on the steps highlighted in blue:

$$\mathrm{E + S} \underset{}{\overset{\text{Step I}}{\rightleftharpoons}} \mathrm{ES} \underset{}{\overset{\text{Step II}}{\rightleftharpoons}} \mathrm{ES^*} \underset{}{\overset{\text{Step III}}{\rightleftharpoons}} \mathrm{EP} \underset{}{\overset{\text{Step IV}}{\rightleftharpoons}} \mathrm{E + P}$$

E + S	ES	ES*	EP	E + P
Enzyme + substrate	Enzyme–substrate complex	Transition state	Enzyme–product complex	Enzyme + product

After the formation of the enzyme-substrate complex in Step I, the flexible enzyme and substrate interact, changing the substrate into a configuration that is no longer energetically stable (Step II). This is the **transition state,** a state in which the substrate is in an intermediate form, having features of both the substrate and the product. This state favors conversion of the substrate into product (Step III) and release of the product (Step IV). Notice that the enzyme is completely unchanged by these events.

What kinds of transition state changes might occur in the substrate that would make a reaction proceed more rapidly?

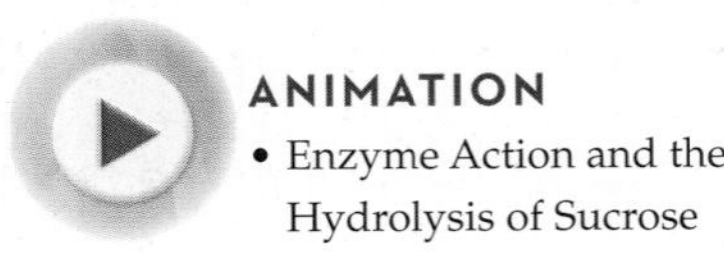

ANIMATION
- Enzyme Action and the Hydrolysis of Sucrose

1. The enzyme might put "stress" on a bond and thereby promote bond breakage, as in the example of sucrase. The enzyme catalyzes the hydrolysis of sucrose into glucose and fructose. The formation of the enzyme-substrate complex (Figures 19.4a and 19.4b) results in a change in the shape of the enzyme. This, in turn, may stretch or distort the bond between glucose and fructose, weakening the bond and allowing it to be broken much more easily than in the absence of the enzyme (Figure 19.4c through e).
2. An enzyme may facilitate a reaction by bringing two reactants into close proximity and in the proper orientation for reaction to occur. If we look at the reaction between glucose and fructose to produce sucrose (Figure 19.5a), we see that each of the sugars has five hydroxyl groups that could undergo condensation to produce a disaccharide. By random molecular collision there is a one in twenty-five chance that the two molecules will collide in the

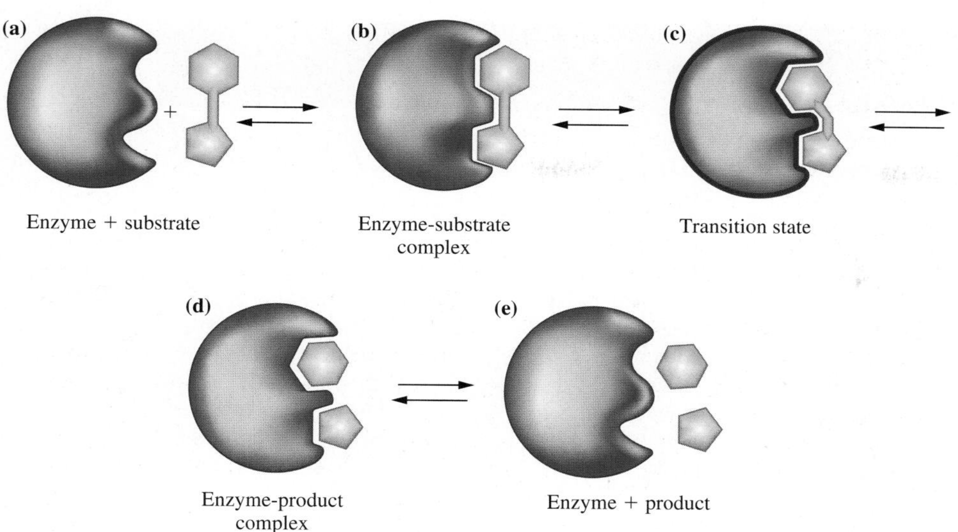

Figure 19.4 Bond breakage is facilitated by the enzyme as a result of stress on a bond. (a, b) The enzyme-substrate complex is formed. (c) In the transition state, the enzyme changes shape and thereby puts stress on the glycosidic bond holding the two monosaccharides together. This lowers the energy of activation of this reaction. (d, e) The bond is broken, and the products are released.

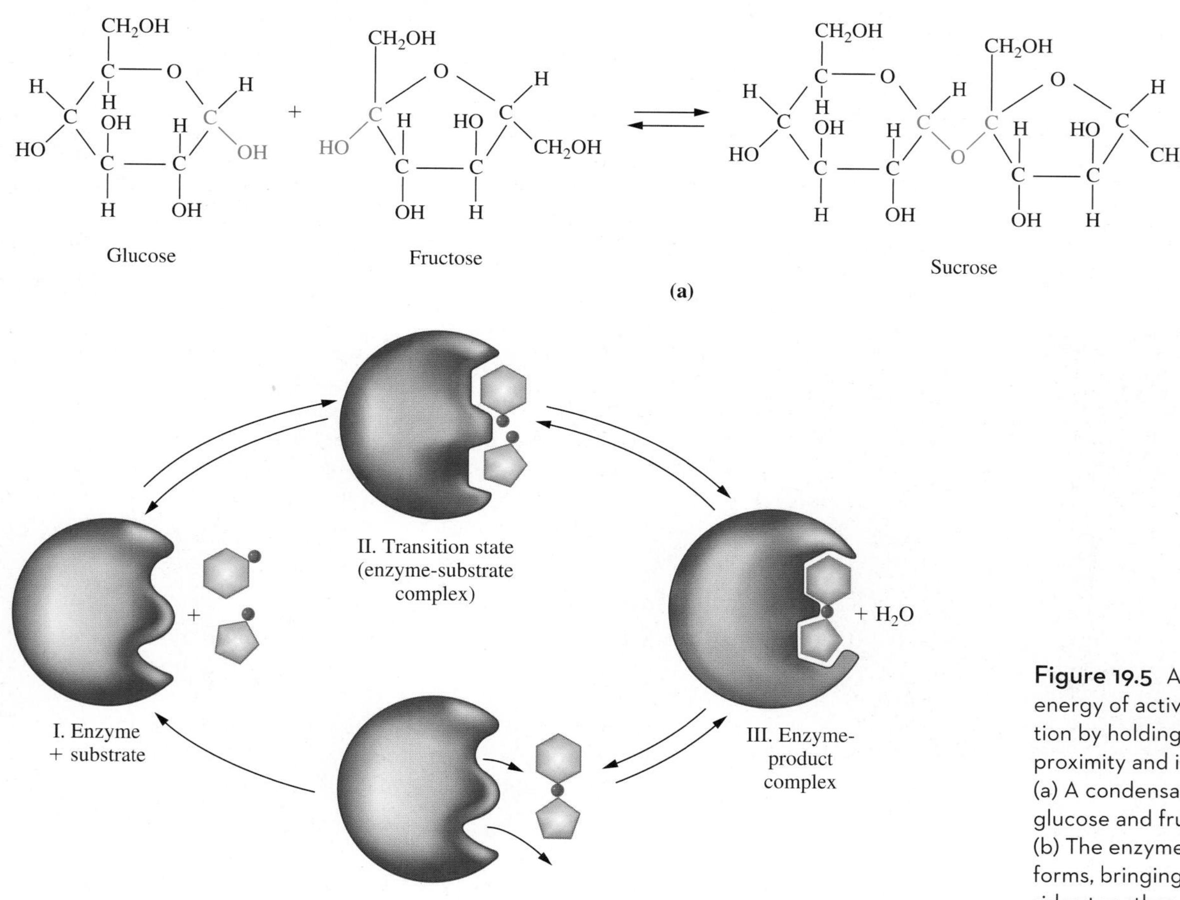

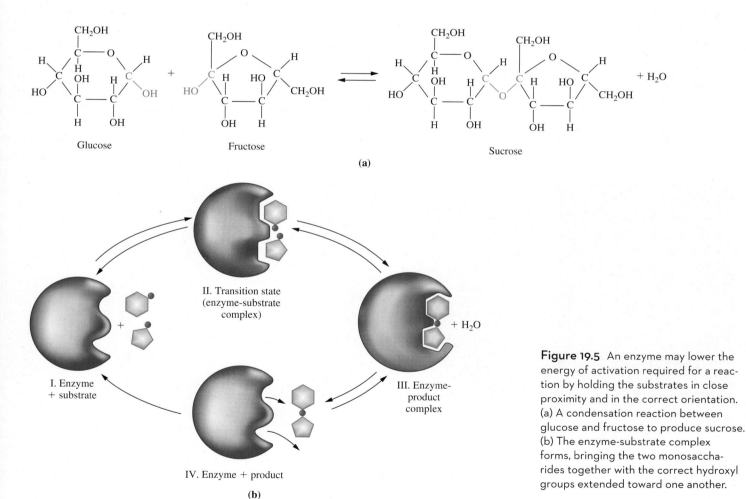

Figure 19.5 An enzyme may lower the energy of activation required for a reaction by holding the substrates in close proximity and in the correct orientation. (a) A condensation reaction between glucose and fructose to produce sucrose. (b) The enzyme-substrate complex forms, bringing the two monosaccharides together with the correct hydroxyl groups extended toward one another.

proper orientation to produce sucrose. The probability that the two will react is actually much less than that because at body temperature, most molecular collisions will not have enough energy to overcome the energy of activation, even if the molecules are in the proper orientation. The enzyme can bring the two molecules close together in the correct alignment (Figure 19.5b), forming the transition state and greatly speeding up the reaction.

A MEDICAL PERSPECTIVE

HIV Protease Inhibitors and Pharmaceutical Drug Design

In 1981 the Centers for Disease Control in Atlanta, Georgia, recognized a new disease syndrome, acquired immune deficiency syndrome (AIDS). The syndrome is characterized by an impaired immune system, a variety of opportunistic infections and cancer, and brain damage that results in dementia. It soon became apparent that the disease was being transmitted by blood and blood products, as well as by sexual contact.

The earliest drugs that proved effective in the treatment of human immunodeficiency virus (HIV) infections all inhibited replication of the genetic material of the virus. While these treatments were initially effective, prolonging the lives of many, it was not long before viral mutants resistant to these drugs began to appear. Clearly, a new approach was needed.

In 1989 a group of scientists revealed the three-dimensional structure of the HIV protease. This structure is shown in the accompanying figure. This enzyme is necessary for viral replication because the virus has an unusual strategy for making all of its proteins. Rather than make each protein individually, it makes large "polyproteins" that must then be cut by the HIV protease to form the final proteins required for viral replication.

Since scientists realized that this enzyme was essential for HIV replication, they decided to engineer a substance that would inhibit the enzyme by binding irreversibly to the active site, in essence plugging it up. The challenge, then, was to design a molecule that would be the plug. Researchers knew the primary structure (amino acid sequence) of the HIV protease from earlier nucleic acid sequencing studies. By 1989 they also had a very complete picture of the three-dimensional nature of the molecule, which they had obtained by X-ray crystallography.

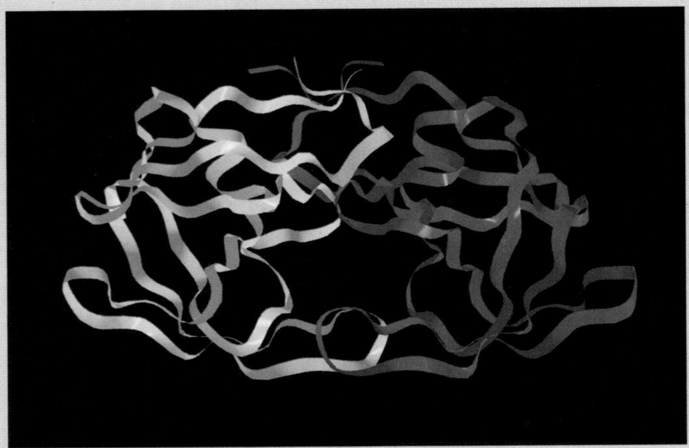

The human immunodeficiency virus protease.

Putting all of this information into a sophisticated computer modeling program, they could look at the protease from any angle. They could see the location of each of the R groups of each of the amino acids in the active site. This kind of information allowed the scientists to design molecules that would be complementary to the shape and charge distribution of the enzyme active site—in other words, structural analogs of the normal protease substrate. It was not long before the scientists had produced several candidates for the HIV protease inhibitor.

But, there are many tests that a drug candidate must pass before it can be introduced into the market as safe and effective. Scientists had to show that the candidate drugs would bind effectively to the HIV protease and block its function, thereby inhibiting virus replication. Properties such as the solubility, the efficiency of absorption by the body, the period of activity in the body, and the toxicity of the drug candidates all had to be determined.

By 1996 there were three protease inhibitors available to combat HIV infection. There are currently seven of these drugs on the market. In many cases development and testing of a drug candidate can take up to 15 years. In the case of the first HIV protease inhibitors, the first three drugs were on the market in less than 8 years. This is a testament both to the urgent need for HIV treatments and to the technology available to attack the problem.

For Further Understanding

- What particular concerns would you have, as a medical researcher, about administering a drug that is a protease inhibitor?
- Often a protease inhibitor is prescribed along with an inhibitor of replication of the viral genetic material. Develop a hypothesis to explain this strategy.

3. The active site of an enzyme may modify the pH of the microenvironment surrounding the substrate. For instance, it may serve as a donor or an acceptor of H^+. This would cause a change in the pH in the vicinity of the substrate without disturbing the normal pH elsewhere in the cell.

Question 19.7 Summarize three ways in which an enzyme might lower the energy of activation of a reaction.

Question 19.8 What is the transition state in an enzyme-catalyzed reaction?

19.7 Cofactors and Coenzymes

LEARNING GOAL

7 Discuss the roles of cofactors and coenzymes in enzyme activity.

In Section 18.6 we saw that some proteins require an additional nonprotein prosthetic group to function. The same is true of some enzymes. In this case, the polypeptide portion is called the **apoenzyme,** and the nonprotein group is called the **cofactor.** Together they form the active enzyme called the **holoenzyme.** Cofactors may be metal ions, organic compounds, or organometallic compounds, and must be bound to the enzyme to maintain the correct shape of the active site (Figure 19.6). Only when the cofactor is bound can the enzyme bind the substrate and catalyze the reaction.

Other enzymes require the temporary binding of a **coenzyme.** Such binding is generally mediated by weak interactions like hydrogen bonds. Coenzymes are organic molecules that serve as carriers of electrons or chemical groups. In chemical reactions, they may either donate groups to the substrate or accept groups that are removed from the substrate. The example in Figure 19.7 shows a coenzyme accepting a functional group from one substrate and donating it to the second substrate in a reaction catalyzed by a transferase.

Often coenzymes contain modified vitamins as part of their structure. A **vitamin** is an organic substance that is required in the diet in only small amounts. Of the water-soluble vitamins, only vitamin C has not been associated with a coenzyme. Table 19.1 is a summary of some coenzymes and the water-soluble vitamins from which they are made.

Nicotinamide adenine dinucleotide (NAD^+), shown in Figure 19.8, is an example of a coenzyme that is of critical importance in the oxidation reactions of the cellular energy-harvesting processes. NAD^+ can accept a hydride ion, a hydrogen atom with two electrons, from the substrate of these reactions. The substrate is oxidized, and the portion of NAD^+ that is derived from the vitamin *niacin* is reduced to produce NADH. The NADH subsequently yields the hydride ion to the first acceptor in an electron transport chain. This regenerates the NAD^+ and provides electrons for the production of ATP, the

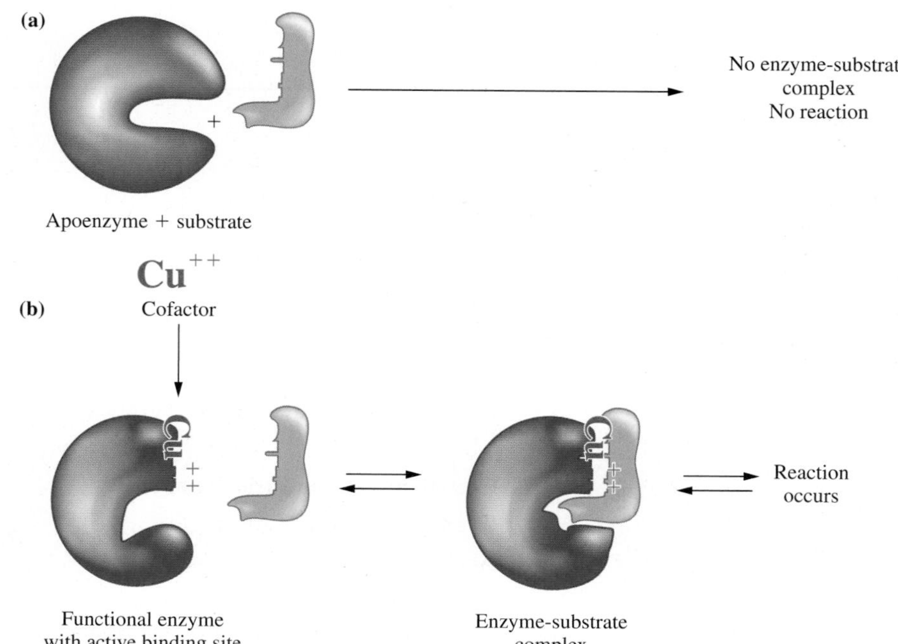

Figure 19.6 (a) The apoenzyme is unable to bind to its substrate. (b) When the required cofactor, in this case a copper ion, Cu^{2+}, is available, it binds to the apoenzyme. Now the active site takes on the correct configuration, the enzyme-substrate complex forms, and the reaction occurs.

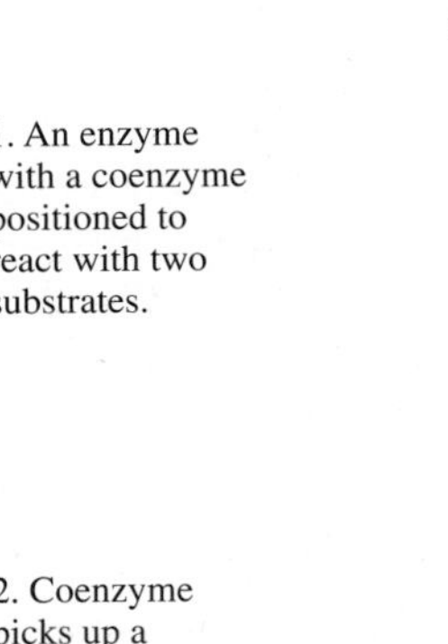

1. An enzyme with a coenzyme positioned to react with two substrates.

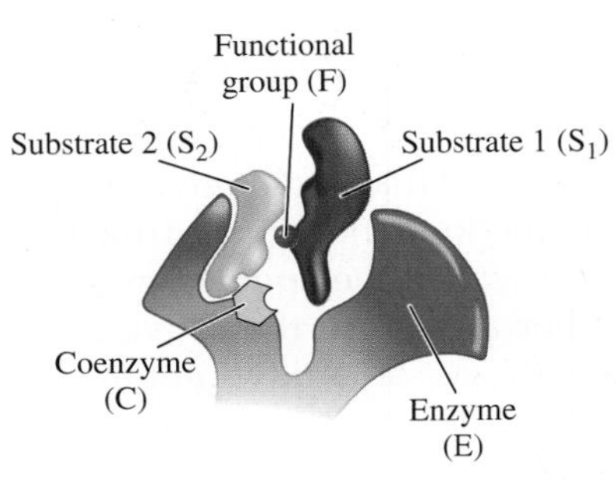

2. Coenzyme picks up a functional group from substrate 1.

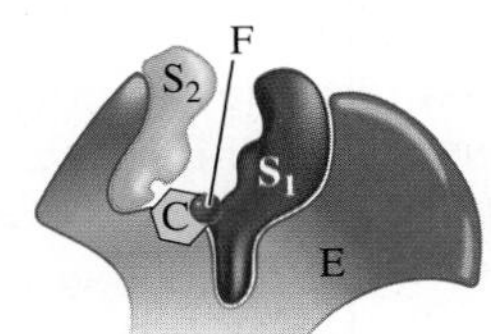

3. Coenzyme transfers the functional group to substrate 2.

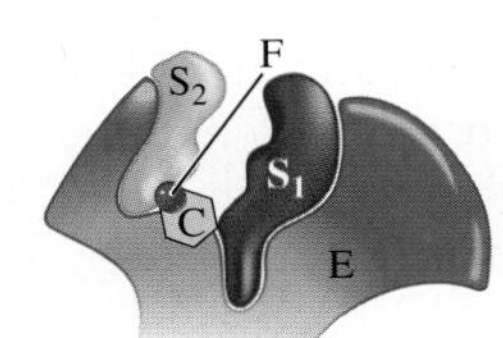

4. Products are released from enzyme.

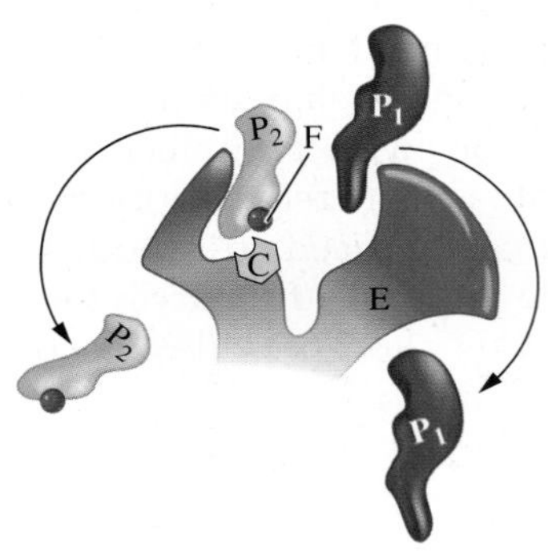

Figure 19.7 Some enzymes require a coenzyme to facilitate the reaction.

TABLE 19.1 The Water-Soluble Vitamins and Their Coenzymes

Vitamin	Coenzyme	Function
Thiamine (B_1)	Thiamine pyrophosphate	Decarboxylation reactions
Riboflavin (B_2)	Flavin mononucleotide (FMN)	Carrier of H atoms
	Flavin adenine dinucleotide (FAD)	
Niacin (B_3)	Nicotinamide adenine dinucleotide (NAD^+)	Carrier of hydride ions
	Nicotinamide adenine dinucleotide phosphate ($NADP^+$)	
Pyridoxine (B_6)	Pyridoxal phosphate	Carriers of amino and carboxyl groups
	Pyridoxamine phosphate	
Cyanocobalamin (B_{12})	Deoxyadenosyl cobalamin	Coenzyme in amino acid metabolism
Folic acid	Tetrahydrofolic acid	Coenzyme for 1-C transfer
Pantothenic acid	Coenzyme A	Acyl group carrier
Biotin	Biocytin	Coenzyme in CO_2 fixation
Ascorbic acid	Unknown	Hydroxylation of proline and lysine in collagen

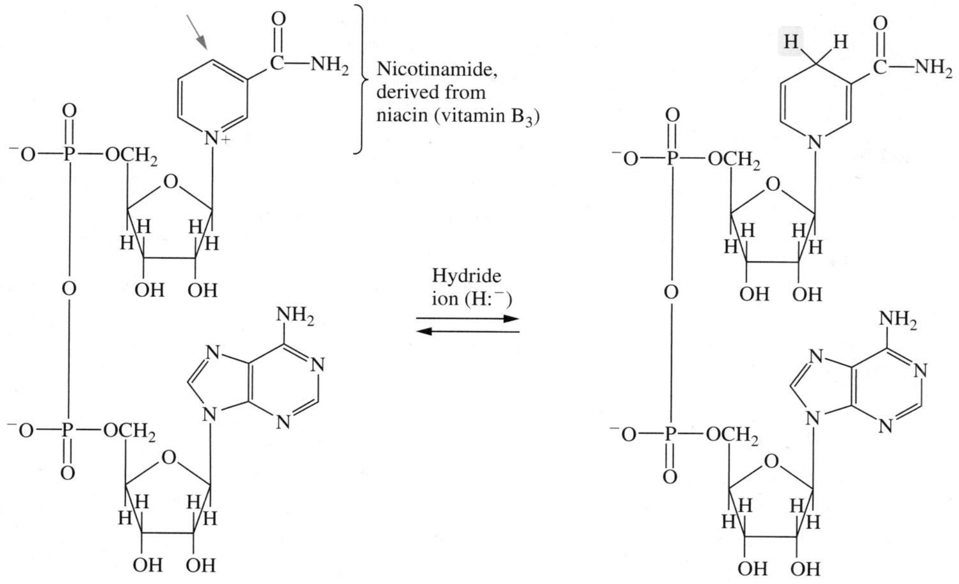

NAD^+
Nicotinamide adenine dinucleotide
(oxidized form)

NADH
(reduced form)

(a)

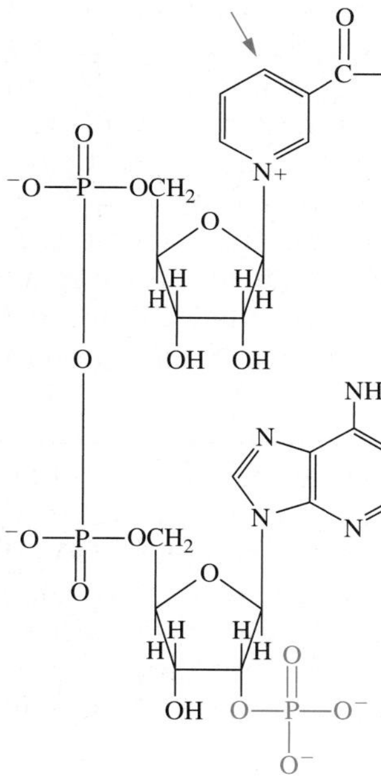

$NADP^+$
Nicotinamide adenine dinucleotide phosphate
(oxidized form)

(b)

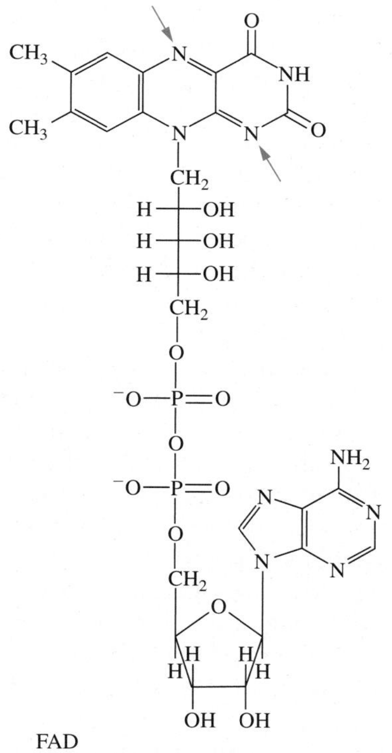

FAD
Flavin adenine dinucleotide
(oxidized form)

(c)

Figure 19.8 The structure of three coenzymes. (a) The oxidized and reduced forms of nicotinamide adenine dinucleotide. (b) The oxidized form of the closely related hydride ion carrier, nicotinamide adenine dinucleotide phosphate ($NADP^+$), which accepts hydride ions at the same position as NAD^+ (colored arrow). (c) The oxidized form of flavin adenine dinucleotide (FAD) accepts hydrogen atoms at the positions indicated by the colored arrows.

ANIMATIONS
- How NAD^+ Works
- B Vitamins

chemical energy required by the cell. Also shown in Figure 19.8 is the hydride carrier $NADP^+$ and the hydrogen atom carrier FAD. Both are used in the oxidation-reduction reactions that harvest energy for the cell. Unlike NADH and $FADH_2$, NADPH serves as "reducing power" for the cell by donating hydride ions in biochemical reactions. Like NAD^+, $NADP^+$ is derived from niacin. FAD is made from the vitamin *riboflavin.*

Question 19.9 Why does the body require the water-soluble vitamins?

Question 19.10 What are the coenzymes formed from each of the following vitamins? What are the functions of each of these coenzymes?

a. Pantothenic acid b. Niacin c. Riboflavin

19.8 Environmental Effects

Effect of pH

LEARNING GOAL

8 Explain how pH and temperature affect the rate of an enzyme-catalyzed reaction.

Most enzymes are active only within a very narrow pH range. The cytoplasm of the cell has a pH of 7, and most enzymes function best at this pH. A plot of reaction rate versus pH for a typical enzyme is shown in Figure 19.9.

The pH at which an enzyme functions optimally is called the **pH optimum.** Making the solution more basic or more acidic sharply decreases the rate of the reaction. These pH changes alter the degree of ionization of amino acid R groups in the protein, as well as the extent to which they can hydrogen bond. This causes the enzyme to lose its biologically active configuration; it becomes *denatured.* Less drastic changes in the R groups of an enzyme active site can also destroy the ability to form the enzyme-substrate complex.

Some environments within the body must function at a pH far from 7. For instance, the pH of the stomach is approximately 2 as a result of the secretion of hydrochloric acid by cells of the stomach lining. The proteolytic digestive enzyme *pepsin* must effectively degrade proteins at this extreme pH. In the case of pepsin the enzyme has evolved an amino acid sequence that can maintain a stable tertiary structure at pH 2 and is most active in the hydrolysis of peptides that have been denatured by very low pH. Thus pepsin has a pH optimum of 2.

In a similar fashion, another proteolytic enzyme, *trypsin,* functions under the conditions of higher pH found in the intestine. Both pepsin and trypsin cleave peptide bonds by virtually identical mechanisms, yet their amino acid sequences have evolved so that they are stable and active in very different environments.

The body has used adaptation of enzymes to different environments to protect itself against one of its own destructive defense mechanisms. Within the cytoplasm of a cell are organelles called *lysosomes.* Christian de Duve, who discovered lysosomes in 1956, called them "suicide bags" because they are membrane-bound vesicles containing about fifty different kinds of hydrolases that degrade large biological molecules into small molecules that are useful for energy-harvesting reactions. For instance, some of the enzymes in the lysosomes can degrade proteins to amino acids, others hydrolyze polysaccharides into monosaccharides, still others degrade lipids and nucleic acids.

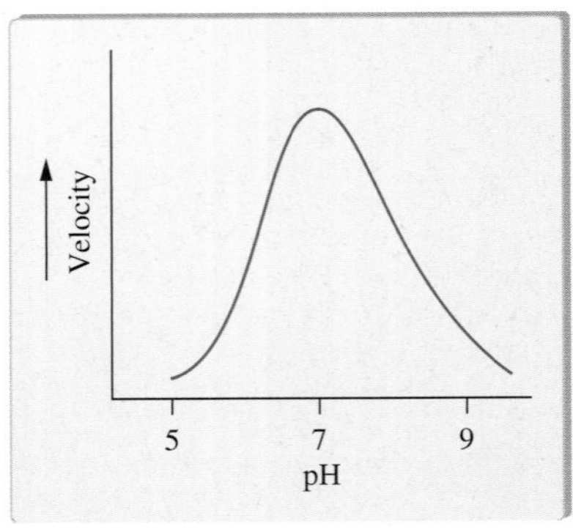

Figure 19.9 Effect of pH on the rate of an enzyme-catalyzed reaction. This enzyme functions most efficiently at pH 7. The rate of the reaction falls rapidly as the solution is made either more acidic or more basic.

If the hydrolytic enzymes of the lysosome were accidentally released into the cytoplasm of the cell, the result would be the destruction of cellular macromolecules and death of the cell. Because of this danger, the cell invests a great deal of energy in maintaining the integrity of the lysosomal membranes. An additional protective mechanism relies on the fact that lysosomal enzymes function optimally at an acid pH (pH 4.8). Should some of these enzymes leak out of the lysosome or should a lysosome accidentally rupture, the cytoplasmic pH of 7.0–7.3 renders them inactive.

A MEDICAL PERSPECTIVE

α_1-Antitrypsin and Familial Emphysema

Nearly two million people in the United States suffer from emphysema. Emphysema is a respiratory disease caused by destruction of the alveoli, the tiny, elastic air sacs of the lung. This damage results from the irreversible destruction of a protein called *elastin,* which is needed for the strength and flexibility of the walls of the alveoli. When elastin is destroyed, the small air passages in the lungs, called *bronchioles,* become narrower or may even collapse. This severely limits the flow of air into and out of the lung, causing respiratory distress, and in extreme conditions, death.

Some people have a genetic predisposition to emphysema. This is called *familial emphysema.* These individuals have a genetic defect in the gene that encodes the human plasma protein α_1-antitrypsin. As the name suggests, α_1-antitrypsin is an inhibitor of the proteolytic enzyme trypsin. But, as we have seen in this chapter, trypsin is just one member of a large family of proteolytic enzymes called the *serine proteases.* In the case of the α_1-antitrypsin activity in the lung, it is the inhibition of the enzyme elastase that is the critical event.

Elastase damages or destroys elastin, which in turn promotes the development of emphysema. People with normal levels of α_1-antitrypsin are protected from familial emphysema because their α_1-antitrypsin inhibits elastase and, thus, protects the elastin. The result is healthy alveoli in the lungs. However, individuals with a genetic predisposition to emphysema have very low levels of α_1-antitrypsin. This is due to a mutation that causes a single amino acid substitution in the protein chain. Because elastase in the lungs is not effectively controlled, severe lung damage characteristic of emphysema occurs.

Emphysema is also caused by cigarette smoking. Is there a link between these two forms of emphysema? The answer is yes; research has revealed that components of cigarette smoke cause the oxidation of a methionine near the amino terminus of α_1-antitrypsin. This chemical damage destroys α_1-antitrypsin activity. There are enzymes in the lung that reduce the methionine, converting it back to its original chemical form and restoring α_1-antitrypsin activity. However, it is obvious that over a long period, smoking seriously reduces the level of α_1-antitrypsin activity. The accumulated lung damage results in emphysema in many chronic smokers.

At the current time the standard treatment of emphysema is the use of inhaled oxygen. Studies have shown that intravenous infusion of α_1-antitrypsin isolated from human blood is both safe and effective. However, the level of α_1-antitrypsin in the blood must be maintained by repeated administration.

The α_1-antitrypsin gene has been cloned. In experiments with sheep it was shown that the protein remains stable when administered as an aerosol. It is still functional after it has passed through the pulmonary epithelium. This research offers hope of an effective treatment for this frightful disease.

For Further Understanding

- Draw the structure of methionine and write an equation showing the reversible oxidation of this amino acid.
- Develop a hypothesis to explain why an excess of elastase causes emphysema. What is the role of elastase in this disease?

Effect of Temperature

Enzymes are rapidly destroyed if the temperature of their environment rises much above 37°C, but they remain stable at much lower temperatures. This is why enzymes used for clinical assays are stored in refrigerators or freezers before use. Figure 19.10 shows the effects of temperature on enzyme-catalyzed and uncatalyzed reactions. The rate of the uncatalyzed reaction steadily increases

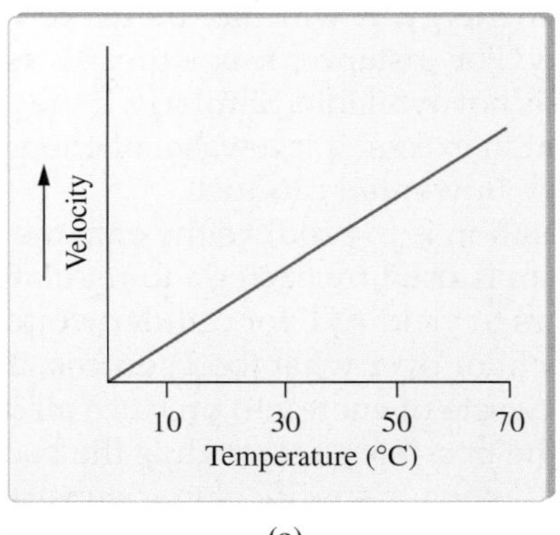

(a)

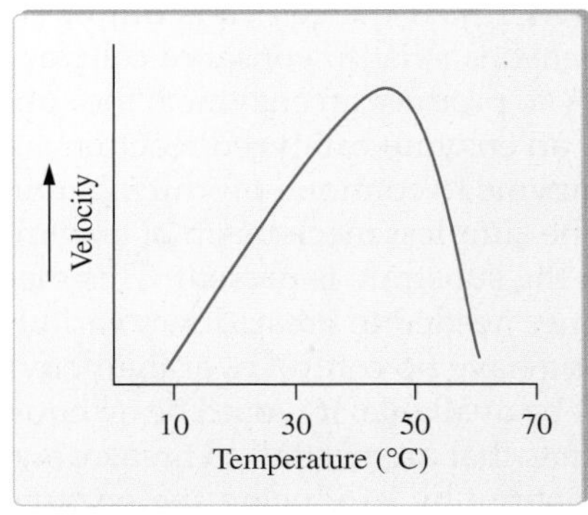

(b)

Figure 19.10 Effect of temperature on (a) uncatalyzed reactions and (b) enzyme-catalyzed reactions.

with increasing temperature because more collisions occur with sufficient energy to overcome the energy barrier for the reaction. The rate of an enzyme-catalyzed reaction also increases with modest increases in temperature because there are increasing numbers of collisions between the enzyme and the substrate. At the **temperature optimum,** the enzyme is functioning optimally and the rate of the reaction is maximal. Above the temperature optimum, increasing temperature begins to increase the vibrational energy of the bonds within the enzyme. Eventually, so many bonds and weak interactions are disrupted that the enzyme becomes denatured, and the reaction stops.

Because heating enzymes and other proteins destroys their three-dimensional structure, and hence their activity, a cell cannot survive very high temperatures. Thus, heat is an effective means of sterilizing medical instruments and solutions for transfusion or clinical tests. Although instruments can be sterilized by dry heat (160°C) applied for at least 2 hours (h) in a dry air oven, autoclaving is a quicker, more reliable procedure. The autoclave works on the principle of the pressure cooker. Air is pumped out of the chamber, and steam under pressure is pumped into the chamber until a pressure of 2 atmospheres (atm) is achieved. The pressure causes the temperature of the steam, which would be 100°C at atmospheric pressure, to rise to 121°C. Within 20 minutes (min), all the bacteria and viruses are killed. This is the most effective means of destroying the very heat-resistant endospores that are formed by many bacteria of clinical interest. These bacteria include the genera *Bacillus* and *Clostridium,* which are responsible for such unpleasant and deadly diseases as anthrax, gas gangrene, tetanus, and botulism food poisoning.

See also the Introduction to this chapter.

However, not all enzymes are inactivated by heating, even to rather high temperatures. Certain bacteria live in such out-of-the-way places as coal slag heaps, which are actually burning. Others live in deep vents on the ocean floor where temperatures and pressures are extremely high. Still others grow in the hot springs of Yellowstone National Park, where they thrive at temperatures near the boiling point of water. These organisms, along with their enzymes, survive under such incredible conditions because the amino acid sequences of their proteins dictate structures that are stable at such seemingly impossible temperature extremes.

Question 19.11 How does a decrease in pH alter the activity of an enzyme?

Question 19.12 Heating is an effective mechanism for killing bacteria on surgical instruments. How does elevated temperature result in cellular death?

19.9 Regulation of Enzyme Activity

LEARNING GOAL

9 Describe the mechanisms used by cells to regulate enzyme activity.

Enzyme activity is often regulated by the cell. Often the reason for this is to conserve energy. If the cell runs out of chemical energy, it will die; therefore many mechanisms exist to conserve cellular energy. For instance, it is a great waste of energy to produce an enzyme if the substrate is not available. Similarly, if the product of an enzyme-catalyzed reaction is present in excess, it is a waste of energy for the enzyme to continue producing more of the unwanted product.

The simplest mechanism of enzyme regulation is to produce the enzyme only when the substrate is present. This mechanism is used by bacteria to regulate the enzymes needed to break down various sugars to yield ATP for cellular work. The bacteria have no control over their environment or over what food sources, if any, might be available. It would be an enormous waste of energy to produce all of the enzymes that are needed to break down all the possible sugars. Thus the bacteria save energy by producing the enzymes only when a specific sugar substrate is available. Other mechanisms for regulating enzyme activity include use of allosteric enzymes, feedback inhibition, production of proenzymes, and protein modification. Let's take a look at these regulatory mechanisms in some detail.

Allosteric Enzymes

Allosteric means "other forms."

One type of enzyme regulation involves enzymes that have more than a single binding site. These enzymes, called **allosteric enzymes,** have active sites that can be altered by binding of small molecules called *effector molecules.* As shown in Figure 19.11, the effector binding alters the shape of the active site of the enzyme. The result can be to convert the active site to an inactive configuration, **negative allosterism,** or to convert the active site to the active configuration, **positive allosterism.** In either case, binding of the effector molecule regulates enzyme activity by determining whether it will be active or inactive.

In upcoming chapters we will study metabolic pathways. A metabolic pathway is a series of biochemical reactions that breaks down or synthesizes one or more biological molecules. One of these is glycolysis, which is the first stage of the breakdown of carbohydrates to produce ATP energy for the cell. This pathway must be responsive to the demands of the body. When more energy is required, the reactions of the pathway should occur more quickly, producing more ATP. However, if the energy demand is low, the reactions should slow down.

The third reaction in glycolysis is the transfer of a phosphoryl group from an ATP molecule to a molecule of fructose-6-phosphate. This reaction, shown here, is catalyzed by an enzyme called *phosphofructokinase:*

$$\text{Fructose-6-phosphate} + \text{ATP} \xrightarrow{\text{Phosphofructokinase}} \text{Fructose-1,6-bisphosphate} + \text{ADP}$$

Fructose-6-phosphate　　　　Fructose-1,6-bisphosphate

Phosphofructokinase activity is sensitive to both positive and negative allosterism. For instance, when ATP is present in abundance, a signal that the body has sufficient energy, it binds to an effector binding site on phosphofructokinase. This inhibits the activity of the enzyme and, thus, slows the entire pathway. An abundance of AMP, which is a precursor of ATP, is evidence that the body needs to

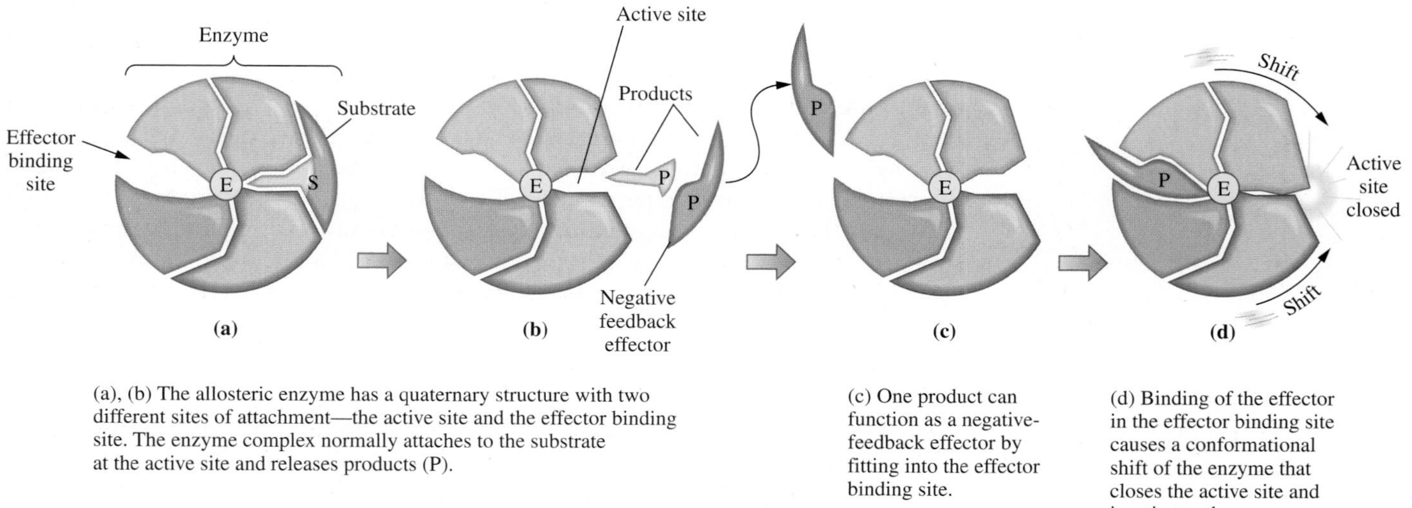

(a), (b) The allosteric enzyme has a quaternary structure with two different sites of attachment—the active site and the effector binding site. The enzyme complex normally attaches to the substrate at the active site and releases products (P).

(c) One product can function as a negative-feedback effector by fitting into the effector binding site.

(d) Binding of the effector in the effector binding site causes a conformational shift of the enzyme that closes the active site and inactivates the enzyme.

Figure 19.11 A mechanism of negative allosterism. This is an example of feedback inhibition.

make ATP. When AMP binds to an effector binding site on phosphofructokinase, enzyme activity is increased, speeding up the reaction and the entire pathway.

Feedback Inhibition

Allosteric enzymes are the basis for **feedback inhibition** of biochemical pathways. This system functions on the same principle as the thermostat on your furnace. You set the thermostat at 70°F; the furnace turns on and produces heat until the sensor in the thermostat registers a room temperature of 70°F. It then signals the furnace to shut off.

ANIMATIONS
- A Biochemical Pathway
- Feedback Inhibition of Biochemical Pathways

Feedback inhibition usually regulates pathways of enzymes involved in the synthesis of a biological molecule. Such a pathway can be shown schematically as follows:

$$A \xrightarrow{E_1} B \xrightarrow{E_2} C \xrightarrow{E_3} D \xrightarrow{E_4} E \xrightarrow{E_5} F$$

In this pathway the starting material, *A*, is converted to *B* by the enzyme E_1. Enzyme E_2 immediately converts *B* to *C*, and so on until the final product, *F*, has been synthesized. If *F* is no longer needed, it is a waste of cellular energy to continue to produce it.

To avoid this waste of energy, the cell uses feedback inhibition, in which the product can shut off the entire pathway for its own synthesis. This is the result of the fact that the product, *F*, acts as a negative allosteric effector on one of the early enzymes of the pathway. For instance, enzyme E_1 may have an effector-binding site for *F*. When *F* is present in excess, it binds to the effector-binding site, causing the active site to close so that it cannot bind to substrate *A*. Thus *A* is not converted to *B*. If no *B* is produced, there is no substrate for enzyme E_2, and the entire pathway ceases to operate. The product, *F*, has turned off all the steps involved in its own synthesis, just as the heat produced by the furnace is ultimately responsible for turning off the furnace itself.

When the concentration of *F* drops, it will dissociate from the effector binding site. When this occurs, the enzyme is once again active. Thus, feedback inhibition is an effective metabolic on-off switch.

Proenzymes

Another means of regulating enzyme activity involves the production of the enzyme in an inactive form called a **proenzyme.** The proenzyme is converted by proteolysis (hydrolysis of the protein) to the active form when it has reached the site of its activity. On first examination it seems wasteful to add a step to the synthesis of an enzyme. But consider for a moment the very destructive nature of some of the enzymes that are necessary for life. The enzymes pepsin, trypsin, and chymotrypsin are all proteolytic enzymes of the digestive tract. They are necessary to life because they degrade dietary proteins into amino acids that are used by the cell. But what would happen to the cells that produce these enzymes if they were synthesized in active form? Those cells would be destroyed. Thus the cells of the stomach that produce pepsin actually produce an inactive proenzyme, called *pepsinogen*. Pepsinogen has an additional forty-two amino acids. In the presence of stomach acid and previously activated pepsin, the extra forty-two amino acids are cleaved off, and the proenzyme is transformed into the active enzyme. Table 19.2 lists several other proenzymes and the enzymes that convert them to active form.

Protein Modification

Protein modification is another mechanism that the cell can use to turn an enzyme on or off. This is a process in which a chemical group is covalently added to or removed from the protein. This covalent modification either activates the enzyme or turns it off.

The most common type of protein modification is phosphorylation or dephosphorylation of an enzyme. Typically, the phosphoryl group is added to (or removed

TABLE 19.2 Proenzymes of the Digestive Tract

Proenzyme	Activator	Enzyme
Proelastase	Trypsin	Elastase
Trypsinogen	Trypsin	Trypsin
Chymotrypsinogen A	Trypsin + chymotrypsin	Chymotrypsin
Pepsinogen	Acid pH + pepsin	Pepsin
Procarboxypeptidases	Trypsin	Carboxypeptidase A, Carboxypeptidase B

from) the R group of a serine, tyrosine, or threonine in the protein chain of the enzyme. Notice that these three amino acids have a free —OH in their R group, which serves as the site for the addition of the phosphoryl group.

The covalent modification of an enzyme's structure is catalyzed by other enzymes. *Protein kinases* add phosphoryl groups to a target enzyme, while *phosphatases* remove them. For some enzymes it is the phosphorylated form that is active. For instance, in adipose tissue, phosphorylation activates the enzyme triacylglycerol lipase, an enzyme that breaks triglycerides down to fatty acids and glycerol. Glycogen phosphorylase, an enzyme involved in the breakdown of glycogen, is also activated by the addition of a phosphoryl group. However, for some enzymes phosphorylation inactivates the enzyme. This is true for glycogen synthase, an enzyme involved in the synthesis of glycogen. When this enzyme is phosphorylated, it becomes inactive.

The convenient aspect of this type of regulation is the reversibility. An enzyme can quickly be turned on or off in response to environmental or physiological conditions.

19.10 Inhibition of Enzyme Activity

LEARNING GOAL

10 Discuss the mechanisms by which certain chemicals inhibit enzyme activity.

Many chemicals can bind to enzymes and either eliminate or drastically reduce their catalytic ability. These chemicals, called *enzyme inhibitors,* have been used for hundreds of years. When she poisoned her victims with arsenic, Lucretia Borgia was unaware that it was binding to the thiol groups of cysteine amino acids in the proteins of her victims and thus interfering with the formation of disulfide bonds needed to stabilize the tertiary structure of enzymes. However, she was well aware of the deadly toxicity of heavy metal salts like arsenic and mercury. When you take penicillin for a bacterial infection, you are taking another enzyme inhibitor. Penicillin inhibits several enzymes that are involved in the synthesis of bacterial cell walls.

Enzyme inhibitors are classified on the basis of whether the inhibition is reversible or irreversible, competitive or noncompetitive. Reversibility deals with whether the inhibitor will eventually dissociate from the enzyme, releasing it in the active form. Competition refers to whether the inhibitor is a structural analog, or look-alike, of the natural substrate. If so, the inhibitor and substrate will compete for the enzyme active site.

Irreversible Inhibitors

Irreversible enzyme inhibitors, such as arsenic, usually bind very tightly, sometimes even covalently, to the enzyme. This generally involves binding of the inhibitor to one of the R groups of an amino acid in the active site. Inhibitor binding may block the active site binding groups so that the enzyme-substrate complex cannot form. Alternatively, an inhibitor may interfere with the catalytic groups of the active site, thereby effectively eliminating catalysis. Irreversible inhibitors, which include snake venoms and nerve gases, generally inhibit many different enzymes.

CHEMISTRY AT THE CRIME SCENE

Enzymes, Nerve Agents, and Poisoning

The transmission of nerve impulses at the *neuromuscular junction* involves many steps, one of which is the activity of a critical enzyme, called *acetylcholinesterase,* which catalyzes the hydrolysis of the chemical messenger, *acetylcholine,* that initiated the nerve impulse. The need for this enzyme activity becomes clear when we consider the events that begin with a message from the nerve cell and end in the appropriate response by the muscle cell. Acetylcholine is a *neurotransmitter,* that is, a chemical messenger that transmits a message from the nerve cell to the muscle cell. Acetylcholine is stored in membrane-bound bags, called *synaptic vesicles,* in the nerve cell ending.

Acetylcholinesterase comes into play in the following way. The arrival of a nerve impulse at the end plate of the nerve axon causes an influx of Ca^{2+}. This causes the acetylcholine-containing vesicles to migrate to the nerve cell membrane that is in contact with the muscle cell. This is called the *presynaptic membrane.* The vesicles fuse with the presynaptic membrane and release the neurotransmitter. The acetylcholine then diffuses across the *nerve synapse* (the space between the nerve and muscle cells) and binds to the acetylcholine receptor protein (R) in the *postsynaptic membrane* of the muscle cell. This receptor then opens pores in the membrane through which Na^+ and K^+ ions flow into and out of the cell, respectively. This generates the nerve impulse and causes the muscle to contract. If acetylcholine remains at the neuromuscular junction, it will continue to stimulate the muscle contraction. To stop this continued stimulation, acetylcholine is hydrolyzed, and hence, destroyed by acetylcholinesterase. When this happens, nerve stimulation ceases.

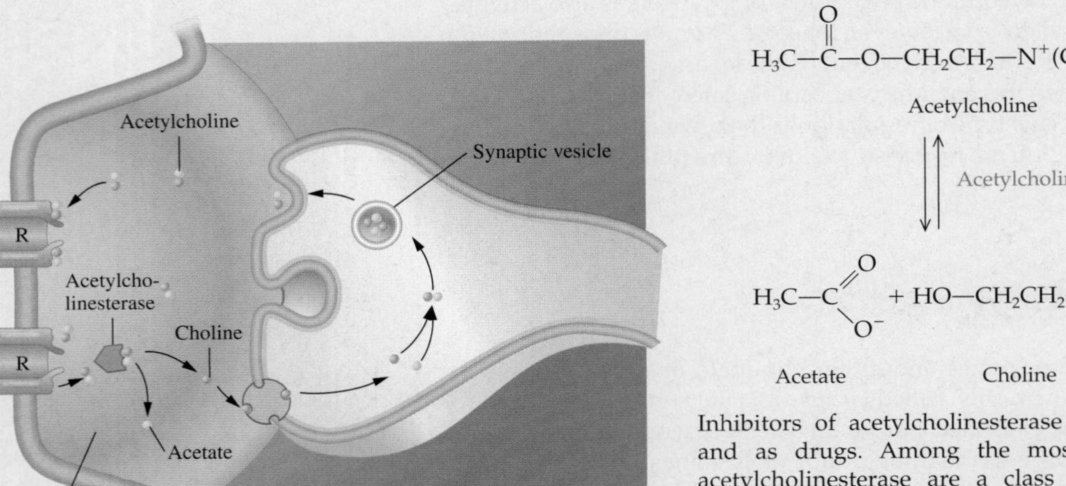

Schematic diagram of the synapse at the neuromuscular junction.

$$H_3C{-}\overset{\overset{\large O}{\|}}{C}{-}O{-}CH_2CH_2{-}N^+(CH_3)_3 + H_2O$$

Acetylcholine

$$\rightleftarrows \quad \text{Acetylcholinesterase}$$

$$H_3C{-}C\begin{smallmatrix}\nearrow O \\ \searrow O^-\end{smallmatrix} + HO{-}CH_2CH_2{-}N^+(CH_3)_3 + H^+$$

Acetate Choline

Inhibitors of acetylcholinesterase are used both as poisons and as drugs. Among the most important inhibitors of acetylcholinesterase are a class of compounds known as *organophosphates.* One of these is the nerve agent Sarin (isopropylmethylfluorophosphate). Sarin forms a covalently bonded intermediate with the active site of acetylcholinesterase. Thus, it acts as an irreversible, noncompetitive inhibitor.

Reversible, Competitive Inhibitors

See A Medical Perspective: Fooling the AIDS Virus with "Look-Alike" Nucleotides online.

Reversible, competitive enzyme inhibitors are often referred to as **structural analogs,** that is, they are molecules that resemble the structure and charge distribution of the natural substrate for a particular enzyme. Because of this resemblance, the inhibitor can occupy the enzyme active site. However, no reaction can occur, and enzyme activity is inhibited (Figure 19.12). This inhibition is competitive because the inhibitor and the substrate compete for binding to the enzyme active site. Thus, the degree of inhibition depends on their relative concentrations. If the inhibitor is in excess or binds more strongly to the active site, it will occupy the active site more frequently, and enzyme activity will be greatly decreased. On

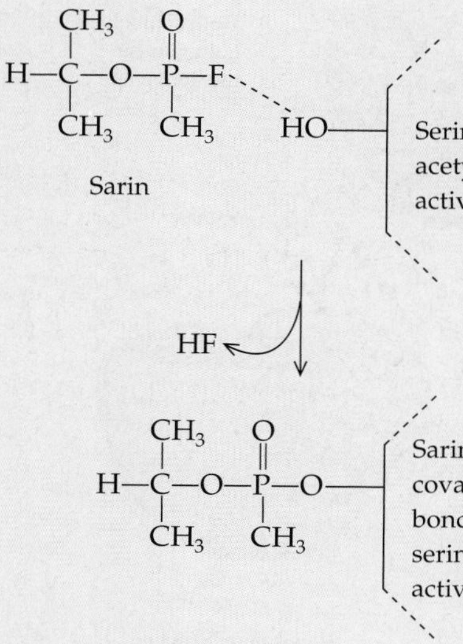

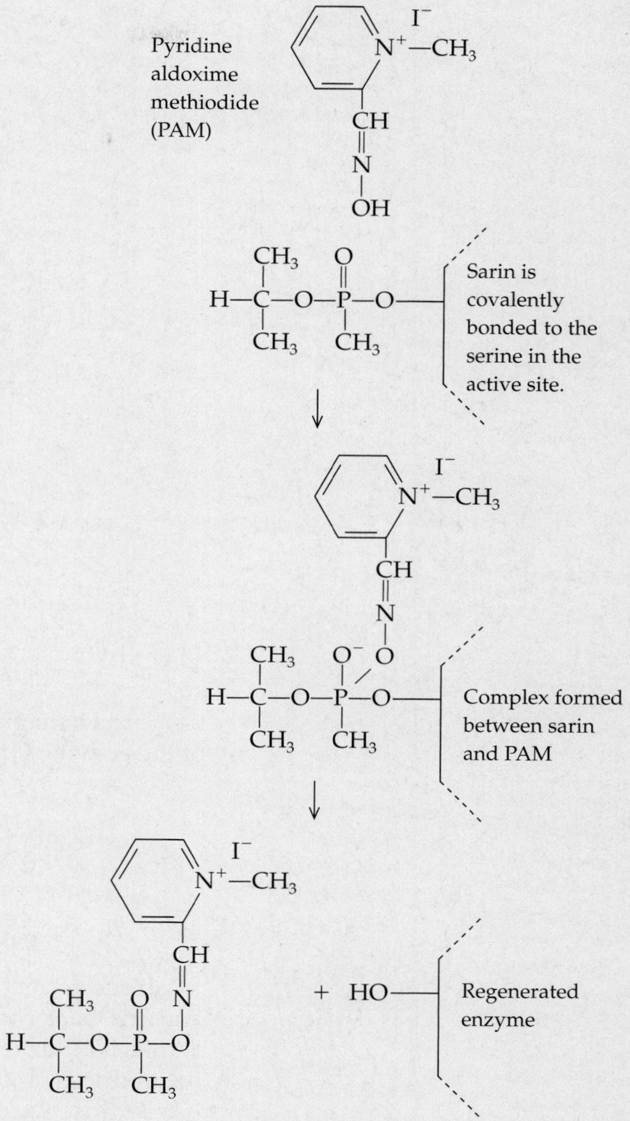

Sarin

Serine in the acetylcholinesterase active site

HF

Sarin is covalently bonded to the serine in the active site.

Pyridine aldoxime methiodide (PAM)

Sarin is covalently bonded to the serine in the active site.

Complex formed between sarin and PAM

Regenerated enzyme

The covalent intermediate is stable, and acetylcholinesterase is therefore inactive, no longer able to break down acetylcholine. Nerve transmission continues, resulting in muscle spasm. Death may occur as a result of laryngeal spasm. Antidotes for poisoning by organophosphates, which include many insecticides and nerve gases, have been developed. The antidotes work by reversing the effects of the inhibitor. One of these antidotes is known as *PAM,* an acronym for *pyridine aldoxime methiodide.* This molecule displaces the organophosphate group from the active site of the enzyme, alleviating the effects of the poison.

For Further Understanding

- Botulinum toxin inhibits release of neurotransmitters from the presynaptic membrane. What symptoms do you predict would result from this?
- Why must Na^+ and K^+ enter and exit the cell through a protein channel?

the other hand, if the natural substrate is present in excess, it will more frequently occupy the active site, and there will be little inhibition.

The sulfa drugs, the first antimicrobics to be discovered, are **competitive inhibitors** of a bacterial enzyme needed for the synthesis of the vitamin folic acid. *Folic acid* is a vitamin required for the transfer of methyl groups in the biosynthesis of methionine and the nitrogenous bases required to make DNA and RNA. Humans cannot synthesize folic acid and must obtain it from the diet. Bacteria, on the other hand, must make folic acid because they cannot take it in from the environment.

para-Aminobenzoic acid (PABA) is the substrate for an early step in folic acid synthesis. The sulfa drugs, the prototype of which was discovered in the 1930s by

In addition to the folic acid supplied in the diet, we obtain folic acid from our intestinal bacteria.

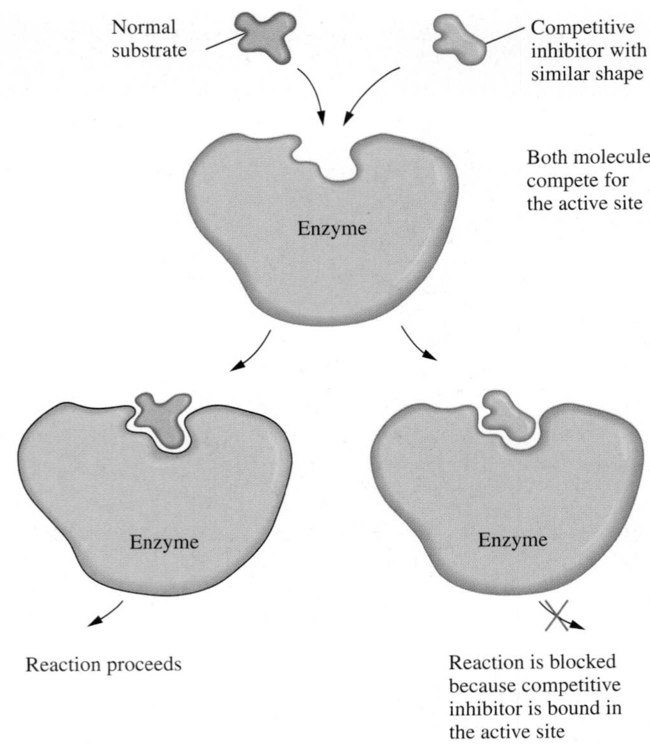

Figure 19.12 Competitive inhibition.

Gerhard Domagk, are structural analogs of PABA and thus competitive inhibitors of the enzyme that uses PABA as its normal substrate.

$$H_2N-C_6H_4-\overset{\overset{O}{\|}}{C}-OH \qquad H_2N-C_6H_4-\underset{\underset{O}{\|}}{\overset{\overset{O}{\|}}{S}}-NH_2$$

p-Aminobenzoic acid — Sulfanilamide

If the correct substrate (PABA) is bound by the enzyme, the reaction occurs, and the bacterium lives. However, if the sulfa drug is present in excess over PABA, it binds more frequently to the active site of the enzyme. No folic acid will be produced, and the bacterial cell will die.

Because we obtain our folic acid from our diets, sulfa drugs do not harm us. However, bacteria are selectively killed. Luckily, we can capitalize on this property for the treatment of bacterial infections, and as a result, sulfa drugs have saved countless lives. Although bacterial infection was the major cause of death before the discovery of sulfa drugs and other antibiotics, death caused by bacterial infection is relatively rare at present.

Reversible, Noncompetitive Inhibitors

Reversible, noncompetitive enzyme inhibitors bind to R groups of amino acids or perhaps to the metal ion cofactors. Unlike the situation of irreversible inhibition, however, the binding is weak, and the enzyme activity is restored when the inhibitor dissociates from the enzyme-inhibitor complex. Binding of these inhibitors modifies the shape of the active site in much the same way that the binding of an allosteric effector does. Since this binding is nonspecific, these inhibitors inactivate a broad range of enzymes.

Question 19.13 Why are irreversible inhibitors considered to be poisons?

Question 19.14 Explain the difference between an irreversible inhibitor and a reversible, noncompetitive inhibitor.

Question 19.15 What is a structural analog?

Question 19.16 How can structural analogs serve as enzyme inhibitors?

19.11 Proteolytic Enzymes

Proteolytic enzymes break the peptide bonds that maintain the primary protein structure. *Chymotrypsin,* for example, is an enzyme that hydrolyzes dietary proteins in the small intestine. It acts specifically at peptide bonds on the carbonyl side of the peptide bond. The C-terminal amino acids of the peptides released by bond cleavage are methionine, tyrosine, tryptophan, and phenylalanine. The specificity of chymotrypsin depends upon the presence of a *hydrophobic pocket,* a cluster of hydrophobic amino acids brought together by the three-dimensional folding of the protein chain. The flat aromatic side chains of certain amino acids (tyrosine, tryptophan, phenylalanine) slide into this pocket, providing the binding specificity required for catalysis (Figure 19.13).

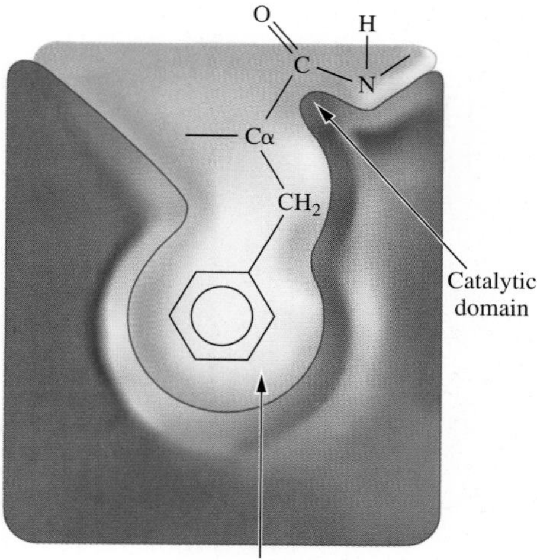

Figure 19.13 The specificity of chymotrypsin is determined by a hydrophobic pocket that holds the aromatic side chain of the substrate. This brings the peptide bond to be cleaved into the catalytic domain of the active site.

LEARNING GOAL

11 Discuss the role of the enzyme chymotrypsin and other serine proteases.

How can we determine which bond is cleaved by a protease such as chymotrypsin? To know which bond is cleaved, we must write out the sequence of amino acids in the region of the peptide that is being cleaved. This can be determined experimentally by amino acid sequencing techniques. Remember that the N-terminal amino acid is written to the left and the C-terminal amino acid to the right. Consider a protein having within it the sequence —Ala-Phe-Gly—. A reaction is set up in which the enzyme, chymotrypsin, is mixed with the protein substrate. After the reaction has occurred, the products are purified, and their amino acid sequences are determined. Experiments of this sort show that chymotrypsin cleaves the bond between phenylalanine and glycine, which is the peptide bond on the carbonyl side of amino acids having an aromatic side chain.

$$H_3^+N—\underset{CH_3}{\overset{H}{C}}—\overset{O}{\overset{\|}{C}}—NH—\underset{CH_2—C_6H_5}{\overset{H}{C}}—\overset{O}{\overset{\|}{C}}—NH—\underset{H}{\overset{H}{C}}—\overset{O}{\overset{\|}{C}}—O^-$$

Peptide bond cleaved

Ala ——— Phe ——— Gly

The **pancreatic serine proteases** trypsin, chymotrypsin, and elastase all hydrolyze peptide bonds. As the name suggests, they are produced in the pancreas and subsequently transported to the small intestine. These enzymes are the result of *divergent evolution* in which a single ancestral gene was first duplicated. Then each copy evolved individually. They have similar primary structures, similar tertiary structures, and virtually identical mechanisms of action. However, as a result of evolution, these enzymes all have different specificities:

- Chymotrypsin cleaves peptide bonds on the carbonyl side of aromatic amino acids and large, hydrophobic amino acids such as methionine.
- Trypsin cleaves peptide bonds on the carbonyl side of basic amino acids.
- Elastase cleaves peptide bonds on the carbonyl side of glycine and alanine.

These enzymes are called *serine proteases* because they have the amino acid serine in the catalytic region of the active site that is essential for hydrolysis of the peptide bond.

These enzymes have different pockets for the side chains of their substrates; *different keys fit different locks.* This difference manifests itself in the substrate specificity alluded to on the previous page. For example, the binding pocket of trypsin is long, narrow, and negatively charged to accommodate lysine or arginine R groups. Yet although the binding pockets have undergone divergent evolution, the catalytic sites have remained unchanged, and the mechanism of proteolytic action is the same for all the serine proteases. In each case, the mechanism involves a serine R group.

Question 19.17 Draw the structural formulas of the following peptides and show which bond would be cleaved by chymotrypsin.

a. ala-phe-ala b. tyr-ala-tyr

Question 19.18 Draw the structural formulas of the following peptides and show which bond would be cleaved by chymotrypsin.

a. trp-val-gly b. phe-ala-pro

Question 19.19 Draw the structural formula of the peptide val-phe-ala-gly-leu. Which bond would be cleaved if this peptide were reacted with chymotrypsin? With elastase?

Question 19.20 Draw the structural formula of the peptide trp-val-lys-ala-ser. Show which bonds would be cleaved by trypsin, chymotrypsin, and elastase.

19.12 Uses of Enzymes in Medicine

LEARNING GOAL

12 Provide examples of medical uses of enzymes.

Analysis of blood serum for levels (concentrations) of certain enzymes can provide a wealth of information about a patient's medical condition. Often, such tests are used to confirm a preliminary diagnosis based on the disease symptoms or clinical picture. These tests, called *enzyme assays,* are very precise and specific because they are based on the specificity of the enzyme-substrate complex.

Acute myocardial infarction (AMI) occurs when the blood supply to the heart muscle is blocked for an extended time. If this lack of blood supply, called *ischemia,* is prolonged, the myocardium suffers irreversible cell damage and muscle death, or infarction. When this happens, the concentration of cardiac enzymes in the blood rises dramatically as the dead cells release their contents into the bloodstream.

Three cardiac biomarkers have become the primary tools used to assess myocardial disease and suspected AMI. These are myoglobin, creatine kinase-MB (CK-MB), and cardiac troponin I. Of these three, only troponin is cardiac specific. In fact, it is so reliable that the American College of Cardiology has stated that any elevation of troponin is "abnormal and represents cardiac injury."

Myoglobin is the smallest of these three proteins and diffuses most rapidly through the vascular system. Thus, it is the first cardiac biomarker to appear, becoming elevated as early as 30 min after onset of chest pain. Myoglobin has another benefit in following a myocardial infarction. It is rapidly cleared from the body by the kidneys, returning to normal levels within 16 to 36 h after a heart attack. If the physician sees this decline in myoglobin levels, followed by a subsequent rise, it is an indication that the patient has had a second myocardial infarction.

Creatine kinase-MB is one of the most important cardiac biomarkers, even though it is found primarily in muscle and brain. Levels typically rise 3 to 8 h after chest pains begin. Within another 48 to 72 h, the CK-MB levels return to normal. As a result, like myoglobin, CK-MB can also be used to diagnose a second AMI.

The physician also has enzymes available to treat a heart attack patient. Most AMIs are the result of a *thrombus,* or clot, within a coronary blood vessel. The clot restricts blood flow to the heart muscle. One technique that shows promise for treatment following a coronary thrombosis, a heart attack caused by the formation of a clot, is destruction of the clot by intravenous or intracoronary injection of an enzyme called *streptokinase.* This enzyme, formerly purified from the pathogenic bacterium *Streptococcus pyogenes* but now available through recombinant DNA techniques, catalyzes the production of the proteolytic enzyme plasmin from its proenzyme, plasminogen. Plasmin can degrade a fibrin clot into subunits. This has the effect of dissolving the clot that is responsible for restricted blood flow to the heart, but there is an additional protective function as well. The subunits produced by plasmin degradation of fibrin clots are able to inhibit further clot formation by inhibiting thrombin.

Recombinant DNA technology has provided medical science with yet another, perhaps more promising, clot-dissolving enzyme. *Tissue-type plasminogen activator (TPA)* is a proteolytic enzyme that occurs naturally in the body as a part of the anti-clotting mechanisms. TPA converts the proenzyme, plasminogen, into the active enzyme, plasmin. Injection of TPA within 2 h of the initial chest pain can significantly improve the circulation to the heart and greatly improve the patient's chances of survival.

Elevated blood serum concentrations of the enzymes amylase and lipase are indications of pancreatitis, an inflammation of the pancreas. Liver diseases such as cirrhosis and hepatitis result in elevated levels of alanine aminotransferase/serum glutamate–pyruvate transaminase (ALT/SGPT) and aspartate aminotransferase/serum glutamate–oxaloacetate transaminase (AST/SGOT) in blood serum. In fact, these two enzymes also increase in concentration following heart attack, but the physician can differentiate between these two conditions by considering the relative increase in the two enzymes. If ALT/SGPT is elevated to a greater extent than AST/SGOT, it can be concluded that the problem is liver dysfunction.

Enzymes are also used as analytical reagents in the clinical laboratory owing to their specificity. They often selectively react with one substance of interest, producing a product that is easily measured. An example of this is the clinical analysis of urea in blood. The measurement of urea levels in blood is difficult because of the complexity of blood. However, if urea is converted to ammonia using the enzyme urease, the ammonia becomes an *indicator* of urea, because it is produced from urea, and it is easily measured. This test, called the *blood urea nitrogen (BUN) test,* is useful in the diagnosis of kidney malfunction and serves as one example of the utility of enzymes in clinical chemistry.

Enzyme replacement therapy can also be used in the treatment of certain diseases. One such disease, Gaucher's disease, is a genetic disorder resulting in a deficiency of the enzyme *glucocerebrosidase.* In the normal situation, this enzyme breaks down a glycolipid called *glucocerebroside,* which is an intermediate in the synthesis and degradation of complex glycosphingolipids found in cellular membranes. Glucocerebrosidase is found in the lysosomes, where it hydrolyzes glucocerebroside into glucose and ceramide.

See A Medical Perspective: Disorders of Sphingolipid Metabolism in Chapter 17.

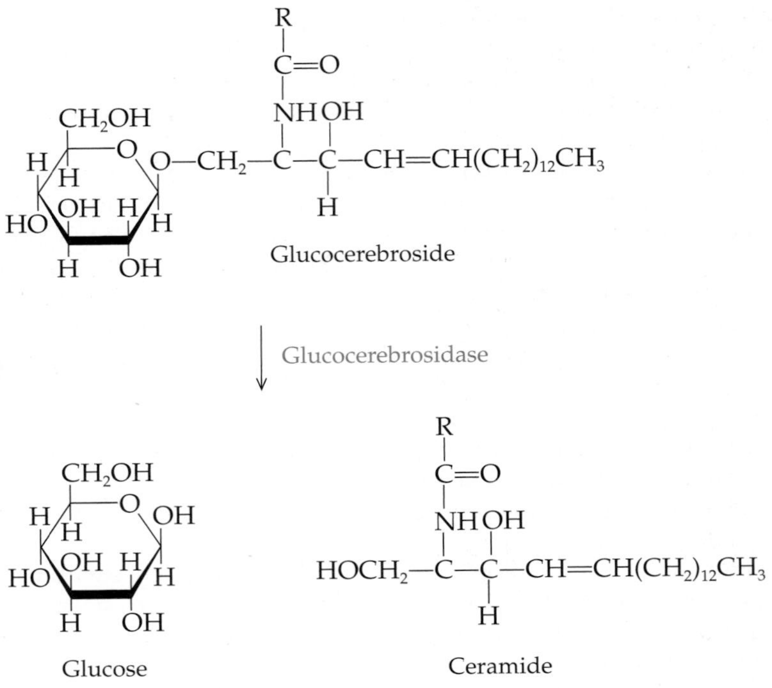

Glucocerebroside

$\downarrow$ Glucocerebrosidase

Glucose

$HOCH_2-C(H)(NH-C(=O)-R)-C(H)(OH)-CH{=}CH(CH_2)_{12}CH_3$

Ceramide

In Gaucher's disease, the enzyme is not present and glucocerebroside builds up in macrophages found in the liver, spleen, and bone marrow. These cells become engorged with excess lipid that cannot be metabolized and then displace healthy, normal cells in bone marrow. The symptoms of Gaucher's disease include severe anemia, thrombocytopenia (reduction in the number of platelets), and hepatosplenomegaly (enlargement of the spleen and liver). There can also be skeletal problems including bone deterioration and secondary fractures.

Recombinant DNA technology has been used by the Genzyme Corporation to produce the human lysosomal enzyme β-glucocerebrosidase. Given the trade name *Cerezyme,* the enzyme hydrolyzes glucocerebroside into glucose and ceramide so that the products can be metabolized normally. Patients receive Cerezyme intravenously over the course of 1 to 2 h. The dosage and treatment schedule can be tailored to the individual. The results of testing are very encouraging. Patients experience improved red blood cell and platelet counts and reduced hepatosplenomegaly.

CHAPTER MAP

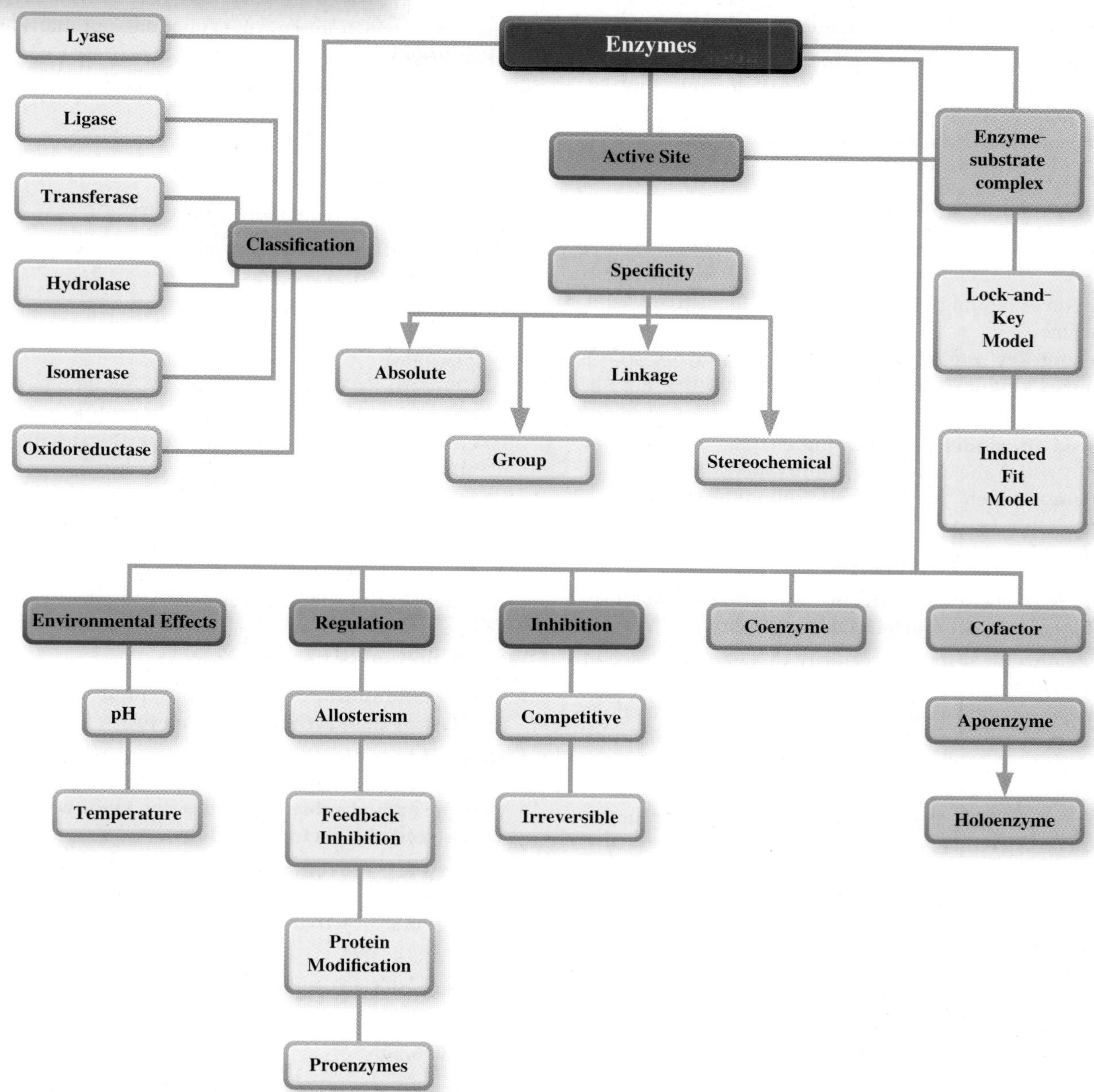

SUMMARY

19.1 Nomenclature and Classification

- **Enzymes** are most frequently named by using the common system of nomenclature.
  - Common names are useful because they are often derived from the name of the substrate and/or the type of reaction catalyzed by the enzyme.
- Enzymes convert one or more **substrates** into one or more **products.**
- There are six classes of enzymes on the basis of function: **oxidoreductases, transferases, hydrolases, lyases, isomerases,** and **ligases.**

19.2 The Effect of Enzymes on the Activation Energy of a Reaction

- Enzymes are biological catalysts that lower the activation energy of a reaction but do not alter the equilibrium constant.

19.3 The Effect of Substrate Concentration on Enzyme-Catalyzed Reactions

- In uncatalyzed reactions, increases in substrate concentration result in an increase in the reaction rate.
- In enzyme-catalyzed reactions, an increase in substrate concentration initially causes an increase in reaction rate, but at a particular concentration the reaction rate reaches a maximum because the enzyme active sites are all filled with substrate.

19.4 The Enzyme-Substrate Complex

- Formation of an **enzyme-substrate complex** is the first step of an enzyme-catalyzed reaction.
  - This involves binding of the substrate to the **active site** of the enzyme.
- The **lock-and-key model** of substrate binding describes the enzyme as a rigid structure into which the substrate fits precisely.
- The **induced fit model** describes the enzyme as a flexible molecule in which the active site approximates the shape of the substrate and then "molds" itself around the substrate.

19.5 Specificity of the Enzyme-Substrate Complex

- There are four classes of **enzyme specificity: absolute, group, linkage,** and **stereochemical specificity.**
  - An enzyme with absolute specificity catalyzes the reaction of only a single substrate.
  - An enzyme with group specificity catalyzes reactions involving similar substrates with the same functional group.
  - An enzyme with linkage specificity catalyzes reactions involving similar substrates with the same kind of bond.
  - An enzyme with stereochemical specificity catalyzes reactions involving only one enantiomer.

19.6 The Transition State and Product Formation

- An enzyme-catalyzed reaction is mediated through an unstable **transition state.**
- Transition states may involve putting "stress" on a bond, bringing reactants into close proximity and in the correct orientation, or altering the local pH.

19.7 Cofactors and Coenzymes

- **Cofactors** are metal ions, organic compounds, or organometallic compounds that bind to an enzyme and help maintain the correct configuration of the active site.
  - The protein portion is the **apoenzyme;** the protein portion bound to the cofactor is the **holoenzyme.**
- **Coenzymes** are organic groups that bind transiently to an enzyme during the reaction and that accept or donate chemical groups.
  - Coenzymes often contain modified **vitamins** as part of their structure.

19.8 Environmental Effects

- Enzymes are sensitive to pH and temperature and are quickly inactivated by extremes of pH or high temperature.
- The pH at which an enzyme functions optimally is the **pH optimum.**
- The **temperature optimum** is the temperature at which an enzyme functions optimally.

19.9 Regulation of Enzyme Activity

- Enzymes may be regulated by the cell.
- Some mechanisms of enzyme regulation include the following:
  - Formation of inactive forms or **proenzymes** that are later converted into active enzymes under the appropriate conditions
  - Allosterism: **Allosteric enzymes** have an effector binding site, as well as an active site. Effector binding renders the enzyme active **(positive allosterism)** or inactive **(negative allosterism).**
  - **Feedback inhibition:** the product of a biosynthetic pathway turns off the entire pathway via negative allosterism.
  - **Protein modification:** adding or removing a covalently bound group either activates or inactivates the enzyme.

19.10 Inhibition of Enzyme Activity

- **Irreversible inhibitors,** or poisons, bind tightly to enzymes and destroy their activity permanently.
- **Reversible competitive inhibitors** are generally **structural analogs** of the natural substrate for the enzyme that compete with the natural substrate for binding to the active side. They are also called **structural analogs.**
- **Reversible noncompetitive inhibitors** bind weakly to amino acid R groups of an enzyme. If they dissociate from the enzyme, its activity is restored.

19.11 Proteolytic Enzymes

- **Proteolytic enzymes** (proteases) catalyze the hydrolysis of peptide bonds.
- The **pancreatic serine proteases** chymotrypsin, trypsin, and elastase have similar structures and mechanisms of action and are thought to have evolved from a common ancestral protease.

19.12 Uses of Enzymes in Medicine

- Analysis of blood serum for unusually high levels of certain enzymes provides valuable information about the condition of a patient and is used to diagnose heart attack, liver disease, pancreatitis, and other conditions.
- Enzymes are used as analytical reagents, as in the blood urea nitrogen (BUN) test, and in the treatment of disease.

ANSWERS TO PRACTICE PROBLEMS

19.1 a. Pyruvate kinase is a transferase.
b. Alanine transaminase is a transferase.
c. Triose phosphate isomerase is an isomerase.
d. Pyruvate dehydrogenase is an oxidoreductase.
e. Lactase is a hydrolase.
f. Phosphofructokinase is a transferase.
g. Lipase is a hydrolase.
h. Acetoacetate decarboxylase is a transferase.
i. Succinate dehydrogenase is an oxidoreductase.

QUESTIONS AND PROBLEMS

Nomenclature and Classification

Foundations

19.21 How are the common names of enzymes often derived?

19.22 What is the most common characteristic used to classify enzymes?

Applications

19.23 Match each of the following substrates with its corresponding enzyme:

1. Urea	**a.** Lipase
2. Hydrogen peroxide	**b.** Glucose-6-phosphatase
3. Lipid	**c.** Peroxidase
4. Aspartic acid	**d.** Sucrase
5. Glucose-6-phosphate	**e.** Urease
6. Sucrose	**f.** Aspartase

19.24 Give a systematic name for the enzyme that would act on each of the following substrates:
a. Alanine
b. Citrate
c. Ampicillin
d. Ribose
e. Methylamine

19.25 Describe the function implied by the name of each of the following enzymes:
a. Citrate decarboxylase
b. Adenosine diphosphate phosphorylase
c. Oxalate reductase
d. Nitrite oxidase
e. *cis-trans* Isomerase

19.26 List the six classes of enzymes based on the type of reaction catalyzed. Briefly describe the function of each class, and provide an example of each.

The Effect of Enzymes on the Activation Energy of a Reaction

Foundations

19.27 Define the term *substrate.*

19.28 Define the term *product.*

Applications

19.29 What is the activation energy of a reaction?

19.30 What is the effect of an enzyme on the activation energy of a reaction?

19.31 Write and explain the equation for the equilibrium constant of an enzyme-mediated reaction. Does the enzyme alter the K_{eq}?

19.32 If an enzyme does not alter the equilibrium constant of a reaction, how does it speed up the reaction?

The Effect of Substrate Concentration on Enzyme-Catalyzed Reactions

Foundations

19.33 What is the effect of doubling the substrate concentration on the rate of a chemical reaction?

19.34 Why doesn't the rate of an enzyme-catalyzed reaction increase indefinitely when the substrate concentration is made very large?

Applications

19.35 What is meant by the term *rate-limiting step?*

19.36 How does the rate-limiting step influence an enzyme-catalyzed reaction?

19.37 Draw a graph that describes the effect of increasing the concentration of the substrate on the rate of an enzyme-catalyzed reaction.

19.38 What does a graph of enzyme activity versus substrate concentration tell us about the nature of enzyme-catalyzed reactions?

The Enzyme-Substrate Complex

Foundations

19.39 Define the term *enzyme-substrate complex.*

19.40 Define the term *active site.*

19.41 What are catalytic groups of an enzyme active site?

19.42 What is the binding site of an enzyme active site?

Applications

19.43 Name three major properties of enzyme active sites.

19.44 If enzyme active sites are small, why are enzymes so large?

19.45 What is the lock-and-key model of enzyme-substrate binding?

19.46 Why is the induced fit model of enzyme-substrate binding a much more accurate model than the lock-and-key model?

Specificity of the Enzyme-Substrate Complex

Foundations

19.47 Define the term *enzyme specificity.*

19.48 What region of an enzyme is responsible for its specificity?

19.49 What is meant by the term *group specificity?*

19.50 What is meant by the term *linkage specificity?*

19.51 What is meant by the term *absolute specificity?*

19.52 What is meant by the term *stereochemical specificity?*

Applications

19.53 Provide an example of an enzyme with group specificity and explain the advantage of group specificity for that particular enzyme.

19.54 Provide an example of an enzyme with linkage specificity and explain the advantage of linkage specificity for that particular enzyme.

19.55 Provide an example of an enzyme with absolute specificity and explain the advantage of absolute specificity for that particular enzyme.

19.56 Provide an example of an enzyme with stereochemical specificity and explain the advantage of stereochemical specificity for that particular enzyme.

The Transition State and Product Formation

Foundations

19.57 Outline the four general stages in an enzyme-catalyzed reaction.

19.58 Describe the transition state.

Applications

19.59 What types of transition states might be envisioned that would decrease the energy of activation of a reaction?

19.60 If an enzyme catalyzed a reaction by modifying the local pH, what kind of amino acid R groups would you expect to find in the active site?

Cofactors and Coenzymes

Foundations

19.61 What is the role of a cofactor in enzyme activity?

19.62 How does a coenzyme function in an enzyme-catalyzed reaction?

Applications

19.63 List each of the vitamins found in modified form in a coenzyme and list the coenzymes.

19.64 List the functions of each of the coenzymes. What classes of enzymes would require these coenzymes?

Environmental Effects

Foundations

19.65 Define the temperature optimum for an enzyme.

19.66 Define the optimum pH for enzyme activity.

19.67 How will each of the following changes in conditions alter the rate of an enzyme-catalyzed reaction?

- **a.** Decreasing the temperature from 37°C to 10°C
- **b.** Increasing the pH of the solution from 7 to 11
- **c.** Heating the enzyme from 37°C to 100°C

19.68 Why does an enzyme lose activity when the pH is drastically changed from optimum pH?

Applications

19.69 High temperature is an effective mechanism for killing bacteria on surgical instruments. How does high temperature result in cellular death?

19.70 An increase in temperature will increase the rate of a reaction if a nonenzymatic catalyst is used; however, an increase in temperature will eventually *decrease* the rate of a reaction when an enzyme catalyst is used. Explain the apparent contradiction of these two statements.

19.71 What is the function of the lysosome?

19.72 Of what significance is it that lysosomal enzymes have a pH optimum of 4.8?

19.73 Why are enzymes that are used for clinical assays in hospitals stored in refrigerators?

19.74 Why do extremes of pH inactivate enzymes?

Regulation of Enzyme Activity

Foundations

19.75 **a.** Why is it important for cells to regulate the level of enzyme activity?

b. Why must synthesis of digestive enzymes be carefully controlled?

19.76 What is an allosteric enzyme?

19.77 What is the difference between positive and negative allosterism?

19.78 **a.** Define feedback inhibition.

b. Describe the role of allosteric enzymes in feedback inhibition.

c. Is this positive or negative allosterism?

19.79 What is a proenzyme?

19.80 Three proenzymes that are involved in digestion of proteins in the stomach and intestines are pepsinogen, chymotrypsinogen, and trypsinogen. What is the advantage of producing these enzymes as inactive peptides?

Applications

19.81 The blood clotting mechanism consists of a set of proenzymes that act in a cascade that results in formation of a blood clot. Develop a hypothesis to explain the value of this mechanism for blood clotting.

19.82 What is the benefit for an enzyme such as triacylglycerol lipase to be regulated by covalent modification, in this case phosphorylation?

Inhibition of Enzyme Activity

Foundations

19.83 Define *competitive enzyme inhibition.*

19.84 How do the sulfa drugs selectively kill bacteria while causing no harm to humans?

19.85 Describe the structure of a structural analog.

19.86 How can structural analogs serve as enzyme inhibitors?

19.87 Define *irreversible enzyme inhibition.*

19.88 Why are irreversible enzyme inhibitors often called *poisons?*

Applications

19.89 Suppose that a certain drug company manufactured a compound that had nearly the same structure as a substrate for a certain enzyme but that could not be acted upon chemically by the enzyme. What type of interaction would the compound have with the enzyme?

19.90 The addition of phenylthiourea to a preparation of the enzyme polyphenoloxidase completely inhibits the activity of the enzyme.

- **a.** Knowing that phenylthiourea binds all copper ions, what conclusion can you draw about whether polyphenoloxidase requires a cofactor?
- **b.** What kind of inhibitor is phenylthiourea?

Proteolytic Enzymes

Foundations

19.91 What is the function of a proteolytic enzyme?

19.92 Where are the proteolytic enzymes pepsin and trypsin formed? Where do they carry out their function?

Applications

19.93 What do the similar structures of chymotrypsin, trypsin, and elastase suggest about their evolutionary relationship?

19.94 What properties are shared by chymotrypsin, trypsin, and elastase?

19.95 Draw the complete structural formula for the peptide tyr-lys-ala-phe. Show which bond would be broken when this peptide is reacted with chymotrypsin.

19.96 Repeat Question 19.95 for the peptide trp-pro-gly-tyr.

19.97 The sequence of a peptide that contains ten amino acids is as follows:

ala-gly-val-leu-trp-lys-ser-phe-arg-pro

Which peptide bond(s) are cleaved by elastase, trypsin, and chymotrypsin?

19.98 What structural features of trypsin, chymotrypsin, and elastase account for their different specificities?

Uses of Enzymes in Medicine

Foundations

19.99 How are blood serum levels of certain enzymes used in medical diagnosis?

19.100 How are enzymes used in medical treatment? Provide an example.

Applications

19.101 List the enzymes whose levels are elevated in blood serum following a myocardial infarction.

19.102 List the enzymes whose levels are elevated as a result of hepatitis or cirrhosis of the liver.

19.103 How is urease used in the diagnosis of kidney malfunction?

19.104 What medical condition is indicated by elevated blood serum levels of amylase and lipase?

CRITICAL THINKING PROBLEMS

1. Ethylene glycol is a poison that causes about fifty deaths a year in the United States. Treating people who have drunk ethylene glycol with massive doses of ethanol can save their lives. Suggest a reason for the effect of ethanol.

2. Generally speaking, feedback inhibition involves regulation of the first step in a pathway. Consider the following hypothetical pathway:

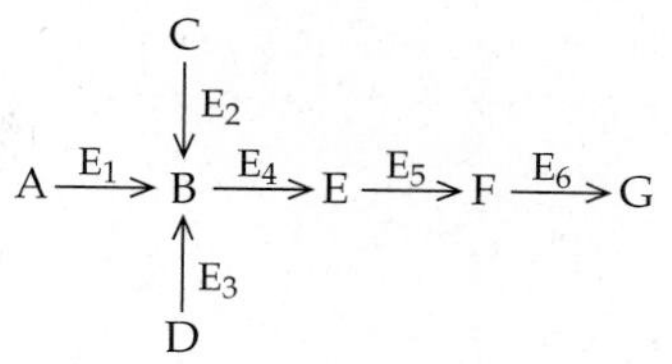

$$C \xrightarrow{E_2} B, \quad D \xrightarrow{E_3} B$$
$$A \xrightarrow{E_1} B \xrightarrow{E_4} E \xrightarrow{E_5} F \xrightarrow{E_6} G$$

Which step in this pathway do you think should be regulated? Explain your reasoning.

3. In an amplification cascade, each step greatly increases the amount of substrate available for the next step, so that a very large amount of the final product is made. Consider the following hypothetical amplification cascade:

$$A_{active}$$
$$\downarrow$$
$$B_{inactive} \longrightarrow B_{active}$$
$$\downarrow$$
$$C_{inactive} \longrightarrow C_{active}$$
$$\downarrow$$
$$D_{inactive} \longrightarrow D_{active}$$

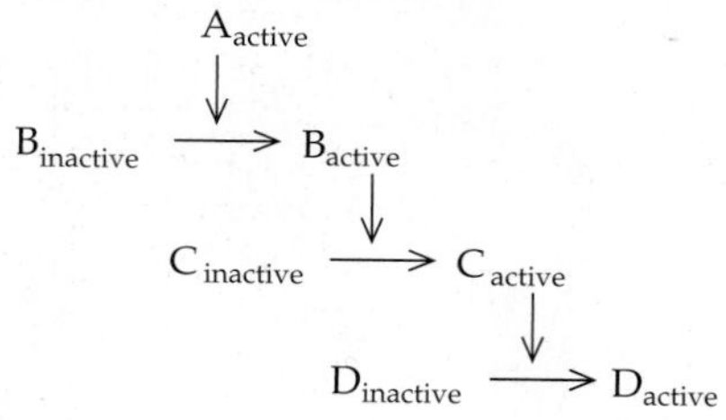

If each active enzyme in the pathway converts 100 molecules of its substrate to active form, how many molecules of D will be produced if the pathway begins with one molecule of A?

4. L-1-(*p*-toluenesulfonyl)-amido-2-phenylethylchloromethyl ketone (TPCK, shown below) inhibits chymotrypsin, but not trypsin. Propose a hypothesis to explain this observation.

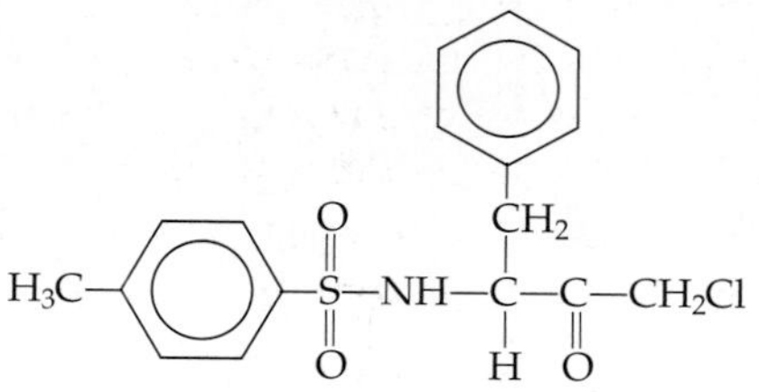

$$H_3C{-}C_6H_4{-}SO_2{-}NH{-}CH(CH_2C_6H_5){-}C(=O){-}CH_2Cl$$

5. A graduate student is trying to make a "map" of a short peptide so that she can eventually determine the amino acid sequence. She digested the peptide with several proteases and determined the sizes of the resultant digestion products.

Enzyme	M.M. of Digestion Products
Trypsin	2000, 3000
Chymotrypsin	500, 1000, 3500
Elastase	500, 1000, 1500, 2000

Suggest experiments that would allow the student to map the order of the enzyme digestion sites along the peptide.

BIOCHEMISTRY

20

Introduction to Molecular Genetics

These twin girls are identical. Explain why this is so.

LEARNING GOALS

1. Draw the general structure of DNA and RNA nucleotides.
2. Describe the structure of DNA and compare it with RNA.
3. Explain DNA replication.
4. List three classes of RNA molecules and describe their functions.
5. Explain the process of transcription.
6. List and explain the three types of post-transcriptional modifications of eukaryotic mRNA.
7. Describe the essential elements of the genetic code, and develop a "feel" for its elegance.
8. Describe the process of translation.
9. Define mutation and understand how mutations cause cancer and cell death.
10. Describe the tools used in the study of DNA and in genetic engineering.
11. Describe the process of polymerase chain reaction and discuss potential uses of the process.
12. Discuss strategies for genome analysis and DNA sequencing.

OUTLINE

Introduction 685

20.1 The Structure of the Nucleotide 685

20.2 The Structure of DNA and RNA 688

A Medical Perspective: Molecular Genetics and Detection of Human Genetic Disorders 693

20.3 DNA Replication 693

20.4 Information Flow in Biological Systems 698

20.5 The Genetic Code 702

20.6 Protein Synthesis 703

20.7 Mutation, Ultraviolet Light, and DNA Repair 708

A Medical Perspective: The Ames Test for Carcinogens 710

20.8 Recombinant DNA 711

20.9 Polymerase Chain Reaction 717

20.10 The Human Genome Project 717

Chemistry at the Crime Scene: DNA Fingerprinting 718

A Medical Perspective: A Genetic Approach to Familial Emphysema 720

INTRODUCTION

Look around at the students in your chemistry class. They all share many traits: upright stance, a head with two eyes, a nose, and a mouth facing forward, one ear on each side of the head, and so on. You would have no difficulty listing the similarities that define you and your classmates as *Homo sapiens*.

As you look more closely at the individuals you begin to notice many differences. Eye color, hair color, skin color, the shape of the nose, height, body build: all these traits, and many more, show amazing variety from one person to the next. Even within one family, in which the similarities may be more pronounced, each individual has a unique appearance. In fact, only identical twins look exactly alike—well, most of the time.

The molecule responsible for all these similarities and differences is deoxyribonucleic acid (DNA). Tightly wound up in structures called *chromosomes* in the nucleus of the cell, DNA carries the genetic code to produce the thousands of different proteins that make us who we are. These proteins include enzymes that are responsible for production of the pigment melanin. The more melanin we are genetically programmed to make, the darker our hair, eyes, and skin will be. Others are structural proteins. The gene for α-keratin that makes up hair determines whether our hair will be wavy, straight, or curly. Thousands of genes carry the genetic information for thousands of proteins that dictate our form and, some believe, our behavior.

Genetic traits are passed from one generation to the next. When a sperm fertilizes an ovum, a zygote is created from a single set of maternal chromosomes and a single set of paternal chromosomes. As this fertilized egg divides, each daughter cell will receive one copy of each of these chromosomes. The genes on these chromosomes will direct fetal development from that fertilized cell to a newborn with all the characteristics we recognize as human.

In this chapter we will explore the structure of DNA and the molecular events that translate the genetic information of a gene into the structure of a protein.

20.1 The Structure of the Nucleotide

Even before the philosopher Aristotle observed that "like begets like," humans were curious about the way in which family likenesses are passed from one generation to the next. In the 1860s Gregor Mendel combined astute observations, careful experimental design, and mathematical analysis to explain inheritance. Presented at a meeting in 1865 and published in 1866, Mendel's brilliant work was largely ignored by a scientific community that simply could not understand it.

LEARNING GOAL

1 Draw the general structure of DNA and RNA nucleotides.

At about the same time (1869), Friedrich Miescher discovered a substance in the nuclei of white blood cells recovered from pus. Chemical analysis of this substance, which he called *nuclein*, revealed that it contained 14% nitrogen and 3% phosphorus in addition to carbon, hydrogen, and oxygen. As microscopes improved in the last decades of the nineteenth century, biologists were able to peer into the nuclei of cells. They observed structures, later called *chromosomes*, which seemed to play a critical role in the process of cell division. Interestingly, egg and sperm cells were observed to have only half the chromosomes of the cells that produced them.

Chemical analysis of chromosomes indicated that they were composed of both protein and nuclein. But which of these molecules represented the genetic material? Most were convinced that the answer to this question was protein. The reasoning was that the genetic material must have a structure that would allow it to encode the enormous variation seen in the biological world. Both nuclein and protein were known to be polymers. However, proteins were polymers of twenty different subunits, the amino acids. Based on the results of Phoebus Levene, working with Emil Fischer and Albrecht Kossel, nuclein was composed of only four subunits. It appeared to lack the complexity required of a molecule responsible for the great diversity seen among plants, animals, and microbes.

In 1950, the genetic information was demonstrated to be nuclein, now called *deoxyribonucleic acid,* or DNA. In 1953, just over 60 years ago, James Watson and Francis Crick published a paper describing the structure of the DNA molecule.

Chemical Composition of DNA and RNA

Two types of nucleic acids are important to the cell. The first is **deoxyribonucleic acid (DNA),** which carries all of the genetic information for an organism. The second type is **ribonucleic acid (RNA),** which is responsible for interpreting the genetic information into proteins that will carry out the essential cellular functions.

The components of these nucleic acids can be released by acid hydrolysis and then identified by chromatography. Treatment of DNA with a strong acid releases the sugar 2′-deoxyribose, phosphate, and four heterocyclic amines called *nitrogenous bases.* These bases are divided into two families known as **pyrimidines** and **purines** (Figure 20.1). Hydrolysis of RNA also releases purine and pyrimidine bases, phosphate, and a sugar; but in this case the sugar is ribose. The pyrimidine bases in DNA are cytosine and thymine. The pyrimidines found in RNA are cytosine and uracil (Figure 20.1). Notice that these three pyrimidines differ from one another only in the positioning of certain functional groups around the ring.

The major purines of both DNA and RNA are adenine and guanine (Figure 20.1). As with the pyrimidines, the purines differ from one another only in the location of functional groups around the ring.

Nucleosides

Nucleosides are produced by the combination of a sugar, either ribose (in RNA) or 2′-deoxyribose (in DNA), with a purine or a pyrimidine base. Because there are two cyclic molecules in a nucleoside, we need an easy way to describe the ring atoms of each. For this reason the ring atoms of the sugar are designated with a prime to distinguish them from atoms in the base (Figure 20.2). The covalent bond between the sugar and the base is called a β-*N-glycosidic linkage.* The general structures of a purine nucleoside and a pyrimidine nucleoside are shown in Figure 20.2.

N-1 of pyrimidines and N-9 of purines participate in the glycosidic bonds of nucleosides. The nucleosides formed with ribose and adenine or guanine are

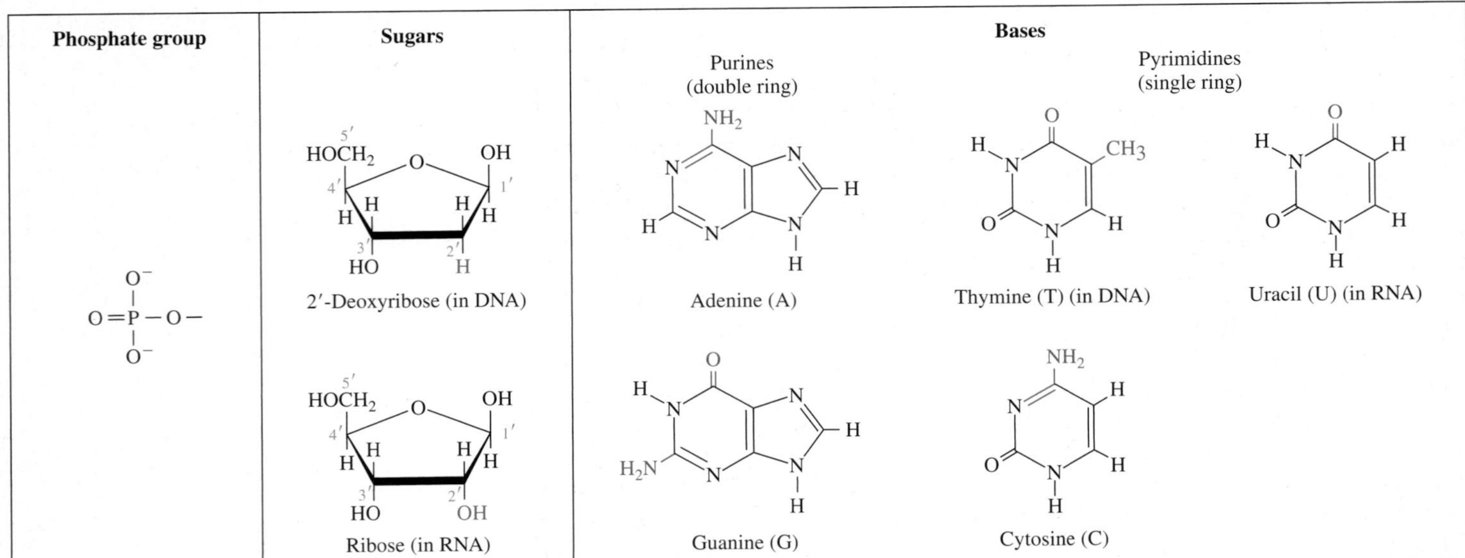

Figure 20.1 The components of nucleic acids include phosphate groups, the five-carbon sugars ribose and deoxyribose, and purine and pyrimidine nitrogenous bases. The ring positions of the sugars are designated with primes (′) to distinguish them from the ring positions of the bases.

called adenosine or guanosine, respectively. If 2′-deoxyribose is the sugar in these nucleosides, they are called 2′-deoxyadenosine and 2′-deoxyguanosine. The ribonucleosides formed from cytosine and uracil are called cytidine and uridine, respectively. The deoxyribonucleosides of cytosine and thymine are called 2′-deoxycytidine and thymidine, respectively. No prefix is needed for thymidine because it is found only in DNA.

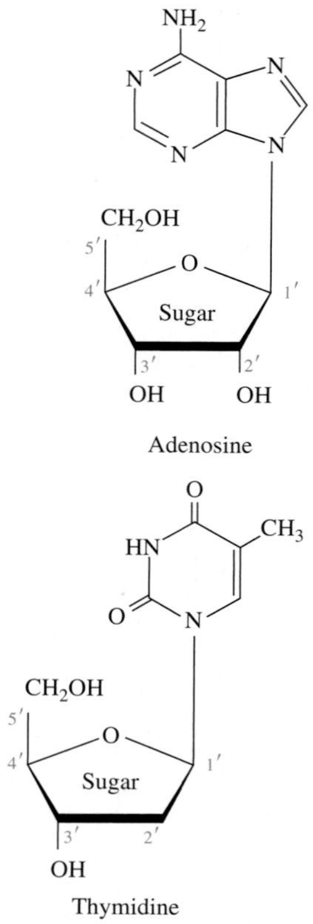

Nucleotide Structure

From the work of Watson and Crick, as well as that of Miescher, Levene, and many others, we now know that deoxyribonucleic acid (DNA) and ribonucleic acid (RNA) are long polymers of **nucleotides.** Every nucleotide is composed of a nitrogenous base, a five-carbon sugar, and at least one phosphoryl group.

Each nucleotide consists of either ribose or deoxyribose, one of the five nitrogenous bases, and one or more phosphoryl groups (Figure 20.3). A nucleotide with the sugar ribose is a **ribonucleotide,** and one having the sugar 2′-deoxyribose is a **deoxyribonucleotide** (Figures 20.1 and 20.3).

The covalent bond between the sugar and the phosphoryl group is a phosphoester bond formed by a condensation reaction between the 5′-OH of the sugar and an —OH of the phosphoryl group. As noted above, the bond between the base and the sugar is a β-*N*-glycosidic linkage that joins the 1′-carbon of the sugar and a nitrogen atom of the base (N-9 of purines and N-1 of pyrimidines).

To name a nucleotide, simply begin with the name of the nitrogenous base, and apply the following simple rules:

- Remove the *-ine* ending, and replace it with either *-osine* for purines or *-idine* for pyrimidines. Uracil is the one exception to this rule. In this case the *-acil* ending is replaced with *-idine,* producing the name *uridine.*

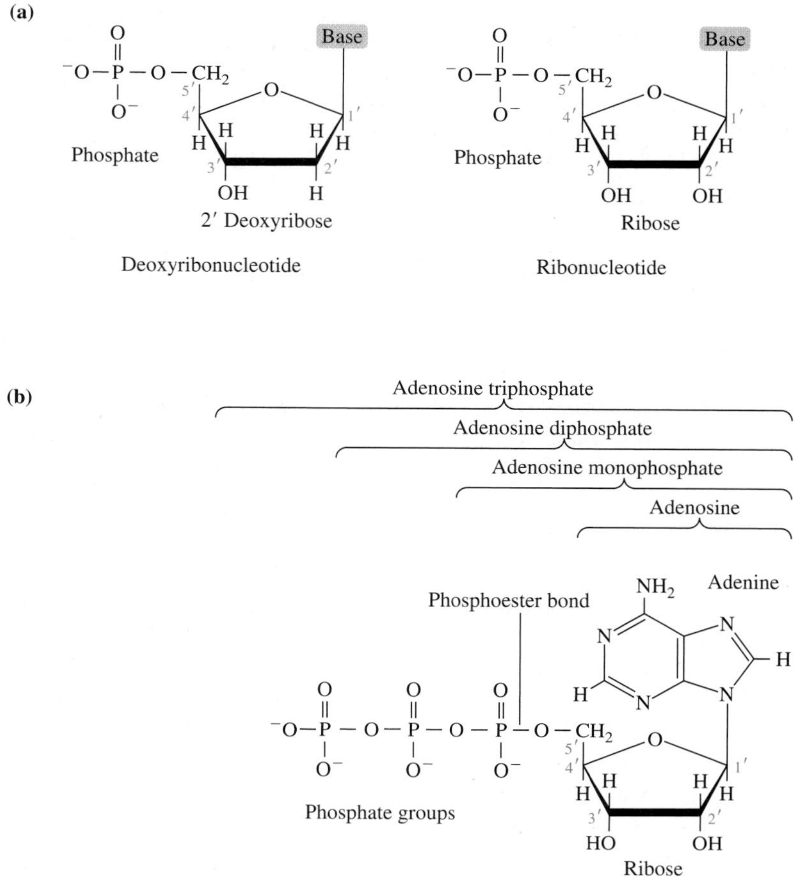

Figure 20.2 General structures of a purine and a pyrimidine nucleoside. Notice that the *N*-glycosidic linkage involves the 1′ carbon of the sugar and either the N-1 of the pyrimidine or N-9 of the purine.

Figure 20.3 (a) The general structures of a deoxyribonucleotide and a ribonucleotide. (b) A specific example of a ribonucleotide, adenosine triphosphate.

TABLE 20.1 Names and Abbreviations of the Ribonucleotides and Deoxyribonucleotides Containing Adenine

Nucleotide	Abbreviation
Deoxyadenosine monophosphate	dAMP
Deoxyadenosine diphosphate	dADP
Deoxyadenosine triphosphate	dATP
Adenosine monophosphate	AMP
Adenosine diphosphate	ADP
Adenosine triphosphate	ATP

- Nucleotides with the sugar ribose are ribonucleotides, and those having the sugar 2′-deoxyribose are deoxyribonucleotides. For a deoxyribonucleotide, the prefix *deoxy-* is placed before the modified nitrogenous base name. No prefix is required for ribonucleotides, or for thymidine, which is found only in DNA.
- Add a prefix to indicate the number of phosphoryl groups that are attached. A *mono*phosphate carries one phosphoryl group; a *di*phosphate carries two phosphoryl groups; and a *tri*phosphate carries three phosphoryl groups.

Because the full names of the nucleotides are so cumbersome, a simple abbreviation is generally used. These abbreviations are summarized in Table 20.1.

Question 20.1 Referring to the structures in Figures 20.1 and 20.3, draw the structures for nucleotides consisting of the following units.

a. Ribose, adenine, two phosphoryl groups
b. 2′-Deoxyribose, guanine, three phosphoryl groups

Question 20.2 Referring to the structures in Figures 20.1 and 20.3, draw the structures for nucleotides consisting of the following units.

a. 2′-Deoxyribose, thymine, one phosphoryl group
b. Ribose, cytosine, three phosphoryl groups
c. Ribose, uracil, one phosphoryl group

20.2 The Structure of DNA and RNA

LEARNING GOAL

2 Describe the structure of DNA and compare it with RNA.

A single strand of DNA is a polymer of nucleotides bonded to one another by 3′–5′ phosphodiester bonds. The backbone of the polymer is called the *sugar-phosphate backbone* because it is composed of alternating units of the five-carbon sugar 2′-deoxyribose and phosphoryl groups in phosphodiester linkage. A nitrogenous base is bonded to each sugar by an *N*-glycosidic linkage (Figure 20.4).

DNA Structure: The Double Helix

James Watson and Francis Crick were the first to describe the three-dimensional structure of DNA, in 1953. They deduced the structure by building models based on the experimental results of others. Irwin Chargaff observed that the amount of adenine in any DNA molecule is equal to the amount of thymine. Similarly, he found that the amounts of cytosine and guanine are also equal. The X-ray diffraction studies of Rosalind Franklin and Maurice Wilkens revealed several repeat distances that characterize the structure of DNA: 0.34 nanometers (nm), 3.4 nm, and 2 nm. (Look at the structure of DNA in Figure 20.5 to see the significance of these measurements.)

With this information, Watson and Crick concluded that DNA is a **double helix** of two strands of DNA wound around one another. The structure of the double helix is often compared to a spiral staircase. The sugar-phosphate backbones

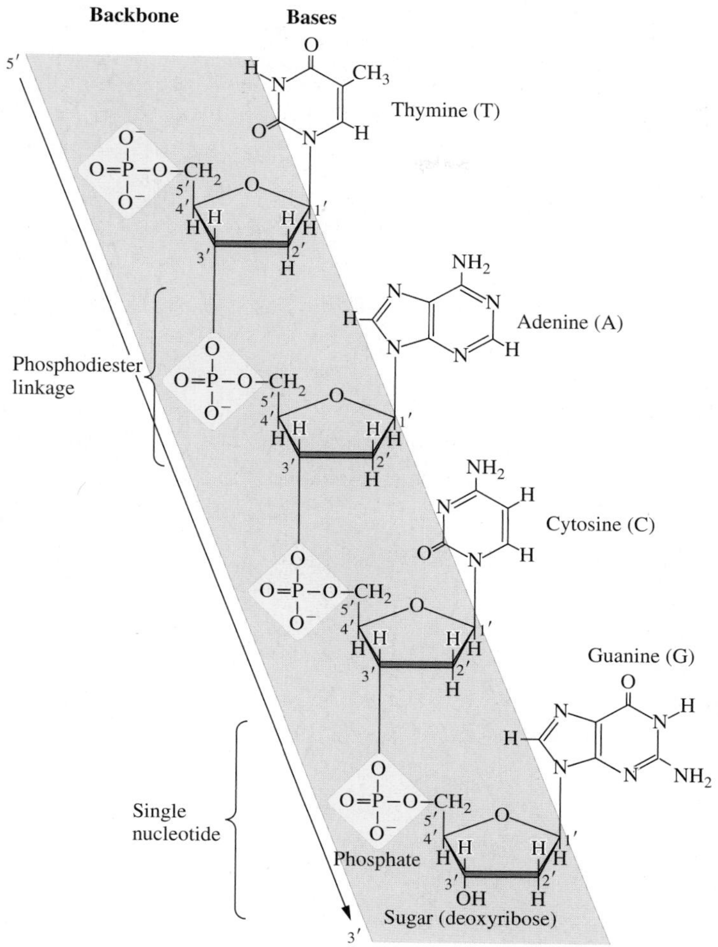

Figure 20.4 The covalent, primary structure of DNA.

of the two strands of DNA spiral around the outside of the helix like the handrails on a spiral staircase. The nitrogenous bases extend into the center at right angles to the axis of the helix. You can imagine the nitrogenous bases forming the steps of the staircase. The structure of this elegant molecule is shown in Figure 20.5.

One noncovalent attraction that helps maintain the double helix structure is hydrogen bonding between the nitrogenous bases in the center of the helix. Adenine forms two hydrogen bonds with thymine, and cytosine forms three hydrogen bonds with guanine (Figure 20.5). These are called **base pairs.** The two strands of DNA are **complementary strands** because the sequence of bases on one automatically determines the sequence of bases on the other. When there is an adenine on one strand, there will always be a thymine in the same location on the opposite strand.

Base-pairing explains Chargaff's observation that the amount of adenine always equals the amount of thymine and the amount of guanine always equals the amount of cytosine for any DNA sample.

The diameter of the double helix is 2.0 nm. This is dictated by the dimensions of the purine-pyrimidine base pairs. The helix completes one turn every ten base pairs. One complete turn is 3.4 nm. Thus, each base pair advances the helix by 0.34 nm. These dimensions explain the repeat distances observed by X-ray diffraction.

One last important feature of the DNA double helix is that the two strands are **antiparallel strands,** as this example shows:

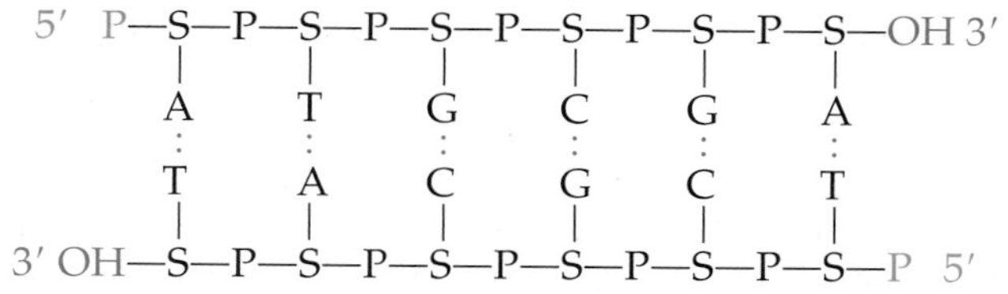

```
5′  P—S—P—S—P—S—P—S—P—S—P—S—OH 3′
      |     |     |     |     |     |
      A     T     G     C     G     A
      :     :     :     :     :     :
      T     A     C     G     C     T
      |     |     |     |     |     |
3′ OH—S—P—S—P—S—P—S—P—S—P—S—P  5′
```

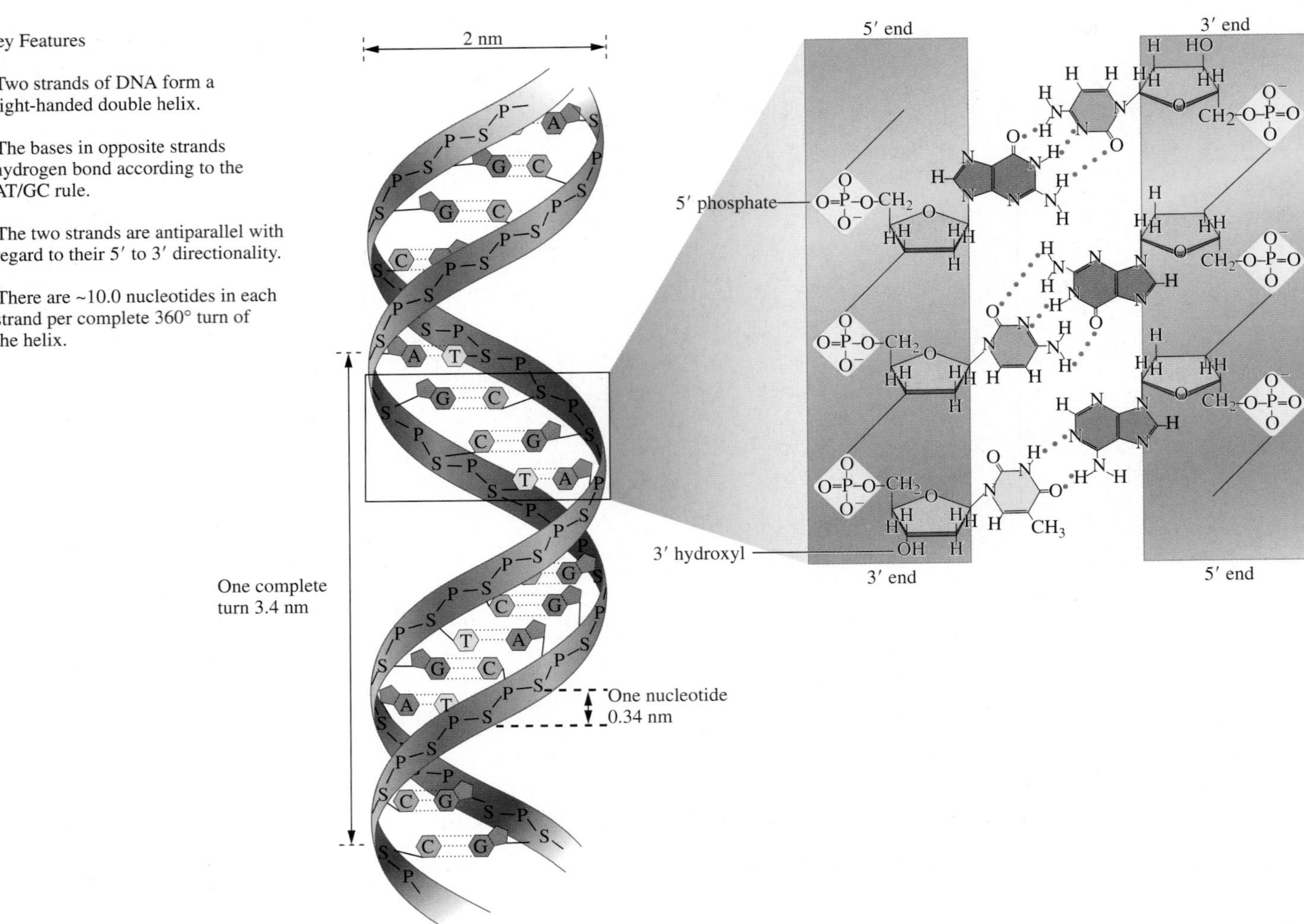

Key Features
• Two strands of DNA form a right-handed double helix.
• The bases in opposite strands hydrogen bond according to the AT/GC rule.
• The two strands are antiparallel with regard to their 5′ to 3′ directionality.
• There are ~10.0 nucleotides in each strand per complete 360° turn of the helix.
2 nm
One complete turn 3.4 nm
One nucleotide 0.34 nm
5′ phosphate
3′ hydroxyl
5′ end
3′ end
3′ end
5′ end

Figure 20.5 Schematic ribbon diagram of the DNA double helix showing the dimensions of the DNA molecule and the antiparallel orientation of the two strands.

In other words, the two strands of the helix run in opposite directions (see Figure 20.5). Only when the two strands are antiparallel can the base pairs form the hydrogen bonds that hold the two strands together.

Chromosomes

Chromosomes are pieces of DNA that carry the genetic instructions, or genes, of an organism. Organisms such as the prokaryotes have only a single chromosome and its structure is relatively simple. Others, the eukaryotes, have many chromosomes, each of which has many different levels of structure. The complete set of genetic information in all the chromosomes of an organism is called the **genome.**

Prokaryotes are organisms with a simple cellular structure in which there is no true nucleus surrounded by a nuclear membrane and there are no true membrane-bound organelles. This group includes all of the bacteria. In these organisms the chromosome is a circular DNA molecule that is supercoiled, which means that the helix is coiled on itself. The supercoiled DNA molecule is attached to a complex of proteins at roughly forty sites along its length, forming a series of loops. This structure, called the nucleoid, can be seen in Figure 20.6.

Eukaryotes are organisms that have cells containing a true nucleus enclosed by a nuclear membrane. They also have a variety of membrane-bound organelles

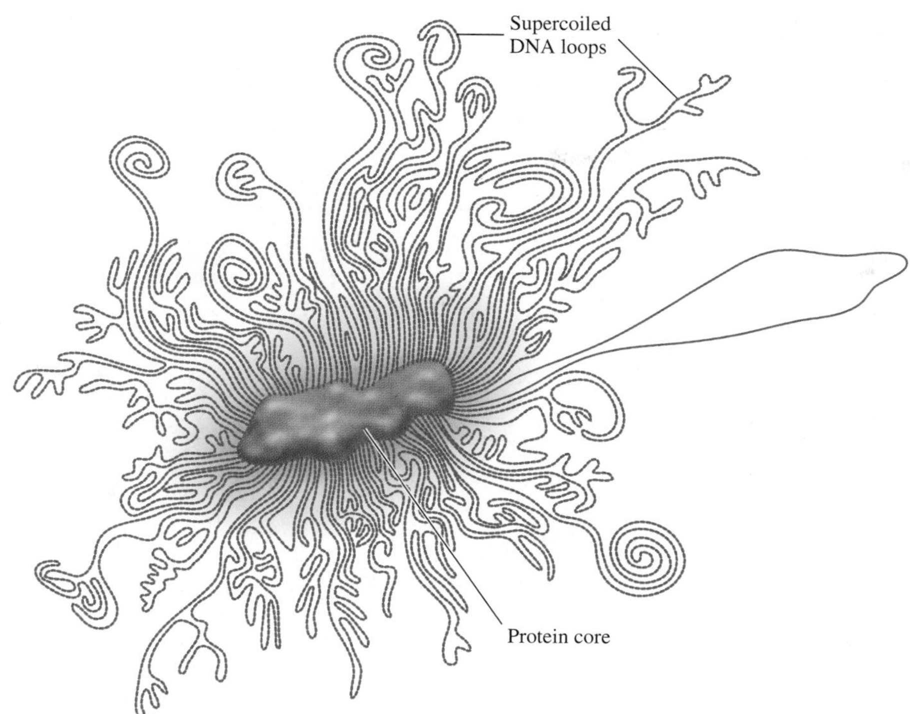

Figure 20.6 Structure of a bacterial nucleoid. The nucleoid is made up of the supercoiled, circular chromosome attached to a protein core.

that segregate different cellular functions into different compartments. As an example, the reactions of aerobic respiration are located within the mitochondria.

All animals, plants, and fungi are eukaryotes. The number and size of the chromosomes of eukaryotes vary from one species to the next. For instance, humans have twenty-three pairs of chromosomes, while the adder's tongue fern has 631 pairs of chromosomes. But the chromosome structure is the same for all those organisms that have been studied.

Eukaryotic chromosomes are very complex structures (Figure 20.7). The first level of structure is the **nucleosome,** which consists of a strand of DNA wrapped around a small disk made up of histone proteins. At this level the DNA looks like beads along a string. The string of beads then coils into a larger structure called the *30 nm fiber.* These, in turn, are further coiled into a *200 nm fiber.* Other proteins are probably involved in the organization of the 200 nm fiber. The full complexities of the eukaryotic chromosome are not yet understood, but there are probably many such levels of coiled structures.

Some human genetic disorders are characterized by unusual chromosome numbers. For instance, Down syndrome is characterized by an extra copy of chromosome 21. The presence of this additional chromosome causes the traits associated with Down syndrome, including varying degrees of mental challenges, a flattened face, and short stature. The presence of an additional chromosome 18 causes Edward syndrome and an extra chromosome 13 causes Patau syndrome. Both of these are extremely rare and result in extreme mental and physical defects and early death. The presence of extra copies of the sex chromosomes, X or Y, is not lethal. Males with two X chromosomes and one Y suffer from Klinefelter syndrome and show sexual immaturity and breast development. Males with an extra Y chromosome are unusually tall, as are women with three X chromosomes. A woman with only a single X chromosome experiences Turner syndrome, including short stature, a webbed neck, and sexual immaturity. All other abnormalities in chromosome number are thought to be lethal to the fetus. In fact, it is thought that 50% of all miscarriages are the result of abnormal chromosome numbers.

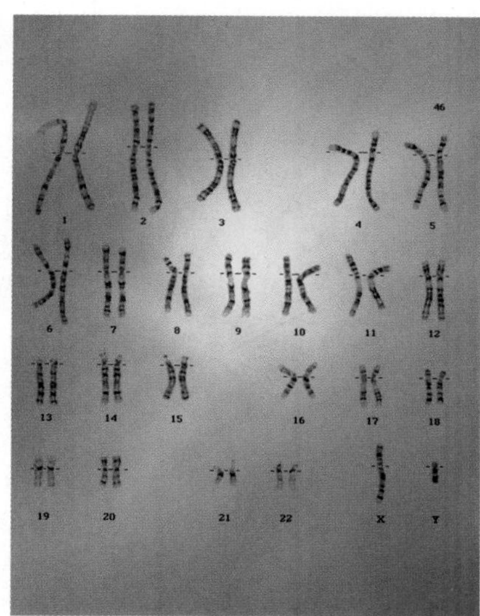

This karyotype shows the twenty-three pairs of chromosomes of humans. What type of genetic disorders could be identified by karyotyping?

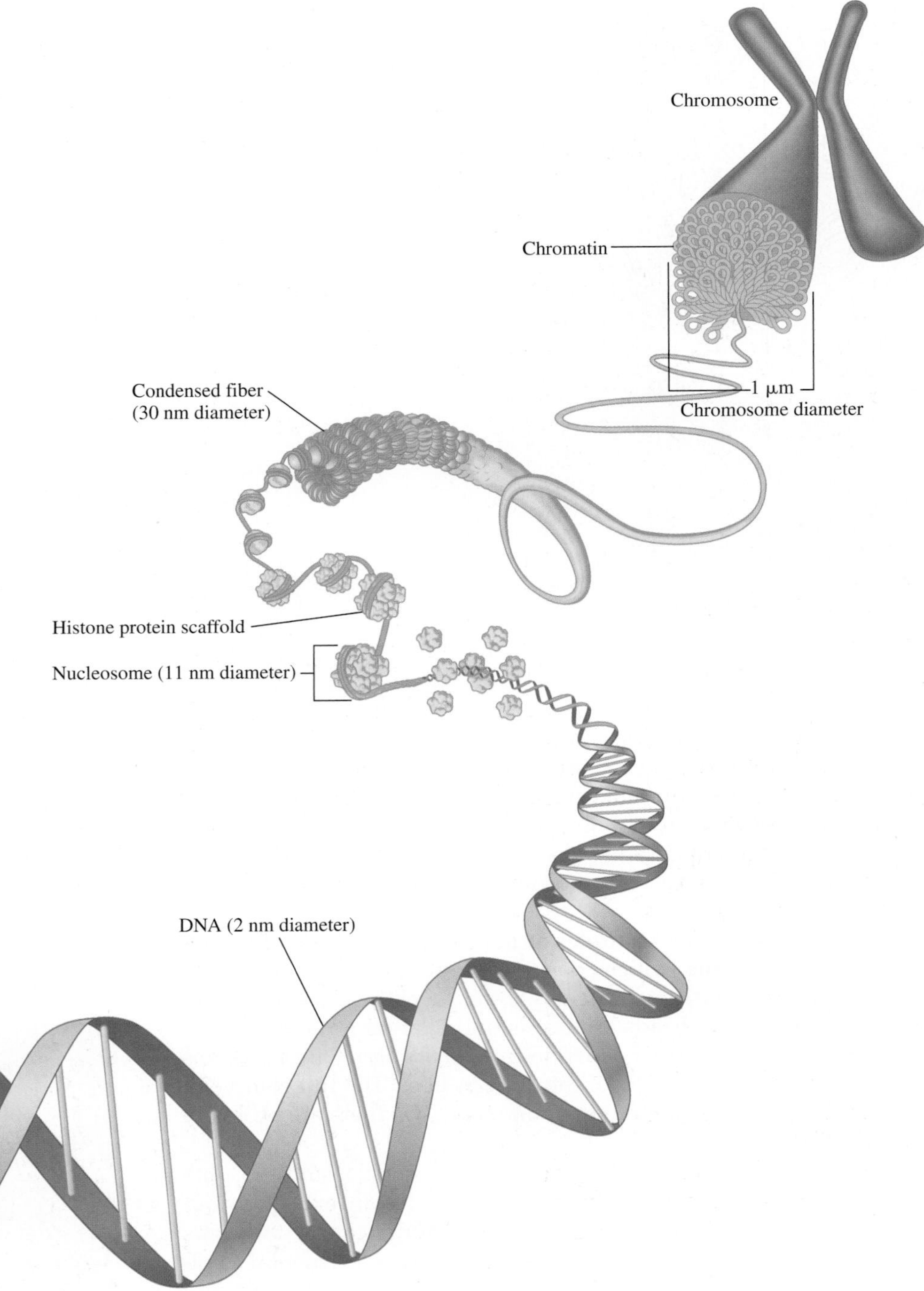

Figure 20.7 The eukaryotic chromosome has many levels of structure.

RNA Structure

The sugar-phosphate backbone of RNA consists of ribonucleotides, also linked by 3′–5′ phosphodiester bonds. These phosphodiester bonds are identical to those found in DNA. However, RNA molecules differ from DNA molecules in three basic properties.

- RNA molecules are usually *single-stranded.*
- The sugar-phosphate backbone of RNA consists of *ribonucleotides* linked by 3′–5′ phosphodiester bonds. Thus the sugar *ribose* is found in place of 2′-deoxyribose.
- The nitrogenous base *uracil* (U) replaces thymine (T).

A MEDICAL PERSPECTIVE

Molecular Genetics and Detection of Human Genetic Disorders

It is estimated that 3–5% of the human population suffers from a serious genetic defect. That's 350 million people! But what if genetic disease could be detected and "cured"? Two new technologies, *gene therapy* and *preimplantation diagnosis,* may help us realize this dream.

For a couple with a history of genetic disorders in the family, pregnancy is a time of anxiety. Through *genetic counseling* these couples can learn the probability that their child has the defect. For several hundred genetic disorders the uncertainty can be eliminated. *Amniocentesis* (removal of 10–20 milliliters (mL) of fluid from the sac around the fetus) and *chorionic villus sampling* (removal of cells from a fetal membrane) are two procedures that are used to obtain fetal cells for genetic testing. Fetal cells are cultured and tested by enzyme assays and DNA tests to look for genetic disorders. If a genetic defect is diagnosed, the parents must make a difficult decision: to abort the fetus or to carry the child to term and deal with the effects of the genetic disorder.

The power of modern molecular genetics is obvious in our ability to find a "bad" gene from just a few cells. But scientists have developed an even more impressive way to test for genetic defects before the embryo implants into the uterine lining. This technique, called *preimplantation diagnosis,* involves fertilizing a human egg and allowing the resulting zygote to divide in a sterile petri dish. When the zygote consists of eight to sixteen cells, *one* cell is removed for genetic testing. Only genetically normal embryos are implanted in the mother. Thus, the genetic defects that we can detect could be eliminated from the population by preimplantation diagnosis because only a zygote with "good" genes is used.

Gene therapy is a second way in which genetic disorders may one day be eliminated. Foreign genes, including one for growth hormone, have been introduced into fertilized mouse eggs and the zygotes implanted in female mice. The baby mice born with the foreign growth hormone gene were about three times larger than their normal littermates! One day, this kind of technology may be used to introduce normal genes into human fertilized eggs carrying a defective gene, thereby replacing the defective gene with a normal one.

In this chapter we will examine the molecules that carry and express our genetic information, DNA and RNA. Only by understanding the structure and function of these molecules have we been able to develop the amazing array of genetic tools that currently exists. We hope that as we continue to learn more about human genetics, we will be able to detect and one day correct most of the known genetic disorders.

For Further Understanding

- Go online to investigate the concerns that limit the use of gene therapy in humans.
- What is the advantage of preimplantation diagnosis?

Although RNA molecules are single-stranded, base pairing between uracil and adenine and between guanine and cytosine can still occur. We will show the importance of this property as we examine the way in which RNA molecules are involved in the expression of the genetic information in DNA.

20.3 DNA Replication

LEARNING GOAL

3 Explain DNA replication.

DNA must be replicated before a cell divides so that each daughter cell inherits a copy of each gene. A cell that is missing a critical gene will die, just as an individual with a genetic disorder, a defect in an important gene, may die early in life. Thus it is essential that the process of DNA replication produces an absolutely accurate copy of the original genetic information. If mistakes are made in critical genes, the result may be lethal mutations.

The structure of the DNA molecule suggested the mechanism for its accurate replication. Since adenine can base pair only with thymine and cytosine with guanine, Watson and Crick first suggested that an enzyme could "read" the nitrogenous bases on one strand of a DNA molecule and add complementary bases to a strand of DNA being synthesized. The product of this mechanism would be a new DNA molecule in which one strand is the original, or parent, strand and the second strand is a newly synthesized, or daughter, strand. This mode of DNA replication is called **semiconservative replication** (Figure 20.8).

Isotopes are atoms of the same element having the same number of protons but different numbers of neutrons and, therefore, different mass numbers.

Experimental evidence for this mechanism of DNA replication was provided by an experiment designed by Matthew Meselson and Franklin Stahl in 1958. *Escherichia coli* cells were grown in a medium in which $^{15}NH_4^+$ was the sole nitrogen source. ^{15}N is a nonradioactive, heavy isotope of nitrogen. Thus, growing the cells in this medium resulted in all of the cellular DNA containing this heavy isotope.

The cells containing only $^{15}NH_4^+$ were then added to a medium containing only the abundant isotope of nitrogen, $^{14}NH_4^+$, and were allowed to grow for one cycle of cell division. When the daughter DNA molecules were isolated and analyzed, it was found that each was made up of one strand of "heavy" DNA, the parental strand, and one strand of "light" DNA, the new daughter strand. After a second round of cell division, half of the isolated DNA contained no ^{15}N and half contained a 50/50 mixture of ^{14}N and ^{15}N-labeled DNA (Figure 20.9). This demonstrated conclusively that each parental strand of the DNA molecule serves as the template for the synthesis of a daughter strand and that each newly synthesized DNA molecule is composed of one parental strand and one newly synthesized daughter strand.

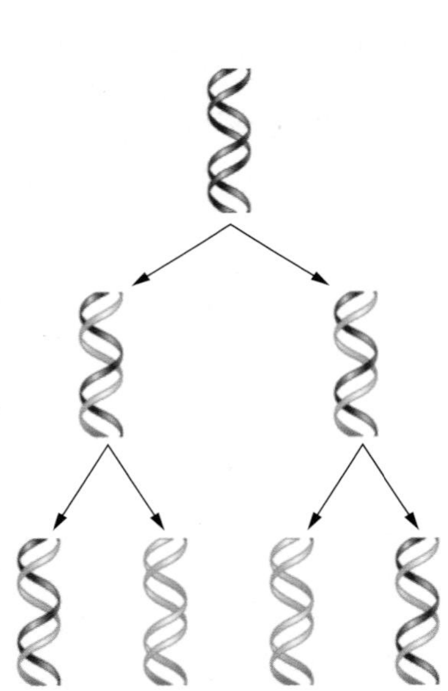

Figure 20.9 Representation of the Meselson and Stahl experiment. The DNA from cells grown in medium containing $^{15}NH_4^+$ is shown in purple. After a single generation in medium containing $^{14}NH_4^+$, the daughter DNA molecules have one ^{15}N-labeled parent strand and one ^{14}N-labeled daughter strand (blue). After a second generation in $^{14}NH_4^+$ containing medium, there are equal numbers of $^{14}N/^{15}N$ DNA molecules and $^{14}N/^{14}N$ DNA molecules.

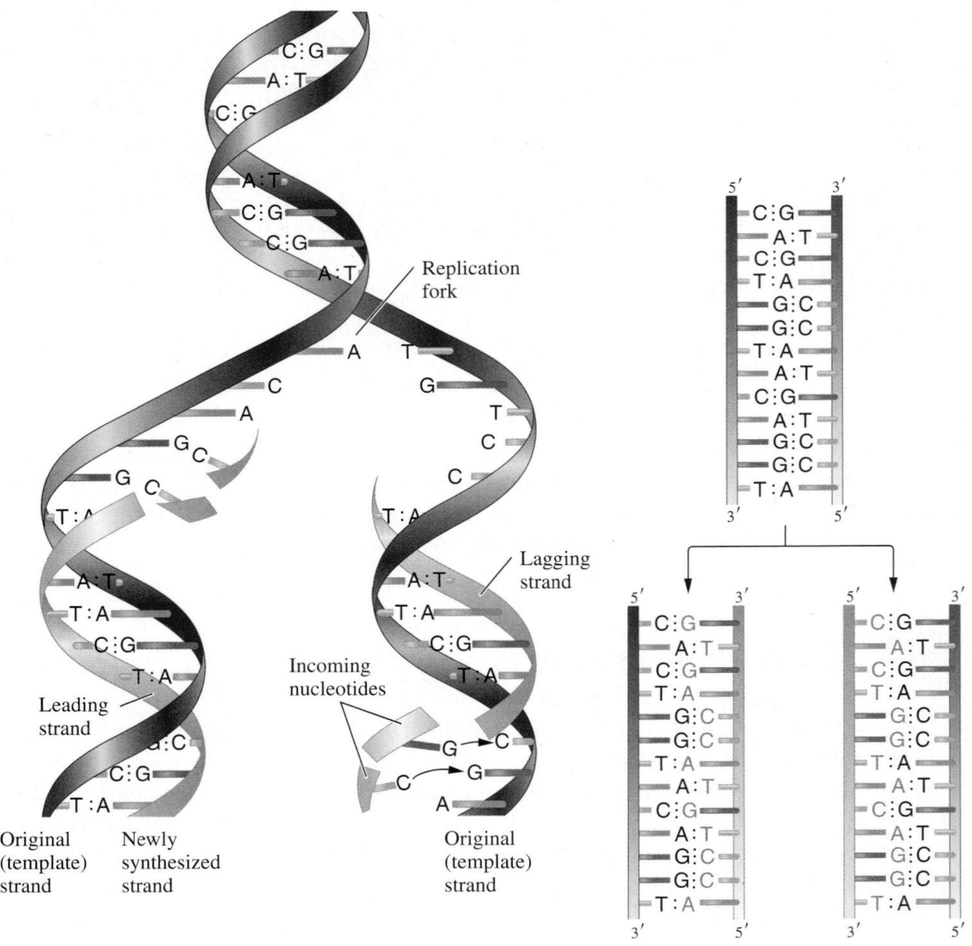

(a) The mechanism of DNA replication (b) The products of replication

Figure 20.8 In semiconservative DNA replication, each parent strand serves as a template for the synthesis of a new daughter strand.

Bacterial DNA Replication

ANIMATIONS
- How Nucleotides Are Added in DNA Replication
- DNA Replication Fork
- Bidirectional DNA Replication
- DNA Replication (*E. coli*)

The bacterial chromosome is a circular molecule of DNA made up of about three million nucleotides. DNA replication begins at a unique sequence on the circular chromosome known as the **replication origin** (Figure 20.10). Replication occurs bidirectionally at the rate of about 500 new nucleotides every second! The point at which the new deoxyribonucleotide is added to the growing daughter strand is called the **replication fork** (Figure 20.10). It is here that the DNA has been opened to allow binding of the various proteins and enzymes responsible for DNA replication. Since DNA synthesis occurs bidirectionally, there are two replication forks moving in opposite directions. Replication is complete when the replication forks collide approximately half way around the circular chromosome.

The first step in DNA replication (Figure 20.11) is the separation of the strands of DNA. The protein *helicase* does this by breaking the hydrogen bonds between the base pairs. This, in turn, causes supercoiling of the molecule. This stress is relieved by the enzyme *topoisomerase,* which travels along the DNA ahead of the replication fork. At this point, *single-strand binding protein* binds to the separated strands, preventing them from coming back together. In the next step, the enzyme *primase* catalyzes the synthesis of a small piece of RNA (ten to twelve nucleotides) called an *RNA primer* that serves to "prime" the process of DNA replication.

Now the enzyme **DNA polymerase III** "reads" each parental strand, also called the *template,* and catalyzes the polymerization of a complementary daughter strand. Deoxyribonucleotide triphosphate molecules are the precursors for DNA replication (Figure 20.12). In this reaction, a pyrophosphate group is released as a phosphoester bond is formed between the 5′-phosphoryl group of the nucleotide being added to the chain and the 3′-OH of the nucleotide on the daughter strand. This is called 5′ to 3′ synthesis.

One complicating factor in the process of DNA replication is the fact that the two strands of DNA are antiparallel to one another. DNA polymerase III can only catalyze DNA chain elongation in the 5′ to 3′ direction, yet the replication fork proceeds in one direction, while both strands are replicated simultaneously. Another complication is the need for an RNA primer to serve as the starting point for DNA replication. As a result of these two obstacles, there are different mechanisms for replication of the two strands. One strand, called the **leading strand,** is replicated continuously. The opposite strand, called the **lagging strand,** is replicated discontinuously.

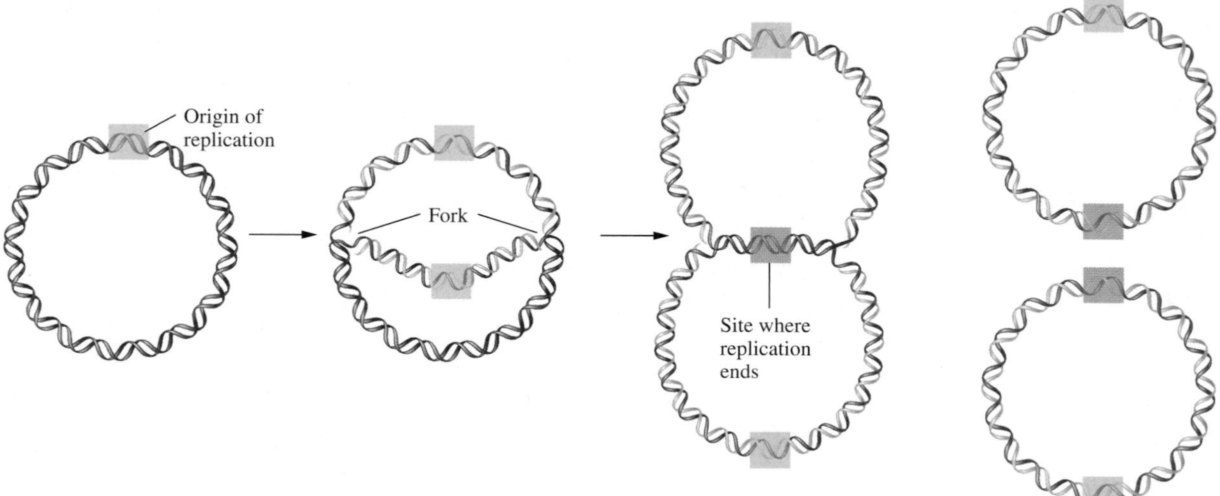

Figure 20.10 Bacterial chromosome replication.

Functions of key proteins involved with DNA replication

- **DNA helicase** breaks the hydrogen bonds between the DNA strands.
- **Topoisomerase** alleviates positive supercoiling.
- **Single-strand binding proteins** keep the parental strands apart.
- **Primase** synthesizes an RNA primer.
- **DNA polymerase III** synthesizes a daughter strand of DNA.
- **DNA polymerase I** excises the RNA primers and fills in with DNA.
- **DNA ligase** covalently links the DNA fragments together.

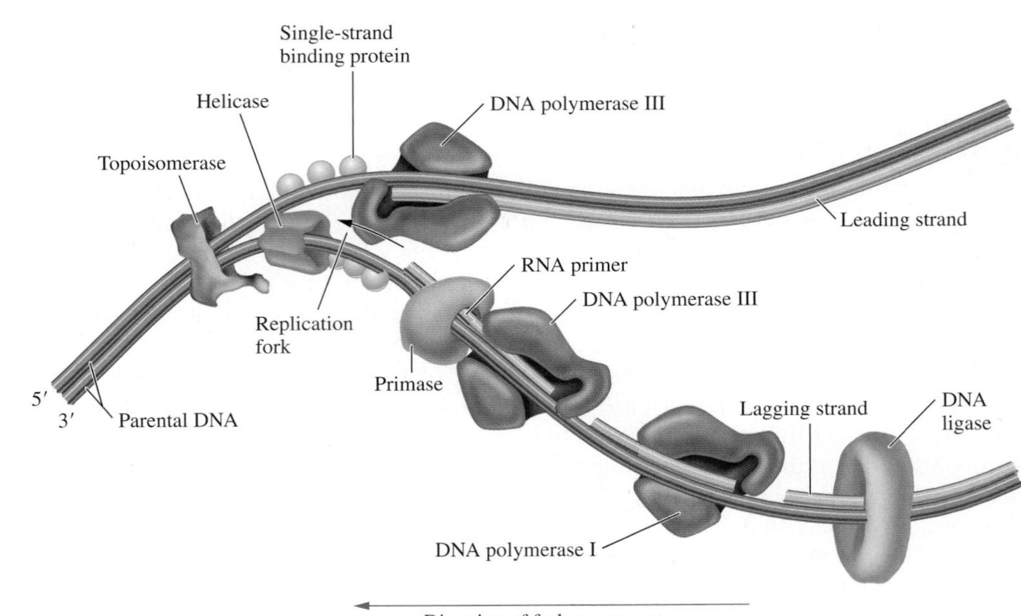

Figure 20.11 Because the two strands of DNA are antiparallel and DNA polymerase can only catalyze 5′ ⟶ 3′ replication, only one of the two DNA strands (top strand) can be read continuously to produce a daughter strand. The other must be synthesized in segments that are extended away from the direction of movement of the replication fork (bottom strand). These discontinuous segments are later covalently joined together by DNA ligase.

The two mechanisms are shown in Figures 20.11 and 20.12. For the leading strand, a single RNA primer is produced at the replication origin and DNA polymerase III continuously catalyzes the addition of nucleotides in the 5′ to 3′ direction, beginning with addition of the first nucleotide to the RNA primer.

On the lagging strand, many RNA primers are produced as the replication fork proceeds along the molecule. DNA polymerase III catalyzes DNA chain elongation from each of these primers. When the new strand "bumps" into a previous one, synthesis stops at that site. Meanwhile, at the replication fork, a new primer is being synthesized by primase. The final steps of synthesis on the lagging strand involve removal of the primers, repair of the gaps, and sealing of the fragments into an intact strand of DNA. The enzyme DNA polymerase I catalyzes the removal of the RNA primer and its replacement with DNA nucleotides. In the final step of the process, the enzyme DNA ligase catalyzes the formation of a phosphoester bond between the two adjacent fragments. It is little wonder that this is referred to as lagging strand replication! A more accurate model of the replication fork is shown in Figure 20.13.

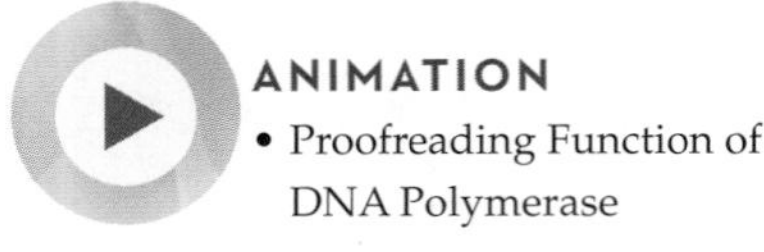

ANIMATION
- Proofreading Function of DNA Polymerase

Because it is critical to produce an accurate copy of the parental DNA, it is very important to avoid errors in the replication process. In addition to catalyzing the replication of new DNA, DNA polymerase III is able to proofread the newly synthesized strand. If the wrong nucleotide has been added to the growing DNA strand, it is removed and replaced with the correct one. In this way, a faithful copy of the parental DNA is ensured.

Eukaryotic DNA Replication

DNA replication in eukaryotes is more complex. The human genome consists of approximately three billion nucleotide pairs. Just one chromosome may be nearly 100 times longer than a bacterial chromosome. To accomplish this huge job, DNA replication begins at many replication origins and proceeds bidirectionally along each chromosome.

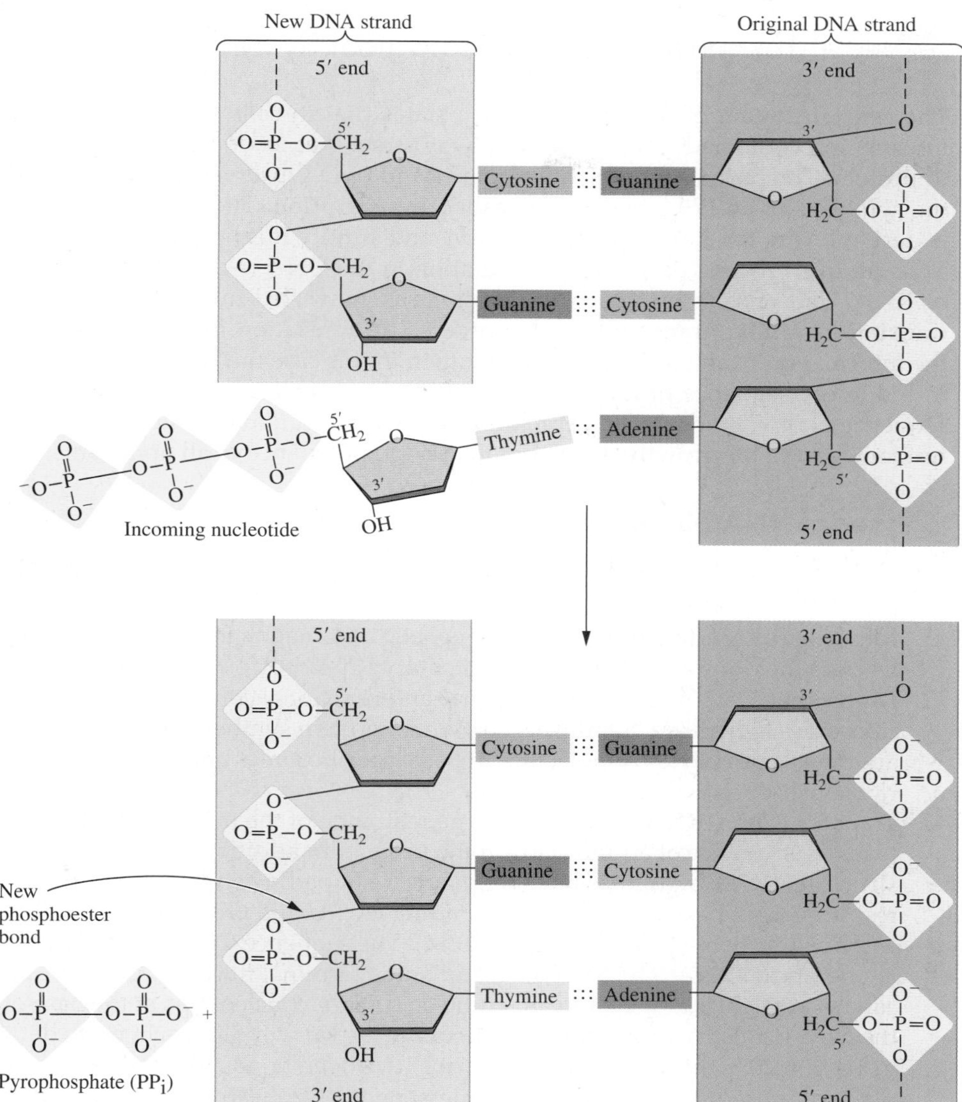

Figure 20.12 The reaction catalyzed by DNA polymerase.

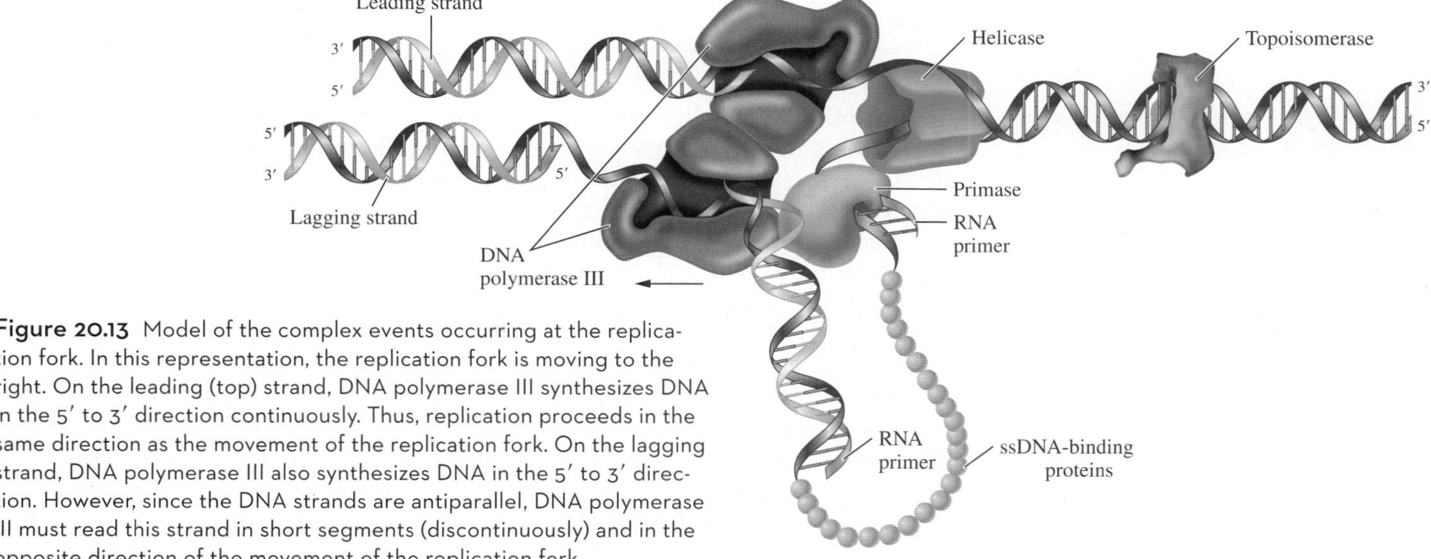

Figure 20.13 Model of the complex events occurring at the replication fork. In this representation, the replication fork is moving to the right. On the leading (top) strand, DNA polymerase III synthesizes DNA in the 5′ to 3′ direction continuously. Thus, replication proceeds in the same direction as the movement of the replication fork. On the lagging strand, DNA polymerase III also synthesizes DNA in the 5′ to 3′ direction. However, since the DNA strands are antiparallel, DNA polymerase III must read this strand in short segments (discontinuously) and in the opposite direction of the movement of the replication fork.

20.4 Information Flow in Biological Systems

The **central dogma** of molecular biology states that in cells the flow of genetic information contained in DNA is a one-way street that leads from DNA to RNA to protein. The process by which a single strand of DNA serves as a template for the synthesis of an RNA molecule is called **transcription.** The word *transcription* is derived from the Latin word *transcribere* and simply means "to make a copy." Thus, in this process, part of the information in the DNA is copied into a strand of RNA. The process by which the message is converted into protein is called **translation.** Unlike transcription, the process of translation involves converting the information from one language to another. In this case the genetic information in the linear sequence of nucleotides is being translated into a protein, a linear sequence of amino acids. The expression of the information contained in DNA is fundamental to the growth, development, and maintenance of all organisms.

Classes of RNA Molecules

LEARNING GOAL

4 List three classes of RNA molecules and describe their functions.

Three classes of RNA molecules are produced by transcription: messenger RNA, transfer RNA, and ribosomal RNA.

1. **Messenger RNA (mRNA)** carries the genetic information for a protein from DNA to the ribosomes. It is a complementary RNA copy of a gene on the DNA.
2. **Ribosomal RNA (rRNA)** is a structural and functional component of the ribosomes, which are "platforms" on which protein synthesis occurs. There are three types of rRNA molecules in bacterial ribosomes and four in the ribosomes of eukaryotes.
3. **Transfer RNA (tRNA)** translates the genetic code of the mRNA into the primary sequence of amino acids in the protein. In addition to the primary structure, tRNA molecules have a cloverleaf-shaped secondary structure resulting from base pair hydrogen bonding (A—U and G—C) and a roughly L-shaped tertiary structure (Figure 20.14). The sequence CCA is found at the 3′ end of the tRNA. The 3′—OH group of the terminal nucleotide, adenosine, can be covalently attached to an amino acid. Three nucleotides at the base of the cloverleaf structure form the **anticodon.** As we will discuss in more detail in Section 20.6, this triplet of bases forms hydrogen bonds to a **codon** (complementary sequence of bases) on a messenger RNA (mRNA) molecule on the surface of a ribosome during protein synthesis. This hydrogen bonding of codon and anticodon brings the correct amino acid to the site of protein synthesis at the appropriate location in the growing peptide chain.

Transcription

LEARNING GOAL

5 Explain the process of transcription.

Transcription, shown in Figure 20.15, is catalyzed by the enzyme **RNA polymerase.** The process occurs in three stages. The first, called *initiation,* involves binding of RNA polymerase to a specific nucleotide sequence, the **promoter,** at the beginning of a gene. This interaction of RNA polymerase with specific promoter DNA sequences allows RNA polymerase to recognize the start point for transcription. It also determines which DNA strand will be transcribed. Unlike DNA replication, transcription produces a complementary copy of only one of the two strands of DNA. As it binds to the DNA, RNA polymerase separates the two strands of DNA so that it can "read" the base sequence of the DNA.

The second stage, chain elongation, begins as the RNA polymerase "reads" the DNA template strand and catalyzes the polymerization of a complementary RNA copy. With each step, RNA polymerase transfers a complementary ribonucleotide to the end of the growing RNA chain and catalyzes the formation of a 3′–5′ phosphodiester bond between the 5′ phosphoryl group of the incoming ribonucleotide and the 3′ hydroxyl group of the last ribonucleotide of the growing RNA chain.

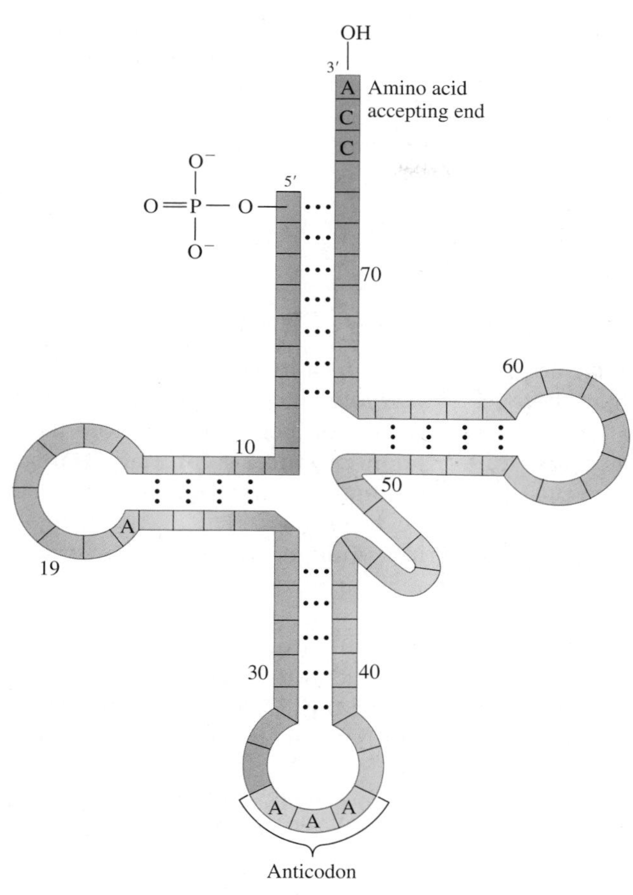

Figure 20.14 Structure of tRNA. The primary structure of a tRNA is the linear sequence of ribonucleotides. Here we see the hydrogen-bonded secondary structure of a tRNA showing the three loops and the amino acid accepting end.

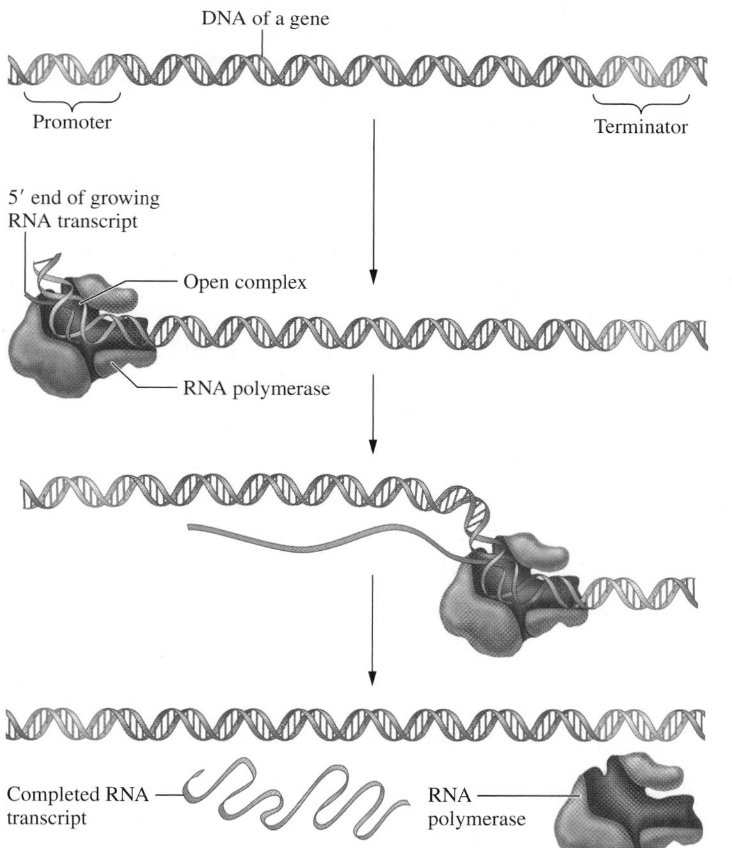

Figure 20.15 The stages of transcription.

Initiation

Elongation/synthesis of the RNA transcript

Termination

The final stage of transcription is termination. The RNA polymerase finds a termination sequence at the end of the gene and releases the newly formed RNA molecule.

Question 20.3 What is the function of RNA polymerase in the process of transcription?

Question 20.4 What is the function of the promoter sequence in the process of transcription?

Post-transcriptional Processing of RNA

LEARNING GOAL

6 List and explain the three types of post-transcriptional modifications of eukaryotic mRNA.

In bacteria, which are prokaryotes, termination releases a mature mRNA for translation. In fact, because prokaryotes have no nuclear membrane separating the DNA from the cytoplasm, translation begins long before the mRNA is completed. In eukaryotes, transcription produces a **primary transcript** that must undergo extensive **post-transcriptional modification** before it is exported out of the nucleus for translation in the cytoplasm.

Eukaryotic primary transcripts undergo three post-transcriptional modifications. These are the addition of a 5′ cap structure and a 3′ poly(A) tail, and RNA splicing.

In the first modification, a **cap structure** is enzymatically added to the 5′ end of the primary transcript. The cap structure (Figure 20.16) consists of 7-methylguanosine attached to the 5′ end of the RNA by a 5′–5′ triphosphate bridge. The first two nucleotides of the mRNA are also methylated. The cap structure is required for efficient translation of the final mature mRNA.

The second modification is the enzymatic addition of a **poly(A) tail** to the 3′ end of the transcript. *Poly(A) polymerase* uses ATP and catalyzes the stepwise

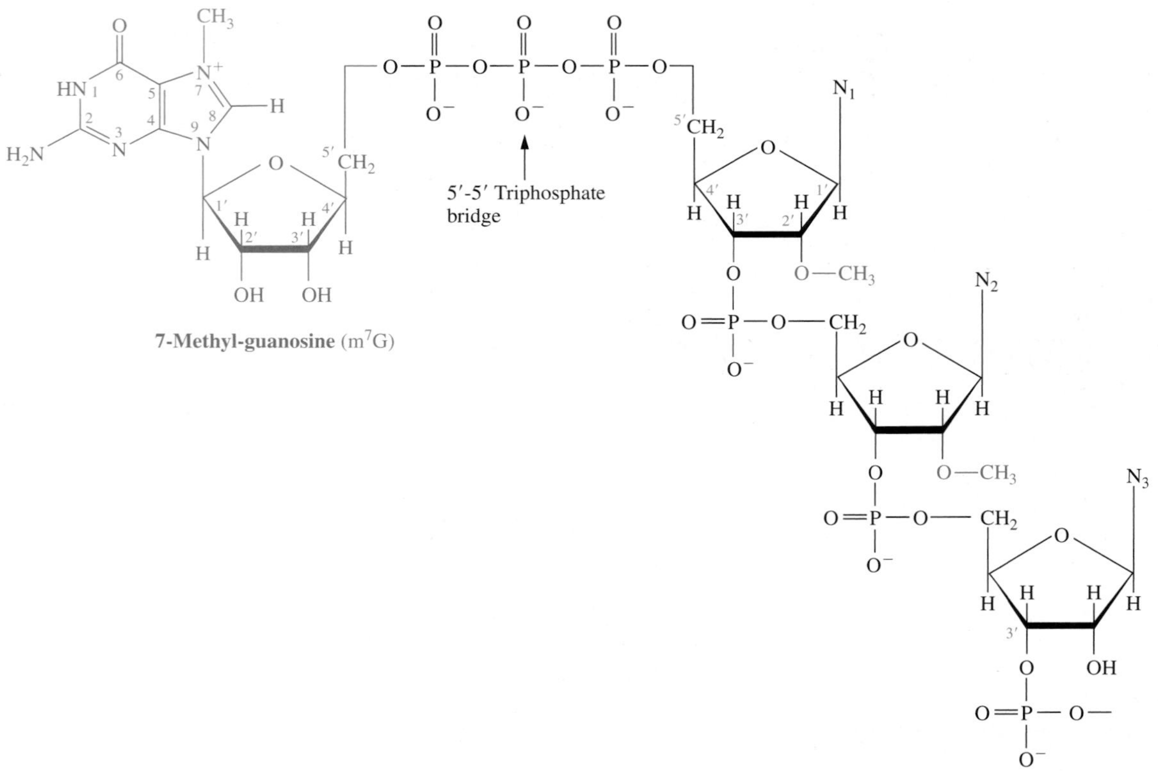

7-Methyl-guanosine (m^7G)

5′-5′ Triphosphate bridge

Figure 20.16 The 5′-methylated cap structure of eukaryotic mRNA. N_1, N_2, and N_3 represent any of the four nitrogenous bases adenine, guanine, cytosine, or uracil.

polymerization of 100 to 200 adenosine nucleotides on the 3′ end of the RNA. The poly(A) tail protects the 3′ end of the mRNA from enzymatic degradation and thus prolongs the lifetime of the mRNA.

The third modification, **RNA splicing,** involves the removal of portions of the primary transcript that are not protein coding. Bacterial genes are continuous; all the nucleotide sequences of the gene are found in the mRNA. However, study of the gene structure of eukaryotes revealed a fascinating difference. Eukaryotic genes are discontinuous; there are *extra* DNA sequences within these genes that do not encode any amino acid sequences for the protein. These sequences are called *intervening sequences* or **introns.** The primary transcript contains both the introns and the protein coding sequences, called **exons.** The presence of introns in the mRNA would make it impossible for the process of translation to synthesize the correct protein. Therefore they must be removed, which is done by the process of RNA splicing.

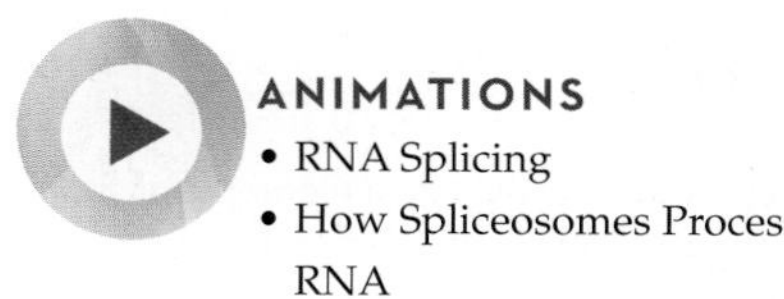

ANIMATIONS
- RNA Splicing
- How Spliceosomes Process RNA

As you can imagine, RNA splicing must be very precise. If too much, or too little, RNA is removed, the mRNA will not carry the correct code for the protein. Thus, there are "signals" in the DNA to mark the boundaries of the introns. The sequence GpU is always found at the intron's 5′ boundary and the sequence ApG is found at the 3′ boundary.

Recognition of the splice boundaries and stabilization of the splicing complex requires the assistance of particles called *spliceosomes.* Spliceosomes are composed of a variety of *small nuclear ribonucleoproteins* (snRNPs, read "snurps"). Each snRNP consists of a small RNA and associated proteins. The RNA components of different snRNPs are complementary to different sequences involved in splicing. By hydrogen bonding to a splice boundary or intron sequences the snRNPs recognize and bring together the sequences involved in the splicing reactions.

One of the first eukaryotic genes shown to contain introns was the gene for the β subunit of adult hemoglobin (Figure 20.17). On the DNA, the gene for β-hemoglobin is 1200 nucleotides long, but only 438 nucleotides carry the genetic information for protein. The remaining sequences are found in two introns of 116 and 646 nucleotides that are removed by splicing before translation. It is interesting that the larger intron is longer than the final β-hemoglobin mRNA! In the genes that have been studied, introns have been found to range in size from 50 to 20,000 nucleotides in length, and there may be many throughout a gene. Thus a typical human gene might be ten to thirty times longer than the final mRNA.

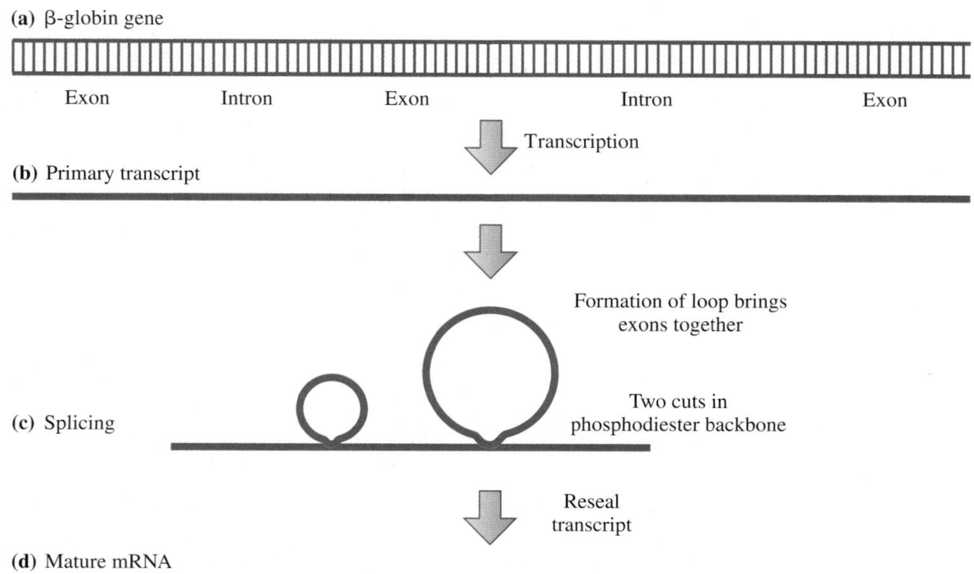

Figure 20.17 Schematic diagram of mRNA splicing. (a) The β-globin gene contains protein coding exons, as well as noncoding sequences called *introns.* (b) The primary transcript of the DNA carries both the introns and the exons. (c) The introns are looped out, the phosphodiester backbone of the mRNA is cut twice, and the pieces are tied together. (d) The final mature mRNA now carries only the coding sequences (exons) of the gene.

20.5 The Genetic Code

LEARNING GOAL

7 Describe the essential elements of the genetic code, and develop a "feel" for its elegance.

The mRNA carries the genetic code for a protein. But what is the nature of this code? In 1954, George Gamow proposed that because there are only four "letters" in the DNA alphabet (A, T, G, and C) and because there are twenty amino acids, the genetic code must contain words made of at least three letters taken from the four letters in the DNA alphabet. How did he come to this conclusion? He reasoned that a code of two-letter words constructed from any combination of the four letters has a "vocabulary" of only sixteen words (4^2). In other words, there are only sixteen different ways to put A, T, C, and G together two bases at a time (AA, AT, AC, AG, TT, TA, etc.). That is not enough to encode all twenty amino acids. A code of four-letter words gives 256 words (4^4), far more than are needed. A code of three-letter words, however, has a possible vocabulary of sixty-four words (4^3), sufficient to encode the twenty amino acids but not too excessive.

A series of elegant experiments proved that Gamow was correct by demonstrating that the genetic code is, indeed, a triplet code. Mutations were introduced into the DNA of a bacterial virus. These mutations inserted (or deleted) one, two, or three nucleotides into a gene. The researchers then looked for the protein encoded by that gene. When one or two nucleotides were inserted, no protein was produced. However, when a third base was inserted, the sense of the mRNA was restored, and the protein was made. You can imagine this experiment by using a sentence composed of only three-letter words. For instance,

THE CAT RAN OUT

What happens to the "sense" of the sentence if we insert one letter?

THE FCA TRA NOU T

The reading frame of the sentence has been altered, and the sentence is now nonsense. Can we now restore the sense of the sentence by inserting a second letter?

THE FAC ATR ANO UT

No, we have not restored the sense of the sentence. Once again, we have altered the reading frame, but because our code has only three-letter words, the sentence is still nonsense. If we now insert a third letter, it should restore the correct reading frame:

THE FAT CAT RAN OUT

Indeed, by inserting three new letters we have restored the sense of the message by restoring the reading frame. This is exactly the way in which the message of the mRNA is interpreted. Each group of three nucleotides in the sequence of the mRNA is called a *codon,* and each codes for a single amino acid. If the sequence is interrupted or changed, it can change the amino acid composition of the protein that is produced or even result in the production of no protein at all.

As we noted, a three-letter genetic code contains sixty-four words, called *codons,* but there are only twenty amino acids. Thus, there are forty-four more codons than are required to specify all of the amino acids found in proteins. Three of the codons—UAA, UAG, and UGA—specify termination signals for the process of translation. But this still leaves us with forty-one additional codons. What is the function of the "extra" code words? Francis Crick (recall Watson and Crick and the double helix) proposed that the genetic code is a **degenerate code.** The term *degenerate* is used to indicate that different triplet codons may serve as code words for the same amino acid.

The complete genetic code is shown in Figure 20.18. We can make several observations about the genetic code. First, methionine and tryptophan are the only amino acids that have a single codon. All others have at least two codons, and serine and leucine have six codons each. The genetic code is also somewhat

FIRST BASE	SECOND BASE				THIRD BASE
	U	C	A	G	
U	UUU Phenylalanine	UCU Serine	UAU Tyrosine	UGU Cysteine	U
U	UUC Phenylalanine	UCC Serine	UAC Tyrosine	UGC Cysteine	C
U	UUA Leucine	UCA Serine	UAA STOP	UGA STOP	A
U	UUG Leucine	UCG Serine	UAG STOP	UGG Tryptophan	G
C	CUU Leucine	CCU Proline	CAU Histidine	CGU Arginine	U
C	CUC Leucine	CCC Proline	CAC Histidine	CGC Arginine	C
C	CUA Leucine	CCA Proline	CAA Glutamine	CGA Arginine	A
C	CUG Leucine	CCG Proline	CAG Glutamine	CGG Arginine	G
A	AUU Isoleucine	ACU Threonine	AAU Asparagine	AGU Serine	U
A	AUC Isoleucine	ACC Threonine	AAC Asparagine	AGC Serine	C
A	AUA Isoleucine	ACA Threonine	AAA Lysine	AGA Arginine	A
A	AUG (*START*) Methionine	ACG Threonine	AAG Lysine	AGG Arginine	G
G	GUU Valine	GCU Alanine	GAU Aspartic acid	GGU Glycine	U
G	GUC Valine	GCC Alanine	GAC Aspartic acid	GGC Glycine	C
G	GUA Valine	GCA Alanine	GAA Glutamic acid	GGA Glycine	A
G	GUG Valine	GCG Alanine	GAG Glutamic acid	GGG Glycine	G

Cys
ACG
tRNA

Asn
UUG
tRNA

Figure 20.18 The genetic code. The table shows the possible codons found in mRNA. To read the universal biological language from this chart, find the first base in the column on the left, the second base from the row across the top, and the third base from the column to the right. This will direct you to one of the sixty-four squares in the matrix. Within that square you will find the codon and the amino acid that it specifies. In the cell this message is decoded by tRNA molecules like those shown to the right of the table.

mutation-resistant. For those amino acids that have multiple codons, the first two bases are often identical and thus identify the amino acid, and only the third position is variable. Mutations—changes in the nucleotide sequence—in the third position therefore often have no effect on the amino acid that is incorporated into a protein.

Question 20.5 Why is the genetic code said to be degenerate?

Question 20.6 Why is the genetic code said to be mutation-resistant?

20.6 Protein Synthesis

LEARNING GOAL

8 Describe the process of translation.

The process of protein synthesis is called *translation*. It involves translating the genetic information from the sequence of nucleotides into the sequence of amino acids in the primary structure of a protein. Figure 20.19 shows the relationship through which the nucleotide sequence of a DNA molecule is transcribed into a

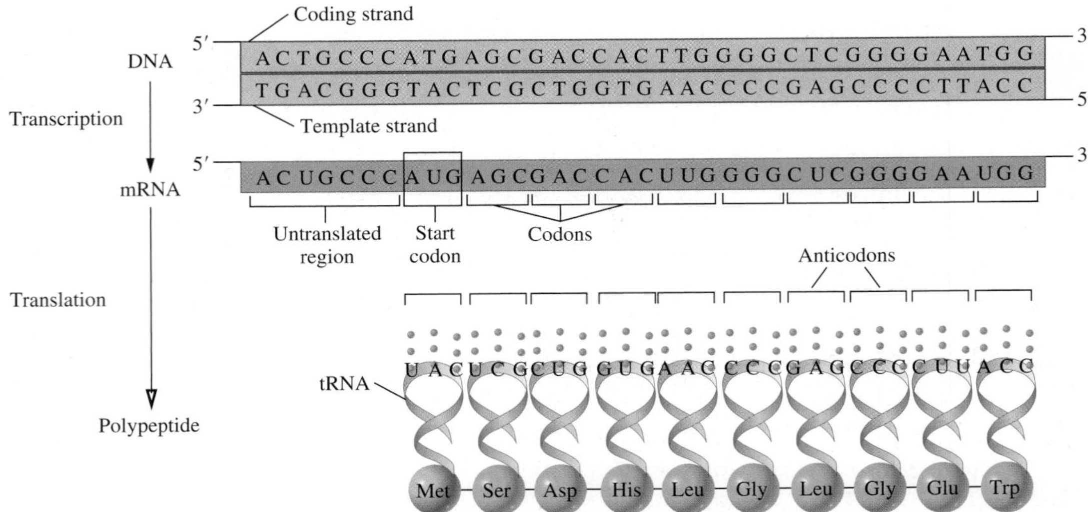

Figure 20.19 Messenger RNA (mRNA) is an RNA copy of one strand of a gene in the DNA. Each codon on the mRNA that specifies a particular amino acid is recognized by the complementary anticodon on a transfer RNA (tRNA).

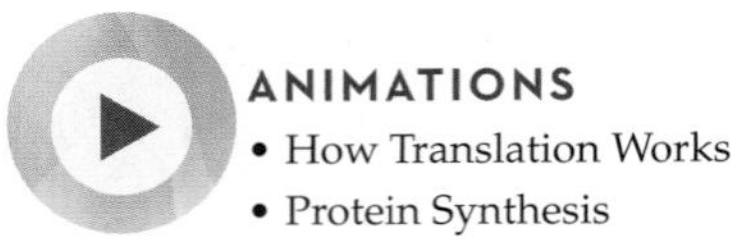

complementary sequence of ribonucleotides, the mRNA molecule. Each mRNA has a short untranslated region followed by the sequences that carry the information for the order of the amino acids in the protein that will be produced in the process of translation. That genetic information is the sequence of codons along the mRNA. The decoding process is carried out by tRNA molecules.

Translation is carried out on **ribosomes,** which are complexes of ribosomal RNA (rRNA) and proteins. Each ribosome is made up of two subunits: a small and a large ribosomal subunit (Figure 20.20a). In eukaryotic cells, the small ribosomal subunit contains one rRNA molecule and thirty-three different ribosomal proteins, and the large subunit contains three rRNA molecules and about forty-nine different proteins.

Protein synthesis involves the simultaneous action of many ribosomes on a single mRNA molecule. These complexes of many ribosomes along a single mRNA are known as *polyribosomes* or **polysomes** (Figure 20.20b). Each ribosome

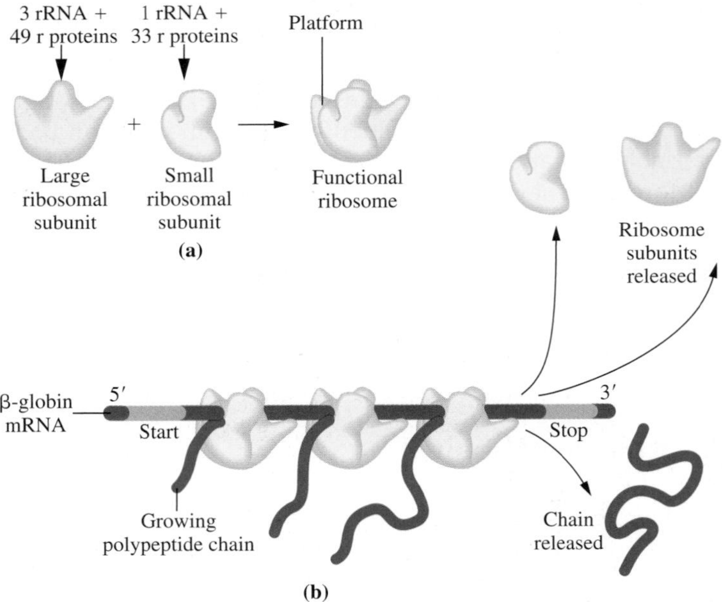

Figure 20.20 Structure of the ribosome. (a) The large and small subunits form the functional complex in association with an mRNA molecule. (b) A polyribosome translating the mRNA for a β-globin chain of hemoglobin.

synthesizes one copy of the protein molecule encoded by the mRNA. Thus, many copies of a protein are simultaneously produced.

The Role of Transfer RNA

The codons of mRNA must be read if the genetic message is to be translated into protein. The molecule that decodes the information in the mRNA molecule into the primary structure of a protein is transfer RNA (tRNA). To decode the genetic message into the primary sequence of a protein, the tRNA must faithfully perform two functions.

First, the tRNA must covalently bind one, and only one, specific amino acid. There is at least one transfer RNA for each amino acid. All tRNA molecules have the sequence CCA at their 3′ ends. This is the site where the amino acid will be covalently attached to the tRNA molecule. Each tRNA is specifically recognized by the active site of an enzyme called an **aminoacyl tRNA synthetase.** This enzyme also recognizes the correct amino acid and covalently links the amino acid to the 3′ end of the tRNA molecule (Figure 20.21). The resulting structure is called an **aminoacyl tRNA.** The covalently bound amino acid will be transferred from the tRNA to a growing polypeptide chain during protein synthesis.

Second, the tRNA must be able to recognize the appropriate codon on the mRNA that calls for that amino acid. This is mediated through a sequence of three bases called the *anticodon,* which is located at the bottom of the tRNA cloverleaf (refer to Figure 20.14). The anticodon sequence for each tRNA is complementary to the codon on the mRNA that specifies a particular amino acid. As you can see in Figure 20.19, the anticodon-codon complementary hydrogen bonding will bring the correct amino acid to the site of protein synthesis.

Question 20.7 How are codons related to anticodons?

Question 20.8 If the sequence of a codon on the mRNA is 5′-AUG-3′, what will the sequence of the anticodon be? Remember that the hydrogen bonding rules require antiparallel strands. It is easiest to write the anticodon first 3′⟶5′ and then reverse it to the 5′⟶3′ order.

The Process of Translation

LEARNING GOAL

8 Describe the process of translation.

Initiation

The first stage of protein synthesis is *initiation.* Proteins called **initiation factors** assist in the formation of a translation complex composed of an mRNA molecule, the small and large ribosomal subunits, and the initiator tRNA. This initiator tRNA recognizes the codon AUG and carries the amino acid methionine.

The ribosome has two sites for binding tRNA molecules. The first site, called the **peptidyl tRNA binding site (P-site),** holds the peptidyl tRNA, the growing peptide bound to a tRNA molecule. The second site, called the **aminoacyl tRNA binding site (A-site),** holds the aminoacyl tRNA carrying the next amino acid to be added to the peptide chain. Each of the tRNA molecules is hydrogen bonded to the mRNA molecule by codon-anticodon complementarity. The entire complex is further stabilized by the fact that the mRNA is also bound to the ribosome. Figure 20.22a shows the series of events that result in the formation of the initiation complex. The initiator methionyl tRNA occupies the P-site in this complex.

Chain Elongation

The second stage of translation is *chain elongation.* This occurs in three steps that are repeated until protein synthesis is complete. We enter the action after a

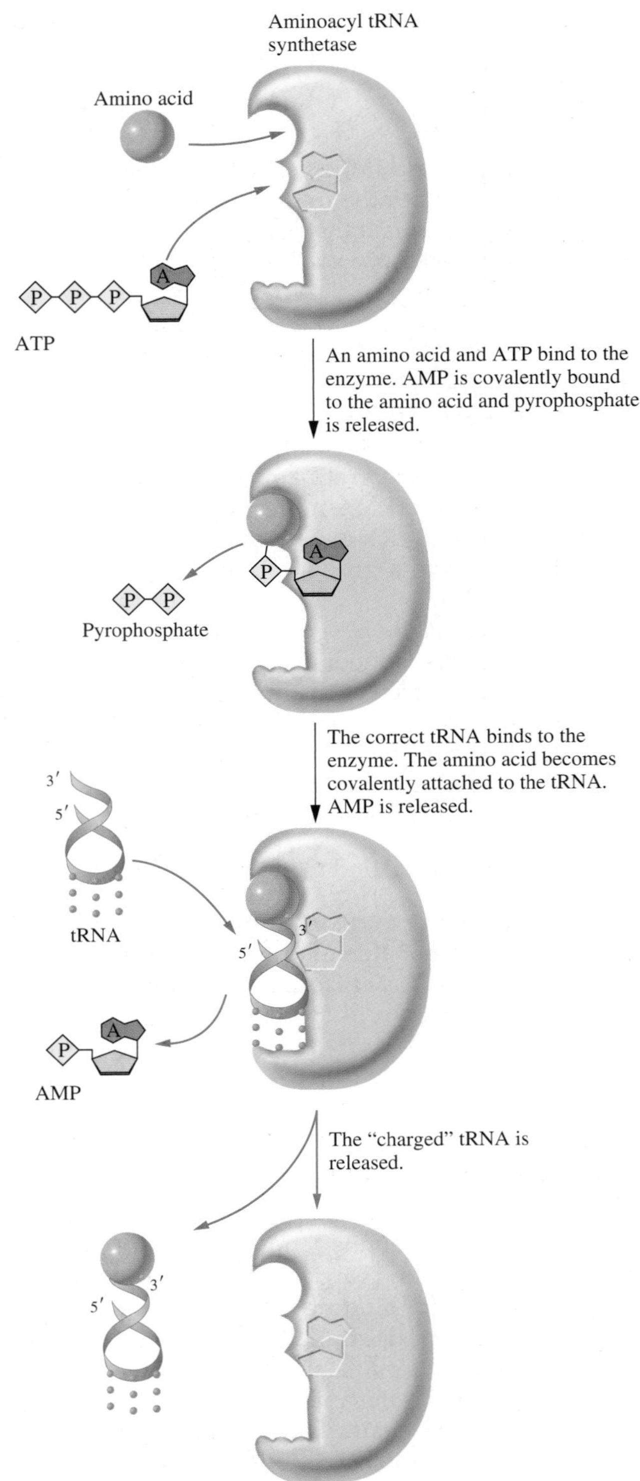
Aminoacyl tRNA synthetase
Amino acid
ATP
An amino acid and ATP bind to the enzyme. AMP is covalently bound to the amino acid and pyrophosphate is released.
Pyrophosphate
The correct tRNA binds to the enzyme. The amino acid becomes covalently attached to the tRNA. AMP is released.
tRNA
AMP
The "charged" tRNA is released.

Figure 20.21 Aminoacyl tRNA synthetase binds the amino acid in one region of the active site and the appropriate tRNA in another. The acylation reaction occurs and the aminoacyl tRNA is released.

tetrapeptide has already been assembled, and a peptidyl tRNA occupies the P-site (Figure 20.22b).

The first event is binding of an aminoacyl-tRNA molecule to the empty A-site. Next, peptide bond formation occurs. This is catalyzed by an enzyme on the ribosome called *peptidyl transferase.* Now the peptide chain is shifted to the tRNA that

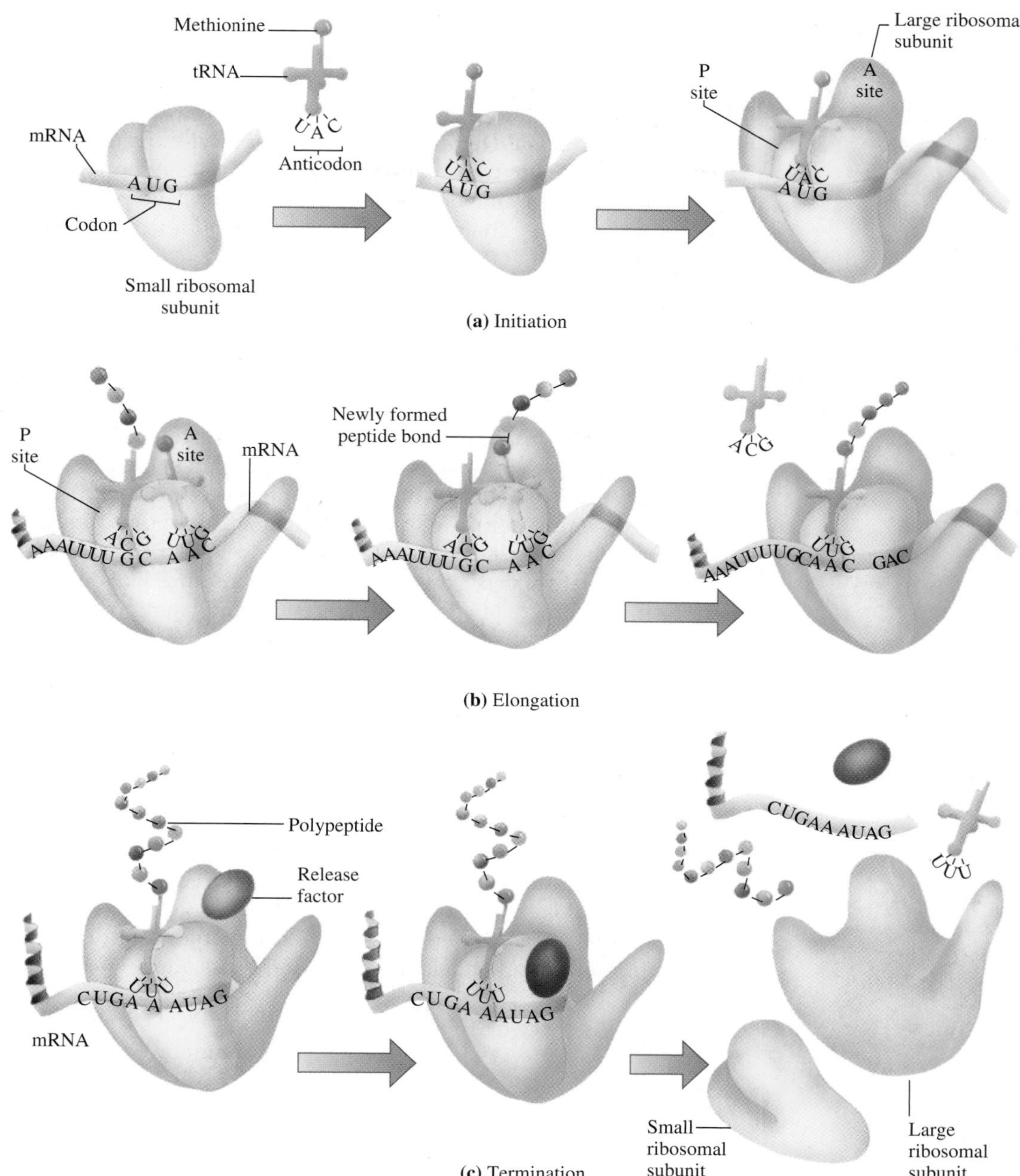

Figure 20.22 (a) Formation of an initiation complex sets protein synthesis in motion. The mRNA and proteins called *initiation factors* bind to the small ribosomal subunit. Next, a charged methionyl tRNA molecule binds, and finally, the initiation factors are released, and the large subunit binds. (b) The elongation phase of protein synthesis involves addition of new amino acids to the C-terminus of the growing peptide. An aminoacyl tRNA molecule binds at the empty A-site, and the peptide bond is formed. The uncharged tRNA molecule is released, and the peptidyl tRNA is shifted to the P-site as the ribosome moves along the mRNA. (c) Termination of protein synthesis occurs when a release factor binds the stop codon on mRNA. This leads to the hydrolysis of the ester bond linking the peptide to the peptidyl tRNA molecule in the P-site. The ribosome then dissociates into its two subunits, releasing the mRNA and the newly synthesized peptide.

occupies the A-site. Finally, the tRNA in the P-site falls away, and the ribosome changes positions so that the next codon on the mRNA occupies the A-site. This movement of the ribosome is called **translocation.** The process shifts the new peptidyl tRNA from the A-site to the P-site. The chain elongation stage of translation requires the hydrolysis of GTP to GDP and P_i. Several **elongation factors** are also involved in this process.

Recent evidence indicates that the peptidyl transferase is a catalytic region of the 28S ribosomal RNA.

Termination

The last stage of translation is *termination.* There are three **termination codons**—UAA, UAG, and UGA—for which there are no corresponding tRNA molecules. When one of these "stop" codons is encountered, translation is terminated. A **release factor** binds the empty A-site. The peptidyl transferase that had previously catalyzed peptide bond formation hydrolyzes the ester bond between the peptidyl tRNA and the last amino acid of the newly synthesized protein (Figure 20.22c). At this point the tRNA, the newly synthesized peptide, and the two ribosomal subunits are released.

Question 20.9 What is the function of the ribosomal P-site in protein synthesis?

Question 20.10 What is the function of the ribosomal A-site in protein synthesis?

Post-translational proteolytic cleavage of digestive enzymes is discussed in Section 19.11.

The quaternary structure of hemoglobin is described in Section 18.8.

The peptide that is released following translation is not necessarily in its final functional form. In some cases the peptide is proteolytically cleaved before it becomes functional. Synthesis of digestive enzymes uses this strategy. Sometimes the protein must associate with other peptides to form a functional protein, as in the case of hemoglobin. Cellular enzymes add carbohydrate or lipid groups to some proteins, especially those that will end up on the cell surface. These final modifications are specific for particular proteins and, like the sequence of the protein itself, are directed by the cellular genetic information.

20.7 Mutation, Ultraviolet Light, and DNA Repair

The Nature of Mutations

LEARNING GOAL

9 Define mutation and understand how mutations cause cancer and cell death.

Changes can occur in the nucleotide sequence of a DNA molecule. Such a genetic change is called a **mutation.** Mutations can arise from mistakes made by DNA polymerase during DNA replication. They also result from the action of chemicals, called **mutagens,** that damage the DNA.

Mutations are classified by the kind of change that occurs in the DNA. The substitution of a single nucleotide for another is called a **point mutation:**

ATGGACTTC: normal DNA sequence
ATGCACTTC: point mutation

Sometimes a single nucleotide or even large sections of DNA are lost. These are called **deletion mutations:**

ATGGACTTC: normal DNA sequence
ATGTTC: deletion mutation

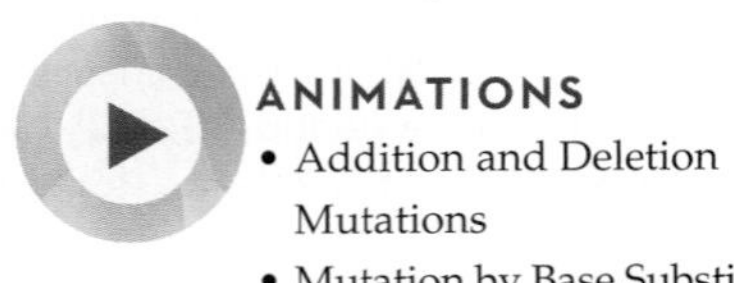

ANIMATIONS
• Addition and Deletion Mutations
• Mutation by Base Substitution

Occasionally, one or more nucleotides are added to a DNA sequence. These are called **insertion mutations:**

ATGGACTTC: normal DNA sequence
ATGCTCGACTTC: insertion mutation

The Results of Mutations

Some mutations are **silent mutations;** that is, they cause no change in the protein. Often, however, a mutation has a negative effect on the health of the organism. The effect of a mutation depends on how it alters the genetic code for a protein. Consider the two codons for glutamic acid: GAA and GAG. A point mutation that alters the third nucleotide of GAA to GAG will still result in the incorporation of glutamic acid at the correct position in the protein. Similarly, a GAG to GAA mutation will also be silent.

Many mutations are not silent. There are approximately four thousand human genetic disorders that result from such mutations. These occur because the mutation in the DNA changes the codon and results in incorporation of the wrong amino acid into the protein. This causes the protein to be nonfunctional or to function improperly.

Consider the human genetic disorder sickle cell anemia. In the normal β-chain of hemoglobin, the sixth amino acid is glutamic acid. In the β-chain of sickle cell hemoglobin, the sixth amino acid is valine. How did this amino acid substitution arise? The answer lies in examination of the codons for glutamic acid and valine:

Glutamic acid:	GAA or GAG
Valine:	GUG, GUC, GUA, or GUU

A point mutation of A $\longrightarrow$ U in the second nucleotide changes some codons for glutamic acid into codons for valine:

Glutamic acid codon		Valine codon
GAA	$\longrightarrow$	GUA
GAG	$\longrightarrow$	GUG

This mutation in a single codon leads to the change in amino acid sequence at position 6 in the β-chain of human hemoglobin from glutamic acid to valine. The result of this seemingly minor change is sickle cell anemia in individuals who inherit two copies of the mutant gene.

Question 20.11 The sequence of a gene on the mRNA is normally AUGCCC-GACUUU. A point mutation in the gene results in the mRNA sequence AUGCGCGACUUU. What are the amino acid sequences of the normal and mutant proteins? Would you expect this to be a silent mutation?

Question 20.12 The sequence of a gene on the mRNA is normally AUGCCC-GACUUU. A point mutation in the gene results in the mRNA sequence AUGCCGGACUUU. What are the amino acid sequences of the normal and mutant proteins? Would you expect this to be a silent mutation?

Mutagens and Carcinogens

Any chemical that causes a change in the DNA sequence is called a *mutagen*. Often, mutagens are also **carcinogens,** cancer-causing chemicals. Most cancers result from mutations in a single normal cell. These mutations result in the loss of normal growth control, causing the abnormal cell to proliferate. If that growth is not controlled or destroyed, it will result in the death of the individual. We are exposed to many carcinogens in the course of our lives. Sometimes we are exposed to a carcinogen by accident, but in some cases it is by choice. Cigarette smoke has about three thousand chemical components and several are potent mutagens. As a result, people who smoke have a much greater chance of developing lung cancer than those who don't.

Ultraviolet Light Damage and DNA Repair

Ultraviolet (UV) light is another agent that causes damage to DNA. Absorption of UV light by DNA causes adjacent pyrimidine bases to become covalently linked. The product is called a **pyrimidine dimer.** As a result of pyrimidine dimer formation, there is no hydrogen bonding between these pyrimidine molecules and the complementary bases on the other DNA strand. This stretch of DNA cannot be replicated or transcribed!

A MEDICAL PERSPECTIVE

The Ames Test for Carcinogens

Each day we come into contact with a variety of chemicals, including insecticides, food additives, hair dyes, automobile emissions, and cigarette smoke. Some of these chemicals have the potential to cause cancer. How do we determine whether these agents are harmful? More particularly, how do we determine whether they cause cancer?

If we consider the example of cigarette smoke, we see that it can be years, even centuries, before a relationship is seen between a chemical and cancer. Europeans and Americans have been smoking since Sir Walter Raleigh introduced tobacco into England in the seventeenth century. However, it was not until three centuries later that physicians and scientists demonstrated the link between smoking and lung cancer. Obviously, this epidemiological approach takes too long, and too many people die. Alternatively, we can test chemicals by treating laboratory animals, such as mice, and observing them for various kinds of cancer. However, this, too, can take years, is expensive, and requires the sacrifice of many laboratory animals. How, then, can chemicals be tested for carcinogenicity (the ability to cause cancer) quickly and inexpensively? In the 1970s it was recognized that most carcinogens are also mutagens. That is, they cause cancer by causing mutations in the DNA, and the mutations cause the cells of the body to lose growth control. Bruce Ames, a biochemist and bacterial geneticist, developed a test using mutants of the bacterium *Salmonella typhimurium* that can demonstrate in 48–72 hours (h) whether a chemical is a mutagen and thus a suspected carcinogen.

Ames chose several mutants of *S. typhimurium* that cannot grow unless the amino acid histidine is added to the growth medium. The Ames test involves subjecting these bacteria to a chemical and determining whether the chemical causes reversion of the mutation. In other words, the researcher is looking for a mutation that reverses the original mutation. When a reversion occurs, the bacteria will be able to grow in the absence of histidine.

The details of the Ames test are shown in the accompanying figure. Both an experimental and a control test are done. The control test contains no carcinogen and will show the number of spontaneous revertants that occur in the culture. A very small amount of histidine is added to the experimental and control cultures to allow a few rounds of DNA replication. This is needed for the formation of the reverse mutations. If there are many colonies on the surface of the experimental plate and only a few colonies on the negative control plate, it can be concluded that the chemical tested is a mutagen. It is therefore possible that the chemical is also a carcinogen.

The Ames test has greatly accelerated our ability to test new compounds for mutagenic and possibly carcinogenic effects. However, once the Ames test identifies a mutagenic compound, testing in animals must be done to show conclusively that the compound also causes cancer.

For Further Understanding

- A researcher carried out the Ames test in which an experimental sample was exposed to a suspected mutagen and a control sample was not. A sample from each tube was grown on a medium containing no histidine. On the experimental plate, he observed forty-three colonies and on the control plate, he observed thirty-one colonies. He concluded that the substance is a mutagen. When he reported his data and conclusion to his supervisor, she told him that his conclusions were not valid. How can the researcher modify his experimental procedure to obtain better data?
- Suppose that the mutation in a strain of *S. typhimurium* produces the codon UUA instead of UUC. What is the amino acid change caused by this mutation? What base substitutions could correct the mutant codon so that it once again calls for the correct amino acid? What base substitutions would not correct the mutant codon?

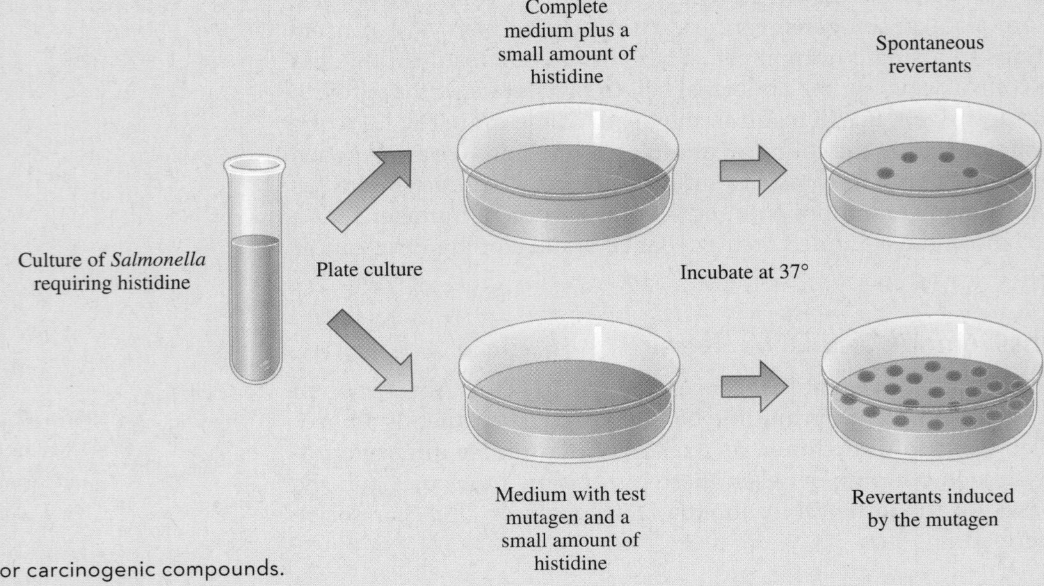

The Ames test for carcinogenic compounds.

Bacteria such as *Escherichia coli* have four different mechanisms to repair UV light damage. However, even a repair process can make a mistake. Mutations occur when the UV damage repair system makes an error and causes a change in the nucleotide sequence of the DNA.

Pyrimidine dimers were originally called thymine dimers because thymine is more commonly involved in these reactions than cytosine.

In medicine, the pyrimidine dimerization reaction is used to advantage in hospitals where germicidal (UV) light is used to kill bacteria in the air and on environmental surfaces, such as in a vacant operating room. This cell death is caused by pyrimidine dimer formation on a massive scale. The repair systems of the bacteria are overwhelmed, and the cells die.

Of course, the same type of pyrimidine dimer formation can occur in human cells as well. Lying out in the sun all day to acquire a fashionable tan exposes the skin to large amounts of UV light. This damages the skin by formation of many pyrimidine dimers. Exposure to high levels of UV from sunlight or tanning booths has been linked to a rising incidence of skin cancer in human populations.

This mother is applying sunscreen to her daughter to shield her from UV radiation. Explain the kind of damage that UV light can cause and what the potential long-term effects may be.

Consequences of Defects in DNA Repair

The human repair system for pyrimidine dimers is quite complex, requiring at least five enzymes. The first step in repair of the pyrimidine dimer is the cleavage of the sugar-phosphate backbone of the DNA near the site of the damage. The enzyme that performs this is called a *repair endonuclease.* If the gene encoding this enzyme is defective, pyrimidine dimers cannot be repaired. The accumulation of mutations combined with a simultaneous decrease in the efficiency of DNA repair mechanisms leads to an increased incidence of cancer. For example, a mutation in the repair endonuclease gene, or in other genes in the repair pathway, results in the genetic skin disorder called *xeroderma pigmentosum.* People who suffer from xeroderma pigmentosum are extremely sensitive to the ultraviolet rays of sunlight and develop multiple skin cancers, usually before the age of twenty.

20.8 Recombinant DNA

Tools Used in the Study of DNA

LEARNING GOAL

10 Describe the tools used in the study of DNA and in genetic engineering.

Scientists are often asked why they study such seemingly unimportant subjects as bacterial DNA replication. One very good reason is that such studies often lend insight into the workings of human genetic systems. A second is that such research often produces the tools that allow great leaps into new technologies. Nowhere is this more true than in the development of recombinant DNA technology. Many of the techniques and tools used in recombinant DNA studies were developed or discovered during basic studies on bacterial DNA replication and gene expression. These include many enzymes that catalyze reactions of DNA molecules, gel electrophoresis, cloning vectors, and hybridization techniques.

Restriction Enzymes

Restriction enzymes, often called *restriction endonucleases,* are bacterial enzymes that "cut" the sugar-phosphate backbone of DNA molecules at specific nucleotide sequences. The first of these enzymes to be purified and studied was called EcoR1. The name is derived from the genus and species name of the bacteria from which it was isolated, in this case *Escherichia coli,* or *E. coli.* The following is the specific nucleotide sequence recognized by EcoR1:

ANIMATION
• Restriction Endonucleases

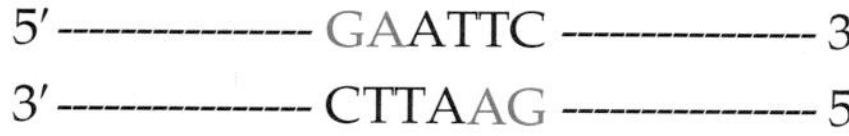

5′ --------------- GAATTC --------------- 3′
3′ --------------- CTTAAG --------------- 5′

When EcoR1 cuts the DNA at this site, it does so in a staggered fashion. Specifically, it cuts between the G and the first A on both strands. Cutting produces two DNA fragments with the following structure:

These staggered termini are called *sticky ends* because they can reassociate with one another by hydrogen bonding. This is a property of the DNA fragments generated by restriction enzymes that is very important to gene cloning.

Examples of other restriction enzymes and their specific recognition sequences are listed in Table 20.2. The sites on the sugar-phosphate backbone that are cut by the enzymes are indicated by slashes.

These enzymes are used to digest large DNA molecules into smaller fragments of specific size. Because a restriction enzyme always cuts at the same site, DNA from a particular individual generates a reproducible set of DNA fragments. This is convenient for the study or cloning of DNA from any source.

Agarose Gel Electrophoresis

One means of studying the DNA fragments produced by restriction enzyme digestion is agarose gel electrophoresis. The digested DNA sample is placed in a sample well in the gel, and an electrical current is applied. The negative charge of the phosphoryl groups in the sugar-phosphate backbone causes the DNA fragment to move through the gel away from the negative electrode (cathode) and toward the positive electrode (anode). The smaller DNA fragments move more rapidly than the larger ones, and as a result the DNA fragments end up distributed throughout the gel according to their size. The size of each fragment can be determined by comparison with the migration pattern of DNA fragments of known size.

Hybridization

Agarose gel electrophoresis allows the determination of the size of a DNA fragment. However, in recombinant DNA research it is also important to identify what gene is carried by a particular DNA fragment.

Hybridization is a technique used to identify the presence of a gene on a particular DNA fragment. This technique is based on the fact that complementary DNA sequences will hydrogen bond, or hybridize, to one another. In fact, even RNA can be used in hybridization studies. RNA can hybridize to DNA molecules or to other RNA molecules.

One technique, called Southern blotting, involves hybridization of DNA fragments from an agarose gel (Figure 20.23a). DNA digested by a restriction

TABLE 20.2 Common Restriction Enzymes and Their Recognition Sequences

Restriction Enzyme	Recognition Sequence
BamHI	5′-G/GATCC-3′
	3′-CCTAG/G-5′
HindIII	5′-A/AGCTT-3′
	3′-TTCGA/A-5′
SalI	5′-G/TCGAC-3′
	3′-CAGCT/G-5′
BglII	5′-A/GATCT-3′
	3′-TCTAG/A-5′
PstI	5′-CTGCA/G-3′
	3′-G/ACGTC-5′

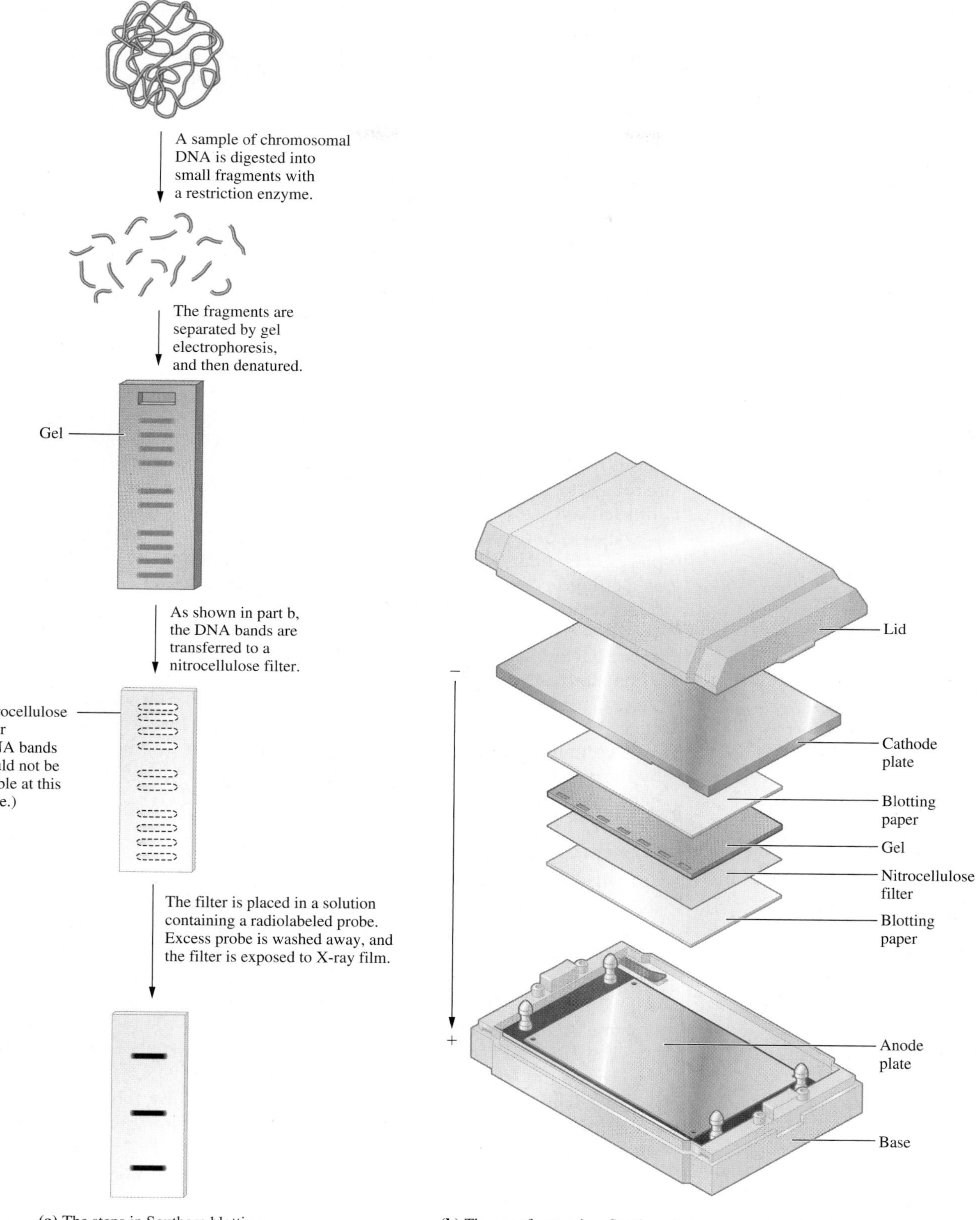
A sample of chromosomal DNA is digested into small fragments with a restriction enzyme.
The fragments are separated by gel electrophoresis, and then denatured.
Gel
As shown in part b, the DNA bands are transferred to a nitrocellulose filter.
Nitrocellulose filter (DNA bands would not be visible at this stage.)
The filter is placed in a solution containing a radiolabeled probe. Excess probe is washed away, and the filter is exposed to X-ray film.
Lid
–
Cathode plate
Blotting paper
Gel
Nitrocellulose filter
Blotting paper
+
Anode plate
Base

(a) The steps in Southern blotting

(b) The transfer step in a Southern blotting experiment

Figure 20.23 Southern blot hybridization. (a) DNA is digested and the fragments are separated by gel electrophoresis. The DNA is transferred from the gel onto a filter and "melted" into single strands. A radioactive probe is applied and the filter exposed to X-ray film. (b) An electroblotting apparatus for the transfer of DNA from a gel onto a filter.

enzyme is run on an agarose gel. Next the DNA fragments are transferred by blotting onto a special membrane filter. Figure 20.23b shows an apparatus that uses an electric field to transfer DNA from a gel onto a filter. In the next step, the DNA molecules on the filter are "melted" into single DNA strands so that they are ready for hybridization. The filter is then bathed in a solution containing a radioactive DNA or RNA molecule. This probe will hybridize to any DNA fragments on the filter that are complementary to it. X-ray film is used to detect any bands where the radioactive probe hybridized, thus locating the gene of interest.

DNA Cloning Vectors

DNA cloning experiments combine these technologies with a few additional tricks to isolate single copies of a gene and then produce billions of copies. To produce multiple copies of a gene, it may be joined to a **cloning vector.** A cloning vector is a piece of DNA having its own replication origin so that it can be replicated inside a host cell. Often the bacterium *E. coli* serves as the host cell in which the vector carrying the cloned DNA is replicated in abundance.

There are two major kinds of cloning vectors. The first are bacterial virus or phage vectors. These are bacterial viruses that have been genetically altered to allow the addition of cloned DNA fragments. These viruses have all the genes required to replicate 100 to 200 copies of the virus (and cloned fragment) per infected cell.

The second commonly used vector is a plasmid vector. Plasmids are extra pieces of circular DNA found in most kinds of bacteria. The plasmids that are used as cloning vectors often contain antibiotic resistance genes that are useful in the selection of cells containing a plasmid.

Each plasmid has its own replication origin to allow efficient DNA replication in the bacterial host cell. Most plasmid vectors also have a *selectable marker,* often a gene for resistance to an antibiotic. Finally, plasmid vectors have a gene that has several restriction enzyme sites useful for cloning. The valuable feature of this gene is that it is inactivated when a DNA fragment has been cloned into it. Thus, cells containing a plasmid carrying a cloned DNA fragment can be recognized by their ability to grow in the presence of antibiotic and by loss of function of the gene into which the cloned DNA has been inserted.

Antibiotic resistance causes countless problems in the treatment of bacterial infections.

Genetic Engineering

ANIMATIONS
• Construction of a Plasmid Vector
• Steps in Cloning a Gene

Now that we have assembled most of the tools needed for a cloning experiment, we must decide which gene to clone. The example that we will use is the cloning of the β-globin genes for normal and sickle cell hemoglobin. DNA from an individual with normal hemoglobin is digested with a restriction enzyme. This is the target DNA. The vector DNA must be digested with the same enzyme (Figure 20.24). In our example, the restriction enzyme cuts within the *lacZ* gene, which codes for the enzyme β-galactosidase.

The digested vector and target DNA are mixed together under conditions that encourage the sticky ends of the target and vector DNA to hybridize with one another. The sticky ends are then covalently linked by the enzyme DNA ligase. This enzyme catalyzes the formation of phosphoester bonds between the two pieces of DNA.

Now the recombinant DNA molecules are introduced into bacterial cells by a process called transformation. Next, the cells of the transformation mixture are plated on a solid nutrient agar medium containing the antibiotic ampicillin and the β-galactosidase substrate X-gal (5-bromo-4-chloro-3-indolyl-β-D-galactoside). Only those cells containing the antibiotic resistance gene will survive and grow

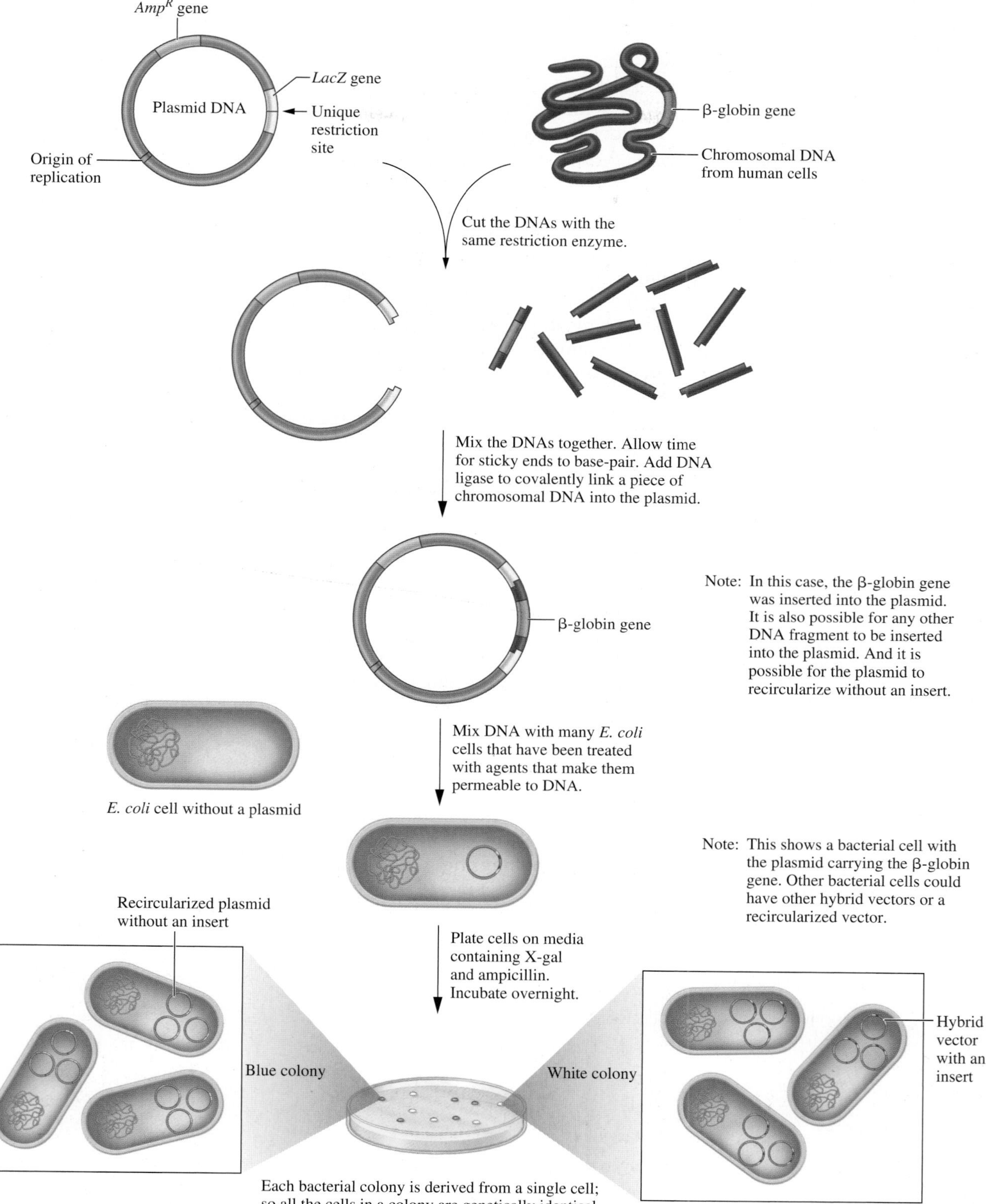

Figure 20.24 Cloning of eukaryotic DNA into a plasmid cloning vector.

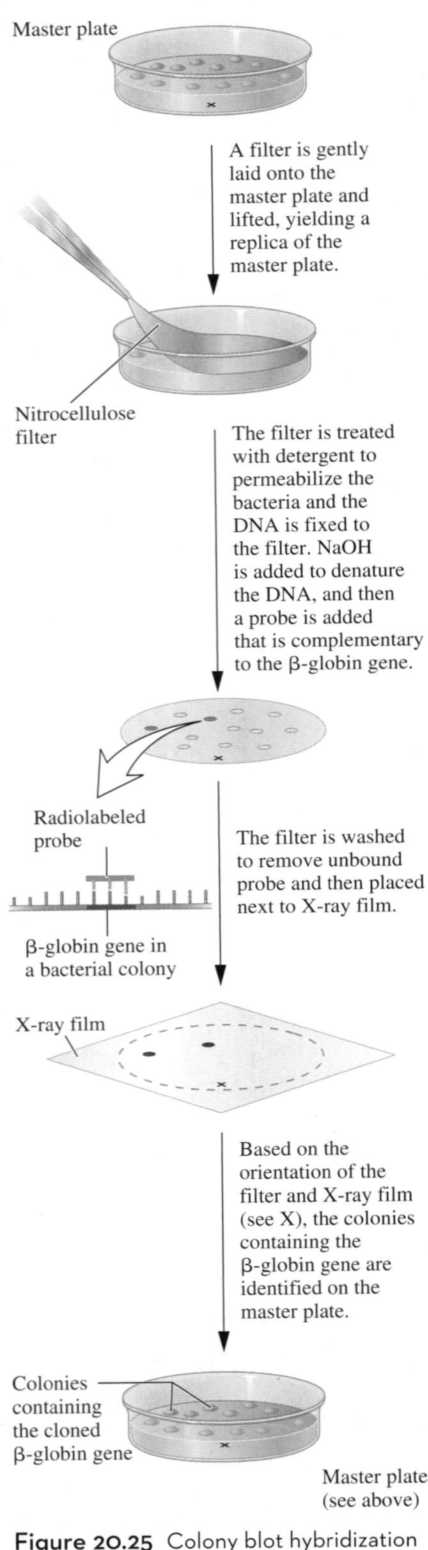

Master plate
A filter is gently laid onto the master plate and lifted, yielding a replica of the master plate.
Nitrocellulose filter
The filter is treated with detergent to permeabilize the bacteria and the DNA is fixed to the filter. NaOH is added to denature the DNA, and then a probe is added that is complementary to the β-globin gene.
Radiolabeled probe
β-globin gene in a bacterial colony
The filter is washed to remove unbound probe and then placed next to X-ray film.
X-ray film
Based on the orientation of the filter and X-ray film (see X), the colonies containing the β-globin gene are identified on the master plate.
Colonies containing the cloned β-globin gene
Master plate (see above)

Figure 20.25 Colony blot hybridization for detection of cells carrying a plasmid clone of the β-chain gene of hemoglobin.

into bacterial colonies. Cells with an intact *lacZ* gene will produce the enzyme β-galactosidase. The enzyme will hydrolyze X-gal to produce a blue product that will cause the colonies to appear blue. If the *lacZ* gene has been inactivated by insertion of a cloned gene, no β-galactosidase will be produced and the colonies will be white.

Now hybridization can be used to detect the clones that carry the β-globin gene. A replica of the experimental plate is made by transferring some cells from each colony onto a membrane filter. These cells are gently broken open so that the released DNA becomes attached to the membrane. When hybridization is carried out on these filters, the radioactive probe will hybridize only to the complementary sequences of the β-globin gene. When the membrane filter is exposed to X-ray film, a "spot" will appear on the developed film only at the site of a colony carrying the desired clone. By going back to the original plate, we can select cells from that colony and grow them for further study (Figure 20.25).

The same procedure can be used to clone the β-chain gene of sickle cell hemoglobin. Then the two can be studied and compared to determine the nature of the genetic defect.

This simple example makes it appear that all gene cloning is very easy and straightforward. This has proved to be far from the truth. Genetic engineers have had to overcome many obstacles to clone eukaryotic genes of particular medical interest. One of the first obstacles encountered was the presence of introns within eukaryotic genes. Bacteria that are used for cloning lack the enzymatic machinery to splice out introns. Molecular biologists found that a DNA copy of a eukaryotic mRNA could be made by using the enzyme reverse transcriptase from a family of viruses called *retroviruses*. Such a DNA copy of the mRNA carries all the protein-coding sequences of a gene but none of the intron sequences. Thus bacteria are able to transcribe and translate the cloned DNA and produce valuable products for use in medicine and other applications.

This is only one of the many technical problems that have been overcome by the amazing developments in recombinant DNA technology. A brief but impressive list of medically important products of genetic engineering is presented in Table 20.3.

TABLE 20.3 A Brief List of Medically Important Proteins Produced by Genetic Engineering

Protein	Medical Condition Treated
Insulin	Insulin-dependent diabetes
Human growth hormone	Pituitary dwarfism
Factor VIII	Type A hemophilia
Factor IX	Type B hemophilia
Tissue plasminogen factor	Stroke, myocardial infarction
Streptokinase	Myocardial infarction
Interferon	Cancer, some virus infections
Interleukin-2	Cancer
Tumor necrosis factor	Cancer
Atrial natriuretic factor	Hypertension
Erythropoietin	Anemia
Thymosin α-1	Stimulate immune system
Hepatitis B virus (HBV) vaccine	Prevent HBV viral hepatitis
Influenza vaccine	Prevent influenza infection

20.9 Polymerase Chain Reaction

A bacterium originally isolated from a hot spring in Yellowstone National Park provides the key to a powerful molecular tool for the study of DNA. Polymerase chain reaction (PCR) allows scientists to produce unlimited amounts of any gene of interest and the bacterium *Thermus aquaticus* produces a heat-stable DNA polymerase (Taq polymerase) that allows the process to work.

The human genome consists of approximately three billion base pairs of DNA. But suppose you are interested in studying only one gene, perhaps the gene responsible for muscular dystrophy or cystic fibrosis. It's like looking for a needle in a haystack. Using PCR, a scientist can make millions of copies of the gene of interest, while ignoring the thousands of other genes on human chromosomes.

The secret to this specificity is the synthesis of a DNA primer, a short piece of single-stranded DNA that will specifically hybridize to the beginning of a particular gene. DNA polymerases require a primer for initiation of DNA synthesis because they act by adding new nucleotides to the 3′—OH of the last nucleotide of the primer.

To perform PCR, a small amount of DNA is mixed with Taq polymerase, the primer, and the four DNA nucleotide triphosphates. The mixture is then placed in an instrument called a *thermocycler*. The temperature in the thermocycler is raised to 94–96°C for several minutes to separate the two strands of DNA. Because the Taq polymerase is heat-stable, it is not denatured by these temperatures. The temperature is then dropped to 50–56°C to allow the primers to hybridize to the target DNA. Finally, the temperature is raised to 72°C to allow Taq polymerase to act, reading the template DNA strand and polymerizing a daughter strand extended from the primer. At the end of this step, the amount of the gene has doubled (Figure 20.26).

Now the three steps are repeated. With each cycle the amount of the gene is doubled. Theoretically after thirty cycles, you have one billion times more DNA than you started with!

PCR can be used in genetic screening to detect the gene responsible for muscular dystrophy. It can also be used to diagnose disease. For instance, it can be used to amplify small amounts of HIV in the blood. It can also be used by forensic scientists to amplify DNA from a single hair follicle or a tiny drop of blood at a crime scene.

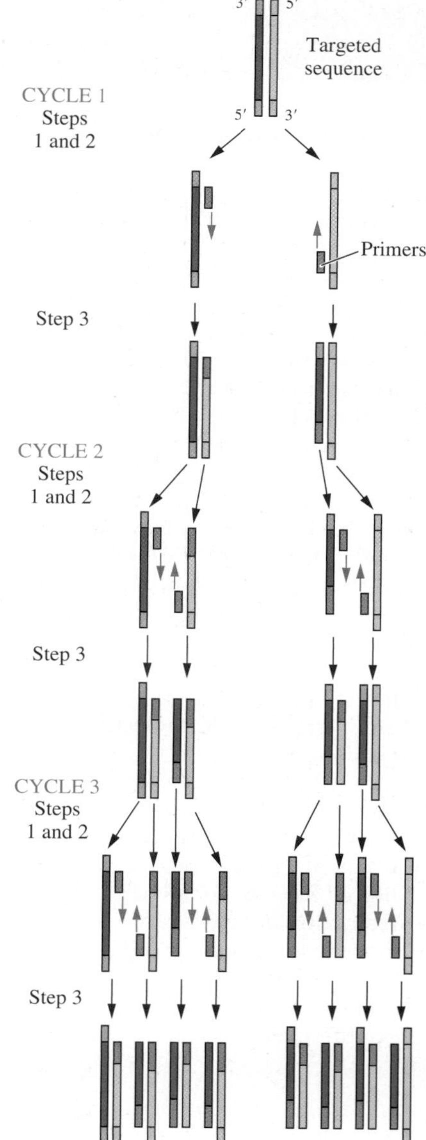

Figure 20.26 Polymerase chain reaction.

LEARNING GOAL

11 Describe the process of polymerase chain reaction and discuss potential uses of the process.

ANIMATIONS
- PCR Reactions
- Polymerase Chain Reaction
- DNA Fingerprinting

LEARNING GOAL

12 Discuss strategies for genome analysis and DNA sequencing.

20.10 The Human Genome Project

In 1990 the Department of Energy and the National Institutes of Health began the Human Genome Project (HGP), a multinational project that would extend into the next millennium. The goals of the HGP were to identify all of the genes in human DNA and to sequence the entire three billion nucleotide pairs of the genome. In order to accomplish these goals, enormous computer databases had to be developed to store the information and computer software had to be designed to analyze it.

Initially, the HGP planned to complete the work by the year 2005. However, as a result of technological advances made by those in the project, a working draft of the human genome was published in February 2001 and the successful completion of the project was announced on April 14, 2003.

Genetic Strategies for Genome Analysis

The strategy for the HGP was rather straightforward. In order to determine the DNA sequence of the human genome, genomic libraries had to be produced. A *genomic library* is a set of clones representing the entire genome. The DNA sequences of each of these clones could then be determined. Of course, once the

CHEMISTRY AT THE CRIME SCENE

DNA Fingerprinting

Four U.S. Army helicopters swept over the field of illicit coca plants (*Erythroxylum* spp.) growing in a mountainous region of northern Colombia. When the soldiers were certain that the fields were unguarded, a fifth helicopter landed. From it emerged a team of researchers from the Agricultural Research Service of the U.S. Department of Agriculture (ARS-USDA). Quickly the scientists gathered leaves from mature plants, as well as from seedlings growing in a coca nursery, and returned to the helicopter with their valuable samples. With a final sweep over the field, the Army helicopters sprayed herbicides to kill the coca plants.

From 1997 to 2001, this scene was repeated in regions of Colombia known to have the highest coca production. The reason for these collections was to study the genetic diversity of the coca plants being grown for the illegal production of cocaine. The tool selected for this study was DNA fingerprinting.

DNA fingerprinting was developed in the 1980s by Alec Jeffries of the University of Leicester in England. The idea grew out of basic molecular genetic studies of the human genome. Scientists observed that some DNA sequences varied greatly from one person to the next. Such hypervariable regions are made up of variable numbers of repeats of short DNA sequences. They are located at many sites on different chromosomes. Each person has a different number of repeats and when his or her DNA is digested with restriction enzymes, a unique set of DNA fragments is generated. Jeffries invented DNA fingerprinting by developing a set of DNA probes that detect these variable number tandem repeats (VNTRs) when used in hybridization with Southern blots.

Coca nursery next to a mature field in Colombia.

Although several variations of DNA fingerprinting exist, the basic technique is quite simple. DNA is digested with restriction enzymes, producing a set of DNA fragments. These are separated by electrophoresis through an agarose gel. The DNA fragments are then transferred to membrane filters and hybridized with the radioactive probe DNA. The bands that hybridize the radioactive probe are visualized by exposing the membrane to X-ray film and developing a "picture" of the gel. The result is what Jeffries calls a *DNA fingerprint*, a set of twenty-five to sixty DNA bands that are unique to an individual.

sequence of each of these clones is determined, there is no way to know how they are arranged along the chromosomes.

A second technique, called *chromosome walking*, provides both DNA sequence information and a method for identifying the DNA sequences next to it on the chromosome. This method requires clones that are overlapping. To accomplish this, libraries of clones are made using many different restriction enzymes. The DNA sequence of a fragment is determined. Then that information is used to develop a probe for any clones in the library that are overlapping. Each time a DNA fragment is sequenced, the information is used to identify overlapping clones. This process continues, allowing scientists to walk along the chromosome in two directions until the entire sequence is cloned, mapped, and sequenced.

DNA Sequencing

The method of DNA sequencing that is used is based on a technique developed by Frederick Sanger. A cloned piece of DNA is separated into its two strands. Each of these will serve as a template strand to carry out DNA replication in test tubes.

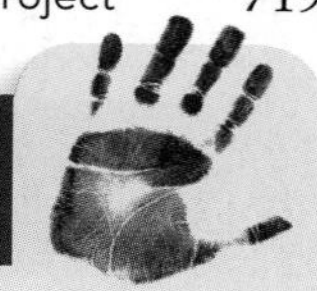

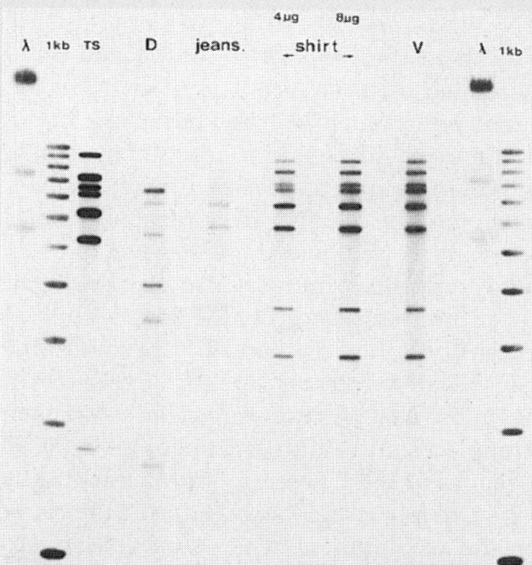

An example of a DNA fingerprint used in a criminal case. The DNA sample designated *V* is that of the victim and the sample designated *D* is that of the defendant. The samples labeled *jeans* and *shirt* were taken from the clothing of the defendant. The DNA bands from the defendant's clothing clearly match the DNA bands of the victim, providing evidence of the guilt of the defendant.

DNA fingerprinting is now routinely used for paternity testing, testing for certain genetic disorders, and identification of the dead in cases where no other identification is available. DNA fingerprints are used as evidence in criminal cases involving rape and murder. In such cases, the evidence may be little more than a hair with an intact follicle on the clothing of the victim.

Less widely known is the use of DNA fingerprinting to study genetic diversity in natural populations of plants and animals. The greater the genetic diversity, the healthier the population is likely to be. Populations with low genetic diversity face a far higher probability of extinction under adverse conditions. Customs officials have used DNA fingerprinting to determine whether confiscated elephant tusks were taken illegally from an endangered population of elephants or were obtained from a legally harvested population.

In the case of the coca plants, ARS wanted to know whether the drug cartels were developing improved strains that might be hardier or more pest resistant or that have a higher concentration of cocaine. Their conclusions, which you can read in *Phytochemistry* (*64:* 187–197, 2003), were that the drug cartels have introduced significant genetic modification into coca plants in Colombia in the last two decades. In addition, some of these new variants, those producing the highest levels of cocaine, have been transplanted to other regions of the country. All of this indicates that the cocaine agribusiness is thriving.

For Further Understanding

- As this sampling of applications suggests, DNA fingerprinting has become an invaluable tool in law enforcement, medicine, and basic research. What other applications of this technology can you think of?
- Do some research on the development of DNA fingerprinting as a research and forensics tool. What is the probability that two individuals will have the same DNA fingerprint? How are these probabilities determined?

A primer strand is also needed. This is a short piece of DNA that will hybridize to the template strand. The primer is the starting point for addition of new nucleotides during DNA synthesis.

The DNA is then placed in four test tubes with all of the enzymes and nucleotides required for DNA synthesis. In addition, each tube contains an unusual nucleotide, called a dideoxynucleotide. These nucleotides differ from the standard nucleotides by having a hydrogen atom at the 3′ position of the deoxyribose, rather than a hydroxyl group. When a dideoxynucleotide is incorporated into a growing DNA chain, it acts as a chain terminator. Because it does not have a 3′-hydroxyl group, no phosphoester bond can be formed with another nucleotide and no further polymerization can occur.

Each of the four tubes containing the DNA, enzymes, and an excess of the nucleotides required for replication will also have a small amount of one of the four dideoxynucleotides. In the tube that receives dideoxyadenosine triphosphate (ddA), for example, DNA synthesis will begin. As replication proceeds, either the standard nucleotide or ddA will be incorporated into the growing strand. Since the

A MEDICAL PERSPECTIVE

A Genetic Approach to Familial Emphysema

Familial emphysema is a human genetic disease resulting from the inability to produce the protein α_1-antitrypsin. See also A Medical Perspective: α_1-Antitrypsin and Familial Emphysema, in Chapter 19. In individuals who have inherited one or two copies of the α_1-antitrypsin gene, this serum protein protects the lungs from the enzyme elastase. Normally, elastase fights bacteria and helps in the destruction and removal of dead lung tissue. However, the enzyme can also cause lung damage. By inhibiting elastase, α_1-antitrypsin prevents lung damage. Individuals who have inherited two defective α_1-antitrypsin genes do not produce this protein and suffer from familial, or A1AD, emphysema. In the absence of α_1-antitrypsin, the elastase and other proteases cause the severe lung damage characteristic of emphysema.

A1AD is the second most common genetic disorder in Caucasians. It is estimated that there are 100,000 sufferers in the United States and that one in five Americans carries the gene. The disorder, discovered in 1963, is often misdiagnosed as asthma or chronic obstructive pulmonary disease. In fact, it is estimated that fewer than 5% of the sufferers are diagnosed with A1AD.

The α_1-antitrypsin gene has been cloned. Early experiments with sheep showed that the protein remains stable when administered as an aerosol and remains functional after it has passed through the pulmonary epithelium. This research offers hope of an effective treatment for this disease.

The current treatment involves weekly IV injections of α_1-antitrypsin. The supply of the protein, purified from human plasma that has been demonstrated to be virus free, is rather limited. Thus, the injections are expensive. In addition, they are painful. These two factors cause some sufferers to refuse the treatment.

Dr. Terry Flotte and his colleagues at the University of Florida have cloned the gene for α_1-antitrypsin into the DNA of adeno-associated virus (AAV). This virus is an ideal vector for human gene replacement therapy because it replicates only in cells that are not dividing and it does not stimulate a strong immune or inflammatory response. The researchers injected the virus carrying the cloned α_1-antitrypsin gene into the muscle tissue of mice, then tested for the level of α_1-antitrypsin in the blood. The results were very promising. Effective levels of α_1-antitrypsin were produced in the muscle cells of the mice and secreted into the bloodstream. Furthermore, the level of α_1-antitrypsin remained at therapeutic levels for more than four months. In the past 10 years three clinical trials in humans have been completed and a fourth is ongoing. In 2009 Dr. Flotte and his colleagues at the University of Massachusetts Medical School and the University of Florida reported that three patients treated with the recombinant AAV were able to produce α_1-antitrypsin for up to 1 year. Although the levels of enzyme produced were not considered to be therapeutic, this clinical trial demonstrated that introduction of a functioning gene can result in production of the protein. Preliminary results of an ongoing Phase 2 clinical trial suggest that therapeutic concentrations of α_1-antitrypsin can be achieved. The research team is optimistic that by modifying the design of the recombinant AAV or the method of delivery into the body, they will be able to develop an effective therapy for familial emphysema.

For Further Understanding

- Of the three treatments described in this perspective, which do you think has the highest probability of success in the long term? Defend your answer.
- Explain the lung damage that results from A1AD.

standard nucleotide is present in excess, the dideoxynucleotide will be incorporated infrequently and randomly. This produces a family of DNA fragments that terminate at the location of one of the deoxyadenosines in the molecule.

The same reaction is done with each of the dideoxynucleotides. The DNA fragments are then separated by gel electrophoresis on a DNA sequencing gel. The four reactions are placed in four wells, side by side, on the gel. Following electrophoresis, the DNA sequence can be read directly from the gel, as shown in Figure 20.27.

When chain termination DNA sequencing was first done, radioactive isotopes were used to label the DNA strands. However, new technology has

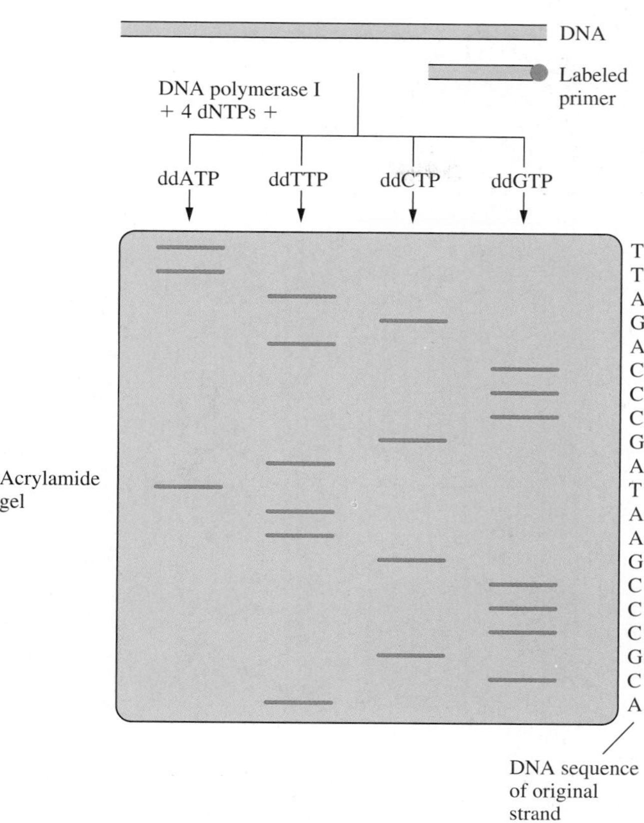

Figure 20.27 DNA sequencing by chain termination requires a template DNA strand and a radioactive primer. These are placed into each of four reaction mixtures that contain DNA polymerase, the four DNA nucleotides (dATP, dCTP, dGTP, and TTP), as well as one of the four dideoxynucleotides. Following the reaction, the products are separated on a DNA sequencing gel. The sequence is read from an autoradiograph of the gel.

resulted in automated systems that employ dideoxynucleotides that are labeled with fluorescent dyes, a different color for each dideoxynucleotide. Because each reaction (A, G, C, and T) will be a different color, all the reactions can be done in a single reaction mixture and the products separated on a single lane of a sequencing gel. A computer then "reads" the gel by distinguishing the color of each DNA band. The sequence information is directly stored into a databank for later analysis.

There is currently a vast amount of DNA information available on the Internet. The complete genomes of many bacteria have been reported, as well as the sequence information generated by the Human Genome Project. Because we know the genetic code, we can predict the amino acid sequence of proteins encoded by the genes. Researchers can also compare the sequences of normal genes with those of people suffering from genetic disorders. The enormity of the DNA information available, as well as the many types of analysis that need to be carried out, have given rise to an entirely new branch of science. The field of **bioinformatics** is a marriage of computer information sciences and DNA technology that is helping to devise methods for understanding, analyzing, and applying the DNA sequence information that we are gathering.

CHAPTER MAP

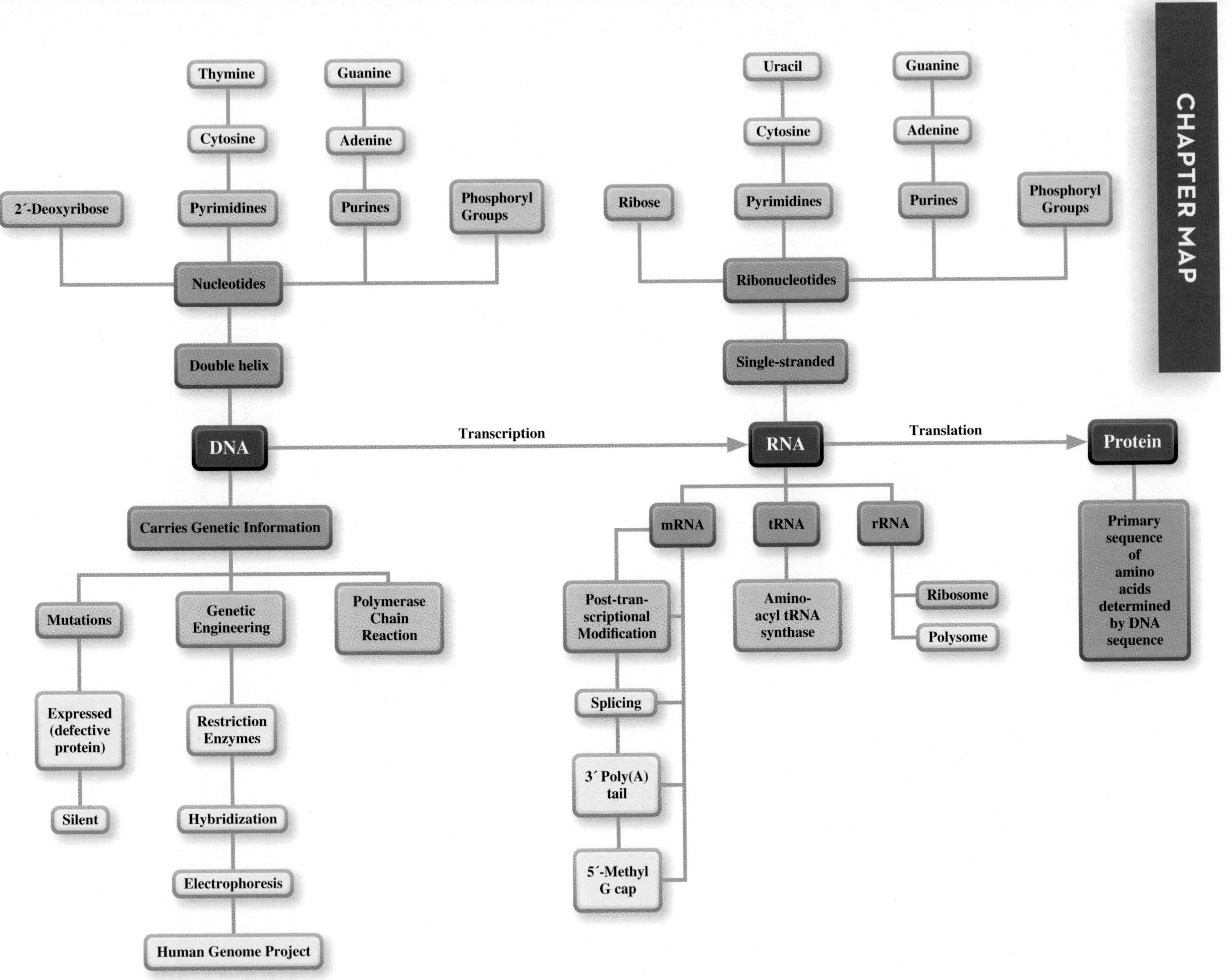

Thymine
Cytosine
Pyrimidines
Guanine
Adenine
Purines
2′-Deoxyribose
Phosphoryl Groups
Nucleotides
Double helix
DNA
Carries Genetic Information
Mutations
Expressed (defective protein)
Silent
Genetic Engineering
Restriction Enzymes
Hybridization
Electrophoresis
Human Genome Project
Polymerase Chain Reaction
Transcription
Uracil
Cytosine
Pyrimidines
Guanine
Adenine
Purines
Ribose
Phosphoryl Groups
Ribonucleotides
Single-stranded
RNA
mRNA
Post-tran-scriptional Modification
Splicing
3′ Poly(A) tail
5′-Methyl G cap
tRNA
Amino-acyl tRNA synthase
rRNA
Ribosome
Polysome
Translation
Protein
Primary sequence of amino acids determined by DNA sequence

SUMMARY

20.1 The Structure of the Nucleotide

- **Deoxyribonucleic acid** (DNA) and **ribonucleic acid** (RNA) are polymers of **nucleotides.**
- **Nucleosides** are produced by the combination of a sugar, either ribose in RNA or 2′-deoxyribose in DNA, and a nitrogenous base.
- Nucleotides are composed of a nucleoside bonded to one, two, or three phosphoryl groups.
- There are two types of nitrogenous bases:
  - **Purines:** adenine and guanine
  - **Pyrimidines:** cytosine, thymine, and uracil
- **Deoxyribonucleotides** are the subunits of DNA.
- **Ribonucleotides** are the subunits of RNA.

20.2 The Structure of DNA and RNA

- Nucleotides are joined by 3′–5′ phosphodiester bonds in both DNA and RNA.
- DNA is a **double helix,** two strands of nucleotide polymers wound around one another with the sugar-phosphate backbone on the outside and complementary pairs of bases extended into the center of the helix.
- **Base pairs** are held together by hydrogen bonds.
  - Adenine base pairs with thymine.
  - Cytosine base pairs with guanine.
- The two **complementary strands** of DNA are **antiparallel** to one another.
- RNA is single-stranded.
- **Prokaryotes** are organisms with a simple cellular structure and in which there is no true membrane-bound nucleus and no true membrane-bound organelles.
- **Eukaryotes** are organisms that have cells containing a true nucleus with a nuclear membrane and a variety of organelles that segregate a variety of cellular functions from one another.
  - Eukaryotic **chromosomes** are complex structure with a first level structure called the **nucleosome.**
- The **genome** is the complete set of genetic information of an organism.

20.3 DNA Replication

- DNA replication involves synthesis of a faithful copy of the DNA molecule.
  - It begins at a **replication origin** and proceeds at the **replication fork.**
- DNA replication is **semiconservative;** each daughter molecule consists of one parental strand and one newly synthesized strand.
- **DNA polymerase III** "reads" each parental strand and synthesizes the complementary daughter strand according to the rules of base pairing.
  - The **leading strand** is replicated continuously.
  - The opposite **lagging strand** is replicated discontinuously.

20.4 Information Flow in Biological Systems

- The **central dogma** states that the flow of biological information in cells is DNA → RNA → protein.
- There are three classes of RNA: **messenger RNA** (mRNA), **transfer RNA** (tRNA), and **ribosomal RNA** (rRNA).
- **Transcription** is the process by which RNA is synthesized and occurs in three stages: initiation, elongation, and termination.
- **RNA polymerase** catalyzes transcription beginning at the **promoter** of the gene.
- Eukaryotic genes contain **introns,** sequences that do not encode protein.
  - Introns are removed from the **primary transcript** by **RNA splicing.**
  - The final RNA contains only the protein coding sequences called **exons.**
- Eukaryotic mRNA undergoes further **post-transcriptional modification,** including addition of a **5′ cap structure** and a **3′ poly(A) tail.**

20.5 The Genetic Code

- The genetic code is a triplet code and each code word is called a **codon.**
- There are sixty-four codons in the genetic code.
  - There are three termination codons: UAA, UAG, and UGA.
  - The remaining sixty-one specify an amino acid.
- Most amino acids have several codons, causing the genetic code to be called **degenerate.**

20.6 Protein Synthesis

- The process of protein synthesis is called **translation.**
- The codons on the mRNA are decoded by tRNA; the **anticodon** on the tRNA is complementary to a codon on the mRNA and the tRNA is covalently linked to the correct amino acid.
  - The tRNA bonded to the correct amino acid is called an **aminoacyl tRNA.**
  - An **aminoacyl tRNA synthetase** catalyzes the bond between the tRNA and the amino acid.
- Hydrogen bonding between the codon and anticodon brings the correct amino acid to the site of protein synthesis.
- The stages of translation are initiation, chain elongation, and termination.
  - **Initiation factors** and **elongation factors** facilitate initiation and chain elongation.
  - **Translocation** is the movement of the ribosome along the mRNA during chain elongation.
  - A **termination codon** signals the end of the translation process.
  - A **release factor** causes peptidyl transferase to hydrolyze the bond between the peptide and the peptidyl tRNA, releasing the completed peptide.
- Protein synthesis occurs on **ribosomes.** The **aminoacyl tRNA binding site** of the ribosome holds the aminoacyl tRNA.

The **peptidyl tRNA binding site** of the ribosome holds the tRNA bonded to the growing peptide chain.

- **Many ribosomes together translating a single mRNA constitute a polysome.**

20.7 Mutation, Ultraviolet Light, and DNA Repair

- **Any change in a DNA sequence is a mutation.**
  - Mutations may be **silent mutations** if they do not cause any change in the function of the protein encoded by the gene.
  - Mutations that destroy or damage the function of a protein may have effects that range from a mild genetic disorder to death.
- **Agents that cause mutations are called mutagens.**
  - Mutagens may be **carcinogens,** cancer-causing chemicals.
- **Mutations are classified by the type of change that occurs in the DNA sequence. They may be point mutations, deletion mutations,** or **insertion mutations.**
- **Ultraviolet light causes the formation of pyrimidine dimers.**
  - Errors in the repair of pyrimidine dimers can cause UV-induced mutations.
  - Germicidal lamps emit UV light that kills bacteria on environmental surfaces.
  - UV light damage to the skin can cause skin cancer.

20.8 Recombinant DNA

- **Restriction enzymes,** agarose gel electrophoresis, **hybridization,** and **cloning vectors** are all tools required for genetic engineering.
- **Cloning a DNA fragment involves digestion of the target and the vector DNA with a restriction enzyme.**
  - DNA ligase joins the target and vector DNA covalently.
  - The recombinant DNA molecules are introduced into bacteria by transformation.
  - The desired clones are located by using antibiotic selection and hybridization.
- **Many eukaryotic genes have been cloned for the purpose of producing medically important proteins.**

20.9 Polymerase Chain Reaction

- **Using a heat-stable DNA polymerase from the bacterium *Thermus aquaticus* and specific DNA primers, polymerase chain reaction (PCR) allows the amplification of specific DNA fragments that are present in small quantities.**
- **PCR is useful in genetic screening, diagnosis of viral or bacterial disease, and in forensic science.**

20.10 The Human Genome Project

- **The Human Genome Project has identified and mapped the genes of the human genome and determined the complete DNA sequence of each of the chromosomes.**
- **DNA libraries were generated and the DNA sequences determined.**
- **Chromosome walking was used to map the sequences along the chromosomes.**
- **DNA sequencing involves reactions in which DNA polymerase copies specific DNA sequences.**
  - Nucleotide analogs that cause chain termination (dideoxynucleotides) are incorporated randomly into the growing DNA chain.
  - This generates a family of DNA fragments that differ in size by one nucleotide.
  - DNA sequencing gels separate these fragments and provide DNA sequence data.
- **Bioinformatics is an interdisciplinary field that uses computer information sciences and DNA technology to develop methods to understand, analyze, and apply DNA sequence information.**

QUESTIONS AND PROBLEMS

The Structure of the Nucleotide

Foundations

20.13 What is a heterocyclic amine?

20.14 What components of nucleic acids are heterocyclic amines?

Applications

20.15 Draw the structure of the purine ring, and indicate the nitrogen that is bonded to sugars in nucleotides.

20.16 **a.** Draw the ring structure of the pyrimidines.
b. In a nucleotide, which nitrogen atom of pyrimidine rings is bonded to the sugar?

20.17 ATP is the universal energy currency of the cell. What components make up the ATP nucleotide?

20.18 One of the energy-harvesting steps of the citric acid cycle results in the production of GTP. What is the structure of the GTP nucleotide?

The Structure of DNA and RNA

Foundations

20.19 The two strands of a DNA molecule are antiparallel. What is meant by this description?

20.20 List three differences between DNA and RNA.

Applications

20.21 What is the significance of the following repeat distances in the structure of the DNA molecule: 0.34 nm, 3.4 nm, and 2 nm?

20.22 Except for the functional groups attached to the rings, the nitrogenous bases are largely flat, hydrophobic molecules. Explain why the arrangement of the purines and pyrimidines found in DNA molecules is very stable.

20.23 Draw the adenine-thymine base pair and indicate the hydrogen bonds that link them.

20.24 Draw the guanine-cytosine base pair and indicate the hydrogen bonds that link them.

20.25 Write the structure that results when deoxycytosine-5′-monophosphate is linked by a $3' \longrightarrow 5'$ phosphodiester bond to thymidine-5′-monophosphate.

20.26 Write the structure that results when adenosine-5′-monophosphate is linked by a $3' \longrightarrow 5'$ phosphodiester bond to uridine-5′-monophosphate.

20.27 Describe the structure of the prokaryotic chromosome.
20.28 Describe the structure of the eukaryotic chromosome.

DNA Replication

Foundations

20.29 What is meant by semiconservative DNA replication?
20.30 Draw a diagram illustrating semiconservative DNA replication.

Applications

20.31 What are the two primary functions of DNA polymerase III?
20.32 **a.** Why is DNA polymerase said to be template-directed?
b. Why is DNA replication a self-correcting process?
20.33 If a DNA strand had the nucleotide sequence

5′-ATGCCCGAGCTGATTGATCAGA-3′

what would the sequence of the complementary daughter strand be?
20.34 If the sequence of a double-stranded DNA molecule is

5′-CATAAGTCGAGACCGTTACTCACTACTGGAC-3′
| | | | | | | | | | | | | | | | | | | | | | | | | | | | | | |
3′-GTATTCAGCTCTGGCAATGAGTGATGACCTG-5′

what would the sequence of the two daughter DNA molecules be after DNA replication? Indicate which strands are newly synthesized and which are parental.
20.35 What is the replication origin of a DNA molecule?
20.36 What is occurring at the replication fork?
20.37 What is the function of the enzyme helicase?
20.38 What is the function of the enzyme primase?
20.39 What role does the RNA primer play in DNA replication?
20.40 Explain the differences between leading strand and lagging strand replication.

Information Flow in Biological Systems

Foundations

20.41 What is the central dogma of molecular biology?
20.42 What are the roles of DNA, RNA, and protein in information flow in biological systems?
20.43 On what molecule is the anticodon found?
20.44 On what molecule is the codon found?

Applications

20.45 If a gene had the nucleotide sequence

5′-TACGGGCATAGGCCTTAAAGCTAGCTT-3′

what would the sequence of the mRNA be?
20.46 If an RNA strand has the nucleotide sequence

5′-AUGCCAUAACGAUACCCAGUC-3′

what was the sequence of the DNA strand that was transcribed?
20.47 What is meant by the term *RNA splicing?*
20.48 The following is the unspliced transcript of a eukaryotic gene:

exon 1 intron A exon 2 intron B exon 3 intron C exon 4

What would the structure of the final mature mRNA look like, and which of the above sequences would be found in the mature mRNA?

20.49 List the three classes of RNA molecules.
20.50 What is the function of each of the classes of RNA molecules?
20.51 What is the function of the spliceosome?
20.52 What are snRNPs? How do they facilitate RNA splicing?
20.53 What is a poly(A) tail?
20.54 What is the purpose of the poly(A) tail on eukaryotic mRNA?
20.55 What is the cap structure?
20.56 What is the function of the cap structure on eukaryotic mRNA?

The Genetic Code

Foundations

20.57 How many codons constitute the genetic code?
20.58 What is meant by a triplet code?
20.59 What is meant by the reading frame of a gene?
20.60 What happens to the reading frame of a gene if a nucleotide is deleted?

Applications

20.61 Which two amino acids are encoded by only one codon?
20.62 Which amino acids are encoded by six codons?
20.63 An essential gene has the codon 5′-UUU-3′ in a critical position. If this codon is mutated to the sequence 5′-UUA-3′, what is the expected consequence for the cell?
20.64 An essential gene has the codon 5′-UUA-3′ in a critical position. If this codon is mutated to the sequence 5′-UUG-3′, what is the expected consequence for the cell?

Protein Synthesis

Foundations

20.65 What is the function of ribosomes?
20.66 What are the two tRNA binding sites on the ribosome?

Applications

20.67 Write one of the possible mRNA sequences that encodes the following peptide: Ala-gly-leu-cys-met-trp-tyr-ser-ile-gly
20.68 Why are there several alternative mRNA sequences that could encode the same peptide?
20.69 Explain how a change in the sequence of nucleotides of a gene, a mutation, may alter the sequence of amino acids in the protein encoded by that gene.
20.70 What peptide sequence would be formed from the mRNA 5′-AUGUGUAGUGACCAACCGAUUUCACUGUGA-3′?

The following diagram shows the reaction that produces an aminoacyl tRNA, in this case methionyl tRNA. Use this diagram to answer Questions 20.71 and 20.72.

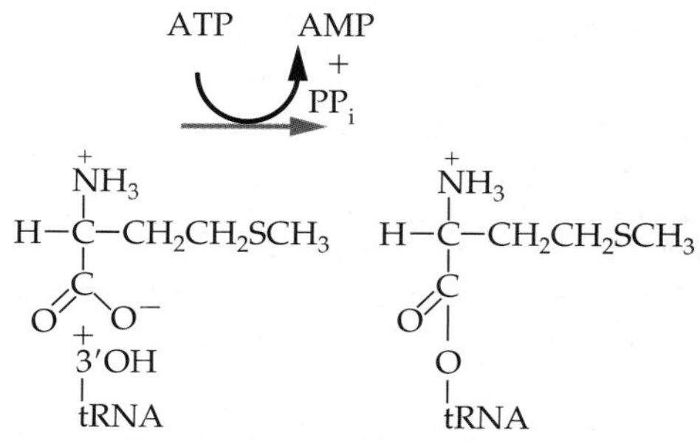

The amino acyl linkage is formed between the 3′—OH of the tRNA and the carboxylate group of the amino acid methionine.

20.71 By what type of bond is an amino acid linked to a tRNA molecule in an aminoacyl tRNA molecule?

20.72 Draw the structure of an alanine residue bound to the 3′ position of adenine at the 3′ end of alanyl tRNA.

Mutation, Ultraviolet Light, and DNA Repair

Foundations

20.73 Define the term *point mutation.*

20.74 What are deletion and insertion mutations?

Applications

20.75 Why are some mutations silent?

20.76 Which is more likely to be a silent mutation, a point mutation or a deletion mutation? Explain your reasoning.

20.77 What damage does UV light cause in DNA, and how does this lead to mutations?

20.78 Explain why UV lights are effective germicides on environmental surfaces.

20.79 What is a carcinogen? Why are carcinogens also mutagens?

20.80 **a.** What causes the genetic disease xeroderma pigmentosum?
b. Why are people who suffer from xeroderma pigmentosum prone to cancer?

Recombinant DNA

Foundations

20.81 What is a restriction enzyme?

20.82 Of what value are restriction enzymes in recombinant DNA research?

20.83 What is a selectable marker?

20.84 What is a cloning vector?

Applications

20.85 Name three products of recombinant DNA that are of value in the field of medicine.

20.86 **a.** What is the ultimate goal of genetic engineering?
b. What ethical issues does this goal raise?

Polymerase Chain Reaction

20.87 After twelve cycles of polymerase chain reaction, how many copies of target DNA would you have for each original molecule in the mixture?

20.88 How is polymerase chain reaction applied in forensic science?

The Human Genome Project

Foundations

20.89 What were the major goals of the Human Genome Project?

20.90 What are the potential benefits of the information gained in the Human Genome Project?

20.91 What is a genome library?

20.92 What is meant by the term *chromosome walking?*

20.93 What is a dideoxynucleotide?

20.94 How does a dideoxynucleotide cause chain termination in DNA replication?

Applications

20.95 A researcher has determined the sequence of the following pieces of DNA. Using this sequence information, map the location of these pieces relative to one another.
a. 5′-AGCTCCTGATTTCATACAGTTTCTAC-TACCTACTA-3′
b. 5′-AGACATTCTATCTACCTAGACTATGTTCAGAA-3′
c. 5′-TTCAGAACTCATTCAGACCTACTACTATACCTT-GGGAGCTCCT-3′
d. 5′-ACCTACTAGACTATACTACTACTAAGGGGAC-TATTCCAGACTT-3′

20.96 Draw a DNA sequencing gel that would represent the sequence shown below. Be sure to label which lanes of the gel represent each of the four dideoxynucleotides in the chain termination reaction mixture.

5′-GACTATCCTAG-3′

CRITICAL THINKING PROBLEMS

1. It has been suggested that the triplet genetic code evolved from a two-nucleotide code. Perhaps there were fewer amino acids in the ancient proteins. Examine the genetic code in Figure 20.18. What features of the code support this hypothesis?
2. The strands of DNA can be separated by heating the DNA sample. The input heat energy breaks the hydrogen bonds between base pairs, allowing the strands to separate from one another. Suppose that you are given two DNA samples. One has a G + C content of 70% and the other has a G + C content of 45%. Which of these samples will require a higher temperature to separate the strands? Explain your answer.
3. A mutation produces a tRNA with a new anticodon. Originally the anticodon was 5′-CCA-3′; the mutant anticodon is 5′-UCA-3′. What effect will this mutant tRNA have on cellular translation?
4. You have just cloned an EcoR1 fragment that is 1650 base pairs (bp) and contains the gene for the hormone leptin. Your first job is to prepare a restriction enzyme map of the recombinant plasmid. You know that you have cloned into a plasmid vector that is 805 bp and that has only one EcoR1 site (the one into which you cloned). There are no other restriction enzyme sites in the plasmid. The following table shows the restriction enzymes used and the DNA fragment sizes that resulted. Draw a map of the circular recombinant plasmid and a representation of the gel from which the fragment sizes were obtained.

Restriction Enzymes	DNA Fragment Sizes (bp)
EcoR1	805, 1650
EcoR1 + BamHI	450, 805, 1200
EcoR1 + SalI	200, 805, 1450
BamHI + SalI	200, 250, 805, 1200

5. A scientist is interested in cloning the gene for blood clotting factor VIII into bacteria so that large amounts of the protein can be produced to treat hemophiliacs. Knowing that bacterial cells cannot carry out RNA splicing, she clones a complementary DNA copy of the factor VIII mRNA and introduces this into bacteria. However, there is no transcription of the cloned factor VIII gene. How could the scientist engineer the gene so that the bacterial cell RNA polymerase will transcribe it?

21

Carbohydrate Metabolism

LEARNING GOALS

1. Discuss the importance of ATP in cellular energy transfer processes.
2. Describe the three stages of catabolism of dietary proteins, carbohydrates, and lipids.
3. Discuss glycolysis in terms of its two major segments.
4. Looking at an equation representing any of the chemical reactions that occur in glycolysis, describe the kind of reaction that is occurring and the significance of that reaction to the pathway.
5. Describe the mechanism of regulation of the rate of glycolysis. Discuss particular examples of that regulation.
6. Discuss the practical and metabolic roles of fermentation reactions.
7. List several products of the pentose phosphate pathway that are required for biosynthesis.
8. Compare glycolysis and gluconeogenesis.
9. Summarize the regulation of blood glucose levels by glycogenesis and glycogenolysis.

All activity requires a source of energy.

OUTLINE

Introduction 728
21.1 ATP: The Cellular Energy Currency 728
21.2 Overview of Catabolic Processes 731
21.3 Glycolysis 733
A Medical Perspective: High Fructose Corn Syrup 741
21.4 Fermentations 742
A Human Perspective: Fermentations: The Good, the Bad, and the Ugly 744
21.5 The Pentose Phosphate Pathway 744
21.6 Gluconeogenesis: The Synthesis of Glucose 746
21.7 Glycogen Synthesis and Degradation 748
A Medical Perspective: Diagnosing Diabetes 752
A Human Perspective: Glycogen Storage Diseases 755

INTRODUCTION

When you awoke this morning, a flood of chemicals called *neurotransmitters* was sent from cell to cell in your nervous system. As these chemical signals accumulated, you gradually became aware of your surroundings. Chemical signals from your nerves to your muscles propelled you out of your warm bed to prepare for your day.

For breakfast you had a glass of milk, two eggs, and buttered toast, thus providing your body with needed molecules in the form of carbohydrates, proteins, lipids, vitamins, and minerals. As you ran out the door, enzymes in your digestive tract were dismantling the macromolecules of your breakfast. Other enzymes in your cells were busy converting the chemical energy of food molecules into adenosine triphosphate (ATP), the universal energy currency of all cells.

Cells need a ready supply of cellular energy for the many cellular functions that support these activities. They need energy for active transport, to move molecules between the environment and the cell. Energy is needed for biosynthesis of all types of molecules, including the neurotransmitters that helped you awake this morning. Finally, energy is needed for mechanical work, including the muscle contractions that allowed you to get out of bed, have breakfast, and run out the door. Other examples of energy-requiring processes are found in Table 21.1.

Our diet includes three major sources of energy: carbohydrates, fats, and proteins. Each of these types of large biological molecules must be broken down into its basic subunits—simple sugars, fatty acids and glycerol, and amino acids—before they can be taken into the cell and used to produce cellular energy. Of these classes of food molecules, carbohydrates are the most readily used. The pathway for the first stage of carbohydrate breakdown is called *glycolysis.* We find the same pathway in organisms as different as the simple bacterium and humans.

Recall that the potential energy of a compound is the bond energy of that compound.

In this chapter we are going to examine the steps of this ancient energy-harvesting pathway. We will see that it is responsible for the capture of some of the bond energy of carbohydrates and the storage of that energy in the molecular form of adenosine triphosphate (ATP). Glycolysis actually releases and stores very little (2.2%) of the potential energy of glucose, but the pathway also serves as a source of biosynthetic building blocks. It also modifies the carbohydrates in such a way that other pathways are able to release as much as 40% of the potential energy.

21.1 ATP: The Cellular Energy Currency

LEARNING GOAL

1 Discuss the importance of ATP in cellular energy transfer processes.

The degradation of fuel molecules, called **catabolism,** provides the energy for cellular energy-requiring functions, including **anabolism,** or biosynthesis. Actually, the energy of a food source can be released in one of two ways: as heat or, more important to the cell, as chemical bond energy. We can envision two alternative modes of aerobic degradation of the simple sugar glucose. Imagine that we simply set the glucose afire. This would result in its complete oxidation to CO_2 and H_2O and would release 686 kilocalories per mole (kcal/mol) of glucose. Yet in terms of a cell, what would be accomplished? Nothing. All of the potential energy of the bonds of glucose is lost as heat and light.

The cell uses a different strategy. With a series of enzymes, biochemical pathways in the cell carry out a step-by-step oxidation of glucose. Small amounts of energy are released at several points in the pathway and that energy is harvested and saved in the bonds of a molecule that has been called the *universal energy currency.* This molecule is **adenosine triphosphate (ATP).**

ATP serves as a "go-between" molecule that couples the *exergonic* (energy releasing) reactions of catabolism and the endergonic (energy requiring) reactions of anabolism. To understand how this molecule harvests the energy and releases it

TABLE 21.1 The Types of Cellular Work That Require Energy

Biosynthesis: Synthesis of Metabolic Intermediates and Macromolecules
Synthesis of glucose from CO_2 and H_2O in the process of photosynthesis in plants
Synthesis of amino acids
Synthesis of nucleotides
Synthesis of lipids
Protein synthesis from amino acids
Synthesis of nucleic acids
Synthesis of organelles and membranes
Active Transport: Movement of Ions and Molecules
Transport of H^+ to maintain constant pH
Transport of food molecules into the cell
Transport of K^+ and Na^+ into and out of nerve cells for transmission of nerve impulses
Secretion of HCl from parietal cells into the stomach
Transport of waste from the blood into the urine in the kidneys
Transport of amino acids and most hexose sugars into the blood from the intestine
Accumulation of calcium ions in the mitochondria
Motility
Contraction and flexion of muscle cells
Separation of chromosomes during cell division
Ability of sperm to swim via flagella
Movement of foreign substances out of the respiratory tract by cilia on the epithelial lining of the trachea
Translocation of eggs into the fallopian tubes by cilia in the female reproductive tract

for energy-requiring reactions, we must take a look at the structure of this amazing molecule (Figure 21.1). ATP is a **nucleotide,** which means that it is a molecule composed of a nitrogenous base; a five-carbon sugar; and one, two, or three phosphoryl groups.

In ATP, a phosphoester bond joins the first phosphoryl group to the five-carbon sugar ribose. The next two phosphoryl groups are joined to one another by phosphoanhydride bonds (Figure 21.1). Recall that the phosphoanhydride bond is a *high-energy bond.* When it is broken or hydrolyzed, a large amount of energy is released.

Nature's high-energy bonds, including phosphoanhydride and phosphoester bonds, are discussed in Section 14.4.

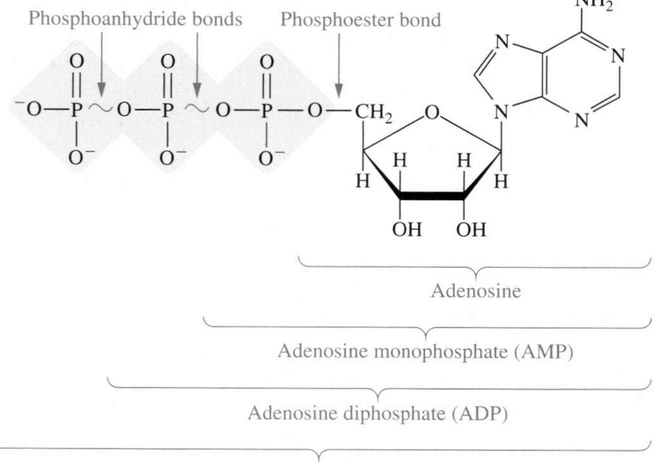

Figure 21.1 The structure of the universal energy currency, ATP.

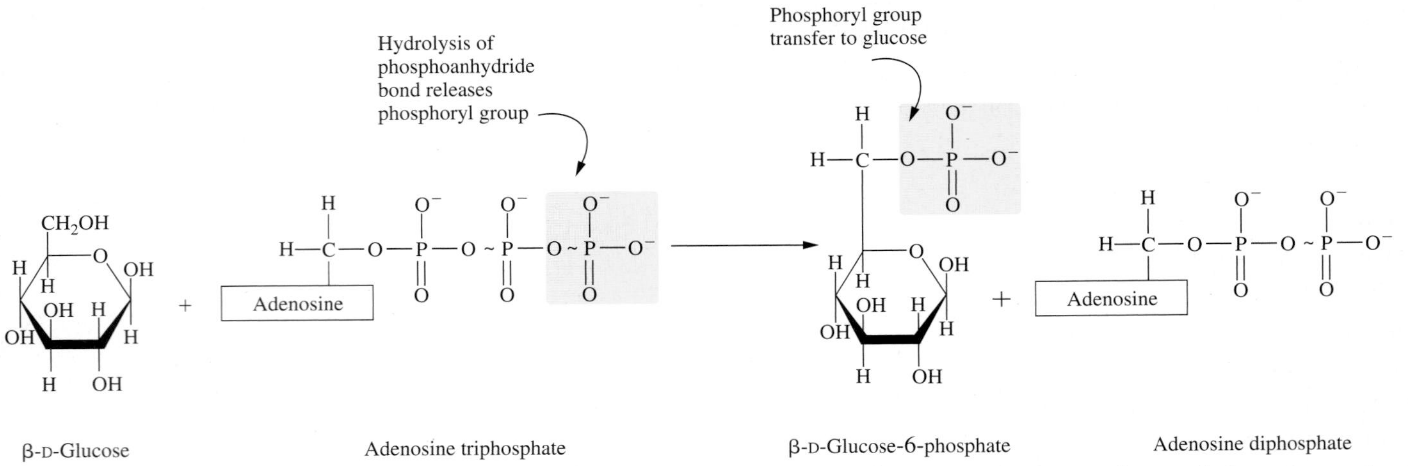

Hydrolysis of phosphoanhydride bond releases phosphoryl group

Phosphoryl group transfer to glucose

β-D-Glucose + Adenosine triphosphate ⟶ β-D-Glucose-6-phosphate + Adenosine diphosphate

Figure 21.2 The hydrolysis of the phosphoanhydride bond of ATP releases inorganic phosphate and energy. In this coupled reaction catalyzed by an enzyme, the phosphoryl group and some of the released energy are transferred to β-D-glucose.

When the phosphoanhydride bond of ATP is broken, the energy that is released can be used for cellular work. These high-energy bonds are indicated as squiggles (~) in Figure 21.1.

See Sections 14.4 and 20.1 for further information on the structure of ATP and hydrolysis of the phosphoanhydride bonds.

Hydrolysis of ATP yields adenosine diphosphate (ADP), an inorganic phosphate group (P_i), and energy (Figure 21.2). The energy released by this hydrolysis of ATP is then used to drive biological processes, for instance, the phosphorylation of glucose or fructose.

An example of the way in which the energy of ATP is used can be seen in the first step of glycolysis, the anaerobic degradation of glucose to harvest chemical energy. The first step involves the transfer of a phosphoryl group, $—PO_3^{2-}$, from ATP to the C-6 hydroxyl group of glucose (Figure 21.2). This reaction is catalyzed by the enzyme hexokinase.

This reaction can be dissected to reveal the role of ATP as a source of energy. Although this is a coupled reaction, we can think of it as a two-step process. The first step is the hydrolysis of ATP to ADP and phosphate, abbreviated P_i. This is an exergonic reaction that *releases* about 7 kcal/mol of energy:

$$\text{ATP} + H_2O \longrightarrow \text{ADP} + P_i + 7\ \text{kcal/mol}$$

The second step, the synthesis of glucose-6-phosphate from glucose and phosphate, is an endergonic reaction that *requires* 3.0 kcal/mol:

$$3.0\ \text{kcal/mol} + \text{glucose} + P_i \longrightarrow \text{glucose-6-phosphate} + H_2O$$

These two chemical reactions can then be added to give the equation showing the way in which ATP hydrolysis is *coupled* to the phosphorylation of glucose:

$$\begin{array}{rcl} \text{ATP} + H_2O & \longrightarrow & \text{ADP} + P_i + 7\ \text{kcal/mol} \\ 3.0\ \text{kcal/mol} + \text{glucose} + P_i & \longrightarrow & \text{glucose-6-phosphate} + H_2O \\ \hline \text{Net: ATP} + \text{glucose} & \longrightarrow & \text{glucose-6-phosphate} + \text{ADP} + 4\ \text{kcal/mol} \end{array}$$

Because the hydrolysis of ATP releases more energy than is required to synthesize glucose-6-phosphate from glucose and phosphate, there is an overall energy release in this process and the reaction proceeds spontaneously to the right. The product, glucose-6-phosphate, has more energy than the reactant, glucose, because it now carries some of the energy from the original phosphoanhydride bond of ATP.

The primary function of all catabolic pathways is to harvest the chemical energy of fuel molecules and to store that energy by the production of ATP.

This continuous production of ATP is what provides the stored potential energy that is used to power most cellular functions.

Question 21.1 Why is ATP called the universal energy currency?

Question 21.2 List five biological activities that require ATP.

21.2 Overview of Catabolic Processes

LEARNING GOAL

2 Describe the three stages of catabolism of dietary proteins, carbohydrates, and lipids.

Although carbohydrates, fats, and proteins can all be degraded to release energy, carbohydrates are the most readily used energy source. We will begin by examining the oxidation of the hexose glucose. In Chapters 22 and 23 we will see how the pathways of glucose oxidation are also used for the degradation of fats and proteins.

Any catabolic process must begin with a supply of nutrients. When we eat a meal, we are eating quantities of carbohydrates, fats, and proteins. From this point the catabolic processes can be broken down into a series of stages. The three stages of catabolism are summarized in Figure 21.3.

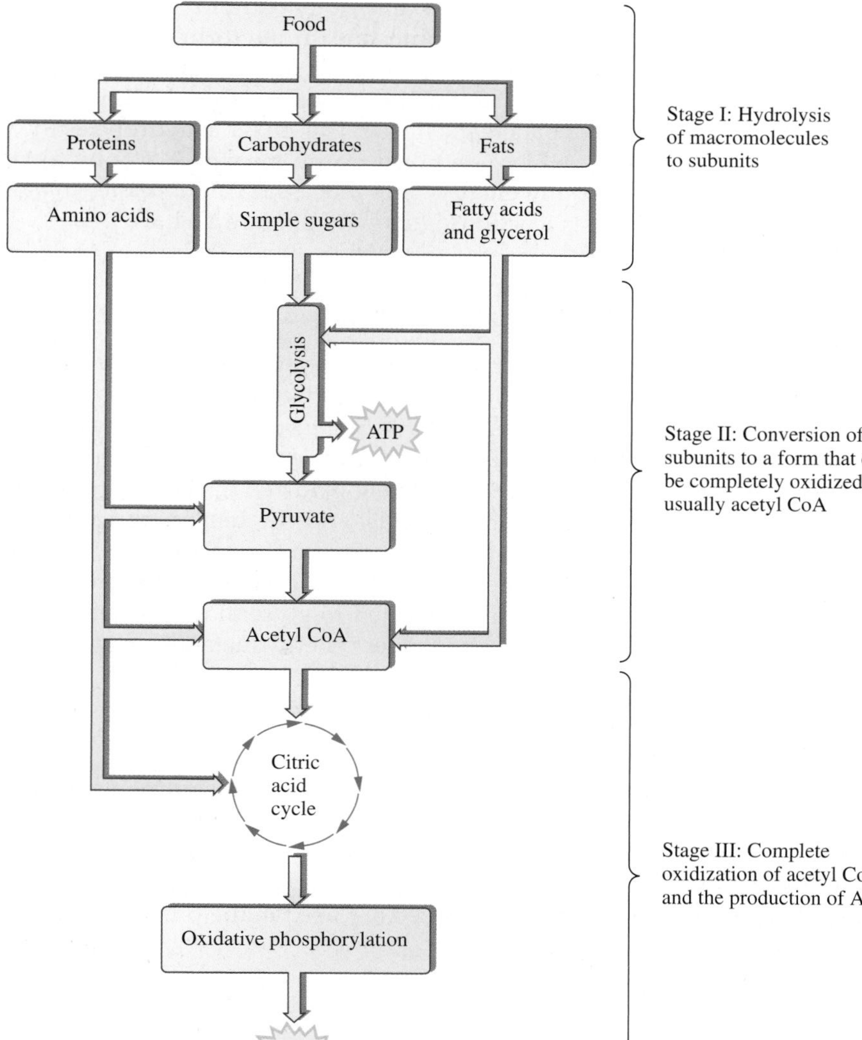

Figure 21.3 The three stages of the conversion of food into cellular energy in the form of ATP.

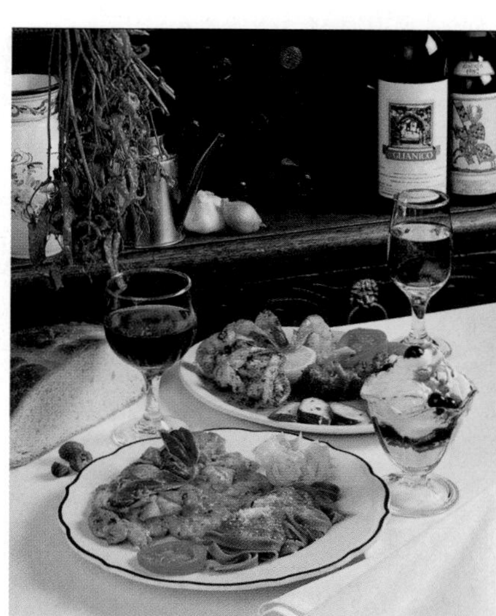

Describe the path of the carbohydrates, lipids, and proteins in this meal from digestion through the biochemical energy-harvesting reactions.

Stage I: Hydrolysis of Dietary Macromolecules into Small Subunits

The purpose of the first stage of catabolism is to degrade large food molecules into their component subunits. These subunits—simple sugars, amino acids, fatty acids, and glycerol—are then taken into the cells of the body for use as an energy source.

Polysaccharides are hydrolyzed to monosaccharides. This process begins in the mouth, where the enzyme amylase begins the hydrolysis of starch. Digestion continues in the small intestine, where pancreatic amylase further hydrolyzes the starch into maltose (a disaccharide of glucose). Maltase catalyzes the hydrolysis of maltose, producing two glucose molecules. Similarly, sucrose is hydrolyzed to glucose and fructose by the enzyme sucrase, and lactose (milk sugar) is degraded into the monosaccharides glucose and galactose by the enzyme lactase in the small intestine. The monosaccharides are taken up by the epithelial cells of the intestine in an energy-requiring process called *active transport.*

In the laboratory, a strong acid or base and high temperatures are required for hydrolysis of amide bonds (Section 15.3). However, this reaction proceeds quickly under physiological conditions when catalyzed by enzymes (Section 19.11).

The digestion of proteins begins in the stomach, where the low pH denatures the proteins so that they are more easily hydrolyzed by the enzyme pepsin. They are further degraded in the small intestine by trypsin, chymotrypsin, elastase, and other proteases. The products of protein digestion—amino acids and short oligopeptides—are taken up by the cells lining the intestine. This uptake also involves an active transport mechanism.

The digestion and transport of fats are considered in greater detail in Chapter 23.

Digestion of fats does not begin until the food reaches the small intestine, even though there are lipases in both the saliva and stomach fluid. Fats arrive in the duodenum, the first portion of the small intestine, in the form of large fat globules. Bile salts produced by the liver break these up into an emulsion of tiny fat droplets. Because the small droplets have a greater surface area, the lipids are now more accessible to the action of pancreatic lipase. This enzyme hydrolyzes the fats into fatty acids and glycerol, which are taken up by intestinal cells by a transport process that does not require energy. This process is called *passive transport.* A summary of these hydrolysis reactions is shown in Figure 21.4.

Stage II: Conversion of Monomers into a Form That Can Be Completely Oxidized

The citric acid cycle is considered in detail in Section 22.4.

The monosaccharides, amino acids, fatty acids, and glycerol must now be assimilated into the pathways of energy metabolism. The two major pathways are glycolysis and the citric acid cycle (see Figure 21.3). Sugars usually enter the glycolysis pathway in the form of glucose or fructose. They are eventually converted to acetyl CoA, which is a form that can be completely oxidized in the citric acid cycle. Amino groups are removed from amino acids, and the remaining carbon skeletons enter the catabolic processes at many steps of the citric acid cycle. Fatty acids are converted to acetyl CoA and enter the citric acid cycle in that form. Glycerol, produced by the hydrolysis of fats, is converted to glyceraldehyde-3-phosphate, one of the intermediates of glycolysis, and enters energy metabolism at that level.

Stage III: The Complete Oxidation of Nutrients and the Production of ATP

Oxidative phosphorylation is described in Section 22.6.

Acetyl CoA carries acetyl groups, two-carbon remnants of the nutrients, to the citric acid cycle. Acetyl CoA enters the cycle, and electrons and hydrogen atoms are harvested during the complete oxidation of the acetyl group to CO_2. Coenzyme A is released (recycled) to carry additional acetyl groups to the pathway. The electrons and hydrogen atoms that are harvested are used in the process of oxidative phosphorylation to produce ATP.

Question 21.3 Briefly describe the three stages of catabolism.

Question 21.4 Discuss the digestion of dietary carbohydrates, lipids, and proteins.

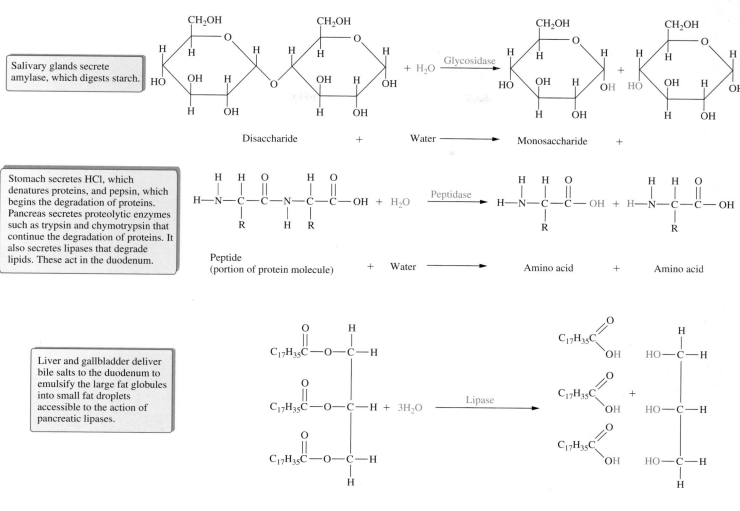

Salivary glands secrete amylase, which digests starch.

Disaccharide + Water —Glycosidase→ Monosaccharide + Monosaccharide

Stomach secretes HCl, which denatures proteins, and pepsin, which begins the degradation of proteins. Pancreas secretes proteolytic enzymes such as trypsin and chymotrypsin that continue the degradation of proteins. It also secretes lipases that degrade lipids. These act in the duodenum.

Peptide (portion of protein molecule) + Water —Peptidase→ Amino acid + Amino acid

Liver and gallbladder deliver bile salts to the duodenum to emulsify the large fat globules into small fat droplets accessible to the action of pancreatic lipases.

Triglyceride + Water ($3H_2O$) —Lipase→ Fatty acids ($C_{17}H_{35}COOH$) + Glycerol

Figure 21.4 A summary of the hydrolysis reactions of carbohydrates, proteins, and fats, and their locations in the digestive tract.

21.3 Glycolysis

An Overview

Glycolysis, also known as the Embden-Meyerhof Pathway, is a pathway for carbohydrate catabolism that begins with the substrate D-glucose. The very fact that all organisms can use glucose as an energy source for glycolysis suggests that glycolysis was the first successful energy-harvesting pathway that evolved on the earth. The pathway evolved at a time when the earth's atmosphere was *anaerobic;* no free oxygen was available. As a result, glycolysis requires no oxygen; it is an anaerobic process. Further, it must have evolved in very simple, single-celled organisms, much like bacteria. These organisms did not have complex organelles in the cytoplasm to carry out specific cellular functions. Thus glycolysis was a process carried out by enzymes that were free in the cytoplasm. To this day, glycolysis remains an anaerobic process carried out by cytoplasmic enzymes, even in cells as complex as our own.

ANIMATIONS
- How Glycolysis Works
- A Biochemical Pathway

The ten steps of glycolysis, catalyzed by ten enzymes, are outlined in Figure 21.5. The first reactions of glycolysis involve an energy investment. ATP molecules are hydrolyzed, energy is released, and phosphoryl groups are added to the hexose sugars. In the remaining steps of glycolysis, energy is harvested to produce a net gain of ATP.

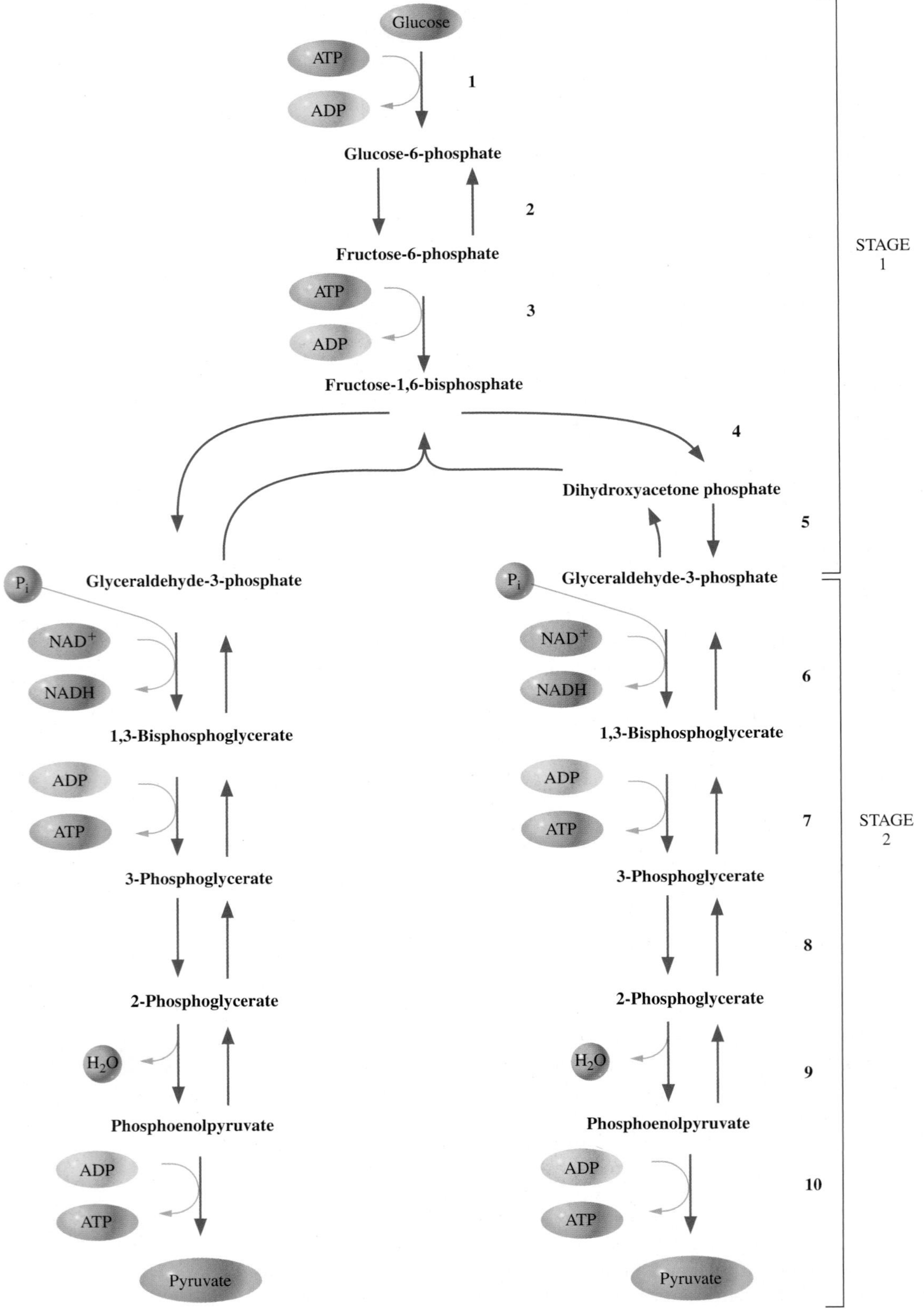

Figure 21.5 A summary of the reactions of glycolysis. These reactions occur in the cell cytoplasm.

The three major products of glycolysis are seen in Figure 21.5. These are chemical energy in the form of ATP, chemical energy in the form of NADH, and two three-carbon pyruvate molecules. Each of these products is considered below:

- **Chemical energy as ATP.** Four ATP molecules are formed by the process of **substrate-level phosphorylation.** This means that a high-energy phosphoryl group from one of the substrates in glycolysis is transferred to ADP to form ATP. The two substrates involved in these transfer reactions are 1,3-bisphosphoglycerate and phosphoenolpyruvate (see Figure 21.5, steps 7 and 10). Although four ATP molecules are produced during glycolysis, the *net* gain is only two ATP molecules because two ATP molecules are used early in glycolysis (Figure 21.5, steps 1 and 3). The two ATP molecules produced represent only 2.2% of the potential energy of the glucose molecule. Thus glycolysis is not a very efficient energy-harvesting process.
- **Chemical energy in the form of reduced NAD^+, NADH. Nicotinamide adenine dinucleotide (NAD^+)** is a coenzyme derived from the vitamin niacin. The reduced form of NAD^+, NADH, carries hydride anions, hydrogen atoms with two electrons ($H:^-$), removed during the oxidation of glyceraldehyde-3-phosphate (see Figure 21.5, step 6). Under aerobic conditions, the electrons and hydrogen atom are transported from the cytoplasm into the mitochondria. Here they enter an electron transport system for the generation of ATP by **oxidative phosphorylation.** Under anaerobic conditions, NADH is used as a source of electrons in fermentation reactions.
- **Two pyruvate molecules.** At the end of glycolysis the six-carbon glucose molecule has been converted into two three-carbon pyruvate molecules. The fate of the pyruvate also depends on whether the reactions are occurring in the presence or absence of oxygen. Under aerobic conditions it is used to produce acetyl CoA destined for the citric acid cycle and complete oxidation. Under anaerobic conditions it is used as an electron acceptor in fermentation reactions.

The structure of NAD^+ and the way it functions as a hydride anion carrier are shown in Figure 19.8 and described in Section 19.7.

In any event these last two products must be used in some way so that glycolysis can continue to function and produce ATP. There are two reasons for this. First, if pyruvate were allowed to build up, it would cause glycolysis to stop, thereby stopping the production of ATP. Thus pyruvate must be used in some kind of follow-up reaction, aerobic or anaerobic. Second, in step 6, glyceraldehyde-3-phosphate is oxidized and NAD^+ is reduced (accepts the hydride anion). The cell has only a small supply of NAD^+. If all the NAD^+ is reduced, none will be available for this reaction, and glycolysis will stop. Therefore NADH must be reoxidized so that glycolysis can continue to produce ATP for the cell.

Biological Effects of Genetic Disorders of Glycolysis

Before we look at each of the reactions of glycolysis in detail, let's consider the symptoms that arise if a person has a genetic defect in some of the enzymes. Symptoms include muscle myopathy (muscle *(myo)* and disorder *(pathy)*), which involves damage to the muscle as a result of the inability to extract energy from food molecules. In its mildest form, myopathy can cause exercise intolerance, which is the onset of fatigue when exercising. In more severe forms it can cause muscle breakdown (rhabdomyolysis), in which the muscle cells, starved of energy, begin to die. Another symptom of rhabdomyolysis is the release of myoglobin into the blood and eventually into the urine. This condition, called *myoglobinuria,* results in urine that is the color of cola soft drinks, and may even damage the kidneys.

Myopathy may include severe muscle pain. Patients often describe it as a cramp, but it is not a cramp since the muscle is not able to contract because of the lack of energy. Rather, the pain is caused by cell death and tissue damage that result from an inability to produce enough ATP.

Another symptom is hemolytic anemia (anemia that results from the lysis of red blood cells). Red blood cells are completely dependent on glycolysis for their ATP. A defect in one of the enzymes of glycolysis results in insufficient ATP and resultant cell death.

Tarui's disease is caused by a deficiency of phosphofructokinase. Although this is not a sex-linked disorder, the great majority of sufferers are males (nine males to one female). The disorder is most frequently found in U.S. Ashkenazi Jews and Italian families. Onset of symptoms typically occurs between the ages of twenty and forty, although some severe cases have been reported in infants and young children. Patients experiencing the late-onset form of Tarui's disease typically experienced exercise intolerance when they were younger. Vigorous exercise results in myoglobinuria and severe muscle pain. Meals high in carbohydrates worsen the exercise intolerance. Early-onset disease is often associated with respiratory failure, cardiomyopathy (heart muscle disease), seizures, and cortical blindness.

Phosphoglycerate kinase deficiency is a sex-linked genetic disorder (located on the X chromosome). As a result, far more males than females suffer from this disease. There are many clinical features associated with this deficiency, although only rarely are they all found in the same patient. These symptoms range from mental challenge and seizures to a slowly progressive myopathy, and hemolytic anemia.

Phosphoglycerate mutase deficiency has been mapped on chromosome 7. The disorder is found predominantly in U.S African American, Italian, and Japanese families. The clinical features include exercise intolerance, muscle pain, and myoglobinuria following more intense exercise.

These are just three of the disorders associated with deficiencies of the enzymes of glycolysis; but they make it clear that the pathway is critical to our health. The most extreme deficiency of one of these enzymes will cause death of the fetus.

Reactions of Glycolysis

LEARNING GOAL

3 Discuss glycolysis in terms of its two major segments.

Glycolysis can be divided into two major segments. The first is the investment of ATP energy. Without this investment, glucose would not have enough energy for glycolysis to continue, and there would be no ATP produced. This segment includes the first five reactions of the pathway. The second major segment involves the remaining reactions of the pathway (steps 6–10), those that result in a net energy yield.

LEARNING GOAL

4 Looking at an equation representing any of the chemical reactions that occur in glycolysis, describe the kind of reaction that is occurring and the significance of that reaction to the pathway.

Reaction 1

The substrate, glucose, is phosphorylated by the enzyme *hexokinase* in a coupled phosphorylation reaction. The source of the phosphoryl group is ATP. At first this reaction seems contrary to the overall purpose of catabolism, the *production* of ATP. The expenditure of ATP in these early reactions must be thought of as an "investment." The cell actually goes into energy "debt" in these early reactions, but this is absolutely necessary to get the pathway started.

The enzyme name can tell us a lot about the reaction (see Section 19.1). The suffix *-kinase* tells us that the enzyme is a transferase that will transfer a phosphoryl group, in this case from an ATP molecule to the substrate. The prefix *hexo-* gives us a hint that the substrate is a six-carbon sugar. Hexokinase predominantly phosphorylates the six-carbon sugar glucose.

$$\text{Glucose} + \text{ATP} \xrightarrow{\text{Hexokinase}} \text{Glucose-6-phosphate} + \text{ADP} + H^+$$

Reaction 2

The glucose-6-phosphate formed in the first reaction is rearranged to produce the structural isomer fructose-6-phosphate. The enzyme *phosphoglucose isomerase* catalyzes this isomerization. The result is that the C-1 carbon of the six-carbon sugar is exposed; it is no longer part of the ring structure. Examination of the open-chain structures reveals that this isomerization converts an aldose into a ketose.

The enzyme name, phosphoglucose isomerase, provides clues to the reaction that is being catalyzed (Section 19.1). *Isomerase* tells us that the enzyme will catalyze the interconversion of one isomer into another. *Phosphoglucose* suggests that the substrate is a phosphorylated form of glucose.

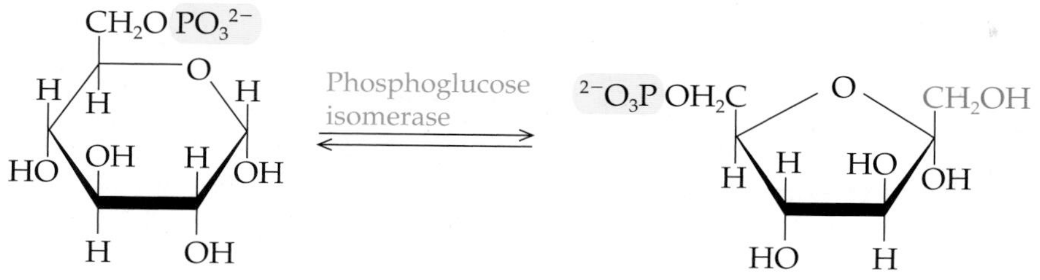

$CH_2OPO_3^{2-}$ ... Phosphoglucose isomerase ⇌ $^{2-}O_3POH_2C$ ... CH_2OH

Glucose-6-phosphate

Fructose-6-phosphate

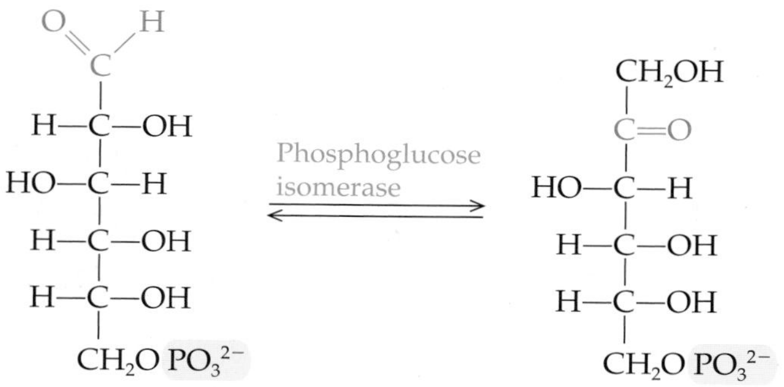

Phosphoglucose isomerase ⇌

Glucose-6-phosphate (an aldose)

Fructose-6-phosphate (a ketose)

Reaction 3

A second energy "investment" is catalyzed by the enzyme *phosphofructokinase.* The phosphoanhydride bond in ATP is hydrolyzed, and a phosphoester linkage between the phosphoryl group and the C-1 hydroxyl group of fructose-6-phosphate is formed. The product is fructose-1,6-bisphosphate.

The suffix *-kinase* in the name of the enzyme tells us that this is a coupled reaction: ATP is hydrolyzed and a phosphoryl group is transferred to another molecule. The prefix *phosphofructo-* tells us the other molecule is a phosphorylated form of fructose.

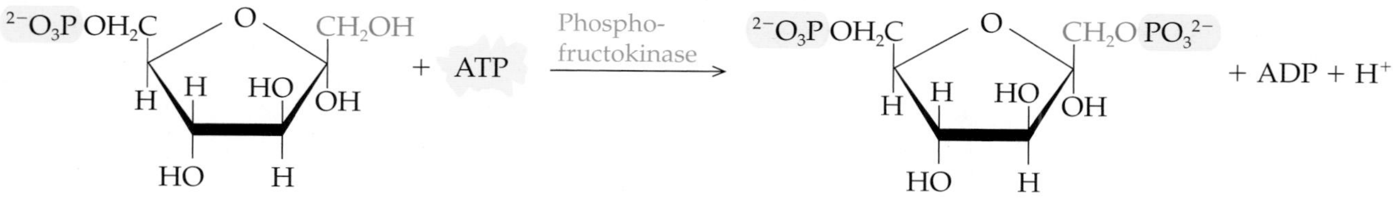

Fructose-6-phosphate + ATP —Phosphofructokinase→ Fructose-1,6-bisphosphate + ADP + H^+

Reaction 4

Fructose-1,6-bisphosphate is split into two three-carbon intermediates in a reaction catalyzed by the enzyme *aldolase.* The products are glyceraldehyde-3-phosphate (G3P) and dihydroxyacetone phosphate.

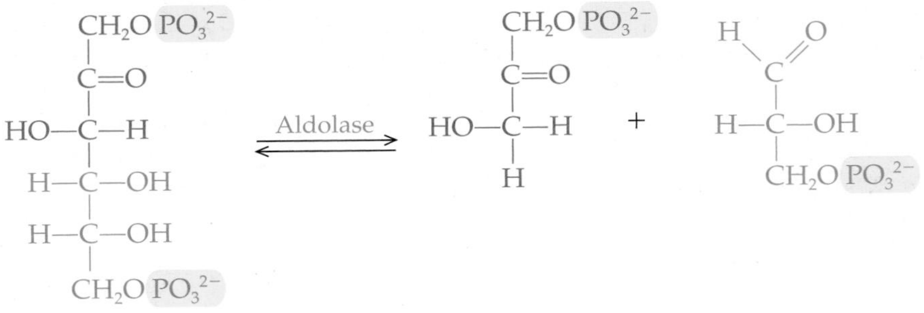

$$\begin{array}{c} CH_2OPO_3^{2-} \\ | \\ C{=}O \\ | \\ HO{-}C{-}H \\ | \\ H{-}C{-}OH \\ | \\ H{-}C{-}OH \\ | \\ CH_2OPO_3^{2-} \end{array} \underset{}{\overset{\text{Aldolase}}{\rightleftharpoons}} \begin{array}{c} CH_2OPO_3^{2-} \\ | \\ C{=}O \\ | \\ HO{-}C{-}H \\ | \\ H \end{array} + \begin{array}{c} H \quad O \\ \diagdown \;\; /\!\!/ \\ C \\ | \\ H{-}C{-}OH \\ | \\ CH_2OPO_3^{2-} \end{array}$$

Fructose-1,6-bisphosphate | Dihydroxyacetone phosphate | Glyceraldehyde-3-phosphate

Reaction 5

Because G3P is the only substrate that can be used by the next enzyme in the pathway, the dihydroxyacetone phosphate is rearranged to become a second molecule of G3P. The enzyme that mediates this isomerization is *triose phosphate isomerase*.

The enzyme name hints that two isomers of a phosphorylated three-carbon sugar are going to be interconverted (Section 19.1). The ketone dihydroxyacetone phosphate and its isomeric aldehyde, glyceraldehyde-3-phosphate are interconverted through an enediol intermediate.

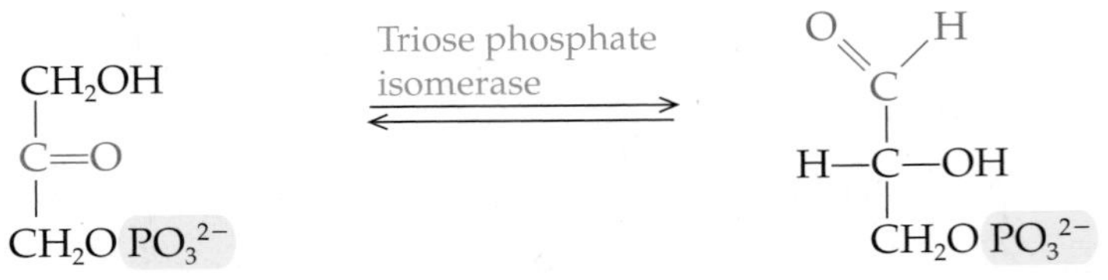

$$\begin{array}{c} CH_2OH \\ | \\ C{=}O \\ | \\ CH_2OPO_3^{2-} \end{array} \underset{}{\overset{\text{Triose phosphate isomerase}}{\rightleftharpoons}} \begin{array}{c} O \quad H \\ \diagdown\!\!\diagdown \;\; / \\ C \\ | \\ H{-}C{-}OH \\ | \\ CH_2OPO_3^{2-} \end{array}$$

Dihydroxyacetone phosphate | Glyceraldehyde-3-phosphate

Reaction 6

In this reaction the aldehyde glyceraldehyde-3-phosphate is oxidized to a carboxylic acid in a reaction catalyzed by *glyceraldehyde-3-phosphate dehydrogenase*. This is the first step in glycolysis that harvests energy, and it involves the reduction of the coenzyme nicotinamide adenine dinucleotide (NAD^+). This reaction occurs in two steps. First, NAD^+ is reduced to NADH as the aldehyde group of glyceraldehyde-3-phosphate is oxidized to a carboxyl group. Second, an inorganic phosphate group is transferred to the carboxyl group to give 1,3-bisphosphoglycerate. Notice that the new bond is denoted with a squiggle (~), indicating that this is a high-energy bond. This, and all remaining reactions of glycolysis, occur twice for each glucose because each glucose has been converted into two molecules of glyceraldehyde-3-phosphate.

The name glyceraldehyde-3-phosphate dehydrogenase tells us that the substrate glyceraldehyde-3-phosphate is going to be oxidized. In this reaction, we see that the aldehyde group has been oxidized to a carboxylate group (Section 13.4).

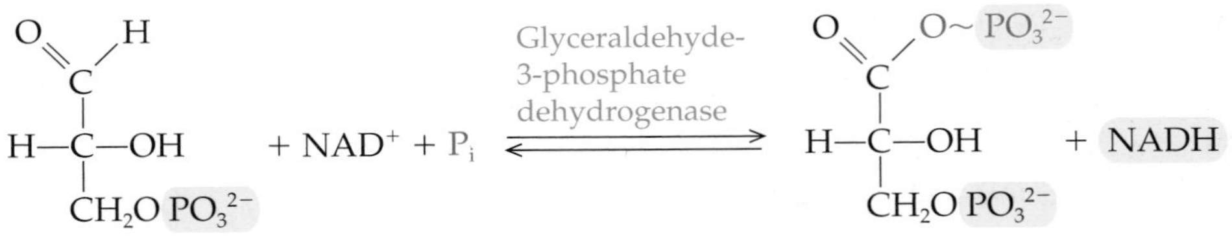

$$\begin{array}{c} O \quad H \\ \diagdown\!\!\diagdown \;\; / \\ C \\ | \\ H{-}C{-}OH \\ | \\ CH_2OPO_3^{2-} \end{array} + NAD^+ + P_i \underset{}{\overset{\text{Glyceraldehyde-3-phosphate dehydrogenase}}{\rightleftharpoons}} \begin{array}{c} O \quad O{\sim}PO_3^{2-} \\ \diagdown\!\!\diagdown \;\; / \\ C \\ | \\ H{-}C{-}OH \\ | \\ CH_2OPO_3^{2-} \end{array} + NADH$$

Glyceraldehyde-3-phosphate | 1,3-Bisphosphoglycerate

Reaction 7

In this reaction, energy is harvested in the form of *ATP*. The enzyme *phosphoglycerate kinase* catalyzes the transfer of the phosphoryl group of 1,3-bisphosphoglycerate to ADP. This is the first substrate-level phosphorylation of glycolysis, and it produces

ATP and 3-phosphoglycerate. It is a coupled reaction in which the high-energy bond is hydrolyzed and the energy released is used to drive the synthesis of ATP.

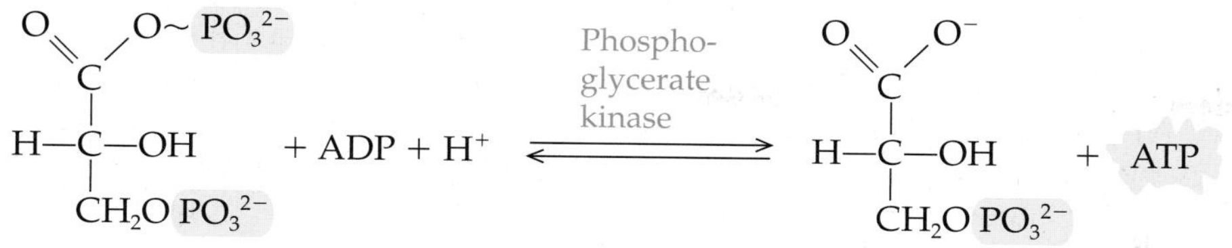

$$\text{1,3-Bisphosphoglycerate} + ADP + H^+ \xrightleftharpoons{\text{Phosphoglycerate kinase}} \text{3-Phosphoglycerate} + ATP$$

1,3-Bisphosphoglycerate 3-Phosphoglycerate

Once again, the enzyme name reveals a great deal about the reaction. The suffix *-kinase* tells us that a phosphoryl group will be transferred. In this case, a phosphoester bond in the substrate 1,3-bisphosphoglycerate is hydrolyzed and ADP is phosphorylated. Note that this is a reversible reaction.

Reaction 8

3-Phosphoglycerate is isomerized to produce 2-phosphoglycerate in a reaction catalyzed by the enzyme *phosphoglycerate mutase*. The phosphoryl group attached to the third carbon of 3-phosphoglycerate is transferred to the second carbon.

$$\text{3-Phosphoglycerate} \xrightleftharpoons{\text{Phosphoglycerate mutase}} \text{2-Phosphoglycerate}$$

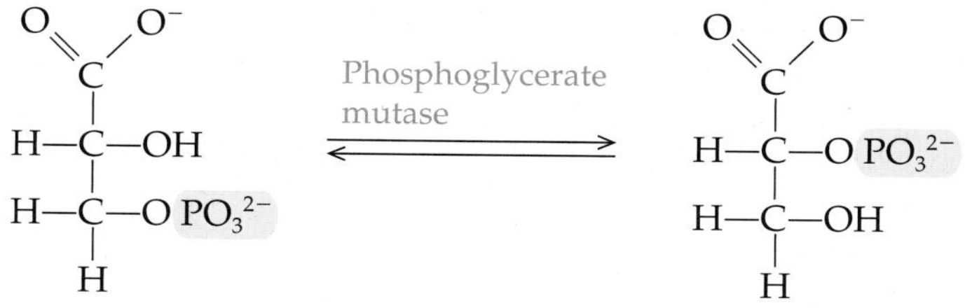

3-Phosphoglycerate 2-Phosphoglycerate

The suffix *-mutase* indicates another type of isomerase. Notice that the chemical formulas of the substrate and reactant are the same. The only difference is in the location of the phosphoryl group.

Reaction 9

In this step the enzyme *enolase* catalyzes the dehydration (removal of a water molecule) of 2-phosphoglycerate. The energy-rich product is phosphoenolpyruvate, the highest energy phosphorylated compound in metabolism.

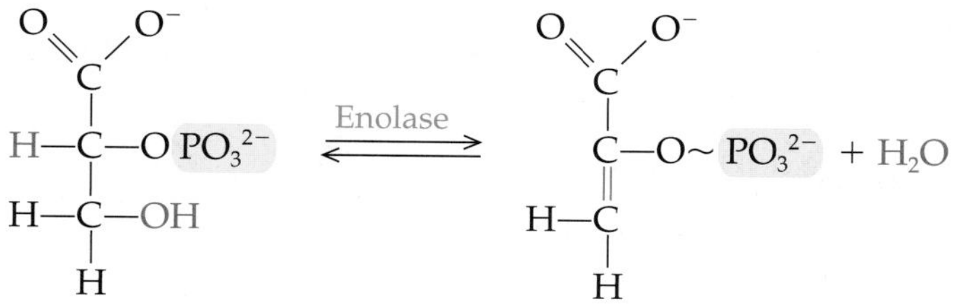

$$\text{2-Phosphoglycerate} \xrightleftharpoons{\text{Enolase}} \text{Phosphoenolpyruvate} + H_2O$$

2-Phosphoglycerate Phosphoenolpyruvate

Reaction 10

Here we see the final substrate-level phosphorylation in the pathway, which is catalyzed by *pyruvate kinase*. Phosphoenolpyruvate serves as a donor of the phosphoryl group that is transferred to ADP to produce ATP. This is another coupled reaction in which hydrolysis of the phosphoester bond in phosphoenolpyruvate provides energy for the formation of the phosphoanhydride bond of ATP. The final product of glycolysis is pyruvate.

$$\text{Phosphoenolpyruvate} + ADP + H^+ \xrightarrow{\text{Pyruvate kinase}} \text{Pyruvate} + ATP$$

Phosphoenolpyruvate Pyruvate

The enzyme name indicates that a phosphoryl group will be transferred (kinase) and that the product will be pyruvate.

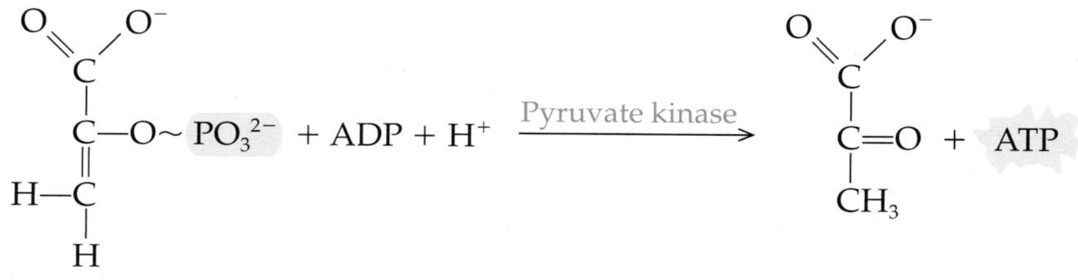

It should be noted that reactions 6 through 10 occur twice per glucose molecule, because the starting six-carbon sugar is split into two three-carbon molecules. Thus in reaction 6, two NADH molecules are generated, and a total of four ATP molecules are made (steps 7 and 10). The net ATP gain from this pathway is, however, only two ATP molecules because there was an energy investment of two ATP molecules in the early steps of the pathway. This investment was paid back by the two ATP molecules produced by substrate-level phosphorylation in step 7. The actual energy yield is produced by substrate-level phosphorylation in reaction 10.

Entry of Fructose into Glycolysis

Depending on the tissue, fructose enters glycolysis in different ways. In the muscle, where hexokinase is abundant, the enzyme phosphorylates fructose to fructose-6-phosphate, which directly enters glycolysis. There is much less hexokinase in the liver, but fructokinase is present. Fructokinase phosphorylates fructose to produce fructose-1-phosphate. This product is cleaved into dihydroxyacetone phosphate (DHAP) and glyceraldehyde by the enzyme fructose-1-phosphate aldolase. The glyceraldehyde is phosphorylated by triose kinase to produce glyceraldehyde-3-phosphate (G3P). The DHAP and G3P enter glycolysis directly.

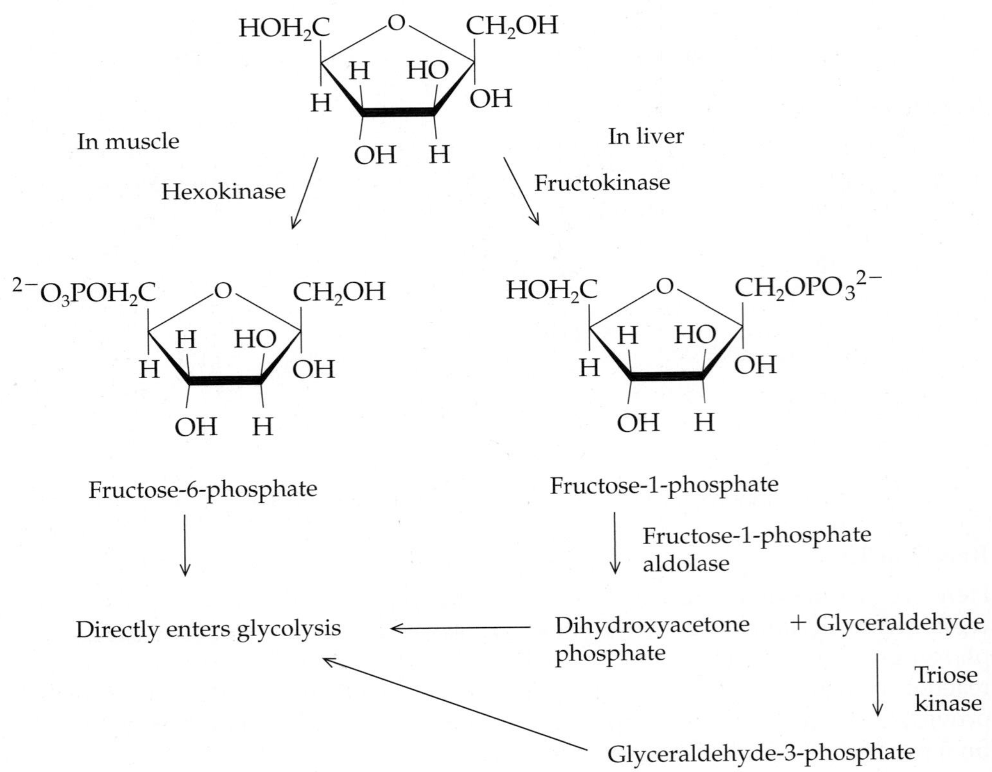

Question 21.5 What is substrate-level phosphorylation?

Question 21.6 What are the major products of glycolysis?

Question 21.7 Describe an overview of the reactions of glycolysis.

Question 21.8 How do the names of the first three enzymes of the glycolytic pathway relate to the reactions they catalyze?

A MEDICAL PERSPECTIVE

High Fructose Corn Syrup

A controversy over the health risks of high fructose corn syrup (HFCS) has been raging in recent years. This sweetener was introduced into the food market forty years ago. Some have made the correlation that the increase in the use of HFCS parallels the increase in obesity in the U.S. population. In 1970, approximately 15% of the population was obese. That level currently stands at 33% of the U.S. population.

Until recently, there were no data to suggest that the observed correlation was valid. But in 2010, Dr. Bart Hoebel and his colleagues at Princeton University carried out two experiments in rats that suggest that there is a relationship between HFCS in the diet and obesity.

In the first experiment, one set of rats was given water sweetened with sucrose at a concentration typical of a soft drink. A second set of rats was provided water sweetened with HFCS at a concentration half that found in soft drinks. Both sets of rats were provided their standard diet of rat chow. Dr. Hoebel's group observed that the rats provided water sweetened with HFCS gained much more weight than those given water with sucrose.

In a long-term study of the effects of HFCS, the group monitored weight gain, blood triglycerides, and body fat over a period of 6 months. In this study, rats on rat chow only were compared with rats on a high HFCS diet. Their results were startling. Not only did the HFCS rats gain 48% more weight, they exhibited significant increases in blood triglycerides and deposition of abdominal fat. These are conditions that, in humans, are associated with metabolic syndrome which, in turn, is associated with coronary artery disease, high blood pressure, cancer, and diabetes.

Both HFCS and sucrose contain glucose and fructose; so what differences might cause these results? The primary difference is that HFCS contains a higher concentration of fructose than sucrose (55% compared to 50%). Could this increased amount of fructose be the cause of the symptoms?

The way the body metabolizes HFCS compared to sucrose may provide some clues. First, sucrose is a disaccharide that must be hydrolyzed before it can be absorbed by cells of the body. HFCS is a mixture of the monosaccharides glucose and fructose; these can be immediately absorbed. In addition, unlike glucose, fructose does not stimulate an increase in insulin levels. Since insulin controls the release of leptin, a hormone that signals the satiety center of the brain, thus reducing hunger, a reduced amount of leptin would promote over-eating and weight gain.

The last observation is that fructose enters glycolysis by a different path than glucose. As we saw in the text, fructose is phosphorylated to fructose-1-phosphate in the liver. This is directly cleaved by fructose-1-phosphate aldolase to produce dihydroxyacetone phosphate (DHAP) and glyceraldehye. The DHAP is quickly isomerized and the glyceraldehyde is phosphorylated; both reactions produce glyceraldehyde-3-phosphate. This leads to the production of acetyl CoA via reactions that are unregulated by the normal regulatory steps of glycolysis. The reactions catalyzed by hexokinase and phosphofructokinase, the two earliest regulatory enzymes in glycolysis, are bypassed in fructose metabolism. The final regulatory step, catalyzed by pyruvate kinase, is mediated by fructose-1,6,-bisphosphate, which is reduced when there is an excess of fructose in the cell. The result, some argue, is that high levels of acetyl CoA produced by this unregulated pathway promote the synthesis of fats that are then deposited in adipose tissue.

We must remember that Dr. Hoebel's experiments involved rats and there has been no direct evidence in humans that HFCS causes obesity. Nonetheless, the results do indicate that we need to learn more about the metabolism of fructose and the presence of HFCS in the diet.

For Further Understanding

- A correlation has been found between the increase of HFCS in the diet and an increase in obesity in the U.S. population. Why is this not proof that a relationship between the two exists?
- Discuss the difficulties of proving the effects of foods such as HFCS in humans.

Regulation of Glycolysis

Energy-harvesting pathways, such as glycolysis, are responsive to the energy needs of the cell. Reactions of the pathway speed up when there is a demand for ATP. They slow down when there is abundant ATP to meet the energy requirements of the cell.

One of the major mechanisms for the control of the rate of glycolysis is the use of *allosteric enzymes*. In addition to the active site, which binds the substrate, allosteric enzymes have an effector binding site, which binds a chemical signal that alters the rate at which the enzyme catalyzes the reaction. Effector binding may increase (positive allosterism) or decrease the rate of reaction (negative allosterism).

The chemical signals, or effectors, that indicate the energy needs of the cell include molecules such as ATP. When the ATP concentration is high, the cell must have sufficient energy. Similarly, ADP and AMP, which are precursors of ATP, are

LEARNING GOAL

5 Describe the mechanism of regulation of the rate of glycolysis. Discuss particular examples of that regulation.

There are additional mechanisms that regulate the rate of glycolysis, but we will focus on those that involve allosteric enzymes (Section 19.9).

indicators that the cell is in need of ATP. In fact, all of these molecules are allosteric effectors that alter the rate of irreversible reactions catalyzed by enzymes in the glycolytic pathway.

The enzyme hexokinase, which catalyzes the phosphorylation of glucose, is allosterically inhibited by the product of the reaction it catalyzes, glucose-6-phosphate. A buildup of this product indicates that the reactions of glycolysis are not proceeding at a rapid rate, presumably because the cell has enough energy.

Phosphofructokinase, the enzyme that catalyzes the third reaction in glycolysis, is a key regulatory enzyme in the pathway. ATP is an allosteric inhibitor of phosphofructokinase, whereas AMP and ADP are allosteric activators. Another allosteric inhibitor of phosphofructokinase is citrate. As we will see in the next chapter, citrate is the first intermediate in the citric acid cycle, a pathway that results in the complete oxidation of the pyruvate. A high concentration of citrate signals that sufficient substrate is entering the citric acid cycle. The inhibition of phosphofructokinase by citrate is an example of *feedback inhibition:* the product, citrate, allosterically inhibits the activity of an enzyme early in the pathway.

The last enzyme in glycolysis, pyruvate kinase, is also subject to allosteric regulation. In this case, fructose-1,6-bisphosphate, the product of the reaction catalyzed by phosphofructokinase, is the allosteric activator. Thus, activation of phosphofructokinase results in the activation of pyruvate kinase. This is an example of *feedforward activation* because the product of an earlier reaction causes activation of an enzyme later in the pathway.

21.4 Fermentations

LEARNING GOAL

6 Discuss the practical and metabolic roles of fermentation reactions.

In the overview of glycolysis, we noted that the pyruvate produced must be used up in some way so that the pathway will continue to produce ATP. Similarly, the NADH produced by glycolysis in step 6 (see Figure 21.5) must be reoxidized at a later time, or glycolysis will grind to a halt as the available NAD^+ is used up. If the cell is functioning under aerobic conditions, NADH will be reoxidized, and pyruvate will be completely oxidized by aerobic respiration. Under anaerobic conditions, however, different types of fermentation reactions accomplish these purposes. **Fermentations** are catabolic reactions that occur with no net oxidation. Pyruvate or an organic compound produced from pyruvate is reduced as NADH is oxidized. We will examine two types of fermentation pathways in detail: lactate fermentation and alcohol fermentation.

Aerobic respiration is discussed in Chapter 22.

Lactate Fermentation

Lactate fermentation is familiar to anyone who has performed strenuous exercise. If you exercise so hard that your lungs and circulatory system can't deliver enough oxygen to the working muscles, your aerobic (oxygen-requiring) energy-harvesting pathways are not able to supply enough ATP to your muscles. But the muscles still demand energy. Under these anaerobic conditions, lactate fermentation begins. In this reaction, the enzyme *lactate dehydrogenase* reduces pyruvate to lactate. NADH is the reducing agent for this process (Figure 21.6). As pyruvate is reduced, NADH is oxidized, and NAD^+ is again available, permitting glycolysis to continue.

When you exercise beyond the ability of your heart and lungs to provide oxygen to muscle, the lactate fermentation kicks in. Write an equation representing the reaction catalyzed by lactate dehydrogenase and explain how this reaction enables muscle to continue working.

$$\underset{\textbf{Pyruvate}}{\overset{O^-}{\underset{\underset{CH_3}{|}}{\overset{|}{\underset{C=O}{C(=O)}}}}} \xrightarrow[\text{NADH} \rightarrow \text{NAD}^+]{\text{Lactate dehydrogenase}} \underset{\textbf{Lactate}}{HO-\overset{COO^-}{\underset{CH_3}{C}}-H}$$

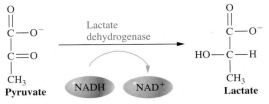

Figure 21.6 The final reaction of lactate fermentation.

The lactate produced in the working muscle passes into the blood. Eventually, if strenuous exercise is continued, the concentration of lactate becomes so high that this fermentation can no longer continue. Glycolysis, and thus ATP production, stops. The muscle, deprived of energy, can no longer function. This point of exhaustion is called the **anaerobic threshold.**

Of course, most of us do not exercise to this point. When exercise is finished, the body begins the process of reclaiming all of the potential energy that was lost in the form of lactate. The liver takes up the lactate from the blood and converts it back to pyruvate. Now that a sufficient supply of oxygen is available, the pyruvate can be completely oxidized in the much more efficient aerobic energy-harvesting reactions to replenish the store of ATP. Alternatively, the pyruvate may be converted to glucose and used to restore the supply of liver and muscle glycogen. This exchange of metabolites between the muscles and liver is called the *Cori Cycle.*

The Cori Cycle is described in Section 21.6 and shown in Figure 21.10.

A variety of bacteria are able to carry out lactate fermentation under anaerobic conditions. This is of great importance in the dairy industry, because these organisms are used to produce yogurt and some cheeses. The tangy flavor of yogurt is contributed by the lactate produced by these bacteria. Unfortunately, similar organisms also cause milk to spoil.

As we saw in A Medical Perspective: Tooth Decay and Simple Sugars (Chapter 16), the lactate produced by oral bacteria is responsible for the gradual removal of calcium from tooth enamel and the resulting dental cavities.

Alcohol Fermentation

Alcohol fermentation has been appreciated, if not understood, since the dawn of civilization. The fermentation process itself was discovered by Louis Pasteur during his studies of the chemistry of wine making and "diseases of wines." Under anaerobic conditions, yeast are able to ferment the sugars produced by fruit and grains. The sugars are broken down to pyruvate by glycolysis. This is followed by the two reactions of alcohol fermentation. First, *pyruvate decarboxylase* removes CO_2 from the pyruvate, producing acetaldehyde (Figure 21.7). Second, *alcohol dehydrogenase* catalyzes the reduction of acetaldehyde to ethanol but, more important, reoxidizes NADH in the process. The regeneration of NAD^+ allows glycolysis to continue, just as in the case of lactate fermentation.

These applications and other fermentations are described in A Human Perspective: Fermentations: The Good, the Bad, and the Ugly.

The two products of alcohol fermentation, then, are ethanol and CO_2. We take advantage of this fermentation in the production of wines and other alcoholic beverages and in the process of bread making.

Question 21.9 How is the alcohol fermentation in yeast similar to lactate production in skeletal muscle?

Question 21.10 Why must pyruvate be used and NADH be reoxidized so that glycolysis can continue?

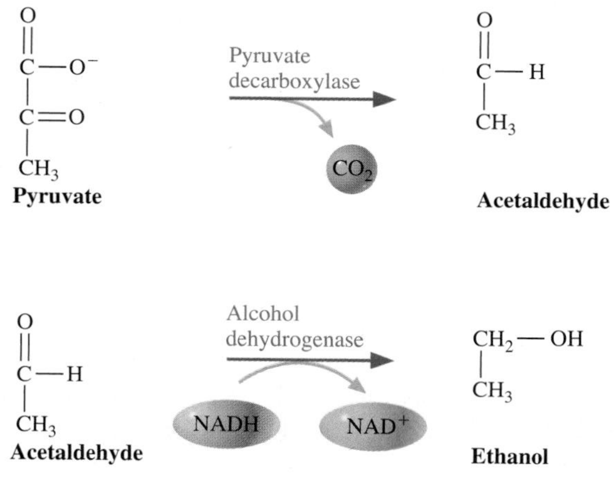

Pyruvate (CH_3–C(=O)–COO^-) —[Pyruvate decarboxylase; releases CO_2]→ Acetaldehyde (CH_3–C(=O)–H)

Acetaldehyde (CH_3–C(=O)–H) —[Alcohol dehydrogenase; NADH → NAD^+]→ Ethanol (CH_3–CH_2–OH)

Figure 21.7 The final two reactions of alcohol fermentation.

A HUMAN PERSPECTIVE

Fermentations: The Good, the Bad, and the Ugly

In this chapter we have seen that fermentation is an anaerobic, cytoplasmic process that allows continued ATP generation by glycolysis. ATP production can continue because the pyruvate produced by the pathway is utilized in the fermentation and because NAD^+ is regenerated.

The stable end products of alcohol fermentation are CO_2 and ethanol. These have been used by humankind in a variety of ways, including the production of alcoholic beverages, bread making, and alternative fuel sources.

If alcohol fermentation is carried out by using fruit juices in a vented vat, the CO_2 will escape, and the result will be a still wine (not bubbly). But conditions must remain anaerobic; otherwise, fermentation will stop, and aerobic energy-harvesting reactions will ruin the wine. Fortunately for vintners (wine makers), when a vat is fermenting actively, enough CO_2 is produced to create a layer that keeps the oxygen-containing air away from the fermenting juice, thus maintaining an anaerobic atmosphere.

Now suppose we want to make a sparkling wine, such as champagne. To do this, we simply have to trap the CO_2 produced. In this case the fermentation proceeds in a sealed bottle, a very strong bottle. Both the fermentation products, CO_2 and ethanol, accumulate. Under pressure within the sealed bottle the CO_2 remains in solution. When the top is "popped," the pressure is released, and the CO_2 comes out of solution in the form of bubbles.

In either case the fermentation continues until the alcohol concentration reaches 12–13%. At that point the yeast "stews in its own juices"! That is, 12–13% ethanol kills the yeast cells that produce it. This points out a last generalization about fermentations. The stable fermentation end product, whether it is lactate or ethanol, eventually accumulates to a concentration that is toxic to the organism. Muscle fatigue is the early effect of lactate buildup in the working muscle. In the same way, continued accumulation of the fermentation product can lead to concentrations that are fatal if there is no means of getting rid of the toxic product or of getting away from it. For single-celled organisms the result is generally death. Our bodies have evolved in such a way that lactate buildup contributes to muscle fatigue that causes the exerciser to stop the exercise. Then the lactate is removed from the blood and converted to glucose by the process of gluconeogenesis.

Another application of alcohol fermentation is the use of yeast in bread making. When we mix the water, sugar, and

The production of bread, wine, and cheese depends on fermentation processes.

21.5 The Pentose Phosphate Pathway

LEARNING GOAL

7 List several products of the pentose phosphate pathway that are required for biosynthesis.

The **pentose phosphate pathway** is an alternative pathway for glucose oxidation. It provides the cell with energy in the form of reducing power for biosynthesis. Specifically, NADPH is produced in the oxidative stage of this pathway. NADPH is the reducing agent required for many biosynthetic pathways.

The details of the pentose phosphate pathway will not be covered in this text. But an overview of the key reactions will allow us to understand the importance of the pathway (Figure 21.8).

$$\text{glucose-6-phosphate} + 2\text{NADP}^+ + H_2O \longrightarrow \text{ribulose-5-phosphate} + 2\text{NADPH} + CO_2$$

The pentose phosphate pathway provides several molecules that are important in biosynthesis. The first is reducing power in the form of NADPH. It also provides sugar phosphates that are required for biosynthesis. For instance, ribose-5-phosphate is used for the synthesis of nucleotides such as ATP. The four-carbon sugar phosphate, *erythrose-4-phosphate,* is produced in the third stage of the pentose phosphate pathway, in a complex set of reactions not shown in the pathway summary in Figure 21.8. It is a precursor of the amino acids phenylalanine, tyrosine, and tryptophan.

dried yeast, the yeast cells begin to grow and carry out the process of fermentation. This mixture is then added to the flour, milk, shortening, and salt, and the dough is placed in a warm place to rise. The yeast continues to grow and ferment the sugar, producing CO_2 that causes the bread to rise. Of course, when we bake the bread, the yeast cells are killed, and the ethanol evaporates, but we are left with a light and airy loaf of bread.

Today, alcohol produced by fermentation is being used as an alternative fuel to replace the use of some fossil fuels. Geneticists and bioengineers are trying to develop strains of yeast that can survive higher alcohol concentrations and thus convert more of the sugar of corn and other grains into alcohol.

Bacteria perform a variety of other fermentations. The propionibacteria produce propionic acid and CO_2. The acid gives Swiss cheese its characteristic flavor, and the CO_2 gas produces the characteristic holes in the cheese. Other bacteria, the clostridia, perform a fermentation that is responsible in part for the horrible symptoms of gas gangrene. When these bacteria are inadvertently introduced into deep tissues by a puncture wound, they find a nice anaerobic environment in which to grow. In fact, these organisms are *obligate anaerobes;* that is, they are killed by even a small amount of oxygen. As they grow, they perform a fermentation called the *butyric acid, butanol, acetone fermentation.* This results in the formation of CO_2, the gas associated with gas gangrene. The CO_2 infiltrates the local tissues and helps to maintain an anaerobic environment because oxygen from the local blood supply cannot enter the area of the wound. Now able to grow well, these bacteria produce a variety of toxins and enzymes that cause extensive tissue death and necrosis. In addition, the fermentation produces acetic acid, ethanol, acetone, isopropanol, butanol, and butyric acid (which is responsible, along with the necrosis, for the characteristic foul smell of gas gangrene). Certainly, the presence of these organic chemicals in the wound enhances tissue death.

Gas gangrene is very difficult to treat. Because the bacteria establish an anaerobic region of cell death and cut off the local circulation, systemic antibiotics do not infiltrate the wound and kill the bacteria. Even our immune response is stymied. Treatment usually involves surgical removal of the necrotic tissue accompanied by antibiotic therapy. In some cases a hyperbaric oxygen chamber is employed. The infected extremity is placed in an environment with a very high partial pressure of oxygen. The oxygen forced into the tissues is poisonous to the bacteria, and they die.

These are but a few examples of the fermentations that have an effect on humans. Regardless of the specific chemical reactions, all fermentations share the following traits:

- They use pyruvate produced in glycolysis.
- They reoxidize the NADH produced in glycolysis.
- They are self-limiting because the accumulated stable fermentation end product eventually kills the cell that produces it.

For Further Understanding

- ▸ Write condensed structural formulas for each of the fermentation products made by clostridia in gas gangrene. Identify the functional groups and provide the IUPAC name for each.
- ▸ Explain the importance of utilizing pyruvate and reoxidizing NADH to the ability of a cell to continue producing ATP.

The pentose phosphate pathway is most active in tissues involved in cholesterol and fatty acid biosynthesis. These two processes require abundant NADPH. Thus the liver, which is the site of cholesterol synthesis and a major site for fatty acid biosynthesis, and adipose (fat) tissue, where active fatty acid synthesis also occurs, have very high levels of pentose phosphate pathway enzymes.

The pathway for fatty acid biosynthesis is discussed in Section 23.4.

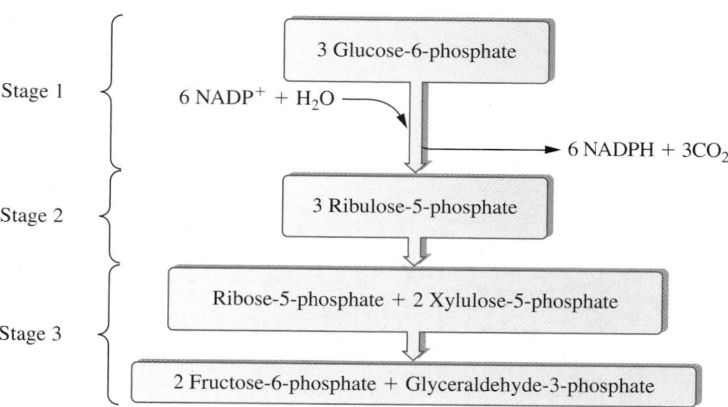

Figure 21.8 Summary of the major stages of the pentose phosphate pathway.

21.6 Gluconeogenesis: The Synthesis of Glucose

LEARNING GOAL

8 Compare glycolysis and gluconeogenesis.

Under extreme conditions of starvation the brain eventually switches to the use of ketone bodies. Ketone bodies are produced, under certain circumstances, from the breakdown of lipids (Section 23.3).

Under normal conditions, we have enough glucose to satisfy our needs. However, under some conditions the body must make glucose. This is necessary following strenuous exercise, to replenish the liver and muscle supplies of glycogen. It also occurs during starvation, so that the body can maintain adequate blood glucose levels to supply the brain cells and red blood cells. Under normal conditions these two tissues use only glucose for energy.

Glucose is produced by the process of **gluconeogenesis** (*gleuko,* Greek *sweet; neo,* Latin *new; genesis,* Latin *produce*), the production of glucose from noncarbohydrate starting materials (Figure 21.9). Gluconeogenesis, an anabolic pathway, occurs primarily in the liver. Lactate, all the amino acids except leucine and lysine, and glycerol from fats can all be used to make glucose. However, the amino acids and glycerol are generally used only under starvation conditions.

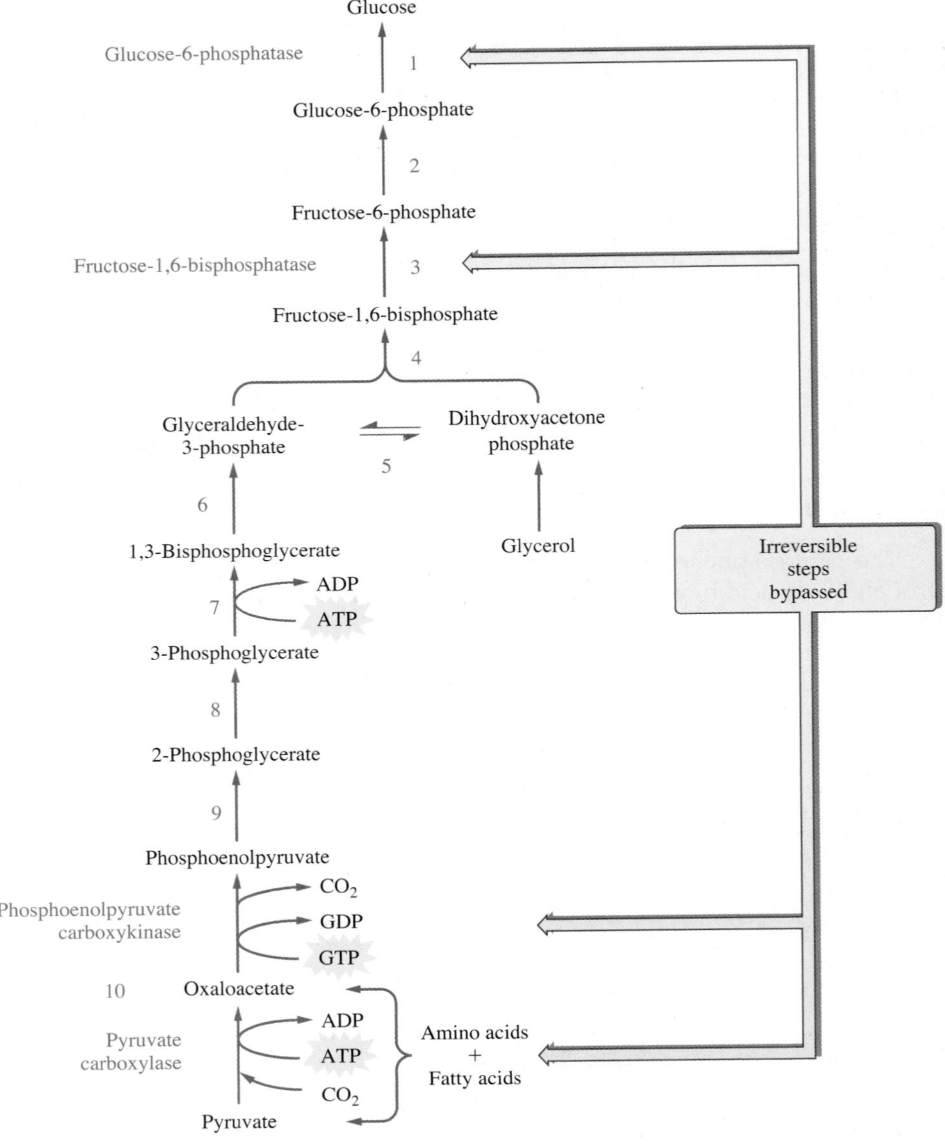

Figure 21.9 Comparison of the reactions of glycolysis and gluconeogenesis.

At first glance, gluconeogenesis appears to be simply the reverse of glycolysis (compare Figures 21.9 and 21.5), because the intermediates of the two pathways are identical. But this is not the case, because steps 1, 3, and 10 of glycolysis are irreversible, and therefore the reverse reactions must be carried out by other enzymes. In step 1 of glycolysis, hexokinase catalyzes the phosphorylation of glucose. In gluconeogenesis the dephosphorylation of glucose-6-phosphate is carried out by the enzyme *glucose-6-phosphatase,* which is found in the liver but not in muscle. Similarly, reaction 3, the phosphorylation of fructose-6-phosphate catalyzed by phosphofructokinase, is irreversible. That step is bypassed in gluconeogenesis by using the enzyme *fructose-1,6-bisphosphatase.* Finally, the phosphorylation of ADP catalyzed by pyruvate kinase, step 10 of glycolysis, cannot be reversed. The conversion of pyruvate to phosphoenolpyruvate actually involves two enzymes and some unusual reactions. First, the enzyme *pyruvate carboxylase* adds CO_2 to pyruvate. The product is the four-carbon compound oxaloacetate. Then *phosphoenolpyruvate carboxykinase* removes the CO_2 and adds a phosphoryl group. The donor of the phosphoryl group in this unusual reaction is **guanosine triphosphate (GTP).** This is a nucleotide like ATP, except that the nitrogenous base is guanine.

This last pair of reactions is complicated by the fact that pyruvate carboxylase is found in the mitochondria, whereas phosphoenolpyruvate carboxykinase is found in the cytoplasm. As we will see in Chapters 22 and 23, mitochondria are organelles in which the final oxidation of food molecules occurs and large amounts of ATP are produced. A complicated shuttle system transports the oxaloacetate produced in the mitochondria through the two mitochondrial membranes and into the cytoplasm. There, phosphoenolpyruvate carboxykinase catalyzes its conversion to phosphoenolpyruvate.

If glycolysis and gluconeogenesis were not regulated in some fashion, the two pathways would occur simultaneously, with the disastrous effect that nothing would get done. Three convenient sites for this regulation are the three bypass reactions. Step 3 of glycolysis is catalyzed by the enzyme phosphofructokinase. This enzyme is stimulated by high concentrations of AMP, ADP, and inorganic phosphate, signals that the cell needs energy. When the enzyme is active, glycolysis proceeds. On the other hand, when ATP is plentiful, phosphofructokinase is inhibited, and fructose-1,6-bisphosphatase is stimulated. The net result is that in times of energy excess (high concentrations of ATP), gluconeogenesis will occur.

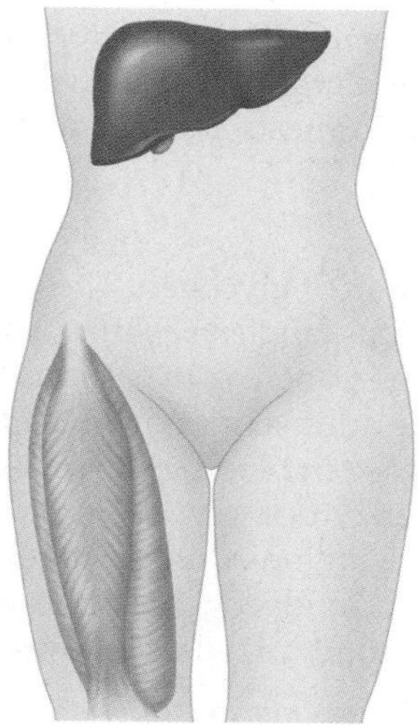

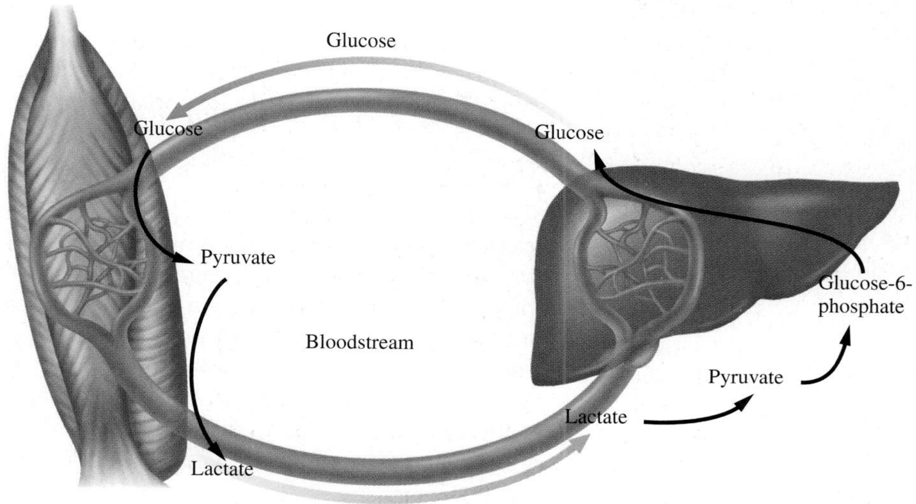

Figure 21.10 The Cori Cycle.

As we have seen, the conversion of lactate into glucose is important in mammals. As the muscles work, they produce lactate, which is converted back to glucose in the liver. The glucose is transported into the blood and from there back to the muscle. In the muscle it can be catabolized to produce ATP, or it can be used to replenish the muscle stores of glycogen. This cyclic process between the liver and skeletal muscles is called the **Cori Cycle** and is shown in Figure 21.10. Through this cycle, gluconeogenesis produces enough glucose to restore the depleted muscle glycogen reservoir within 48 hours (h).

Question 21.11 What are the major differences between gluconeogenesis and glycolysis?

Question 21.12 What do the three irreversible reactions of glycolysis have in common?

21.7 Glycogen Synthesis and Degradation

LEARNING GOAL

9 Summarize the regulation of blood glucose levels by glycogenesis and glycogenolysis.

Glucose is the sole source of energy of mammalian red blood cells and the major source of energy for the brain. Neither red blood cells nor the brain can store glucose; thus a constant supply must be available as blood glucose. This is provided by dietary glucose and by the production of glucose either by gluconeogenesis or by **glycogenolysis,** the degradation of glycogen. Glycogen is a long, branched-chain polymer of glucose. Stored in the liver and skeletal muscles, it is the principal storage form of glucose.

The total amount of glucose in the blood of a 70-kilogram (kg) (approximately 150-pound) adult is about 20 grams (g), but the brain alone consumes 5–6 g of glucose per h. Breakdown of glycogen in the liver mobilizes the glucose when hormonal signals register a need for increased levels of blood glucose. Skeletal muscle also contains substantial stores of glycogen, which provide energy for rapid muscle contraction. However, this glycogen is not able to contribute to blood glucose because muscle cells do not have the enzyme glucose-6-phosphatase. Because glucose cannot be formed from the glucose-6-phosphate, it cannot be released into the bloodstream.

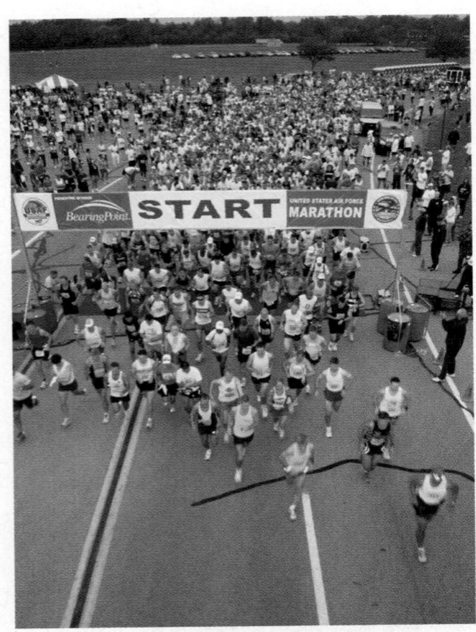

Marathon runners often carbo-load in the days before a race. The goal is to build stores of muscle glycogen. Carbo-loading involves reduced exercise the week before the race, along with a diet that is as high as 70% carbohydrate. Explain how this helps build the runner's endurance.

The Structure of Glycogen

Glycogen is a highly branched glucose polymer in which the "main chain" is linked by α (1→4) glycosidic bonds. The polymer also has numerous α (1→6) glycosidic bonds, which provide many branch points along the chain (Figure 21.11). **Glycogen granules** with a diameter of 10–40 nanometers (nm) are found in the cytoplasm of liver and muscle cells. These granules exist in complexes with the enzymes that are responsible for glycogen synthesis and degradation.

Glycogenolysis: Glycogen Degradation

Two hormones control glycogenolysis, the degradation of glycogen. These are **glucagon,** a peptide hormone synthesized in the pancreas, and *epinephrine,* produced in the adrenal glands. Glucagon is released from the pancreas in response to low blood glucose, and epinephrine is released from the adrenal glands in response to a threat or a stress. Both situations require an increase in blood glucose, and both hormones function by altering the activity of two enzymes, glycogen phosphorylase and glycogen synthase. *Glycogen phosphorylase* is involved in glycogen degradation and is activated; *glycogen synthase* is involved in glycogen synthesis and is inactivated. The steps in glycogen degradation are summarized as follows.

Step 1. The enzyme glycogen phosphorylase catalyzes *phosphorolysis* of a glucose at one end of a glycogen polymer (Figure 21.11). The reaction involves the displacement of a glucose unit of glycogen by a phosphate

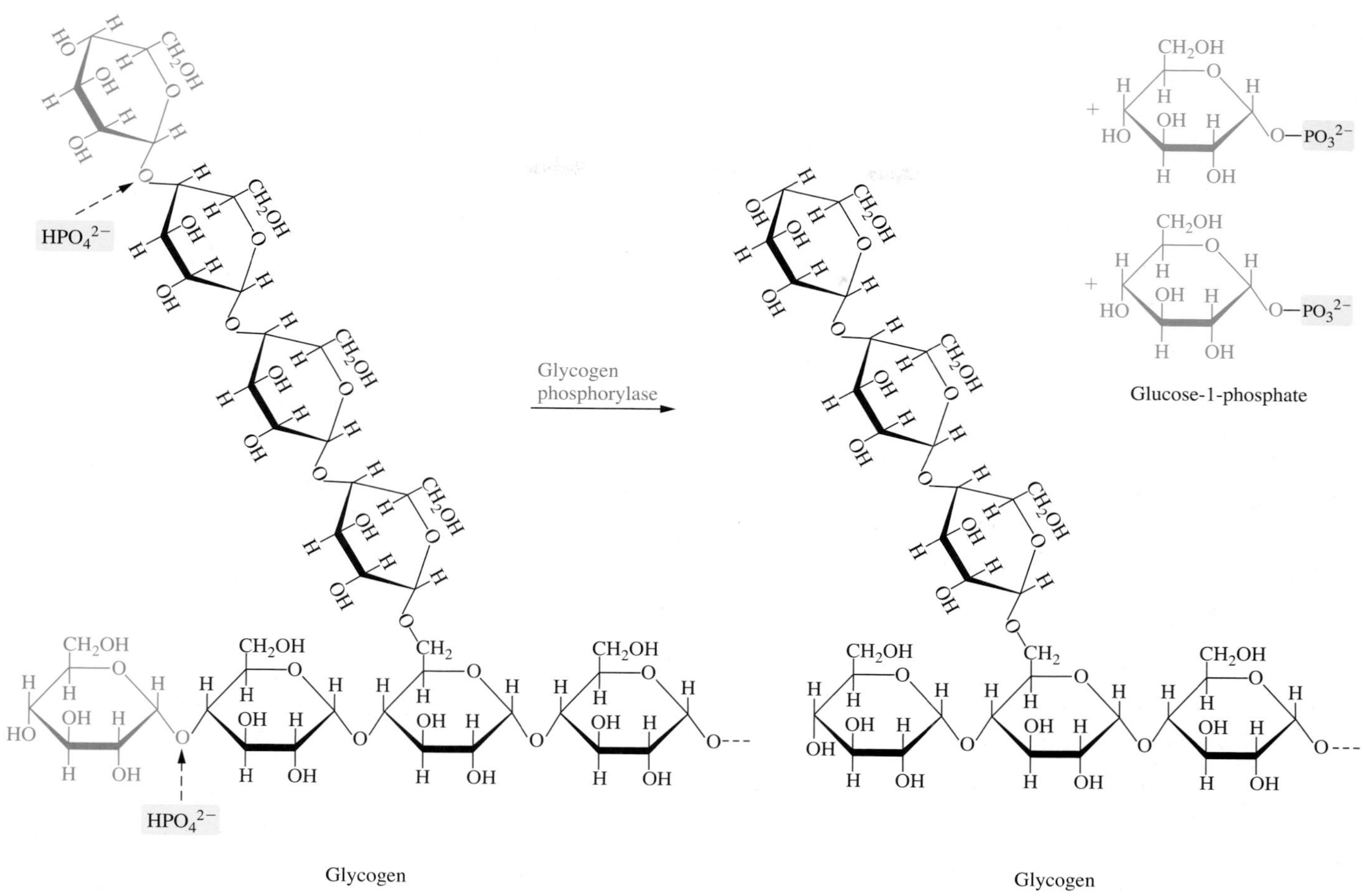

General reaction:

$$\text{Glycogen (glucose)}_x + n\,HPO_4^{2-} \xrightarrow[\text{phosphorylase}]{\text{Glycogen}} \text{Glycogen (glucose)}_{x-n} + n \text{ glucose-1-phosphate}$$

Figure 21.11 The action of glycogen phosphorylase in glycogenolysis.

group. As a result of phosphorolysis, glucose-1-phosphate is produced without using ATP as the phosphoryl group donor.

Step 2. Glycogen contains many branches bound to the α (1→4) backbone by α (1→6) glycosidic bonds. These branches must be removed to allow the complete degradation of glycogen. The extensive action of glycogen phosphorylase produces a smaller polysaccharide with a single glucose bound by an α (1→6) glycosidic bond to the main chain. The enzyme α (1→6) *glycosidase,* also called the *debranching enzyme,* hydrolyzes the α (1→6) glycosidic bond at a branch point and frees one molecule of glucose (Figure 21.12). This molecule of glucose can be phosphorylated and utilized in glycolysis, or it may be released into the bloodstream for use elsewhere. Hydrolysis of the branch bond liberates another stretch of α (1→4)-linked glucose for the action of glycogen phosphorylase.

Step 3. Glucose-1-phosphate is converted to glucose-6-phosphate by *phosphoglucomutase* (Figure 21.13). Glucose originally stored in glycogen enters glycolysis through the action of phosphoglucomutase. Alternatively, in the liver and kidneys it may be dephosphorylated for transport into the bloodstream.

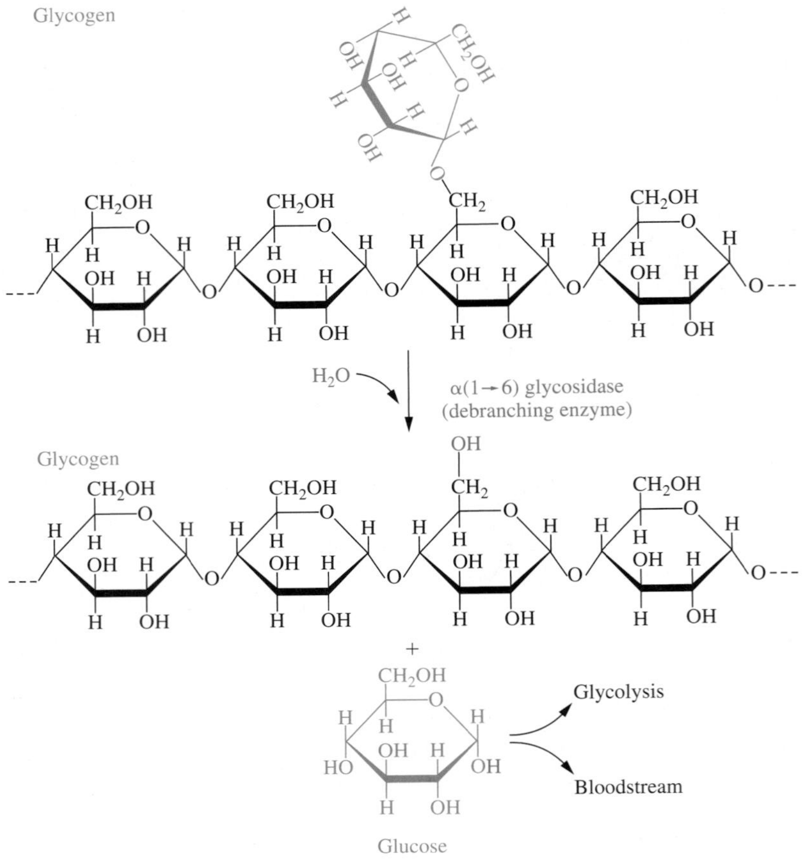

Figure 21.12 The action of α (1⟶6) glycosidase (debranching enzyme) in glycogen degradation.

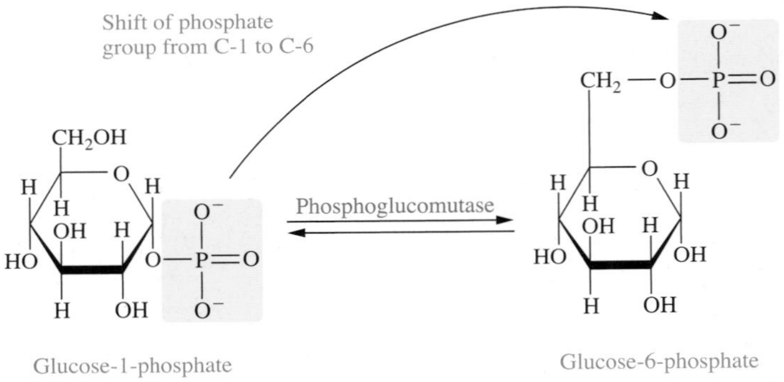

Figure 21.13 The action of phosphoglucomutase in glycogen degradation.

Question 21.13 Explain the role of glycogen phosphorylase in glycogenolysis.

Question 21.14 How does the action of glycogen phosphorylase and phosphoglucomutase result in an energy savings for the cell if the product, glucose-6-phosphate, is used directly in glycolysis?

Glycogenesis: Glycogen Synthesis

The hormone **insulin,** produced by the pancreas in response to high blood glucose levels, stimulates the synthesis of glycogen, **glycogenesis.** Insulin is perhaps one of the most influential hormones in the body because it directly alters the metabolism and uptake of glucose in all but a few cells.

When blood glucose rises, as after a meal, the beta cells of the pancreas secrete insulin. It immediately accelerates the uptake of glucose by all the cells of the body except the brain and certain blood cells. In these cells the uptake of glucose is insulin-independent. The increased uptake of glucose is especially marked in the liver, heart, skeletal muscle, and adipose tissue.

In the liver, insulin promotes glycogen synthesis and storage by inhibiting glycogen phosphorylase, thus inhibiting glycogen degradation. It also stimulates glycogen synthase and glucokinase, two enzymes that are involved in glycogen synthesis.

Although glycogenesis and glycogenolysis share some reactions in common, the two pathways are not simply the reverse of one another. Glycogenesis involves some very unusual reactions, which we will now examine in detail.

The first reaction of glycogen synthesis in the liver traps glucose within the cell by phosphorylating it. In this reaction, catalyzed by the enzyme *glucokinase,* ATP serves as a phosphoryl donor, and glucose-6-phosphate is formed:

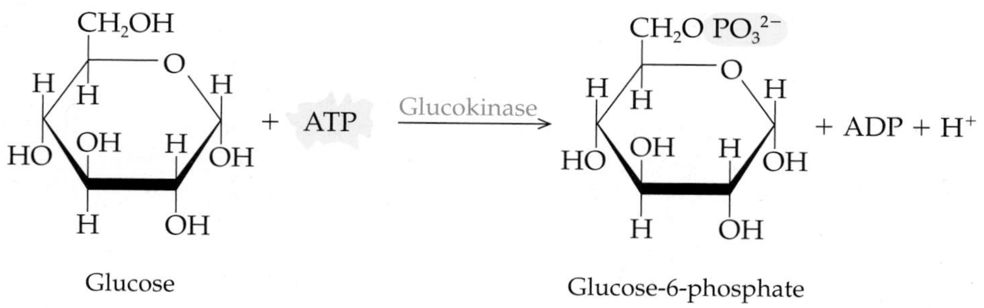

$$\text{Glucose} + \text{ATP} \xrightarrow{\text{Glucokinase}} \text{Glucose-6-phosphate} + \text{ADP} + \text{H}^+$$

Glucose Glucose-6-phosphate

The second reaction of glycogenesis is the reverse of one of the reactions of glycogenolysis. The glucose-6-phosphate formed in the first step is isomerized to glucose-1-phosphate. The enzyme that catalyzes this step is phosphoglucomutase:

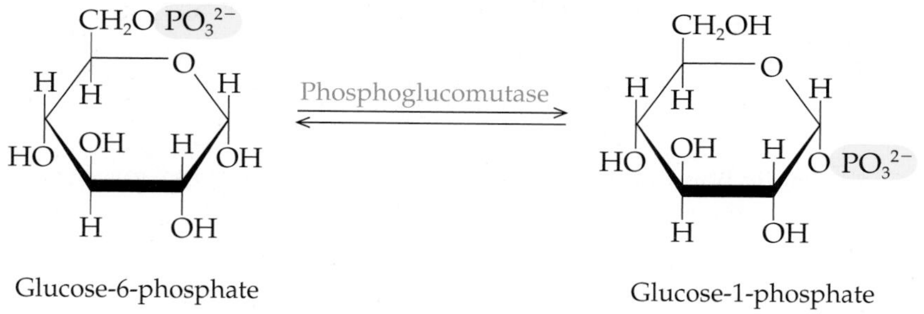

$$\text{Glucose-6-phosphate} \xrightleftharpoons{\text{Phosphoglucomutase}} \text{Glucose-1-phosphate}$$

Glucose-6-phosphate Glucose-1-phosphate

The glucose-1-phosphate must now be activated before it can be added to the growing glycogen chain. The high-energy compound that accomplishes this is the nucleotide **uridine triphosphate (UTP).** In this reaction, mediated by the enzyme *pyrophosphorylase,* the C-1 phosphoryl group of glucose is linked to the α-phosphoryl group of UTP to produce UDP-glucose:

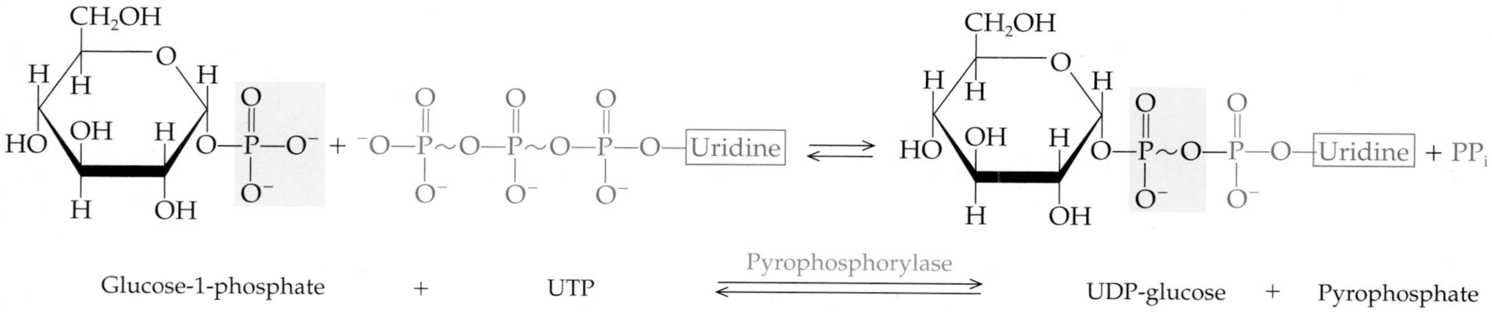

$$\text{Glucose-1-phosphate} + \text{UTP} \xrightleftharpoons{\text{Pyrophosphorylase}} \text{UDP-glucose} + \text{Pyrophosphate}$$

Glucose-1-phosphate + UTP Pyrophosphorylase UDP-glucose + Pyrophosphate

This is accompanied by the release of a pyrophosphate group (PP_i). The structure of UDP-glucose is shown in Figure 21.14.

The UDP-glucose can now be used to extend glycogen chains. The enzyme glycogen synthase breaks the phosphoester linkage of UDP-glucose and forms an

A MEDICAL PERSPECTIVE

Diagnosing Diabetes

When diagnosing diabetes, doctors take many factors and symptoms into consideration. However, there are two primary tests that are performed to determine whether an individual is properly regulating blood glucose levels. First and foremost is the fasting blood glucose test. A person who has fasted since midnight should have a blood glucose level between 70 and 110 milligrams per deciliter (mg/dL) in the morning. If the level is 140 mg/dL on at least two occasions, a diagnosis of diabetes is generally made.

The second commonly used test is the glucose tolerance test. For this test the subject must fast for at least 10 h. A beginning blood sample is drawn to determine the fasting blood glucose level. This will serve as the background level for the test. The subject ingests 50–100 g of glucose (40 g/m^2 body surface), and the blood glucose level is measured at 30 minutes (min), and at 1, 2, and 3 h after ingesting the glucose.

A graph is made of the blood glucose levels over time. For a person who does not have diabetes, the curve will show a peak of blood glucose at approximately 1 h. There will be a reduction in the level, and perhaps a slight hypoglycemia (low blood glucose level) over the next hour. Thereafter, the blood glucose level stabilizes at normal levels.

An individual is said to have impaired glucose tolerance if the blood glucose level remains between 140 and 200 mg/dL 2 h after ingestion of the glucose solution. This suggests that there is a risk of the individual developing diabetes and is reason to prescribe periodic testing to allow early intervention.

If the blood glucose level remains at or above 200 mg/dL after 2 h, a tentative diagnosis of diabetes is made. However, this result warrants further testing on subsequent days to rule out transient problems, such as the effect of medications on blood glucose levels.

It was recently suggested that the upper blood glucose level of 200 mg/dL should be lowered to 180 mg/dL as the standard to diagnose impaired glucose tolerance and diabetes. This would allow earlier detection and intervention. Considering the grave nature of long-term diabetic complications, it is thought to be very beneficial to begin treatment at an early stage to maintain constant blood glucose levels. For more information on diabetes, see A Medical Perspective: Diabetes Mellitus and Ketone Bodies, in Chapter 23.

For Further Understanding

- Draw a graph representing blood glucose levels for a normal glucose tolerance test.
- Draw a similar graph for an individual who would be diagnosed as diabetic.

α (1→4) glycosidic bond between the glucose and the growing glycogen chain. UDP is released in the process.

UDP-glucose + Glycogen primer (n residues) —Glycogen synthase→ Glycogen ($n + 1$ residues) + UDP

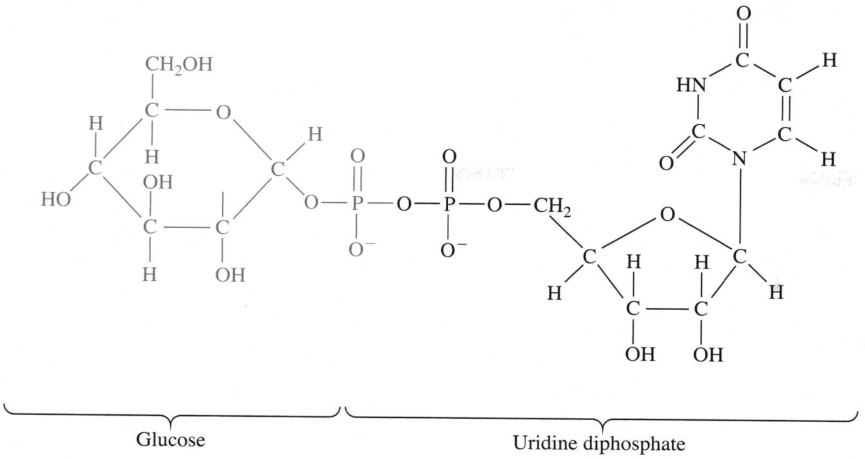

Figure 21.14 The structure of UDP-glucose.

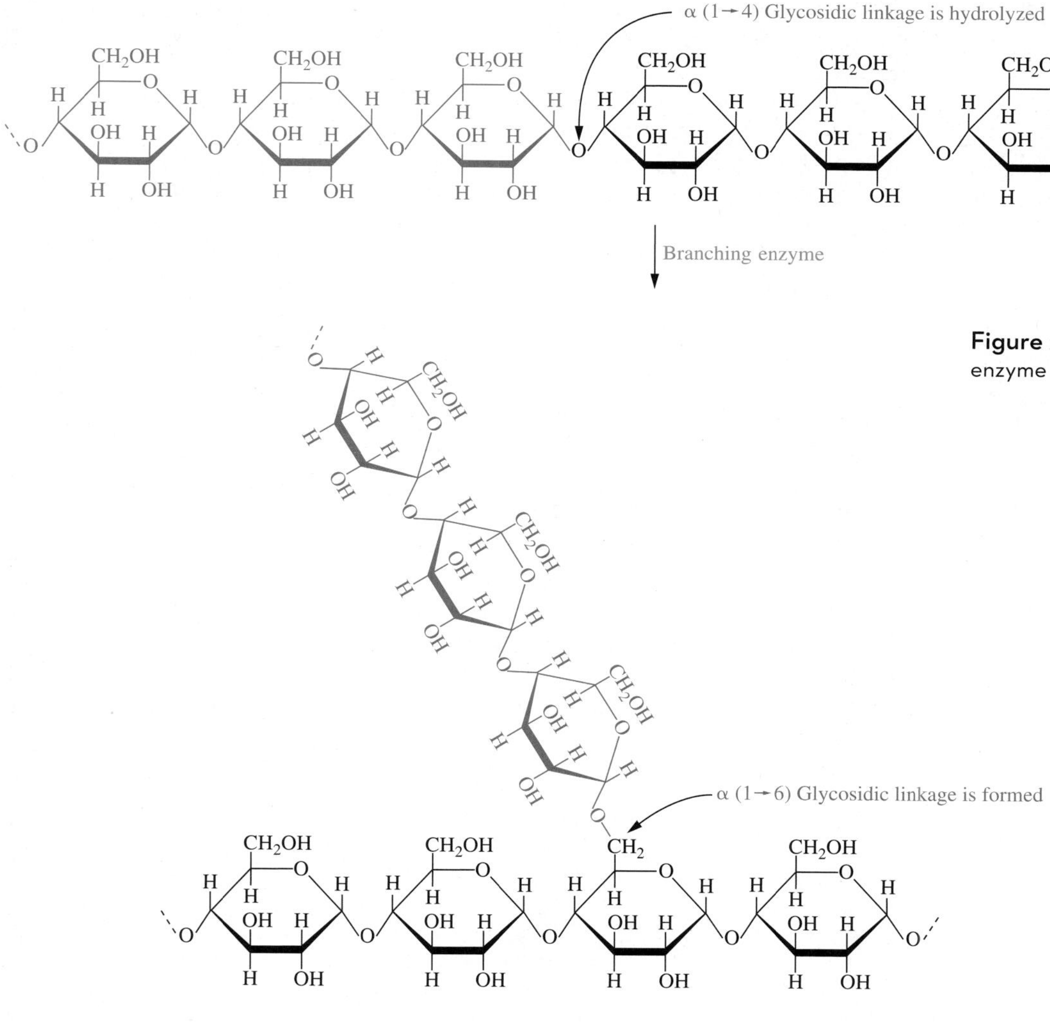

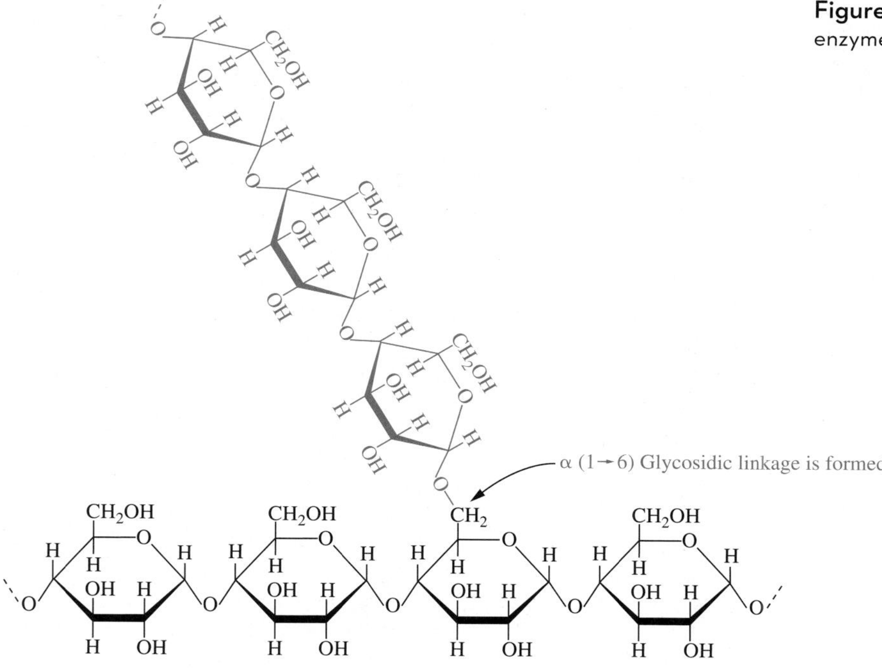

Figure 21.15 The action of the branching enzyme in glycogen synthesis.

Finally, we must introduce the α(1→6) glycosidic linkages to form the branches. The branches are quite important to proper glycogen utilization. As Figure 21.15 shows, the *branching enzyme* removes a section of the linear α(1→4) linked glycogen and reattaches it in α(1→6) glycosidic linkage elsewhere in the chain.

Question 21.15 Describe the way in which glucokinase traps glucose inside liver cells.

Question 21.16 Describe the reaction catalyzed by the branching enzyme.

Compatibility of Glycogenesis and Glycogenolysis

As was the case with glycolysis and gluconeogenesis, it would be futile for the cell to carry out glycogen synthesis and degradation simultaneously. The results achieved by the action of one pathway would be undone by the other. This problem is avoided by a series of hormonal controls that activate the enzymes of one pathway while inactivating the enzymes of the other pathway.

When the blood glucose level is too high, a condition known as **hyperglycemia,** insulin stimulates the uptake of glucose via a transport mechanism. It further stimulates the trapping of the glucose by the elevated activity of glucokinase. Finally, it activates glycogen synthase, the last enzyme in the synthesis of glycogen chains. To further accelerate storage, insulin *inhibits* the first enzyme in glycogen degradation, glycogen phosphorylase. The net effect, seen in Figure 21.16, is that glucose is removed from the bloodstream and converted into glycogen in the liver. When the glycogen stores are filled, excess glucose is converted to fat and stored in adipose tissue.

Glucagon is produced in response to low blood glucose levels, a condition known as **hypoglycemia,** and has an effect opposite to that of insulin. It stimulates glycogen phosphorylase, which catalyzes the first stage of glycogen degradation. This accelerates glycogenolysis and release of glucose into the bloodstream. The effect is further enhanced because glucagon inhibits glycogen synthase. The opposing effects of insulin and glucagon are summarized in Figure 21.16.

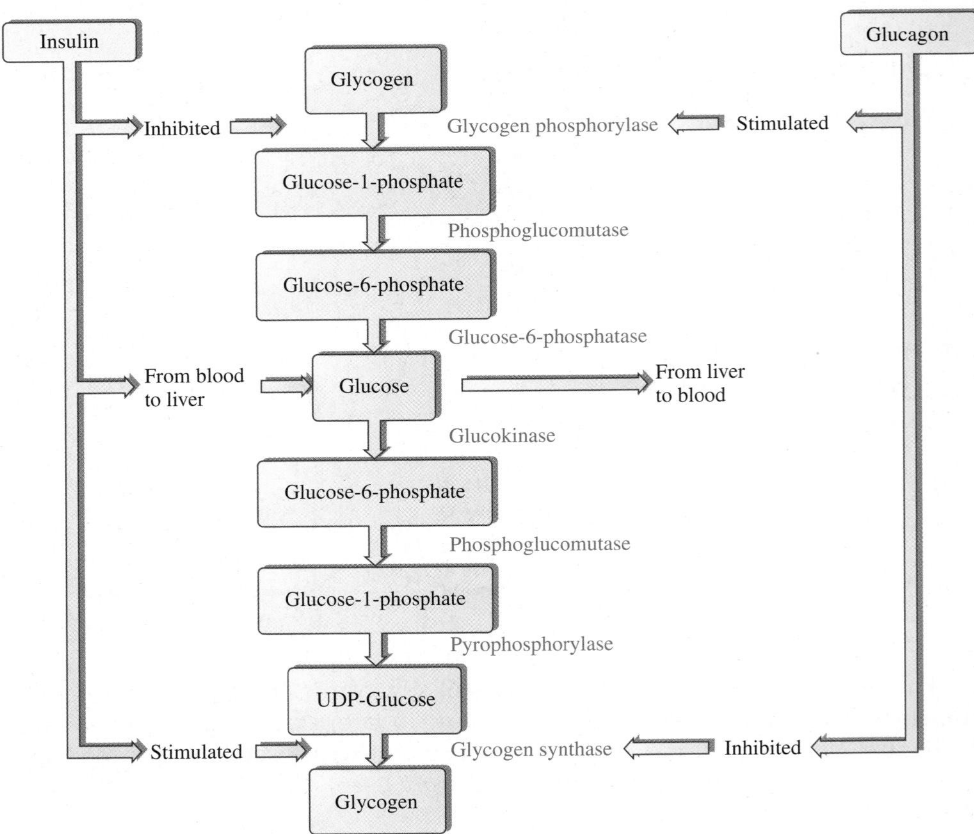

Figure 21.16 The opposing effects of the hormones insulin and glucagon on glycogen metabolism.

A HUMAN PERSPECTIVE

Glycogen Storage Diseases

Glycogen metabolism is important for the proper function of many aspects of cellular metabolism. Many diseases of glycogen metabolism have been discovered. Generally, these are diseases that result in the excessive accumulation of glycogen in the liver, muscle, and tubules of the kidneys. Often they are caused by defects in one of the enzymes involved in the degradation of glycogen.

One example is an inherited defect of glycogen metabolism known as *von Gierke's disease.* This disease results from a defective gene for glucose-6-phosphatase, which catalyzes the final step of gluconeogenesis and glycogenolysis. People who lack glucose-6-phosphatase cannot convert glucose-6-phosphate to glucose. As we have seen, the liver is the primary source of blood glucose, and much of this glucose is produced by gluconeogenesis. Glucose-6-phosphate, unlike glucose, cannot cross the cell membrane, and the liver of a person suffering from von Gierke's disease cannot provide him or her with glucose. The blood sugar level falls precipitously low between meals. In addition, the lack of glucose-6-phosphatase also affects glycogen metabolism. Because glucose-6-phosphatase is absent, the supply of glucose-6-phosphate in the liver is large. This glucose-6-phosphate can also be converted to glycogen. A person suffering from von Gierke's disease has a massively enlarged liver as a result of enormously increased stores of glycogen.

Defects in other enzymes of glycogen metabolism also exist. *Cori's disease* is caused by a genetic defect in the debranching enzyme. As a result, individuals who have this disease cannot completely degrade glycogen and thus use their glycogen stores very inefficiently.

On the other side of the coin, *Andersen's disease* results from a genetic defect in the branching enzyme. Individuals who have this disease produce very long, unbranched glycogen chains. This genetic disorder results in decreased efficiency of glycogen storage.

A final example of a glycogen storage disease is *McArdle's disease.* In this syndrome, the muscle cells lack the enzyme glycogen phosphorylase and cannot degrade glycogen to glucose. Individuals who have this disease have little tolerance for physical exercise because their muscles cannot provide enough glucose for the necessary energy-harvesting processes. It is interesting to note that the liver enzyme glycogen phosphorylase is perfectly normal, and these people respond appropriately with a rise of blood glucose levels under the influence of glucagon or epinephrine.

For Further Understanding

- Write equations showing the reactions catalyzed by the enzymes that are defective in each of the genetic disorders described in this perspective.
- There are different forms of glycogen phosphorylase, one found in the liver and the other in skeletal muscle. Discuss the differences you would expect between a defect in the muscle enzyme and a defect in the liver enzyme.

This elegant system of hormonal control ensures that the reactions involved in glycogen degradation and synthesis do not compete with one another. In this way they provide glucose when the blood level is too low, and they cause the storage of glucose in times of excess.

Question 21.17 Explain how glucagon affects the synthesis and degradation of glycogen.

Question 21.18 How does insulin affect the storage and degradation of glycogen?

CHAPTER MAP

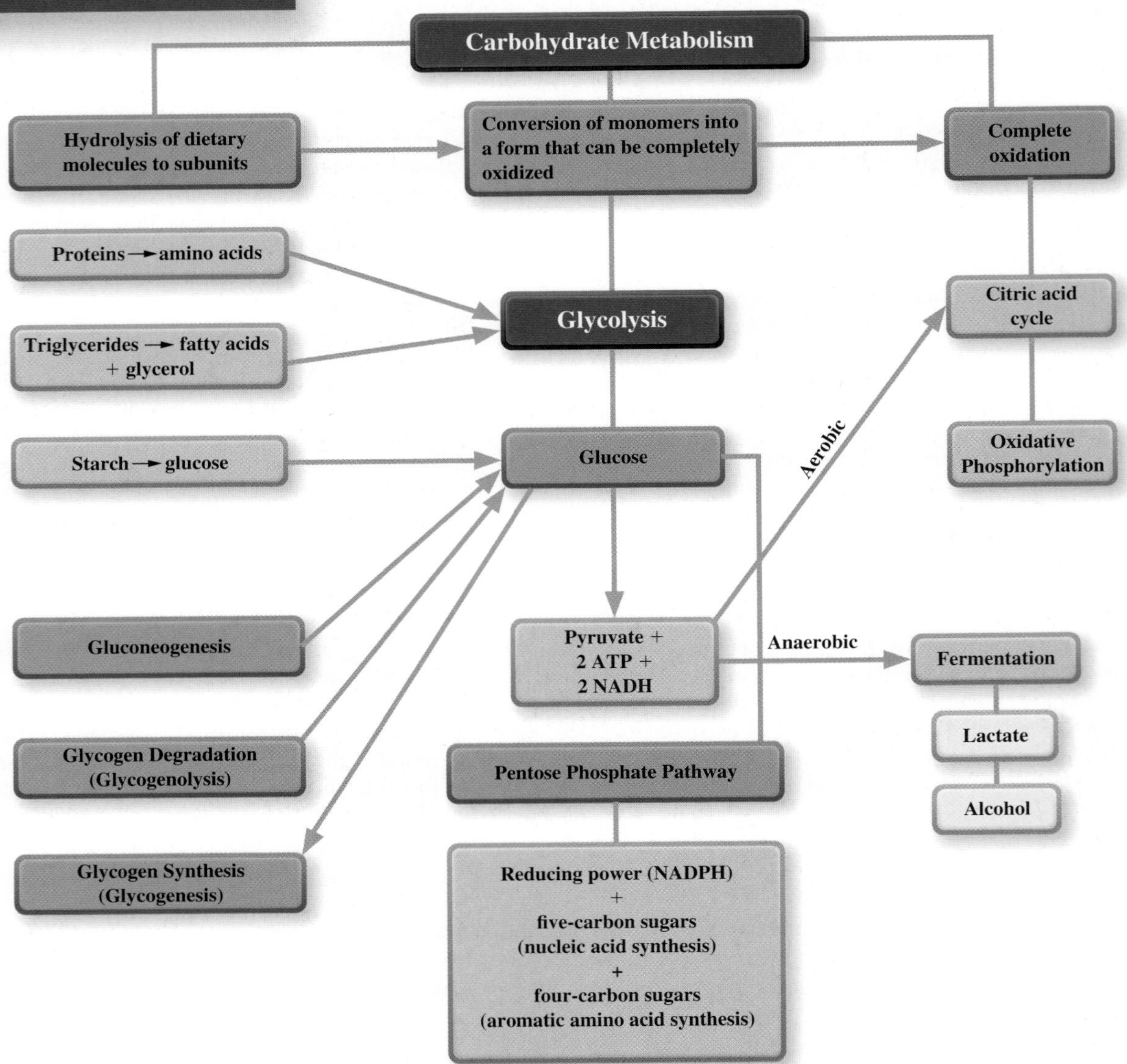

SUMMARY

21.1 ATP: The Cellular Energy Currency

- **Adenosine triphosphate (ATP)** is a **nucleotide** composed of adenine, the sugar ribose, and a triphosphate group.
- The energy released by the hydrolysis of the phosphoanhydride bond between the second and third phosphoryl groups provides the energy for most cellular work.
- The energy harvested during the degradation of fuel molecules, **catabolism,** is stored in ATP.
- Biosynthetic reactions, **anabolism,** utilize ATP as an energy source.

21.2 Overview of Catabolic Processes

- The body needs a supply of ATP to carry out life processes.
- To provide this ATP, we consume a variety of energy-rich food molecules: carbohydrates, lipids, and proteins.
- In digestion, these food molecules are degraded into smaller molecules that are absorbed by our cells: monosaccharides, fatty acids and glycerol, and amino acids.
- Through catabolic reactions, these molecules are used to produce ATP.

21.3 Glycolysis

- **Glycolysis** is the pathway for glucose catabolism that leads to pyruvate. Glycolysis:
  - is anaerobic
  - occurs in the cytoplasm of the cell

- produces a net harvest of two ATP and two NADH (formed from the coenzyme **nicotinamide adenine dinucleotide** (NAD^+))

► **The ATP is produced by substrate-level phosphorylation.**

► **Under aerobic conditions, the electrons carried by NADH are used to produce ATP by oxidative phosphorylation.**

► **The rate of glycolysis responds to the energy demands of the cell.**

- This regulation of the rate of glycolysis occurs through the allosteric enzymes hexokinase, phosphofructokinase, and pyruvate kinase.

21.4 Fermentations

► **Fermentations are catabolic reactions that occur with no net oxidation.**

► **Under anaerobic conditions the NADH produced by glycolysis is used to reduce pyruvate.**

► **The lactate fermentation reduces pyruvate to produce lactate.**

- This occurs in working muscles when there is not enough oxygen to provide ATP through aerobic catabolic reactions.
- If lactate builds up to a high enough concentration, it can inhibit glycolysis and thus ATP production. At this point, the **anaerobic threshold,** there is not enough energy for muscles to continue to function.

► **The alcohol fermentation reduces pyruvate to ethanol.**

- The alcohol fermentation is used to produce wines and other alcoholic beverages.
- The alcohol fermentation is also used in bread making.

21.5 The Pentose Phosphate Pathway

► **The pentose phosphate pathway is an alternative pathway for glucose degradation and is particularly abundant in the liver and adipose tissue.**

► **Products of the pathway include:**

- NADPH, a reducing agent for biosynthetic reaction.
- Ribose-5-phosphate for nucleotide synthesis.
- Erythrose-4-phosphate for biosynthesis of several amino acids (tryptophan, tyrosine, and phenylalanine).

21.6 Gluconeogenesis: The Synthesis of Glucose

► **Gluconeogenesis is the pathway for glucose synthesis from noncarbohydrate starting materials.**

- It occurs in the mammalian liver.
- Starting materials include lactate and all amino acids except lysine and leucine, and glycerol.

► **Gluconeogenesis is not simply the reverse of glycolysis.**

- Three steps in glycolysis in which ATP is produced or consumed are bypassed by gluconeogenesis by using other enzymes.
- All the other enzymes in the two pathways are the same.
- **Guanosine triphosphate (GTP)** is a phosphoryl group donor in a reaction that converts oxaloacetate into phosphoenolpyruvate. The oxaloacetate is produced by the carboxylation of pyruvate.

► **The Cori Cycle is a metabolic pathway in which lactate produced by working muscle is taken up by the liver and converted to glucose by gluconeogenesis.**

21.7 Glycogen Synthesis and Degradation

► **Glycogen is a long, branched-chain polymer of glucose.**

- It is stored in **glycogen granules** that consist of glycogen and the enzymes required for glycogen synthesis and degradation.
- It is found in the liver and muscle.

► **Glycogenolysis is the pathway by which the glycogen polymer is broken down into individual monomers (glucose molecules).**

► **Glycogenesis is the metabolic pathway by which the polymer glycogen is synthesized from glucose molecules.**

- **Uridine triphosphate (UTP)** is a ribonucleotide involved in glycogenesis.

► **Glycogen synthesis and degradation are under hormonal control.**

- **Insulin** inhibits glycogen degradation and stimulates glycogen synthesis when blood glucose levels are too high **(hyperglycemia).**
- **Glucagon** inhibits glycogen synthesis and stimulates glycogen degradation when blood glucose levels are too low **(hypoglycemia).**

QUESTIONS AND PROBLEMS

ATP: The Cellular Energy Currency

Foundations

21.19 What molecule is primarily responsible for conserving the energy released in catabolism?

21.20 Describe the structure of ATP.

Applications

21.21 Write a reaction showing the hydrolysis of the terminal phosphoanhydride bond of ATP.

21.22 What is meant by the term *high-energy bond?*

21.23 What is meant by a coupled reaction?

21.24 Compare and contrast anabolism and catabolism in terms of their roles in metabolism and their relationship to ATP.

Overview of Catabolic Processes

Foundations

21.25 What is the most readily used energy source in the diet?

21.26 What is a hydrolysis reaction?

Applications

21.27 Write an equation showing the hydrolysis of maltose.

21.28 Write an equation showing the hydrolysis of sucrose.

21.29 Write a balanced equation showing the hydrolysis of the following peptide: phe-ala-glu-met-lys.

21.30 Describe the stages of protein digestion, including the location of each.

21.31 Write an equation showing the hydrolysis of a triglyceride consisting of glycerol, oleic acid, linoleic acid, and stearic acid.

21.32 How are fatty acids taken up into the cell?

21.33 Write an equation showing the hydrolysis of the dipeptide alanyl-leucine.

21.34 How are amino acids transported into the cell?

Glycolysis

Foundations

21.35 Define glycolysis and describe its role in cellular metabolism.

21.36 What are the end products of glycolysis?

21.37 Why does glycolysis require a supply of NAD^+ to function?

21.38 Why must the NADH produced in glycolysis be reoxidized to NAD^+?

21.39 What is the net energy yield of ATP in glycolysis?

21.40 How many molecules of ATP are produced by substrate-level phosphorylation during glycolysis?

21.41 Explain how muscle is able to carry out rapid contraction for prolonged periods even though its supply of ATP is sufficient only for a fraction of a second of rapid contraction.

21.42 Where in the muscle cell does glycolysis occur?

21.43 Write the balanced chemical equation for glycolysis.

21.44 Write a chemical equation for the transfer of a phosphoryl group from ATP to fructose-6-phosphate.

21.45 Match each of the following enzymes with the reaction that it catalyzes.

a. Phosphoglucose isomerase
b. Phosphofructokinase
c. Triose phosphate isomerase
d. Aldolase
e. Hexokinase
f. Enolase
g. Glyceraldehyde-3-phosphate dehydrogenase
h. Phosphoglycerate kinase
i. Pyruvate kinase
j. Phosphoglycerate mutase

1. Phosphorylation of glucose
2. Phosphorylation of fructose-6-phosphate
3. Dephosphorylation of pyruvate
4. Conversion of fructose-1,6-bisphosphate to dihydroxyacetone phosphate and glyceraldehyde-3-phosphate
5. Phosphorylation and oxidation of glyceraldehyde-3-phosphate to produce 1,3-bisphosphoglycerate and NADH
6. Conversion of dihydroxyacetone phosphate into glyceraldehyde-3-phosphate
7. Isomerization of glucose-6-phosphate into fructose-6-phosphate
8. Isomerization of 3-phosphoglycerate into 2-phosphoglycerate
9. Dehydration of 2-phosphoglycerate to produce phosphoenolpyruvate
10. Substrate-level phosphorylation involving transfer of a phosphoryl group from 1,3-bisphosphoglycerate to ADP

21.46 Match each of the following enzymes with the appropriate class of enzymes that it represents. (*Hint:* An enzyme classification may be used more than once or not at all.)

a. Phosphoglucose isomerase
b. Phosphofructokinase
c. Triose phosphate isomerase
d. Aldolase
e. Hexokinase
f. Enolase
g. Glyceraldehyde-3-phosphate dehydrogenase
h. Phosphoglycerate kinase
i. Pyruvate kinase
j. Phosphoglycerate mutase

1. Transferase
2. Oxidoreductase
3. Kinase
4. Hydrolase
5. Lyase
6. Isomerase

Applications

21.47 Describe the symptoms associated with a genetic deficiency of an enzyme in the glycolysis pathway.

21.48 Why are red blood cells particularly susceptible to a deficiency of an enzyme in the glycolysis pathway?

21.49 What is the cause of myoglobinuria?

21.50 Describe exercise intolerance and the cause of the condition.

Examine the following pair of equations and use them to answer Questions 21.51–21.54.

(a) O=C—H, H—C—OH, HO—C—H, H—C—OH, H—C—OH, H—C—H, O, $^-$O—P(=O)—O$^-$ ⇌ (b) CH_2OH, C=O, HO—C—H, H—C—OH, H—C—OH, H—C—H, O, $^-$O—P(=O)—O$^-$

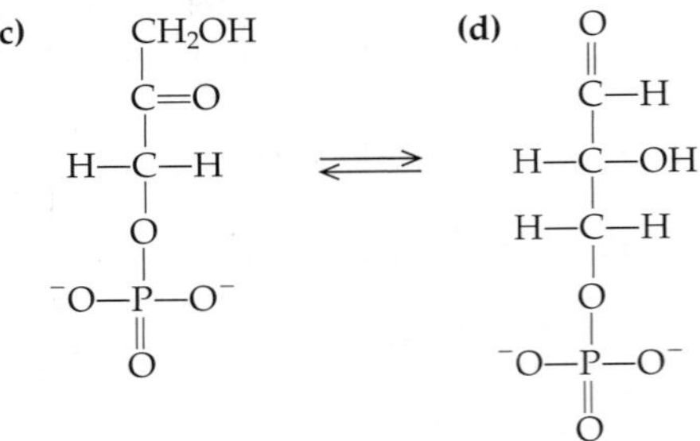

21.51 What type of enzyme would catalyze each of these reactions?

21.52 To which family of organic molecules do a and d belong? To which family of organic molecules do b and c belong?

21.53 What is the name of the type of intermediate formed in each of these reactions?

21.54 Draw the intermediate that would be formed in each of these reactions.

21.55 When an enzyme has the term *kinase* in the name, what type of reaction do you expect it to catalyze?

21.56 What features do the reactions catalyzed by hexokinase and phosphofructokinase share in common?

21.57 What is the role of NAD^+ in a biochemical oxidation reaction?

21.58 Write the equation for the reaction catalyzed by glyceraldehyde-3-phosphate dehydrogenase. Highlight the chemical changes that show this to be an oxidation reaction.

21.59 What is the importance of the regulation of glycolysis?

21.60 Explain the role of allosteric enzymes in control of glycolysis.

21.61 What molecules serve as allosteric effectors of phosphofructokinase?

21.62 What molecule serves as an allosteric inhibitor of hexokinase?

21.63 Explain the role of citrate in the feedback inhibition of glycolysis.

21.64 Explain the feedforward activation mechanism that results in the activation of pyruvate kinase.

Fermentations

Foundations

21.65 Write a balanced chemical equation for the conversion of acetaldehyde to ethanol.

21.66 Write a balanced chemical equation for the conversion of pyruvate to lactate.

Applications

21.67 After running a 100-meter (m) dash, a sprinter had a high concentration of muscle lactate. What process is responsible for production of lactate?

21.68 If the muscle of an organism had no lactate dehydrogenase, could anaerobic glycolysis occur in those muscle cells? Explain your answer.

21.69 What food products are the result of lactate fermentation?

21.70 Explain the value of alcohol fermentation in bread making.

21.71 What enzyme catalyzes the reduction of pyruvate to lactate?

21.72 What enzymes catalyze the conversion of pyruvate to ethanol and carbon dioxide?

21.73 A child was brought to the doctor's office suffering from a strange set of symptoms. When the child exercised hard, she became giddy and behaved as though drunk. What do you think is the metabolic basis of these symptoms?

21.74 A family started a batch of wine by adding yeast to grape juice and placing the mixture in a sealed bottle. Two weeks later, the bottle exploded. What metabolic reactions—and specifically, what product of those reactions—caused the bottle to explode?

The Pentose Phosphate Pathway

21.75 Of what value are the ribose-5-phosphate and erythrose-4-phosphate that are produced in the pentose phosphate pathway?

21.76 Of what value is the NADPH that is produced in the pentose phosphate pathway?

Gluconeogenesis: The Synthesis of Glucose

21.77 Define gluconeogenesis and describe its role in metabolism.

21.78 What is the role of guanosine triphosphate in gluconeogenesis?

21.79 What organ is primarily responsible for gluconeogenesis?

21.80 What is the physiological function of gluconeogenesis?

21.81 Lactate can be converted to glucose by gluconeogenesis. To what metabolic intermediate must lactate be converted so that it can be a substrate for the enzymes of gluconeogenesis?

21.82 L-Alanine can be converted to pyruvate. Can L-alanine also be converted to glucose? Explain your answer.

21.83 Explain why gluconeogenesis is not simply the reversal of glycolysis.

21.84 In step 10 of glycolysis, phosphoenolpyruvate is converted to pyruvate, and ATP is produced by substrate-level phosphorylation. How is this reaction bypassed in gluconeogenesis?

21.85 Which steps in the glycolysis pathway are irreversible?

21.86 What enzymatic reactions of gluconeogenesis bypass the irreversible steps of glycolysis?

Glycogen Synthesis and Degradation

Foundations

21.87 What organs are primarily responsible for maintaining the proper blood glucose level?

21.88 Why must the blood glucose level be carefully regulated?

21.89 What does the term *hypoglycemia* mean?

21.90 What does the term *hyperglycemia* mean?

Applications

21.91 **a.** What enzymes involved in glycogen metabolism are stimulated by insulin?
b. What effect does this have on glycogen metabolism?
c. What effect does this have on blood glucose levels?

21.92 **a.** What enzyme is stimulated by glucagon?
b. What effect does this have on glycogen metabolism?
c. What effect does this have on blood glucose levels?

21.93 Explain how a defect in glycogen metabolism can cause hypoglycemia.

21.94 What defects of glycogen metabolism would lead to a large increase in the concentration of liver glycogen?

21.95 Write a "word" equation showing the reaction catalyzed by glycogen phosphorylase.

21.96 Describe the function of the debranching enzyme in glycogen degradation.

21.97 Write a balanced equation for the reaction catalyzed by phosphoglucomutase. What is the role of this enzyme in glycogen degradation? What is the role of this enzyme in glycogen synthesis?

21.98 Draw the structure of UDP-glucose and describe its role in glycogen synthesis.

21.99 Write a balanced equation for the reaction catalyzed by glucokinase. What is the function of this enzyme in glycogen synthesis?

21.100 Write a "word" equation showing the reaction catalyzed by glycogen synthase.

CRITICAL THINKING PROBLEMS

1. An enzyme that hydrolyzes ATP (an ATPase) bound to the plasma membrane of certain tumor cells has an abnormally high activity. How will this activity affect the rate of glycolysis?
2. Explain why no net oxidation occurs during anaerobic glycolysis followed by lactate fermentation.
3. A certain person was found to have a defect in glycogen metabolism. The liver of this person could (a) make glucose-6-phosphate from lactate and (b) synthesize glucose-6-phosphate from glycogen but (c) could not synthesize glycogen from glucose-6-phosphate. What enzyme is defective?
4. A scientist added phosphate labeled with radioactive phosphorus (^{32}P) to a bacterial culture growing anaerobically (without O_2). She then purified all the compounds produced during glycolysis. Look carefully at the steps of the pathway. Predict which of the intermediates of the pathway would be the first one to contain radioactive phosphate. On which carbon of this compound would you expect to find the radioactive phosphate?
5. A 2-month-old baby was brought to the hospital suffering from seizures. He deteriorated progressively over time, showing psychomotor retardation. Blood tests revealed a high concentration of lactate and pyruvate. Although blood levels of alanine were high, they did not stimulate gluconeogenesis. The doctor measured the activity of pyruvate carboxylase in the baby and found it to be only 1% of the normal level. What reaction is catalyzed by pyruvate carboxylase? How could this deficiency cause the baby's symptoms and test results?

22

Aerobic Respiration and Energy Production

Rock climbing demands a great deal of energy.

LEARNING GOALS

1. Name the regions of the mitochondria and the function of each region.
2. Describe the reaction that results in the conversion of pyruvate to acetyl CoA, describing the location of the reaction and the components of the pyruvate dehydrogenase complex.
3. Summarize the reactions of aerobic respiration.
4. Looking at an equation representing any of the chemical reactions that occur in the citric acid cycle, describe the kind of reaction that is occurring and the significance of that reaction to the pathway.
5. Explain the mechanisms for the control of the citric acid cycle.
6. Describe the process of oxidative phosphorylation.
7. Describe the conversion of amino acids to molecules that can enter the citric acid cycle.
8. Explain the importance of the urea cycle and describe its essential steps.
9. Discuss the cause and effect of hyperammonemia.
10. Summarize the role of the citric acid cycle in catabolism and anabolism.

OUTLINE

Introduction 762
22.1 The Mitochondria 762
A Human Perspective: Exercise and Energy Metabolism 764
22.2 Conversion of Pyruvate to Acetyl CoA 764
22.3 An Overview of Aerobic Respiration 767
22.4 The Citric Acid Cycle (The Krebs Cycle) 768
22.5 Control of the Citric Acid Cycle 772
22.6 Oxidative Phosphorylation 774
A Human Perspective: Brown Fat: The Fat That Makes You Thin? 776
22.7 The Degradation of Amino Acids 778
22.8 The Urea Cycle 782
A Medical Perspective: Pyruvate Carboxylase Deficiency 785
22.9 Overview of Anabolism: The Citric Acid Cycle as a Source of Biosynthetic Intermediates 786

INTRODUCTION

In this chapter we will be studying the amazing, intricate set of reactions that allow us to completely degrade fuel molecules such as sugars and amino acids. These oxygen-requiring reactions, called *aerobic respiration*, occur in cellular organelles called *mitochondria*.

We are used to thinking of the organelles as a collection of membrane-bound structures that are synthesized under the direction of the genetic information in the nucleus of the cell. Not so with the mitochondria. These organelles have their own genetic information and are able to make some of their own proteins. They grow and multiply in a way very similar to simple bacteria. This, along with other information on the structure and activities of mitochondria, has led researchers to conclude that the mitochondria are actually the descendants of bacteria captured by eukaryotic cells millions of years ago.

We inherit all of our mitochondria from our mothers and, like the mitochondria themselves, some genetic diseases of energy metabolism are maternally inherited. One such disease, Leber's hereditary optic neuropathy (LHON), causes blindness and heart problems. People with LHON have a reduced ability to make ATP. As a result, sensitive tissues that demand a great deal of energy eventually die. LHON sufferers eventually lose their sight because the optic nerve dies from lack of energy.

Researchers have identified and cloned a mutant mitochondrial gene that is responsible for LHON. The defect is a mutant form of *NADH dehydrogenase*, a huge, complex enzyme that accepts electrons from NADH and sends them on through an electron transport system. Passage of electrons through the electron transport system allows the synthesis of ATP. If NADH dehydrogenase is defective, passage of electrons through the electron transport system is less efficient, and less ATP is made. In LHON sufferers, the result is eventual blindness.

In this chapter and the next, we will study some of the important biochemical reactions that occur in the mitochondria. Here, the final oxidations of carbohydrates, lipids, and proteins occur. Here, also, the electrons that are harvested in these oxidation reactions are used to make ATP. In these remarkably efficient reactions, nearly 40% of the potential energy of glucose is stored as ATP.

22.1 The Mitochondria

LEARNING GOAL

1 Name the regions of the mitochondria and the function of each region.

Mitochondria are football-shaped organelles that are roughly the size of a bacterial cell. They are surrounded by an **outer mitochondrial membrane** and an **inner mitochondrial membrane** (Figure 22.1). The space between the two membranes is the **intermembrane space,** and the space inside of the inner membrane is the **matrix space.** The enzymes of the citric acid cycle, of the β-oxidation pathway for the breakdown of fatty acids, and for the degradation of amino acids are all found in the mitochondrial matrix space.

An organelle is a compartment within the cytoplasm that has a specialized function.

Structure and Function

The outer mitochondrial membrane has many small pores through which small molecules (less than 10,000 g/mol) can pass. Thus, the small molecules to be oxidized for the production of ATP can easily enter the mitochondrial intermembrane space.

The inner membrane is highly folded to create a large surface area. The folded membranes are known as **cristae.** The inner mitochondrial membrane is almost completely impermeable to most substances. For this reason it has many transport proteins to bring particular fuel molecules into the matrix space. Also embedded

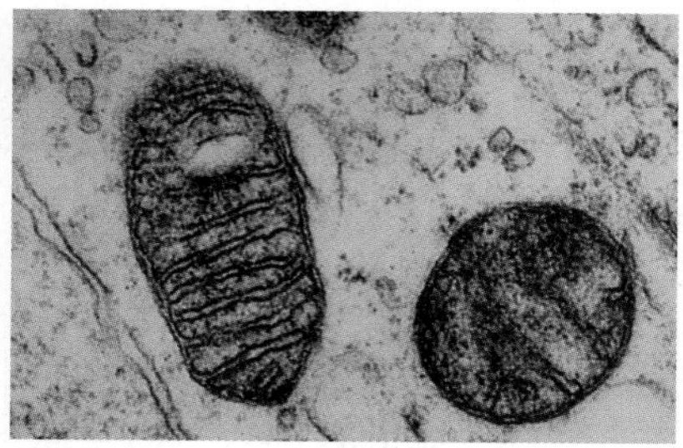

(a)

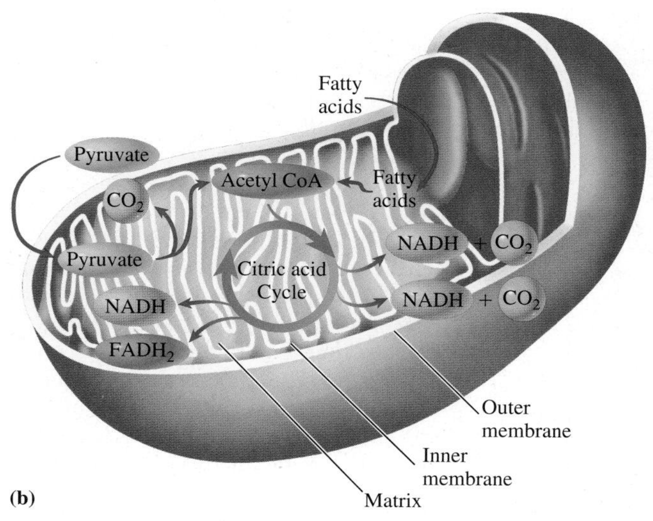

(b)

Figure 22.1 Structure of the mitochondrion. (a) Electron micrograph of mitochondria. (b) Schematic drawing of the mitochondrion.

within the inner mitochondrial membrane are the protein electron carriers of the *electron transport system,* and *ATP synthase.* ATP synthase is a large complex of many proteins that catalyzes the synthesis of ATP.

Origin of the Mitochondria

Not only are mitochondria roughly the size of bacteria, they have several other features that have led researchers to suspect that they may once have been free-living bacteria that were "captured" by eukaryotic cells. They have their own genetic information (DNA). They also make their own ribosomes that are very similar to those of bacteria. These ribosomes allow the mitochondria to synthesize some of their own proteins. Finally, mitochondria are actually self-replicating; they grow in size and divide to produce new mitochondria. All of these characteristics suggest that the mitochondria that produce the majority of the ATP for our cells evolved from bacteria "captured" perhaps as long as 1.5×10^9 years ago.

As we saw in Chapter 20, ribosomes are complexes of protein and RNA that serve as small platforms for protein synthesis.

Question 22.1 What is the function of the mitochondria?

Question 22.2 How do the mitochondria differ from the other components of eukaryotic cells?

Question 22.3 Draw a schematic diagram of a mitochondrion, and label the parts of this organelle.

Question 22.4 Describe the evidence that suggests that mitochondria evolved from free-living bacteria.

A HUMAN PERSPECTIVE

Exercise and Energy Metabolism

The Olympic sprinters get set in the blocks. The gun goes off, and roughly 10 seconds (s) later the 100-meter (m) dash is over. Elsewhere, the marathoners line up. They will run 26 miles (mi) and 385 yards (yd) in a little over 2 hours (h). Both sports involve running, but they utilize very different sources of energy.

Let's look at the sprinter first. The immediate source of energy for the sprinter is stored ATP. But the quantity of stored ATP is very small, only about 3 ounces (oz). This allows the sprinter to run as fast as he or she can for about 3 s. Obviously, another source of stored energy must be tapped, and that energy store is *creatine phosphate:*

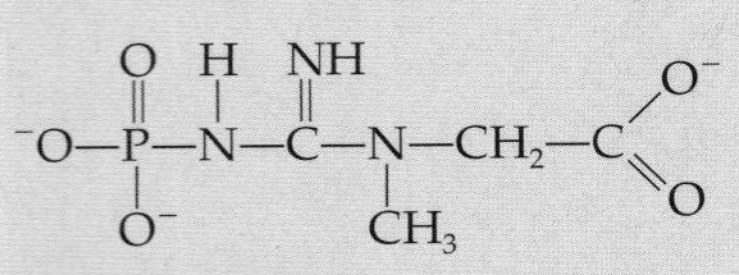

$$^{-}O-\overset{\overset{\displaystyle O}{\|}}{\underset{\underset{\displaystyle O^-}{|}}{P}}-\overset{\overset{\displaystyle H}{|}}{N}-\overset{\overset{\displaystyle NH}{\|}}{C}-\underset{\underset{\displaystyle CH_3}{|}}{N}-CH_2-C\begin{matrix}\diagup O^- \\ \diagdown\!\!\diagdown O\end{matrix}$$

The structure of creatine phosphate.

Creatine phosphate, stored in the muscle, donates its high-energy phosphate to ADP to produce new supplies of ATP.

This will keep our runner in motion for another 5 or 6 s before the store of creatine phosphate is also depleted. This is almost enough energy to finish the 100-m dash, but in reality, all the runners are slowing down, owing to energy depletion, and the winner is the sprinter who is slowing down the least!

Consider a longer race, the 400-m or the 800-m. These runners run at maximum capacity for much longer. When they have depleted their ATP and creatine phosphate stores, they must synthesize more ATP. Of course, the cells have been making ATP all the time, but now the demand for energy is much greater. To supply this increased demand, the anaerobic energy-generating reactions (glycolysis and lactate fermentation, Chapter 21) and aerobic processes (citric acid cycle and oxidative phosphorylation) begin to function much more rapidly. Often, however, these athletes are running so strenuously that they cannot provide enough oxygen to the exercising muscle to allow oxidative phosphorylation to function efficiently. When this happens, the muscles must rely on glycolysis and lactate fermentation to provide *most* of the energy requirement. The chemical by-product of these anaerobic processes, lactate, builds up in the muscle and diffuses into the bloodstream. However, the concentration of lactate inevitably builds up in the working muscle and causes muscle fatigue and, eventually, muscle failure. Thus, exercise that depends primarily on anaerobic ATP production cannot continue for very long.

The marathoner presents us with a different scenario. This runner will deplete his or her stores of ATP and creatine phosphate as quickly as a short-distance runner. The anaerobic glycolytic pathway will begin to degrade glucose provided by the blood at a more rapid rate, as will the citric acid cycle and oxidative phosphorylation. The major difference in ATP production between the long-distance runner and the short- or middle-distance runner is that the muscles of the long-distance runner derive almost all their energy through aerobic pathways. These individuals continue to run long distances at a pace that allows them to supply virtually all the oxygen needed by the exercising muscle. In fact, only aerobic pathways can provide a constant supply of ATP for exercise that goes on for hours. Theoretically, under such conditions our runner could run indefinitely, utilizing first his or her stored glycogen and eventually stored lipids. Of course, in reality, other factors such as dehydration and fatigue place limits on the athlete's ability to continue.

From this we can conclude that long-distance runners must have a great capacity to produce ATP aerobically, in the mitochondria, whereas short- and middle-distance runners need a great capacity to produce energy anaerobically, in the

$$^{-}O-\overset{\overset{\displaystyle O}{\|}}{\underset{\underset{\displaystyle O^-}{|}}{P}}-\overset{\overset{\displaystyle H}{|}}{N}-\overset{\overset{\displaystyle NH}{\|}}{C}-\underset{\underset{\displaystyle CH_3}{|}}{N}-CH_2-C\begin{matrix}\diagup O^- \\ \diagdown\!\!\diagdown O\end{matrix} + ADP \xrightarrow{\text{Creatine kinase}} H_2N-\overset{\overset{\displaystyle NH}{\|}}{C}-\underset{\underset{\displaystyle CH_3}{|}}{N}-CH_2-C\begin{matrix}\diagup O^- \\ \diagdown\!\!\diagdown O\end{matrix} + ATP$$

Phosphoryl group transfer from creatine phosphate to ADP is catalyzed by the enzyme creatine kinase.

22.2 Conversion of Pyruvate to Acetyl CoA

LEARNING GOAL

2 Describe the reaction that results in the conversion of pyruvate to acetyl CoA, describing the location of the reaction and the components of the pyruvate dehydrogenase complex.

As we saw in Chapter 21, under *anaerobic* conditions, glucose is broken down into two pyruvate molecules that are then converted to a stable fermentation product. This limited degradation of glucose releases very little of the potential energy of glucose. Under *aerobic* conditions the cells can use oxygen and completely oxidize glucose to CO_2 in a metabolic pathway called the *citric acid cycle.*

This pathway is often referred to as the *Krebs cycle* in honor of Sir Hans Krebs, who worked out the steps of this cyclic pathway from his own experimental data and that of other researchers. It is also called the *tricarboxylic acid (TCA) cycle* because several of the early intermediates in the pathway have three carboxyl groups.

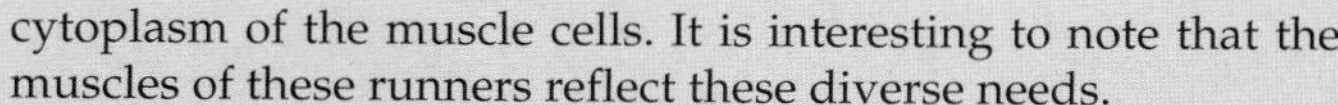

The sprinter relies on fast-twitch muscle fibers.

The marathon runner largely uses slow-twitch muscle fibers.

cytoplasm of the muscle cells. It is interesting to note that the muscles of these runners reflect these diverse needs.

When researchers examine muscle tissue that has been surgically removed, they find two predominant types of muscle fibers. *Fast-twitch muscle fibers* are large, relatively plump, pale cells. They have only a few mitochondria but contain a large reserve of glycogen and high concentrations of the enzymes that are needed for glycolysis and lactate fermentation. These muscle fibers fatigue rather quickly because fermentation is inefficient, quickly depleting the cell's glycogen store and causing the accumulation of lactate.

Slow-twitch muscle fiber cells are about half the diameter of fast-twitch muscle cells and are red. The red color is a result of the high concentrations of myoglobin in these cells. Recall that myoglobin stores oxygen for the cell (Section 18.8) and facilitates rapid diffusion of oxygen throughout the cell. In addition, slow-twitch muscle fiber cells are packed with mitochondria. With this abundance of oxygen and mitochondria these cells have the capacity for extended ATP production via aerobic pathways—ideal for endurance sports like marathon racing.

It is not surprising, then, that researchers have found that the muscles of sprinters have many more fast-twitch muscle fibers and those of endurance athletes have many more slow-twitch muscle fibers. One question that many researchers are trying to answer is whether the type of muscle fibers an individual has is a function of genetic makeup or training. Is a marathon runner born to be a long-distance runner, or are his or her abilities due to the type of training the runner undergoes? There is no doubt that the training regimen for an endurance runner does indeed increase the number of slow-twitch muscle fibers and that of a sprinter increases the number of fast-twitch muscle fibers. But there is intriguing new evidence to suggest that the muscles of endurance athletes have a greater proportion of slow-twitch muscle fibers before they ever begin training. It appears that some of us truly were born to run.

For Further Understanding

- It has been said that the winner of the 100-m race is the one who is slowing down the least. Explain this observation in terms of energy-harvesting pathways.
- Design an experiment to safely test whether the type of muscle fibers a runner has are the result of training or genetic makeup.

Once pyruvate enters the mitochondria, it must be converted to a two-carbon acetyl group. This acetyl group must be "activated" to enter the reactions of the citric acid cycle. Activation occurs when the acetyl group is bonded to the thiol group of coenzyme A. **Coenzyme A** is a large thiol derived from ATP and the vitamin pantothenic acid (Figure 22.2). It is an acceptor of acetyl groups (in red in Figure 22.2), which are bonded to it through a high-energy thioester bond. The acetyl coenzyme A **(acetyl CoA)** formed is the "activated" form of the acetyl group.

Coenzyme A is described in Sections 12.8 and 14.4.

Figure 22.3 shows us the reaction that converts pyruvate to acetyl CoA. First, pyruvate is decarboxylated, which means that it loses a carboxyl group that is released as CO_2. Next it is oxidized, and the hydride anion that is removed is accepted by NAD^+. Finally, the remaining acetyl group, CH_3CO—, is linked to coenzyme A by a thioester bond. This very complex reaction is carried out by

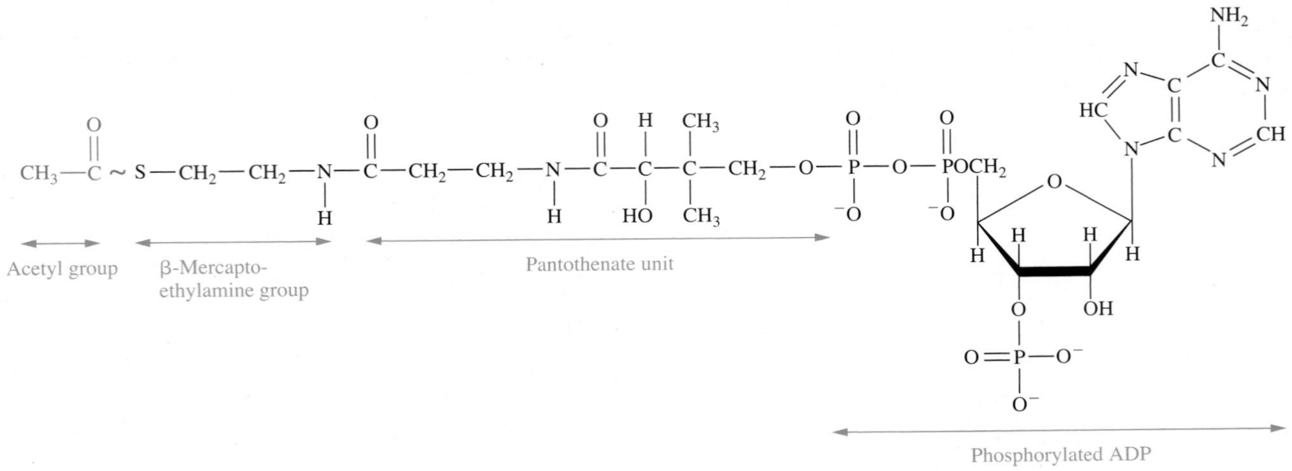

Acetyl group β-Mercapto-ethylamine group Pantothenate unit Phosphorylated ADP

Acetyl coenzyme A
(acetyl CoA)

Figure 22.2 The structure of acetyl CoA. The bond between the acetyl group and coenzyme A is a high-energy thioester bond.

Figure 22.3 The decarboxylation and oxidation of pyruvate to produce acetyl CoA. (a) The overall reaction in which CO_2 and an H:$^-$ are removed from pyruvate and the remaining acetyl group is attached to coenzyme A. This requires the concerted action of three enzymes and five coenzymes. (b) The pyruvate dehydrogenase complex that carries out this reaction is actually a cluster of enzymes and coenzymes. The substrate is passed from one enzyme to the next as the reaction occurs.

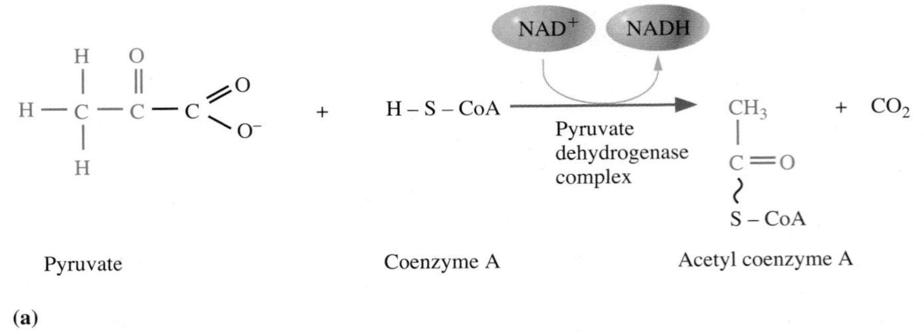

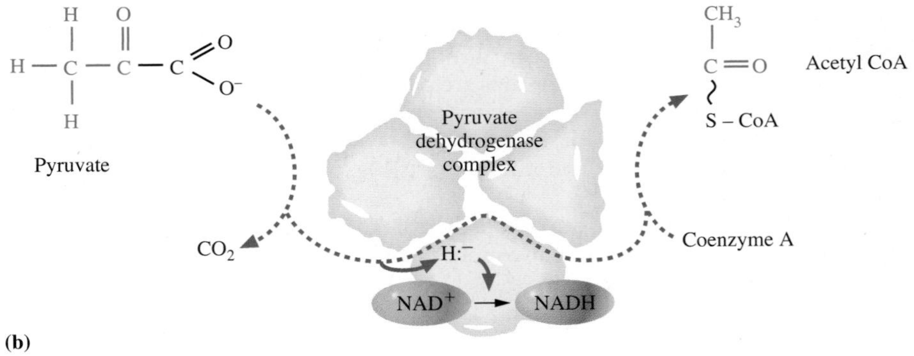

(a) Pyruvate + Coenzyme A (H – S – CoA) → (Pyruvate dehydrogenase complex; NAD^+ → NADH) Acetyl coenzyme A + CO_2

(b) Pyruvate → Pyruvate dehydrogenase complex → Acetyl CoA; CO_2; H:$^-$; NAD^+ → NADH; Coenzyme A

Thioester bonds are discussed in Section 14.4.

three enzymes and five coenzymes that are organized together in a single bundle called the **pyruvate dehydrogenase complex** (see Figure 22.3). This organization allows the substrate to be passed from one enzyme to the next as each chemical reaction occurs. A schematic representation of this "disassembly line" is shown in Figure 22.3b.

This single reaction requires four coenzymes made from four different vitamins, in addition to the coenzyme lipoamide. These are thiamine pyrophosphate, derived from thiamine (Vitamin B_1); FAD, derived from riboflavin (Vitamin B_2); NAD^+, derived from niacin; and coenzyme A, derived from pantothenic acid. Obviously, a deficiency in any of these vitamins would seriously reduce the

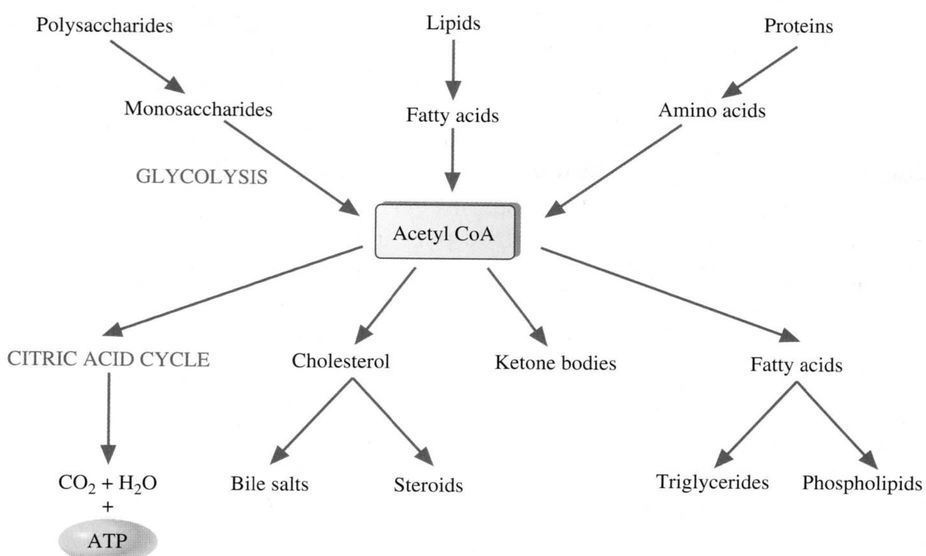

Figure 22.4 The central role of acetyl CoA in cellular metabolism.

amount of acetyl CoA that our cells could produce. This, in turn, would limit the amount of ATP that the body could make and would contribute to vitamin-deficiency diseases. Fortunately, a well-balanced diet provides an adequate supply of these and other vitamins.

In Figure 22.4, we see that acetyl CoA is a central character in cellular metabolism. It is produced by the degradation of glucose, fatty acids, and some amino acids. The major function of acetyl CoA in energy-harvesting pathways is to carry the acetyl group to the citric acid cycle, in which it will be used to produce large amounts of ATP. In addition to these catabolic duties, the acetyl group of acetyl CoA can also be used for *anabolic* or biosynthetic reactions to produce cholesterol and fatty acids. It is through this intermediate, acetyl CoA, that all the energy sources (fats, proteins, and carbohydrates) are interconvertible.

ANIMATION
- B Vitamins

Question 22.5 What vitamins are required for acetyl CoA production from pyruvate?

Question 22.6 What is the major role of coenzyme A in catabolic reactions?

22.3 An Overview of Aerobic Respiration

LEARNING GOAL

3 Summarize the reactions of aerobic respiration.

Aerobic respiration is the oxygen-requiring breakdown of food molecules and production of ATP. The different steps of aerobic respiration occur in different compartments of the mitochondria.

The enzymes for the citric acid cycle are found in the mitochondrial matrix space. The first enzyme catalyzes a reaction that joins the acetyl group of acetyl CoA (two carbons) to a four-carbon molecule (oxaloacetate) to produce citrate (six carbons). The remaining enzymes catalyze a series of rearrangements, decarboxylations (removal of CO_2), and oxidation-reduction reactions. The eventual products of this cyclic pathway are two CO_2 molecules and oxaloacetate—the molecule we began with.

At several steps in the citric acid cycle, a substrate is oxidized. In three of these steps, a pair of electrons is transferred from the substrate to NAD^+, producing NADH (three NADH molecules per turn of the cycle). At another step a pair of electrons is transferred from a substrate to FAD, producing $FADH_2$ (one $FADH_2$ molecule per turn of the cycle).

Remember (Section 19.7) that it is really the hydride anion with its pair of electrons ($H:^-$) that is transferred to NAD^+ to produce NADH. Similarly, a pair of hydrogen atoms (and thus two electrons) are transferred to FAD to produce $FADH_2$.

The electrons are passed from NADH or $FADH_2$, through an electron transport system located in the inner mitochondrial membrane, and finally to the terminal electron acceptor, molecular oxygen (O_2). The transfer of electrons through the electron transport system causes protons (H^+) to be pumped from the mitochondrial matrix into the intermembrane compartment. The result is a high-energy H^+ reservoir.

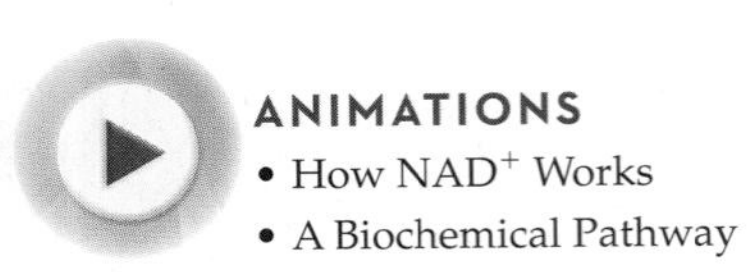

ANIMATIONS
- How NAD^+ Works
- A Biochemical Pathway

In the final step, the energy of the H^+ reservoir is used to make ATP. This last step is carried out by the enzyme complex ATP synthase. As protons flow back into the mitochondrial matrix through a pore in the ATP synthase complex, the enzyme catalyzes the synthesis of ATP.

This long, involved process is called *oxidative phosphorylation,* because the energy of electrons from the *oxidation* of substrates in the citric acid cycle is used to *phosphorylate* ADP and produce ATP. The details of each of these steps will be examined in upcoming sections.

Question 22.7 What is meant by the term *oxidative phosphorylation?*

Question 22.8 What does the term *aerobic respiration* mean?

22.4 The Citric Acid Cycle (The Krebs Cycle)

Biological Effects of Disorders of the Citric Acid Cycle

In Chapter 21 we saw that deficiencies of the enzymes involved in glycolysis cause debilitating conditions and, in severe form, result in death. This is also true of deficiencies of enzymes in the citric acid cycle (Table 22.1). A number of these deficiencies and the mutations that cause them have been studied and, up to this date, no treatment has been found for any of them. As with glycolysis, these genetic deficiencies emphasize the importance of the citric acid cycle to the life of the organism.

Mutations in the fumarase gene cause encephalopathy, which is a syndrome with a variety of symptoms that include neurological symptoms ranging from subtle personality changes to psychosis, lethargy, involuntary muscle spasms, tremors, and seizures. A newborn with a fumarase deficiency may exhibit muscle weakness (hypotonia) and poor feeding. As the child ages, the neurological symptoms become more severe and include severe developmental delay, brain deformation, psychomotor deficits, and seizures. Many children with this deficiency die in infancy or childhood.

A deficiency of α-ketoglutarate dehydrogenase is characterized by chronic lactic acidosis and progressive encephalopathy and hypotonia. The life expectancy of a child born with this deficiency is 2 to 3 years, with death resulting from neurological deterioration.

TABLE 22.1 Some Citric Acid Cycle Enzyme Deficiencies and the Associated Disorders

Enzyme Deficiency	Disorder
Fumarase	Early encephalopathy, seizures, and muscular hypotonia
α-Ketoglutarate dehydrogenase	Hypotonia, severe encephalopathy, psychotic behavior
Succinate dehydrogenase	Leigh disease (subacute necrotizing encephalomyelopathy), paraganglioma
Aconitase	Friedreich ataxia

A variety of mutations in the succinate dehydrogenase gene have been identified. One of these, SdhA, has been associated with Leigh disease, a disorder that generally affects children between 3 months and 2 years of age. It results in loss of motor skills and eventual death. Other mutations lead to tumors called *paragangliomas.* These are typically found in the head and neck regions and, depending on the nature of the mutation, may be malignant or benign.

One manifestation of aconitase deficiency is characterized by myopathy and exercise intolerance. In fact, physical exertion may prove fatal for some patients as a result of circulatory shock. A second manifestation is Friedreich ataxia. Typically symptoms appear in children between the ages of five and fifteen and include muscle weakness, loss of coordination, impaired hearing or speech, and heart disorders.

Reactions of the Citric Acid Cycle

The **citric acid cycle** is the final stage of the breakdown of carbohydrates, fats, and amino acids released from dietary proteins (Figure 22.5). To understand this important cycle, let's follow the fate of the acetyl group of an acetyl CoA as it passes through the citric acid cycle. The numbered steps listed below correspond to the steps in the citric acid cycle that are summarized in Figure 22.5.

LEARNING GOAL

4 Looking at an equation representing any of the chemical reactions that occur in the citric acid cycle, describe the kind of reaction that is occurring and the significance of that reaction to the pathway.

Reaction 1. This is a condensation reaction between the acetyl group of acetyl CoA and oxaloacetate. It is catalyzed by the enzyme *citrate synthase.* The product that is formed is citrate:

$$
\begin{array}{c} COO^- \\ | \\ C{=}O \\ | \\ CH_2 \\ | \\ COO^- \end{array}
+ H_3C{-}\overset{\displaystyle O}{\overset{\|}{C}}{\sim}S{-}CoA + H_2O
\xrightarrow[\text{synthase}]{\text{Citrate}}
\begin{array}{c} COO^- \\ | \\ CH_2 \\ | \\ HO{-}C{-}COO^- \\ | \\ H{-}C{-}H \\ | \\ COO^- \end{array}
+ HS{-}CoA + H^+
$$

Oxaloacetate | Acetyl CoA | Citrate | Coenzyme A

ANIMATION
- How the Krebs Cycle Works

Reaction 2. The enzyme *aconitase* catalyzes the dehydration of citrate, producing *cis*-aconitate. The same enzyme, aconitase, then catalyzes addition of a water molecule to the *cis*-aconitate, converting it to isocitrate. The net effect of these two steps is the isomerization of citrate to isocitrate:

Notice that the conversion of citrate to cis*-aconitate is a biological example of the dehydration of an alcohol to produce an alkene (Section 12.4). The conversion of* cis*-aconitate to isocitrate is a biochemical example of the hydration of an alkene to produce an alcohol (Sections 11.5 and 12.4).*

$$
\begin{array}{c} COO^- \\ | \\ CH_2 \\ | \\ HO{-}C{-}COO^- \\ | \\ H{-}C{-}H \\ | \\ COO^- \end{array}
\xrightarrow{\text{Aconitase}}
\begin{array}{c} COO^- \\ | \\ CH_2 \\ | \\ C{-}COO^- \\ \| \\ C{-}H \\ | \\ COO^- \end{array}
+ H_2O
\xrightarrow{\text{Aconitase}}
\begin{array}{c} COO^- \\ | \\ CH_2 \\ | \\ H{-}C{-}COO^- \\ | \\ HO{-}C{-}H \\ | \\ COO^- \end{array}
$$

Citrate | *cis*-Aconitate | Isocitrate

Reaction 3. The first oxidative step of the citric acid cycle is catalyzed by *isocitrate dehydrogenase.* It is a complex reaction in which three things happen:

a. the hydroxyl group of isocitrate is oxidized to a ketone,
b. carbon dioxide is released, and
c. NAD^+ is reduced to NADH.

The oxidation of a secondary alcohol produces a ketone (Sections 12.4 and 13.4).

Figure 22.5 The reactions of the citric acid cycle.

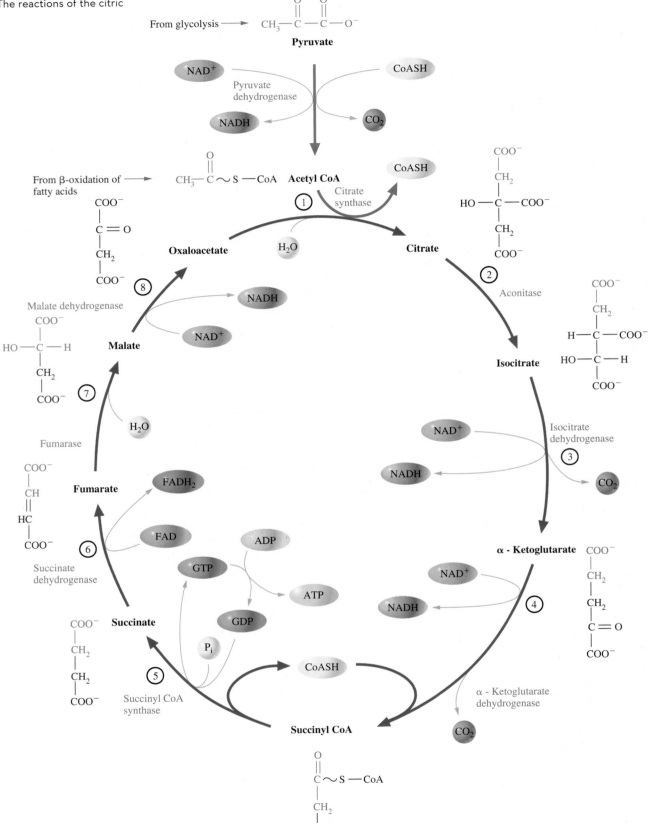

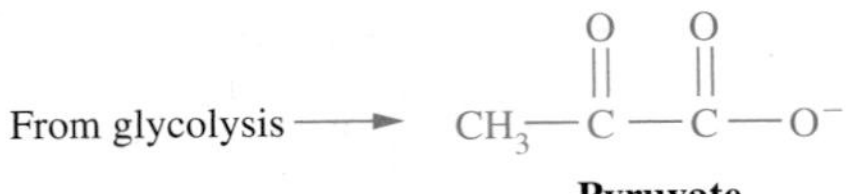

This is an oxidative decarboxylation reaction and the product is α-ketoglutarate:

The structure of NAD^+ and its reduction to NADH are shown in Figure 19.8.

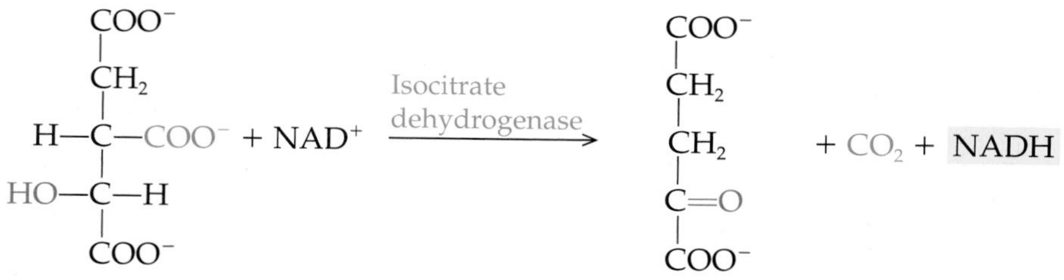

$$\text{Isocitrate: } {}^-OOC{-}CH_2{-}CH(COO^-){-}CH(OH){-}COO^- + NAD^+ \xrightarrow{\text{Isocitrate dehydrogenase}} {}^-OOC{-}CH_2{-}CH_2{-}C(=O){-}COO^- + CO_2 + NADH$$

Isocitrate → α-Ketoglutarate

Remember, in organic (and thus biochemical) reactions, oxidation can be recognized as a gain of oxygen or loss of hydrogen (Section 12.5).

Reaction 4. Coenzyme A enters the picture again as the *α-ketoglutarate dehydrogenase* complex carries out a complex series of reactions similar to those catalyzed by the pyruvate dehydrogenase complex. The same coenzymes are required and, once again, three chemical events occur:

The pyruvate dehydrogenase complex was described in Section 22.2 and shown in Figure 22.3.

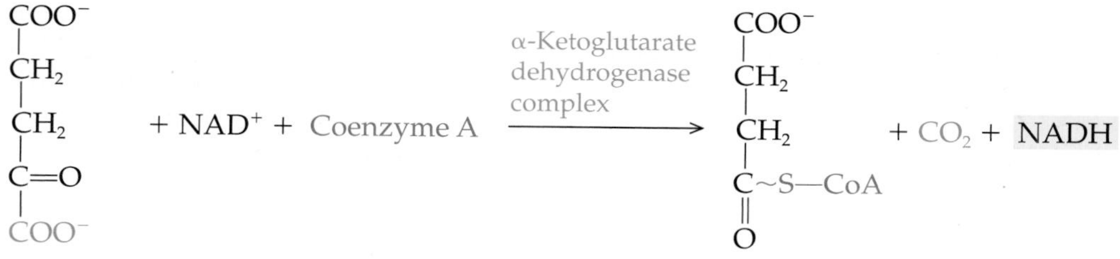

a. α-ketoglutarate loses a carboxylate group as CO_2,
b. it is oxidized and NAD^+ is reduced to NADH, and
c. coenzyme A combines with the product, succinate, to form succinyl CoA. The bond formed between succinate and coenzyme A is a high-energy thioester bond.

$$\text{α-Ketoglutarate: } {}^-OOC{-}CH_2{-}CH_2{-}C(=O){-}COO^- + NAD^+ + \text{Coenzyme A} \xrightarrow{\text{α-Ketoglutarate dehydrogenase complex}} {}^-OOC{-}CH_2{-}CH_2{-}C(=O){\sim}S{-}CoA + CO_2 + NADH$$

α-Ketoglutarate → Succinyl CoA

Reaction 5. Succinyl CoA is converted to succinate in this step, which once more is chemically very involved. The enzyme *succinyl CoA synthase* catalyzes a coupled reaction in which the high-energy thioester bond of succinyl CoA is hydrolyzed and an inorganic phosphate group is added to GDP to make GTP:

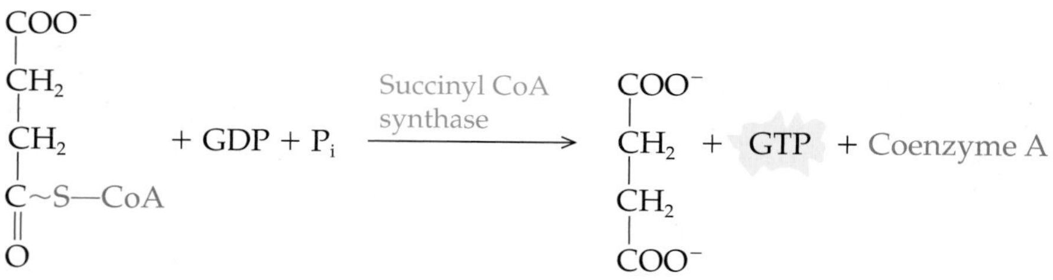

$$\text{Succinyl CoA: } {}^-OOC{-}CH_2{-}CH_2{-}C(=O){\sim}S{-}CoA + GDP + P_i \xrightarrow{\text{Succinyl CoA synthase}} {}^-OOC{-}CH_2{-}CH_2{-}COO^- + GTP + \text{Coenzyme A}$$

Succinyl CoA → Succinate

Another enzyme, *dinucleotide diphosphokinase,* then catalyzes the transfer of a phosphoryl group from GTP to ADP to make ATP:

$$GTP + ADP \xrightarrow{\text{Dinucleotide diphosphokinase}} GDP + ATP$$

The structure of FAD was shown in Figure 19.8.

Reaction 6. *Succinate dehydrogenase* then catalyzes the oxidation of succinate to fumarate in the next step. The oxidizing agent, *flavin adenine dinucleotide (FAD)*, is reduced in this step:

We studied hydrogenation of alkenes to produce alkanes in Section 11.5. This is simply the reverse.

$$\underset{\text{Succinate}}{\begin{array}{c}COO^-\\ |\\ CH_2\\ |\\ CH_2\\ |\\ COO^-\end{array}} + FAD \xrightarrow{\text{Succinate dehydrogenase}} \underset{\text{Fumarate}}{\begin{array}{c}COO^-\\ |\\ C-H\\ \|\\ H-C\\ |\\ COO^-\end{array}} + FADH_2$$

Reaction 7. Addition of H_2O to the double bond of fumarate gives malate. The enzyme *fumarase* catalyzes this reaction:

This reaction is a biological example of the hydration of an alkene to produce an alcohol (Sections 11.5 and 12.4).

$$\underset{\text{Fumarate}}{\begin{array}{c}COO^-\\ |\\ C-H\\ \|\\ H-C\\ |\\ COO^-\end{array}} + H_2O \xrightarrow{\text{Fumarase}} \underset{\text{Malate}}{\begin{array}{c}COO^-\\ |\\ HO-C-H\\ |\\ H-C-H\\ |\\ COO^-\end{array}}$$

This reaction is a biochemical example of the oxidation of a secondary alcohol to a ketone, which we studied in Sections 12.4 and 13.4.

Reaction 8. In the final step of the citric acid cycle, *malate dehydrogenase* catalyzes the reduction of NAD^+ to NADH and the oxidation of malate to oxaloacetate. Because the citric acid cycle "began" with the addition of an acetyl group to oxaloacetate, we have come full circle.

$$\underset{\text{Malate}}{\begin{array}{c}COO^-\\ |\\ HO-C-H\\ |\\ CH_2\\ |\\ COO^-\end{array}} + NAD^+ \xrightarrow{\text{Malate dehydrogenase}} \underset{\text{Oxaloacetate}}{\begin{array}{c}COO^-\\ |\\ C=O\\ |\\ CH_2\\ |\\ COO^-\end{array}} + NADH$$

22.5 Control of the Citric Acid Cycle

LEARNING GOAL

5 Explain the mechanisms for the control of the citric acid cycle.

Just like glycolysis, the citric acid cycle is responsive to the energy needs of the cell. The pathway speeds up when there is a greater demand for ATP, and it slows down when ATP energy is in excess. In the last chapter we saw that several of the enzymes that catalyze the reactions of glycolysis are *allosteric enzymes.* Similarly, four enzymes or enzyme complexes involved in the complete oxidation of pyruvate are allosteric enzymes. Because the control of the pathway must be precise, there are several enzymatic steps that are regulated. These are summarized in Figure 22.6 and below:

1. *Conversion of pyruvate to acetyl CoA.* The pyruvate dehydrogenase complex is inhibited by high concentrations of ATP, acetyl CoA, and NADH. Of course, the presence of these compounds in abundance signals that the cell has an adequate supply of energy, and thus energy metabolism is slowed.
2. *Synthesis of citrate from oxaloacetate and acetyl CoA.* The enzyme citrate synthase is an allosteric enzyme. In this case, the negative effector is ATP. Again, this is logical because an excess of ATP indicates that the cell has an abundance of energy.

3. *Oxidation and decarboxylation of isocitrate to α-ketoglutarate.* Isocitrate dehydrogenase is also an allosteric enzyme; however, the enzyme is controlled by the positive allosteric effector, ADP. ADP is a signal that the levels of ATP must be low, and therefore the rate of the citric acid cycle should be increased. Interestingly, isocitrate dehydrogenase is also *inhibited* by high levels of NADH and ATP.
4. *Conversion of α-ketoglutarate to succinyl CoA.* The α-ketoglutarate dehydrogenase complex is inhibited by high levels of the products of the reactions that it catalyzes, namely, NADH and succinyl CoA. It is further inhibited by high concentrations of ATP.

Allosteric enzymes bind to effectors, such as ATP or ADP, that alter the shape of the enzyme active site, either stimulating the rate of the reaction (positive allosterism) or inhibiting the reaction (negative allosterism). For more detail, see Section 19.9.

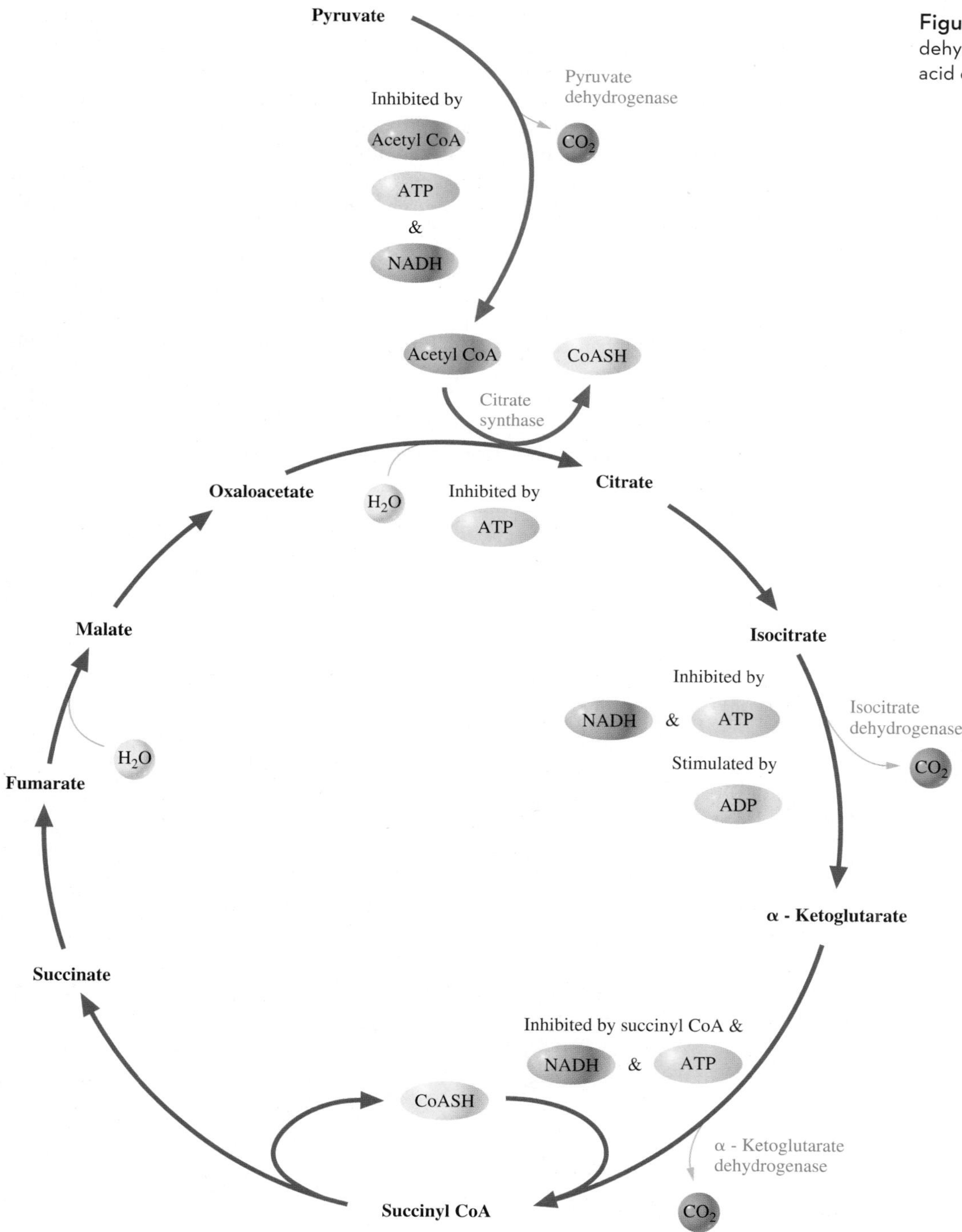

Figure 22.6 Regulation of the pyruvate dehydrogenase complex and the citric acid cycle.

22.6 Oxidative Phosphorylation

In Section 22.3 we noted that the electrons carried by NADH can be used to produce three ATP molecules, and those carried by $FADH_2$ can be used to produce two ATP molecules. We turn now to the process by which the energy of electrons carried by these coenzymes is converted to ATP energy. It is a series of reactions called **oxidative phosphorylation,** which couples the oxidation of NADH and $FADH_2$ to the phosphorylation of ADP to generate ATP.

LEARNING GOAL

6 Describe the process of oxidative phosphorylation.

ANIMATION

- Electron Transport System and ATP Synthesis

Electron Transport Systems and the Hydrogen Ion Gradient

Before we try to understand the mechanism of oxidative phosphorylation, let's first look at the molecules that carry out this complex process. Embedded within the mitochondrial inner membrane are **electron transport systems.** These are made up of a series of electron carriers, including coenzymes and cytochromes. All these molecules are located within the membrane in an arrangement that allows them to pass electrons from one to the next. This array of electron carriers is called the *respiratory electron transport system* (Figure 22.7). As you would expect in such sequential oxidation-reduction reactions, the electrons lose some energy with each transfer. Some of this energy is used to make ATP.

At three sites in the electron transport system, protons (H^+) can be pumped from the mitochondrial matrix to the intermembrane space. These H^+ contribute to a high-energy H^+ reservoir. At each of the three sites, enough H^+ are pumped into the H^+ reservoir to produce one ATP molecule. The first site is NADH dehydrogenase. Because electrons from NADH enter the electron transport system by being transferred to NADH dehydrogenase, all three sites actively pump H^+, and three ATP molecules are made (see Figure 22.7). $FADH_2$ is a less "powerful" electron donor. It transfers its electrons to an electron carrier that follows NADH

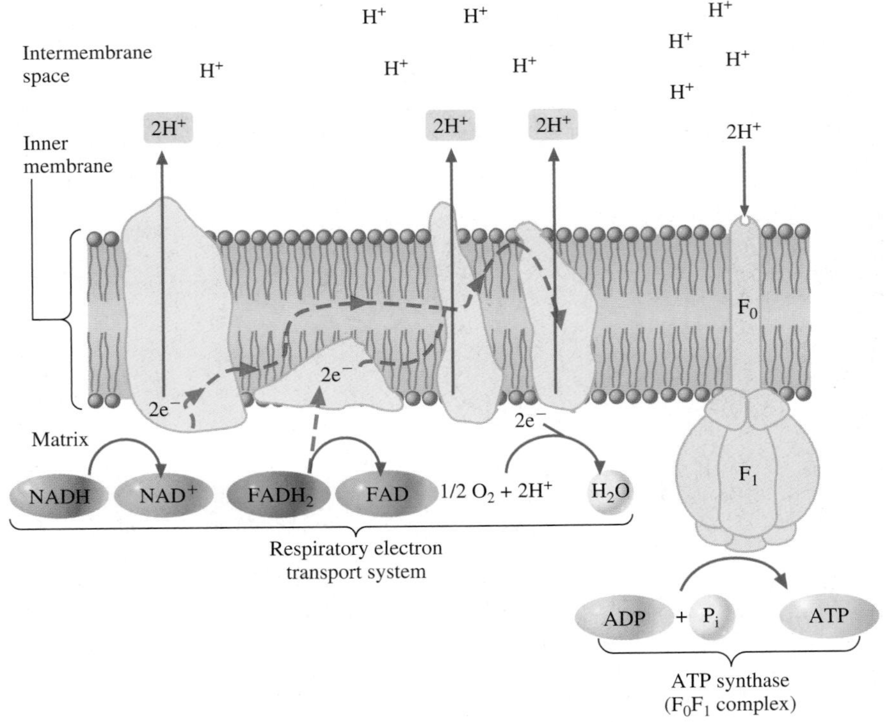

Figure 22.7 Electrons flow from NADH to molecular oxygen through a series of electron carriers embedded in the inner mitochondrial membrane. Protons are pumped from the mitochondrial matrix space into the intermembrane space. This results in a hydrogen ion reservoir in the intermembrane space. As protons pass through the channel in ATP synthase, their energy is used to phosphorylate ADP and produce ATP.

dehydrogenase. As a result, when $FADH_2$ is oxidized, only the second and third sites pump H^+, and only two ATP molecules are made.

The last component needed for oxidative phosphorylation is a multiprotein complex called **ATP synthase,** also called the **F_0F_1 complex** (see Figure 22.7). The F_0 portion of the molecule is a channel through which H^+ pass. It spans the inner mitochondrial membrane, as shown in Figure 22.7. The F_1 part of the molecule is an enzyme that catalyzes the phosphorylation of ADP to produce ATP.

ATP Synthase and the Production of ATP

How does all this complicated machinery actually function? NADH carries electrons, originally from glucose, to the first carrier of the electron transport system, NADH dehydrogenase (see Figure 22.7). There, NADH is oxidized to NAD^+, which returns to the site of the citric acid cycle to be reduced again. As the dashed red line shows, the pair of electrons is passed to the next electron carrier, and H^+ are pumped to the intermembrane compartment. The electrons are passed sequentially through the electron transport system, and at two additional sites, H^+ from the matrix are pumped into the intermembrane compartment. With each transfer the electrons lose some of their potential energy. It is this energy that is used to transport H^+ across the inner mitochondrial membrane and into the H^+ reservoir. As mentioned above, $FADH_2$ donates its electrons to a carrier of lower energy and fewer H^+ are pumped into the reservoir.

Finally, the electrons arrive at the last carrier. They now have too little energy to accomplish any more work, but they *must* be donated to some final electron acceptor so that the electron transport system can continue to function. In aerobic organisms the **terminal electron acceptor** is molecular oxygen, O_2, and the product is water.

The importance of keeping the electron transport system functioning becomes obvious when we consider what occurs in cyanide poisoning. Cyanide binds to the heme group iron of cytochrome oxidase, one of the electron carriers in the electron transport system, instantly stopping electron transfers and causing death within minutes!

As the electron transport system continues to function, a high concentration of protons builds up in the intermembrane space. This creates an H^+ gradient across the inner mitochondrial membrane. Such a gradient is an enormous energy source, like water stored behind a dam. The mitochondria make use of the potential energy of the gradient to synthesize ATP energy.

ATP synthase harvests the energy of this gradient by making ATP. H^+ pass through the F_0 channel back into the matrix. This causes F_1 to become an active enzyme that catalyzes the phosphorylation of ADP to produce ATP. In this way the energy of the H^+ reservoir is harvested to make ATP.

Question 22.9 Write a balanced chemical equation for the reduction of NAD^+.

Question 22.10 Write a balanced chemical equation for the reduction of FAD.

Summary of the Energy Yield

Now that we have studied the reactions of the citric acid cycle and oxidative phosphorylation, we can calculate the total energy yield, in ATP, that is produced from a single glucose molecule.

In some tissues of the body there is a more efficient shuttle system that results in the production of three ATP per cytoplasmic NADH. This system is described online.

One turn of the citric acid cycle results in the production of two CO_2 molecules, three NADH molecules, one $FADH_2$ molecule, and one ATP molecule. Oxidative phosphorylation yields three ATP molecules per NADH molecule and two ATP molecules per $FADH_2$ molecule. The only exception to these energy yields is the NADH produced in the cytoplasm during glycolysis. Oxidative phosphorylation yields only two ATP molecules per cytoplasmic NADH molecule. The reason for this is that energy must be expended to shuttle electrons from NADH in the cytoplasm to $FADH_2$ in the mitochondrion.

A HUMAN PERSPECTIVE

Brown Fat: The Fat That Makes You Thin?

Humans have two types of fat, or adipose, tissue. *White fat* is distributed throughout the body and is composed of aggregations of cells having membranous vacuoles containing stored triglycerides. The size and number of these storage vacuoles determine whether a person is overweight or not. The other type of fat is *brown fat.* Brown fat is a specialized tissue for heat production, called *nonshivering thermogenesis.* As the name suggests, this is a means of generating heat in the absence of the shivering response. The cells of brown fat look nothing like those of white fat. They do contain small fat vacuoles; however, the distinguishing feature of brown fat is the huge number of mitochondria within the cytoplasm. In addition, brown fat tissue contains a great many blood vessels. These provide oxygen for the thermogenic metabolic reactions.

Brown fat is most pronounced in newborns, cold-adapted mammals, and hibernators. One major difficulty faced by a newborn is temperature regulation. The baby leaves an environment in which he or she was bathed in fluid of a constant 37°C, body temperature. Suddenly, the child is thrust into a world that is much colder and in which he or she must generate his or her own warmth internally. By having a good reserve of active brown fat to generate that heat, the newborn is protected against cold shock at the time of birth. However, this thermogenesis literally burns up most of the brown fat tissue, and adults typically have so little brown fat that it can be found only by using a special technique called *thermography,* which detects temperature differences throughout a body. However, in some individuals, brown fat is very highly developed. For instance, the Korean diving women who spend 6–7 h every day diving for pearls in cold water have a massive amount of brown fat to warm them by nonshivering thermogenesis. Thus, development of brown fat is a mechanism of cold adaptation.

When it was noticed that such cold-adapted individuals were seldom overweight, a correlation was made between the amount of brown fat in the body and the tendency to become overweight. Studies done with rats suggest that, to some degree, fatness is genetically determined. In other words, you are as lean as your genes allow you to be. In these studies, cold-adapted and non-cold-adapted rats were fed cafeteria food—as much as they wanted—and their weight gain was monitored. In every case the cold-adapted rats, with their greater quantity of brown fat, gained significantly less weight than their non-cold-adapted counterparts, despite the fact that they ate as much as the non-cold-adapted rats. This and other studies led researchers to conclude that brown fat burns excess fat in a highly caloric diet.

How does brown fat generate heat and burn excess calories? For the answer we must turn to the mitochondrion. In addition to the ATP synthase and the electron transport system proteins that are found in all mitochondria, there is a protein in the inner mitochondrial membrane of brown fat tissue called *thermogenin.* This protein has a channel in the center through which the protons (H^+) of the intermembrane space could pass back into the mitochondrial matrix. Under normal conditions, this channel is plugged by a GDP molecule so that it remains closed and the proton gradient can continue to drive ATP synthesis by oxidative phosphorylation.

When brown fat is "turned on," by cold exposure or in response to certain hormones, there is an immediate increase in the rate of glycolysis and β-oxidation of the stored fat (Chapter 23). These reactions produce acetyl CoA, which then fuels the citric acid cycle. The citric acid cycle, of course, produces NADH and $FADH_2$, which carry electrons to the electron transport system. Finally, the electron transport system pumps protons into the intermembrane space. Under usual conditions, the energy of the proton gradient would be used to synthesize ATP. However, when brown fat is stimulated, the GDP that had plugged the pore in thermogenin is lost. Now protons pass freely back into the matrix space, and the proton gradient is dissipated. The energy of the gradient, no longer useful for generating ATP, is released as *heat,* the heat that warms and protects newborns and cold-adapted individuals.

Brown fat is just one of the body's many systems for maintaining a constant internal environment regardless of the conditions in the external environment. Such mechanisms, called *homeostatic mechanisms,* are absolutely essential to allow the body to adapt to and survive in an ever-changing environment.

For Further Understanding

- Hibernators eat a great deal in preparation for their long winter nap. Explain their lifestyle in terms of energy requirements and heat production.
- Explain why cold-adapted mammals can eat a high caloric diet and remain thin.

Knowing this information and keeping in mind that two turns of the citric acid cycle are required, we can sum up the total energy yield from the complete oxidation of one glucose molecule.

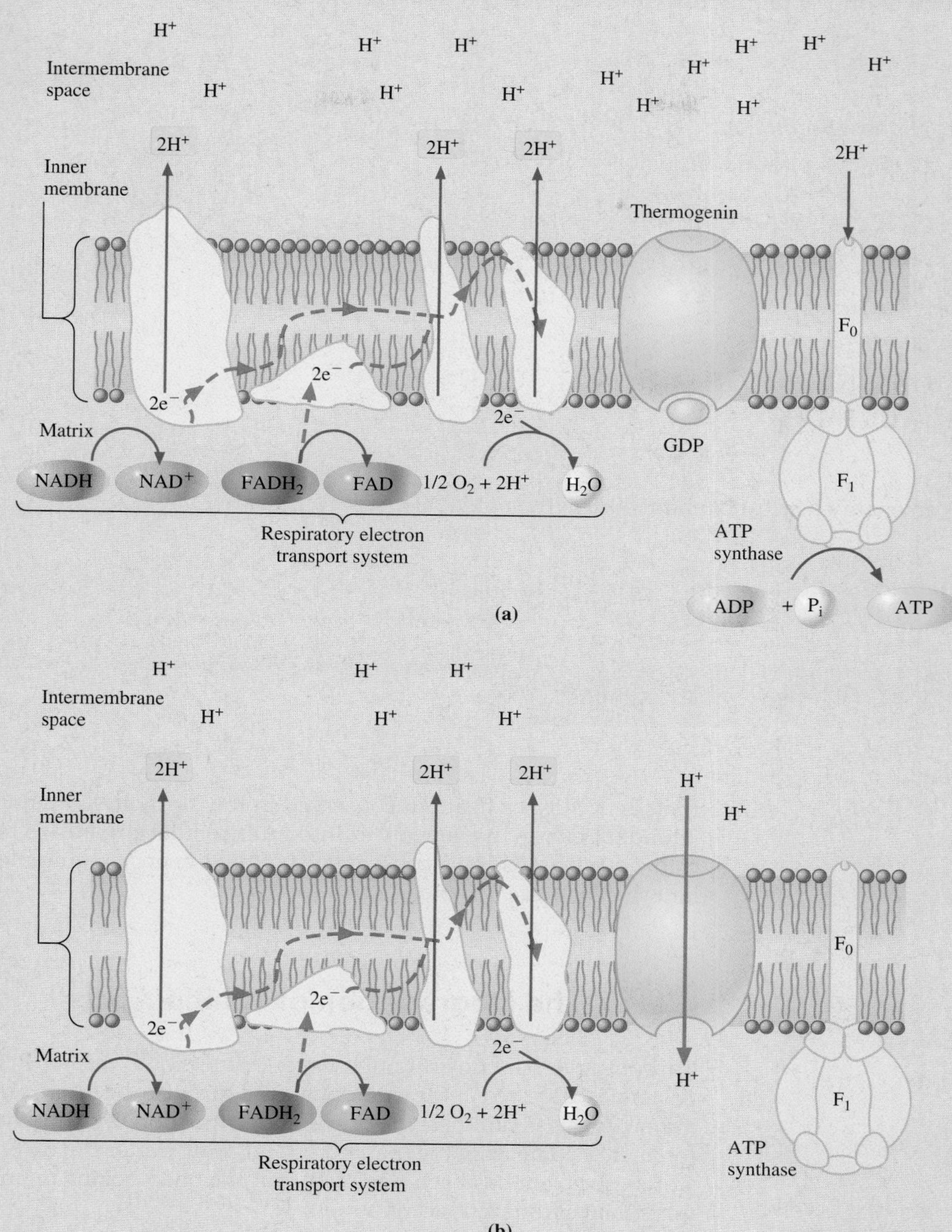

(a) The inner membrane of brown fat mitochondria contains thermogenin. In the normal state, the pore in the center of thermogenin is plugged by a GDP molecule. (b) When brown fat is activated for thermogenesis, the GDP molecule is removed from the pore, and the protons from the H^+ reservoir are free to flow back into the matrix of the mitochondrion. As the gradient dissipates, heat energy is released.

Aerobic metabolism is very much more efficient than anaerobic metabolism. The abundant energy harvested by aerobic metabolism has had enormous consequences for the biological world. Much of the energy released by the oxidation of

EXAMPLE 22.1 **Determining the Yield of ATP from Aerobic Respiration**

Calculate the number of ATP produced by the complete oxidation of one molecule of glucose.

Solution

Glycolysis:

Substrate-level phosphorylation	2 ATP
2 NADH × 2 ATP/cytoplasmic NADH	4 ATP

Conversion of 2 pyruvate molecules to 2 acetyl CoA molecules:

2 NADH × 3 ATP/NADH	6 ATP

Citric acid cycle (two turns):

2 GTP × 1 ATP/GTP	2 ATP
6 NADH × 3 ATP/NADH	18 ATP
2 $FADH_2$ × 2 ATP/$FADH_2$	4 ATP
	36 ATP

This represents an energy harvest of about 40% of the potential energy of glucose.

Practice Problem 22.1

Calculate the number of ATP produced by the complete oxidation of pyruvate.

► For Further Practice: **Questions 22.41, 22.42, and 22.44.**

fuels is not lost as heat but conserved in the form of ATP. Organisms that possess abundant energy have evolved into multicellular organisms and developed specialized functions. As a consequence of their energy requirements, all multicellular organisms are aerobic.

22.7 The Degradation of Amino Acids

LEARNING GOAL

7 Describe the conversion of amino acids to molecules that can enter the citric acid cycle.

Carbohydrates are not our only source of energy. As we saw in Chapter 21, dietary protein is digested to amino acids that can also be used as an energy source, although this is not their major metabolic function. Most of the amino acids used for energy come from the diet. In fact, it is only under starvation conditions, when stored glycogen has been depleted, that the body begins to burn its own protein, for instance from muscle, as a fuel.

The fate of the mixture of amino acids provided by digestion of protein depends upon a balance between the need for amino acids for biosynthesis and the need for cellular energy. Only those amino acids that are not needed for protein synthesis are eventually converted into citric acid cycle intermediates and used as fuel.

The degradation of amino acids occurs primarily in the liver and takes place in two stages. The first stage is the removal of the α-amino group, and the second is the degradation of the carbon skeleton. In land mammals the amino group generally ends up in urea, which is excreted in the urine. The carbon skeletons can be converted into a variety of compounds, including citric acid cycle intermediates, pyruvate, acetyl CoA, or acetoacetyl CoA. The degradation of the carbon

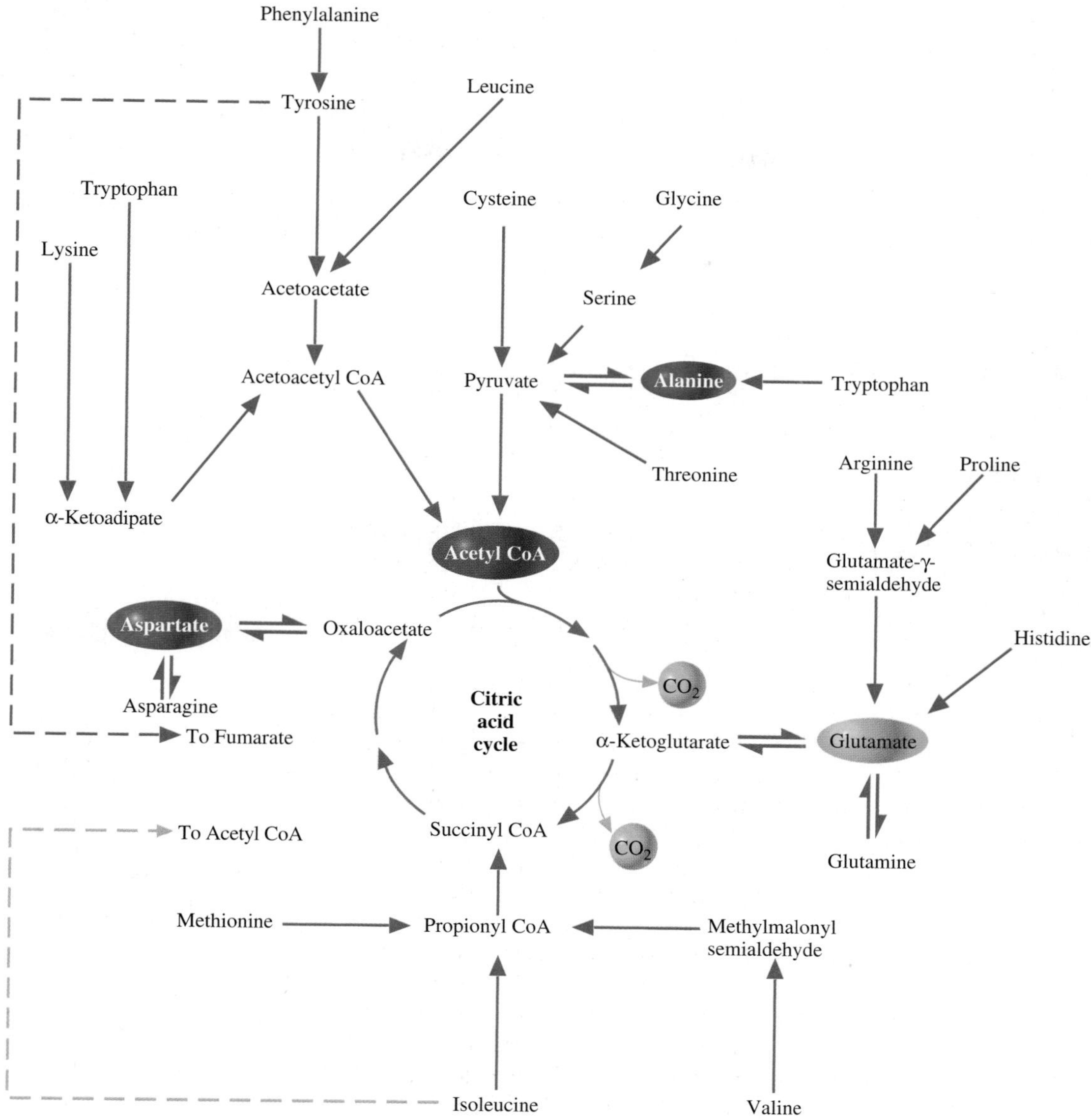

Figure 22.8 The carbon skeletons of amino acids can be converted to citric acid cycle intermediates and completely oxidized to produce ATP energy.

skeletons is summarized in Figure 22.8. Deamination reactions and the fate of the carbon skeletons of amino acids are the focus of this section.

Removal of α-Amino Groups: Transamination

The first stage of amino acid degradation, the removal of the α-amino group, is usually accomplished by a **transamination** reaction. **Transaminases** catalyze the transfer of the α-amino group from an α-amino acid to an α-keto acid:

$$\underset{\text{Donor amino acid}}{\mathrm{H{-}\overset{\overset{+}{N}H_3}{\underset{R^1}{C}}{-}COO^-}} + \underset{\text{Acceptor keto acid}}{\mathrm{\overset{O}{\underset{R^2}{\overset{\|}{C}}}{-}COO^-}} \xrightleftharpoons{\text{Transaminase}} \underset{\text{α-Keto acid of amino acid}}{\mathrm{\overset{O}{\underset{R^1}{\overset{\|}{C}}}{-}COO^-}} + \underset{\text{New amino acid}}{\mathrm{H{-}\overset{\overset{+}{N}H_3}{\underset{R^2}{C}}{-}COO^-}}$$

Pyridoxine (vitamin B_6)

Pyridoxal phosphate

Figure 22.9 The structure of pyridoxal phosphate, the coenzyme required for all transamination reactions, and pyridoxine, vitamin B_6, the vitamin from which it is derived.

The α-amino group of a great many amino acids is transferred to α-ketoglutarate to produce the amino acid glutamate and a new keto acid. This glutamate family of transaminases is especially important because the α-keto acid corresponding to glutamate is α-ketoglutarate, a citric acid cycle intermediate. The glutamate transaminases thus provide a direct link between amino acid degradation and the citric acid cycle.

Aspartate transaminase catalyzes the transfer of the α-amino group of aspartate to α-ketoglutarate, producing oxaloacetate and glutamate:

$$\underset{\text{Aspartate}}{H{-}C(\overset{+}{N}H_3){-}COO^-\,/\,H{-}C{-}H\,/\,COO^-} + \underset{\alpha\text{-Ketoglutarate}}{C(=O){-}COO^-\,/\,H{-}C{-}H\,/\,H{-}C{-}H\,/\,COO^-} \rightleftharpoons \underset{\text{Oxaloacetate}}{C(=O){-}COO^-\,/\,H{-}C{-}H\,/\,COO^-} + \underset{\text{Glutamate}}{H{-}C(\overset{+}{N}H_3){-}COO^-\,/\,H{-}C{-}H\,/\,H{-}C{-}H\,/\,COO^-}$$

Another important transaminase in mammalian tissues is *alanine transaminase,* which catalyzes the transfer of the α-amino group of alanine to α-ketoglutarate and produces pyruvate and glutamate:

$$\underset{\text{Alanine}}{H{-}C(\overset{+}{N}H_3){-}COO^-\,/\,H{-}C{-}H\,/\,H} + \underset{\alpha\text{-Ketoglutarate}}{C(=O){-}COO^-\,/\,H{-}C{-}H\,/\,H{-}C{-}H\,/\,COO^-} \rightleftharpoons \underset{\text{Pyruvate}}{C(=O){-}COO^-\,/\,H{-}C{-}H\,/\,H} + \underset{\text{Glutamate}}{H{-}C(\overset{+}{N}H_3){-}COO^-\,/\,H{-}C{-}H\,/\,H{-}C{-}H\,/\,COO^-}$$

For more information on vitamins and the coenzymes that are made from them, look online.

All of the more than fifty transaminases that have been discovered require the coenzyme **pyridoxal phosphate.** This coenzyme is derived from vitamin B_6 (pyridoxine, Figure 22.9).

The transamination reactions shown above appear to be a simple transfer, but in reality, the reaction is much more complex. The transaminase binds the amino acid (aspartate in Figure 22.10a) in its active site. Then the α-amino group of aspartate is transferred to pyridoxal phosphate, producing pyridoxamine phosphate and oxaloacetate (Figure 22.10b). The amino group is then transferred to an α-keto acid, in this case, α-ketoglutarate (Figure 22.10c), to produce the amino acid glutamate (Figure 22.10d). Next we will examine the fate of the amino group that has been transferred to α-ketoglutarate to produce glutamate.

Question 22.11 What is the role of pyridoxal phosphate in transamination reactions?

Question 22.12 What is the function of a transaminase?

Removal of α-Amino Groups: Oxidative Deamination

In the next stage of amino acid degradation, ammonium ion is liberated from the glutamate formed by the transaminase. This breakdown of glutamate, catalyzed by the enzyme *glutamate dehydrogenase,* occurs as follows:

$$\underset{\text{Glutamate}}{\begin{array}{c} \overset{+}{N}H_3 \\ | \\ H-C-COO^- \\ | \\ H-C-H \\ | \\ H-C-H \\ | \\ COO^- \end{array}} + NAD^+ + H_2O \rightleftharpoons NH_4^+ + \underset{\alpha\text{-Ketoglutarate}}{\begin{array}{c} O \\ \| \\ C-COO^- \\ | \\ H-C-H \\ | \\ H-C-H \\ | \\ COO^- \end{array}} + NADH$$

This is an example of an **oxidative deamination,** an oxidation-reduction process in which NAD^+ is reduced to NADH and the amino acid is deaminated (the amino group is removed). A summary of the deamination reactions described is shown in Figure 22.11.

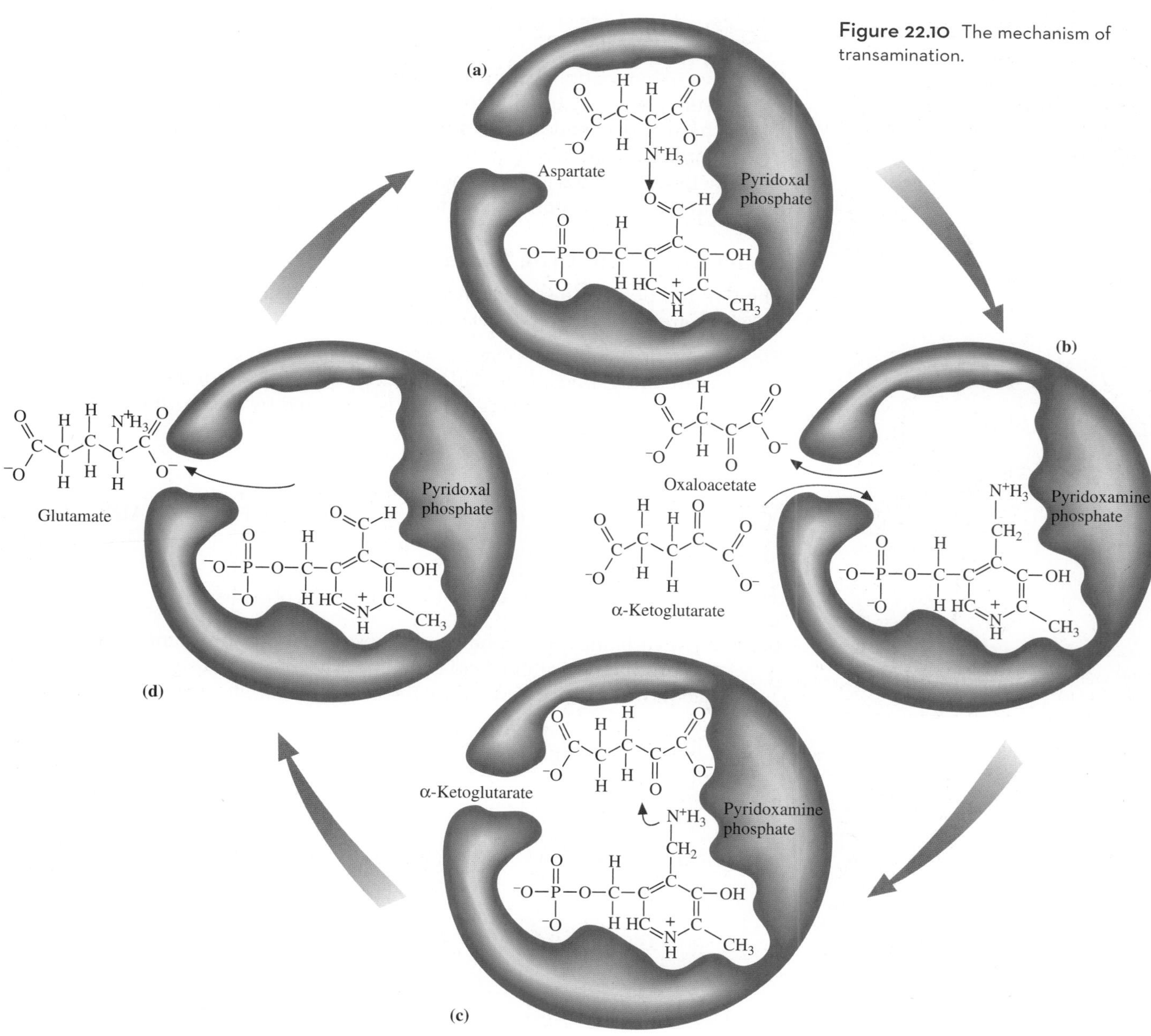

Figure 22.10 The mechanism of transamination.

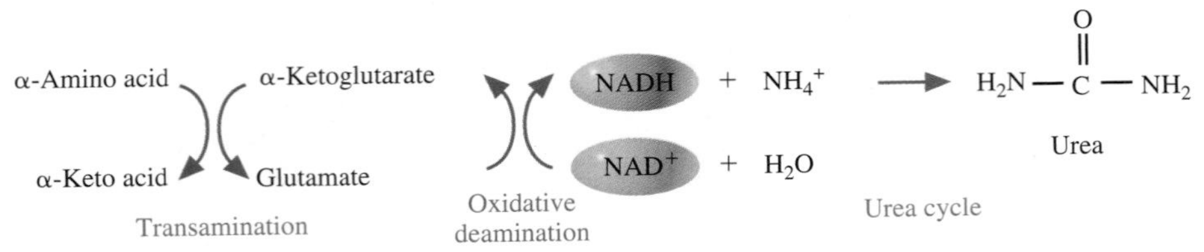

Figure 22.11 Summary of the deamination of an α-amino acid and the fate of the ammonium ion (NH_4^+).

The Fate of Amino Acid Carbon Skeletons

The carbon skeletons produced by these and other deamination reactions enter glycolysis or the citric acid cycle at many steps. For instance, we have seen that transamination converts aspartate to oxaloacetate and alanine to pyruvate. The positions at which the carbon skeletons of various amino acids enter the energy-harvesting pathways are summarized in Figure 22.8.

22.8 The Urea Cycle

LEARNING GOAL

8 Explain the importance of the urea cycle and describe its essential steps.

Oxidative deamination produces large amounts of ammonium ion. Because ammonium ions are extremely toxic, they must be removed from the body, regardless of the energy expenditure required. In humans, they are detoxified in the liver by converting the ammonium ions into urea. This pathway, called the **urea cycle,** is the method by which toxic ammonium ions are kept out of the blood. The excess ammonium ions incorporated in urea are excreted in the urine (Figure 22.12).

Reactions of the Urea Cycle

The five reactions of the urea cycle are shown in Figure 22.12, and details of the reactions are summarized as follows.

Step 1. The first step of the cycle is a reaction in which CO_2 and NH_4^+ form carbamoyl phosphate. This reaction, which also requires ATP and H_2O, occurs in the mitochondria and is catalyzed by the enzyme *carbamoyl phosphate synthase.*

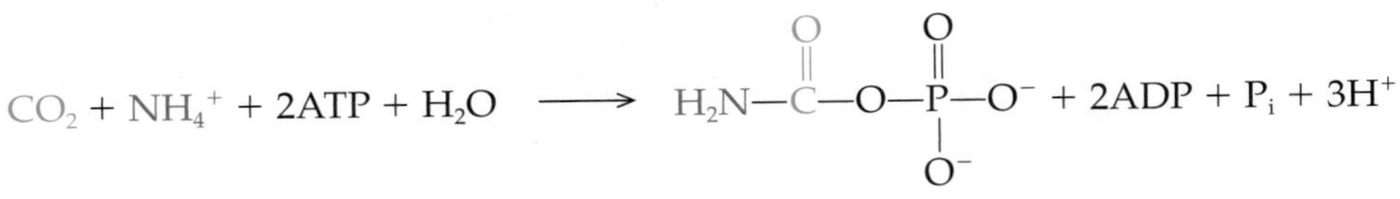

$$CO_2 + NH_4^+ + 2ATP + H_2O \longrightarrow H_2N{-}\overset{\overset{\large O}{\|}}{C}{-}O{-}\overset{\overset{\large O}{\|}}{\underset{\underset{\large O^-}{|}}{P}}{-}O^- + 2ADP + P_i + 3H^+$$

Carbamoyl phosphate

Step 2. The carbamoyl phosphate now condenses with the amino acid ornithine to produce the amino acid citrulline. This reaction also occurs in the mitochondria and is catalyzed by the enzyme *ornithine transcarbamoylase.*

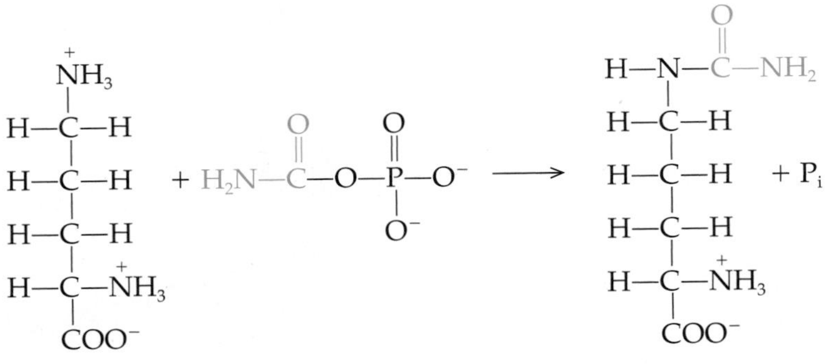

The urea cycle involves several unusual amino acids that are not found in polypeptides.

$$\begin{array}{c} \overset{+}{N}H_3 \\ | \\ H{-}C{-}H \\ | \\ H{-}C{-}H \\ | \\ H{-}C{-}H \\ | \\ H{-}C{-}\overset{+}{N}H_3 \\ | \\ COO^- \end{array} + H_2N{-}\overset{\overset{\large O}{\|}}{C}{-}O{-}\overset{\overset{\large O}{\|}}{\underset{\underset{\large O^-}{|}}{P}}{-}O^- \longrightarrow \begin{array}{c} H{-}N{-}\overset{\overset{\large O}{\|}}{C}{-}NH_2 \\ | \\ H{-}C{-}H \\ | \\ H{-}C{-}H \\ | \\ H{-}C{-}H \\ | \\ H{-}C{-}\overset{+}{N}H_3 \\ | \\ COO^- \end{array} + P_i$$

Ornithine — Carbamoyl phosphate — Citrulline

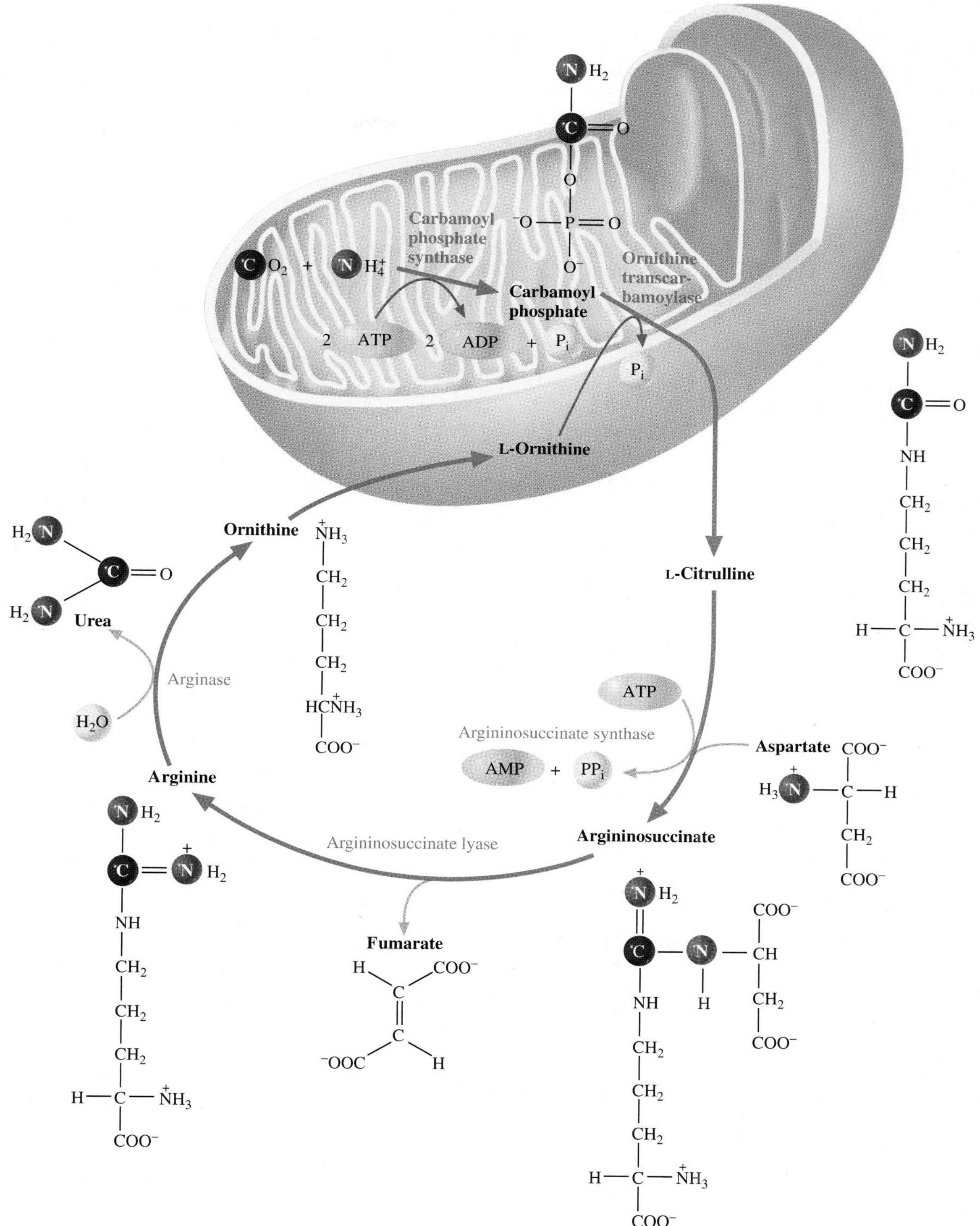

Figure 22.12 The urea cycle converts ammonium ions into urea, which is less toxic. The intracellular locations of the reactions are indicated. Citrulline, formed in the reaction between ornithine and carbamoyl phosphate, is transported out of the mitochondrion and into the cytoplasm. Ornithine, a substrate for the formation of citrulline, is transported from the cytoplasm into the mitochondrion.

The abbreviation PP_i represents the pyrophosphate group, which consists of two phosphate groups joined by a phosphoanhydride bond:

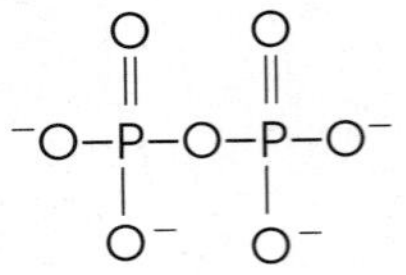

$$^{-}O-P(=O)(O^{-})-O-P(=O)(O^{-})-O^{-}$$

Step 3. Citrulline is transported into the cytoplasm and now condenses with aspartate to produce argininosuccinate. This reaction, which requires energy released by the hydrolysis of ATP, is catalyzed by the enzyme *argininosuccinate synthase.*

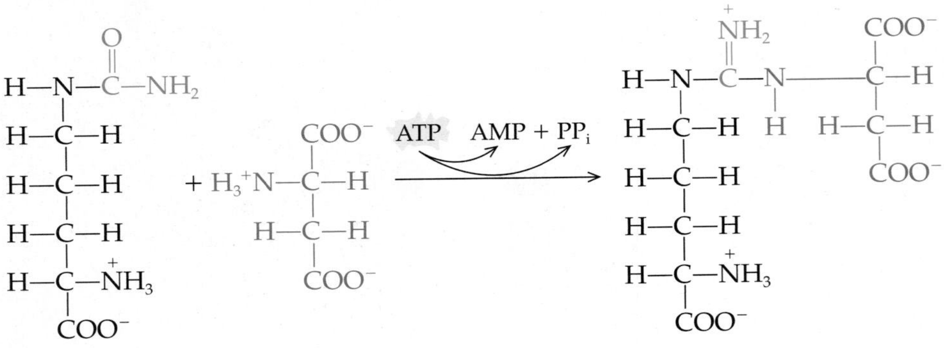

$$\text{Citrulline} + \text{Aspartate} \xrightarrow{\text{ATP} \;\to\; \text{AMP} + PP_i} \text{Argininosuccinate}$$

Citrulline Aspartate Argininosuccinate

Step 4. Now the argininosuccinate is cleaved to produce the amino acid arginine and the citric acid cycle intermediate fumarate. This reaction is catalyzed by the enzyme *argininosuccinate lyase.*

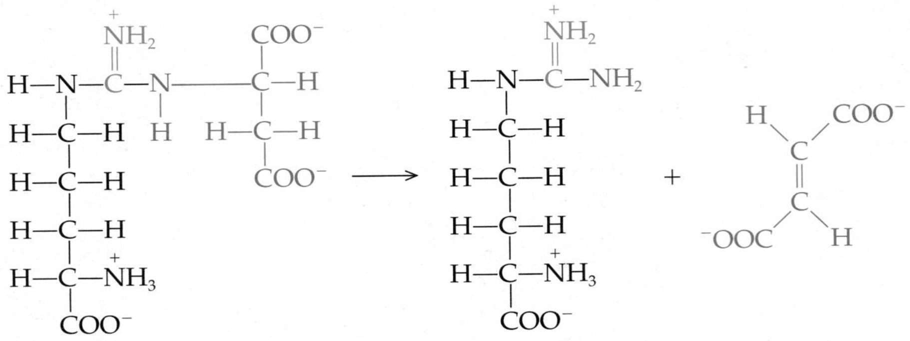

$$\text{Argininosuccinate} \longrightarrow \text{Arginine} + \text{Fumarate}$$

Argininosuccinate Arginine Fumarate

Step 5. Finally, arginine is hydrolyzed to generate urea, the product of the reaction to be excreted, and ornithine, the original reactant in the cycle. *Arginase* is the enzyme that catalyzes this reaction.

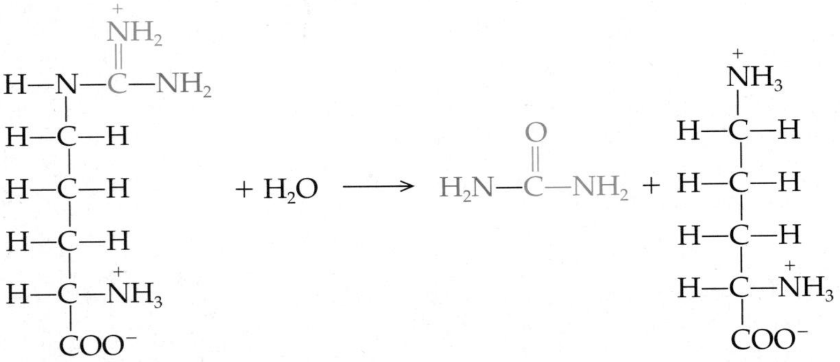

$$\text{Arginine} + H_2O \longrightarrow H_2N-C(=O)-NH_2 + \text{Ornithine}$$

Arginine Water Urea Ornithine

Note that one of the amino groups in urea is derived from the ammonium ion and the second is derived from the amino acid aspartate.

A MEDICAL PERSPECTIVE

Pyruvate Carboxylase Deficiency

Pyruvate carboxylase is the enzyme that converts pyruvate to oxaloacetate.

$$\text{Pyruvate} + CO_2 + \text{ATP} + H_2O \longrightarrow \text{Oxaloacetate} + \text{ADP} + 2H^+$$

This reaction is important because it provides oxaloacetate for the citric acid cycle when the supplies have run low because of the demands of biosynthesis. It is also the enzyme that catalyzes the first step in gluconeogenesis, the pathway that provides the body with needed glucose in times of starvation or periods of exercise that deplete glycogen stores. But somehow these descriptions don't fill us with a sense of the importance of this enzyme and its jobs. It is not until we investigate a case study of a child born with pyruvate carboxylase deficiency that we see the full impact of this enzyme.

Pyruvate carboxylase deficiency is found in about 1 in 250,000 births; however, there is an increased incidence in native North American Indians who speak the Algonquin dialect and in the French. There are two types of genetic disorders that have been described. In the neonatal form of the disease, there is a complete absence of the enzyme. Symptoms are apparent at birth and the child is born with brain abnormalities. In the infantile form, the patient develops symptoms early in infancy. Again, it is neurological symptoms that draw attention to the condition. The infants do not develop mental or psychomotor skills. They may develop seizures and/or respiratory depression. In both cases, it is the brain that suffers the greatest damage. In fact, this is the case in most of the disorders that reduce energy metabolism because the brain has such high energy requirements.

Biochemically, patients exhibit quite a variety of symptoms. They show acidosis (low blood pH) due to accumulations of lactate and extremely high pyruvate concentrations in the blood. Blood levels of alanine are also high and large doses of alanine do not stimulate gluconeogenesis. Furthermore, a patient's cells accumulate lipid.

We can understand each of these symptoms by considering the pathways affected by the absence of this single enzyme. Lactic acidosis results from the fact that the body must rely on glycolysis and lactate fermentation for most of its energy needs. Alanine levels are high because it isn't being transaminated to pyruvate efficiently, because pyruvate levels are so high. In addition, alanine can't be converted to glucose by gluconeogenesis. Although the excess alanine is taken up by the liver and converted to pyruvate, the pyruvate can't be converted to glucose. Lipids accumulate because a great deal of pyruvate is converted to acetyl CoA. However, the acetyl CoA is not used to produce citrate as a result of the absence of oxaloacetate. So, the acetyl CoA is thus used to synthesize fatty acids, which are stored as triglycerides.

Dietary intervention has been tried. One such regimen is to supplement with aspartic acid and glutamic acid. The theory behind this treatment is as complex as the many symptoms of the disorder. Both amino acids can be aminated (amino groups added) in non-nervous tissue. This produces asparagine and glutamine, both of which are able to cross the blood-brain barrier. Glutamine is deaminated to glutamate, which is then transaminated to α-ketoglutarate, indirectly replenishing oxaloacetate. Asparagine can be deaminated to aspartate, which can be converted to oxaloacetate. This serves as a second supply of oxaloacetate. To date, these attempts at dietary intervention have not proved successful. Perhaps in time research will provide the tools for enzyme replacement therapy or gene therapy that could alleviate the symptoms.

For Further Understanding

- Write an equation showing the reaction catalyzed by pyruvate carboxylase using structural formulas for pyruvate and oxaloacetate.
- Supplementing the diet with asparagine and glutamine was tried as a treatment for pyruvate carboxylase deficiency. Write equations showing the reactions that convert these amino acids into citric acid cycle intermediates.

There are genetically transmitted diseases that result from a deficiency of one of the enzymes of the urea cycle. The importance of the urea cycle is apparent when we consider the terrible symptoms suffered by afflicted individuals. A deficiency of urea cycle enzymes causes an elevation of the concentration of NH_4^+, a condition known as **hyperammonemia.** If there is a complete deficiency of one of the enzymes of the urea cycle, the result is death in early infancy. If there is a partial deficiency of one of the enzymes of the urea cycle, the result may be mental challenge, convulsions, and vomiting. In these milder forms of hyperammonemia, a low-protein diet leads to a lower concentration of NH_4^+ in blood and less severe clinical symptoms.

LEARNING GOAL

9 Discuss the cause and effect of hyperammonemia.

Question 22.13 What is the purpose of the urea cycle?

Question 22.14 Where do the reactions of the urea cycle occur?

22.9 Overview of Anabolism: The Citric Acid Cycle as a Source of Biosynthetic Intermediates

LEARNING GOAL

10 Summarize the role of the citric acid cycle in catabolism and anabolism.

So far, we have talked about the citric acid cycle only as an energy-harvesting mechanism. We have seen that dietary carbohydrates and amino acids enter the pathway at various stages and are oxidized to generate NADH and $FADH_2$, which, by means of oxidative phosphorylation, are used to make ATP.

However, the role of the citric acid cycle in cellular metabolism involves more than just **catabolism.** It plays a key role in **anabolism,** or biosynthesis, as well. Figure 22.13 shows the central role of glycolysis and the citric acid cycle as energy-harvesting reactions, as well as their role as a source of biosynthetic precursors.

As you may already suspect from the fact that amino acids can be converted into citric acid cycle intermediates, these same citric acid cycle intermediates can also be used as starting materials for the synthesis of amino acids. Oxaloacetate provides the carbon skeleton for the one-step synthesis of the amino acid aspartate by the transamination reaction:

$$\text{oxaloacetate} + \text{glutamate} \rightleftharpoons \text{aspartate} + \alpha\text{-ketoglutarate}$$

Aside from providing aspartate for protein synthesis, this reaction provides aspartate for the urea cycle.

Asparagine is made from aspartate by the amination reaction

$$\text{aspartate} + NH_4^+ + \text{ATP} \longrightarrow \text{asparagine} + \text{AMP} + PP_i + H^+$$

The nine amino acids not shown in Figure 22.13 (histidine, isoleucine, leucine, lysine, methionine, phenylalanine, threonine, tryptophan, and valine) are called the essential amino acids (Section 18.11) because they cannot be synthesized by humans. Arginine is an essential amino acid for infants and adults under physical stress.

α-Ketoglutarate serves as the starting carbon chain for the family of amino acids including glutamate, glutamine, proline, and arginine. Glutamate is especially important because it serves as the donor of the α-amino group of almost all other amino acids. It is synthesized from NH_4^+ and α-ketoglutarate in a reaction mediated by glutamate dehydrogenase. This is the reverse of the reaction shown in Figure 22.11 and previously described. In this case the coenzyme that serves as the reducing agent is NADPH.

$$NH_4^+ + \alpha\text{-ketoglutarate} + \text{NADPH} \rightleftharpoons \text{L-glutamate} + \text{NADP}^+ + H_2O$$

Glutamine, proline, and arginine are synthesized from glutamate.

Actually, in humans tyrosine is made from the essential amino acid phenylalanine.

Examination of Figure 22.13 reveals that serine, glycine, and cysteine are synthesized from 3-phosphoglycerate; alanine is synthesized from pyruvate; and tyrosine is produced from phosphoenolpyruvate and the four-carbon sugar erythrose-4-phosphate, which, in turn, is synthesized from glucose-6-phosphate in the pentose phosphate pathway. In addition to the amino acid precursors, glycolysis and the citric acid cycle also provide precursors for lipids and the nitrogenous bases that are required to make DNA, the molecule that carries the genetic information. They also generate precursors for heme, the prosthetic group that is required for hemoglobin, myoglobin, and the cytochromes.

Clearly, the reactions of glycolysis and the citric acid cycle are central to both anabolic and catabolic cellular activities. Metabolic pathways that function in both anabolism and catabolism are called **amphibolic pathways.** Consider for a moment the difficulties that the dual nature of these pathways could present to the cell. When the cell is actively growing, there is a great demand for biosynthetic precursors to build new cell structures. A close look at Figure 22.13 shows us that periods of active cell growth and biosynthesis may deplete the supply of citric acid cycle intermediates. The problem is, the processes of growth and biosynthesis also require a great deal of ATP!

The solution to this problem is to have an alternative pathway for oxaloacetate synthesis that can produce enough oxaloacetate to supply the anabolic and catabolic requirements of the cell. Although bacteria and plants have several mechanisms, the only way that mammalian cells can produce more oxaloacetate is by the

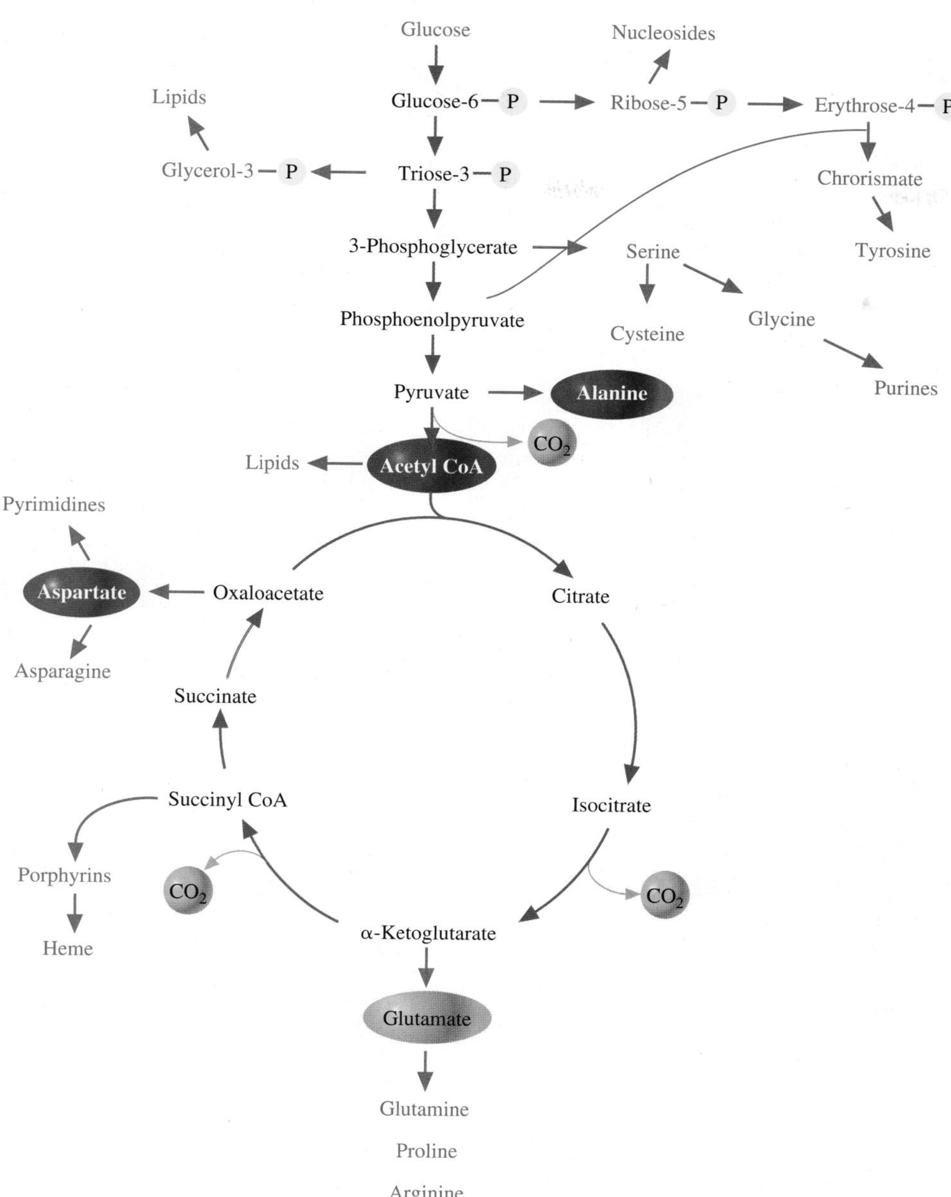

Figure 22.13 Glycolysis, the pentose phosphate pathway, and the citric acid cycle also provide a variety of precursors for the biosynthesis of amino acids, nitrogenous bases, and porphyrins.

carboxylation of pyruvate, a reaction that is also important in gluconeogenesis. This reaction is

Carboxylation of pyruvate during gluconeogenesis is discussed in Section 21.6.

$$\text{pyruvate} + CO_2 + \text{ATP} \longrightarrow \text{oxaloacetate} + \text{ADP} + P_i$$

The enzyme that catalyzes this reaction is *pyruvate carboxylase.* It is a conjugated protein having as its covalently linked prosthetic group the vitamin *biotin.* This enzyme is "turned on" by high levels of acetyl CoA, a signal that the cell requires high levels of the citric acid cycle intermediates, particularly oxaloacetate, the beginning substrate.

See also A Medical Perspective: Pyruvate Carboxylase Deficiency earlier in this chapter.

The reaction catalyzed by pyruvate carboxylase is called an **anaplerotic reaction.** The term *anaplerotic* means "to fill up." Indeed, this critical enzyme must constantly replenish the oxaloacetate and thus indirectly all the citric acid cycle intermediates that are withdrawn as biosynthetic precursors for the reactions summarized in Figure 22.13.

Question 22.15 Explain how the citric acid cycle serves as an amphibolic pathway.

Question 22.16 What is the function of an anaplerotic reaction?

CHAPTER MAP

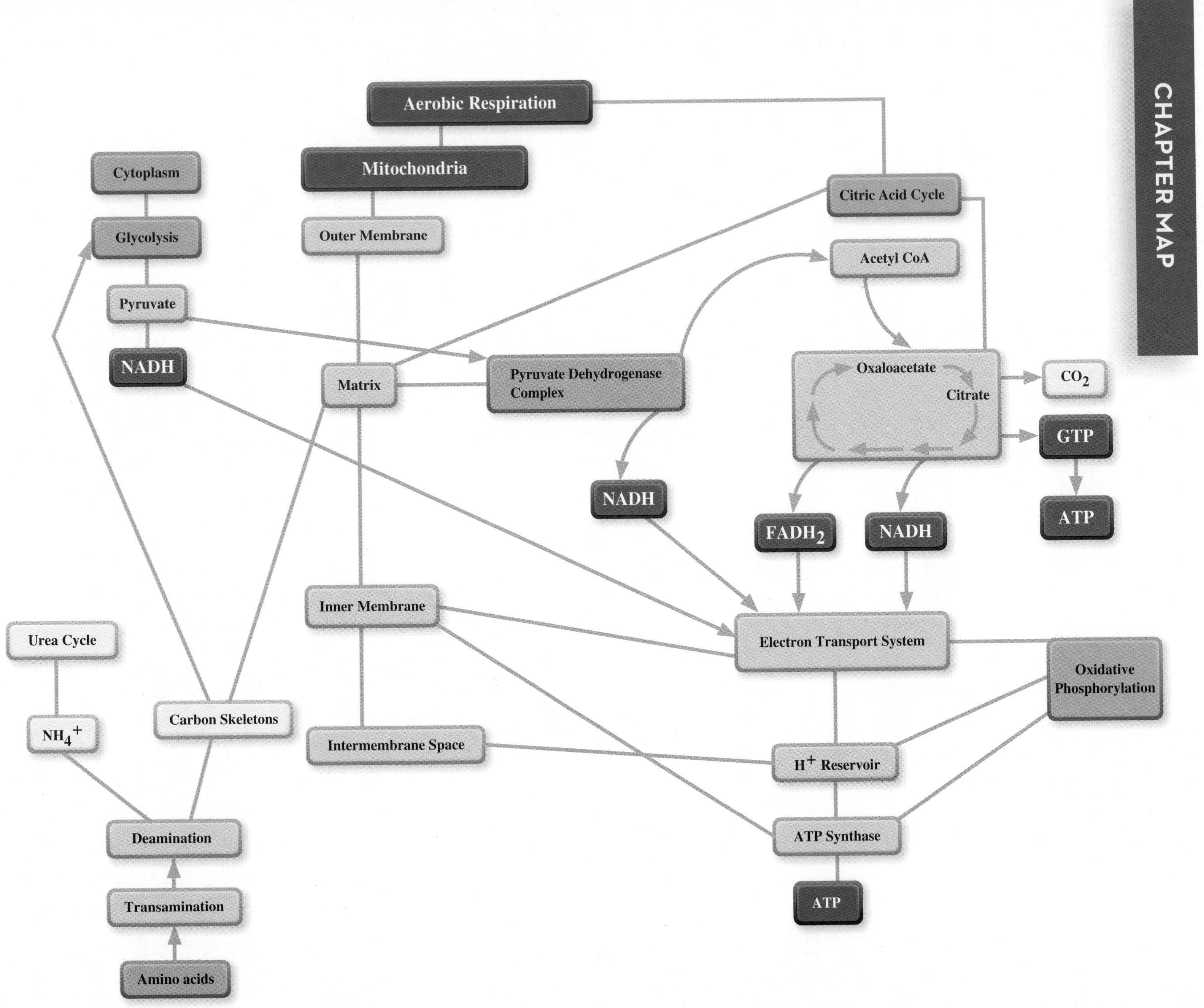

Aerobic Respiration
Mitochondria
Outer Membrane
Matrix
Inner Membrane
Intermembrane Space
Citric Acid Cycle
Acetyl CoA
Oxaloacetate
Citrate
CO_2
GTP
ATP
NADH
$FADH_2$
Electron Transport System
Oxidative Phosphorylation
H^+ Reservoir
ATP Synthase
ATP
Pyruvate Dehydrogenase Complex
NADH
Cytoplasm
Glycolysis
Pyruvate
NADH
Carbon Skeletons
Deamination
Transamination
Amino acids
Urea Cycle
NH_4^+

SUMMARY

22.1 The Mitochondria

- **Mitochondria are aerobic cell organelles that are responsible for most of the ATP production in eukaryotic cells.**
- **Mitochondria are enclosed by a double membrane.**
  - The **outer mitochondrial membrane** permits low-molar-mass molecules to pass through.
  - The **inner mitochondrial membrane** is almost completely impermeable to most molecules.
    - It is the site of oxidative phosphorylation.
    - It is highly folded into **cristae** to increase the surface area.
  - The **intermembrane space** is the site of the high-energy H^+ reservoir.
  - The **matrix space** contains the enzymes of the citric acid cycle.

22.2 Conversion of Pyruvate to Acetyl CoA

- **Under aerobic conditions, pyruvate is oxidized by the pyruvate dehydrogenase complex.**
- **In this reaction, coenzyme A bonds to an acetyl group through a thioester bond to produce acetyl coenzyme A or acetyl CoA.**
- **Acetyl CoA is a central molecule in both anabolism and catabolism.**

22.3 An Overview of Aerobic Respiration

- **Aerobic respiration** is the oxygen-requiring degradation of food molecules and production of ATP.
- **Oxidative phosphorylation is the process that uses high-energy electrons harvested by oxidation of substrates of the citric acid cycle to produce ATP.**

22.4 The Citric Acid Cycle (The Krebs Cycle)

- **The citric acid cycle is the final pathway for the degradation of carbohydrates, amino acids, and fatty acids.**
- **This pathway carries out the complete oxidation of carbon skeletons of food molecules.**
- **The enzymes of the citric acid cycle are found in the matrix space of the mitochondria.**

22.5 Control of the Citric Acid Cycle

- **Because the rate of ATP production by the cell must vary with the amount of available oxygen and the energy requirements of the body, the citric acid cycle is regulated at several steps. These are:**
  - Conversion of pyruvate to acetyl CoA (pyruvate dehydrogenase)
  - Synthesis of citrate from oxaloacetate and acetyl CoA (citrate synthase)
  - Oxidation and decarboxylation of isocitrate to α-ketoglutarate (isocitrate dehydrogenase)
  - Conversion of α-ketoglutarate to succinyl CoA (α-ketoglutarate dehydrogenase)
- **This regulation allows the cells to produce more ATP when it is needed for activity and less ATP when the body is at rest and the requirement for ATP is lower.**

22.6 Oxidative Phosphorylation

- **Oxidative phosphorylation is the process by which NADH and $FADH_2$ are oxidized and ATP is produced.**
  - Two molecules of ATP are produced when one $FADH_2$ is oxidized.
  - Three molecules of ATP are produced when one NADH is oxidized.
- **The electron transport system is the series of electron transport proteins embedded within the inner mitochondrial membrane that accepts high-energy electrons from NADH and $FADH_2$ and transfers them in stepwise fashion to O_2.**
  - At three sites in the electron transport system, H^+ are pumped into the high-energy H^+ reservoir in the intermembrane space.
  - **ATP synthase,** or the **F_0F_1 complex,** is a protein complex in the inner mitochondrial membrane.
    - H^+ pass through the F_0 portion of the complex and return to the matrix space.
    - The F_1 portion catalyzes the phosphorylation of ADP to form ATP.
  - The **terminal electron acceptor** is molecular oxygen (O_2).
- **The complete oxidation of a glucose molecule by glycolysis, the citric acid cycle, and oxidative phosphorylation produces thirty-six ATP molecules.**

22.7 The Degradation of Amino Acids

- **Amino acid degradation occurs in the liver and has two stages.**
  - Removal of the α-amino group
  - Degradation of the carbon skeleton
- **Removal of the α-amino group occurs in a transamination reaction and is catalyzed by a transaminase.**
- **All transaminases require the coenzyme pyridoxal phosphate.**
- **Oxidative deamination is the reaction by which the glutamate produced in transamination is deaminated.**
- **The carbon skeletons of the amino acids enter a number of reactions of glycolysis and the citric acid cycle and are completely oxidized.**

22.8 The Urea Cycle

- **In the urea cycle the toxic ammonium ions released by deamination of amino acids are incorporated into urea, which is excreted through the urine.**
- **Hyperammonemia is a genetic condition that results from a mutation of one of the enzymes of the urea cycle.**

22.9 Overview of Anabolism: The Citric Acid Cycle as a Source of Biosynthetic Intermediates

- **The reactions of the citric acid cycle have key roles in both anabolism and catabolism.**
- **Amino acids, lipids, and nitrogenous bases for nucleic acids all can be synthesized from many intermediates in the citric acid cycle and glycolysis.**
- **Metabolic pathways that function in both anabolism and catabolism are called amphibolic pathways.**
- **An anaplerotic reaction replenishes a substrate needed for a biochemical reaction.**

ANSWERS TO PRACTICE PROBLEMS

22.1 The ATP yield from one molecule of pyruvate can be summarized as follows:

Conversion of pyruvate to acetyl CoA

1 NADH × 3 ATP/NADH = 3 ATP

Citric Acid Cycle

1 GTP × 1 ATP/GTP	= 1 ATP
3 NADH × 3 ATP/NADH	= 9 ATP
1 $FADH_2$ × 2 ATP/$FADH_2$	= 2 ATP
Total	= 15 ATP

QUESTIONS AND PROBLEMS

The Mitochondria

Foundations

22.17 Define the term *mitochondrion.*

22.18 Define the term *cristae.*

Applications

22.19 What is the function of the intermembrane compartment of the mitochondria?

22.20 What biochemical processes occur in the matrix space of the mitochondria?

22.21 In what important way do the inner and outer mitochondrial membranes differ?

22.22 What kinds of proteins are found in the inner mitochondrial membrane?

Conversion of Pyruvate to Acetyl CoA

Foundations

22.23 What is coenzyme A?

22.24 What is the role of coenzyme A in the reaction catalyzed by pyruvate dehydrogenase?

22.25 In the reaction catalyzed by pyruvate dehydrogenase, pyruvate is decarboxylated. What is meant by the term *decarboxylation?*

22.26 In the reaction catalyzed by pyruvate dehydrogenase, pyruvate is also oxidized. What substance is reduced when pyruvate is oxidized? What is the product of that reduction reaction?

Applications

22.27 Under what metabolic conditions is pyruvate converted to acetyl CoA?

22.28 Write a chemical equation for the production of acetyl CoA from pyruvate. Under what conditions does this reaction occur?

22.29 How could a deficiency of riboflavin, thiamine, niacin, or pantothenic acid reduce the amount of ATP the body can produce?

22.30 In what form are the vitamins riboflavin, thiamine, niacin, and pantothenic acid needed by the pyruvate dehydrogenase complex?

The Citric Acid Cycle (The Krebs Cycle)

Foundations

22.31 The reaction catalyzed by citrate synthase is a condensation reaction. Define the term *condensation.*

22.32 The pair of reactions catalyzed by aconitase results in the conversion of isocitrate to its isomer citrate. What are isomers?

22.33 What general type of reaction is occurring in the conversion of isocitrate to α-ketoglutarate?

22.34 Write the equation for the conversion of isocitrate to α-ketoglutarate and circle the chemical change that reveals the type of reaction that is occurring.

22.35 The reaction catalyzed by succinate dehydrogenase is a dehydrogenation reaction. What is meant by the term *dehydrogenation reaction?*

22.36 The reaction catalyzed by fumarase is an example of the hydration of an alkene to produce an alcohol. Write the equation for this reaction. What is meant by the term *hydration reaction?*

22.37 Match each of the following enzymes with the class of enzyme to which it belongs. (*Hint:* An enzyme classification may be used more than once or not at all.)

a. Citrate synthase	**1.** Transferase
b. Aconitase	**2.** Oxidoreductase
c. Isocitrate dehydrogenase	**3.** Kinase
d. α-Ketoglutarate dehydrogenase	**4.** Hydrolase
e. Succinyl CoA synthase	**5.** Lyase
f. Succinate dehydrogenase	**6.** Isomerase
g. Fumarase	
h. Malate dehydrogenase	

22.38 Describe the reaction catalyzed by each of the enzymes listed in Question 22.37.

22.39 Is the following statement true or false? If false, rewrite the statement to make it accurate. Acetyl CoA transfers an acetyl group from pyruvate to citrate.

22.40 Are the following statements true or false? If false, rewrite the statements to make them accurate. Glycolysis and the citric acid cycle are aerobic processes. These anabolic processes occur in the mitochondria and the cytoplasm, respectively.

22.41 How many ions of NAD^+ are reduced to molecules of NADH during one turn of the citric acid cycle?

22.42 How many molecules of FAD are converted to $FADH_2$ during one turn of the citric acid cycle?

22.43 What is the net yield of ATP for anaerobic glycolysis?

22.44 How many molecules of ATP are produced by the complete degradation of glucose via glycolysis, the citric acid cycle, and oxidative phosphorylation?

22.45 What is the function of acetyl CoA in the citric acid cycle?

22.46 What is the function of oxaloacetate in the citric acid cycle?

22.47 GTP is formed in one step of the citric acid cycle. How is this GTP converted into ATP?

22.48 What is the chemical meaning of the term *decarboxylation?* Give an example of a decarboxylase.

Applications

22.49 Fumarase converts fumarate to malate. Explain this reaction in terms of the chemistry of alcohols and alkenes.

22.50 The enzyme aconitase catalyzes the isomerization of citrate into isocitrate. Discuss the two reactions catalyzed by aconitase in terms of the chemistry of alcohols and alkenes.

22.51 A bacterial culture is given ^{14}C-labeled pyruvate as its sole source of carbon and energy. The following is the structure of the radiolabeled pyruvate.

$$^{*}CH_3{-}\overset{\overset{\displaystyle O}{\|}}{C}{-}\overset{\overset{\displaystyle O}{\|}}{C}{-}O^-$$

Follow the fate of the radioactive carbon through the reactions of the citric acid cycle.

22.52 A bacterial culture is given ^{14}C-labeled pyruvate as its sole source of carbon and energy. The following is the structure of the radiolabeled pyruvate.

$$CH_3{-}\overset{\overset{\displaystyle O}{\|}}{C}{}^{*}{-}\overset{\overset{\displaystyle O}{\|}}{C}{-}O^-$$

Follow the fate of the radioactive carbon through the reactions of the citric acid cycle.

22.53 In the oxidation of malate to oxaloacetate, what is the structural evidence that an oxidation reaction has occurred? What functional groups are involved?

22.54 In the oxidation of succinate to fumarate, what is the structural evidence that an oxidation reaction has occurred? What functional groups are involved?

22.55 To what class of enzymes does dinucleotide diphosphokinase belong? Explain your answer.

22.56 To what class of enzymes does succinate dehydrogenase belong? Explain your answer.

22.57 Explain why mutations of the citric acid cycle enzymes frequently appear first in the central nervous system.

22.58 Why would a deficiency of α-ketoglutarate dehydrogenase cause chronic lactic acidosis?

22.59 Explain why deficiencies of citric acid cycle enzymes cause hypotonia.

22.60 Why is myoglobinuria associated with genetic disorders of the enzymes of the citric acid cycle?

Control of the Citric Acid Cycle

Foundations

22.61 Define the term *allosteric enzyme.*

22.62 Define the term *effector.*

22.63 Why are allosteric enzymes an efficient means to regulate a biochemical pathway?

22.64 Why are ADP and ATP efficient effector molecules for allosteric enzymes that regulate a biochemical pathway such as the citric acid cycle?

Applications

22.65 What four allosteric enzymes or enzyme complexes are responsible for the regulation of the citric acid cycle?

22.66 Which of the four allosteric enzymes or enzyme complexes in the citric acid cycle are under negative allosteric control? Which are under positive allosteric control?

22.67 What is the importance of the regulation of the citric acid cycle?

22.68 Explain the role of allosteric enzymes in control of the citric acid cycle.

22.69 What molecule serves as a signal to increase the rate of the reactions of the citric acid cycle?

22.70 What molecules serve as signals to decrease the rate of the reactions of the citric acid cycle?

Oxidative Phosphorylation

Foundations

22.71 Define the term *electron transport system.*

22.72 What is the terminal electron acceptor in aerobic respiration?

Applications

22.73 How many molecules of ATP are produced when one molecule of NADH is oxidized by oxidative phosphorylation?

22.74 How many molecules of ATP are produced when one molecule of $FADH_2$ is oxidized by oxidative phosphorylation?

22.75 What is the source of energy for the synthesis of ATP in mitochondria?

22.76 What is the name of the enzyme that catalyzes ATP synthesis in mitochondria?

22.77 What is the function of the electron transport systems of the mitochondria?

22.78 What is the cellular location of the electron transport systems?

22.79 **a.** Compare the number of molecules of ATP produced by glycolysis to the number of ATP molecules produced by oxidation of glucose by aerobic respiration.
b. Which pathway produces more ATP? Explain.

22.80 At which steps in the citric acid cycle do oxidation-reduction reactions occur?

The Degradation of Amino Acids

Foundations

22.81 What chemical transformation is carried out by transaminases?

22.82 Write a chemical equation for the transfer of an amino group from alanine to α-ketoglutarate, catalyzed by a transaminase.

22.83 Why is the glutamate family of transaminases so important?

22.84 What biochemical reaction is catalyzed by glutamate dehydrogenase?

Applications

22.85 Into which citric acid cycle intermediate is each of the following amino acids converted?

a. Alanine
b. Glutamate
c. Aspartate
d. Phenylalanine
e. Threonine
f. Arginine

22.86 What is the net ATP yield for degradation of each of the amino acids listed in Question 22.85?

22.87 Explain the mechanism of transamination.

22.88 What is the role of vitamin B_6 in transamination?

The Urea Cycle

22.89 What metabolic condition is produced if the urea cycle does not function properly?

22.90 What is hyperammonemia? How are mild forms of this disease treated?

22.91 The structure of urea is

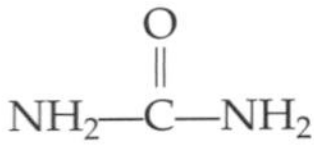

a. What substances are the sources of each of the amino groups in the urea molecule?

b. What substance is the source of the carbonyl group?

22.92 What is the energy source used for the urea cycle?

Overview of Anabolism: The Citric Acid Cycle as a Source of Biosynthetic Intermediates

Foundations

22.93 Define the term *anabolism.*

22.94 Define the term *catabolism.*

Applications

22.95 From which citric acid cycle intermediate is the amino acid glutamate synthesized?

22.96 What amino acids are synthesized from α-ketoglutarate?

22.97 What is the role of the citric acid cycle in biosynthesis?

22.98 How are citric acid cycle intermediates replenished when they are in demand for biosynthesis?

22.99 What is meant by the term *essential amino acid?*

22.100 What are the nine essential amino acids?

22.101 Write a balanced equation for the reaction catalyzed by pyruvate carboxylase.

22.102 How does the reaction described in Question 22.101 allow the citric acid cycle to fulfill its roles in both catabolism and anabolism?

CRITICAL THINKING PROBLEMS

1. A 1-month-old baby boy was brought to the hospital showing severely delayed development and cerebral atrophy. Blood tests showed high levels of lactate and pyruvate. By 3 months of age, very high levels of succinate and fumarate were found in the urine. Fumarase activity was absent in the liver and muscle tissue. The baby died at 5 months of age. This was the first reported case of fumarase deficiency and the defect was recognized too late for effective therapy to be administered. What reaction is catalyzed by fumarase? How would a deficiency of this mitochondrial enzyme account for the baby's symptoms and test results?
2. A certain bacterium can grow with ethanol as its only source of energy and carbon. Propose a pathway to describe how ethanol can enter a pathway that would allow ATP production and synthesis of precursors for biosynthesis.
3. Fluoroacetate has been used as a rat poison and can be fatal when eaten by humans. Patients with fluoroacetate poisoning accumulate citrate and fluorocitrate within the cells. What enzyme is inhibited by fluoroacetate? Explain your reasoning.
4. The pyruvate dehydrogenase complex is activated by removal of a phosphoryl group from *pyruvate dehydrogenase.* This reaction is catalyzed by the enzyme pyruvate dehydrogenase phosphate phosphatase. A baby is born with a defect in this enzyme. What effects would this defect have on the rate of each of the following pathways: aerobic respiration, glycolysis, lactate fermentation? Explain your reasoning.
5. Pyruvate dehydrogenase phosphate phosphatase is stimulated by Ca^{2+}. In muscles, the Ca^{2+} concentration increases dramatically during muscle contraction. How would the elevated Ca^{2+} concentration affect the rate of glycolysis and the citric acid cycle?
6. Liver contains high levels of nucleic acids. When excess nucleic acids are degraded, ribose-5-phosphate is one of the degradation products that accumulate in the cell. Can this substance be used as a source of energy? What pathway would be used?
7. In birds, arginine is an essential amino acid. Can birds produce urea as a means of removing ammonium ions from the blood? Explain your reasoning.

23

Fatty Acid Metabolism

Olive oil, prepared by pressing ripe olives, is a healthy alternative in our diet.

LEARNING GOALS

1. Summarize the digestion and storage of lipids.
2. Describe the degradation of fatty acids by β-oxidation.
3. Explain the role of acetyl CoA in fatty acid metabolism.
4. Understand the role of ketone body production in β-oxidation.
5. Compare β-oxidation of fatty acids and fatty acid biosynthesis.
6. Describe the regulation of lipid and carbohydrate metabolism in relation to the liver, adipose tissue, muscle tissue, and the brain.
7. Summarize the antagonistic effects of glucagon and insulin.

OUTLINE

Introduction 794

23.1 Lipid Metabolism in Animals 794

A Medical Perspective: Obesity: A Genetic Disorder? 797

23.2 Fatty Acid Degradation 798

A Medical Perspective: Carnitine: The Fat Mover 802

23.3 Ketone Bodies 804

A Human Perspective: Losing Those Unwanted Pounds of Adipose Tissue 807

23.4 Fatty Acid Synthesis 808

23.5 The Regulation of Lipid and Carbohydrate Metabolism 810

A Medical Perspective: Diabetes Mellitus and Ketone Bodies 811

23.6 The Effects of Insulin and Glucagon on Cellular Metabolism 813

INTRODUCTION

Triglycerides are our most concentrated energy reserve, yielding 9 kilocalories per gram (kcal/g) when completely oxidized. Compare this with the energy yield for carbohydrates, which is only 4 kcal/g. Lipid metabolism in mammals is extremely complex. There is great concern about the epidemic of obesity that is afflicting the United States (see A Medical Perspective: Obesity: A Genetic Disorder? later in this chapter). No matter the source of dietary calories, when excess calories are ingested, our bodies store them as triglycerides in adipose tissue.

For some animals, large lipid stores are essential for survival. Animals such as bears that may hibernate for as many as 7 months rely solely on their fat reserves as the source of metabolic energy. The ruby-throated hummingbird migrates from New England to the West Indies in the fall of the year. As the time of migration nears, the hummingbirds accumulate as much as 40% of their body weight as triglycerides. This provides them the energy to fly nonstop at speeds of nearly 30 miles per hour (mph) for as long as 60 hours (h).

The metabolism of fatty acids and lipids revolves around the fate of acetyl CoA. We saw in Chapter 22 that, under aerobic conditions, pyruvate is converted to acetyl CoA, which feeds into the citric acid cycle. Fatty acids are also degraded to acetyl CoA and oxidized by the citric acid cycle. Moreover, acetyl CoA is itself the starting material for the biosynthesis of fatty acids, cholesterol, and steroid hormones. Acetyl CoA is thus a key intermediary in lipid metabolism.

23.1 Lipid Metabolism in Animals

Digestion and Absorption of Dietary Triglycerides

LEARNING GOAL

1 Summarize the digestion and storage of lipids.

Triglycerides are highly hydrophobic ("water fearing"). Because of this they must be processed before they can be digested, absorbed, and metabolized. Because processing of dietary lipids occurs in the small intestine, the water-soluble **lipases,** enzymes that hydrolyze triglycerides, which are found in the stomach and in the saliva are not very effective. In fact, most dietary fat arrives in the duodenum, the first part of the small intestine, in the form of fat globules. These fat globules stimulate the secretion of bile from the gallbladder. **Bile** is composed of micelles of lecithin, cholesterol, protein, bile salts, inorganic ions, and bile pigments. **Micelles** (Figure 23.1) are aggregations of molecules having a polar region and a nonpolar region. The nonpolar ends of bile salts tend to bunch together when placed in water. The hydrophilic ("water loving") regions of these molecules interact with water. Bile salts are made in the liver and stored in the gallbladder, awaiting the stimulus to be secreted into the duodenum. The major bile salts in humans are cholate and chenodeoxycholate (Figure 23.2).

See Sections 14.2 and 17.2 for a discussion of micelles.

Cholesterol is almost completely insoluble in water, but the conversion of cholesterol to bile salts creates *detergents* whose polar heads make them soluble in the aqueous phase and whose hydrophobic tails bind triglycerides. After a meal is eaten, bile flows through the common bile duct into the duodenum, where bile salts emulsify the fat globules into tiny droplets. This increases the surface area of the lipid molecules, allowing them to be more easily hydrolyzed by lipases (Figure 23.3).

Triglycerides are described in Section 17.3.

Much of the lipid in these droplets is in the form of **triglycerides,** or triacylglycerols, which are fatty acid esters of glycerol. A protein called **colipase** binds to the surface of the lipid droplets and helps pancreatic lipases to stick to the surface and hydrolyze the ester bonds between the glycerol and fatty acids of the triglycerides (Figure 23.4). In this process, two of the three fatty acids are liberated, and the monoglycerides and free fatty acids produced mix freely with the

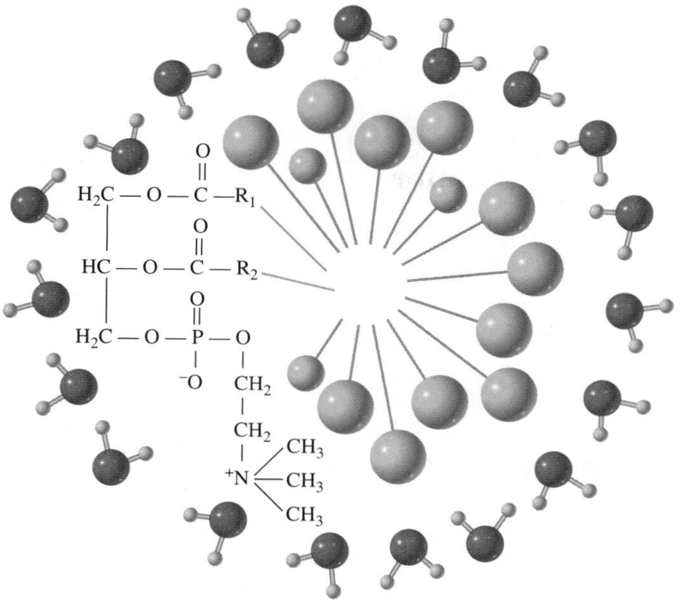

Figure 23.1 The structure of a micelle formed from the phospholipid lecithin. The straight lines represent the long hydrophobic fatty acid tails, and the spheres represent the hydrophilic heads of the phospholipid.

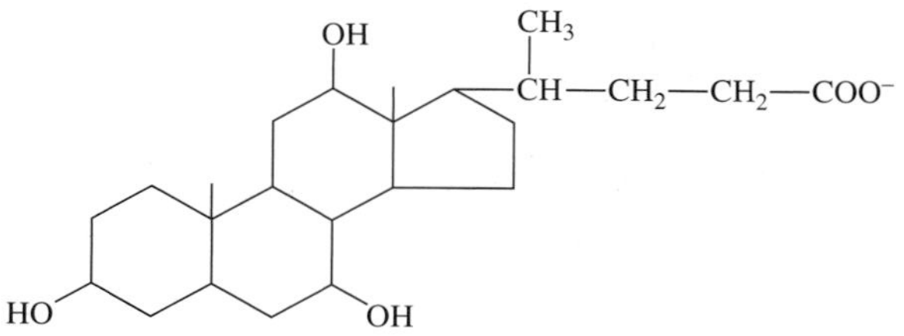

Figure 23.2 Structures of the most common bile salts in human bile: cholate and chenodeoxycholate.

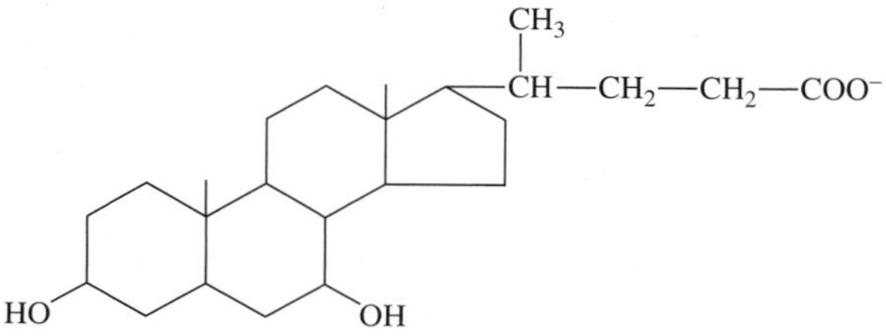

micelles of bile. These micelles are readily absorbed through the membranes of the intestinal epithelial cells (Figure 23.3).

Surprisingly, the monoglycerides and fatty acids are then reassembled into triglycerides that are combined with protein to produce the class of plasma lipoproteins called **chylomicrons** (Figure 23.3). These collections of lipid and protein are secreted into small lymphatic vessels and eventually arrive in the bloodstream. In the bloodstream the triglycerides are once again hydrolyzed to produce glycerol and free fatty acids that are then absorbed by the cells. If the body needs energy, these molecules are degraded to produce ATP. If the body does not need energy, these energy-rich molecules are stored.

Plasma lipoproteins are described in Section 17.5.

Lipid Storage

Fatty acids are stored in the form of triglycerides. Most of the body's triglyceride molecules are stored as fat droplets in the cytoplasm of **adipocytes** (fat cells) that make up **adipose tissue.** Each adipocyte contains a large fat droplet

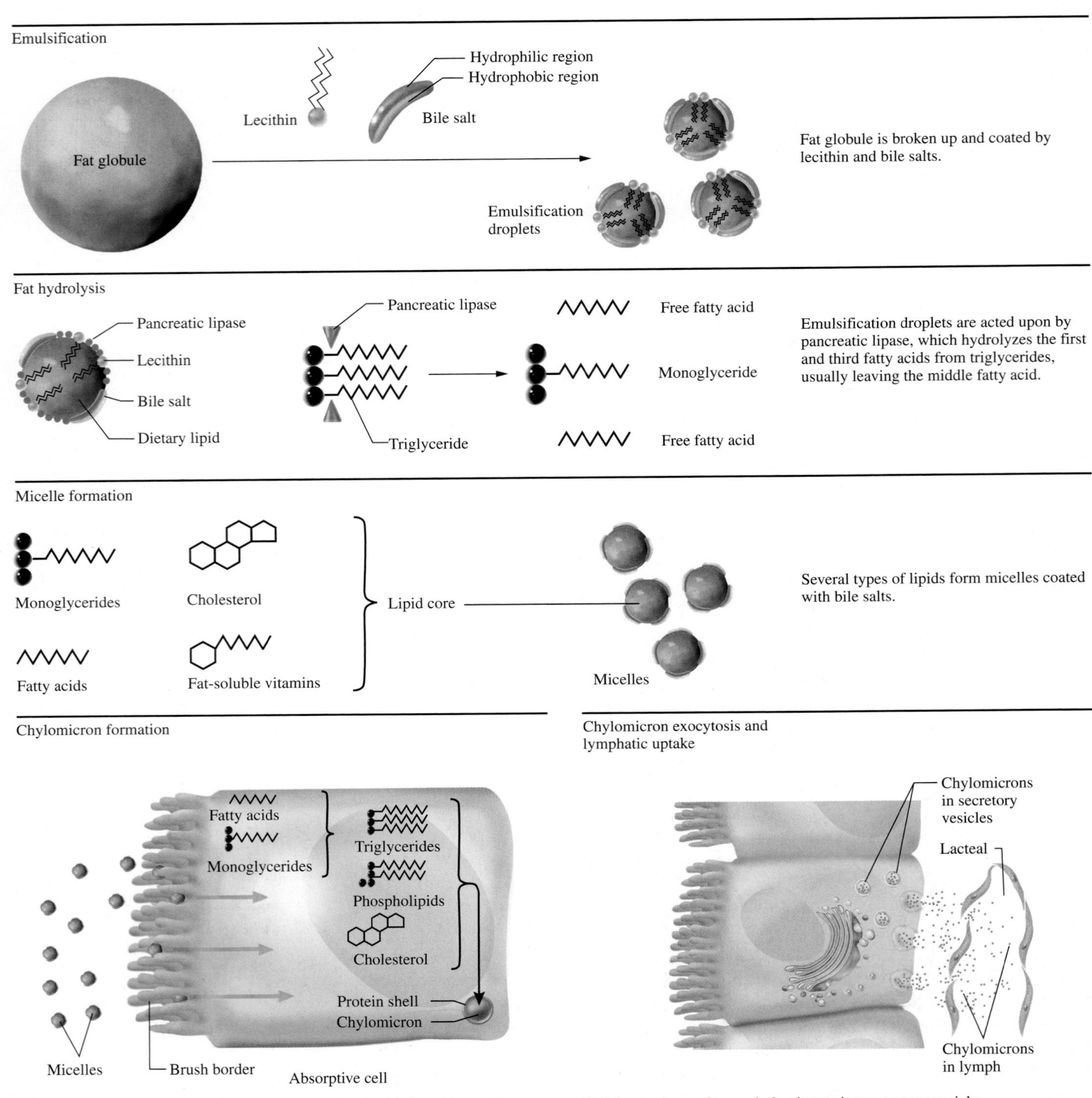

Figure 23.3 Stages of lipid digestion in the intestinal tract.

that accounts for nearly the entire volume of the cell. Other cells, such as those of cardiac muscle, contain a few small fat droplets. In these cells the fat droplets are surrounded by mitochondria. When the cells need energy, triglycerides are hydrolyzed to release fatty acids that are transported into the matrix space

A MEDICAL PERSPECTIVE

Obesity: A Genetic Disorder?

Approximately a third of all Americans are obese; that is, they are more than 20% overweight. One million are morbidly obese; they carry so much extra weight that it threatens their health. Many obese people simply eat too much and exercise too little, but others actually gain weight even though they eat fewer calories than people of normal weight. This observation led many researchers to the hypothesis that obesity in some people is a genetic disorder.

This hypothesis was supported by the 1950 discovery of an obesity mutation in mice. Selective breeding produced a strain of genetically obese mice from the original mutant mouse. The hypothesis was further strengthened by the results of experiments performed in the 1970s by Douglas Coleman. Coleman connected the circulatory systems of a genetically obese mouse and a normal mouse. The obese mouse started eating less and lost weight. Coleman concluded that there was a substance in the blood of normal mice that signals the brain to decrease the appetite. Obese mice, he hypothesized, can't produce this "satiety factor," and thus they continue to eat and gain weight.

In 1987, Jeffrey Friedman assembled a team of researchers to map and then clone the obesity gene that was responsible for appetite control. In 1994, after 7 years of intense effort, the scientists achieved their goal, but they still had to demonstrate that the protein encoded by the cloned obesity gene did, indeed, have a metabolic effect. The gene was modified to be compatible with the genetic system of bacteria so that they could be used to manufacture the protein. When the engineered gene was then introduced into bacteria, they produced an abundance of the protein product. The protein was then purified in preparation for animal testing.

The researchers calculated that a normal mouse has about 12.5 milligrams (mg) of the protein in its blood. They injected that amount into each of ten mice that were so fat they couldn't squeeze into the feeding tunnels used for normal mice. The day after the first injection, graduate student Jeff Halaas observed that the mice had eaten less food. Injections were given daily, and each day the obese mice ate less. After 2 weeks of treatment, each of the ten mice had lost about 30% of its weight. In addition, the mice had become more active and their metabolisms had speeded up.

When normal mice underwent similar treatment, their body fat fell from 12.2% to 0.67%, which meant that these mice had no extra fat tissue. The 0.67% of their body weight represented by fat was accounted for by the membranes that surround each of the cells of their bodies! Because of the dramatic results, Friedman and his colleagues called the protein *leptin*, from the Greek word *leptos*, meaning slender.

The leptin protein is a hormone that functions as a signal in a metabolic thermostat. Fat cells produce leptin and secrete it into the bloodstream. As a result, the leptin concentration in a normal person is proportional to the amount of body fat. The blood concentration of the hormone is monitored by the hypothalamus, a region known to control appetite and set metabolic rates. When the concentration reaches a certain level, it triggers the hypothalamus to suppress the appetite. If no leptin or only small amounts of it are produced, the hypothalamus "thinks" that the individual has too little body fat or is starving. Under these circumstances it does not send a signal to suppress hunger and the individual continues to eat.

The human leptin gene also has been cloned and shown to correct genetic obesity in mice. Unfortunately, the dramatic results achieved with mice were *not* observed with humans. Why? It seems that nearly all of the obese volunteers already produced an abundance of leptin. In fact, fewer than ten people have been found, to date, who do not produce leptin and many obese people have very high levels of leptin in the blood. It appears that, as with type 2 diabetes and insulin, these people are no longer sensitive to the leptin produced by their fat cells.

Ghrelin is another hormone that influences appetite. Produced in the stomach, ghrelin stimulates appetite. As you would predict, the level of ghrelin is high before a meal and decreases following a meal. Many obese people have high levels of ghrelin and therefore experience constant hunger.

Obestatin is another hormone that has been discovered to influence body weight. This hormone decreases appetite. Interestingly, both ghrelin and obestatin are encoded in a single gene. When the protein is produced, it is cleaved into the two peptide hormones.

Clearly lipid metabolism in animals is a complex process and is not yet fully understood. In this chapter we will study other aspects of lipid metabolism: the pathways for fatty acid degradation and biosynthesis and the processes by which dietary lipids are digested and excess lipids are stored.

For Further Understanding

- Go online to learn the cause of type 2 diabetes. Develop a hypothesis to explain the similarities between this condition and leptin insensitivity.
- Design an experiment to demonstrate the opposing effects of ghrelin and obestatin.

of the mitochondria. There the fatty acids are completely oxidized, and ATP is produced.

The fatty acids provided by the hydrolysis of triglycerides are a very rich energy source for the body. The complete oxidation of fatty acids releases much more energy than the oxidation of a comparable amount of glycogen.

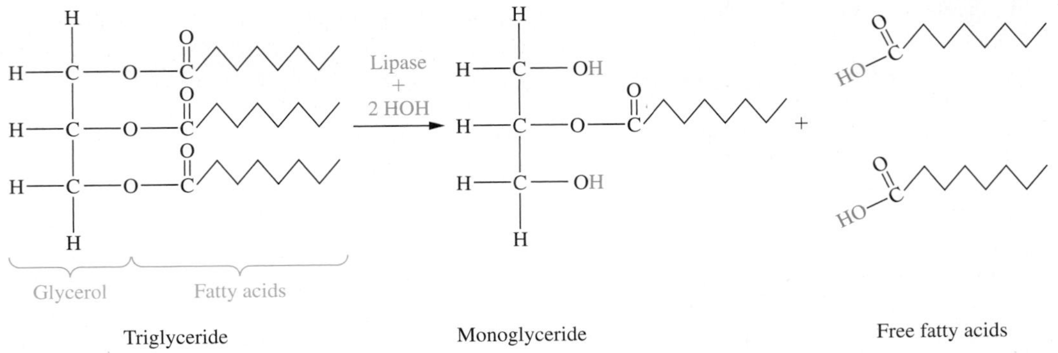

Figure 23.4 The action of pancreatic lipase in the hydrolysis of dietary lipids.

Question 23.1 How do bile salts aid in the digestion of dietary lipids?

Question 23.2 Why must dietary lipids be processed before enzymatic digestion can be effective?

23.2 Fatty Acid Degradation

An Overview of Fatty Acid Degradation

LEARNING GOAL

2 Describe the degradation of fatty acids by β-oxidation.

LEARNING GOAL

3 Explain the role of acetyl CoA in fatty acid metabolism.

This pathway is called β-oxidation because it involves the stepwise oxidation of the β-carbon of the fatty acid.

Early in the twentieth century, a very clever experiment was done to determine how fatty acids are degraded. Recall from Chapter 9 that radioactive elements can be attached to biological molecules and followed through the body. A German biochemist, Franz Knoop, devised a similar kind of labeling experiment long before radioactive tracers were available. Knoop fed dogs fatty acids in which the usual terminal methyl group had a phenyl group attached to it. Such molecules are called ω-labeled (omega-labeled) fatty acids (Figure 23.5). When he isolated the metabolized fatty acids from the urine of the dogs, he found that phenyl acetate was formed when the fatty acid had an even number of carbon atoms in the chain. But benzoate was formed when the fatty acid had an odd number of carbon atoms. Knoop interpreted these data to mean that the degradation of fatty acids occurs by the removal of two-carbon acetate groups from the carboxyl end of the fatty acid. We now know that the two-carbon fragments produced by the degradation of fatty acids are not acetate, but acetyl CoA. The pathway for the breakdown of fatty acids into acetyl CoA is called **β-oxidation.**

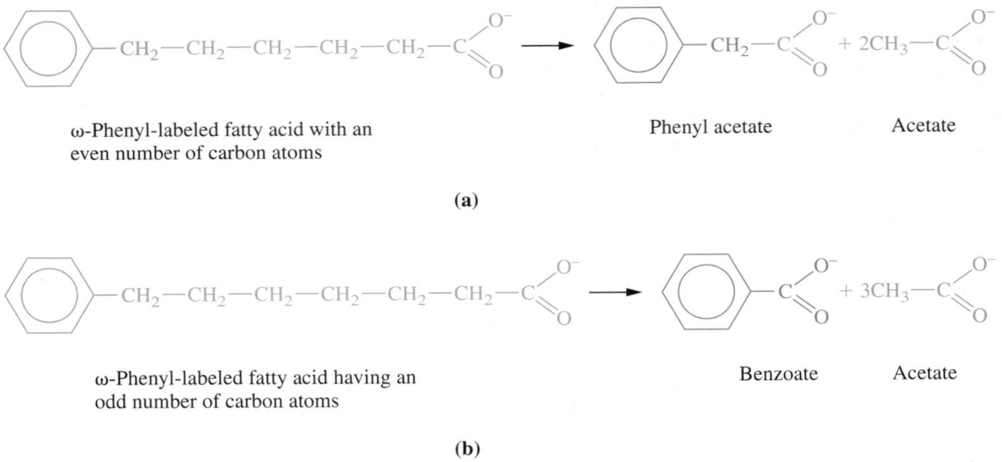

Figure 23.5 The last carbon of the chain is called the ω-carbon (omega-carbon), so the attached phenyl group is an ω-phenyl group. (a) Oxidation of ω-phenyl-labeled fatty acids occurs two carbons at a time. Fatty acids having an even number of carbon atoms are degraded to phenyl acetate and "acetate." (b) Oxidation of ω-phenyl-labeled fatty acids that contain an odd number of carbon atoms yields benzoate and "acetate."

The β-oxidation cycle (steps 2–5, Figure 23.6) consists of a set of four reactions whose overall form is similar to the last four reactions of the citric acid cycle. Each trip through the sequence of reactions releases acetyl CoA and returns a fatty acyl CoA molecule that has two fewer carbons. One molecule of $FADH_2$, equivalent to two ATP molecules, and one molecule of NADH, equivalent to three ATP molecules, are produced for each cycle of β-oxidation.

Review Section 22.6 for the ATP yields that result from oxidation of $FADH_2$ and NADH.

EXAMPLE 23.1 **Predicting the Products of β-Oxidation of a Fatty Acid**

LEARNING GOAL

2 Describe the degradation of fatty acids by β-oxidation.

What products would be produced by the β-oxidation of 10-phenyldecanoic acid?

Solution

This ten-carbon fatty acid would be broken down into four acetyl CoA molecules and one phenyl acetate molecule. Because four cycles through β-oxidation are required to break down a ten-carbon fatty acid, four NADH molecules and four $FADH_2$ molecules would also be produced.

Practice Problem 23.1

What products would be formed by β-oxidation of each of the following fatty acids?

a. 9-Phenylnonanoic acid
b. 8-Phenyloctanoic acid
c. 7-Phenylheptanoic acid
d. 12-Phenyldodecanoic acid

► Further Practice: **Questions 23.41 and 23.42.**

The Reactions of β-Oxidation

The enzymes that catalyze the β-oxidation of fatty acids are located in the matrix space of the mitochondria. Special transport mechanisms are required to bring fatty acid molecules into the mitochondrial matrix. Once inside, the fatty acids are degraded by the reactions of β-oxidation. As we will see, these reactions interact with oxidative phosphorylation and the citric acid cycle to produce ATP.

LEARNING GOAL

2 Describe the degradation of fatty acids by β-oxidation.

Reaction 1. The first step is an *activation* reaction that results in the production of a fatty acyl CoA molecule. A thioester bond is formed between coenzyme A and the fatty acid:

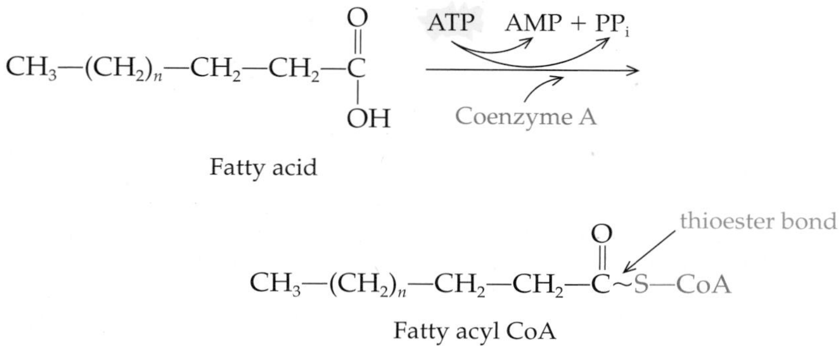

$$CH_3{-}(CH_2)_n{-}CH_2{-}CH_2{-}\overset{\displaystyle O}{\overset{\|}{C}}{-}OH \xrightarrow[\text{Coenzyme A}]{\text{ATP} \quad \text{AMP} + \text{PP}_i}$$

Fatty acid

$$CH_3{-}(CH_2)_n{-}CH_2{-}CH_2{-}\overset{\displaystyle O}{\overset{\|}{C}}{\sim}S{-}CoA$$

thioester bond

Fatty acyl CoA

This reaction requires energy in the form of ATP, which is cleaved to AMP and pyrophosphate. This involves hydrolysis of two phosphoanhydride bonds. Here again we see the need to invest a small amount

Figure 23.6 The reactions in β-oxidation of fatty acids.

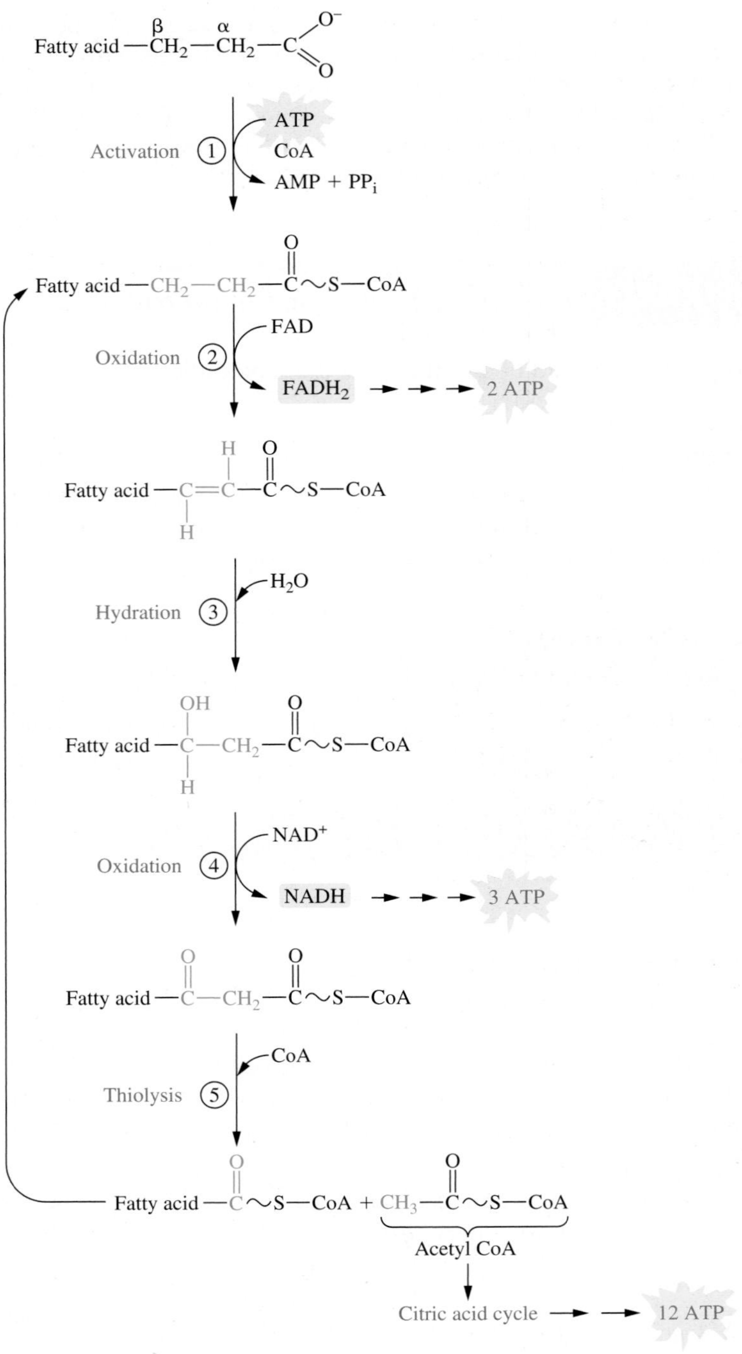

$\text{Fatty acid}-\overset{\beta}{C}H_2-\overset{\alpha}{C}H_2-COO^-$

Activation ① : ATP, CoA → AMP + PP_i

$\text{Fatty acid}-CH_2-CH_2-\overset{O}{\overset{\|}{C}}\sim S-CoA$

Oxidation ② : FAD → $FADH_2$ → → → 2 ATP

$\text{Fatty acid}-\underset{H}{C}=\overset{H}{C}-\overset{O}{\overset{\|}{C}}\sim S-CoA$

Hydration ③ : H_2O

$\text{Fatty acid}-\underset{H}{\overset{OH}{C}}-CH_2-\overset{O}{\overset{\|}{C}}\sim S-CoA$

Oxidation ④ : NAD^+ → NADH → → → 3 ATP

$\text{Fatty acid}-\overset{O}{\overset{\|}{C}}-CH_2-\overset{O}{\overset{\|}{C}}\sim S-CoA$

Thiolysis ⑤ : CoA

$\text{Fatty acid}-\overset{O}{\overset{\|}{C}}\sim S-CoA + \underbrace{CH_3-\overset{O}{\overset{\|}{C}}\sim S-CoA}_{\text{Acetyl CoA}}$

Acetyl CoA → Citric acid cycle → → 12 ATP

Acyl group transfer reactions are described in Section 14.4.

of energy so that a much greater amount of energy can be harvested later in the pathway. Coenzyme A is also required for this step. The product, a fatty acyl CoA, has a *high-energy* thioester bond between the fatty acid and coenzyme A. *Acyl-CoA ligase,* which catalyzes this reaction, is located in the outer membrane of the mitochondria. The mechanism that brings the fatty acyl CoA into the mitochondrial matrix involves a carrier molecule called L-*carnitine.* The first step, catalyzed by the enzyme *carnitine acyltransferase I,* is the transfer of the fatty acyl group to carnitine, producing acylcarnitine and coenzyme A (Figure 23.7a). Next a carrier protein located in the mitochondrial inner membrane transfers the acylcarnitine into the mitochondrial

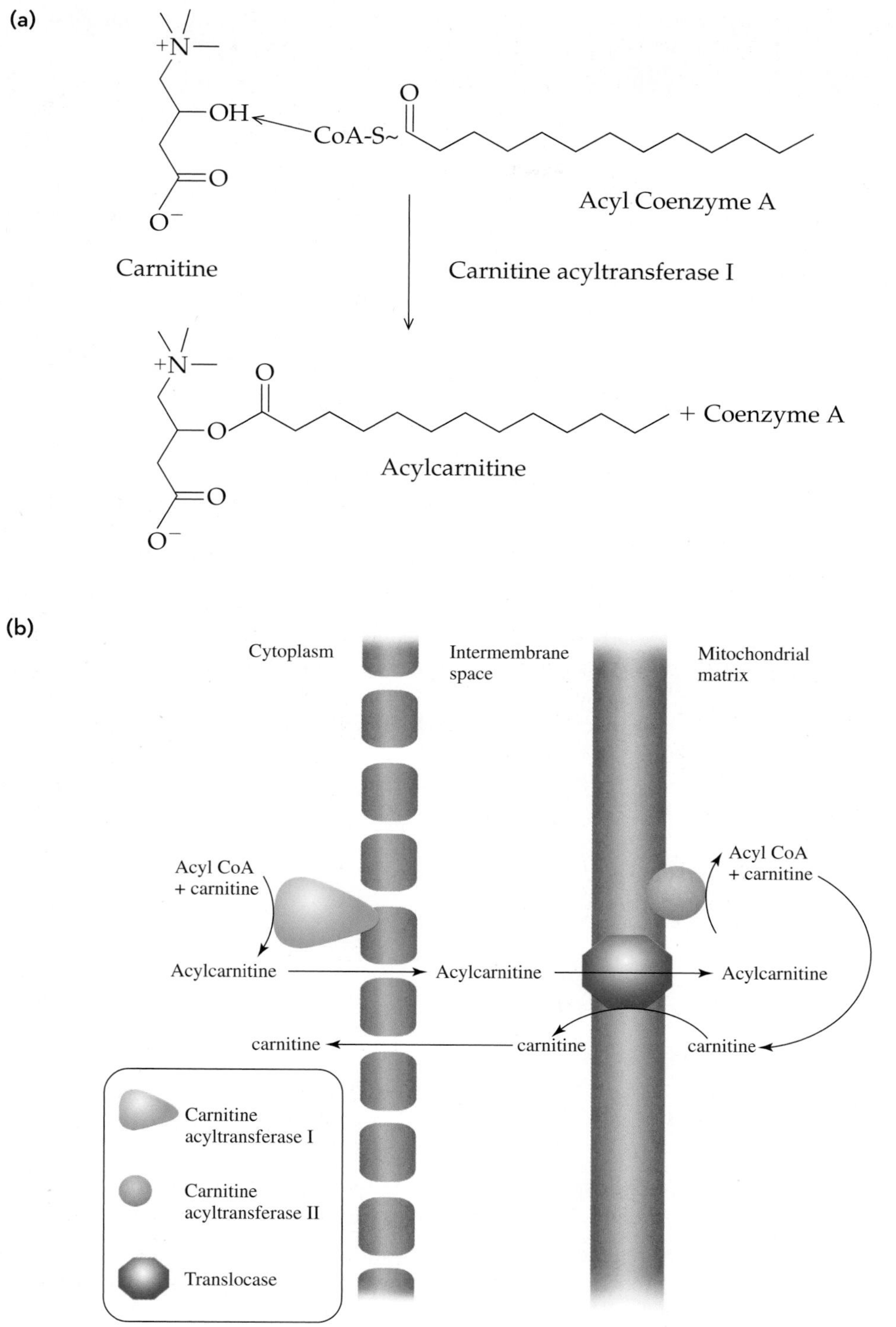

(a)

(b)

Figure 23.7 (a) The reaction catalyzed by carnitine acyltransferase I. (b) The transport of fatty acids into the mitochondrial matrix.

matrix. There *carnitine acyltransferase II* catalyzes the regeneration of fatty acyl CoA, which now becomes involved in the remaining reactions of β-oxidation (Figure 23.7b).

Reaction 2. The next reaction is an *oxidation* reaction that removes a pair of hydrogen atoms from the fatty acid. These are used to reduce FAD to produce $FADH_2$. This *dehydrogenation* reaction is catalyzed by

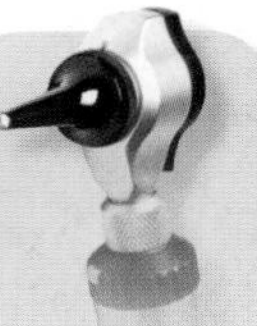

A MEDICAL PERSPECTIVE

Carnitine: The Fat Mover

Carnitine is a quaternary ammonium compound synthesized in the liver and kidneys from the amino acids lysine and methionine. This synthesis requires vitamin C. Carnitine can also be obtained through the diet. Red meats are an excellent source of carnitine, but it can be found also in nuts, legumes, broccoli, fruits, and cereals.

$$(CH_3)_3N^+-CH_2-CH(OH)-CH_2-C(=O)-O^-$$

Carnitine

L-Carnitine, the active enantiomer of carnitine, has been sold as a weight-loss supplement. The idea behind this is that additional carnitine will transport more fatty acids to the site of β-oxidation and in that way promote weight loss. Although the idea is clever, there has never been any scientific evidence to demonstrate that the claim of enhanced weight loss is true. However, a research study in 2007 did find evidence that regular supplements of L-carnitine in the elderly improved energy metabolism and neurotransmitter function in the brain. Further study will be required to fully understand the use of L-carnitine as a nutritional supplement.

Physicians have observed L-carnitine deficiency in children. Systemic primary carnitine deficiency is caused by a mutation in the membrane transport system that brings L-carnitine into the cell. As a result, β-oxidation of fatty acids is defective. The disorder produces a variety of symptoms that present in infancy or childhood. Among these is metabolic decompensation between 3 months and 2 years of age. Decompensation is the inability of the heart to maintain adequate blood circulation, which results in edema and labored breathing. Other symptoms that are more episodic include hypoglycemia, lethargy, irritability, and an enlarged liver. Some children exhibit myopathy of the heart and skeletal muscles between the ages of 2 and 4 years.

If diagnosed before there is irreversible organ damage, the symptoms can be treated with L-carnitine taken orally. A dose of 100–400 mg/kg/day brings about improvement of metabolic decompensation, as well as improved cardiac and skeletal muscle function. Thereafter, the condition can be managed through oral administration of L-carnitine.

For Further Understanding

- Design an experiment that might demonstrate whether L-carnitine promotes weight loss.
- Explain why cardiac and skeletal muscles are particularly susceptible to damage as a result of primary carnitine deficiency.

the enzyme *acyl-CoA dehydrogenase* and results in the formation of a carbon-carbon double bond:

$$CH_3-(CH_2)_n-CH_2-CH_2-\overset{O}{\overset{\|}{C}}\sim S-CoA \xrightarrow{FAD \;\; FADH_2} CH_3-(CH_2)_n-\underset{H}{C}=\overset{H}{C}-\overset{O}{\overset{\|}{C}}\sim S-CoA$$

Oxidative phosphorylation yields two ATP molecules for each molecule of $FADH_2$ produced by this oxidation-reduction reaction.

Reaction 3. The third reaction involves the *hydration* of the double bond produced in reaction 2. As a result, the β-carbon is hydroxylated. This reaction is catalyzed by the enzyme *enoyl-CoA hydrase.*

$$CH_3-(CH_2)_n-\underset{H}{C}=\overset{H}{C}-\overset{O}{\overset{\|}{C}}\sim S-CoA \xrightarrow{H_2O} CH_3-(CH_2)_n-\underset{H}{\overset{OH}{C}}-CH_2-\overset{O}{\overset{\|}{C}}\sim S-CoA$$

Reaction 4. In this *oxidation* reaction the hydroxyl group of the β-carbon is now dehydrogenated. NAD^+ is reduced to form NADH that is subsequently used to produce three ATP molecules by oxidative phosphorylation. L-β-*Hydroxyacyl-CoA dehydrogenase* catalyzes this reaction.

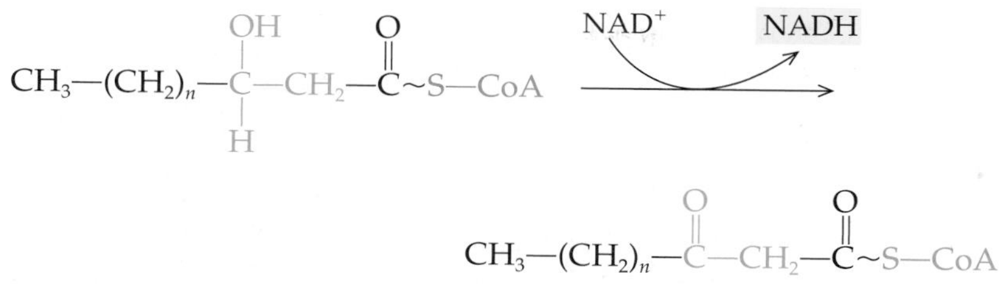

$$CH_3{-}(CH_2)_n{-}\underset{\underset{H}{|}}{\overset{\overset{OH}{|}}{C}}{-}CH_2{-}\overset{\overset{O}{\|}}{C}{\sim}S{-}CoA \xrightarrow{NAD^+ \;\rightarrow\; NADH} CH_3{-}(CH_2)_n{-}\overset{\overset{O}{\|}}{C}{-}CH_2{-}\overset{\overset{O}{\|}}{C}{\sim}S{-}CoA$$

Reaction 5. The final reaction, catalyzed by the enzyme *thiolase,* is the cleavage that releases acetyl CoA. This is accomplished by *thiolysis,* attack of a molecule of coenzyme A on the β-carbon. The result is the release of acetyl CoA and a fatty acyl CoA that is two carbons shorter than the beginning fatty acid:

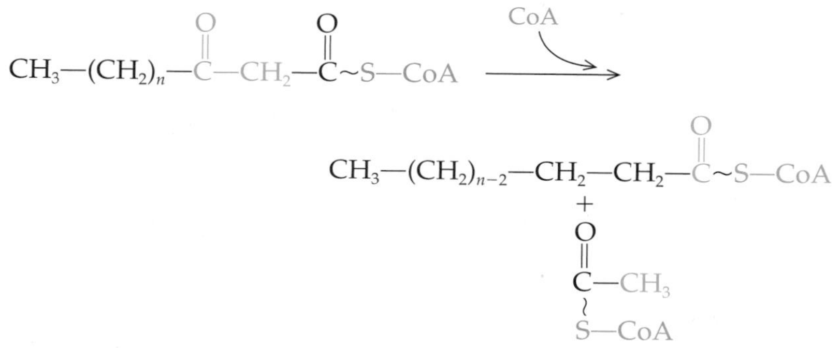

$$CH_3{-}(CH_2)_n{-}\overset{\overset{O}{\|}}{C}{-}CH_2{-}\overset{\overset{O}{\|}}{C}{\sim}S{-}CoA \xrightarrow{CoA} CH_3{-}(CH_2)_{n-2}{-}CH_2{-}CH_2{-}\overset{\overset{O}{\|}}{C}{\sim}S{-}CoA + CoA{-}S{\sim}\overset{\overset{O}{\|}}{C}{-}CH_3$$

The shortened fatty acyl CoA is further oxidized by cycling through reactions 2–5 until the fatty acid carbon chain is completely degraded to acetyl CoA. The acetyl CoA produced by β-oxidation of fatty acids then enters the reactions of the citric acid cycle. Of course, this eventually results in the production of 12 ATP molecules per molecule of acetyl CoA released during β-oxidation.

As an example of the energy yield from β-oxidation, the balance sheet for ATP production when the sixteen-carbon fatty acid palmitic acid is degraded by β-oxidation is summarized in Figure 23.8. Complete oxidation of palmitate results in production of 129 molecules of ATP, *three and one half times more energy than results from the complete oxidation of an equivalent amount of glucose.*

EXAMPLE 23.2 Calculating the Amount of ATP Produced in Complete Oxidation of a Fatty Acid

LEARNING GOAL

2 Describe the degradation of fatty acids by β-oxidation.

How many molecules of ATP are produced in the complete oxidation of stearic acid, an eighteen-carbon saturated fatty acid?

Solution

Step 1 (activation)	−2 ATP
Steps 2–5:	
8 $FADH_2$ × 2 ATP/$FADH_2$	16 ATP
8 NADH × 3 ATP/NADH	24 ATP

Continued...

9 acetyl CoA (to citric acid cycle):

9×1 GTP $\times$ 1 ATP/GTP	9 ATP
9×3 NADH $\times$ 3 ATP/NADH	81 ATP
9×1 $FADH_2$ $\times$ 2 ATP/$FADH_2$	18 ATP
	146 ATP

Practice Problem 23.2

Write out the sequence of steps for β-oxidation of butyryl CoA. What is the energy yield from the complete degradation of butyryl CoA via β-oxidation, the citric acid cycle, and oxidative phosphorylation?

▸ For Further Practice: **Questions 23.43 and 23.44.**

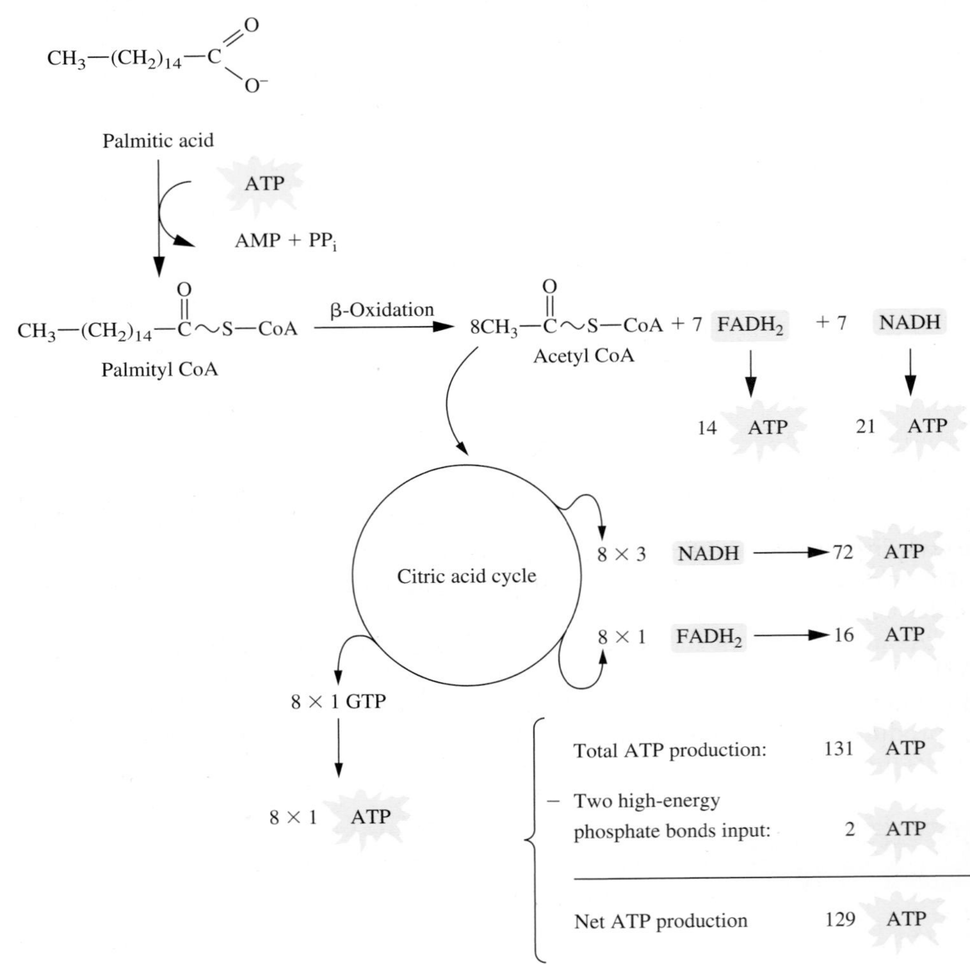

Figure 23.8 Complete oxidation of palmitic acid yields 129 molecules of ATP. Note that the activation step is considered to be an expenditure of two high-energy phosphoanhydride bonds because ATP is hydrolyzed to AMP + PP_i.

23.3 Ketone Bodies

LEARNING GOAL

4 Understand the role of ketone body production in β-oxidation.

For the acetyl CoA produced by the β-oxidation of fatty acids to efficiently enter the citric acid cycle, there must be an adequate supply of oxaloacetate. If glycolysis and β-oxidation are occurring at the same rate, there will be a steady supply of pyruvate (from glycolysis) that can be converted to oxaloacetate. But what happens

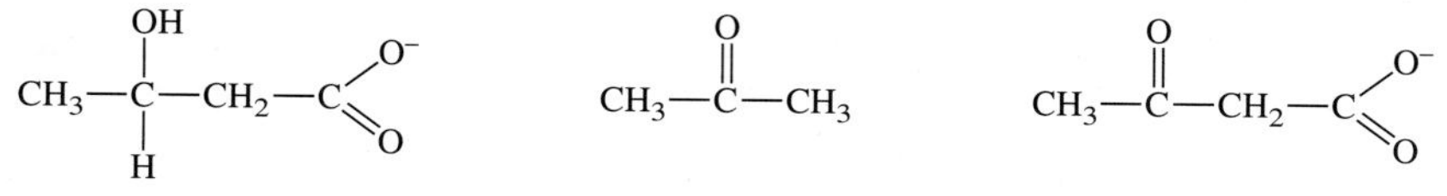

$$\mathrm{CH_3{-}\overset{\displaystyle OH}{\underset{\displaystyle H}{C}}{-}CH_2{-}C\begin{smallmatrix}O^-\\ \| \\ O\end{smallmatrix}}$$

β-Hydroxybutyrate

$$\mathrm{CH_3{-}\overset{\displaystyle O}{\overset{\|}{C}}{-}CH_3}$$

Acetone

$$\mathrm{CH_3{-}\overset{\displaystyle O}{\overset{\|}{C}}{-}CH_2{-}C\begin{smallmatrix}O^-\\ \| \\ O\end{smallmatrix}}$$

Acetoacetate

Figure 23.9 Structures of ketone bodies.

if the supply of oxaloacetate is too low to allow all of the acetyl CoA to enter the citric acid cycle? Under these conditions, acetyl CoA is converted to the so-called **ketone bodies:** β-hydroxybutyrate, acetone, and acetoacetate (Figure 23.9).

See Section 22.9 for a review of the reactions that provide oxaloacetate.

Ketosis

Ketosis, abnormally high levels of blood ketone bodies, is a situation that arises under some pathological conditions, such as starvation, a diet that is extremely low in carbohydrates (as with the high-protein diets), or uncontrolled **diabetes mellitus.** The carbohydrate intake of a diabetic is normal, but the carbohydrates cannot get into the cell to be used as fuel. Thus diabetes amounts to starvation in the midst of plenty. In diabetes the very high concentration of ketone acids in the blood leads to **ketoacidosis.** The ketone acids are relatively strong acids and therefore readily dissociate to release H^+. Under these conditions the blood pH becomes acidic, which can lead to death.

Diabetes mellitus is a disease characterized by the appearance of glucose in the urine as a result of high blood glucose levels. The disease is often caused by the inability to produce the hormone insulin.

Ketogenesis

The pathway for the production of ketone bodies (Figure 23.10) begins with a "reversal" of the last step of β-oxidation. When oxaloacetate levels are low, the enzyme that normally carries out the last reaction of β-oxidation now catalyzes the fusion of two acetyl CoA molecules to produce acetoacetyl CoA:

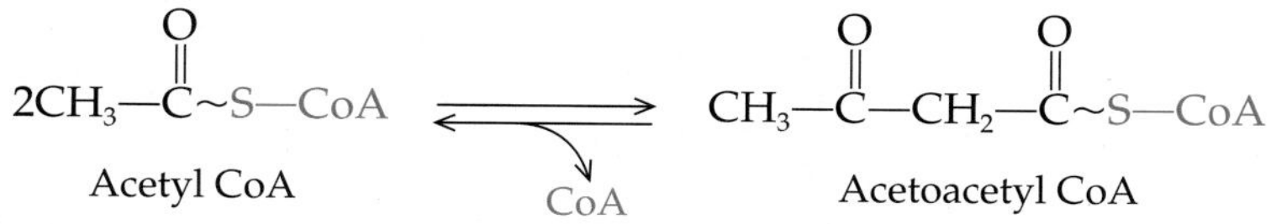

$$\underset{\text{Acetyl CoA}}{\mathrm{2CH_3{-}\overset{\displaystyle O}{\overset{\|}{C}}{\sim}S{-}CoA}} \xrightleftharpoons[\text{CoA}]{} \underset{\text{Acetoacetyl CoA}}{\mathrm{CH_3{-}\overset{\displaystyle O}{\overset{\|}{C}}{-}CH_2{-}\overset{\displaystyle O}{\overset{\|}{C}}{\sim}S{-}CoA}}$$

Acetoacetyl CoA can react with a third acetyl CoA molecule to yield β-hydroxy-β-methylglutaryl CoA (HMG-CoA):

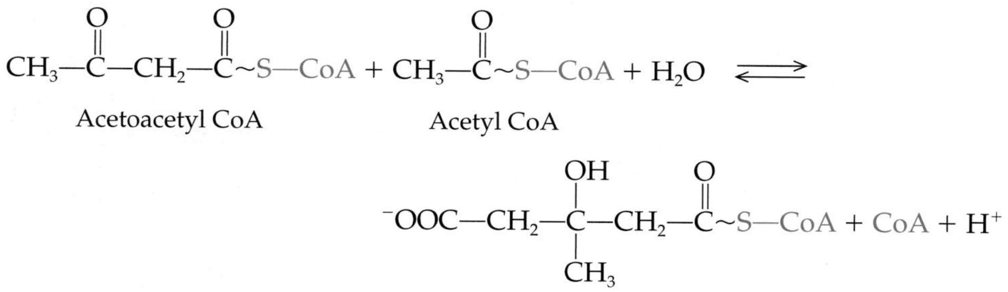

$$\underset{\text{Acetoacetyl CoA}}{\mathrm{CH_3{-}\overset{\displaystyle O}{\overset{\|}{C}}{-}CH_2{-}\overset{\displaystyle O}{\overset{\|}{C}}{\sim}S{-}CoA}} + \underset{\text{Acetyl CoA}}{\mathrm{CH_3{-}\overset{\displaystyle O}{\overset{\|}{C}}{\sim}S{-}CoA}} + \mathrm{H_2O} \rightleftharpoons$$

$$\underset{\text{HMG-CoA}}{\mathrm{{}^-OOC{-}CH_2{-}\overset{\displaystyle OH}{\underset{\displaystyle CH_3}{C}}{-}CH_2{-}\overset{\displaystyle O}{\overset{\|}{C}}{\sim}S{-}CoA}} + \mathrm{CoA} + \mathrm{H^+}$$

If HMG-CoA were formed in the cytoplasm, it would serve as a precursor for cholesterol biosynthesis. But ketogenesis, like β-oxidation, occurs in the mitochondrial matrix, and here HMG-CoA is cleaved to yield acetoacetate and acetyl CoA:

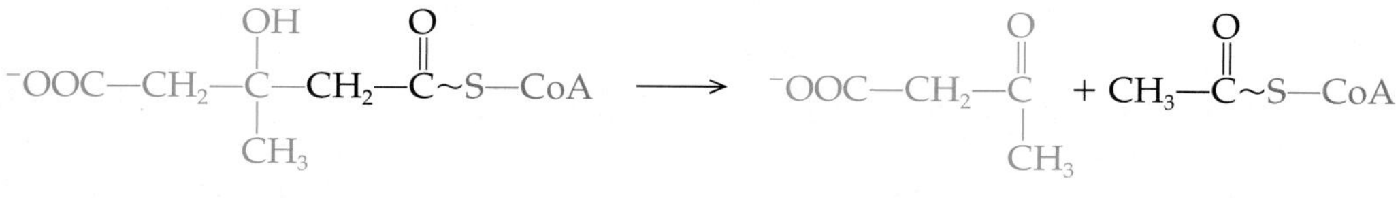

$$\underset{\text{HMG-CoA}}{\mathrm{{}^-OOC{-}CH_2{-}\overset{\displaystyle OH}{\underset{\displaystyle CH_3}{C}}{-}CH_2{-}\overset{\displaystyle O}{\overset{\|}{C}}{\sim}S{-}CoA}} \longrightarrow \underset{\text{Acetoacetate}}{\mathrm{{}^-OOC{-}CH_2{-}\overset{\displaystyle O}{\overset{\|}{\underset{\displaystyle CH_3}{C}}}}} + \underset{\text{Acetyl CoA}}{\mathrm{CH_3{-}\overset{\displaystyle O}{\overset{\|}{C}}{\sim}S{-}CoA}}$$

Figure 23.10 Summary of the reactions involved in ketogenesis.

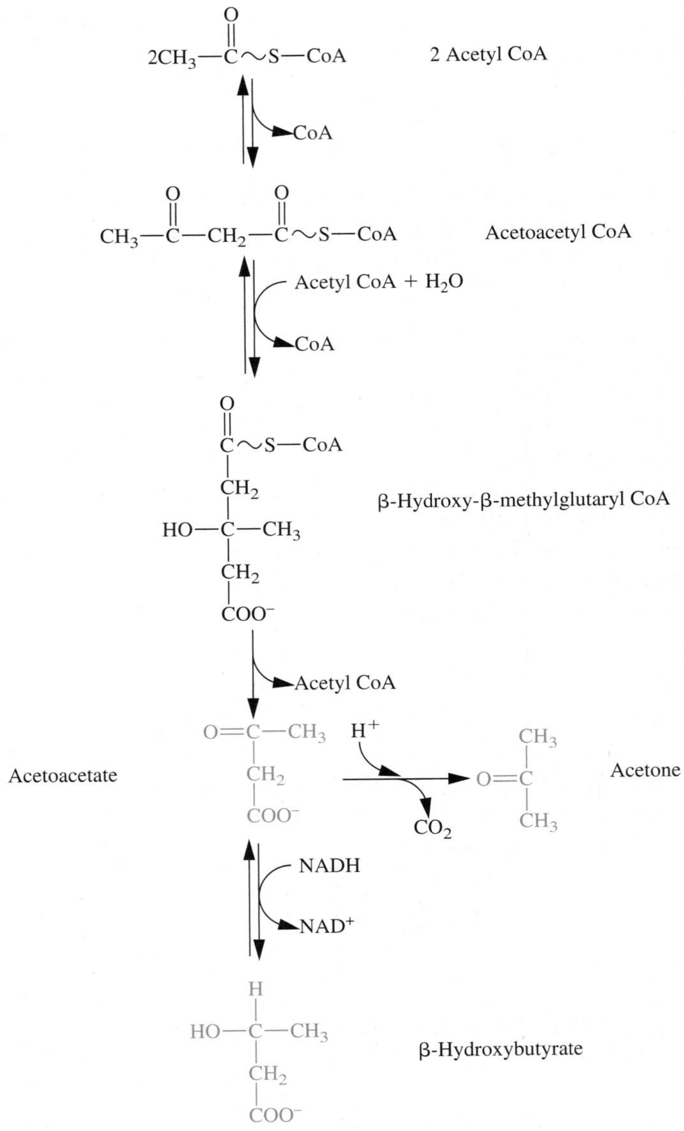

$$2CH_3-\overset{O}{\overset{\|}{C}}\sim S-CoA \quad \text{2 Acetyl CoA}$$

$$\rightleftharpoons \; (\rightarrow CoA)$$

$$CH_3-\overset{O}{\overset{\|}{C}}-CH_2-\overset{O}{\overset{\|}{C}}\sim S-CoA \quad \text{Acetoacetyl CoA}$$

$$\rightleftharpoons \; (\text{Acetyl CoA} + H_2O \rightarrow CoA)$$

$$\text{β-Hydroxy-β-methylglutaryl CoA: } \overset{O}{\overset{\|}{C}}\sim S-CoA-CH_2-C(OH)(CH_3)-CH_2-COO^-$$

$$\downarrow \; (\rightarrow \text{Acetyl CoA})$$

$$\text{Acetoacetate: } O=C(CH_3)-CH_2-COO^- \xrightarrow[CO_2]{H^+} O=C(CH_3)_2 \;\text{Acetone}$$

$$\rightleftharpoons \; (NADH \rightarrow NAD^+)$$

$$\text{β-Hydroxybutyrate: } HO-C(H)(CH_3)-CH_2-COO^-$$

In very small amounts, acetoacetate spontaneously loses carbon dioxide to give acetone. This is the reaction that causes the "acetone breath" that is often associated with uncontrolled diabetes mellitus.

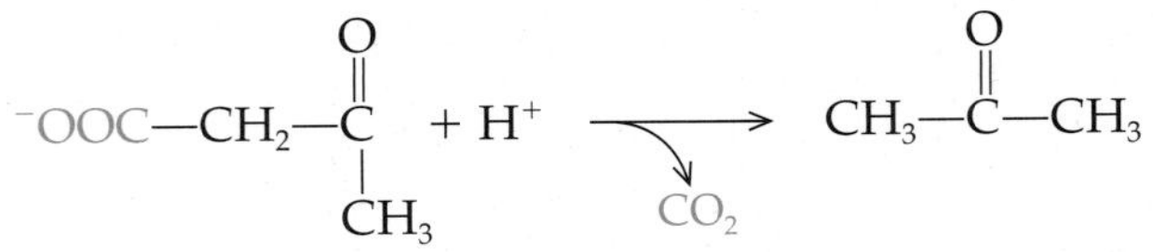

$$^-OOC-CH_2-\overset{O}{\overset{\|}{C}}-CH_3 + H^+ \xrightarrow[CO_2]{} CH_3-\overset{O}{\overset{\|}{C}}-CH_3$$

Acetoacetate → Acetone

More frequently, it undergoes NADH-dependent reduction to produce β-hydroxybutyrate:

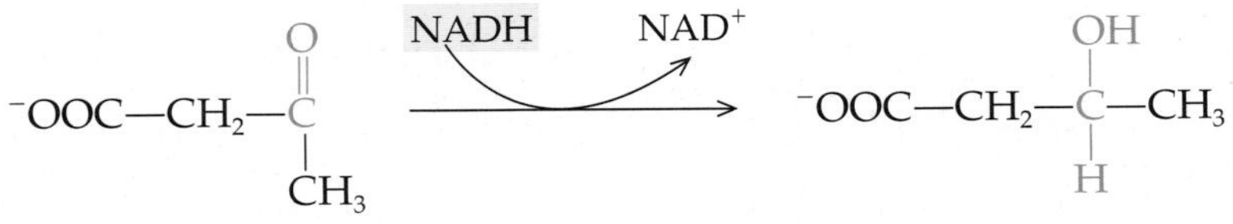

$$^-OOC-CH_2-\overset{O}{\overset{\|}{C}}-CH_3 \xrightarrow{NADH \rightarrow NAD^+} {}^-OOC-CH_2-\underset{H}{\overset{OH}{C}}-CH_3$$

Acetoacetate → β-Hydroxybutyrate

A HUMAN PERSPECTIVE

Losing Those Unwanted Pounds of Adipose Tissue

Weight, or overweight, is a topic of great concern to the American populace. A glance through almost any popular magazine quickly informs us that by today's standards, "beautiful" is synonymous with "thin." The models in all these magazines are extremely thin, and there are literally dozens of ads for weight-loss programs. Americans spend millions of dollars each year trying to attain this slim ideal of the fashion models.

Studies have revealed that this slim ideal is often below a desirable, healthy body weight. In fact, the suggested weight for a 6-foot (ft) tall male between 18 and 39 years of age is 179 pounds (lb). For a 5′6″ female in the same age range, the desired weight is 142 lb. For a 5′1″ female, 126 lb is recommended. Just as being too thin can cause health problems, so too can obesity.

What is obesity, and does it have disadvantages beyond aesthetics? An individual is considered to be obese if his or her body weight is more than 20% above the ideal weight for his or her height. Overweight carries with it a wide range of physical problems, including elevated blood cholesterol levels; high blood pressure; increased incidence of diabetes, cancer, and heart disease; and increased probability of early death. It often causes psychological problems as well, such as guilt and low self-esteem.

Many factors may contribute to obesity. These include genetic factors, a sedentary lifestyle, and a preference for high-calorie, high-fat foods. However, the real concern is how to lose weight. How can we lose weight wisely and safely and keep the weight off for the rest of our lives? Unfortunately, the answer is *not* the answer that most people want to hear. The prevalence and financial success of the quick-weight-loss programs suggest that the majority of people want a program that is rapid and effortless. Unfortunately, most programs that promise dramatic weight reduction with little effort are usually ineffective or, worse, unsafe. The truth is that weight loss and management are best obtained by a program involving three elements.

1. *Reduced caloric intake.* One pound of body fat is equivalent to 3500 Calories (Cal). So if you want to lose 2 lb each week, a reasonable goal, you must reduce your caloric intake by 1000 Cal per day. Remember that diets recommending fewer than 1200 Cal per day are difficult to maintain because they are not very satisfying and may be unsafe because they don't provide all the required vitamins and minerals. The best way to decrease Cal is to reduce fat and increase complex carbohydrates in the diet.
2. *Exercise.* Increase energy expenditures by 200–400 Cal each day. You may choose walking, running, or mowing the lawn; the type of activity doesn't matter, as long as you get moving. Exercise has additional benefits. It increases cardiovascular fitness, provides a psychological lift, and may increase the base rate at which you burn calories after exercise is finished.
3. *Behavior modification.* For some people, overweight is as much a psychological problem as it is a physical problem, and half the battle is learning to recognize the triggers that cause overeating. Several principles of behavior modification have been found to be very helpful.

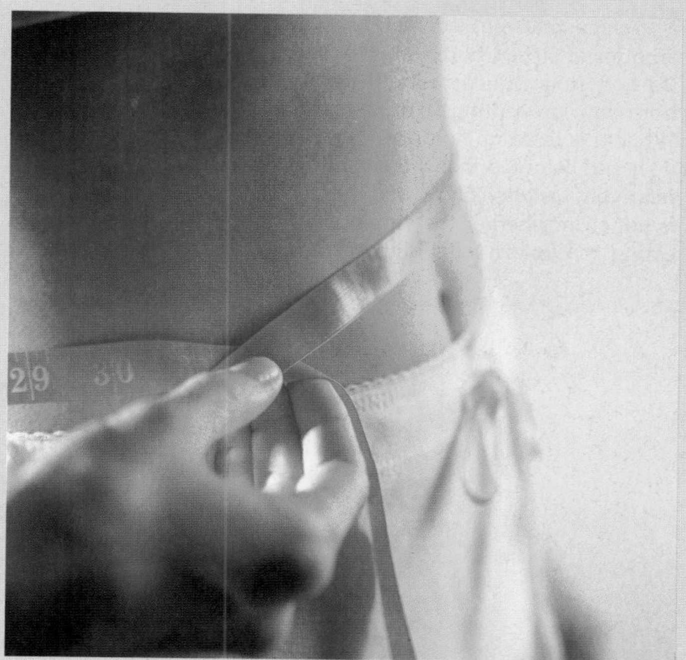

Reduced caloric intake and exercise are the keys to permanent weight loss.

   a. Keep a diary. Record the amount of foods eaten and the circumstances—for instance, a meal at the kitchen table or a bag of chips in the car on the way home.
   b. Identify your eating triggers. Do you eat when you feel stress, boredom, fatigue, joy?
   c. Develop a plan for avoiding or coping with your trigger situations or emotions. You might exercise when you feel that stress-at-the-end-of-the-day trigger or carry a bag of carrot sticks for the midmorning-boredom trigger.
   d. Set realistic goals, and reward yourself when you reach them. The reward should not be food related.

Traditionally, there has been no "quick fix" for safe, effective weight control. A commitment has to be made to modify existing diet and exercise habits. Most important, those habits have to be avoided forever and replaced by new, healthier behaviors and attitudes.

Frustrated by attempts to modify their diet and exercise, growing numbers of people are turning to bariatric surgery, such as the gastric bypass and the reversible laparoscopic stomach banding (lap-band) surgery. One study suggests that the gastric bypass surgery works not only because it reduces the size of the stomach, but because it also reduces the amount of ghrelin produced. Ghrelin is a hormone produced in the stomach that stimulates appetite.

Another interesting approach to the problem of weight loss has been the development of an antiobesity vaccine. A group of researchers at the Scripps Research Institute has developed

Continued...

Losing Those Unwanted Pounds of Adipose Tissue *(continued)*

a vaccine that slowed weight gain in rats and reduced the amount of stored body fat. The vaccine works by stimulating the body to produce antibodies against ghrelin. These bind the hormone, preventing it from reaching its target in the brain. While this research holds out hope for a safe obesity treatment, it should be noted that the rats in the study were given low-fat, relatively tasteless chow and were rather lean to begin with. It is not clear whether the vaccine would be effective in humans eating a "Western" diet high in calories and fat.

For Further Understanding

- In terms of the energy-harvesting reactions we have studied in Chapters 22 and 23, explain how reduced caloric intake and increase in activity level contribute to weight loss.
- If you increased your energy expenditure by 200 Cal per day and did not change your eating habits, how long would it take you to lose 10 lb?

Acetoacetate and β-hydroxybutyrate are produced primarily in the liver. These metabolites diffuse into the blood and are circulated to other tissues, where they may be reconverted to acetyl CoA and used to produce ATP. In fact, the heart muscle derives most of its metabolic energy from the oxidation of ketone bodies, not from the oxidation of glucose. Other tissues that are best adapted to the use of glucose will increasingly rely on ketone bodies for energy when glucose becomes unavailable or limited. This is particularly true of the brain.

Question 23.3 What conditions lead to excess production of ketone bodies?

Question 23.4 What is the cause of the characteristic "acetone breath" that is associated with uncontrolled diabetes mellitus?

23.4 Fatty Acid Synthesis

LEARNING GOAL

5 Compare β-oxidation of fatty acids and fatty acid biosynthesis.

All organisms possess the ability to synthesize fatty acids. In humans the excess acetyl CoA produced by carbohydrate degradation is used to make fatty acids that are then stored as triglycerides.

A Comparison of Fatty Acid Synthesis and Degradation

On first examination, fatty acid synthesis appears to be simply the reverse of β-oxidation. Specifically, the fatty acid chain is constructed by the sequential addition of two-carbon acetyl groups (Figure 23.11). Although the chemistry of fatty acid synthesis and breakdown are similar, there are several major differences between β-oxidation and fatty acid biosynthesis. These are summarized as follows.

- **Intracellular location.** The enzymes responsible for fatty acid biosynthesis are located in the cytoplasm of the cell, whereas those responsible for the degradation of fatty acids are in the mitochondria.
- **Acyl group carriers.** The activated intermediates of fatty acid biosynthesis are bound to a carrier molecule called the **acyl carrier protein (ACP)** (Figure 23.12). In β-oxidation the acyl group carrier was coenzyme A. However, there are important similarities between these two carriers. Both contain the **phosphopantetheine** group, which is made from the vitamin pantothenic acid. In both cases the fatty acyl group is bound by a thioester bond to the phosphopantetheine group.
- **Enzymes involved.** Fatty acid biosynthesis is carried out by a multienzyme complex known as *fatty acid synthase.* The enzymes responsible for fatty acid degradation are not physically associated in such complexes.

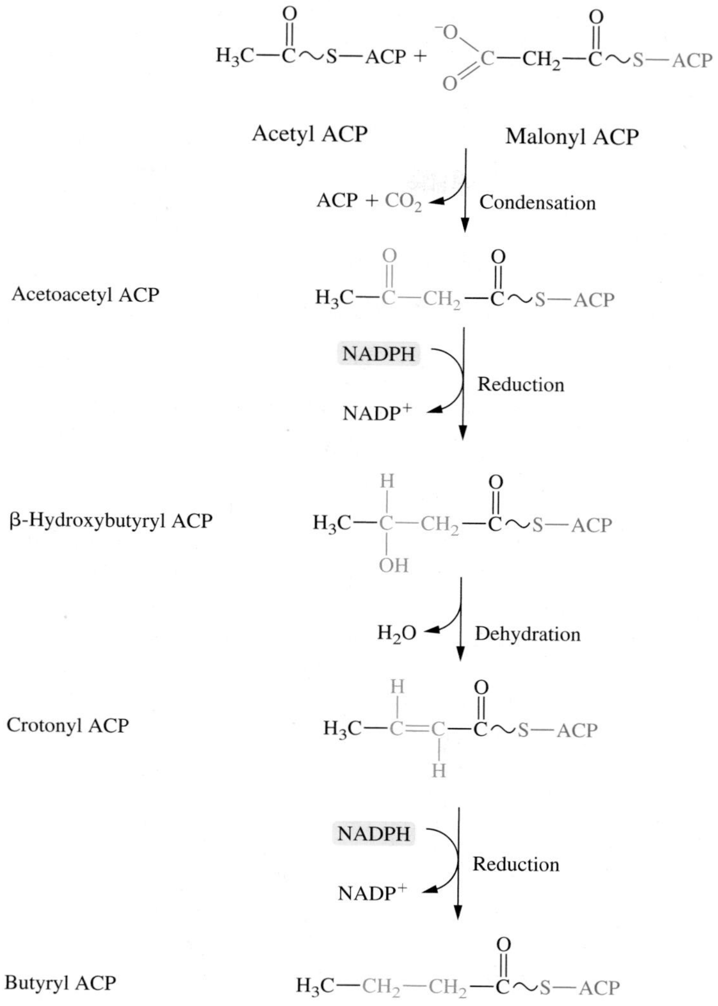

Acetyl ACP: $H_3C-C(=O)\sim S-ACP$ + Malonyl ACP: $^-O(O=)C-CH_2-C(=O)\sim S-ACP$

Condensation ($\rightarrow$ ACP + CO_2)

Acetoacetyl ACP: $H_3C-C(=O)-CH_2-C(=O)\sim S-ACP$

Reduction (NADPH $\rightarrow$ $NADP^+$)

β-Hydroxybutyryl ACP: $H_3C-CH(OH)-CH_2-C(=O)\sim S-ACP$

Dehydration ($\rightarrow H_2O$)

Crotonyl ACP: $H_3C-CH=CH-C(=O)\sim S-ACP$

Reduction (NADPH $\rightarrow$ $NADP^+$)

Butyryl ACP: $H_3C-CH_2-CH_2-C(=O)\sim S-ACP$

Figure 23.11 Summary of fatty acid synthesis. Malonyl ACP is produced in two reactions: carboxylation of acetyl CoA to produce malonyl CoA and transfer of the malonyl acyl group from malonyl CoA to ACP.

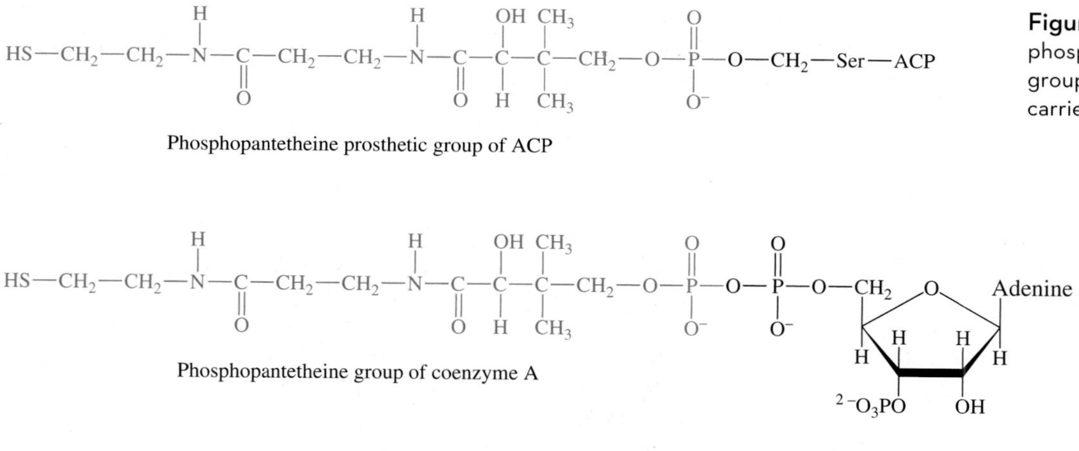

$HS-CH_2-CH_2-NH-C(=O)-CH_2-CH_2-NH-C(=O)-CH(OH)-C(CH_3)_2-CH_2-O-P(=O)(O^-)-O-CH_2-Ser-ACP$

Phosphopantetheine prosthetic group of ACP

$HS-CH_2-CH_2-NH-C(=O)-CH_2-CH_2-NH-C(=O)-CH(OH)-C(CH_3)_2-CH_2-O-P(=O)(O^-)-O-P(=O)(O^-)-O-CH_2$–(ribose: H, H, H, H, $^{2-}O_3PO$, OH)–Adenine

Phosphopantetheine group of coenzyme A

Figure 23.12 The structure of the phosphopantetheine group, the reactive group common to coenzyme A and acyl carrier protein, is highlighted in red.

- **Electron carriers.** NADH and $FADH_2$ are produced by fatty acid oxidation, whereas NADPH is the reducing agent for fatty acid biosynthesis. As a general rule, *NADH is produced by catabolic reactions, and NADPH is the reducing agent of biosynthetic reactions.* These two coenzymes differ only by the presence of a phosphate group bound to the ribose ring of NADPH (Figure 23.13). The enzymes that use these coenzymes, however, are easily able to distinguish them on this basis.

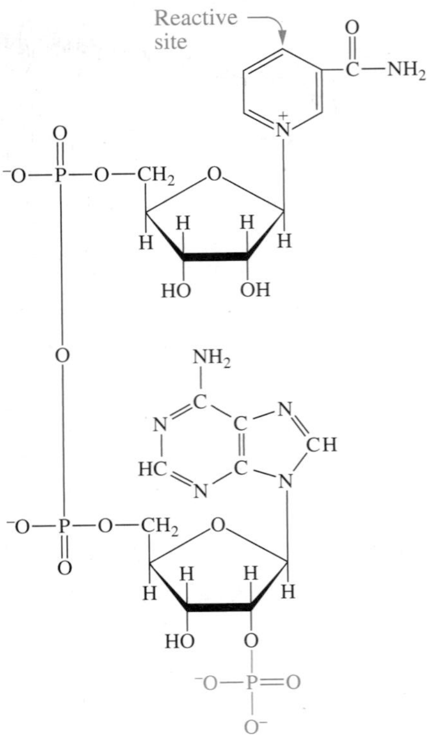

Figure 23.13 Structure of NADPH. The phosphate group shown in red is the structural feature that distinguishes NADPH from NADH.

Question 23.5 List the four major differences between β-oxidation and fatty acid biosynthesis that reveal that the two processes are not just the reverse of one another.

Question 23.6 What chemical group is part of coenzyme A and acyl carrier protein and allows both molecules to form thioester bonds to fatty acids?

23.5 The Regulation of Lipid and Carbohydrate Metabolism

LEARNING GOAL

6 Describe the regulation of lipid and carbohydrate metabolism in relation to the liver, adipose tissue, muscle tissue, and the brain.

The metabolism of fatty acids and carbohydrates occurs to a different extent in different organs. As we will see in this section, the regulation of these two related aspects of metabolism is of great physiological importance.

The Liver

The liver provides a steady supply of glucose for muscle and brain and plays a major role in the regulation of blood glucose concentration. This regulation is under hormonal control. Recall that the hormone insulin causes blood glucose to be taken up by the liver and stored as glycogen (*glycogenesis*). In this way the liver reduces the blood glucose levels when they are too high.

The hormone glucagon, on the other hand, stimulates the breakdown of glycogen and the release of glucose into the bloodstream. Lactate produced by muscles under anaerobic conditions is also taken up by liver cells and is converted to glucose by gluconeogenesis. Both glycogen degradation (*glycogenolysis*) and *gluconeogenesis* are pathways that produce glucose for export to other organs when energy is needed (Figure 23.14).

The liver also plays a central role in lipid metabolism. When excess fuel is available, the liver synthesizes fatty acids. These are used to produce triglycerides that are transported from the liver to adipose tissues by very low density lipoprotein (VLDL) complexes. In fact, VLDL complexes provide adipose tissue with its major source of fatty acids. This transport is particularly active when more calories are eaten than are burned! During fasting or starvation conditions, however, the liver converts fatty acids to acetoacetate and other ketone bodies. The liver cannot use these ketone bodies because it lacks an enzyme for the conversion of acetoacetate to acetyl CoA. Therefore the ketone bodies produced by the liver are exported to other organs where they are oxidized to make ATP.

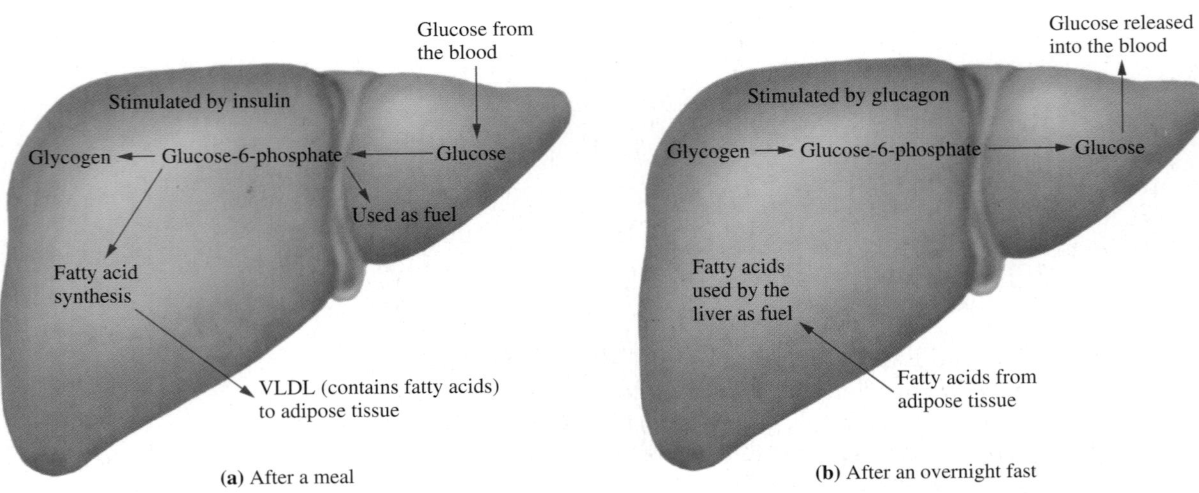

Figure 23.14 The liver controls the concentration of blood glucose.

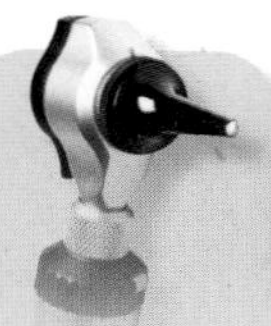

A MEDICAL PERSPECTIVE

Diabetes Mellitus and Ketone Bodies

More than one person, found unconscious on the streets of some metropolis, has been carted to jail only to die of complications arising from uncontrolled diabetes mellitus. Others are fortunate enough to arrive in hospital emergency rooms. A quick test for diabetes mellitus–induced coma is the odor of acetone on the breath of the afflicted person. Acetone is one of several metabolites produced by diabetics that are known collectively as *ketone bodies.*

The term *diabetes* was used by the ancient Greeks to designate diseases in which excess urine is produced. Two thousand years later, in the eighteenth century, the urine of certain individuals was found to contain sugar, and the name *diabetes mellitus* (Latin: *mellitus,* sweetened with honey) was given to this disease. People suffering from diabetes mellitus waste away as they excrete large amounts of sugar-containing urine.

The cause of insulin-dependent diabetes mellitus is inadequate production of insulin by the body. Insulin is secreted in response to high blood glucose levels. It binds to the membrane receptor protein on its target cells. Binding increases the rate of transport of glucose across the membrane and stimulates glycogen synthesis, lipid biosynthesis, and protein synthesis. As a result, the blood glucose level is reduced. Clearly, the inability to produce sufficient insulin seriously impairs the body's ability to regulate metabolism.

Individuals suffering from diabetes mellitus do not produce enough insulin to properly regulate blood glucose levels. This generally results from the destruction of the β-cells of the islets of Langerhans. One theory to explain the mysterious disappearance of these cells is that a virus infection stimulates the immune system to produce antibodies that cause the destruction of the β-cells.

In the absence of insulin the uptake of glucose into the tissues is not stimulated, and a great deal of glucose is eliminated

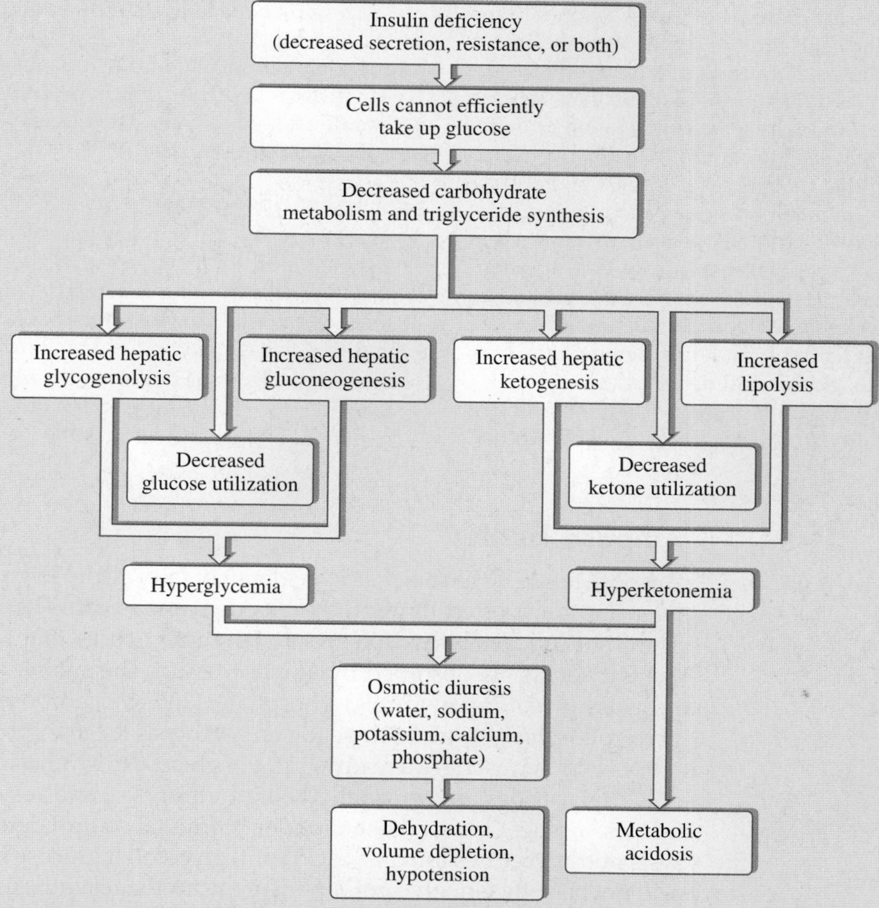

The metabolic events that occur in uncontrolled diabetes and that can lead to coma and death.

Continued...

Diabetes Mellitus and Ketone Bodies *(continued)*

in the urine. Without insulin, then, adipose cells are unable to take up the glucose required to synthesize triglycerides. As a result, the rate of fat hydrolysis is much greater than the rate of fat resynthesis, and large quantities of free fatty acids are liberated into the bloodstream. Because glucose is not being efficiently taken into cells, carbohydrate metabolism slows, and there is an increase in the rate of lipid catabolism. In the liver this lipid catabolism results in the production of ketone bodies: acetone, acetoacetate, and β-hydroxybutyrate.

A similar situation can develop from improper eating, fasting, or dieting—any situation in which the body is not provided with sufficient energy in the form of carbohydrates. These ketone bodies cannot all be oxidized by the citric acid cycle, which is limited by the supply of oxaloacetate. The acetone concentration in blood rises to levels so high that acetone can be detected in the breath of untreated diabetics. The elevated concentration of ketones in the blood can overwhelm the buffering capacity of the blood, resulting in ketoacidosis. Ketones, too, will be excreted through the kidney. In fact, the presence of excess ketones in the urine can raise the osmotic concentration of the urine so that it behaves as an "osmotic diuretic," causing the excretion of enormous amounts of water. As a result, the patient may become severely dehydrated. In extreme cases the combination of dehydration and ketoacidosis may lead to coma and death.

It has been observed that diabetics also have a higher than normal level of glucagon in the blood. As we have seen, glucagon stimulates lipid catabolism and ketogenesis. It may be that the symptoms previously described result from both the deficiency of insulin and the elevated glucagon levels. The absence of insulin may cause the elevated blood glucose and fatty acid levels, whereas the glucagon, by stimulating ketogenesis, may be responsible for the ketoacidosis and dehydration.

There is no cure for diabetes. However, when the problem is the result of the inability to produce active insulin, blood glucose levels can be controlled moderately well by the injection of human insulin produced from the cloned insulin gene. Unfortunately, one or even a few injections of insulin each day cannot mimic the precise control of blood glucose accomplished by the pancreas.

As a result, diabetics suffer progressive tissue degeneration that leads to early death. One primary cause of this degeneration is atherosclerosis, the deposition of plaque on the walls of blood vessels. This causes a high frequency of strokes, heart attack, and gangrene of the feet and lower extremities, often necessitating amputation. Kidney failure causes the death of about 20% of diabetics under 40 years of age, and diabetic retinopathy (various kinds of damage to the retina of the eye) ranks fourth among the leading causes of blindness in the United States. Nerves are also damaged, resulting in neuropathies that can cause pain or numbness, particularly of the feet.

There is no doubt that insulin injections prolong the life of diabetics, but only the presence of a fully functioning pancreas can allow a diabetic to live a life free of the complications noted here. At present, pancreas transplants do not have a good track record. Only about 50% of the transplants are functioning after 1 year. It is hoped that improved transplantation techniques will be developed so that diabetics can live a normal life span, free of debilitating disease.

For Further Understanding

- The Atkins' low carbohydrate diet recommends that dieters test their urine for the presence of ketone bodies as an indicator that the diet is working. In terms of lipid and carbohydrate metabolism, explain why ketone bodies are being produced and why this is an indication that the diet is working.
- An excess of ketone bodies in the blood causes ketoacidosis. Consider the chemical structure of the ketone bodies and explain why they are acids.

Adipose Tissue

Adipose tissue is the major storage depot of fatty acids. Triglycerides produced by the liver are transported through the bloodstream as components of VLDL complexes. The triglycerides are hydrolyzed by the same lipases that act on chylomicrons, and the fatty acids are absorbed by adipose tissue. The synthesis of triglycerides in adipose tissue requires glycerol-3-phosphate. However, adipose tissue is unable to make glycerol-3-phosphate and depends on glycolysis for its supply of this molecule. Thus adipose cells must have a ready source of glucose to synthesize and store triglycerides.

```
      H
      |
  H—C—OH
      |
  H—C—OH   O
      |    ||
  H—C——O—P—O⁻
      |    |
      H    O⁻
```

Glycerol-3-phosphate

Triglycerides are constantly being hydrolyzed and resynthesized in the cells of adipose tissue. Lipases that are under hormonal control determine the rate of hydrolysis of triglycerides into fatty acids and glycerol. If glucose is in limited supply, there will not be sufficient glycerol-3-phosphate for the resynthesis of triglycerides, and the fatty acids and glycerol are exported to the liver for further processing (Figure 23.15).

Muscle Tissue

The energy demand of resting muscle is generally supplied by the β-oxidation of fatty acids. The heart muscle actually prefers ketone bodies over glucose.

Working muscle, however, obtains energy by degradation of its own supply of glycogen. Glycogen degradation produces glucose-6-phosphate, which is directly funneled into glycolysis. If the muscle is working so hard that it doesn't get enough oxygen, it produces large amounts of lactate. This fermentation end product, as well as alanine (from catabolism of proteins and transamination of pyruvate), is exported to the liver. Here they are converted to glucose by gluconeogenesis (Figure 23.16).

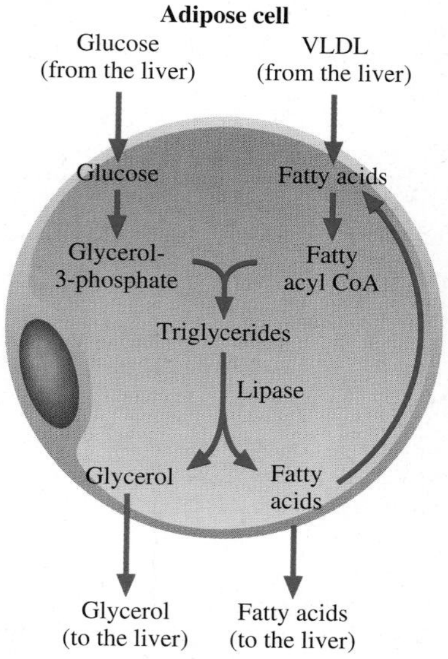

Figure 23.15 Synthesis and degradation of triglycerides in adipose tissue.

The Brain

Under normal conditions the brain uses glucose as its sole source of metabolic energy. When the body is in the resting state, about 60% of the free glucose of the body is used by the brain. Starvation depletes glycogen stores, and the amount of glucose available to the brain drops sharply. The ketone bodies acetoacetate and β-hydroxybutyrate are then used by the brain as an alternative energy source. Fatty acids are transported in the blood in complexes with proteins and cannot cross the blood-brain barrier to be used by brain cells as an energy source. But ketone bodies, which have a free carboxyl group, are soluble in blood and can enter the brain.

Question 23.7 How does the liver regulate blood glucose levels?

Question 23.8 Why is regulation of blood glucose levels important to the efficient function of the brain?

23.6 The Effects of Insulin and Glucagon on Cellular Metabolism

LEARNING GOAL

7 Summarize the antagonistic effects of glucagon and insulin.

The hormone **insulin** is produced by the β-cells of the islets of Langerhans in the pancreas. It is secreted from these cells in response to an increase in the blood glucose level. Insulin lowers the concentration of blood glucose by causing a number of changes in metabolism (Table 23.1).

The simplest way to lower blood glucose levels is to stimulate storage of glucose, both as glycogen and as triglycerides. *Insulin therefore activates biosynthetic processes and inhibits catabolic processes.*

The effect of insulin on glycogen metabolism is described in Section 21.7.

Insulin acts only on those cells, known as *target cells,* that possess a specific insulin receptor protein in their plasma membranes. The major target cells for insulin are liver, adipose, and muscle cells.

Figure 23.16 Metabolic relationships between liver and muscle.

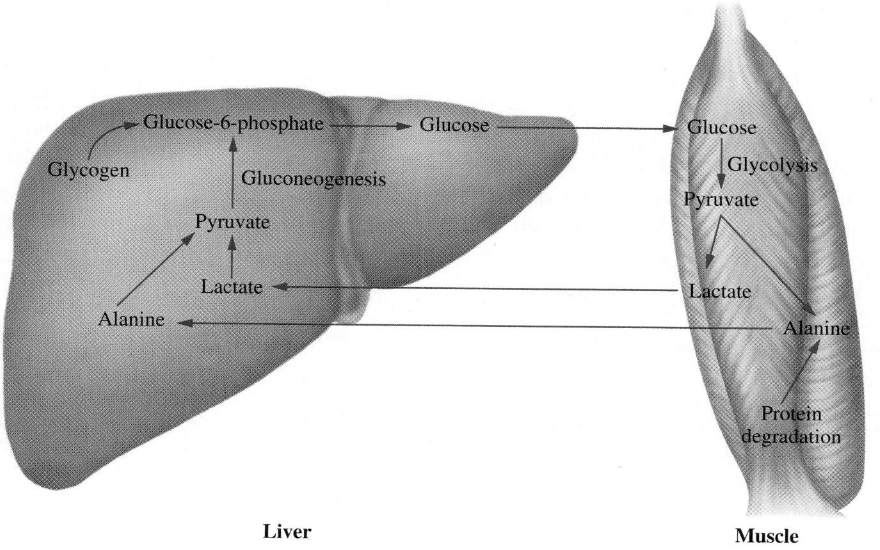

TABLE 23.1 Comparison of the Metabolic Effects of Insulin and Glucagon

Actions	Insulin	Glucagon
Cellular glucose transport	Increased	No effect
Glycogen synthesis	Increased	Decreased
Glycogenolysis in liver	Decreased	Increased
Gluconeogenesis	Decreased	Increased
Amino acid uptake and protein synthesis	Increased	No effect
Inhibition of amino acid release and protein degradation	Decreased	No effect
Lipogenesis	Increased	No effect
Lipolysis	Decreased	Increased
Ketogenesis	Decreased	Increased

The blood glucose level is normally about 10 millimolar (mM). However, a substantial meal increases the concentration of blood glucose considerably and stimulates insulin secretion. Subsequent binding of insulin to the plasma membrane insulin receptor increases the rate of transport of glucose across the membrane and into cells.

Insulin exerts a variety of effects on all aspects of cellular metabolism:

- **Carbohydrate metabolism.** Insulin stimulates glycogen synthesis. At the same time it inhibits glycogenolysis and gluconeogenesis. The overall result of these activities is the storage of excess glucose.
- **Protein metabolism.** Insulin stimulates transport and uptake of amino acids, as well as the incorporation of amino acids into proteins.
- **Lipid metabolism.** Insulin stimulates uptake of glucose by adipose cells, as well as the synthesis and storage of triglycerides. As we have seen, storage of lipids requires a source of glucose, and insulin helps the process by increasing the available glucose. At the same time, insulin inhibits the breakdown of stored triglycerides.

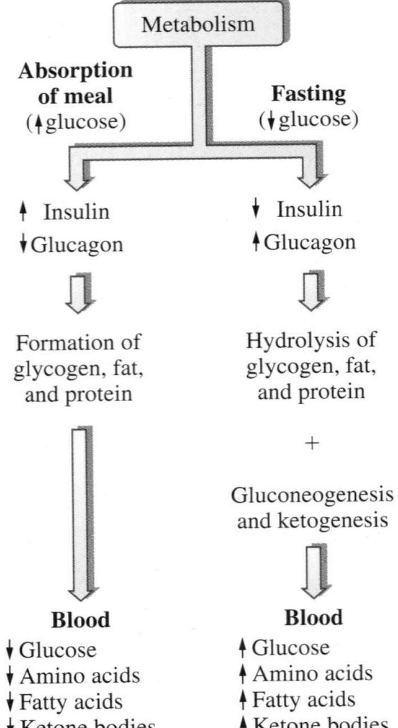

Figure 23.17 A summary of the antagonistic effects of insulin and glucagon.

As you may have already guessed, insulin is only part of the overall regulation of cellular metabolism in the body. A second hormone, **glucagon,** is secreted by the α-cells of the islets of Langerhans in response to decreased blood glucose levels. The effects of glucagon, generally the opposite of the effects of insulin, are summarized in Table 23.1. Although it has no direct effect on glucose uptake, glucagon inhibits glycogen synthesis and stimulates glycogenolysis and gluconeogenesis. It also stimulates the breakdown of fats and ketogenesis.

The antagonistic effects of these two hormones, seen in Figure 23.17, are critical for the maintenance of adequate blood glucose levels. During fasting, low blood glucose levels stimulate production of glucagon, which increases blood glucose by stimulating the breakdown of glycogen and the production of glucose by gluconeogenesis. This ensures a ready supply of glucose for the tissues, especially the brain. On the other hand, when blood glucose levels are too high, insulin is secreted. It stimulates the removal of the excess glucose by enhancing uptake and inducing pathways for storage.

Question 23.9 Summarize the effects of the hormone insulin on carbohydrate, lipid, and amino acid metabolism.

Question 23.10 Summarize the effects of the hormone glucagon on carbohydrate and lipid metabolism.

CHAPTER MAP

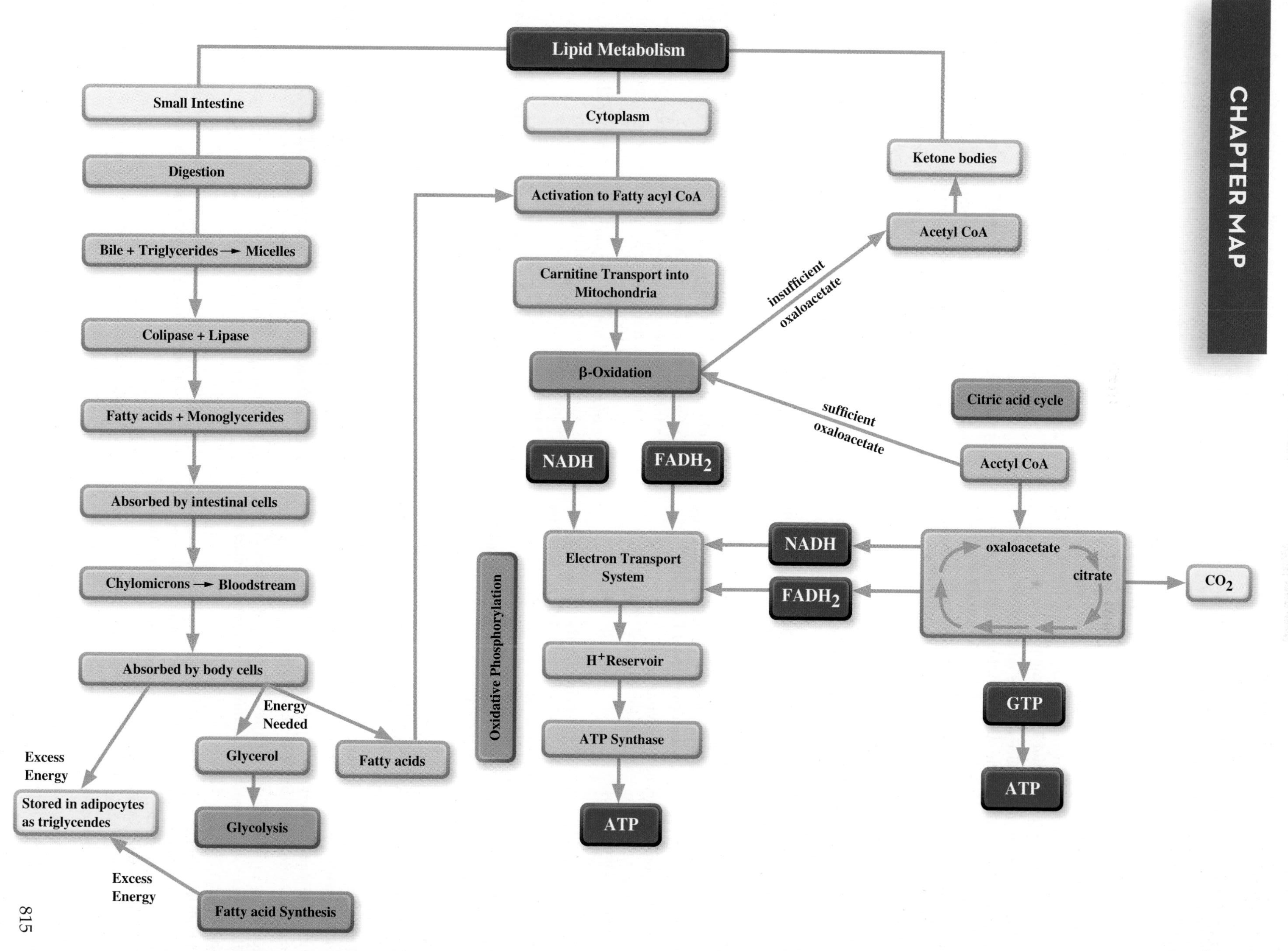

Lipid Metabolism
Small Intestine
Digestion
Bile + Triglycerides → Micelles
Colipase + Lipase
Fatty acids + Monoglycerides
Absorbed by intestinal cells
Chylomicrons → Bloodstream
Absorbed by body cells
Energy Needed
Glycerol
Glycolysis
Fatty acids
Excess Energy
Stored in adipocytes as triglycendes
Excess Energy
Fatty acid Synthesis
Cytoplasm
Activation to Fatty acyl CoA
Carnitine Transport into Mitochondria
β-Oxidation
NADH
$FADH_2$
Oxidative Phosphorylation
Electron Transport System
H^+Reservoir
ATP Synthase
ATP
Ketone bodies
Acetyl CoA
insufficient oxaloacetate
sufficient oxaloacetate
Citric acid cycle
Acctyl CoA
NADH
$FADH_2$
oxaloacetate
citrate
CO_2
GTP
ATP

SUMMARY

23.1 Lipid Metabolism in Animals

- ▶ **Dietary lipids (triglycerides) are emulsified into tiny fat droplets in the intestine by the action of bile. Bile is composed of micelles consisting of lecithin, cholesterol, protein, bile salts, inorganic ions, and bile pigments.**
- ▶ **Colipase binds to the surface of these fat droplets and helps pancreatic lipase stick to the surface so that it can catalyze the hydrolysis of triglycerides into monoglycerides and fatty acids.**
- ▶ **These are absorbed by the intestinal epithelial cells, reassembled into triglycerides, and packaged with proteins to form chylomicrons.**
- ▶ **Chylomicrons are transported to the cells of the body through the bloodstream.**
- ▶ **Fatty acids are stored as triglycerides (triacylglycerols) in fat droplets in the cytoplasm of adipocytes.**
- ▶ **Adipose tissue is composed of adipocytes and is a means of energy storage in the body.**

23.2 Fatty Acid Degradation

- ▶ **Fatty acids are degraded to acetyl CoA in the mitochondria by the β-oxidation pathway, which consists of five steps:**
  - Production of a fatty acyl CoA molecule
  - Oxidation of the fatty acid by an FAD-dependent dehydrogenase
  - Hydration
  - Oxidation by an NAD^+-dependent dehydrogenase
  - Cleavage of the chain with release of acetyl CoA and a fatty acyl CoA that is two carbons shorter than the beginning fatty acid.
- ▶ **The last four reactions are repeated until the fatty acid is completely degraded to acetyl CoA.**

23.3 Ketone Bodies

- ▶ **Under some conditions, fatty acid degradation occurs more rapidly than glycolysis.**
- ▶ **This results in a large amount of acetyl CoA from β-oxidation, but an insufficient amount of oxaloacetate from glycolysis.**
- ▶ **In this situation, acetyl CoA is converted to ketone bodies: acetone, acetoacetate, and β-hydroxybutyrate.**
- ▶ **Ketosis, an abnormally high level of ketone bodies in the blood, may result from starvation or uncontrolled diabetes mellitus.**
- ▶ **A high level of ketone bodies in the blood causes ketoacidosis because the ketone acids β-hydroxybutyrate and acetoacetate are relatively strong acids. When they dissociate, the blood pH may drop to life-threatening levels.**

23.4 Fatty Acid Synthesis

- ▶ **Fatty acid biosynthesis occurs by sequential addition of acetyl groups, but is not the reverse of β-oxidation.**
- ▶ **Although the chemical reactions are similar, fatty acid synthesis differs from β-oxidation in the following ways:**
  - It occurs in the cytoplasm.
  - It utilizes **acyl carrier protein (ACP)** rather than coenzyme A, both of which have the **phosphopantetheine** group as the functional part of the molecule that binds to the acetyl or acyl group.
  - It utilizes NADPH, rather than NADH.
  - It is carried out by a multienzyme complex called *fatty acid synthase.*

23.5 The Regulation of Lipid and Carbohydrate Metabolism

- ▶ **The liver regulates the flow of metabolites to brain, muscle, and adipose tissue, and ultimately controls the blood glucose level.**
- ▶ **In adipose tissue, the major storage depot for fatty acids, triglycerides are constantly hydrolyzed and resynthesized.**
- ▶ **Muscle can oxidize glucose, fatty acids, and ketone bodies.**
- ▶ **The brain uses only glucose as a fuel except in prolonged starvation or fasting, when it will use ketone bodies as fuel.**

23.6 The Effects of Insulin and Glucagon on Cellular Metabolism

- ▶ **Insulin activates biosynthetic processes and inhibits catabolic processes as follows:**
  - Stimulates glycogen synthesis
  - Inhibits glycogen degradation and gluconeogenesis
  - Stimulates transport and uptake of amino acids and their incorporation into proteins
  - Stimulates uptake of glucose by adipose cells, as well as synthesis and storage of triglycerides
  - Inhibits breakdown of stored triglycerides
  - Inhibits ketogenesis
- ▶ **The effects of glucagon are generally the opposite of those of insulin in the following ways:**
  - Inhibits glycogen synthesis
  - Stimulates glycogen breakdown and gluconeogenesis
  - Stimulates the breakdown of stored triglycerides
  - Stimulates ketogenesis

ANSWERS TO PRACTICE PROBLEMS

23.1 a. The products of the β-oxidation of 9-phenylnonanoic acid are 4 acetyl CoA, 1 benzoate, 4 NADH, and 4 $FADH_2$.

b. The products of the β-oxidation of 8-phenyloctanoic acid are 3 acetyl CoA, 1 phenyl acetate, 3 NADH, and 3 $FADH_2$.

c. The products of the β-oxidation of 7-phenylheptanoic acid are 3 acetyl CoA, 1 benzoate, 3 NADH, and 3 $FADH_2$.

d. The products of the β-oxidation of 12-phenyldodecanoic acid are 5 acetyl CoA, 1 phenyl acetate, 5 NADH, and 5 $FADH_2$.

23.2 The following equations show the steps for the β-oxidation of butyryl CoA:

$$CH_3CH_2CH_2—\overset{O}{\overset{\|}{C}}\sim S—CoA$$

$$\downarrow \; FAD$$

$$CH_3CH{=}CH—\overset{O}{\overset{\|}{C}}\sim S—CoA + FADH_2$$

$$\downarrow \; H_2O$$

$$CH_3\overset{OH}{\overset{|}{C}H}—CH_2—\overset{O}{\overset{\|}{C}}\sim S—CoA$$

$$\downarrow \; NAD^+$$

$$CH_3—\overset{O}{\overset{\|}{C}}—CH_2—\overset{O}{\overset{\|}{C}}\sim S—CoA + NADH$$

$$\downarrow \; \text{Coenzyme A}$$

$$2\ CH_3—\overset{O}{\overset{\|}{C}}\sim S—CoA$$

The energy yield from the complete degradation of butyryl CoA via β-oxidation, the citric acid cycle, and oxidative phosphorylation is summarized below:

Butyryl CoA has already been activated, so no ATP investment is needed.

β-Oxidation:

1 $FADH_2$ × 2 ATP/$FADH_2$	2 ATP
1 NADH × 3 ATP/NADH	3 ATP

Citric acid cycle (2 acetyl CoA):

6 NADH × 3 ATP/NADH	18 ATP
2 $FADH_2$ × 2 ATP/$FADH_2$	4 ATP
2 GTP × 1 ATP/GTP	2 ATP
	29 ATP

QUESTIONS AND PROBLEMS

Lipid Metabolism in Animals

Foundations

23.11 Draw the structures of the bile salts cholate and chenodeoxycholate.
23.12 To what class of lipids do the bile salts belong?
23.13 Define the term *micelle.*
23.14 In Figure 23.1, a micelle composed of the phospholipid lecithin is shown. Why is lecithin a good molecule for the formation of micelles?
23.15 Define the term *triglyceride.*
23.16 Draw the structure of a triglyceride composed of glycerol, palmitoleic acid, linolenic acid, and oleic acid.
23.17 Describe the structure of chylomicrons.
23.18 Why is colipase needed for lipid digestion?

Applications

23.19 What is the major storage form of fatty acids?
23.20 What tissue is the major storage depot for lipids?
23.21 What is the outstanding structural feature of an adipocyte?
23.22 What is the major metabolic function of adipose tissue?
23.23 What is the general reaction catalyzed by lipases?
23.24 Why are the lipases that are found in saliva and in the stomach not very effective at digesting triglycerides?
23.25 List three major biological molecules for which acetyl CoA is a precursor.
23.26 Why are triglycerides more efficient energy-storage molecules than glycogen?
23.27 What is the function of chylomicrons?
23.28 **a.** What are very low density lipoproteins?
b. Compare the function of VLDLs with that of chylomicrons.
23.29 What is the function of the bile salts in the digestion of dietary lipids?
23.30 What is the function of colipase in the digestion of dietary lipids?
23.31 Describe the stages of lipid digestion.
23.32 Describe the transport of lipids digested in the lumen of the intestines to the cells of the body.

Fatty Acid Degradation

Foundations

23.33 What is the energy source for the activation of a fatty acid in preparation for β-oxidation?
23.34 Which bond in fatty acyl CoA is a high-energy bond?
23.35 What is carnitine?
23.36 Explain the mechanism by which a fatty acyl group is brought into the mitochondrial matrix.
23.37 Explain why the reaction catalyzed by acyl-CoA dehydrogenase is an example of an oxidation reaction.
23.38 What is the reactant that is oxidized in the reaction catalyzed by acyl-CoA dehydrogenase? What is the reactant that is reduced in this reaction?
23.39 What is the product of the hydration of an alkene?
23.40 Which reaction in β-oxidation is a hydration reaction? What is the name of the enzyme that catalyzes this reaction? Write an equation representing this reaction.

Applications

23.41 What products are formed when the ω-phenyl-labeled carboxylic acid 14-phenyltetradecanoic acid is degraded by β-oxidation?
23.42 What products are formed when the ω-phenyl-labeled carboxylic acid 5-phenylpentanoic acid is degraded by β-oxidation?
23.43 Calculate the number of ATP molecules produced by complete β-oxidation of the fourteen-carbon saturated fatty acid tetradecanoic acid (common name: myristic acid).
23.44 **a.** Write the sequence of steps that would be followed for one round of β-oxidation of hexanoic acid.
b. Calculate the number of ATP molecules produced by complete β-oxidation of hexanoic acid.
23.45 Calculate the number of ATP molecules produced by complete β-oxidation of lauric acid.
23.46 Calculate the number of ATP molecules produced by the complete β-oxidation of eicosanoic acid.

23.47 What is the fate of the acetyl CoA produced by β-oxidation?
23.48 How many ATP molecules are produced from each acetyl CoA molecule generated in β-oxidation that enters the citric acid cycle?

Ketone Bodies

Foundations

23.49 What are ketone bodies?
23.50 What are the chemical properties of ketone bodies?
23.51 What is ketosis?
23.52 Define *ketoacidosis.*
23.53 In what part of the cell does ketogenesis occur? Be specific.
23.54 What would be the fate of HMG-CoA produced in ketogenesis if it were produced in the cell cytoplasm?

Applications

23.55 Draw the structures of acetoacetate and β-hydroxybutyrate.
23.56 Describe the relationship between the formation of ketone bodies and β-oxidation.
23.57 Why do uncontrolled diabetics produce large amounts of ketone bodies?
23.58 How does the presence of ketone bodies in the blood lead to ketoacidosis?
23.59 When does the heart use ketone bodies?
23.60 When does the brain use ketone bodies?

Fatty Acid Synthesis

Foundations

23.61 Where in the cell does fatty acid biosynthesis occur?
23.62 What is the acyl group carrier in fatty acid biosynthesis?
23.63 Draw the structure of NADPH.
23.64 What is the function of NADPH in fatty acid biosynthesis?

Applications

23.65 **a.** What is the role of the phosphopantetheine group in fatty acid biosynthesis?
b. From what molecule is phosphopantetheine made?
23.66 What molecules involved in fatty acid degradation and fatty acid biosynthesis contain the phosphopantetheine group?
23.67 How does the structure of fatty acid synthase differ from that of the enzymes that carry out β-oxidation?
23.68 In what cellular compartments do fatty acid biosynthesis and β-oxidation occur?

The Regulation of Lipid and Carbohydrate Metabolism

Foundations

23.69 Define the term *glycogenesis.*
23.70 Define the term *glycogenolysis.*
23.71 Define the term *gluconeogenesis.*
23.72 How are the fatty acids synthesized in the liver transported to adipose tissue?

Applications

23.73 Which pathway provides the majority of the ATP for *resting* muscle?
23.74 Why is the liver unable to utilize ketone bodies as an energy source?
23.75 What is the major metabolic function of the liver?
23.76 What is the fate of lactate produced in skeletal muscle during rapid contraction?
23.77 What are the major fuels of the heart, brain, and liver?
23.78 Why can't the brain use fatty acids as fuel?
23.79 Briefly describe triglyceride metabolism in an adipocyte.
23.80 What is the source of the glycerol molecule that is used in the synthesis of triglycerides?

The Effects of Insulin and Glucagon on Cellular Metabolism

Foundations

23.81 In general, what is the effect of insulin on catabolic and anabolic or biosynthetic processes?
23.82 What is the trigger that causes insulin to be secreted into the bloodstream?
23.83 What is meant by the term *target cell?*
23.84 What are the primary target cells of insulin?
23.85 What is the trigger that causes glucagon to be secreted into the bloodstream?
23.86 What are the primary target cells of glucagon?

Applications

23.87 Where is insulin produced?
23.88 Where is glucagon produced?
23.89 How does insulin affect carbohydrate metabolism?
23.90 How does glucagon affect carbohydrate metabolism?
23.91 How does insulin affect lipid metabolism?
23.92 How does glucagon affect lipid metabolism?
23.93 Explain the importance of the antagonistic effects of insulin and glucagon.
23.94 How does the presence of the insulin receptor on the surface of a cell identify that cell as a target cell?

CRITICAL THINKING PROBLEMS

1. Suppose that fatty acids were degraded by sequential oxidation of the α-carbon. What product(s) would Knoop have obtained with fatty acids with even numbers of carbon atoms? What product(s) would he have obtained with fatty acids with odd numbers of carbon atoms?
2. Oil-eating bacteria can oxidize long-chain alkanes. In the first step of the pathway, the enzyme monooxygenase catalyzes a reaction that converts the long-chain alkane into a primary alcohol. Data from research studies indicate that three more reactions are required to allow the primary alcohol to enter the β-oxidation pathway. Propose a pathway that would convert the long-chain alcohol into a product that could enter the β-oxidation pathway.
3. A young woman sought the advice of her physician because she was 30 lb overweight. The excess weight was in the form of triglycerides carried in adipose tissue. Yet when the woman described her diet, it became obvious that she actually ate very moderate amounts of fatty foods. Most of her caloric intake was in the form of carbohydrates. This included candy, cake, beer, and soft drinks. Explain how the excess calories

consumed in the form of carbohydrates ended up being stored as triglycerides in adipose tissue.

4. Olestra is a fat substitute that provides no calories, yet has a creamy, tongue-pleasing consistency. Because it can withstand heating, it can be used to prepare foods such as potato chips and crackers. Olestra is a sucrose polyester produced by esterification of six, seven, or eight fatty acids to molecules of sucrose. Develop a hypothesis to explain why olestra is not a source of dietary calories.

5. Carnitine is a tertiary amine found in mitochondria that is involved in transporting the acyl groups of fatty acids from the cytoplasm into the mitochondria. The fatty acyl group is transferred from a fatty acyl CoA molecule and esterified to carnitine. Inside the mitochondria, the reaction is reversed and the fatty acid enters the β-oxidation pathway.

   A 17-year-old male went to a university medical center complaining of fatigue and poor exercise tolerance. Muscle biopsies revealed droplets of triglycerides in his muscle cells. Biochemical analysis showed that he had only one-fifth of the normal amount of carnitine in his muscle cells.

   What effect will carnitine deficiency have on β-oxidation? What effect will carnitine deficiency have on glucose metabolism?

6. Acetyl CoA carboxylase catalyzes the formation of malonyl CoA from acetyl CoA and the bicarbonate anion, a reaction that requires the hydrolysis of ATP. Write a balanced equation showing this reaction.

   The reaction catalyzed by acetyl CoA carboxylase is the rate-limiting step in fatty acid biosynthesis. The malonyl group is transferred from coenzyme A to acyl carrier protein; similarly, the acetyl group is transferred from coenzyme A to acyl carrier protein. This provides the two beginning substrates of fatty acid biosynthesis shown in Figure 23.11.

   Consider the following case study. A baby boy was brought to the emergency room with severe respiratory distress. Examination revealed muscle pathology, poor growth, and severe brain damage. A liver biopsy revealed that the child didn't make acetyl CoA carboxylase. What metabolic pathway is defective in this child? How is this defect related to the respiratory distress suffered by the baby?

Glossary

A

absolute specificity (19.5) the property of an enzyme that allows it to bind and catalyze the reaction of only one substrate

accuracy (1.4) the nearness of an experimental value to the true value

acetal (13.4) the family of organic compounds formed via the reaction of two molecules of alcohol with an aldehyde or a ketone in the presence of an acid catalyst

acetyl coenzyme A (acetyl CoA) (14.4, 22.2) a molecule composed of coenzyme A and an acetyl group; the intermediate that provides acetyl groups for complete oxidation by aerobic respiration

acid (8.1) a substance that behaves as a proton donor

acid anhydride (14.3) the product formed by the combination of an acid chloride and a carboxylate ion; structurally they are two carboxylic acids with a water molecule removed:

$$\text{(Ar)R}-\overset{\overset{\displaystyle O}{\|}}{C}-O-\overset{\overset{\displaystyle O}{\|}}{C}-\text{R(Ar)}$$

acid-base reaction (4.4) reaction that involves the transfer of a hydrogen ion (H^+) from one reactant to another

acid chloride (14.3) member of the family of organic compounds with the general formula

$$\text{(Ar)R}-\overset{\overset{\displaystyle O}{\|}}{C}-Cl$$

activated complex (7.3) the arrangement of atoms at the top of the potential energy barrier as a reaction proceeds

activation energy (7.3) the threshold energy that must be overcome to produce a chemical reaction

active site (19.4) the cleft in the surface of an enzyme that is the site of substrate binding

acyl carrier protein (ACP) (23.4) the protein that forms a thioester linkage with fatty acids during fatty acid synthesis

acyl group (14.3, 15.3) the functional group found in carboxylic acid derivatives that contains the carbonyl group attached to one alkyl or aryl group:

$$\text{(Ar)R}-\overset{\overset{\displaystyle O}{\|}}{C}-$$

addition polymer (11.5) polymers prepared by the sequential addition of a monomer

addition reaction (11.5, 13.4) a reaction in which two molecules add together to form a new molecule; often involves the addition of one molecule to a double or triple bond in an unsaturated molecule; e.g., the addition of alcohol to an aldehyde or ketone to form a hemiacetal

adenosine triphosphate (ATP) (14.4, 21.1) a nucleotide composed of the purine adenine, the sugar ribose, and three phosphoryl groups; the primary energy storage and transport molecule used by the cells in cellular metabolism

adipocyte (23.1) a fat cell

adipose tissue (23.1) fatty tissue that stores most of the body lipids

aerobic respiration (22.3) the oxygen-requiring degradation of food molecules and production of ATP

alcohol (12.1) an organic compound that contains a hydroxyl group (—OH) attached to an alkyl group

aldehyde (13.1) a class of organic molecules characterized by a carbonyl group; the carbonyl carbon is bonded to a hydrogen atom and to another hydrogen or an alkyl or aryl group. Aldehydes have the following general structure:

$$\text{(Ar)}-\overset{\overset{\displaystyle O}{\|}}{C}-H \qquad R-\overset{\overset{\displaystyle O}{\|}}{C}-H$$

aldose (16.2) a sugar that contains an aldehyde (carbonyl) group

aliphatic hydrocarbon (10.1) any member of the alkanes, alkenes, and alkynes or the substituted alkanes, alkenes, and alkynes

alkali metal (2.4) an element within Group IA (1) of the periodic table

alkaline earth metal (2.4) an element within Group IIA (2) of the periodic table

alkaloid (15.2) a class of naturally occurring compounds that contain one or more nitrogen heterocyclic rings; many of the alkaloids have medicinal and other physiological effects

alkane (10.2) a hydrocarbon that contains only carbon and hydrogen and is bonded together through carbon-hydrogen and carbon-carbon single bonds; a saturated hydrocarbon with the general molecular formula C_nH_{2n+2}

alkene (11.1) a hydrocarbon that contains one or more carbon-carbon double bonds; an unsaturated hydrocarbon with the general formula C_nH_{2n}

alkyl group (10.2) a hydrocarbon group that results from the removal of one hydrogen from the original hydrocarbon (e.g., methyl, $—CH_3$; ethyl, $—CH_2CH_3$)

alkyl halide (10.5) a substituted hydrocarbon with the general structure R—X, in which R— represents any alkyl group and X = a halogen (F—, Cl—, Br—, or I—)

alkylammonium ion (15.1) the ion formed when the lone pair of electrons of the nitrogen atom of an amine is shared with a proton (H^+) from a water molecule

alkyne (11.1) a hydrocarbon that contains one or more carbon-carbon triple bonds; an unsaturated hydrocarbon with the general formula C_nH_{2n-2}

allosteric enzyme (19.9) an enzyme that has an effector binding site and an active site; effector binding changes the shape of the active site, rendering it either active or inactive

alpha particle (9.1) a particle consisting of two protons and two neutrons; the alpha particle is identical to a helium nucleus

amide bond (15.3) the bond between the carbonyl carbon of a carboxylic acid and the amino nitrogen of an amine

amides (15.3) the family of organic compounds formed by the reaction between a carboxylic acid derivative and an amine and characterized by the amide group

amines (15.1) the family of organic molecules with the general formula RNH_2, R_2NH, or R_3N (R— can represent either an alkyl or aryl group); they may be viewed as substituted ammonia molecules in which one or more of the ammonia hydrogens has been substituted by a more complex organic group

α-amino acid (15.4, 18.1) the subunits of proteins composed of an α-carbon bonded to a carboxylate group, a protonated amino group, a hydrogen atom, and a variable R group

aminoacyl group (15.4) the functional group that is characteristic of an amino acid; the aminoacyl group has the following general structure:

$$H_3\overset{+}{N}-\underset{\underset{\displaystyle R}{|}}{\overset{\overset{\displaystyle H}{|}}{C}}-\overset{\overset{\displaystyle O}{\|}}{C}-$$

aminoacyl tRNA (20.6) the transfer RNA covalently linked to the correct amino acid

aminoacyl tRNA binding site of ribosome (A-site) (20.6) a pocket on the surface of a ribosome that holds the aminoacyl tRNA during translation

aminoacyl tRNA synthetase (20.6) an enzyme that recognizes one tRNA and covalently links the appropriate amino acid to it

amorphous solid (5.3) a solid with no organized, regular structure

amphibolic pathway (22.9) a metabolic pathway that functions in both anabolism and catabolism

amphiprotic (8.1) a substance that can behave either as a Brønsted acid or a Brønsted base

amylopectin (16.6) a highly branched form of amylose; the branches are attached to the C-6 hydroxyl by $\alpha(1 \longrightarrow 6)$ glycosidic linkage; a component of starch

amylose (16.6) a linear polymer of α-D-glucose molecules bonded in $\alpha(1 \longrightarrow 4)$ glycosidic linkage that is a component of starch; a polysaccharide storage form

anabolism (21.1, 22.9) all of the cellular energy-requiring biosynthetic pathways

anaerobic threshold (21.4) the point at which the level of lactate in the exercising muscle inhibits glycolysis and the muscle, deprived of energy, ceases to function

analgesic (15.2) any drug that acts as a painkiller, e.g., aspirin, acetaminophen

anaplerotic reaction (22.9) a reaction that replenishes a substrate needed for a biochemical pathway

anesthetic (15.2) a drug that causes a lack of sensation in part of the body (local anesthetic) or causes unconsciousness (general anesthetic)

anion (2.6) a negatively charged atom or group of atoms

anode (8.5) the positively charged electrode in an electrical cell

anomers (16.4) isomers of cyclic monosaccharides that differ from one another in the arrangement of bonds around the hemiacetal carbon

antibodies (18: Intro) immunoglobulins; specific glycoproteins produced by cells of the immune system in response to invasion by infectious agents

anticodon (20.6) a sequence of three ribonucleotides on a tRNA that are complementary to a codon on the mRNA; codon-anticodon binding results in delivery of the correct amino acid to the site of protein synthesis

antigen (18: Intro) any substance that is able to stimulate the immune system; generally a protein or large carbohydrate

antiparallel strands (20.2) a term describing the polarities of the two strands of the DNA double helix; on one strand the sugar-phosphate backbone advances in the $5' \longrightarrow 3'$ direction; on the opposite, complementary strand, the sugar-phosphate backbone advances in the $3' \longrightarrow 5'$ direction

apoenzyme (19.7) the protein portion of an enzyme that requires a cofactor to function in catalysis

aqueous solution (6.1) any solution in which the solvent is water

arachidonic acid (17.2) a fatty acid derived from linoleic acid; the precursor of the prostaglandins

aromatic hydrocarbon (10.1, 11.6) an organic compound that contains the benzene ring or a derivative of the benzene ring

Arrhenius theory (8.1) a theory that describes an acid as a substance that dissociates to produce H^+, and a base as a substance that dissociates to produce OH^-

artificial radioactivity (9.5) radiation that results from the conversion of a stable nucleus to another, unstable nucleus

atherosclerosis (17.4) deposition of excess plasma cholesterol and other lipids and proteins on the walls of arteries, resulting in decreased artery diameter and increased blood pressure

atom (2.1) the smallest unit of an element that retains the properties of that element

atomic mass (2.1, 4.1) the mass of an atom expressed in atomic mass units

atomic mass unit (4.1) 1/12 of the mass of a ^{12}C atom, equivalent to 1.661×10^{-24} g

atomic number (2.1) the number of protons in the nucleus of an atom; it is a characteristic identifier of an element

atomic orbital (2.3, 2.5) a specific region of space where an electron may be found

ATP synthase (22.6) a multiprotein complex within the inner mitochondrial membrane that uses the energy of the proton (H^+) gradient to produce ATP

autoionization (8.1) also known as *self-ionization,* the reaction of a substance, such as water, with itself to produce a positive and a negative ion

Avogadro's law (5.1) a law that states that the volume is directly proportional to the number of moles of gas particles, assuming that the pressure and temperature are constant

Avogadro's number (4.1) 6.022×10^{23} particles of matter contained in 1 mol of a substance

B

background radiation (9.6) the radiation that emanates from natural sources

barometer (5.1) a device for measuring pressure

base (8.1) a substance that behaves as a proton acceptor

base pair (20.2) a hydrogen-bonded pair of bases within the DNA double helix; the standard base pairs always involve a purine and a pyrimidine; in particular, adenine always base pairs with thymine and cytosine with guanine

Benedict's reagent (16.4) a buffered solution of Cu^{2+} ions that can be used to test for reducing sugars or to distinguish between aldehydes and ketones

Benedict's test (13.4) a test used to determine the presence of reducing sugars or to distinguish between aldehydes and ketones; it requires a buffered solution of Cu^{2+} ions that are reduced to Cu^+, which precipitates as brick-red Cu_2O

bent structure (3.4) a planar molecule with bond angles other than 180°

beta particle (9.1) an electron formed in the nucleus by the conversion of a neutron into a proton

bile (23.1) micelles of lecithin, cholesterol, bile salts, protein, inorganic ions, and bile pigments that aid in lipid digestion by emulsifying fat droplets

binding energy (9.3) the energy required to break down the nucleus into its component parts

bioinformatics (20.10) an interdisciplinary field that uses computer information sciences and DNA technology to devise methods for understanding, analyzing, and applying DNA sequence information

boat conformation (10.4) a form of a six-member cycloalkane that resembles a rowboat. It is less stable than the chair conformation because the hydrogen atoms are not perfectly staggered

boiling point (3.3) the temperature at which the vapor pressure of a liquid is equal to the atmospheric pressure

bond energy (3.4) the amount of energy necessary to break a chemical bond

Boyle's law (5.1) a law stating that the volume of a gas varies inversely with the pressure exerted if the temperature and number of moles of gas are constant

breeder reactor (9.4) a nuclear reactor that produces its own fuel in the process of providing electrical energy

Brønsted-Lowry theory (8.1) a theory that describes an acid as a proton donor and a base as a proton acceptor

buffer capacity (8.4) a measure of the ability of a solution to resist large changes in pH when a strong acid or strong base is added

buffer solution (8.4) a solution containing a weak acid or base and its salt (the conjugate base or acid) that is resistant to large changes in pH upon addition of strong acids or bases

buret (8.3) a device calibrated to deliver accurately known volumes of liquid, as in a titration

C

C-terminal amino acid (18.2) the amino acid in a peptide that has a free α-CO_2^- group; the last amino acid in a peptide

calorimetry (7.2) the measurement of heat energy changes during a chemical reaction

cap structure (20.4) a 7-methylguanosine unit covalently bonded to the 5′ end of a mRNA by a 5′–5′ triphosphate bridge

carbinol carbon (12.1) that carbon in an alcohol to which the hydroxyl group is attached

carbohydrate (16.1) generally sugars and polymers of sugars; the primary source of energy for the cell

carbonyl group (13: Intro) the functional group that contains a carbon-oxygen double bond: —C═O; the functional group found in aldehydes and ketones

carboxyl group (14.1) the —COOH functional group; the functional group found in carboxylic acids

carboxylic acid (14.1) a member of the family of organic compounds that contain the —COOH functional group

carboxylic acid derivative (14.2) any of several families of organic compounds, including the esters and amides, that are derived from carboxylic acids and have the general formula

$$\text{(Ar)}—\overset{\overset{\displaystyle O}{\|}}{C}—Z \qquad R—\overset{\overset{\displaystyle O}{\|}}{C}—Z$$

Z = —OR or OAr for the esters, and Z = $—NH_2$ for the amides

carcinogen (20.7) any chemical or physical agent that causes mutations in the DNA that lead to uncontrolled cell growth or cancer

catabolism (21.1, 22.9) the degradation of fuel molecules and production of ATP for cellular functions

catalyst (7.3) any substance that increases the rate of a chemical reaction (by lowering the activation energy of the reaction) and that is not destroyed in the course of the reaction

cathode (8.5) the negatively charged electrode in an electrical cell

cation (2.6) a positively charged atom or group of atoms

cellulose (16.6) a polymer of β-D-glucose linked by β(1 ⟶ 4) glycosidic bonds

central dogma (20.4) a statement of the directional transfer of the genetic information in cells: DNA ⟶ RNA ⟶ Protein

chain reaction (9.4) the process in a fission reactor that involves neutron production and causes subsequent reactions accompanied by the production of more neutrons in a continuing process

chair conformation (10.4) the most stable conformation for a six-member cycloalkane; so-called for its resemblance to a lawn chair

Charles's law (5.1) a law stating that the volume of a gas is directly proportional to the temperature of the gas, assuming that the pressure and number of moles of the gas are constant

chemical bond (3.1) the attractive force holding two atomic nuclei together in a chemical compound

chemical change (1.2) a process in which one or more atoms of a substance is rearranged, removed, replaced, or added to produce a new substance

chemical equation (4.3) a record of chemical change, showing the conversion of reactants to products

chemical equilibrium (7.4) the state of a reaction in which the rates of the forward and reverse reactions are equal

chemical formula (4.2) the representation of a compound or ion in which elemental symbols represent types of atoms and subscripts show the relative numbers of atoms

chemical properties (1.2) characteristics of a substance that relate to the substance's participation in a chemical reaction

chemical reaction (1.2) a process in which atoms are rearranged to produce new combinations

chemistry (1.1) the study of matter and the changes that matter undergoes

chiral carbon (16.3) a carbon atom bonded to four different atoms or groups of atoms

chiral molecule (16.3) molecule capable of existing in mirror-image forms

cholesterol (17.4) a twenty-seven-carbon steroid ring structure that serves as the precursor of the steroid hormones

chromosome (20.2) a piece of DNA that carries the genetic instructions, or genes, of an organism

chylomicron (17.5, 23.1) a plasma lipoprotein (aggregate of protein and triglycerides) that carries triglycerides from the intestine to all body tissues via the bloodstream

***cis-trans* isomers** (10.3) isomers that differ from one another in the placement of substituents on a double bond or ring

citric acid cycle (22.4) a cyclic biochemical pathway that is the final stage of degradation of carbohydrates, fats, and amino acids. It results in the complete oxidation of acetyl groups derived from these dietary fuels

cloning vector (20.8) a DNA molecule that can carry a cloned DNA fragment into a cell and that has a replication origin that allows the DNA to be replicated abundantly within the host cell

coagulation (18.10) the process by which proteins in solution are denatured and aggregate with one another to produce a solid

codon (20.5) a group of three ribonucleotides on the mRNA that specifies the addition of a specific amino acid onto the growing peptide chain

coenzyme (19.7) an organic group required by some enzymes; it generally serves as a donor or acceptor of electrons or a functional group in a reaction

coenzyme A (22.2) a molecule derived from ATP and the vitamin pantothenic acid; coenzyme A functions in the transfer of acetyl groups in lipid and carbohydrate metabolism

cofactor (19.7) an inorganic group, usually a metal ion, that must be bound to an apoenzyme to maintain the correct configuration of the active site

colipase (23.1) a protein that aids in lipid digestion by binding to the surface of lipid droplets and facilitating binding of pancreatic lipase

colligative property (6.4) property of a solution that is dependent only on the concentration of solute particles

colloidal suspension (6.1) a heterogeneous mixture of solute particles in a solvent; distribution of solute particles is not uniform because of the size of the particles

combination reaction (4.3) a reaction in which two substances join to form another substance

combined gas law (5.1) an equation that describes the behavior of a gas when volume, pressure, and temperature may change simultaneously

combustion (10.5) the oxidation of hydrocarbons by burning in the presence of air to produce carbon dioxide and water

competitive inhibitor (19.10) a structural analog; a molecule that has a structure very similar to the natural substrate of an enzyme, competes with the natural substrate for binding to the enzyme active site, and inhibits the reaction

complementary strands (20.2) the opposite strands of the double helix are hydrogen-bonded to one another such that adenine and thymine or guanine and cytosine are always paired

complete protein (18.11) a protein source that contains all the essential and nonessential amino acids

complex lipid (17.5) a lipid bonded to other types of molecules

compound (1.2) a substance that is characterized by constant composition and that can be chemically broken down into elements

concentration (1.6, 6.2) a measure of the quantity of a substance contained in a specified volume of solution

concentration gradient (6.4) region where concentration decreases over distance

condensation (5.2) the conversion of a gas to a liquid

condensation polymer (14.2) a polymer, which is a large molecule formed by combination of many small molecules (monomers) that results from joining of monomers in a reaction that forms a small molecule, such as water or an alcohol

condensed formula (10.2) a structural formula showing all of the atoms in a molecule and placing them in a sequential arrangement that details which atoms are bonded to each other; the bonds themselves are not shown

conformations, conformers (10.4) discrete, distinct isomeric structures that may be converted, one to the other, by rotation about the bonds in the molecule

conjugate acid (8.1) substance that has one more proton than the base from which it is derived

conjugate acid-base pair (8.1) two species related to each other through the gain or loss of a proton

conjugate base (8.1) substance that has one fewer proton than the acid from which it is derived

constitutional isomers (10.2) two molecules having the same molecular formulas, but different chemical structures

Cori Cycle (21.6) a metabolic pathway in which the lactate produced by working muscle is taken up by cells in the liver and converted back to glucose by gluconeogenesis

corrosion (8.5) the unwanted oxidation of a metal

covalent bonding (3.1) a pair of electrons shared between two atoms

covalent solid (5.3) a collection of atoms held together by covalent bonds

cristae (22.1) the folds of the inner membrane of the mitochondria

crystal lattice (3.1) a unit of a solid characterized by a regular arrangement of components

crystalline solid (5.3) a solid having a regular repeating atomic structure

curie (9.7) the quantity of radioactive material that produces 3.7×10^{10} nuclear disintegrations per second

cycloalkane (10.3) a cyclic alkane; a saturated hydrocarbon that has the general formula C_nH_{2n}

D

Dalton's law (5.1) also called the law of partial pressures; states that the total pressure exerted by a gas mixture is the sum of the partial pressures of the component gases

data (1.1) facts resulting from an experiment

decomposition reaction (4.3) the breakdown of a substance into two or more substances

defense proteins (18: Intro) proteins that defend the body against infectious diseases; antibodies are defense proteins

degenerate code (20.5) a term used to describe the fact that several triplet codons may be used to specify a single amino acid in the genetic code

dehydration (of alcohols) (12.4) a reaction that involves the loss of a water molecule, in this case the loss of water from an alcohol and the simultaneous formation of an alkene

deletion mutation (20.7) a mutation that results in the loss of one or more nucleotides from a DNA sequence

denaturation (18.10) the process by which the organized structure of a protein is disrupted, resulting in a completely disorganized, nonfunctional form of the protein

density (1.6) mass per unit volume of a substance

deoxyribonucleic acid (DNA) (20.1) the nucleic acid molecule that carries all of the genetic information of an organism; the DNA molecule is a double helix composed of two strands, each of which is composed of phosphate groups, deoxyribose, and the nitrogenous bases thymine, cytosine, adenine, and guanine

deoxyribonucleotide (20.1) a nucleoside phosphate or nucleotide composed of a nitrogenous base in β-*N*-glycosidic linkage to the 1′ carbon of the sugar 2′-deoxyribose and with one, two, or three phosphoryl groups esterified at the hydroxyl of the 5′ carbon

diabetes mellitus (23.3) a disease caused by the production of insufficient levels of insulin and characterized by the appearance of very high levels of glucose in the blood and urine

dialysis (6.5) the removal of waste material via transport across a membrane

diastereomers (16.3) stereoisomers with at least two chiral carbons that are not mirror images of one another

diffusion (6.4) net movement of solute or solvent molecules from a region of high concentration to a region of low concentration

diglyceride (17.3) the product of esterification of glycerol at two positions

dipole-dipole interactions (5.2) attractive forces between polar molecules

disaccharide (16.1) a sugar composed of two monosaccharides joined through an oxygen atom bridge

dissociation (3.3) production of positive and negative ions when an ionic compound dissolves in water

disulfide (12.8) an organic compound that contains a disulfide group (—S—S—)

DNA polymerase III (20.3) the enzyme that catalyzes the polymerization of daughter DNA strands using the parental strand as a template

double bond (3.4) a bond in which two pairs of electrons are shared by two atoms

double helix (20.2) the spiral staircase–like structure of the DNA molecule characterized by two sugar-phosphate backbones wound around the outside and nitrogenous bases extending into the center

double-replacement reaction (4.3) a chemical change in which cations and anions "exchange partners"

dynamic equilibrium (7.4) the state that exists when the rate of change in the concentration of products and reactants is equal, resulting in no net concentration change

E

eicosanoid (17.2) any of the derivatives of twenty-carbon fatty acids, including the prostaglandins, leukotrienes, and thromboxanes

electrolysis (8.5) an electrochemical process that uses electrical energy to cause nonspontaneous oxidation-reduction reactions to occur

electrolyte (3.3, 6.1) a material that dissolves in water to produce a solution that conducts an electrical current

electromagnetic radiation (2.3) energy that is propagated as waves at the speed of light

electron (2.1) a negatively charged particle outside of the nucleus of an atom

electron affinity (2.7) the energy released when an electron is added to an isolated atom

electron configuration (2.5) the arrangement of electrons around the nucleus of an atom, an ion, or a collection of nuclei of a molecule

electron density (2.3) the probability of finding the electron in a particular location

electron transport system (22.6) the series of electron transport proteins embedded in the inner mitochondrial membrane that accept high-energy electrons from NADH and $FADH_2$ and transfer them in stepwise fashion to molecular oxygen (O_2)

electronegativity (3.1) a measure of the tendency of an atom in a molecule to attract shared electrons

element (1.2) a substance that cannot be decomposed into simpler substances by chemical or physical means

elimination reaction (12.4) a reaction in which a molecule loses atoms or ions from its structure

elongation factor (20.6) proteins that facilitate the elongation phase of translation

emulsifying agent (17.3) a bipolar molecule that aids in the suspension of fats in water

enantiomers (16.3) stereoisomers that are nonsuperimposable mirror images of one another

endothermic reaction (7.1) a chemical or physical change in which energy is absorbed

energy (1.6) the capacity to do work

energy level (2.3) one of numerous atomic regions where electrons may be found

enol (13.4) a tautomer containing a carbon-carbon double bond and a hydroxyl group

enthalpy (7.1) a term that represents heat energy

entropy (7.1) a measure of randomness or disorder

enzyme (18: Intro, 19: Intro) a protein that serves as a biological catalyst

enzyme specificity (19.5) the ability of an enzyme to bind to only one, or a very few, substrates and thus catalyze only a single reaction

enzyme-substrate complex (19.4) a molecular aggregate formed when the substrate binds to the active site of the enzyme

equilibrium constant (7.4) number equal to the ratio of the equilibrium concentrations of products to the equilibrium concentrations of reactants, each raised to the power corresponding to its coefficient in the balanced equation

equivalence point (8.3) the situation in which reactants have been mixed in the molar ratio corresponding to the balanced equation

error (1.4) the difference between the true value and the experimental value for data or results

essential amino acid (18.11) an amino acid that cannot be synthesized by the body and must therefore be supplied by the diet

essential fatty acids (17.2) the fatty acids linolenic and linoleic acids that must be supplied in the diet because they cannot be synthesized by the body

ester (14.2) a carboxylic acid derivative formed by the reaction of a carboxylic acid and an alcohol. Esters have the following general formula:

$$R{-}\overset{\overset{O}{\|}}{C}{-}R \quad R{-}\overset{\overset{O}{\|}}{C}{-}(Ar) \quad (Ar){-}\overset{\overset{O}{\|}}{C}{-}(Ar)$$

esterification (17.2) the formation of an ester in the reaction of a carboxylic acid and an alcohol

ether (12.7) an organic compound that contains two alkyl and/or aryl groups attached to an oxygen atom; R—O—R, Ar—O—R, and Ar—O—Ar

eukaryote (20.2) an organism having cells containing a true nucleus enclosed by a nuclear membrane and having a variety of membrane-bound organelles that segregate different cellular functions into different compartments

evaporation (5.2) the conversion of a liquid to a gas below the boiling point of the liquid

excited state (2.3) an electronic state of an atom when energy has been adsorbed by the ground state atom and one or more electrons are promoted into a higher energy level

exon (20.4) protein-coding sequences of a gene found on the final mature mRNA

exothermic reaction (7.1) a chemical or physical change that releases energy

extensive property (1.2) a property of a substance that depends on the quantity of the substance

F

F_0F_1 complex (22.6) an alternative term for ATP synthase, the multiprotein complex in the inner mitochondrial membrane that uses the energy of the proton gradient to produce ATP

fatty acid (14.1, 17.2) any member of the family of continuous-chain carboxylic acids that generally contain four to twenty carbon atoms; the most concentrated source of energy used by the cell

feedback inhibition (19.9) the process whereby excess product of a biosynthetic pathway turns off the entire pathway for its own synthesis

fermentation (12.3, 21.4) anaerobic (in the absence of oxygen) catabolic reactions that occur with no net oxidation. Pyruvate or an organic compound produced from pyruvate is reduced as NADH is oxidized

fibrous protein (18.4) a protein composed of peptides arranged in long sheets or fibers

Fischer Projection (16.3) a two-dimensional drawing of a molecule, that shows a chiral carbon at the intersection of two lines and horizontal lines representing bonds projecting out of the page and vertical lines representing bonds that project into the page

fission (9.4) the splitting of heavy nuclei into lighter nuclei accompanied by the release of large quantities of energy

fluid mosaic model (17.6) the model of membrane structure that describes the fluid nature of the lipid bilayer and the presence of numerous proteins embedded within the membrane

formula (3.2) the representation of the fundamental compound unit using chemical symbols and numerical subscripts

formula mass (4.2) the mass of a formula unit of a compound relative to a standard (carbon-12)

formula unit (4.2) the smallest collection of atoms from which the formula of a compound can be established

free energy (7.1) the combined contribution of entropy and enthalpy for a chemical reaction

fructose (16.4) a ketohexose that is also called levulose and fruit sugar; the sweetest of all sugars, abundant in honey and fruits

fuel value (7.2) the amount of energy derived from a given mass of material

functional group (10.1) an atom (or group of atoms and their bonds) that imparts specific chemical and physical properties to a molecule

fusion (9.4) the joining of light nuclei to form heavier nuclei, accompanied by the release of large amounts of energy

G

galactose (16.4) an aldohexose that is a component of lactose (milk sugar)

galactosemia (16.5) a human genetic disease caused by the inability to convert galactose to a phosphorylated form of glucose (glucose-1-phosphate) that can be used in cellular metabolic reactions

gamma ray (9.1) a high-energy emission from nuclear processes, traveling at the speed of light; the high-energy region of the electromagnetic spectrum

gaseous state (1.2) a physical state of matter characterized by a lack of fixed shape or volume and ease of compressibility

genome (20.2) the complete set of genetic information in all the chromosomes of an organism

geometric isomer (10.3, 11.3) an isomer that differs from another isomer in the placement of substituents on a double bond or a ring

globular protein (18.5) a protein composed of polypeptide chains that are tightly folded into a compact spherical shape

glucagon (21.7, 23.6) a peptide hormone synthesized by the α-cells of the islets of Langerhans in the pancreas and secreted in response to low blood glucose levels; glucagon promotes glycogenolysis and gluconeogenesis and thereby increases the concentration of blood glucose

gluconeogenesis (21.6) the synthesis of glucose from noncarbohydrate precursors

glucose (16.4) an aldohexose, the most abundant monosaccharide; it is a component of many disaccharides, such as lactose and sucrose, and of polysaccharides, such as cellulose, starch, and glycogen

glyceraldehyde (16.4) an aldotriose that is the simplest carbohydrate; phosphorylated forms of glyceraldehyde are important intermediates in cellular metabolic reactions

glyceride (17.3) a lipid that contains glycerol

glycogen (16.6, 21.7) a long, branched polymer of glucose stored in liver and muscles of animals; it consists of a linear backbone of α-D-glucose in α(1 ⟶ 4) linkage, with numerous short branches attached to the C-6 hydroxyl group by α(1 ⟶ 6) linkage

glycogenesis (21.7) the metabolic pathway that results in the addition of glucose to growing glycogen polymers when blood glucose levels are high

glycogen granule (21.7) a core of glycogen surrounded by enzymes responsible for glycogen synthesis and degradation

glycogenolysis (21.7) the biochemical pathway that results in the removal of glucose molecules from glycogen polymers when blood glucose levels are low

glycolysis (21.3) the enzymatic pathway that converts a glucose molecule into two molecules of pyruvate; this anaerobic process generates a net energy yield of two molecules of ATP and two molecules of NADH

glycoprotein (18.6) a protein bonded to sugar groups

glycosidic bond (16.1) the bond between the hydroxyl group of the C-1 carbon of one sugar and a hydroxyl group of another sugar

ground state (2.3) the electronic state of an atom in which all of the electrons are in the lowest possible energy levels

group (2.4) any one of eighteen vertical columns of elements; often referred to as a *family*

group specificity (19.5) an enzyme that catalyzes reactions involving similar substrate molecules having the same functional groups

guanosine triphosphate (GTP) (21.6) a nucleotide composed of the purine guanosine, the sugar ribose, and three phosphoryl groups

H

half-life ($t_{1/2}$) (9.3, 9.6) the length of time required for one-half of the initial mass of an isotope to decay to products

halogen (2.4) an element found in Group VIIA (17) of the periodic table

halogenation (10.5, 11.5) a reaction in which one of the C—H bonds of a hydrocarbon is replaced with a C—X bond (X = Br or Cl generally)

Haworth projection (16.4) a means of representing the orientation of substituent groups around a cyclic sugar molecule

heat (7.1) energy transferred between a system and its surroundings due to a temperature difference between system and surroundings

α-helix (18.4) a right-handed coiled secondary structure maintained by hydrogen bonds between the amide hydrogen of one amino acid and the carbonyl oxygen of an amino acid four residues away

heme group (18.8) the chemical group found in hemoglobin and myoglobin that is responsible for the ability to carry oxygen

hemiacetal (13.4, 16.4) the family of organic compounds formed via the reaction of one molecule of alcohol with an aldehyde or a ketone in the presence of an acid catalyst; or a ketone

hemoglobin (18.8) the major protein component of red blood cells; the function of this red, iron-containing protein is transport of oxygen

Henderson-Hasselbalch equation (8.4) an equation for calculating the pH of a buffer system:

$$pH = pK_a + \log\frac{[\text{conjugate base}]}{[\text{weak acid}]}$$

Henry's law (6.1) a law stating that the number of moles of a gas dissolved in a liquid at a given temperature is proportional to the partial pressure of the gas

heterocyclic amine (15.2) a heterocyclic compound that contains nitrogen in at least one position in the ring skeleton

heterocyclic aromatic compound (11.7) cyclic aromatic compound having at least one atom other than carbon in the structure of the aromatic ring

heterogeneous mixture (1.2) a mixture of two or more substances characterized by nonuniform composition

heteropolysaccharide (16.6) a polysaccharide composed of two or more different monosaccharides

hexose (16.2) a six-carbon monosaccharide

high-density lipoprotein (HDL) (17.5) a plasma lipoprotein that transports cholesterol from peripheral tissue to the liver

holoenzyme (19.7) an active enzyme consisting of an apoenzyme bound to a cofactor

homogeneous mixture (1.2) a mixture of two or more substances characterized by uniform composition

homopolysaccharide (16.6) a polysaccharide composed of identical monosaccharides

hybridization (20.8) a technique for identifying DNA or RNA sequences that is based on specific hydrogen bonding between a radioactive probe and complementary DNA or RNA sequences

hydrate (4.2) any substance that has water molecules incorporated in its structure

hydration (11.5, 12.4) a reaction in which water is added to a molecule, e.g., the addition of water to an alkene to form an alcohol

hydrocarbon (10.1) a compound composed solely of the elements carbon and hydrogen

hydrogen bonding (5.2) the attractive force between a hydrogen atom covalently bonded to a small, highly electronegative atom and another atom containing an unshared pair of electrons

hydrogenation (11.5, 13.4, 17.2) a reaction in which hydrogen (H_2) is added to a double or a triple bond

hydrohalogenation (11.5) the addition of a hydrohalogen (HCl, HBr, or HI) to an unsaturated bond

hydrolase (19.1) an enzyme that catalyzes hydrolysis reactions

hydrolysis (14.2) a chemical change that involves the reaction of a molecule with water; the process by which molecules are broken into their constituents by addition of water

hydronium ion (8.1) a protonated water molecule, H_3O^+

hydrophilic amino acid (18.1) "water loving"; a polar or ionic amino acid that has a high affinity for water

hydrophobic amino acid (18.1) "water fearing"; a nonpolar amino acid that prefers contact with other nonpolar molecules over contact with water

hydroxide ion (8.1) the anion consisting of one oxygen atom and one hydrogen atom ($—OH^-$)

hydroxyl group (12.1) the —OH functional group that is characteristic of alcohols

hyperammonemia (22.8) a genetic defect in one of the enzymes of the urea cycle that results in toxic or even fatal elevation of the concentration of ammonium ions in the body

hyperglycemia (21.7) blood glucose levels that are higher than normal

hypertonic solution (6.4) the more concentrated solution of two separated by a semipermeable membrane

hypoglycemia (21.7) blood glucose levels that are lower than normal

hypothesis (1.1) an attempt to explain observations in a commonsense way

hypotonic solution (6.4) the more dilute solution of two separated by a semipermeable membrane

I

ideal gas (5.1) a gas in which the particles do not interact and the volume of the individual gas particles is assumed to be negligible

ideal gas law (5.1) a law stating that for an ideal gas the product of pressure and volume is proportional to the product of the number of moles of the gas and its temperature; the proportionality constant for an ideal gas is symbolized R

incomplete protein (18.11) a protein source that does not contain all the essential and nonessential amino acids

indicator (8.3) a solute that shows some condition of a solution (such as acidity or basicity) by its color

induced fit model (19.4) the theory of enzyme-substrate binding that assumes that the enzyme is a flexible molecule and that both the substrate and the enzyme change their shapes to accommodate one another as the enzyme-substrate complex forms

initiation factors (20.6) proteins that are required for formation of the translation initiation complex, which is composed of the large and small ribosomal subunits, the mRNA, and the initiator tRNA, methionyl tRNA

inner mitochondrial membrane (22.1) the highly folded, impermeable membrane within the mitochondrion that is the location of the electron transport system and ATP synthase

insertion mutation (20.7) a mutation that results in the addition of one or more nucleotides to a DNA sequence

insulin (21.7, 23.6) a hormone released from the pancreas in response to high blood glucose levels; insulin stimulates glycogenesis, fat storage, and cellular uptake and storage of glucose from the blood

intensive property (1.2) a property of a substance that is independent of the quantity of the substance

intermembrane space (22.1) the region between the outer and inner mitochondrial membranes, which is the location of the proton (H^+) reservoir that drives ATP synthesis

intermolecular force (3.5) any attractive force that occurs between molecules

intramolecular force (3.5) any attractive force that occurs within molecules

intron (20.4) a noncoding sequence within a eukaryotic gene that must be removed from the primary transcript to produce a functional mRNA

ion (2.6) an electrically charged particle formed by the gain or loss of electrons

ionic bonding (3.1) an electrostatic attractive force between ions resulting from electron transfer

ionic solid (5.3) a solid composed of positive and negative ions in a regular three-dimensional crystalline arrangement

ionization energy (2.7) the energy needed to remove an electron from an atom in the gas phase

ionizing radiation (9.1, 9.5) radiation that is sufficiently high in energy to cause ion formation upon impact with an atom

ion product for water (8.1) the product of the hydronium and hydroxide ion concentrations in pure water at a specified temperature; at 25°C, it has a value of 1.0×10^{-14}

irreversible enzyme inhibitor (19.10) a chemical that binds strongly to the R groups of an amino acid in the active site and eliminates enzyme activity

isoelectronic (2.6) atoms, ions, and molecules containing the same number of electrons

isomerase (19.1) an enzyme that catalyzes the conversion of one isomer to another

isomers (3.4) molecules having the same molecular formula but different chemical structures

isotonic solution (6.4) a solution that has the same solute concentration as another solution with which it is being compared; a solution that has the same osmotic pressure as a solution existing within a cell

isotope (2.1) atom of the same element that differs in mass because it contains different numbers of neutrons

IUPAC Nomenclature System (10.2) the International Union of Pure and Applied Chemistry (IUPAC) standard, universal system for the nomenclature of organic compounds

K

α-keratin (18.4) a member of the family of fibrous proteins that form the covering of most land animals; major components of fur, skin, beaks, and nails

ketoacidosis (23.3) a drop in the pH of the blood caused by elevated levels of ketone bodies

ketone (13.1) a family of organic molecules characterized by a carbonyl group; the carbonyl carbon is bonded to two alkyl groups, two aryl groups, or one alkyl and one aryl group; ketones have the following general structures:

$$R-\overset{\overset{\displaystyle O}{\|}}{C}-OR \quad R-\overset{\overset{\displaystyle O}{\|}}{C}-O(Ar) \quad (Ar)-\overset{\overset{\displaystyle O}{\|}}{C}-O(Ar)$$

ketone bodies (23.3) acetone, acetoacetone, and β-hydroxybutyrate produced from fatty acids in the liver via acetyl CoA

ketose (16.2) a sugar that contains a ketone (carbonyl) group

ketosis (23.3) an abnormal rise in the level of ketone bodies in the blood

kinetic energy (1.6) the energy resulting from motion of an object [kinetic energy = 1/2(mass)(velocity)^2]

kinetic molecular theory (5.1) the fundamental model of particle behavior in the gas phase

kinetics (7.3) the study of rates of chemical reactions

L

lactose (16.5) a disaccharide composed of β-D-galactose and either α- or β-D-glucose in β(1 ⟶ 4) glycosidic linkage; milk sugar

lactose intolerance (16.5) the inability to produce the digestive enzyme lactase, which degrades lactose to galactose and glucose

lagging strand (20.3) in DNA replication, the strand that is synthesized discontinuously from numerous RNA primers

law (1.1) a summary of a large quantity of information

law of conservation of mass (4.3) a law stating that, in chemical change, matter cannot be created or destroyed

leading strand (20.3) in DNA replication, the strand that is synthesized continuously from a single RNA primer

LeChatelier's principle (7.4) a law stating that when a system at equilibrium is disturbed, the equilibrium shifts in the direction that minimizes the disturbance

lethal dose (LD_{50}) (9.7) the quantity of toxic material (such as radiation) that causes the death of 50% of a population of an organism

Lewis structure (3.1) representation of a molecule (or polyatomic ion) that shows valence electron arrangement among the atoms in a molecule (or polyatomic ion)

Lewis symbol (3.1) representation of an atom (or ion) using the atomic symbol (for the nucleus and core electrons) and dots to represent valence electrons

ligase (19.1) an enzyme that catalyzes the joining of two molecules

linear structure (3.4) the structure of a molecule in which the bond angle(s) about the central atom(s) is (are) 180°

line formula (10.2) the simplest representation of a molecule, in which it is assumed that there is a carbon atom at any location where two or more lines intersect, there is a carbon at the end of any line, and each carbon is bonded to the correct number of hydrogen atoms

linkage specificity (19.5) the property of an enzyme that allows it to catalyze reactions involving only one kind of bond in the substrate molecule

lipase (23.1) an enzyme that hydrolyzes the ester linkage between glycerol and the fatty acids of triglycerides

lipid (17.1) a member of the group of biological molecules of varying composition that are classified together on the basis of their solubility in nonpolar solvents

liquid state (1.2) a physical state of matter characterized by a fixed volume and the absence of a fixed shape

lock-and-key model (19.4) the theory of enzyme-substrate binding that depicts enzymes as inflexible molecules; the substrate fits into the rigid active site in the same way a key fits into a lock

London dispersion forces (5.2) weak attractive forces between molecules that result from short-lived dipoles that occur because of the continuous movement of electrons in the molecules

lone pair (3.4) an electron pair that is not involved in bonding

low-density lipoprotein (LDL) (17.5) a plasma lipoprotein that carries cholesterol to peripheral tissues and helps to regulate cholesterol levels in those tissues

lyase (19.1) an enzyme that catalyzes a reaction involving double bonds

M

maltose (16.5) a disaccharide composed of α-D-glucose and a second glucose molecule in α(1 ⟶ 4) glycosidic linkage

Markovnikov's rule (11.5) the rule stating that a hydrogen atom, adding to a carbon-carbon double bond, will add to the carbon having the larger number of hydrogens attached to it

mass (1.3) a quantity of matter

mass/mass percent [% (m/m)] (6.2) the concentration of a solution expressed as a ratio of mass of solute to mass of solution multiplied by 100%

mass number (2.1) the sum of the number of protons and neutrons in an atom

mass/volume percent [% (m/V)] (6.2) the concentration of a solution expressed as a ratio of grams of solute to milliliters of solution multiplied by 100%

matrix space (22.1) the region of the mitochondrion within the inner membrane; the location of the enzymes that carry out the reactions of the citric acid cycle and β-oxidation of fatty acids

matter (1.1) anything that has mass and occupies space

melting point (3.3, 5.2) the temperature at which a solid converts to a liquid

meso compound (16.3) a special case of stereoisomers that occurs when a molecule has two chiral carbons and each chiral carbon has identical substituents; these molecules are achiral because they have a plane of symmetry within the molecule

messenger RNA (20.4) an RNA species produced by transcription and that specifies the amino acid sequence for a protein

metal (2.4) an element located on the left side of the periodic table (left of the "staircase" boundary)

metallic bond (5.3) a bond that results from the orbital overlap of metal atoms

metallic solid (5.3) a solid composed of metal atoms held together by metallic bonds

metalloid (2.4) an element along the "staircase" boundary between metals and nonmetals; metalloids exhibit both metallic and nonmetallic properties

metastable isotope (9.3) an isotope that will give up some energy to produce a more stable form of the same isotope

micelle (23.1) an aggregation of molecules having nonpolar and polar regions; the nonpolar regions of the molecules aggregate, leaving the polar regions facing the surrounding water

mitochondria (22.1) the cellular "power plants" in which the reactions of the citric acid cycle, β-oxidation of fatty acids, the electron transport system, and ATP synthase function to produce ATP

mixture (1.2) a material composed of two or more substances

molality (6.4) the number of moles of solute per kilogram of solvent

molar mass (4.1, 4.2) the mass in grams of 1 mol of a substance

molar volume (5.1) the volume occupied by 1 mol of a substance

molarity (6.3) the number of moles of solute per liter of solution

mole (4.1) the amount of substance containing Avogadro's number of particles

molecular formula (10.2) a formula that provides the atoms and number of each type of atom in a molecule but gives no information regarding the bonding pattern involved in the structure of the molecule

molecular solid (5.3) a solid in which the molecules are held together by dipole-dipole and London dispersion forces (van der Waals forces)

molecule (3.1) a unit in which the atoms of two or more elements are held together by chemical bonds

monatomic ion (3.2) an ion formed by electron gain or loss from a single atom

monoglyceride (17.3) the product of the esterification of glycerol at one position

monomer (11.5) the individual molecules from which a polymer is formed

monosaccharide (16.1) the simplest type of carbohydrate consisting of a single saccharide unit

movement protein (18: Intro) a protein involved in any aspect of movement in an organism, for instance, actin and myosin in muscle tissue and flagellin that composes bacterial flagella

mutagen (20.7) any chemical or physical agent that causes changes in the nucleotide sequence of a gene

mutation (20.7) any change in the nucleotide sequence of a gene

myoglobin (18.8) the oxygen storage protein found in muscle

N

N-terminal amino acid (18.2) the amino acid in a peptide that has a free $\alpha\text{-N}^+H_3$ group; the first amino acid of a peptide

natural radioactivity (9.5) the spontaneous decay of a nucleus to produce high-energy particles or rays

negative allosterism (19.9) effector binding inactivates the active site of an allosteric enzyme

neurotransmitter (15.5) a chemical that carries a message, or signal, from a nerve cell to a target cell

neutral glyceride (17.3) the product of the esterification of glycerol at one, two, or three positions

neutralization (8.3) the reaction between an acid and a base

neutron (2.1) an uncharged particle, with the same mass as the proton, in the nucleus of an atom

nicotinamide adenine dinucleotide (NAD $^+$) (21.3) a molecule synthesized from the vitamin niacin and the nucleotide ATP and that serves as a carrier of hydride anions; a coenzyme that is an oxidizing agent used in a variety of metabolic processes

noble gas (2.4) elements in Group VIIIA (18) of the periodic table

nomenclature (3.2) a system for naming chemical compounds

nonelectrolyte (3.3, 6.1) a substance that, when dissolved in water, produces a solution that does not conduct an electrical current

nonessential amino acid (18.11) any amino acid that can be synthesized by the body

nonmetal (2.4) an element located on the right side of the periodic table (right of the "staircase" boundary)

nonreducing sugar (16.5) a sugar that cannot be oxidized by Benedict's or Tollens' reagent

normal boiling point (5.2) the temperature at which a substance will boil at 1 atm of pressure

nuclear equation (9.2) a balanced equation accounting for the products and reactants in a nuclear reaction

nuclear imaging (9.5) the generation of images of components of the body (organs, tissues) using techniques based on the measurement of radiation

nuclear medicine (9.5) a field of medicine that uses radioisotopes for diagnostic and therapeutic purposes

nuclear reactor (9.4) a device for conversion of nuclear energy into electrical energy

nucleoside (20.1) a molecule composed of a nitrogenous base and a five-carbon sugar

nucleosome (20.2) the first level of chromosome structure consisting of a strand of DNA wrapped around a small disk of histone proteins

nucleotide (20.1, 21.1) a molecule composed of a nitrogenous base, a five-carbon sugar, and one, two, or three phosphoryl groups

nucleus (2.1) the small, dense center of positive charge in the atom

nuclide (9.1) any atom characterized by an atomic number and a mass number

nutrient protein (18: Intro) a protein that serves as a source of amino acids for embryos or infants

nutritional Calorie (7.2) equivalent to 1 kilocalorie (1000 calories); also known as a large Calorie

O

octet rule (2.6) a rule predicting that atoms form the most stable molecules or ions when they are surrounded by eight electrons in their highest occupied energy level

oligosaccharide (16.1) an intermediate-sized carbohydrate composed of from three to ten monosaccharides

osmosis (6.4) net flow of a solvent across a semipermeable membrane in response to a concentration gradient

osmotic pressure (6.4) the net force with which water enters a solution through a semipermeable membrane; alternatively, the pressure required to stop net transfer of solvent across a semipermeable membrane

outer mitochondrial membrane (22.1) the membrane that surrounds the mitochondrion and separates it from the contents of the cytoplasm; it is highly permeable to small "food" molecules

β-oxidation (23.2) the biochemical pathway that results in the oxidation of fatty acids and the production of acetyl CoA

oxidation (8.5, 12.4, 13.4, 14.1) a loss of electrons; in organic compounds it may be recognized as a loss of hydrogen atoms or the gain of oxygen

oxidation-reduction reaction (4.4) also called *redox reaction*, a reaction involving the transfer of one or more electrons from one reactant to another

oxidative deamination (22.7) an oxidation-reduction reaction in which NAD^+ is reduced and the amino acid is deaminated

oxidative phosphorylation (21.3, 22.6) production of ATP using the energy of electrons harvested during biological oxidation-reduction reactions

oxidizing agent (8.5) a substance that oxidizes, or removes electrons from, another substance; the oxidizing agent is reduced in the process

oxidoreductase (19.1) an enzyme that catalyzes an oxidation-reduction reaction

P

pancreatic serine proteases (19.11) a family of proteolytic enzymes, including trypsin, chymotrypsin, and elastase, that arose by divergent evolution

parent compound or parent chain (10.2) in the IUPAC Nomenclature System the parent compound is the longest carbon-carbon chain containing the principal functional group in the molecule that is being named

partial pressure (5.1) the pressure exerted by one component of a gas mixture

parts per million (6.2) number of parts of solute in one million parts of solvent

parts per thousand (6.2) number of parts of solute per thousand parts of solvent

pentose (16.2) a five-carbon monosaccharide

pentose phosphate pathway (21.5) an alternative pathway for glucose degradation that provides the cell with reducing power in the form of NADPH

peptide bond (15.4, 18.2) the amide bond between two amino acids in a peptide chain

peptidyl tRNA binding site of ribosome (P-site) (20.6) a pocket on the surface of the ribosome that holds the tRNA bound to the growing peptide chain

percent yield (4.5) the ratio of the actual and theoretical yields of a chemical reaction multiplied by 100%

period (2.4) any one of seven horizontal rows of elements in the periodic table

periodic law (2.4) a law stating that properties of elements are periodic functions of their atomic numbers (Note that Mendeleev's original statement was based on atomic masses.)

peripheral membrane protein (17.6) a protein bound to either the inner or the outer surface of a membrane

phenol (12.6) an organic compound that contains a hydroxyl group (—OH) attached to a benzene ring

phenyl group (11.6) a benzene ring that has had a hydrogen atom removed, C_6H_5—

pH optimum (19.8) the pH at which an enzyme catalyzes the reaction at maximum efficiency

phosphatidate (17.3) a molecule of glycerol with fatty acids esterified to C-1 and C-2 of glycerol and a free phosphoryl group esterified at C-3

phosphoanhydride (14.4) the bond formed when two phosphate groups react with one another and a water molecule is lost

phosphoester (14.4) the product of the reaction between phosphoric acid and an alcohol

phosphoglyceride (17.3) a molecule with fatty acids esterified at the C-1 and C-2 positions of glycerol and a phosphoryl group esterified at the C-3 position

phospholipid (17.3) a lipid containing a phosphoryl group

phosphopantetheine (23.4) the portion of coenzyme A and the acyl carrier protein that is derived from the vitamin pantothenic acid

pH scale (8.2) a numerical representation of acidity or basicity of a solution; $pH = -\log[H_3O^+]$

physical change (1.2) a change in the form of a substance but not in its chemical composition; no chemical bonds are broken in a physical change

physical property (1.2) a characteristic of a substance that can be observed without the substance undergoing change (examples include color, density, melting and boiling points)

plasma lipoprotein (17.5) a complex composed of lipid and protein that is responsible for the transport of lipids throughout the body

β-pleated sheet (18.4) a common secondary structure of a peptide chain that resembles the pleats of an Oriental fan

point mutation (20.7) the substitution of one nucleotide pair for another within a gene

polar covalent bond (3.1) a covalent bond in which the electrons are not equally shared

poly(A) tail (20.4) a tract of 100–200 adenosine monophosphate units covalently attached to the 3′ end of eukaryotic messenger RNA molecules

polyatomic ion (3.2) an ion containing a number of atoms

polymer (11.5) a very large molecule formed by the combination of many small molecules (called *monomers*) (e.g., polyamides, nylons)

polyprotic substance (8.3) a substance that can accept or donate more than one proton per molecule

polysaccharide (16.1) a large, complex carbohydrate composed of long chains of monosaccharides

polysome (20.6) complexes of many ribosomes all simultaneously translating a single mRNA

positive allosterism (19.9) effector binding activates the active site of an allosteric enzyme

positron (9.1) particle that has the same mass as an electron but opposite (+) charge

post-transcriptional modification (20.4) alterations of the primary transcripts produced in eukaryotic cells; these include addition of a poly(A) tail to the 3′ end of the mRNA, addition of the cap structure to the 5′ end of the mRNA, and RNA splicing

potential energy (1.6) stored energy or energy caused by position or composition

precipitate (4.4, 6.1) an insoluble substance formed and separated from a solution

precision (1.4) the degree of agreement among replicate measurements of the same quantity

pressure (5.1) a force per unit area

primary (1°) alcohol (12.1) an alcohol with the general formula RCH_2OH

primary (1°) amine (15.1) an amine with the general formula RNH_2

primary (1°) carbon (10.2) a carbon atom that is bonded to only one other carbon atom

primary structure (of a protein) (18.3) the linear sequence of amino acids in a protein chain determined by the genetic information of the gene for each protein

primary transcript (20.4) the RNA product of transcription in eukaryotic cells, before post-transcriptional modifications are carried out

principal energy level (2.5) a region where electrons may be found; has integral values $n = 1, n = 2$, and so forth

product (4.3, 19.1) the chemical species that results from a chemical reaction and that appears on the right side of a chemical equation

proenzyme (19.9) the inactive form of a proteolytic enzyme

prokaryote (20.2) an organism with simple cellular structure in which there is no true nucleus enclosed by a nuclear membrane and there are no true membrane-bound organelles in the cytoplasm

promoter (20.4) the sequence of nucleotides immediately before a gene that is recognized by the RNA polymerase and signals the start point and direction of transcription

properties (1.2) characteristics of matter

prostaglandins (17.2) a family of hormonelike substances derived from the twenty-carbon fatty acid, arachidonic acid; produced by many cells of the body, they regulate many body functions

prosthetic group (18.6) the nonprotein portion of a protein that is essential to the biological activity of the protein; often a complex organic compound

protein (18: Intro) a macromolecule whose primary structure is a linear sequence of α-amino acids and whose final structure results from folding of the chain into a specific three-dimensional structure; proteins serve as catalysts, structural components, and nutritional elements for the cell

protein modification (19.9) a means of enzyme regulation in which a chemical group is covalently added to or removed from a protein. The chemical modification either turns the enzyme on or turns it off

proteolytic enzyme (19.11) an enzyme that hydrolyzes the peptide bonds between amino acids in a protein chain

proton (2.1) a positively charged particle in the nucleus of an atom

pure substance (1.2) a substance with constant composition

purine (20.1) a family of nitrogenous bases (heterocyclic amines) that are components of DNA and RNA and consist of a six-sided ring fused to a five-sided ring; the common purines in nucleic acids are adenine and guanine

pyridoxal phosphate (22.7) a coenzyme derived from vitamin B_6 that is required for all transamination reactions

pyrimidine (20.1) a family of nitrogenous bases (heterocyclic amines) that are components of nucleic acids and consist of a single six-sided ring; the common pyrimidines of DNA are cytosine and thymine; the common pyrimidines of RNA are cytosine and uracil

pyrimidine dimer (20.7) UV light–induced covalent bonding of two adjacent pyrimidine bases in a strand of DNA

pyruvate dehydrogenase complex (22.2) a complex of all the enzymes and coenzymes required for the synthesis of CO_2 and acetyl CoA from pyruvate

Q

quaternary ammonium salt (15.1) an amine salt with the general formula $R_4N^+A^-$ (in which R— can be an alkyl or aryl group or a hydrogen atom and A^- can be any anion)

quaternary (4°) carbon (10.2) a carbon atom that is bonded to four other carbon atoms

quaternary structure (of a protein) (18.6) aggregation of more than one folded peptide chain to yield a functional protein

R

rad (9.7) abbreviation for *radiation absorbed dose,* the absorption of 2.4×10^{-3} calories of energy per kilogram of absorbing tissue

radioactivity (9.1) the process by which atoms emit high-energy particles or rays; the spontaneous decomposition of a nucleus to produce a different nucleus

radiocarbon dating (9.3) the estimation of the age of objects through measurement of isotopic ratios of carbon

Raoult's law (6.4) a law stating that the vapor pressure of a component is equal to its mole fraction times the vapor pressure of the pure component

rate constant (7.3) the proportionality constant that relates the rate of a reaction and the concentration of reactants

rate law (7.3) expresses the rate of a reaction in terms of reactant concentration and a rate constant

rate of chemical reaction (7.3) the change in concentration of a reactant or product per unit time

reactant (4.3) starting material for a chemical reaction, appearing on the left side of a chemical equation

reaction order (7.3) the exponent of each concentration term in the rate equation

reducing agent (8.5) a substance that reduces, or donates electrons to, another substance; the reducing agent is itself oxidized in the process

reducing sugar (16.4) a sugar that can be oxidized by Benedict's or Tollens' reagents; includes all monosaccharides and most disaccharides

reduction (8.5, 12.4) the gain of electrons; in organic compounds it may be recognized by a gain of hydrogen or loss of oxygen

regulatory proteins (18: Intro) proteins that control cell functions such as metabolism and reproduction

release factor (20.6) a protein that binds to the termination codon in the empty A-site of the ribosome and causes the peptidyl transferase to hydrolyze the bond between the peptide and the peptidyl tRNA

rem (9.7) abbreviation for *roentgen equivalent for man,* the product of rad and RBE

replication fork (20.3) the point at which new nucleotides are added to the growing daughter DNA strand

replication origin (20.3) the region of a DNA molecule where DNA replication always begins

representative element (2.4) member of the groups of the periodic table designated as A

resonance (3.4) a condition that occurs when more than one valid Lewis structure can be written for a particular molecule

restriction enzyme (20.8) a bacterial enzyme that recognizes specific nucleotide sequences on a DNA molecule and cuts the sugar-phosphate backbone of the DNA at or near that site

result (1.1) the outcome of a designed experiment, often determined from individual bits of data

reversible, competitive enzyme inhibitor (19.10) a chemical that resembles the structure and charge distribution of the natural substrate and competes with it for the active site of an enzyme

reversible, noncompetitive enzyme inhibitor (19.10) a chemical that binds weakly to an amino acid R group of an enzyme and inhibits activity; when the inhibitor dissociates, the enzyme is restored to its active form

reversible reaction (7.4) a reaction that will proceed in either direction, reactants to products or products to reactants

ribonucleic acid (RNA) (20.1) single-stranded nucleic acid molecules that are composed of phosphoryl groups, ribose, and the nitrogenous bases uracil, cytosine, adenine, and guanine

ribonucleotide (20.1) a ribonucleoside phosphate or nucleotide composed of a nitrogenous base in β-*N*-glycosidic linkage to the 1′ carbon of the sugar ribose and with one, two, or three phosphoryl groups esterified at the hydroxyl of the 5′ carbon of the ribose

ribose (16.4) a five-carbon monosaccharide that is a component of RNA and many coenzymes

ribosomal RNA (rRNA) (20.4) the RNA species that are structural and functional components of the small and large ribosomal subunits

ribosome (20.6) an organelle composed of a large and a small subunit, each of which is made up of ribosomal RNA and proteins; the platform on which translation occurs and that carries the enzymatic activity that forms peptide bonds

RNA polymerase (20.4) the enzyme that catalyzes the synthesis of RNA molecules using DNA as the template

RNA splicing (20.4) removal of portions of the primary transcript that do not encode protein sequences

roentgen (9.7) the dose of radiation producing 2.1×10^9 ions in 1 cm^3 of air at 0°C and 1 atm of pressure

S

saccharide (16.1) a sugar molecule

saponification (14.2, 17.3) a reaction in which a soap is produced; more generally, the hydrolysis of an ester by an aqueous base

saturated fatty acid (17.2) a long-chain monocarboxylic acid in which each carbon of the chain is bonded to the maximum number of hydrogen atoms

saturated hydrocarbon (10.1) an alkane; a hydrocarbon that contains only carbon and hydrogen bonded together through carbon-hydrogen and carbon-carbon single bonds

saturated solution (6.1) one in which undissolved solute is in equilibrium with the solution

scientific method (1.1) the process of studying our surroundings that is based on experimentation

scientific notation (1.4) a system used to represent numbers as powers of ten

secondary (2°) alcohol (12.1) an alcohol with the general formula R_2CHOH

secondary (2°) amine (15.1) an amine with the general formula R_2NH

secondary (2°) carbon (10.2) a carbon atom that is bonded to two other carbon atoms

secondary structure (of a protein) (18.4) folding of the primary structure of a protein into an α-helix or a β-pleated sheet; folding is maintained by hydrogen bonds between the amide hydrogen and the carbonyl oxygen of the peptide bond

selectively permeable membrane (6.4) a membrane that restricts diffusion of some ions and molecules (based on size and charge) across the membrane

semiconservative DNA replication (20.3) DNA polymerase "reads" each parental strand of DNA and produces a complementary daughter strand; thus, all newly synthesized DNA molecules consist of one parental and one daughter strand

semipermeable membrane (6.4) a membrane permeable to the solvent but not the solute; a material that allows the transport of certain substances from one side of the membrane to the other

shielding (9.6) material used to provide protection from radiation

sickle cell anemia (18.8) a human genetic disorder resulting from inheriting mutant hemoglobin genes from both parents

significant figures (1.4) all digits in a number known with certainty and the first uncertain digit

silent mutation (20.7) a mutation that changes the sequence of the DNA but does not alter the amino acid sequence of the protein encoded by the DNA

single bond (3.4) a bond in which one pair of electrons is shared by two atoms

single-replacement reaction (4.3) also called *substitution reaction,* one in which one atom in a molecule is displaced by another

soap (14.1) any of a variety of the alkali metal salts of fatty acids

solid state (1.2) a physical state of matter characterized by its rigidity and fixed volume and shape

solubility (3.5, 6.1) the amount of a substance that will dissolve in a given volume of solvent at a specified temperature

solute (6.1) a component of a solution that is present in lesser quantity than the solvent

solution (6.1) a homogeneous (uniform) mixture of two or more substances

solvent (6.1) the solution component that is present in the largest quantity

specific gravity (1.6) the ratio of the density of a substance to the density of water at 4°C or any specified temperature

specific heat (7.2) the quantity of heat (calories) required to raise the temperature of 1 g of a substance 1 degree Celsius

spectroscopy (2.3) the measurement of intensity and energy of electromagnetic radiation

speed of light (2.3) 2.99×10^8 m/s in a vacuum

sphingolipid (17.4) a phospholipid that is derived from the amino alcohol sphingosine rather than from glycerol

sphingomyelin (17.4) a sphingolipid found in abundance in the myelin sheath that surrounds and insulates cells of the central nervous system

standard solution (8.3) a solution whose concentration is accurately known

standard temperature and pressure (STP) (5.1) defined as 273 K and 1 atm

stereochemical specificity (19.5) the property of an enzyme that allows it to catalyze reactions involving only one enantiomer of the substrate

stereochemistry (16.3) the study of the spatial arrangement of atoms in a molecule

stereoisomers (10.3, 16.3) a pair of molecules having the same structural formula and bonding pattern but differing in the arrangement of the atoms in space

steroid (17.4) a lipid derived from cholesterol and composed of one five-sided ring and three six-sided rings; the steroids include sex hormones and anti-inflammatory compounds

structural analog (19.10) a chemical having a structure and charge distribution very similar to those of a natural enzyme substrate

structural formula (10.2) a formula showing all of the atoms in a molecule and exhibiting all bonds as lines

structural isomers (10.2) molecules having the same molecular formula but different chemical structures

structural protein (18: Intro) a protein that provides mechanical support for large plants and animals

sublevel (2.5) a set of equal-energy orbitals within a principal energy level

sublimation (5.3) a process whereby some molecules in the solid state convert directly to the gaseous state

substituted hydrocarbon (10.1) a hydrocarbon in which one or more hydrogen atoms is replaced by another atom or group of atoms

substitution reaction (10.5, 11.6) a reaction that results in the replacement of one group for another

substrate (19.1) the reactant in a chemical reaction that binds to an enzyme active site and is converted to product

substrate-level phosphorylation (21.3) the production of ATP by the transfer of a phosphoryl group from the substrate of a reaction to ADP

sucrose (16.5) a disaccharide composed of α-D-glucose and β-D-fructose in ($\alpha 1 \longrightarrow \beta 2$) glycosidic linkage; table sugar

supersaturated solution (6.1) a solution that is more concentrated than a saturated solution (Note that such a solution is not at equilibrium.)

surface tension (5.2) a measure of the strength of the attractive forces at the surface of a liquid

surfactant (5.2) a substance that decreases the surface tension of a liquid

surroundings (7.1) the universe outside of the system

suspension (6.1) a heterogeneous mixture of particles; the suspended particles are larger than those found in a colloidal suspension

system (7.1) the process under study

T

tautomers (13.4) structural isomers that differ from one another in the placement of a hydrogen atom and a double bond

temperature (1.6) a measure of the relative "hotness" or "coldness" of an object

temperature optimum (19.8) the temperature at which an enzyme functions optimally and the rate of reaction is maximal

terminal electron acceptor (22.6) the final electron acceptor in an electron transport system that removes the low-energy electrons from the system; in aerobic organisms the terminal electron acceptor is molecular oxygen

termination codon (20.6) a triplet of ribonucleotides with no corresponding anticodon on a tRNA; as a result, translation will end because there is no amino acid to transfer to the peptide chain

terpene (17.4) the general term for lipids that are synthesized from isoprene units; the terpenes include steroids, bile salts, lipid-soluble vitamins, and chlorophyll

tertiary (3°) alcohol (12.1) an alcohol with the general formula R_3COH

tertiary (3°) amine (15.1) an amine with the general formula R_3N

tertiary (3°) carbon (10.2) a carbon atom that is bonded to three other carbon atoms

tertiary structure (of a protein) (18.5) the globular, three-dimensional structure of a protein that results from folding the regions of secondary structure; this folding occurs spontaneously as a result of interactions of the side chains or R groups of the amino acids

tetrahedral structure (3.4) a molecule consisting of four groups attached to a central atom that occupy the four corners of an imagined regular tetrahedron

tetrose (16.2) a four-carbon monosaccharide

theoretical yield (4.5) the maximum amount of product that can be produced from a given amount of reactant

theory (1.1) a hypothesis supported by extensive testing that explains and predicts facts

thermodynamics (7.1) the branch of science that deals with the relationship between energies of systems, work, and heat

thioester (14.4) the product of a reaction between a thiol and a carboxylic acid

thiol (12.8) an organic compound that contains a thiol group (—SH)

titration (8.3) the process of adding a solution from a buret to a sample until a reaction is complete, at which time the volume is accurately measured and the concentration of the sample is calculated

Tollens' test (13.4) a test reagent (silver nitrate in ammonium hydroxide) used to distinguish aldehydes and ketones; also called the Tollens' silver mirror test

tracer (9.5) a radioisotope that is rapidly and selectively transmitted to the part of the body for which diagnosis is desired

transaminase (22.7) an enzyme that catalyzes the transfer of an amino group from one molecule to another

transamination (22.7) a reaction in which an amino group is transferred from one molecule to another

transcription (20.4) the synthesis of RNA from a DNA template

transferase (19.1) an enzyme that catalyzes the transfer of a functional group from one molecule to another

transfer RNA (tRNA) (15.4, 20.4) small RNAs that bind to a specific amino acid at the 3′ end and mediate its addition at the appropriate site in a growing peptide chain; accomplished by recognition of the correct codon on the mRNA by the complementary anticodon on the tRNA

transition element (2.4) any element located between Groups IIA (2) and IIIA (13) in the long periods of the periodic table

transition state (19.6) the unstable intermediate in catalysis in which the enzyme has altered the form of the substrate so that it now shares properties of both the substrate and the product

translation (20.6) the synthesis of a protein from the genetic code carried on the mRNA

translocation (20.6) movement of the ribosome along the mRNA during translation

transmembrane protein (17.6) a protein that is embedded within a membrane and crosses the lipid bilayer, protruding from the membrane both inside and outside the cell

transport protein (18: Intro) a protein that transports materials across the cell membrane or throughout the body

triglyceride (17.3, 23.1) triacylglycerol; a molecule composed of glycerol esterified to three fatty acids

trigonal planar (3.4) a molecular geometry in which a central atom is bonded to three atoms that lie at the vertices of an equilateral triangle. All atoms lie within one plane and all bond angles are 120°

trigonal pyramidal molecule (3.4) a nonplanar structure involving three groups bonded to a central atom in which each group is equidistant from the central atom

triose (16.2) a three-carbon monosaccharide

triple bond (3.4) a bond in which three pairs of electrons are shared by two atoms

U

uncertainty (1.4) the degree of doubt in a single measurement

unit (1.3) a determinate quantity (of length, time, etc.) that has been adopted as a standard of measurement

unsaturated fatty acid (17.2) a long-chain monocarboxylic acid having at least one carbon-to-carbon double bond

unsaturated hydrocarbon (10.1, 11: Intro) a hydrocarbon containing at least one multiple (double or triple) bond

urea cycle (22.8) a cyclic series of reactions that detoxifies ammonium ions by incorporating them into urea, which is excreted from the body

uridine triphosphate (UTP) (21.7) a nucleotide composed of the pyrimidine uracil, the sugar ribose, and three phosphoryl groups and that serves as a carrier of glucose-1-phosphate in glycogenesis

V

valence electron (2.6) electron in the outermost shell (principal quantum level) of an atom

valence-shell electron-pair repulsion (VSEPR) theory (3.4) a model that predicts molecular geometry using the premise that electron pairs will arrange themselves as far apart as possible, to minimize electron repulsion

van der Waals forces (5.2) a general term for intermolecular forces that include dipole-dipole and London dispersion forces

vapor pressure lowering (6.4) the decrease in the tendency of a liquid to become a gas when a solute is added

vapor pressure of a liquid (5.2) the pressure exerted by the vapor at the surface of a liquid at equilibrium

very low density lipoprotein (VLDL) (17.5) a plasma lipoprotein that binds triglycerides synthesized by the liver and carries them to adipose tissue for storage

viscosity (5.2) a measure of the resistance to flow of a substance at constant temperature

vitamin (19.7) an organic substance that is required in the diet in small amounts; water-soluble vitamins are used in the synthesis of coenzymes required for the function of cellular enzymes; lipid-soluble vitamins are involved in calcium metabolism, vision, and blood clotting

voltaic cell (8.5) an electrochemical cell that converts chemical energy into electrical energy

W

wax (17.4) a collection of lipids that are generally considered to be esters of long-chain alcohols

weight (1.3) the force exerted on an object by gravity

Z

Zaitsev's rule (12.4) states that in an elimination reaction, the alkene with the greatest number of alkyl groups on the double-bonded carbon (the more highly substituted alkene) is the major product of the reaction

Answers to Odd-Numbered Problems

Chapter 10

10.1 The student could test the solubility of the substance in water and in an organic solvent, such as hexane. Solubility in hexane would suggest an organic substance; whereas solubility in water would indicate an inorganic compound. The student could also determine the melting and boiling points of the substance. If the melting and boiling points are very high, an inorganic substance would be suspected.

10.3

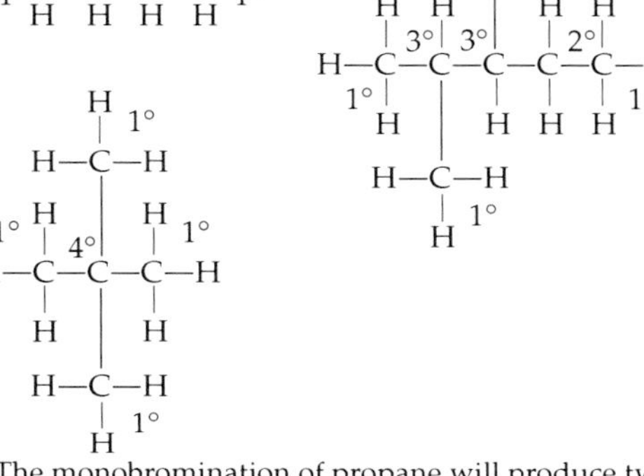

10.5 a. The monobromination of propane will produce two products, as shown in the following two equations:

$CH_3CH_2CH_3 + Br_2 \xrightarrow{\text{Light or heat}} CH_3CH_2CH_2Br + HBr$

$CH_3CH_2CH_3 + Br_2 \xrightarrow{\text{Light or heat}} CH_3CHBrCH_3 + HBr$

b. The monochlorination of butane will produce two products, as shown in the following two equations:

$CH_3CH_2CH_2CH_3 + Cl_2 \xrightarrow{\text{Light or heat}} CH_3CH_2CH_2CH_2Cl + HCl$

$CH_3CH_2CH_2CH_3 + Cl_2 \xrightarrow{\text{Light or heat}} CH_3CH_2CHClCH_3 + HCl$

c. The monochlorination of cyclobutane:

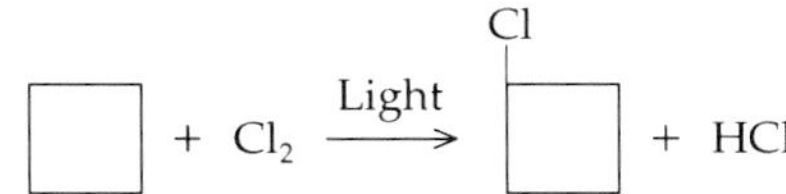

d. The monobromination of pentane will produce three products as shown in the following equations:

$CH_3CH_2CH_2CH_2CH_3 + Br_2 \xrightarrow{\text{Light or heat}} CH_3CH_2CH_2CH_2CH_2Br + HBr$

$CH_3CH_2CH_2CH_2CH_3 + Br_2 \xrightarrow{\text{Light or heat}} CH_3CH_2CH_2CHBrCH_3 + HBr$

$CH_3CH_2CH_2CH_2CH_3 + Br_2 \xrightarrow{\text{Light or heat}} CH_3CH_2CHBrCH_2CH_3 + HBr$

10.7 The number of organic compounds is nearly limitless because carbon forms stable covalent bonds with other carbon atoms in a variety of different patterns. In addition, carbon can form stable bonds with other elements and functional groups. Finally, carbon can form double or triple bonds with other carbon atoms to produce organic molecules with different properties.

10.9 Because ionic substances often form three-dimensional crystals made up of many positive and negative ions, they generally have much higher melting and boiling points than covalent compounds.

10.11 a. $LiCl > H_2O > CH_4$ b. $NaCl > C_3H_8 > C_2H_6$

10.13 a. LiCl would be a solid; H_2O would be a liquid; and CH_4 would be a gas.

b. NaCl would be a solid; both C_3H_8 and C_2H_6 would be gases.

10.15 a. Water-soluble inorganic compounds
b. Inorganic compounds
c. Organic compounds
d. Inorganic compounds
e. Organic compounds

10.17 a. $C_{19}H_{40}$

b.

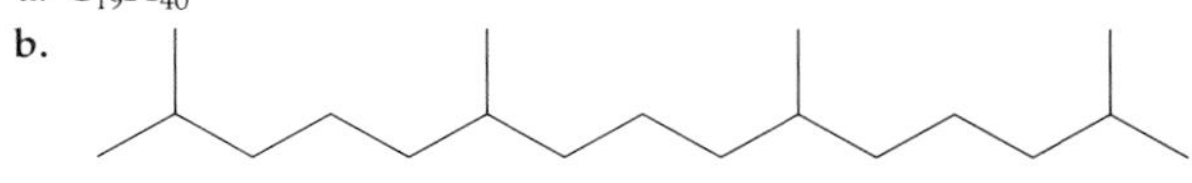

$CH(CH_3)_2(CH_2)_3CH(CH_3)(CH_2)_3CH(CH_3)(CH_2)_3CH(CH_3)_2$

c. 268.51 g/mol

10.19 a. $CH_3CH_2CH(CH_3)_2$
b. $CH_3CH_2C(CH_3)_2(CH_2)_2CH(CH_3)_2$
c. $CH_3CH_2C(CH_3)_2(CH_2)_3CH(CH_3)CH(CH_3)_2$

10.21 a. b. c.

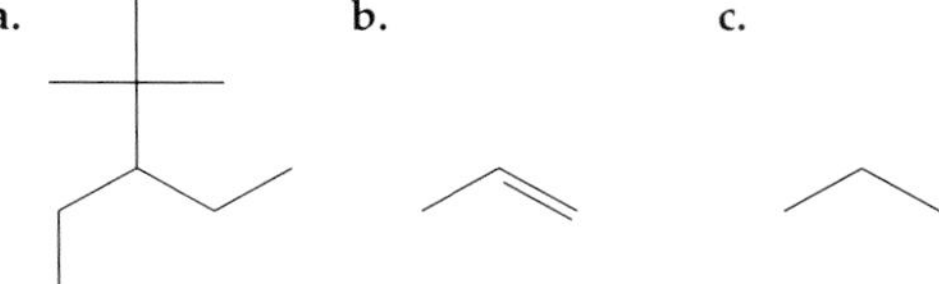

10.23 a. $(CH_3)_3CCH(CH_2CH_3)_2$
b. CH_3CHCH_2
c. $CH_3CH_2CH_3$

10.25

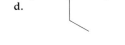

a. b.

c. d.

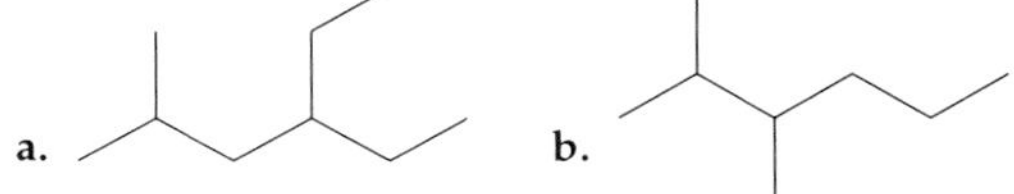

10.27 a. Tricosane.

Pentacosane.

Heptacosane.

b. Tricosane: 324.61 g/mol
Pentacosane: 352.67 g/mol
Heptacosane: 380.72 g/mol

10.29

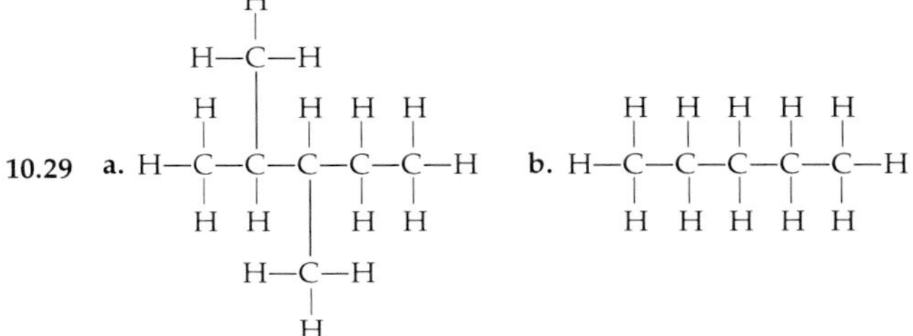

10.31

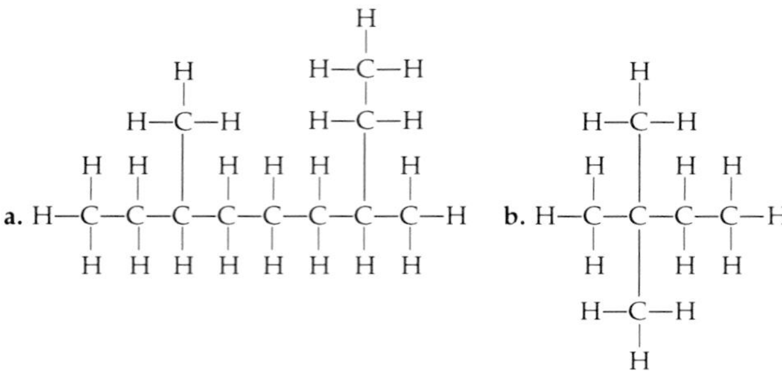

10.33 a. Hydroxyl group
b. Amino group
c. Carbonyl group
d. Carboxyl group
e. Ester group
f. Ether group
g. Halide

10.35 a. C_nH_{2n+2}
b. C_nH_{2n-2}
c. C_nH_{2n}
d. C_nH_{2n}
e. C_nH_{2n-2}

10.37 Alkanes have only carbon-to-carbon and carbon-to-hydrogen single bonds, as in the molecule ethane:

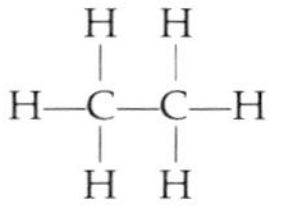

```
    H  H
    |  |
 H—C—C—H
    |  |
    H  H
```

Alkenes have at least one carbon-to-carbon double bond, as in the molecule ethene:

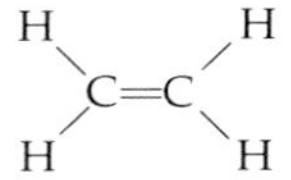

```
 H       H
  \     /
   C=C
  /     \
 H       H
```

Alkynes have at least one carbon-to-carbon triple bond, as in the molecule ethyne:

H—C≡C—H

10.39 a. A carboxylic acid:

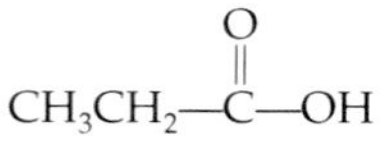

```
           O
           ‖
 CH3CH2—C—OH
```

b. An amine: $CH_3CH_2CH_2$—NH_2
c. An alcohol: $CH_3CH_2CH_2$—OH
d. An ether: CH_3CH_2—O—CH_2CH_3

10.41

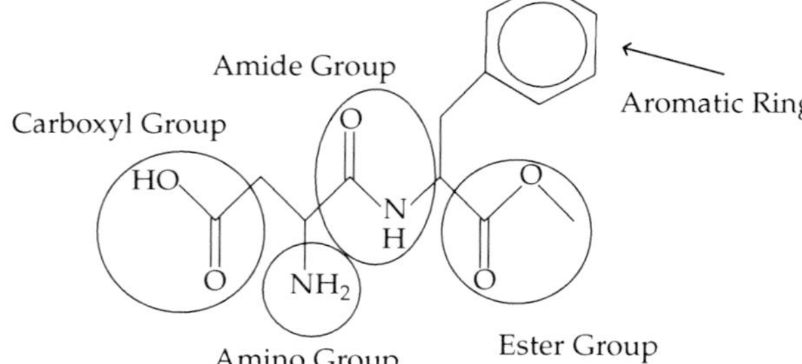

10.43 Hydrocarbons are nonpolar molecules, and hence are not soluble in water.

10.45 a. Heptane > Hexane > Butane > Ethane
b. $CH_3CH_2CH_2CH_2CH_2CH_2CH_2CH_2CH_3$ > $CH_3CH_2CH_2CH_2CH_3$ > $CH_3CH_2CH_3$

10.47 a. Heptane and hexane would be liquid at room temperature; butane and ethane would be gases.
b. $CH_3CH_2CH_2CH_2CH_2CH_2CH_2CH_2CH_3$ and $CH_3CH_2CH_2CH_2CH_3$ would be liquids at room temperature; $CH_3CH_2CH_3$ would be a gas.

10.49 Nonane: $CH_3CH_2CH_2CH_2CH_2CH_2CH_2CH_2CH_3$
Pentane: $CH_3CH_2CH_2CH_2CH_3$
Propane: $CH_3CH_2CH_3$

10.51 a. Br

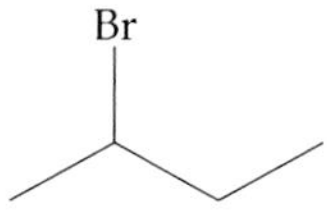

b. Cl

c.

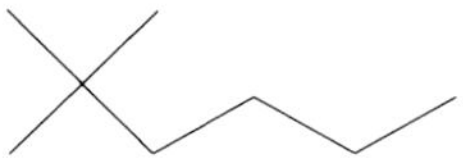

10.53 a. 2,2-Dibromobutane:

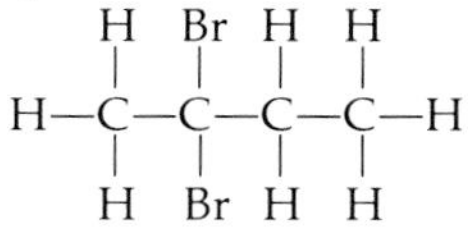

```
    H  Br  H  H
    |  |   |  |
 H—C—C—C—C—H
    |  |   |  |
    H  Br  H  H
```

b. 2-Iododecane:

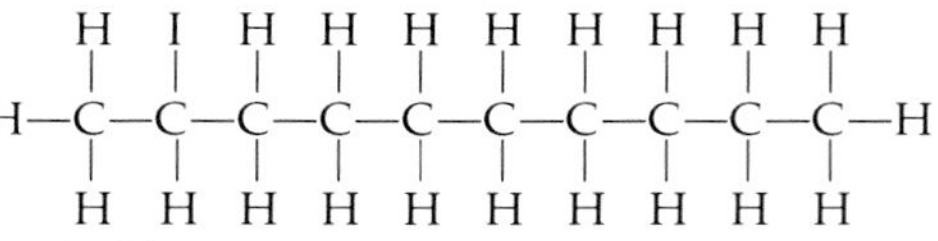

c. 1,2-Dichloropentane:

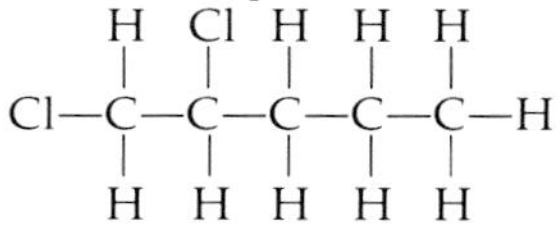

```
     H  Cl  H  H  H
     |  |   |  |  |
 Cl—C—C—C—C—C—H
     |  |   |  |  |
     H  H   H  H  H
```

d. 1-Bromo-2-methylpentane:

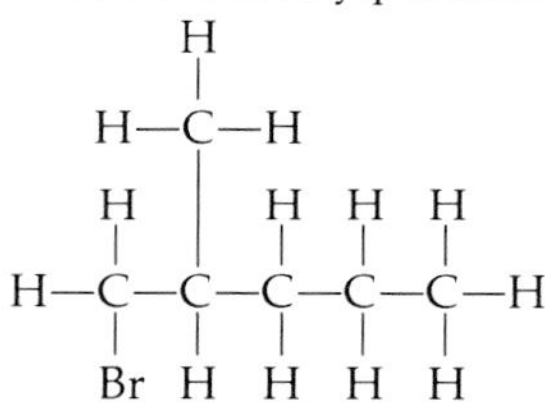

10.55 a. 3-Methylpentane
b. 2,5-Dimethylhexane
c. 1-Bromoheptane
d. 1-Chloro-3-methylbutane

10.57 a. 2-Chloropropane
b. 2-Iodobutane
c. 2,2-Dibromopropane
d. 1-Chloro-2-methylpropane
e. 2-Iodo-2-methylpropane

10.59 a. The straight chain isomers of molecular formula C_4H_9Br:

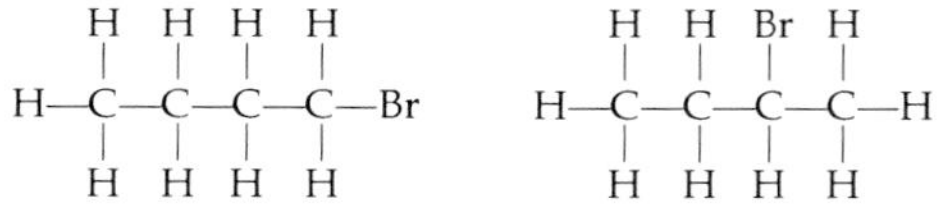

```
    H  H  H  H              H  H  Br H
    |  |  |  |              |  |  |  |
 H—C—C—C—C—Br          H—C—C—C—C—H
    |  |  |  |              |  |  |  |
    H  H  H  H              H  H  H  H
```

b. The straight chain isomers of molecular formula $C_4H_8Br_2$:

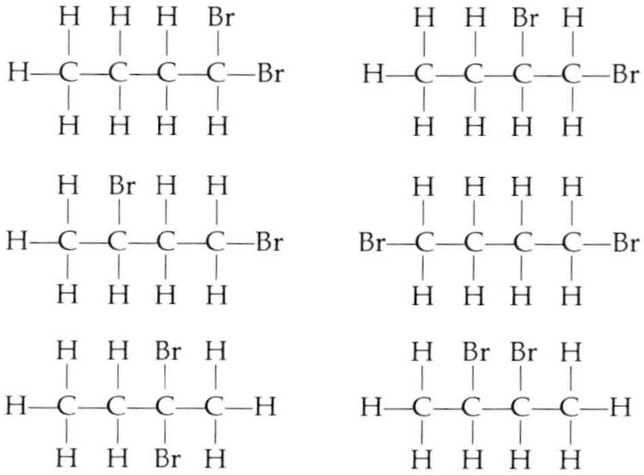

```
    H  H  H  Br             H  H  Br H
    |  |  |  |              |  |  |  |
 H—C—C—C—C—Br          H—C—C—C—C—Br
    |  |  |  |              |  |  |  |
    H  H  H  H              H  H  H  H

    H  Br H  H               H  H  H  H
    |  |  |  |               |  |  |  |
 H—C—C—C—C—Br          Br—C—C—C—C—Br
    |  |  |  |               |  |  |  |
    H  H  H  H               H  H  H  H

    H  H  Br H              H  Br Br H
    |  |  |  |              |  |  |  |
 H—C—C—C—C—H           H—C—C—C—C—H
    |  |  |  |              |  |  |  |
    H  H  Br H              H  H  H  H
```

10.61 a. 2-Chlorohexane c. 3-Chloropentane
b. 1,4-Dibromobutane d. 2-Methylheptane

10.63 a. The first pair of molecules are constitutional isomers: hexane and 2-methylpentane.
b. The second pair of molecules are identical. Both are heptane.

10.65 Structures "a" and "c"

10.67 a. Incorrect: 3-Methylhexane c. Incorrect: 3-Methylheptane
b. Incorrect: 2-Methylbutane d. Correct

10.69 a.
CH_3
|
$CH_3CHCH_2CHCH_3$
|
CH_3
The name given in the problem is correct.

b.
CH_3
|
$CH_3CH_2CH_2CHCH_2CH_2CH_3$
The correct name is 4-methylheptane.

c. $I—CH_2CH_2CH_2CH_2CH_2—I$ The name given in the problem is correct.

d. $CH_3CH_2CH_2CH_2CH_2CHCH_2CH_2CH_3$
|
CH_2CH_3
The correct name is 4-ethylnonane.

e. Br Br
| |
$CH_2CH_2CH_2CH_2CH_2CCH_2CH_3$
|
CH_3
The name given in the problem is correct.

10.71 Cycloalkanes are a family of molecules having carbon-to-carbon bonds in a ring structure.

10.73 The general formula for a cycloalkane is C_nH_{2n}.

10.75 a. Chlorocyclopropane
b. *cis*-1,2-Dichlorocyclopropane
c. *trans*-1,2-Dichlorocyclopropane
d. Bromocyclopropane

10.77 a. c.

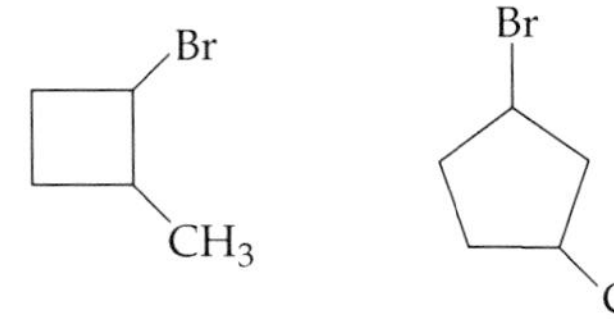

b. d.

Br
Br
CH_3

10.79 There are three structural isomers of dichlorocyclopropane. Two of these isomers are geometric isomers.

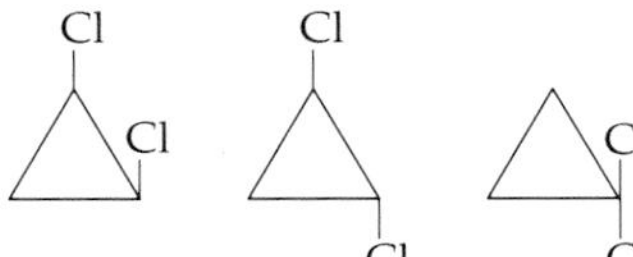

10.81 a. Incorrect—1,2-Dibromocyclobutane
b. Incorrect—1,2-Diethylcyclobutane
c. Correct
d. Incorrect—1,2,3-Trichlorocyclohexane

10.83 a. *cis*-1,3-Dibromocyclopentane c. *cis*-1, 2-Dichlorocyclopropane

Br Br

Cl
Cl

b. *trans*-1,2-Dimethylcyclobutane d. *trans*-1,4-Diethylcyclohexane

CH_3
CH_3

CH_2CH_3
CH_2CH_3

10.85 a. *cis*-1,2-Dibromocyclopentane
b. *trans*-1,3-Dibromocyclopentane
c. *cis*-1,2-Dimethylcyclohexane
d. *cis*-1,2-Dimethylcyclopropane

10.87 Conformational isomers are distinct isomeric structures that may be converted into one another by rotation about the bonds in the molecule.

10.89 In the chair conformation the hydrogen atoms, and thus the electron pairs of the C—H bonds, are farther from one another. As a result, there is less electron repulsion and the structure is more stable. In the boat conformation, the electron pairs are more crowded. This causes greater electron repulsion, producing a less stable conformation.

10.91 Combustion is the oxidation of hydrocarbons by burning in the presence of air to produce carbon dioxide and water.

10.93 a. $C_3H_8 + 5O_2 \rightarrow 4H_2O + 3CO_2$
b. $C_7H_{16} + 11O_2 \rightarrow 8H_2O + 7CO_2$
c. $C_9H_{20} + 14O_2 \rightarrow 10H_2O + 9CO_2$
d. $2C_{10}H_{22} + 31O_2 \rightarrow 22H_2O + 20CO_2$

10.95 $2C_{16}H_{34} + 49O_2 \rightarrow 32CO_2 + 34H_2O$

10.97 a. $8CO_2 + 10H_2O$
b.
CH_3 CH_3
| |
$Br—C—CH_3 + CH_3CHCH_2Br + 2HBr$
|
CH_3
c. Cl_2 and light

10.99 The following molecules are all isomers of C_6H_{14}.

$CH_3CH_2CH_2CH_2CH_2CH_3$
Hexane

CH_3
|
$CH_3CHCH_2CH_2CH_3$
2-Methylpentane

CH_3
|
$CH_3CH_2CHCH_2CH_3$
3-Methylpentane

CH_3
|
$CH_3CHCHCH_3$
|
CH_3
2,3-Dimethylbutane

CH_3
|
$CH_3CCH_2CH_3$
|
CH_3
2,2-Dimethylbutane

a. 2,3-Dimethylbutane produces only two monobrominated derivatives: 1-bromo-2,3-dimethylbutane and 2-bromo-2, 3-dimethylbutane.
b. Hexane produces three monobrominated products: 1-bromohexane, 2-bromohexane, and 3-bromohexane. 2,2-Dimethylbutane also produces three monobrominated products: 1-bromo-2,2-dimethylbutane, 2-bromo-3, 3-dimethylbutane, and 1-bromo-3,3-dimethylbutane.

c. 3-Methylpentane produces four monobrominated products: 1-bromo-3-methylpentane, 2-bromo-3-methylpentane, 3-bromo-3-methylpentane, and 1-bromo-2-ethylbutane.

10.101 The hydrocarbon is cyclooctane, and it has the molecular formula C_8H_{16}.

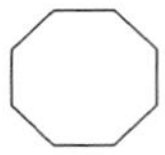

$$\text{(cyclooctane)} + 12\ O_2 \longrightarrow 8\ CO_2 + 8\ HO_2 + \text{heat energy}$$

Chapter 11

11.1 a. $CH_2BrCH_2C{\equiv}CCH_2CH_3$

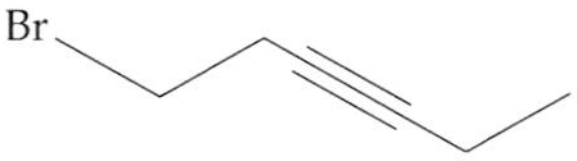

b. $CH_3C{\equiv}CCH_3$

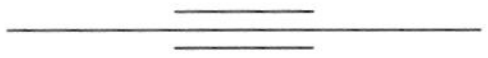

c. $ClC{\equiv}CCl$

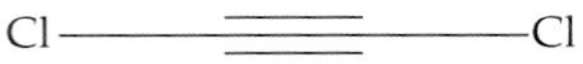

d. $HC{\equiv}C(CH_2)_7I$

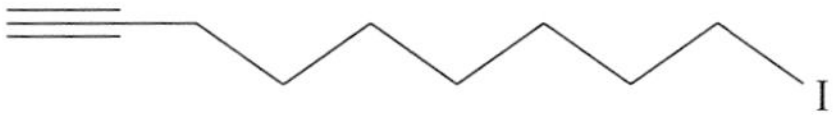

11.3 a. 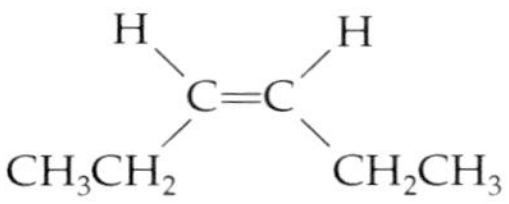 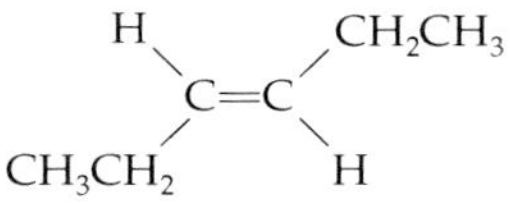 cis-3-Hexene; trans-3-Hexene

b. 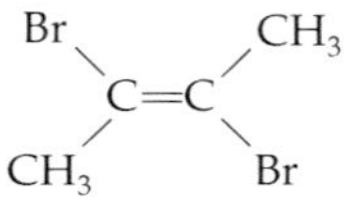 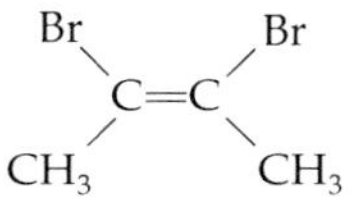 trans-2,3-Dibromo-2-butene; cis-2,3-Dibromo-2-butene

11.5 Molecule "c" can exist as *cis*- and *trans*-isomers because there are two different groups on each of the carbon atoms attached by the double bond.

11.7 a. 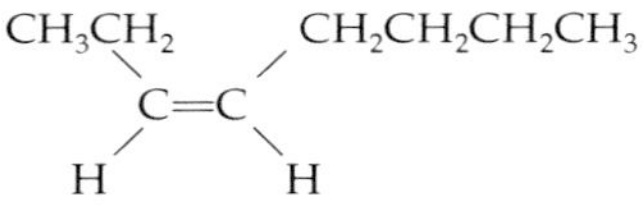 $CH_3CH_2(H)C{=}C(H)CH_2CH_2CH_2CH_3$

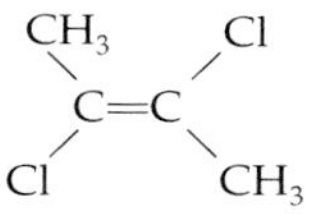

b. 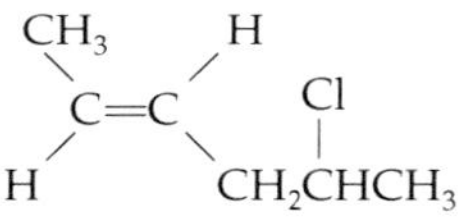 $CH_3(H)C{=}C(H)CH_2CHClCH_3$

c. $CH_3(Cl)C{=}C(Cl)CH_3$

11.9 The hydrogenation of the *cis* and *trans* isomers of 2-pentene would produce the same product, pentane.

11.11 a.

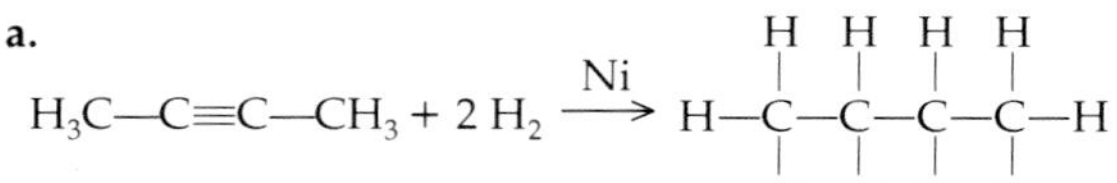

$$H_3C{-}C{\equiv}C{-}CH_3 + 2\ H_2 \xrightarrow{Ni} CH_3CH_2CH_2CH_3$$

2-Butyne → Butane

b.

$$H_3C{-}C{\equiv}C{-}CH_2CH_3 + 2\ H_2 \xrightarrow{Ni} CH_3CH_2CH_2CH_2CH_3$$

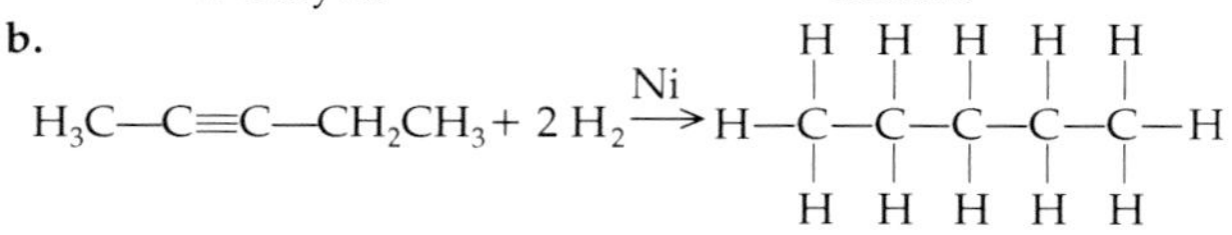

2-Pentyne → Pentane

11.13

a. $CH_3CH{=}CH_2 + Br_2 \longrightarrow CH_3CHBrCH_2Br$

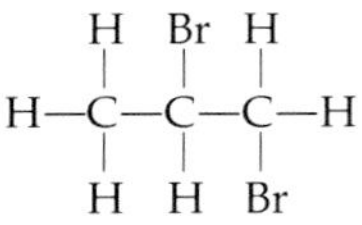

b. $CH_3CH{=}CHCH_3 + Br_2 \longrightarrow CH_3CHBrCHBrCH_3$

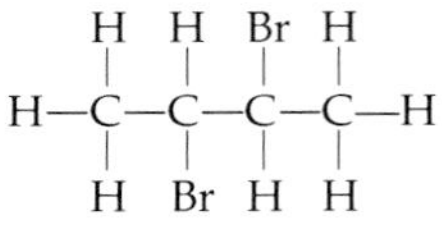

11.15

a. $CH_3C{\equiv}CCH_3 + 2Cl_2 \longrightarrow CH_3CCl_2CCl_2CH_3$

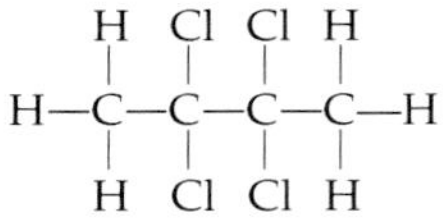

b. $CH_3C{\equiv}CCH_2CH_3 + 2Cl_2 \longrightarrow CH_3CCl_2CCl_2CH_2CH_3$

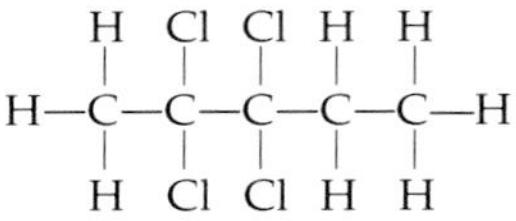

11.17 a. $CH_3CH{=}CHCH_3 + H_2O \xrightarrow{H+} CH_3CHOHCH_2CH_3$

b. $H_2C{=}CHCH_2CH_2CH(CH_3)_2 + H_2O \xrightarrow{H+}$ $CH_3CHOHCH_2CH_2CH(CH_3)_2$ (Major product)

$H_2C{=}CHCH_2CH_2CH(CH_3)_2 + H_2O \xrightarrow{H+}$ $CH_2OHCH_2CH_2CH_2CH(CH_3)_2$ (Major product)

c. $CH_3CH_2CH_2CH{=}CHCH_2CH_3 + H_2O \xrightarrow{H+}$ $CH_3CH_2CH_2CHOHCH_2CH_2CH_3$

$CH_3CH_2CH_2CH{=}CHCH_2CH_3 + H_2O \xrightarrow{H+}$ $CH_3CH_2CH_2CH_2CHOHCH_2CH_3$

d. $CH_3CHClCH{=}CHCHClCH_3 + H_2O \xrightarrow{H+}$ $CH_3CHClCHOHCH_2CHClCH_3$ Only product

11.19 a. $H_3CC{\equiv}CH + H_2O \xrightarrow{H^+} CH_3C(OH){=}CH_2 \longrightarrow CH_3COCH_3$

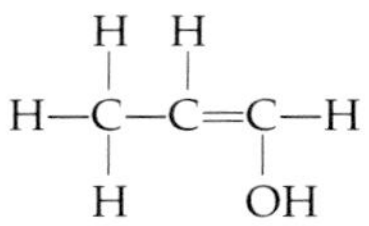

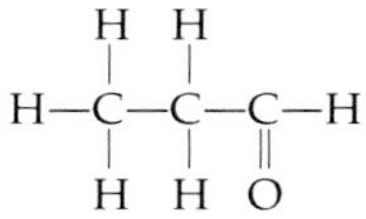

Or

$H_3CC{\equiv}CH + H_2O \xrightarrow{H^+} CH_3CH{=}CHOH \longrightarrow CH_3CH_2CHO$

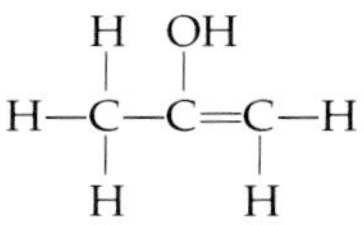

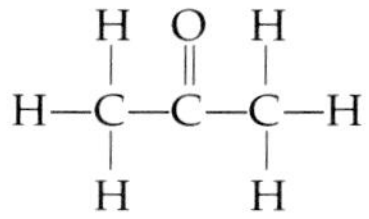

b.

$$H_3CC{\equiv}CCH_2CH_3 + H_2O \xrightarrow{H^+} H{-}\underset{H}{\overset{H}{C}}{-}\overset{H}{C}{=}\underset{OH}{C}{-}\underset{H}{\overset{H}{C}}{-}\underset{H}{\overset{H}{C}}{-}H \longrightarrow H{-}\underset{H}{\overset{H}{C}}{-}\underset{H}{\overset{H}{C}}{-}\underset{O}{\overset{\|}{C}}{-}\underset{H}{\overset{H}{C}}{-}\underset{H}{\overset{H}{C}}{-}H$$

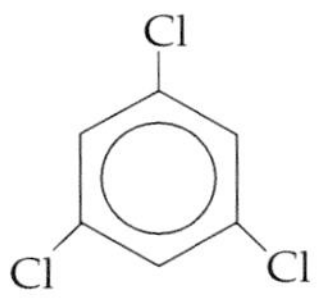

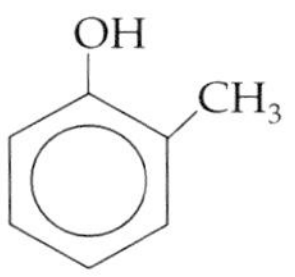

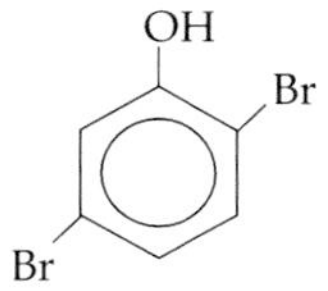

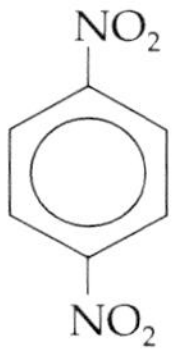

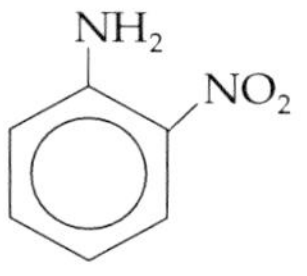

Or

$$H_3CC{\equiv}CCH_2CH_3 + H_2O \xrightarrow{H^+} H{-}\underset{H}{\overset{H}{C}}{-}\overset{OH}{C}{=}\underset{H}{C}{-}\underset{H}{\overset{H}{C}}{-}\underset{H}{\overset{H}{C}}{-}H \longrightarrow H{-}\underset{H}{\overset{H}{C}}{-}\overset{O}{\overset{\|}{C}}{-}\underset{H}{\overset{H}{C}}{-}\underset{H}{\overset{H}{C}}{-}\underset{H}{\overset{H}{C}}{-}H$$

11.21 a. Cl, Cl, Cl (benzene ring)
b. OH, CH_3 (benzene ring)
c. OH, Br, Br (benzene ring)
d. NO_2, NO_2 (benzene ring)
e. NH_2, NO_2 (benzene ring)
f. CH_3, NO_2 (benzene ring)

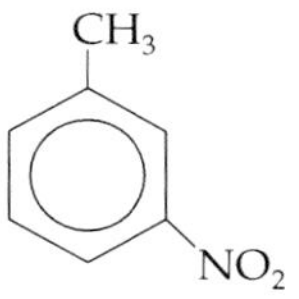

11.23 As the length of the hydrocarbon chain increases, the London dispersion forces between the molecules increase. The stronger these attractive forces between molecules are, the higher the boiling point will be.

11.25 The general formula for an alkane is C_nH_{2n+2}.
The general formula for an alkene is C_nH_{2n}.
The general formula for an alkyne is C_nH_{2n-2}.

11.27 Ethene is a planar molecule. All of the bond angles are 120°.

11.29 In alkanes, such as ethane, the four bonds around each carbon atom have tetrahedral geometry. The bond angles are 109.5°. In alkenes, such as ethene, each carbon is bonded by two single bonds and one double bond. The molecule is planar and each bond angle is approximately 120°.

11.31 Ethyne is a linear molecule. All of the bond angles are 180°.

11.33 In alkanes, such as ethane, the four bonds around each carbon atom have tetrahedral geometry. The bond angles are 109.5°. In alkenes, such as ethene, each carbon is bonded by two single bonds and one double bond. The molecule is planar and each bond angle is approximately 120°. In alkynes, such as ethyne, each carbon is bonded by one single bond and one triple bond. The molecule is linear and the bond angles are 180°.

11.35 a. 2-Pentyne > Propyne > Ethyne
b. 3-Decene > 2-Butene > Ethene

11.37 Identify the longest carbon chain containing the carbon-to-carbon double or triple bond. Replace the *-ane* suffix of the alkane name with *-ene* for an alkene or *-yne* for an alkyne. Number the chain to give the lowest number to the first of the two carbons involved in the double or triple bond. Determine the name and carbon number of each substituent group and place that information as a prefix in front of the name of the parent compound.

11.39 Geometric isomers of alkenes differ from one another in the placement of substituents attached to each of the carbon atoms of the double bond. Of the pair of geometric isomers, the *cis-* isomer is the one in which identical groups are on the same side of the double bond.

11.41 a. $(H_3C)(H_3C)C{=}C(CH_2CH_2CH_3)(H)$
H_3C and H_3C on left carbon; $CH_2CH_2CH_3$ (top) and H (bottom) on right carbon

b. CH_3CH_2 (top) and H (bottom) on left carbon; H (top) and $CH_2CH_2CH_3$ (bottom) on right carbon

c. $ClCH_2$ (top) and H (bottom) on left carbon; CH_2CH_3 (top) and H (bottom) on right carbon

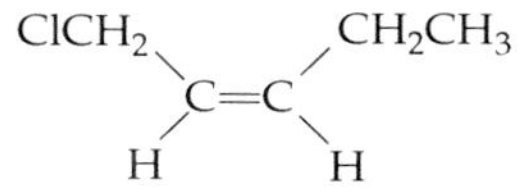

d. $(H_3C)_2CCl$ (top) and H (bottom) on left carbon; $CH_2CH_2CH_3$ (top) and H (bottom) on right carbon

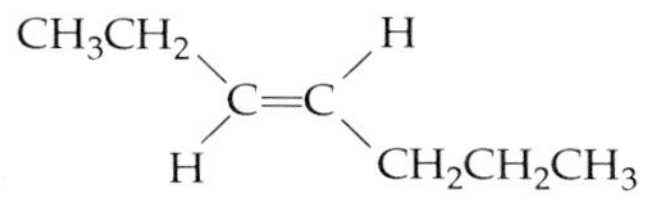

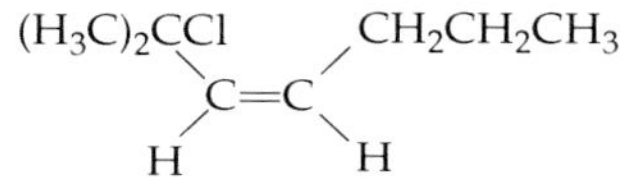

e. $(H_3C)_2CH$ (top) and H (bottom) on left carbon; H (top) and $CHBrCH(CH_3)CH_2CH_3$ (bottom) on right carbon

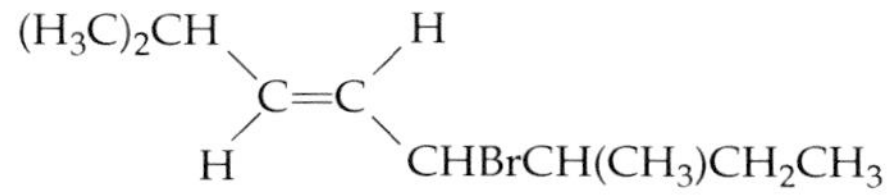

11.43 a. 3-Methyl-1-pentene
b. 7-Bromo-1-heptene
c. 5-Bromo-3-heptene
d. 1-*t*-Butyl-4-methylcyclohexene

11.45 a. $CH_2FCH_2CHFCH_2CH_2F$
b. H (top) and H_3C (bottom) on left carbon; H (top) and $CH_2CH_2CH_2CH_2CH_3$ (bottom) on right carbon
c. $CH_3CH_2CH_2C{\equiv}CCH_2CH_2CH_3$

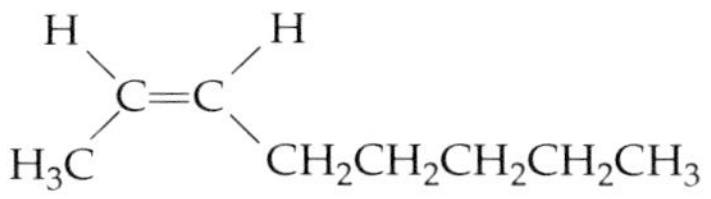

11.47 a. 1-Heptene can only be drawn one way. Therefore, a *cis-trans* isomer does not exist.
b. 2-Heptene can be drawn two ways. Therefore, *cis-trans* isomers do exist.
c. 3-Heptene can be drawn two ways. Therefore, *cis-trans* isomers do exist.
d. 2-Methyl-2-hexene can only be drawn one way. Therefore, *cis-trans* isomers do not exist.
e. 3-Methyl-2-hexene can be drawn two ways. Therefore, *cis-trans* isomers do exist.

11.49 Alkenes b and c would not exhibit *cis-trans* isomerism.

11.51 Alkenes b and d can exist as both *cis-* and *trans-* isomers.

11.53 a. 1,5-Nonadiene c. 2,5-Octadiene
b. 1,4,7-Nonatriene d. 4-Methyl-2,5-heptadiene

11.55 $R_2C{=}CR_2 + H_2 \xrightarrow[\text{heat or pressure}]{\text{Pt, Pd, or Ni}} R{-}C(H)(R){-}C(R)(H){-}R$

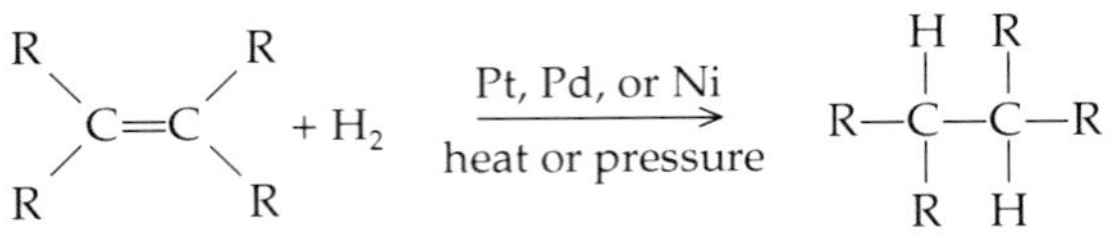

11.57 $R_2C{=}CR_2 + X_2 \longrightarrow R{-}C(X)(R){-}C(R)(X){-}R$

11.59 $R_2C{=}CR_2 + H_2O \xrightarrow{H^+} R{-}C(H)(R){-}C(R)(OH){-}R$

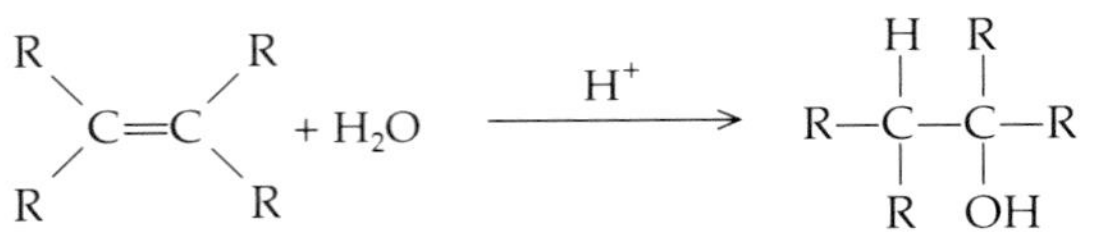

11.61 The primary difference between complete hydrogenation of an alkene and an alkyne is that 2 moles of H_2 are required for the complete hydrogenation of an alkyne.

11.63 a. $CH_2{=}CH(CH_2)_4CH_3 + H_2O \xrightarrow{H^+}$ $CH_3CHOH(CH_2)_4CH_3$ Major Product + $CH_2OH(CH_2)_5CH_3$ Minor Product

b. $CH_3CH{=}CH(CH_2)_3CH_3 + HBr \longrightarrow$ $CH_3CH_2CHBr(CH_2)_3CH_3$ + $CH_3CHBr(CH_2)_4CH_3$

c. $CH_3CH_2CH{=}CH(CH_2)_2CH_3 + H_2 \xrightarrow[\text{heat or pressure}]{\text{Pt, Pd, or Ni}}$ $CH_3(CH_2)_5CH_3$

d. $CH_3C(CH_3){=}CHCH_2CH_2CH_3 + HCl \longrightarrow$ $CH_3CCl(CH_3)(CH_2)_3CH_3$ Major Product + $CH_3CH(CH_3)CHCl(CH_2)_2CH_3$ Minor Product

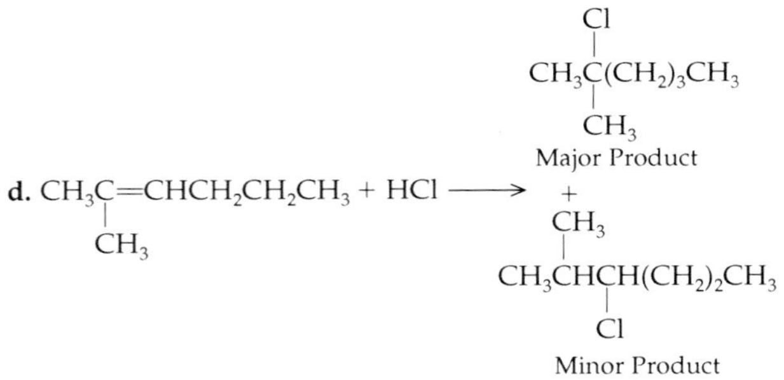

11.65 a. H_2 d. $19O_2 \rightarrow 12CO_2 + 14H_2O$
b. H_2O e. Cl_2
c. HBr f. (cyclopentene)

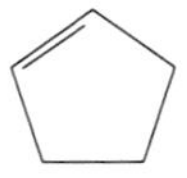

11.67 a.

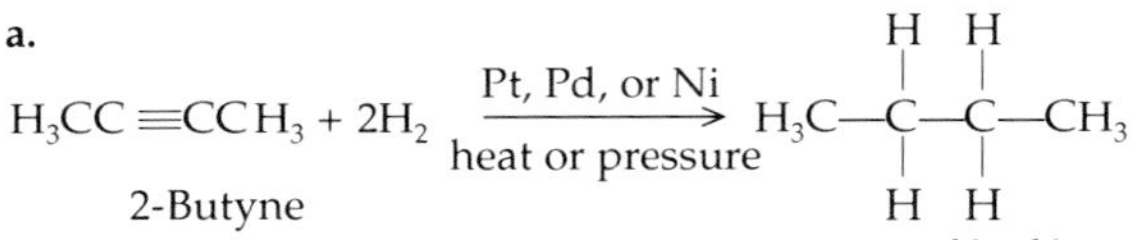

$H_3CC{\equiv}CCH_3 + 2H_2 \xrightarrow[\text{heat or pressure}]{\text{Pt, Pd, or Ni}} H_3C{-}CH_2{-}CH_2{-}CH_3$

2-Butyne

b.

$CH_3CH_2C{\equiv}CCH_3 + 2X_2 \longrightarrow CH_3CH_2{-}CX_2{-}CX_2{-}CH_3$

2-Pentyne

11.69 a. Reactant—*cis*-2-butene; Only product—butane
b. Reactant—1-butene; Major product—2-butanol
c. Reactant—2-butene; Only product—2,3-dichlorobutane
d. Reactant—1-pentene; Major product— 2-bromopentane

11.71 $CH_2{=}CHCH_2CH_2CH_3$, $CH_3CH{=}CHCH_2CH_3$, $CH_3C(CH_3){=}CHCH_3$, $CH_2{=}C(CH_3)CH_2CH_3$, $CH_2{=}CHCH(CH_3)CH_3$

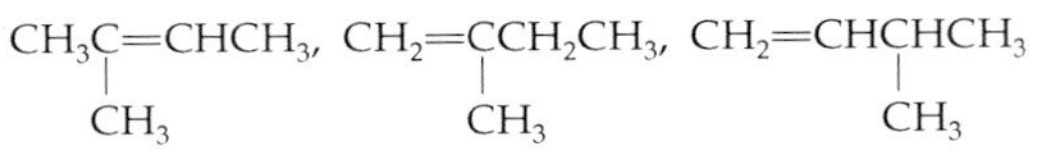

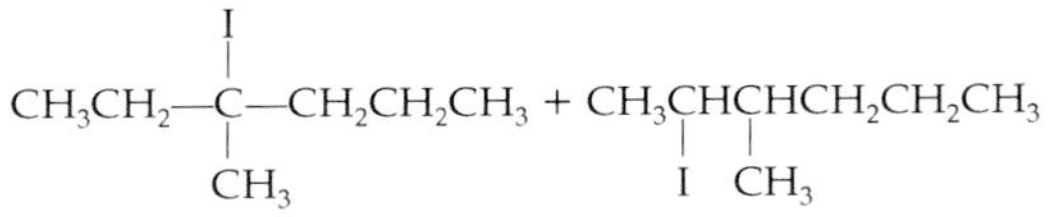

11.73 a. $CH_3CHBrCH_2CH_3$

b. $CH_3CH_2{-}CI(CH_3){-}CH_2CH_2CH_3$ (Major product) + $CH_3CHICH(CH_3)CH_2CH_2CH_3$ (Minor product)

c. (chlorocyclopentane)

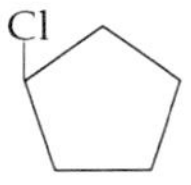

11.75 A polymer is a macromolecule composed of repeating structural units called *monomers*.

11.77 Polyvinyl chloride (PVC) is used in pipes, detergent bottles, and cleanser bottles.

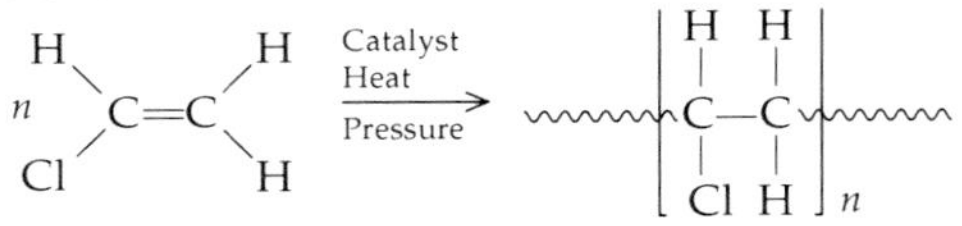

$n\ CH(Cl){=}CH_2 \xrightarrow[\text{Pressure}]{\text{Catalyst, Heat}} [{-}CH(Cl){-}CH_2{-}]_n$

11.79 The IUPAC name for (a) is 2-pentene, for (b) is 3-bromo-1-propene, and for (c) is 3,4-dimethylcyclohexene.

a. These products will be formed in approximately equal amounts.

$CH_3CH{=}CHCH_2CH_3 + H_2O \xrightarrow{H^+} CH_3CHOHCH_2CH_2CH_3$

$CH_3CH{=}CHCH_2CH_3 + H_2O \xrightarrow{H^+} CH_3CH_2CHOHCH_2CH_3$

b. $CH_3BrCH{=}CH_2 + H_2O \xrightarrow{H^+}$ $CH_2BrCH_2CH_2OH$ Minor product + $CH_2BrCHOHCH_3$ Major product

c. These products will be formed in approximately equal amounts.

3,4-dimethylcyclohexene $+ H_2O \xrightarrow{H^+}$ 2,3-dimethylcyclohexanol (OH, CH_3, CH_3)

3,4-dimethylcyclohexene $+ H_2O \xrightarrow{H^+}$ 3,4-dimethylcyclohexanol (HO, CH_3, CH_3)

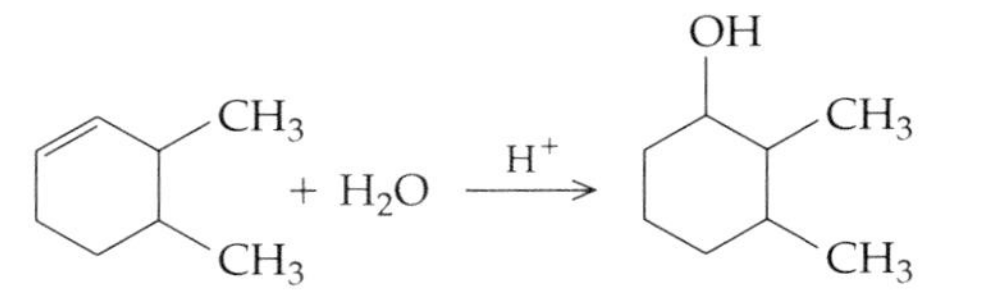

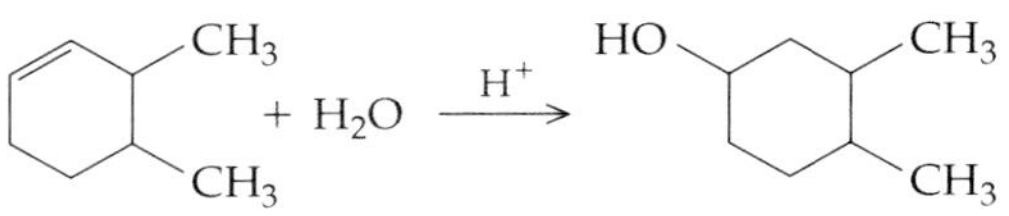

11.81 a. This is the minor product of this reaction.

$$H_2C{=}CHCH_2CH(CH_3)_2 + H_2O \xrightarrow{H^+} CH_2OHCH_2CH_2CH(CH_3)_2$$

b. $$CH_3CH{=}CHCH_2CH_2CH_3 + HBr \xrightarrow{H^+} CH_3CH_2CHBrCH_2CH_2CH_3$$

and

$$CH_3CH_2CH{=}CHCH_2CH_3 + HBr \longrightarrow CH_3CH_2CHBrCH_2CH_2CH_3$$

c. (methylcyclohexene, CH_3) + HBr ⟶ (Br, CH_3 cyclohexane)

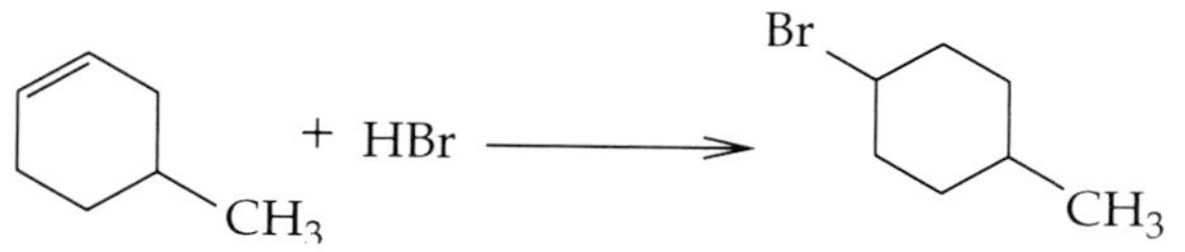

d. (ethylcyclopentene) $-CH_2CH_3 + H_2O \xrightarrow{H^+}$ (cyclopentane) $-CH_2CH_3$, OH

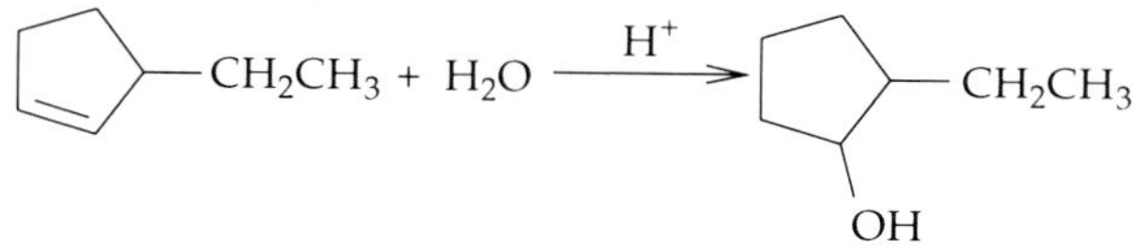

11.83 a.

$$CH_2{=}CHCH_2CH{=}CHCH_3 + 2H_2 \xrightarrow[\text{heat}]{\text{Pt}} CH_3(CH_2)_4CH_3$$

1,4-Hexadiene → Hexane

b.

$$CH_3CH{=}CHCH{=}CHCH{=}CHCH_3 + 3H_2 \xrightarrow[\text{heat}]{\text{Ni}} CH_3(CH_2)_6CH_3$$

2,4,6-Octatriene → Octane

c. (1,3-cyclohexadiene) $+ 2H_2 \xrightarrow[\text{Pressure}]{\text{Pd}}$ (cyclohexane)

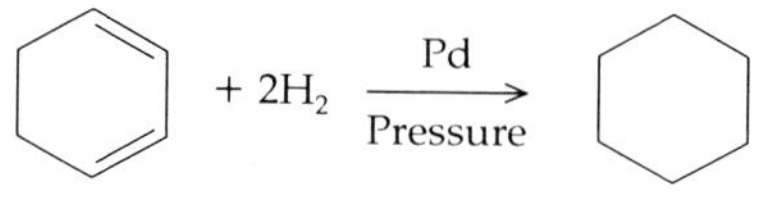

1,3-Cyclohexadiene → Cyclohexane

d. (1,3,5-cyclooctatriene) $+ 3H_2 \xrightarrow[\text{heat}]{\text{Ni}}$ (cyclooctane)

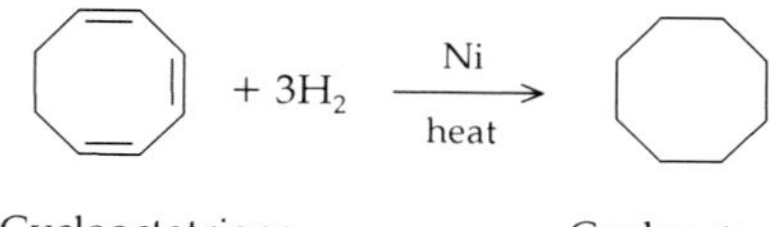

1,3,5-Cyclooctatriene → Cyclooctane

11.85 The term aromatic hydrocarbon was first used as a term to describe the pleasant-smelling resins of tropical trees.

11.87 Resonance hybrids are molecules for which more than one valid Lewis structure can be written.

11.89 a.

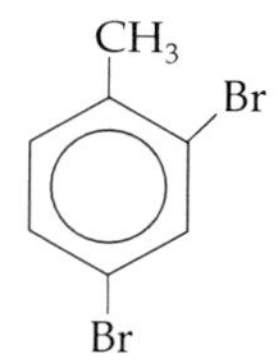

b. CH_2CH_3, CH_2CH_3, CH_2CH_3 (benzene ring)

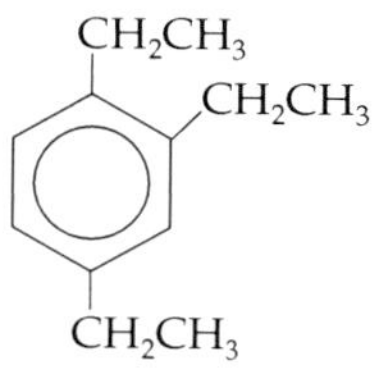

c. CH_3CHCH_3

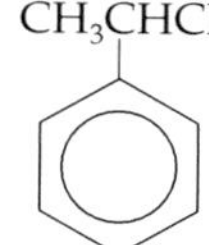

d. CH_3, Br, Cl (benzene ring)

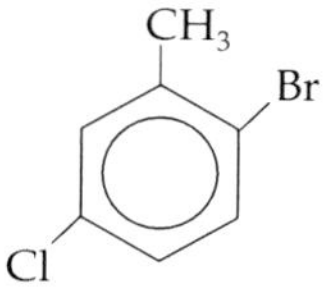

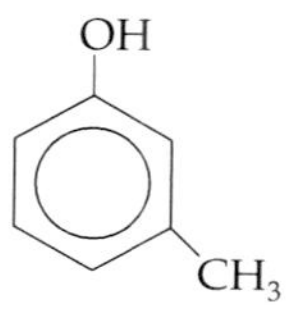

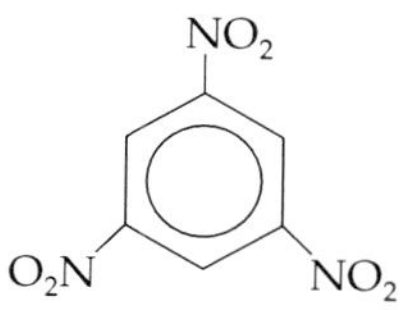

11.91 a. OH, CH_3 (benzene ring) b. $CH_2CH_2CH_3$ (benzene ring)

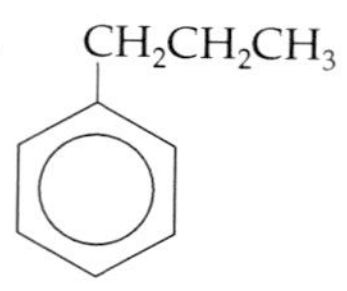

c. NO_2, O_2N, NO_2 (benzene ring) d. CH_3, Cl (benzene ring)

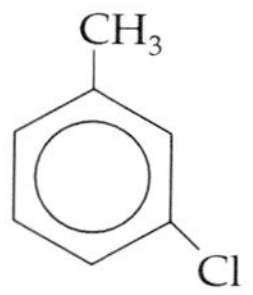

11.93 Kekulé proposed that single and double carbon-carbon bonds alternate around the benzene ring. To explain why benzene does not react like other unsaturated compounds, he proposed that the double and single bonds shift positions rapidly.

11.95 An addition reaction involves addition of a molecule to a double or triple bond in an unsaturated molecule. In a substitution reaction, one chemical group replaces another.

11.97 a. (benzene) $+ Br_2 \xrightarrow{FeBr_3}$ (bromobenzene, Br) + HBr

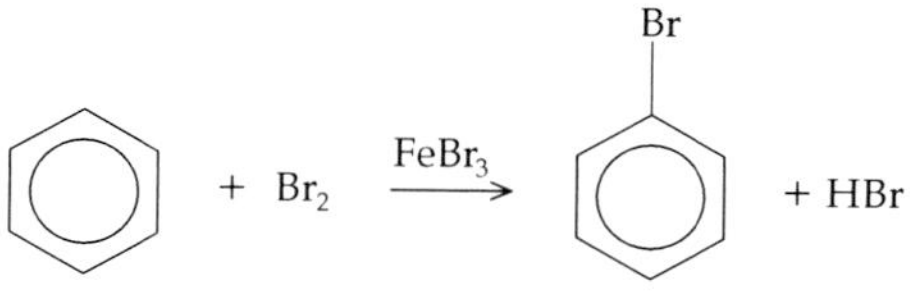

b. (benzene) $+ Cl_2 \xrightarrow{FeCl_3}$ (chlorobenzene, Cl) + HCl

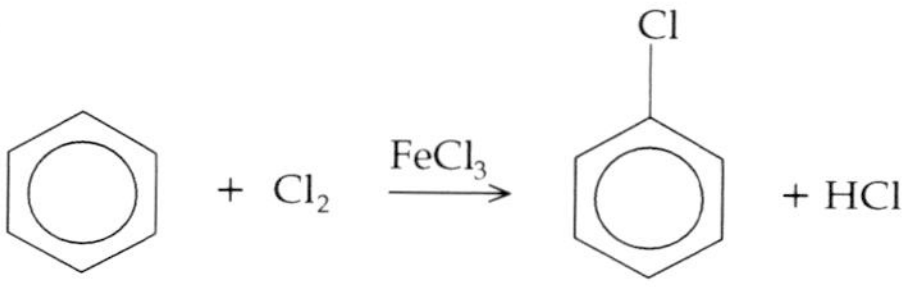

c.

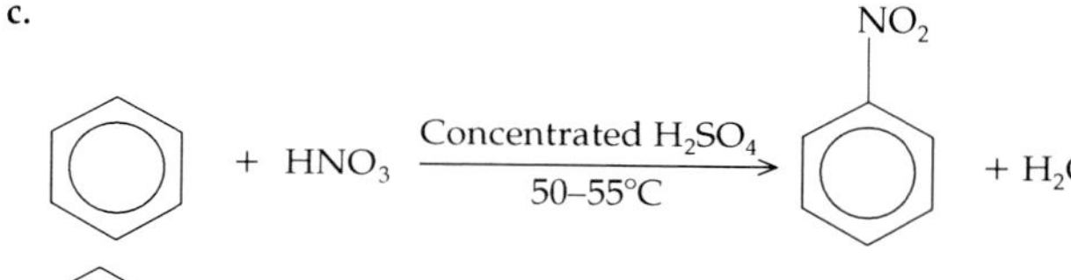

11.99

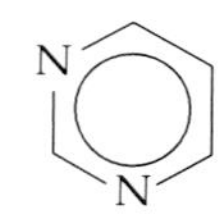

Pyrimidine

11.101 (N, N, N, N–H)

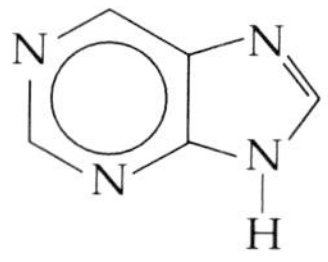

Purine

Chapter 12

12.1 a. 2-Methyl-1-propanol

CH_3CHCH_2OH with CH_3 on C-2

b. 2-Chlorocyclopentanol

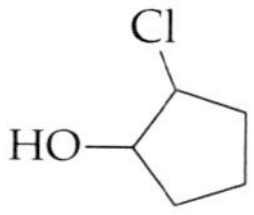

Cl, HO– (cyclopentane)

c. 2,4-Dimethylcyclohexanol

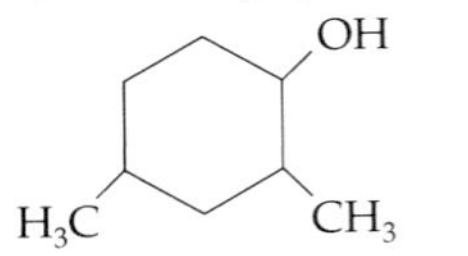

OH

H_3C CH_3

d. 2,3-Dichloro-3-hexanol

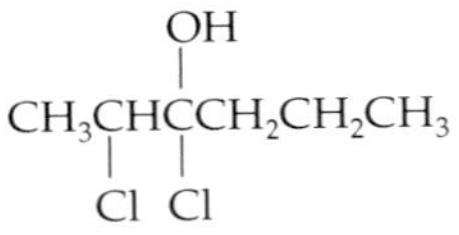

$$\begin{array}{c} \text{OH} \\ | \\ CH_3CHCCH_2CH_2CH_3 \\ \;\;\;|\;\;| \\ \;\;\;\text{Cl Cl} \end{array}$$

12.3 IUPAC name: 1-Butanol
Common name: Butyl alcohol
Primary alcohol

12.5 a. Ethanol is a primary alcohol. The product is ethene.
b. 2-Propanol is a secondary alcohol. The product is propene.
c. 4-Methyl-3-hexanol is a secondary alcohol. The products are 3-methyl-3-hexene and 4-methyl-2-hexene.
d. 2-Methyl-2-propanol is a tertiary alcohol. The product is 2-methyl-1-propene.

12.7 a. The reactant is 2-butanol and the product is butanone.
b. The reactant is 2-pentanol and the product is 2-pentanone.

12.9 Simple phenols are somewhat soluble in water because they have the polar hydroxyl group.

12.11 Ethers have much lower boiling points than alcohols because ether molecules cannot hydrogen bond to one another.

12.13 The longer the hydrocarbon tail of an alcohol becomes, the less water soluble it will be.

12.15 The carbinol carbon is the one to which the hydroxyl group is bonded.

12.17 a. Primary alcohol
b. Secondary alcohol
c. Tertiary alcohol
d. Tertiary alcohol
e. Tertiary alcohol

12.19 a. Primary alcohol
b. Secondary alcohol
c. Primary alcohol
d. Primary alcohol
e. Secondary alcohol

12.21 a. 2-Nonanol is a secondary alcohol:
$CH_3CHOHCH_2CH_2CH_2CH_2CH_2CH_2CH_3$
b. 2-Heptanol is a secondary alcohol:
$CH_3CHOHCH_2CH_2CH_2CH_2CH_3$
c. 2-Undecanol is a secondary alcohol:
$CH_3CHOHCH_2CH_2CH_2CH_2CH_2CH_2CH_2CH_2CH_3$

12.23 a < d < c < b

12.25 a. CH_3CH_2OH
b. $CH_3CH_2CH_2CH_2OH$
c. CH_3CHCH_3 (with OH on C-2)

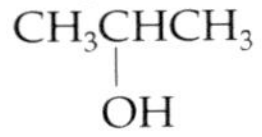

12.27 The IUPAC rules for the nomenclature of alcohols require you to name the parent compound, that is the longest continuous carbon chain bonded to the —OH group. Replace the *–e* ending of the parent alkane with *–ol* of the alcohol. Number the parent chain so that the carbon bearing the hydroxyl group has the lowest possible number. Name and number all other substituents. If there is more than one hydroxyl group, the *–ol* ending will be modified to reflect the number. If there are two —OH groups, the suffix *–diol* is used; if it has three —OH groups, the suffix *–triol* is used, etc.

12.29 a. 1,4-Hexanediol
b. 2,3-Pentanediol
c. 2-Methyl-3-pentanol

12.31 a. OH

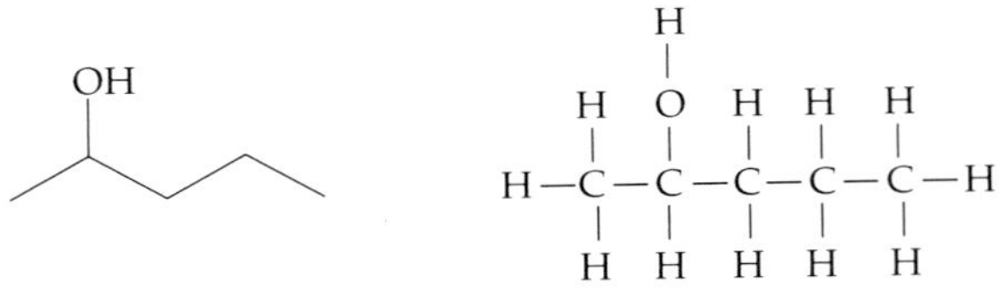

H–C–C–C–C–C–H (C-2 bears O–H; all other positions H)

b. OH OH OH

H–C–C–C–C–C–C–C–H (O–H on C-1, C-2 and C-4; all other positions H)

c. OH

(cyclopentane ring with C bearing O–H and adjacent C bearing CH_3; all other positions H)

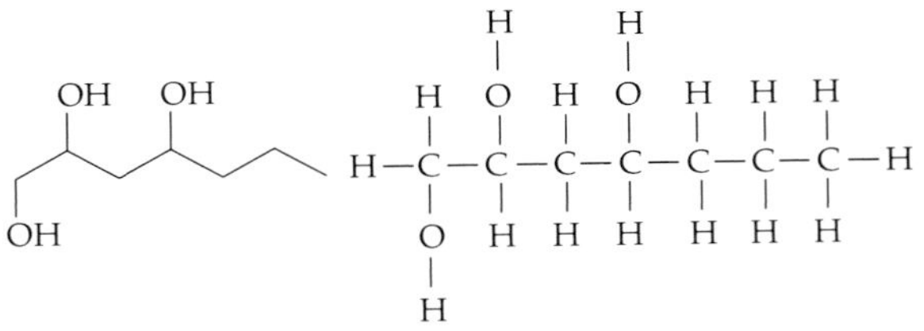

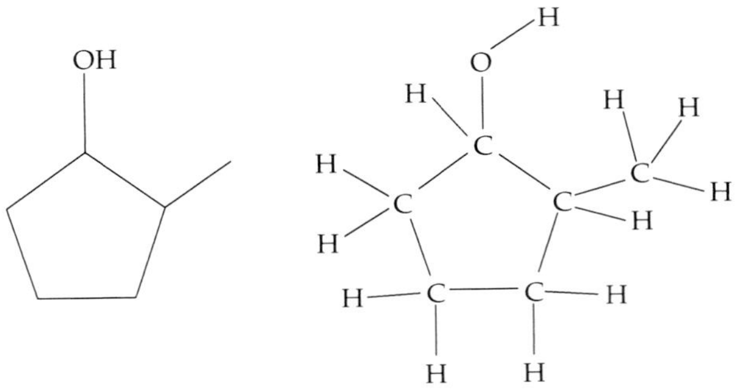

12.33 a. Cyclopentanol
b. Cycloheptanol
c. 3-Methylcyclohexanol

12.35 a. Methyl alcohol
b. Ethyl alcohol
c. Ethylene glycol
d. Propyl alcohol

12.37 a. $CH_3CHOHCH_2CH(CH_3)CH_2CH_3$
b. $CH(CH_3)_2CH_2OH$
c. $CH_2OH(CH_2)_3CH_2OH$
d. $CH_3CHOH(CH_2)_6CH_3$
e. OH

HO OH

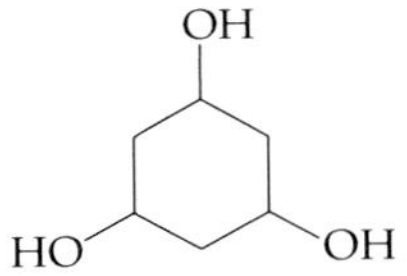

12.39 Denatured alcohol is 100% ethanol to which benzene or methanol is added. The additive makes the ethanol unfit to drink and prevents illegal use of pure ethanol.

12.41 Fermentation is the anaerobic degradation of sugar that involves no net oxidation. The alcohol fermentation, carried out by yeast, produces ethanol and carbon dioxide.

12.43 When the ethanol concentration in a fermentation reaches 12–13%, the yeast producing the ethanol are killed by it. To produce a liquor of higher alcohol concentration, the product of the original fermentation must be distilled.

12.45 $R_2C{=}CR_2 + H_2O \xrightarrow{H^+} R{-}C(OH)(R){-}C(H)(R){-}R$

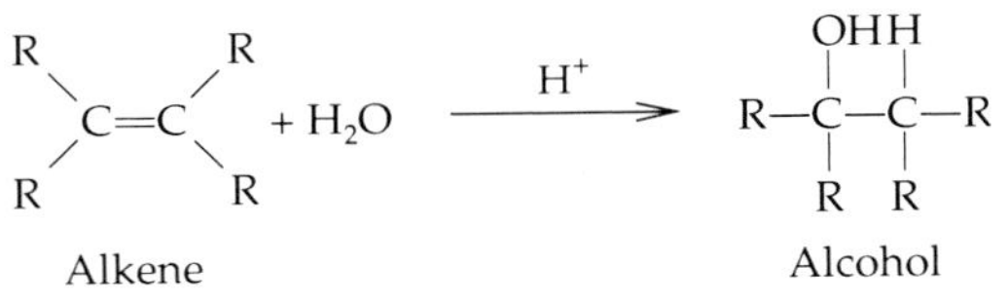

Alkene Alcohol

12.47 $R{-}C(OH)(R){-}C(H)(R){-}R \xrightarrow{H^+,\ \text{heat}} R_2C{=}CR_2 + H_2O$

Alcohol Alkene

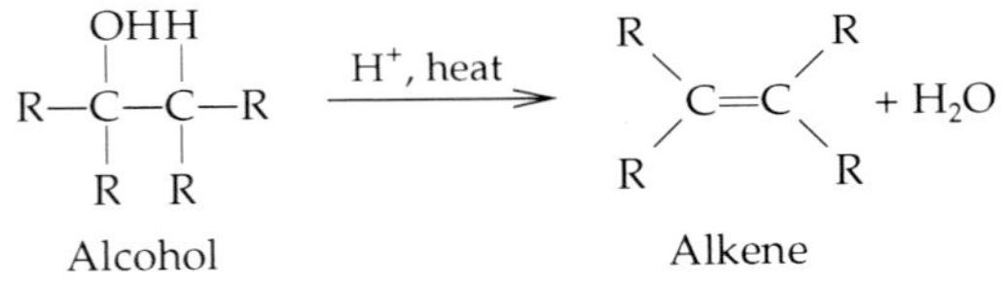

12.49

$$R_2CH{-}OH \xrightarrow{[O]} R{-}C({=}O){-}R$$

Secondary alcohol → Ketone

12.51 **a.** The predicted products are 1-hexanol (minor) and 2-hexanol (major).

b. The predicted products are 2-hexanol and 3-hexanol. These products will be formed in approximately equal amounts.

c. The predicted products are 5-methyl-3-hexanol and 2-methyl-3-hexanol. These products will be formed in approximately equal amounts.

d. The predicted products are 2,2-dimethyl-4-heptanol and 2,2-dimethyl-3-heptanol. These products will be formed in approximately equal amounts.

12.53 **a.**

$$CH_3CH{=}CHCH_2CH_2CH_3 + H_2O \xrightarrow{H^+}$$

2-Hexene

$CH_3CH(OH)CH_2CH_2CH_2CH_3$ — 2-Hexanol

and

$CH_3CH_2CH(OH)CH_2CH_2CH_3$ — 3-Hexanol

These products will be formed in approximately equal amounts.

b. Cyclopentene $+ H_2O \xrightarrow{H^+}$ Cyclopentanol

c. $CH_2{=}CHCH_2CH_2CH_2CH_2CH_2CH_3 + H_2O \xrightarrow{H^+}$

1-Octene

$CH_3CH(OH)CH_2CH_2CH_2CH_2CH_2CH_3$ — 2-Octanol (Major product)

and

$CH_2(OH)CH_2CH_2CH_2CH_2CH_2CH_2CH_3$ — 1-Octanol (Minor product)

d. 1-Methylcyclohexene $+ H_2O \xrightarrow{H^+}$ 1-Methylcyclohexanol (Major product) and 2-Methylcyclohexanol (Minor product)

12.55 **a.** Butanone **b.** N.R. **c.** Cyclohexanone **d.** N.R.

12.57 **a.** 3-Pentanol; 3-Pentanone

b. 1-Propanol; Propanal (Upon further oxidation, propanoic acid would be formed.)

c. 4-Methyl-2-pentanol; 4-Methyl-2-pentanone

d. 2-Methyl-2-butanol; N.R.

e. 3-Phenyl-1-propanol; 3-Phenylpropanal (Upon further oxidation, 3-phenylpropanoic acid will be formed.)

12.59

$$CH_3CH_2OH \xrightarrow{\text{liver enzymes}} CH_3{-}C({=}O){-}H$$

Ethanol → Ethanal

The product, ethanal, is responsible for the symptoms of a hangover.

12.61 The reaction in which a water molecule is added to 1-butene is a hydration reaction.

$$CH_3CH_2CH{=}CH_2 + H_2O \xrightarrow{H^+} CH_3CH_2CH(OH)CH_3$$

1-Butene → 2-Butanol

12.63

$$CH_3CH{=}CH_2 \xrightarrow{H_2O,\ H^+} CH_3CH(OH)CH_3 \xrightarrow{[O]} CH_3C({=}O)CH_3$$

Propene (propylene) → 2-Propanol (isopropanol) → Propanone (acetone)

12.65 **a.** Hexanal $+ H_2 \xrightarrow{\text{catalyst}}$ 1-hexanol

b. 2-Hexanone $+ H_2 \xrightarrow{\text{catalyst}}$ 2-hexanol

c. 2-Methylbutanal $+ H_2 \xrightarrow{\text{catalyst}}$ 2-methyl-1-butanol

d. 5-Ethyl-2-heptanone $+ H_2 \xrightarrow{\text{catalyst}}$ 5-ethyl-2-heptanol

12.67 Oxidation is a loss of electrons, whereas reduction is a gain of electrons.

12.69

$$CH_3CH_2CH_3 < CH_3CH_2CH_2OH < CH_3CH_2C({=}O){-}H < CH_3CH_2C({=}O){-}OH$$

12.71 Phenols are compounds with an —OH attached to a benzene ring.

12.73 Picric acid: 2,4,6-trinitrophenol (OH with NO_2 groups at 2, 4, 6) 2,4,6,-Trinitrotoluene: (CH_3 with NO_2 groups at 2, 4, 6)

Picric acid is water-soluble because of the polar hydroxyl group that can form hydrogen bonds with water.

12.75 Hexachlorophene, hexylresorcinol, and *o*-phenylphenol are phenol compounds used as antiseptics or disinfectants.

12.77 Ethers have much lower boiling points than alcohols of similar molar mass, but higher boiling points than alkanes of similar molar mass. The boiling points are higher than alkanes because the R—O—R bond is polar. However, there is no —OH group, so ether molecules cannot hydrogen bond to one another. This is the reason that the boiling points are lower than alcohols of similar molar mass.

12.79 Alcohols of molecular formula $C_4H_{10}O$

$CH_3CH_2CH_2CH_2OH$, $CH_3CH(OH)CH_2CH_3$,

$CH_3CH(CH_3)CH_2OH$, $CH_3C(OH)(CH_3)CH_3$

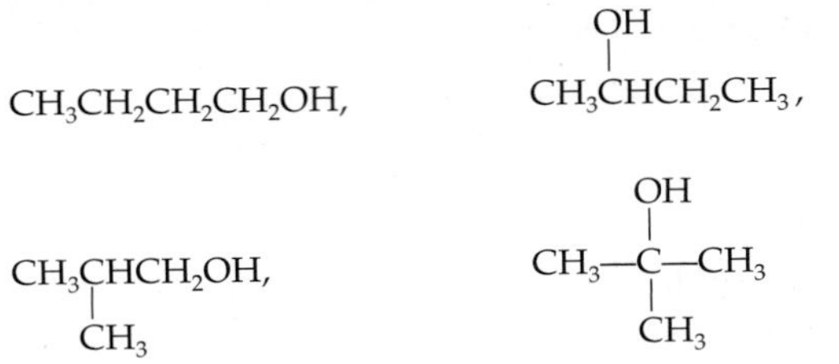

Ethers of molecular formula $C_4H_{10}O$

$CH_3—O—CH_2CH_2CH_3$ $CH_3CH_2—O—CH_2CH_3$

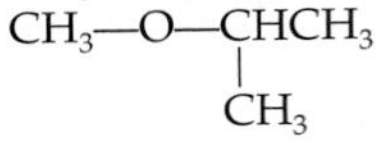

$CH_3—O—CH(CH_3)CH_3$

12.81 Penthrane: 2,2-Dichloro-1,1-difluoro-1-methoxyethane
Enthrane: 2-Chloro-1-(difluoromethoxy)-1,1,2-trifluoroethane

12.83
a. $CH_3CH_2—O—CH_2CH_3 + H_2O$
b. $CH_3CH_2—O—CH_2CH_3 + CH_3—O—CH_3 + CH_3—O—CH_2CH_3 + H_2O$
c. $CH_3—O—CH_3 + CH_3—O—CH(CH_3)CH_3 + CH_3CH(CH_3)—O—CH(CH_3)CH_3 + H_2O$
d. (cyclopentyl)—O—(cyclopentyl) $+ H_2O$

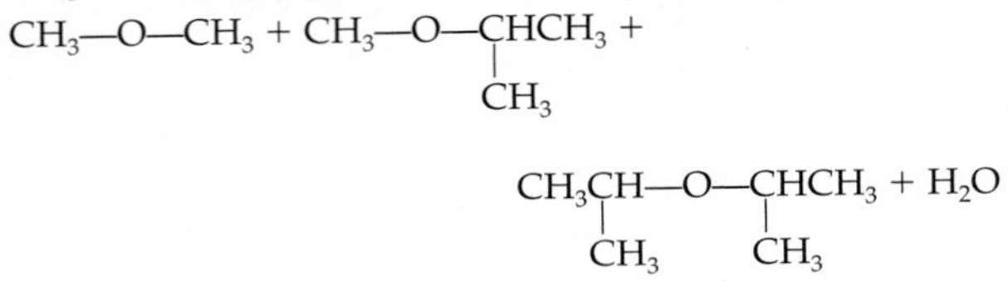

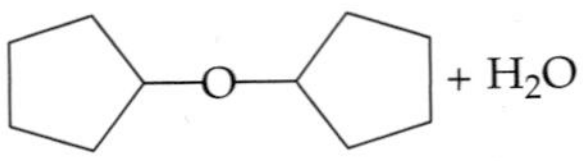

12.85
a. 2-Ethoxypentane
b. 2-Methoxybutane
c. 1-Ethoxybutane
d. Methoxycyclopentane

12.87
a. $CH_3CH_2CH_2CH_2—O—CH_2CH_2CH_2CH_3$ (full structural formula with all H shown)
b. $CH_3CH_2CH_2CH_2CH_2CH_2CH_2—O—CH_2CH_3$ (full structural formula with all H shown)
c. $CH_3CH_2CH_2—O—CH_2CH_2CH_2CH_2CH_3$ (full structural formula with all H shown)
d. $CH_3CH_2CH_2CH_2CH_2CH_2—O—C(CH_3)_2CH_3$ (full structural formula with all H shown)

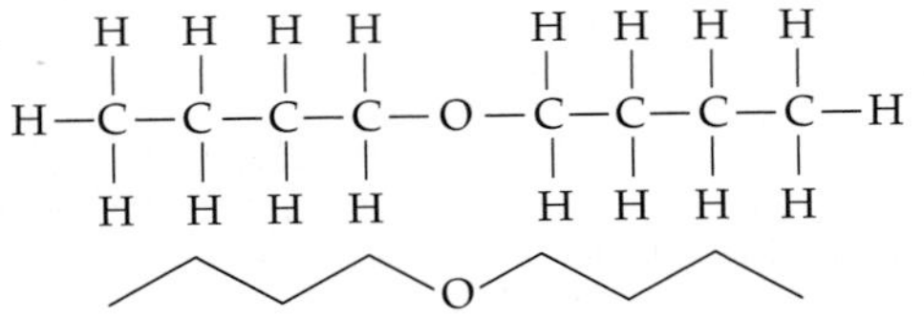

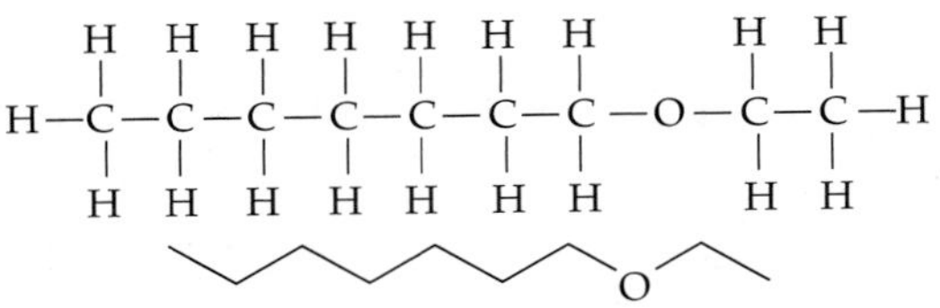

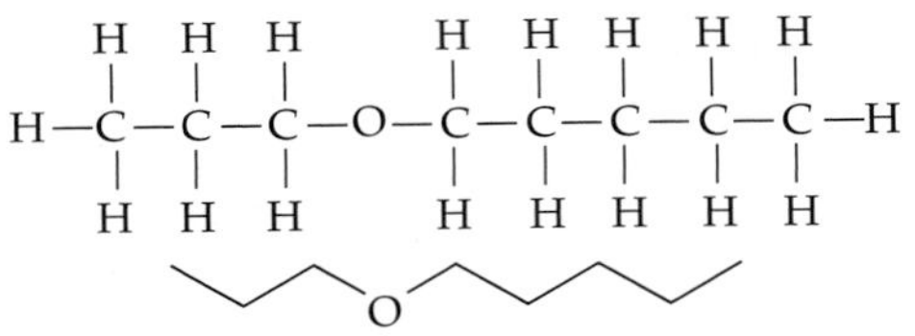

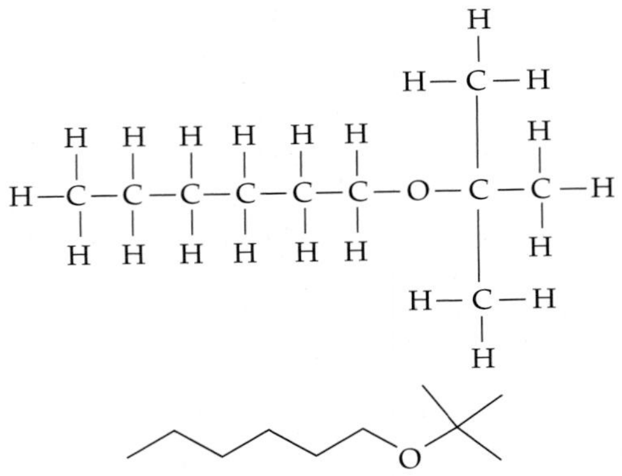

12.89 Thiols contain the sulfhydryl group (—SH). The sulfhydryl group is similar to the hydroxyl group (—OH) of alcohols, except that a sulfur atom replaces the oxygen atom.

12.91 Cystine:

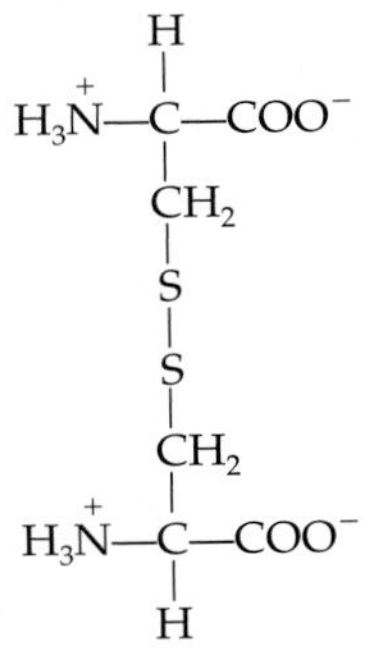

$\overset{+}{H_3N}—CH(COO^-)—CH_2—S—S—CH_2—CH(COO^-)—\overset{+}{N}H_3$

12.93
a. 1-Propanethiol
b. 2-Butanethiol
c. 2-Methyl-2-butanethiol
d. 1,4-Cyclohexanedithiol

Chapter 13

13.1
a. $CH_3—C(=O)—CH_3$
b. $CH_3CH(OH)CH_2CH_2CH_3$

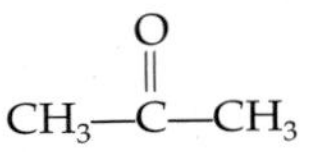

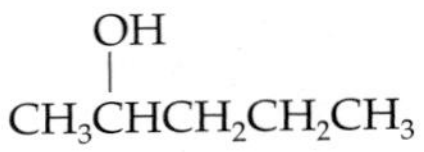

13.3
a. $CH_3CH_2C(=O)—OH$
b. $CH_3C(=O)—OH$

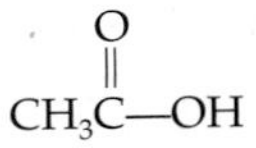

13.5
a. 2,3-Dichloropentanal 
$CH_3CH_2CHClCHClCH(=O)$
b. 2-Bromobutanal 
$CH_3CH_2CHBrCH(=O)$
c. 4-Methylhexanal 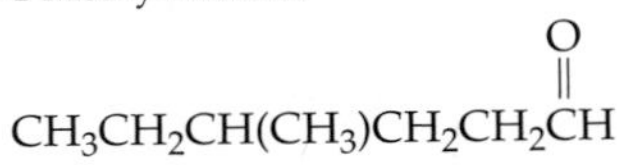
$CH_3CH_2CH(CH_3)CH_2CH_2CH(=O)$
d. Butanal 
$CH_3CH_2CH_2CH(=O)$
e. 2,4-Dimethylpentanal
$CH_3CH(CH_3)CH_2CH(CH_3)CH(=O)$

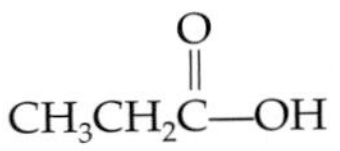

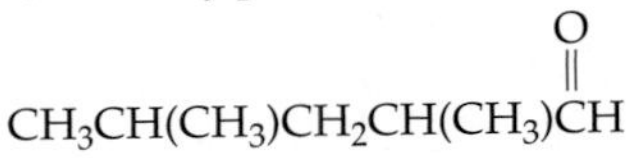

13.7
a. 3-Iodobutanone
b. 4-Methyl-2-octanone
c. 3-Methylbutanone
d. 2-Methyl-3-pentanone
e. 2-Fluoro-3-pentanone

13.9
$CH_3—C(=O)—H$

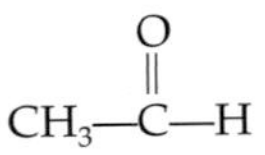

13.11 a. Reduction
b. Reduction
c. Reduction
d. Oxidation
e. Reduction

13.13 a. Hemiacetal
b. Acetal
c. Acetal
d. Hemiacetal

13.15 As the carbon chain length increases, the compounds become less polar and more hydrocarbon-like. As a result, their solubility in water decreases.

13.17 A good solvent should dissolve a wide range of compounds. Simple ketones are considered to be universal solvents because they have both a polar carbonyl group and nonpolar side chains. As a result, they dissolve organic compounds and are also miscible in water.

13.19

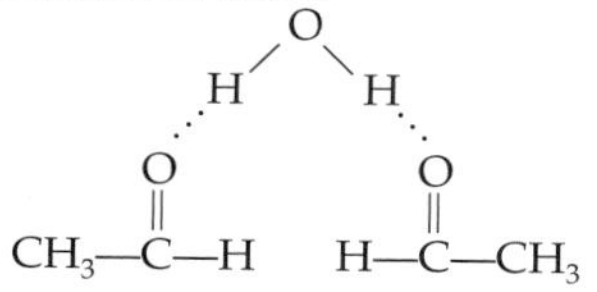

$CH_3-\overset{O}{\overset{\|}{C}}-H \cdots H-O-H \cdots H-\overset{O}{\overset{\|}{C}}-CH_3$

13.21 Alcohols have higher boiling points than aldehydes or ketones of comparable molar mass because alcohol molecules can form intermolecular hydrogen bonds with one another. Aldehydes and ketones cannot form intermolecular hydrogen bonds.

13.23 a.

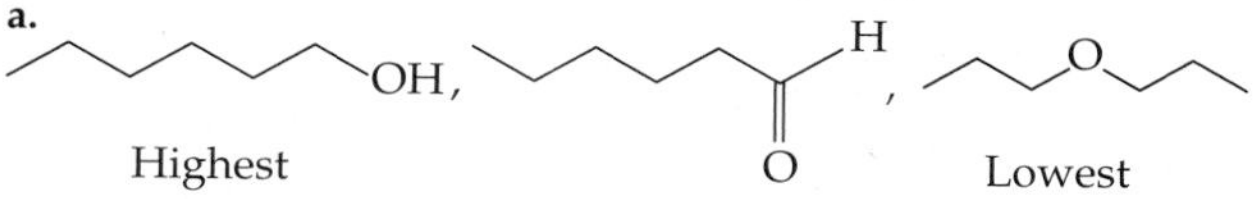

OH, H(C=O), O

Highest → Lowest

b.

OH, O, O, (alkane)

Highest → Lowest

13.25 To name an aldehyde using the IUPAC Nomenclature System, identify and name the longest carbon chain containing the carbonyl group. Replace the final *-e* of the alkane name with *-al*. Number and name all substituents as usual. Remember that the carbonyl carbon is always carbon-1 and does not need to be numbered in the name of the compound.

13.27 The common names of aldehydes are derived from the same Latin roots as the corresponding carboxylic acids. For instance, methanal is formaldehyde; ethanal is acetaldehyde; propanal is propionaldehyde, *etc.*

Substituted aldehydes are named as derivatives of the straight-chain parent compound. Greek letters are used to indicate the position of substituents. The carbon nearest the carbonyl group is the α-carbon, the next is the β-carbon, and so on.

13.29 a. $CH_3\overset{O}{\overset{\|}{C}}H$

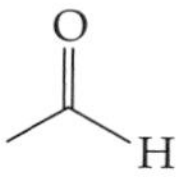

b. $(CH_3)_2CHCH(CH_3)CH_2\overset{O}{\overset{\|}{C}}H$

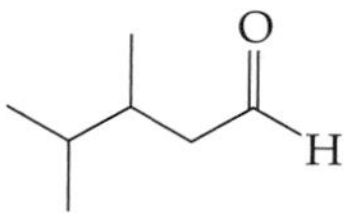

c. $CH_3(CH_2)_4CH(CH_2CH_3)\overset{O}{\overset{\|}{C}}H$

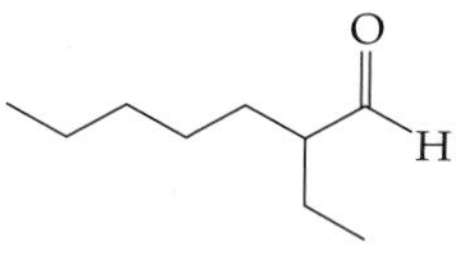

d. $CH_2ClCH_2CHCl(CH_2)_3\overset{O}{\overset{\|}{C}}H$

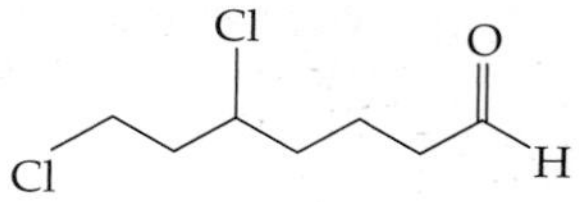

13.31 a. $CH_3CH(CH_3)\overset{O}{\overset{\|}{C}}CH_2CH_3$

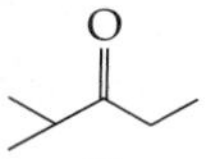

b. $CH_3(CH_2)_2\overset{O}{\overset{\|}{C}}CH_2CH_3$

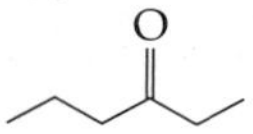

c. $CH_3(CH_2)_3\overset{O}{\overset{\|}{C}}(CH_2)_3CH_3$

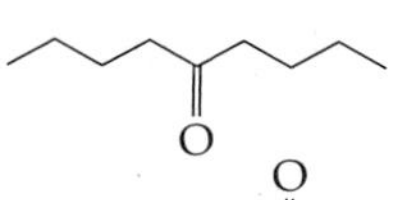

d. $CH_3(CH_2)_5\overset{O}{\overset{\|}{C}}(CH_2)_6CH_3$

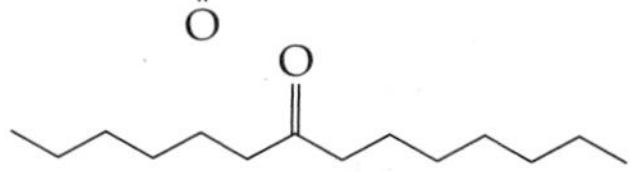

13.33 a. Butanone
b. 2-Ethylhexanal

13.35 a. 3-Nitrobenzaldehyde
b. 3,4-Dihydroxycyclopentanone

13.37 7-Hydroxy-3,7-dimethyloctanal

13.39 a. 4,6-Dimethyl-3-heptanone
b. 3,3-Dimethylcyclopentanone

13.41 a. Acetone
b. Ethyl methyl ketone
c. Acetaldehyde
d. Propionaldehyde
e. Methyl isopropyl ketone

13.43 a. 3-Hydroxybutanal

$CH_3CHOHCH_2\overset{O}{\overset{\|}{C}}H$

b. 2-Methylpentanal

$CH_3(CH_2)_2CH(CH_3)\overset{O}{\overset{\|}{C}}H$

c. 4-Bromohexanal

$CH_3CH_2CHBr(CH_2)_2\overset{O}{\overset{\|}{C}}H$

d. 3-Iodopentanal

$CH_3CH_2CHICH_2\overset{O}{\overset{\|}{C}}H$

e. 2-Hydroxy-3-methylheptanal

$CH_3(CH_2)_3CH(CH_3)CHOH\overset{O}{\overset{\|}{C}}H$

13.45 Acetone is a good solvent because it can dissolve a wide range of compounds. It has both a polar carbonyl group and nonpolar side chains. As a result, it dissolves organic compounds and is also miscible in water.

13.47 The liver

13.49 In organic molecules, oxidation may be recognized as a gain of oxygen or a loss of hydrogen. An aldehyde may be oxidized to form a carboxylic acid as in the following example in which ethanal is oxidized to produce ethanoic acid.

$$H_3C-\overset{O}{\overset{\|}{C}}-H \xrightarrow{[O]} H_3C-\overset{O}{\overset{\|}{C}}-OH$$

Ethanal → Ethanoic acid

13.51 Addition reactions of aldehydes or ketones are those in which a second molecule is added to the double bond of the carbonyl group.

13.53 The following equation represents the oxidation of an aldehyde. The product is a carboxylic acid.

$$R-\overset{O}{\overset{\|}{C}}-H \xrightarrow{[O]} R-\overset{O}{\overset{\|}{C}}-OH$$

Aldehyde → Carboxylic acid

13.55 The following general equation represents the addition of one alcohol molecule to an aldehyde:

$$\mathrm{R{-}\overset{\overset{\large O}{\|}}{C}{-}H} + \mathrm{R'OH} \underset{}{\overset{H^+}{\rightleftharpoons}} \mathrm{R{-}\underset{\underset{\large H}{|}}{\overset{\overset{\large OH}{|}}{C}}{-}OR'}$$

Aldehyde — Hemiacetal

The following general equation represents the addition of one alcohol molecule to a ketone:

$$\mathrm{R{-}\overset{\overset{\large O}{\|}}{C}{-}R} + \mathrm{R'OH} \overset{H^+}{\rightleftharpoons} \mathrm{R{-}\underset{\underset{\large R}{|}}{\overset{\overset{\large OH}{|}}{C}}{-}OR'}$$

Ketone — Hemiacetal

13.57 a. OH $\xrightarrow{[O]}$ O

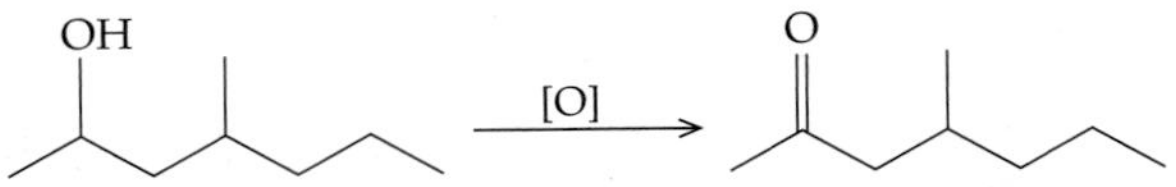

4-Methyl-2-heptanol → 4-Methyl-2-heptanone

b. OH $\xrightarrow{[O]}$ O, H

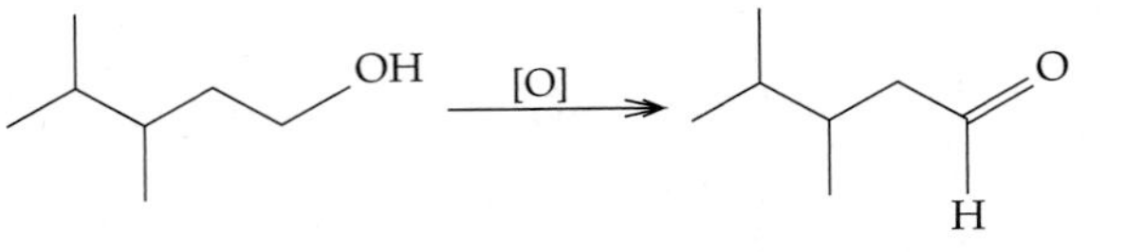

3,4-Dimethyl-1-pentanol → 3,4-Dimethylpentanal

c. OH $\xrightarrow{[O]}$ O

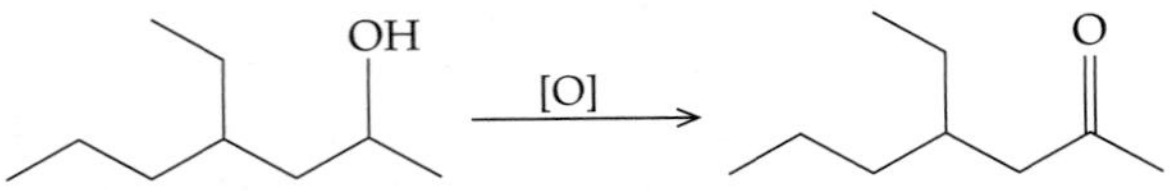

4-Ethyl-2-heptanol → 4-Ethyl-2-heptanone

d. OH Cl Cl $\xrightarrow{[O]}$ O Cl Cl

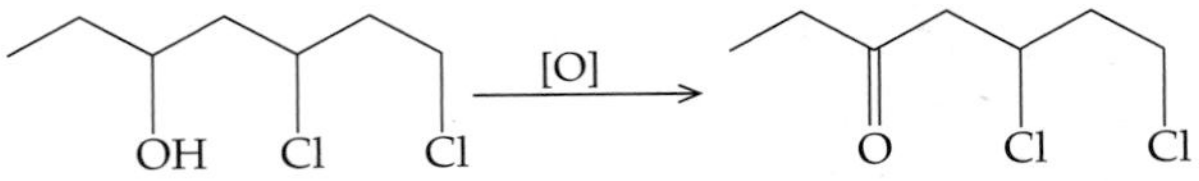

5,7-Dichloro-3-heptanol → 5,7-Dichloro-3-heptanone

13.59

$$\mathrm{R{-}CH_2OH} \xrightarrow{[O]} \mathrm{R{-}\overset{\overset{\large O}{\|}}{C}{-}H} \xrightarrow{[O]} \mathrm{R{-}\overset{\overset{\large O}{\|}}{C}{-}OH}$$

Primary alcohol — Aldehyde — Carboxylic acid

13.61 a. Reduction reaction

$$\mathrm{CH_3{-}\overset{\overset{\large O}{\|}}{C}{-}H + H_2 \xrightarrow{Pt} CH_3CH_2OH}$$

Ethanal — Ethanol

b. Reduction reaction

$$\text{(cyclohexane)}{=}\mathrm{O + H_2 \xrightarrow{Pt}} \text{(cyclohexane)}{-}\mathrm{OH}$$

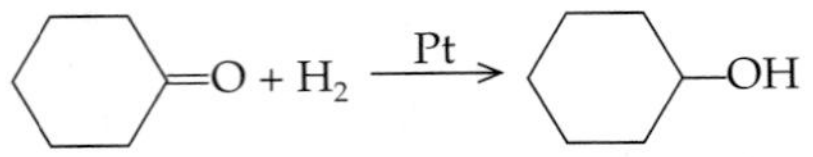

Cyclohexanone — Cyclohexanol

c. Oxidation reaction

$$\mathrm{CH_3\overset{\overset{\large OH}{|}}{C}HCH_3 \xrightarrow{[O]} CH_3{-}\overset{\overset{\large O}{\|}}{C}{-}CH_3}$$

2-Propanol — Propanone

13.63 a. O, H + H_2 $\xrightarrow{Pt}$ OH

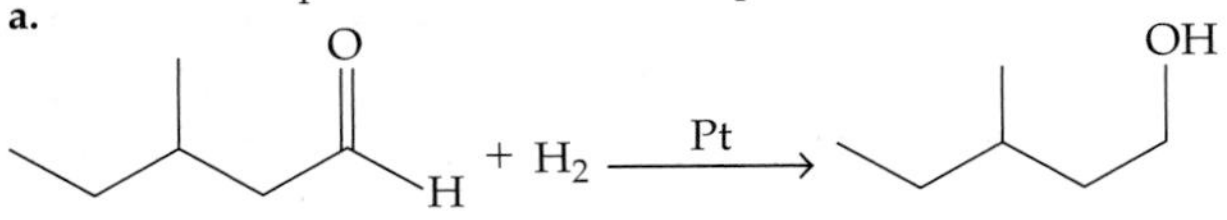

b. OH, H, O + H_2 $\xrightarrow{Pt}$ OH, OH

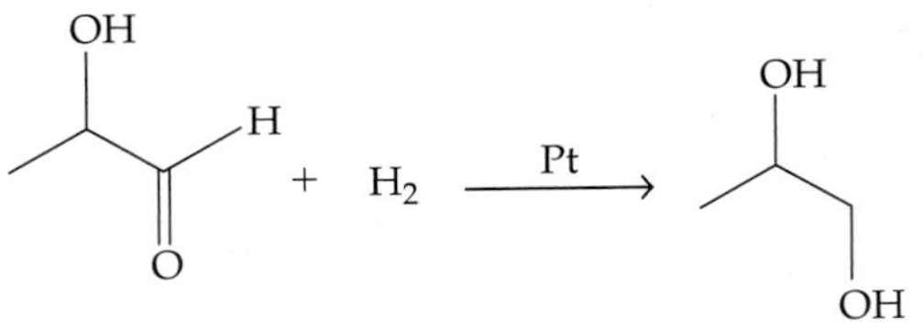

c. H, O + H_2 $\xrightarrow{Pt}$ OH

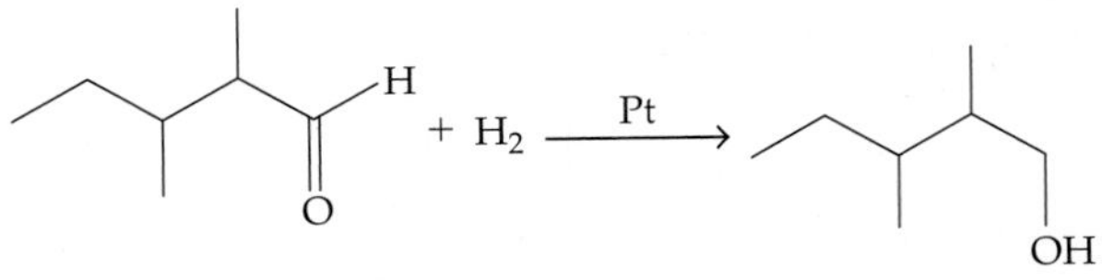

d. Cl, H, O + H_2 $\xrightarrow{Pt}$ Cl, OH

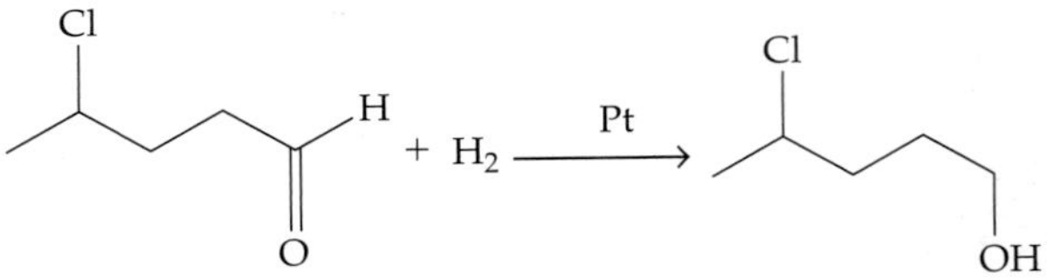

13.65 a.

$$\mathrm{CH_3CH_2CH_2\overset{\overset{\large O}{\|}}{C}H + H_2 \xrightarrow{Pt} CH_3CH_2CH_2CH_2OH}$$

Butanal — 1-Butanol

b.

$$\mathrm{CH_3CH_2\underset{\underset{\large CH_3}{|}}{C}HCH_2\overset{\overset{\large O}{\|}}{C}H + H_2 \xrightarrow{Pt} CH_3CH_2\underset{\underset{\large CH_3}{|}}{C}HCH_2CH_2OH}$$

3-Methylpentanal — 3-Methyl-1-pentanol

c.

$$\mathrm{CH_3\underset{\underset{\large CH_3}{|}}{C}H\overset{\overset{\large O}{\|}}{C}H + H_2 \xrightarrow{Pt} CH_3\underset{\underset{\large CH_3}{|}}{C}HCH_2OH}$$

2-Methylpropanal — 2-Methyl-1-propanol

13.67 Only (c) 3-methylbutanal and (f) acetaldehyde would give a positive Tollens' test.

13.69 a.

$$\mathrm{CH_3CH_2\overset{\overset{\large O}{\|}}{C}H + CH_3CH_2OH \xrightarrow{H^+} CH_3CH_2{-}\underset{\underset{\large OCH_2CH_3}{|}}{\overset{\overset{\large OH}{|}}{C}}{-}H}$$

b.

$$\mathrm{CH_3\overset{\overset{\large O}{\|}}{C}H + CH_3CH_2OH \xrightarrow{H^+} CH_3{-}\underset{\underset{\large OCH_2CH_3}{|}}{\overset{\overset{\large OH}{|}}{C}}{-}H}$$

13.71

a.

$$\mathrm{CH_3CH_2\overset{\overset{\large O}{\|}}{C}H + 2\,CH_3OH \xrightarrow{H^+} CH_3CH_2{-}\underset{\underset{\large OCH_3}{|}}{\overset{\overset{\large OCH_3}{|}}{C}}{-}H + H_2O}$$

b.

$$\mathrm{CH_3\overset{\overset{\large O}{\|}}{C}H + 2\,CH_3OH \xrightarrow{H^+} CH_3{-}\underset{\underset{\large OCH_3}{|}}{\overset{\overset{\large OCH_3}{|}}{C}}{-}H + H_2O}$$

13.73

a. OH, O

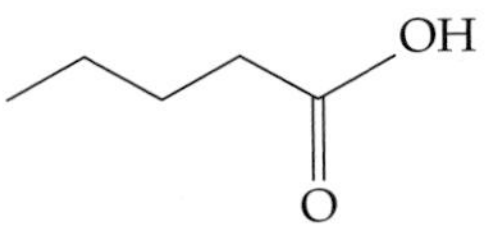

b. (skeletal structure: hexanoic acid, O / OH)

c. (skeletal structure: heptanoic acid, O / OH)

d. (skeletal structure: octanoic acid, O / OH)

13.75 a. Methanal b. Propanal

13.77 a. False c. False
b. True d. False

13.79 $CH_3C(=O)CH_3$ — Keto form of Propanone; $H_2C=C(OH)CH_3$ — Enol form of Propanone

13.81 a. $CH_3CH_2CH_2—C(OH)(OCH_2CH_3)—CH_3$
b. $C_6H_5—C(OH)(OCH_2CH_3)—CH_3$
c. Cyclopentane bearing OH and OCH_2CH_3

13.83 (1) $2CH_3CH_2OH$
(2) $KMnO_4/OH^-$
(3) $CH_3CH=CH_2$

Chapter 14

14.1 a. Ketone c. Alkane
b. Ketone

14.3 The carboxyl group consists of two very polar groups, the carbonyl group and the hydroxyl group. Thus, carboxylic acids are very polar, in addition to which, they can hydrogen bond to one another. Aldehydes are polar, as a result of the carbonyl group, but cannot hydrogen bond to one another. As a result, carboxylic acids have higher boiling points than aldehydes of the same carbon chain length.

14.5 a. 3-Methylcyclohexanecarboxylic acid
b. 2-Ethylcyclopentanecarboxylic acid

14.7 a. $CH_3COOH + CH_3CH_2CH_2OH$
Ethanoic acid 1-Propanol
b. $CH_3CH_2CH_2CH_2CH_2COO^-K^+ + CH_3CH_2CH_2OH$
Potassium hexanoate 1-Propanol
c. $CH_3CH_2CH_2CH_2COO^-Na^+ + CH_3OH$
Sodium pentanoate Methanol
d. $CH_3CH_2CH_2CH_2CH_2COOH + CH_3CH(OH)CH_2CH_2CH_3$
Hexanoic acid 2-Pentanol

14.9 a. $CH_3CH(CH_3)CH_2C(=O)—Cl \xrightarrow{CH_3CH(CH_3)CH_2C(=O)—O^-} CH_3CH(CH_3)CH_2C(=O)—O—C(=O)CH_2CH(CH_3)CH_3 + Cl^-$
3-Methylbutanoyl chloride; 3-Methylbutanoate ion; 3-Methylbutanoic anhydride

b. $H—C(=O)—Cl \xrightarrow{CH_3C(=O)—O^-} H—C(=O)—O—C(=O)—CH_3 + Cl^-$
Methanoyl chloride; Ethanoate ion; Ethanoic methanoic anhydride

14.11 Aldehydes are polar, as a result of the carbonyl group, but cannot hydrogen bond to one another. Alcohols are polar and can hydrogen bond as a result of the polar hydroxyl group. The carboxyl group of the carboxylic acids consists of both of these groups: the carbonyl group and the hydroxyl group. Thus, carboxylic acids are more polar than either aldehydes or alcohols, in addition to which, they can hydrogen bond to one another. As a result, carboxylic acids have higher boiling points than aldehydes or alcohols of comparable molar mass.

14.13 a. Pentanoic acid
b. 2-Pentanol
c. 2-Pentanol

14.15 Propanoic acid > 2-Butanol > Butanal > 2-Methylbutane

14.17 a. Heptanoic acid c. Pentanoic acid
b. 1-Propanol d. Butanoic acid

14.19 The smaller carboxylic acids are water-soluble. They have sharp, sour tastes and unpleasant aromas.

14.21 Citric acid is found naturally in citrus fruits. It is added to foods to give them a tart flavor or to act as a food preservative and antioxidant.

14.23 Glutaric acid is useful in the synthesis of condensation polymers because it has an odd number of carbons in the chain, which reduces the elasticity of the polymer.

14.25 Determine the name of the parent compound, that is, the longest carbon chain containing the carboxyl group. Change the *-e* ending of the alkane name to *-oic* acid. Number the chain so that the carboxyl carbon is carbon-1. Name and number substituents in the usual way.

14.27 The IUPAC name for adipic acid is hexanedioic acid. Adipic acid is a natural food additive that reduces spoilage by lowering the pH and thereby inhibiting the growth of bacteria and fungi.

14.29 **a.** $CH_3(CH_2)_2CH(CH_3)CH_2COOH$ (OH, O)

b. $CH_3(CH_2)_2C(CH_3)(CH_2CH_3)COOH$ (OH, O)

c. (O, C, HO, H_2 C, CH, CH_3, CH, $H_2C—CH_2$; O, HO)

14.31 **a.** IUPAC name: Methanoic acid
Common name: Formic acid
b. IUPAC name: 3-Methylbutanoic acid
Common name: β-Methylbutyric acid
c. IUPAC name: Cyclopentanecarboxylic acid
Common name: Cyclovalericcarboxylic acid

14.33

H–C(H)(H)–C(H)(H)–C(H)(H)–C(=O)–OH

Butanoic acid

H–C(H)(H)–C(H)(CH₃)–C(=O)–OH

Methylpropanoic acid

14.35 **a.** $CH_3CH_2C(CH_3)_2CH_2CH_2COOH$

b. $CH_3CH(CH_3)CH(Br)CH_2COOH$

c. (benzene ring with COOH, O_2N, NO_2)

d.

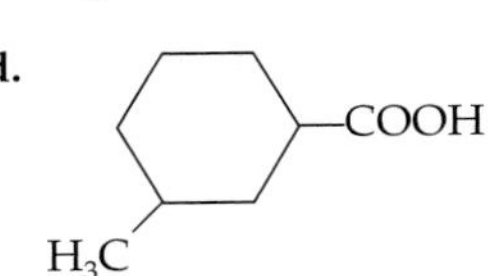

14.37 **a.** IUPAC name: 2-Hydroxypropanoic acid
Common name: α-Hydroxypropionic acid
b. IUPAC name: 3-Hydroxybutanoic acid
Common name: β-Hydroxybutyric acid
c. IUPAC name: 4,4-Dimethylpentanoic acid
Common name: γ,γ-Dimethylvaleric acid
d. IUPAC name: 3, 3-Dichloropentanoic acid
Common name: β,β-Dichlorovaleric acid

14.39 **a.** 3-Bromobenzoic acid (or *meta*-bromobenzoic acid or *m*-bromobenzoic acid)
b. 2-Ethylbenzoic acid (or *ortho*-ethylbenzoic acid or *o*-ethylbenzoic acid)
c. 4-Hydroxybenzoic acid (or *para*-hydroxybenzoic acid or *p*-hydroxybenzoic acid)

14.41 In organic molecules, oxidation may be recognized as a gain of oxygen or a loss of hydrogen. An aldehyde may be oxidized to form a carboxylic acid as in the following example in which ethanal is oxidized to produce ethanoic acid.

$$H_3C—\overset{O}{\overset{\|}{C}}—H \xrightarrow{[O]} H_3C—\overset{O}{\overset{\|}{C}}—OH$$

Ethanal → Ethanoic acid

14.43 The following general equation represents the dissociation of a carboxylic acid.

$$R—\overset{O}{\overset{\|}{C}}—OH \rightleftharpoons R—\overset{O}{\overset{\|}{C}}—O^- + H^+$$

14.45 When a strong base is added to a carboxylic acid, neutralization occurs.

14.47 Soaps are made from water, a strong base, and natural fats or oils.

14.49
a. (1-pentanol, OH) $\xrightarrow{[O]}$ (pentanal, H, O) $\xrightarrow{[O]}$ (pentanoic acid, OH, O)
b. (H, O) $\xrightarrow{[O]}$ (OH, O)
c. (ketone, O) $\xrightarrow{[O]}$ No Reaction

14.51 **a.** CH_3COOH
b.

$$CH_3CH_2CH_2—\overset{O}{\overset{\|}{C}}—O—CH_3 + H_2O$$

c. CH_3OH

14.53 **a.** The oxidation of 1-pentanol yields pentanal.
b. Continued oxidation of pentanal yields pentanoic acid.

14.55
a. (pentanoic acid, OH, O) + NaOH ⟶ (O⁻Na⁺, O) + H_2O
b. (pentanoic acid, OH, O) + KOH ⟶ (O⁻K⁺, O) + H_2O
c. 2 (pentanoic acid, OH, O) + $Ca(OH)_2$ ⟶ (Ca^{2+} ⁻O, O⁻, O) + $2H_2O$

14.57 The structure of the calcium salt of propionic acid is $[CH_3CH_2COO^-]_2Ca^{2+}$. The common name of this salt is calcium propionate and the IUPAC name is calcium propanoate.

14.59 Esters are slightly polar as a result of the polar carbonyl group within the structure.

14.61 Esters are formed in the reaction of a carboxylic acid with an alcohol. The name is derived by using the alkyl or aryl portion of the alcohol IUPAC name as the first name. The *-ic* acid ending of the IUPAC name of the carboxylic acid is replaced with *-ate* and follows the name of the aryl or alkyl group.

14.63 **a.** (benzene ring with $\overset{O}{\overset{\|}{C}}—OCH_3$)

b.

$$CH_3CH_2CH_2CH_2CH_2CH_2CH_2CH_2CH_2—\overset{O}{\overset{\|}{C}}—O—CH_2CH_2CH_2CH_3$$

c.

$$CH_3CH_2—\overset{O}{\overset{\|}{C}}—O—CH_3$$

d.

$$CH_3CH_2—\overset{O}{\overset{\|}{C}}—O—CH_2CH_3$$

14.65 **a.** Ethyl ethanoate **b.** Methyl propanoate **c.** Methyl-3-methylbutanoate **d.** Cyclopentyl benzoate

14.67 The following equation shows the general reaction for the preparation of an ester:

$$\underset{\text{Carboxylic acid}}{R{-}\overset{O}{\overset{\|}{C}}{-}OH} + \underset{\text{Alcohol}}{R{-}OH} \underset{}{\overset{H^+,\ \text{heat}}{\rightleftharpoons}} \underset{\text{Ester}}{R{-}\overset{O}{\overset{\|}{C}}{-}OR} + \underset{\text{Water}}{H_2O}$$

14.69 The following equation shows the general reaction for the acid-catalyzed hydrolysis of an ester:

$$\underset{\text{Ester}}{R{-}\overset{O}{\overset{\|}{C}}{-}OR} + \underset{\text{Water}}{H_2O} \overset{H^+,\ \text{heat}}{\rightleftharpoons} \underset{\text{Carboxylic acid}}{R{-}\overset{O}{\overset{\|}{C}}{-}OH} + \underset{\text{Alcohol}}{R{-}OH}$$

14.71 A hydrolysis reaction is the cleavage of any bond by the addition of a water molecule.

14.73 **a.**

$$CH_3CH_2CH_2{-}\overset{O}{\overset{\|}{C}}{-}O{-}CH_2CH_3$$

b.

$$CH_3CH_2{-}\overset{O}{\overset{\|}{C}}{-}OH + CH_3CH_2OH$$

c. $CH_3CH_2CH_2OH$

d.

$$CH_3CH_2\underset{}{\overset{Br}{\overset{|}{C}}}HCH_2{-}\overset{O}{\overset{\|}{C}}{-}O^- + CH_3CH_2OH$$

14.75 **a.** Isobutyl methanoate is made from isobutyl alcohol (IUPAC name 2-methyl-1-propanol) and methanoic acid.

$$\underset{\text{Isobutyl alcohol}}{CH_3\overset{CH_3}{\overset{|}{C}}HCH_2OH} + \underset{\text{Methanoic acid}}{HCOOH} \rightarrow \underset{\text{Isobutyl methanoate}}{H\overset{O}{\overset{\|}{C}}OCH_2\overset{CH_3}{\overset{|}{C}}HCH_3}$$

Isobutyl alcohol is an allowed starting material, but methanoic acid is not. However, it can easily be produced by the oxidation of its corresponding alcohol, methanol:

$$\underset{\text{Methanol}}{CH_3OH} \xrightarrow{[O]} \underset{\text{Methanal}}{HCHO} \xrightarrow{[O]} \underset{\text{Methanoic acid}}{HCOOH}$$

b. Pentyl butanoate is made from 1-pentanol and butanoic acid.

$$\underset{\text{1-Pentanol}}{CH_3(CH_2)_3CH_2OH} + \underset{\text{Butanoic acid}}{CH_3CH_2CH_2COOH} \rightarrow \underset{\text{Pentyl butanoate}}{CH_3CH_2CH_2\overset{O}{\overset{\|}{C}}OCH_2(CH_2)_3CH_3}$$

Pentanol is an allowed starting material but butanoic acid is not. However, it can easily be produced by the oxidation of its corresponding alcohol, 1-butanol:

$$\underset{\text{1-Butanol}}{CH_3CH_2CH_2CH_2OH} \xrightarrow{[O]} \underset{\text{Butanal}}{CH_3CH_2CH_2CHO} \xrightarrow{[O]} \underset{\text{Butanoic acid}}{CH_3CH_2CH_2COOH}$$

14.77 Saponification is a reaction in which soap is produced. More generally, it is the hydrolysis of an ester in the presence of a base. The following reaction shows the base-catalyzed hydrolysis of an ester:

$$CH_3(CH_2)_{14}{-}\overset{O}{\overset{\|}{C}}{-}O{-}CH_3 + NaOH \longrightarrow CH_3(CH_2)_{14}{-}\overset{O}{\overset{\|}{C}}{-}O^-\ Na^+ + CH_3OH$$

14.79

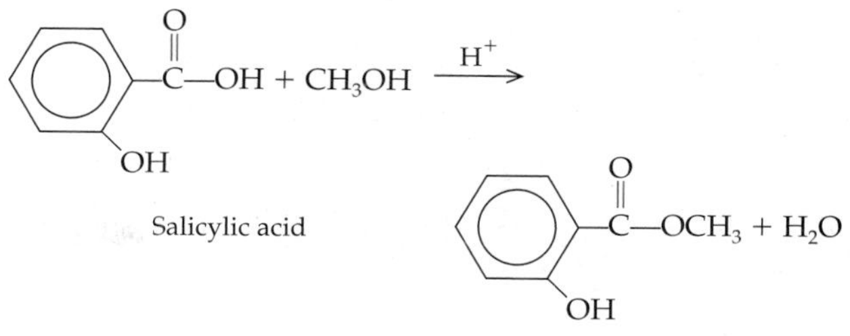

$$\underset{\text{Salicylic acid}}{(o\text{-HO})C_6H_4{-}\overset{O}{\overset{\|}{C}}{-}OH} + CH_3OH \xrightarrow{H^+} \underset{\text{Methyl salicylate}}{(o\text{-HO})C_6H_4{-}\overset{O}{\overset{\|}{C}}{-}OCH_3} + H_2O$$

14.81 Compound A is

$$CH_3CH_2CH_2CH_2{-}\overset{O}{\overset{\|}{C}}{-}O{-}CH_3$$

Compound B is

$$CH_3CH_2CH_2CH_2{-}\overset{O}{\overset{\|}{C}}{-}OH$$

Compound C is CH_3OH

14.83 **a.**

$$\underset{\text{Propyl propanoate}}{CH_3CH_2{-}\overset{O}{\overset{\|}{C}}{-}OCH_2CH_2CH_3} \overset{H^+,\ \text{heat}}{\rightleftharpoons} \underset{\text{Propanoic acid}}{CH_3CH_2{-}\overset{O}{\overset{\|}{C}}{-}OH} + \underset{\text{1-Propanol}}{CH_3CH_2CH_2OH}$$

b.

$$\underset{\text{Butyl methanoate}}{H{-}\overset{O}{\overset{\|}{C}}{-}OCH_2CH_2CH_2CH_3} \overset{H^+,\ \text{heat}}{\rightleftharpoons} \underset{\text{Methanoic acid}}{H{-}\overset{O}{\overset{\|}{C}}{-}OH} + \underset{\text{1-Butanol}}{CH_3CH_2CH_2CH_2OH}$$

c.

$$\underset{\text{Ethyl methanoate}}{H{-}\overset{O}{\overset{\|}{C}}{-}OCH_2CH_3} \overset{H^+,\ \text{heat}}{\rightleftharpoons} \underset{\text{Methanoic acid}}{H{-}\overset{O}{\overset{\|}{C}}{-}OH} + \underset{\text{Ethanol}}{CH_3CH_2OH}$$

d.

$$\underset{\text{Methyl pentanoate}}{CH_3CH_2CH_2CH_2{-}\overset{O}{\overset{\|}{C}}{-}OCH_3} \overset{H^+,\ \text{heat}}{\rightleftharpoons} \underset{\text{Pentanoic acid}}{CH_3CH_2CH_2CH_2{-}\overset{O}{\overset{\|}{C}}{-}OH} + \underset{\text{Methanol}}{CH_3OH}$$

14.85 Acid chlorides are noxious, irritating chemicals. They are slightly polar and have boiling points similar to comparable aldehydes or ketones. They cannot be dissolved in water because they react violently with it.

14.87 Acid anhydrides have much lower boiling points than carboxylic acids of comparable molar mass. They are also less soluble in water, and often react with it.

14.89 **a.**

$$CH_3(CH_2)_8{-}\overset{O}{\overset{\|}{C}}{-}O{-}\overset{O}{\overset{\|}{C}}{-}(CH_2)_8CH_3$$

b.

$$CH_3{-}\overset{O}{\overset{\|}{C}}{-}O{-}\overset{O}{\overset{\|}{C}}{-}CH_3$$

14.91 a. $CH_3(CH_2)_6\overset{O}{\overset{\|}{C}}Cl$ 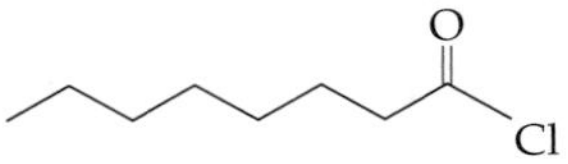

b. $CH_3(CH_2)_2\overset{O}{\overset{\|}{C}}Cl$ 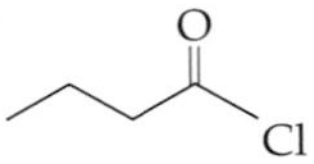

c. $CH_3(CH_2)_7\overset{O}{\overset{\|}{C}}Cl$ 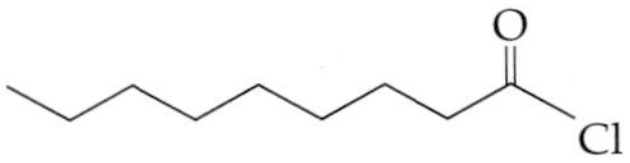

14.93 The following equation represents the synthesis of methanoic anhydride:

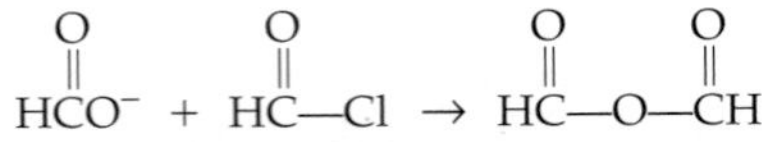

Methanoate anion, Methanoic chloride, Methanoic anhydride

14.95 a.

$$CH_3CH_2OH + CH_3CH_2-\overset{O}{\overset{\|}{C}}-O-\overset{O}{\overset{\|}{C}}-CH_2CH_3 \longrightarrow CH_3CH_2-\overset{O}{\overset{\|}{C}}-OCH_2CH_3 + CH_3CH_2-\overset{O}{\overset{\|}{C}}-OH$$

b.

$$CH_3CH_2OH + CH_3-\overset{O}{\overset{\|}{C}}-O-\overset{O}{\overset{\|}{C}}-CH_3 \longrightarrow CH_3-\overset{O}{\overset{\|}{C}}-OCH_2CH_3 + CH_3-\overset{O}{\overset{\|}{C}}-OH$$

c.

$$CH_3CH_2OH + H-\overset{O}{\overset{\|}{C}}-O-\overset{O}{\overset{\|}{C}}-H \longrightarrow H-\overset{O}{\overset{\|}{C}}-OCH_2CH_3 + H-\overset{O}{\overset{\|}{C}}-OH$$

14.97 a. Monoester:

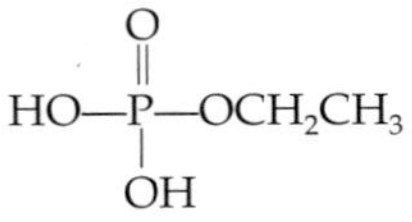

b. Diester:

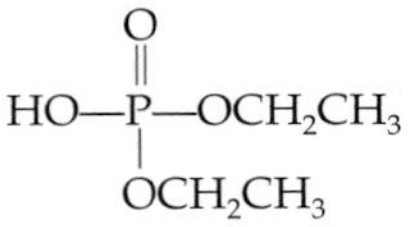

c. Triester:

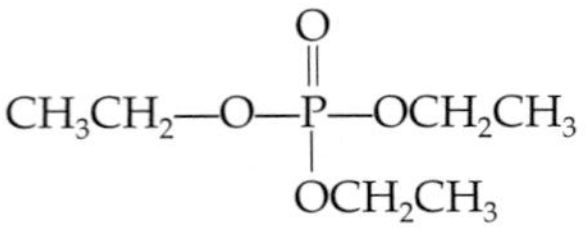

14.99 ATP is the molecule used to store the energy released in metabolic reactions. The energy is stored in the phosphoanhydride bonds between two phosphoryl groups. The energy is released when the bond is hydrolyzed. A portion of the energy can be transferred to another molecule if the phosphoryl group is transferred from ATP to the other molecule.

14.101

$$CH_3-\overset{O}{\overset{\|}{C}}\sim S-\text{COENZYME A}$$

The squiggle denotes a high energy bond.

14.103

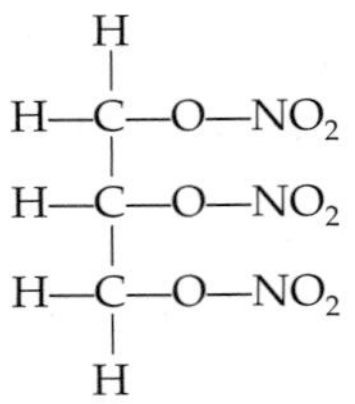

Chapter 15

15.1

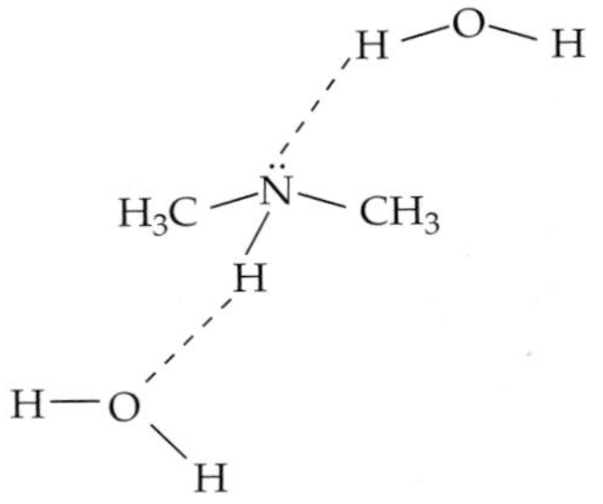

15.3 a.

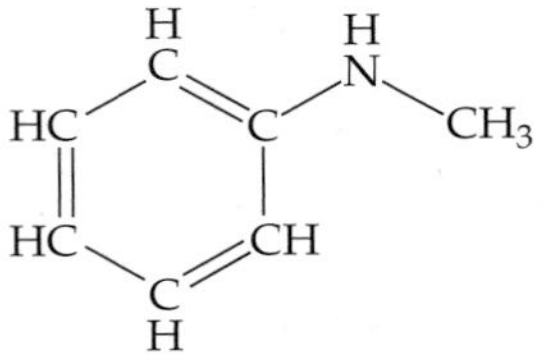

b.

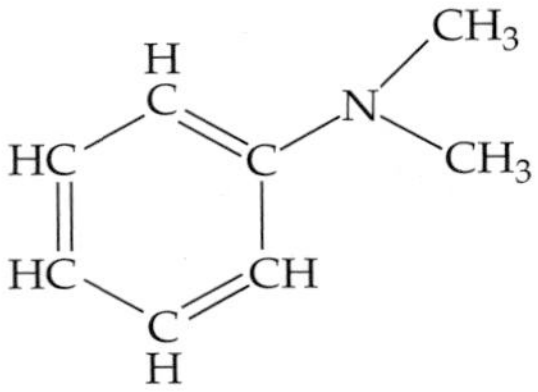

c.

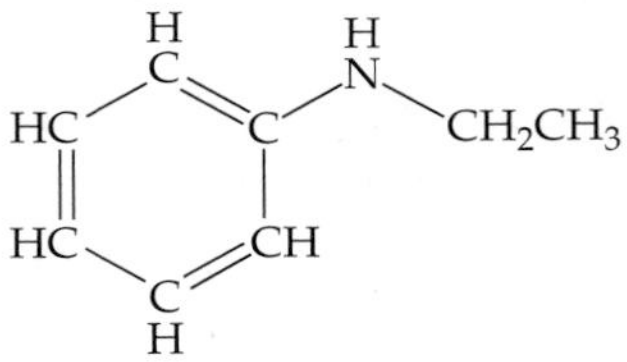

d.

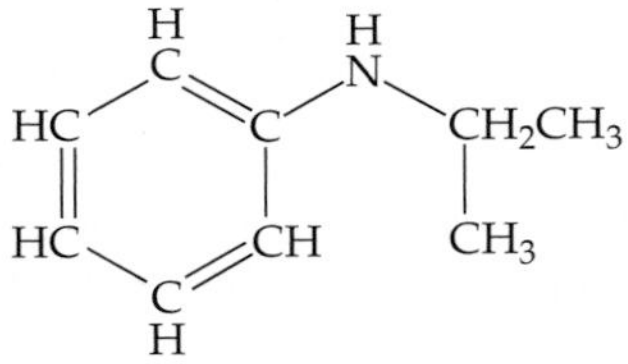

15.5 a.

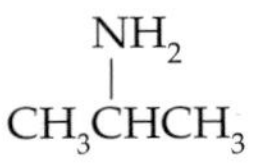

b.

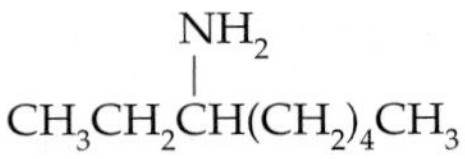

c.

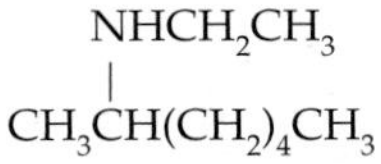

d. $NH_2C(CH_3)_2(CH_2)_2CH_3$

e. $NH_2(CH_2)_3CHCH(CH_2)_3CH_3$ (Cl and I on the two CH carbons)

f. $(CH_3CH_2)_2N(CH_2)_4CH_3$

15.7 a. Cyclopentyl–$N^+H_3Br^-$

b. $CH_3CH_2—N^+H_2—CH_3 + OH^-$

c. $CH_3—N^+H_3 + OH^-$

15.9 a. $CH_3—NH_2$

b. $CH_3—NH—CH_3$

15.11 The nitrogen atom is more electronegative than the hydrogen atom in amines; thus, the N—H bond is polar and hydrogen bonding can occur between primary or secondary amine molecules. Thus, amines have a higher boiling point than alkanes, which are nonpolar. Because nitrogen is not as electronegative as oxygen, the N—H bond is not as polar as the O—H. As a result, intermolecular hydrogen bonds between primary and secondary amine molecules are not as strong as the hydrogen bonds between alcohol molecules. Thus, alcohols have a higher boiling point.

15.13 In systematic nomenclature, primary amines are named by determining the name of the parent compound, the longest continuous carbon chain containing the amine group. The *-e* ending of the alkane chain is replaced with *-amine.* Thus, an alkane becomes an alkanamine. The parent chain is then numbered to give the carbon bearing the amine group the lowest possible number. Finally, all substituents are named and numbered and added as prefixes to the "alkanamine" name.

15.15 Amphetamines elevate blood pressure and pulse rate. They also decrease the appetite.

15.17 a. 1-Pentamine would be more soluble in water because it has a polar amine group that can form hydrogen bonds with water molecules.

b. 2-Butamine would be more soluble in water because it has a polar amine group that can form hydrogen bonds with water molecules.

15.19 Triethylamine molecules cannot form hydrogen bonds with one another, but 1-hexanamine molecules are able to do so.

15.21 a. 2-Butanamine
b. 3-Hexanamine
c. Cyclopentanamine
d. 2-Methyl-2-propanamine

15.23 a. $CH_3CH_2NHCH_2CH_3$ (line structure with N–H)

b. $CH_3(CH_2)_3NH_2$ (line structure with NH_2)

c. $CH_3(CH_2)_6CHCH_2CH_3$ with NH_2 on the CH (line structure with NH_2)

d. $CH_3CHCHCH_2CH_3$ with NH_2 on C-2 and Br on C-3 (line structure with NH_2 and Br)

e. Triphenylamine (structure with HC/CH ring atoms; N bonded to three benzene rings)

15.25 a. $CH_3CH_2CH(NH)(CH_2)_2CH_3$

b. $CH_3(CH_2)_5NH(CH_2)_4CH_3$

c. Cyclobutane ring ($H_2C—CH$, $H_2C—CH_2$) with NH_2 on CH

d. Cyclopentane ring (H_2C, CH, $H_2C—CH_2$) with NH_2 on CH and CH_3 on the adjacent CH

e. $CH_3CH_2N^+HCH_2CH_3$ with CH_2CH_3 on N, Cl^-

15.27

Structure	Name
$CH_3CH_2CH_2CH_2NH_2$	1-Butanamine (Primary amine)
$CH_3CH_2CHCH_3$ with NH_2 on C-2	2-Butanamine (Primary amine)
$CH_3CHCH_2NH_2$ with CH_3 on C-2	2-Methyl-1-propanamine (Primary amine)
$CH_3—C(CH_3)—CH_3$ with NH_2 on central C	2-Methyl-2-propanamine (Primary amine)
$CH_3CH_2—N(CH_3)—CH_3$	*N,N*-Dimethylethanamine (Tertiary amine)
$CH_3CH_2—NH—CH_2CH_3$	*N*-Ethylethanamine (Secondary amine)
CH_3CHCH_3 with $NH—CH_3$ on C-2	*N*-Methyl-2-propanamine (Secondary amine)
$CH_3CH_2CH_2—NH—CH_3$	*N*-Methyl-1-propanamine (Secondary amine)

15.29 a. Primary
b. Secondary
c. Primary
d. Tertiary

15.31 a.

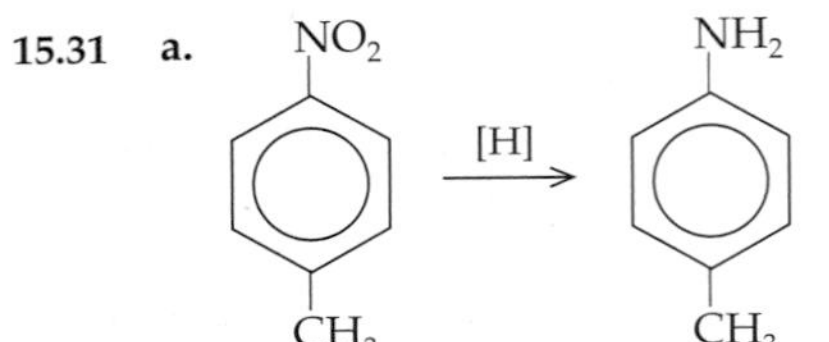

b. NO_2, OH $\xrightarrow{[H]}$ NH_2, OH

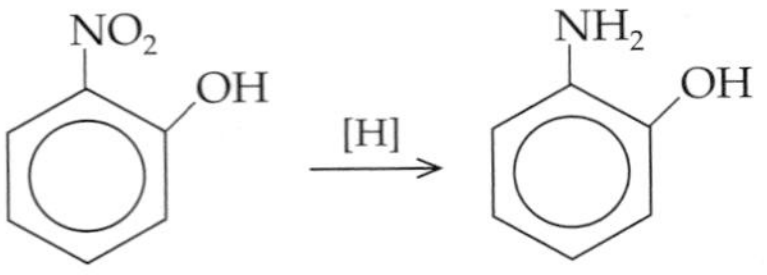

c. NO_2 $\xrightarrow{[H]}$ NH_2

d. O=C—NH_2 $\xrightarrow{[H]}$ H_2C—NH_2

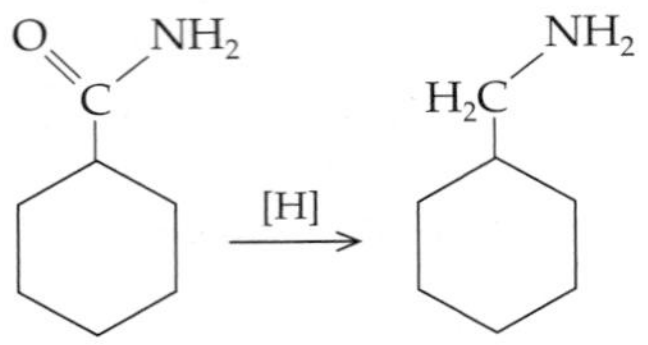

15.33 a. H_2O
b. HBr
c. $CH_3CH_2CH_2—N^+H_3$
d. $CH_3CH_2—N^+H_2Cl^-$ with CH_2CH_3

15.35
a. $CH_3(CH_2)_4\overset{O}{\overset{\|}{C}}NH_2 \xrightarrow{[H]} CH_3(CH_2)_5NH_2$
b. $CH_3(CH_2)_2\overset{O}{\overset{\|}{C}}NHCH_3 \xrightarrow{[H]} CH_3(CH_2)_3NHCH_3$
c. $CH_3CH_2\overset{O}{\overset{\|}{C}}NCH_3$ (CH_3 on N) $\xrightarrow{[H]} CH_3(CH_2)_2NCH_3$ (CH_3 on N)

15.37 Lower molar mass amines are soluble in water because the N—H bond is polar and can form hydrogen bonds with water molecules.

15.39 Drugs containing amine groups are generally administered as ammonium salts because the salt is more soluble in water and, hence, in body fluids.

15.41 Putrescine (1,4-Butanediamine):
$CH_2CH_2CH_2CH_2$ with NH_2 on each terminal carbon

Cadaverine (1,5-Pentanediamine):
$CH_2CH_2CH_2CH_2CH_2$ with NH_2 on each terminal carbon

15.43 a.

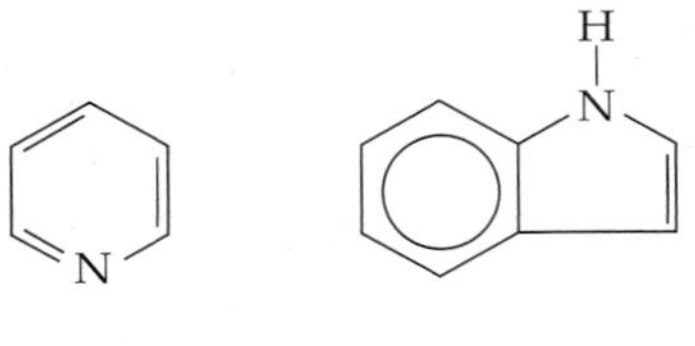

Pyridine   Indole

b. The indole ring is found in lysergic acid diethylamide, which is a hallucinogenic drug. The pyridine ring is found in vitamin B_6, an essential water-soluble vitamin.

15.45 Morphine, codeine, quinine, and vitamin B_6

15.47 Amides have very high boiling points because the amide group consists of two very polar functional groups, the carbonyl group and the amino group. Strong intermolecular hydrogen bonding between the N—H bond of one amide and the C=O group of a second amide results in very high boiling points.

15.49 The IUPAC names of amides are derived from the IUPAC names of the carboxylic acids from which they are derived. The *-oic acid* ending of the carboxylic acid is replaced with the *-amide* ending.

15.51 Barbiturates are often called "downers" because they act as sedatives. They are sometimes used as anticonvulsants for epileptics and people suffering from other disorders that manifest as neurosis, anxiety, or tension.

15.53 a. IUPAC name: Propanamide
Common name: Propionamide
b. IUPAC name: Pentanamide
Common name: Valeramide
c. IUPAC name: *N,N*-Dimethylethanamide
Common name: *N,N*-Dimethylacetamide

15.55 a. $CH_3CH_2\overset{O}{\overset{\|}{C}}NH_2$
b. $CH_3(CH_2)_2\overset{O}{\overset{\|}{C}}N(CH_2CH_3)_2$
c. $(CH_3CH_2)_2CHCH(CH_2CH_3)\overset{O}{\overset{\|}{C}}NH_2$
d. $CH_3(CH_2)_4\overset{O}{\overset{\|}{C}}NHCH_3$

15.57 a. $CH_3—\overset{O}{\overset{\|}{C}}—NH_2$, (line structure with O, NH_2)
b. $CH_3CH_2—\overset{O}{\overset{\|}{C}}—NHCH_3$, (line structure with O, H, N)
c. $C_6H_5—\overset{O}{\overset{\|}{C}}—N—CH_2CH_3$ (CH_2CH_3 on N), (line structure with O, N)
d. $CH_3CH_2\overset{CH_3}{CH}\underset{Br}{CH}CH_2—\overset{O}{\overset{\|}{C}}—NH_2$, (line structure with Br, O, NH_2) 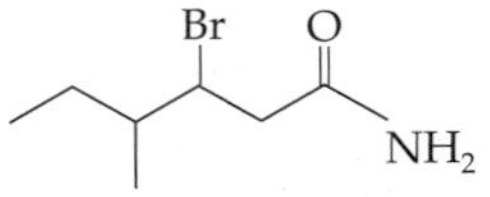
e. $CH_3—\overset{O}{\overset{\|}{C}}—N—CH_3$ (CH_3 on N), (line structure with O, N)

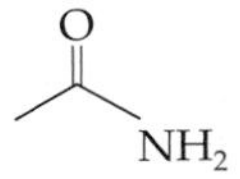

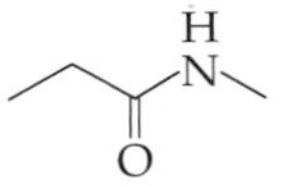

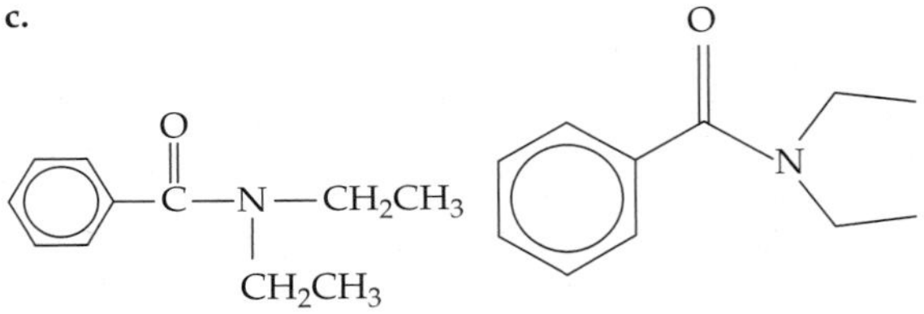

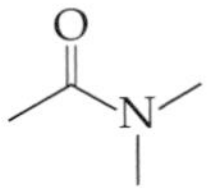

15.59 *N,N*-Diethyl-*m*-toluamide:

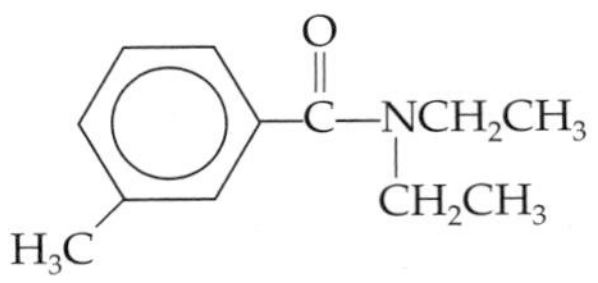

H_3C—C_6H_4—$\overset{O}{\overset{\|}{C}}$—$NCH_2CH_3$ (CH_2CH_3 on N)

Hydrolysis of this compound would release the carboxylic acid *m*-toluic acid and the amine *N*-ethylethanamine (diethylamine).

15.61 Amides are not proton acceptors (bases) because the highly electronegative carbonyl oxygen has a strong attraction for the nitrogen lone pair of electrons. As a result they cannot "hold" a proton.

15.63

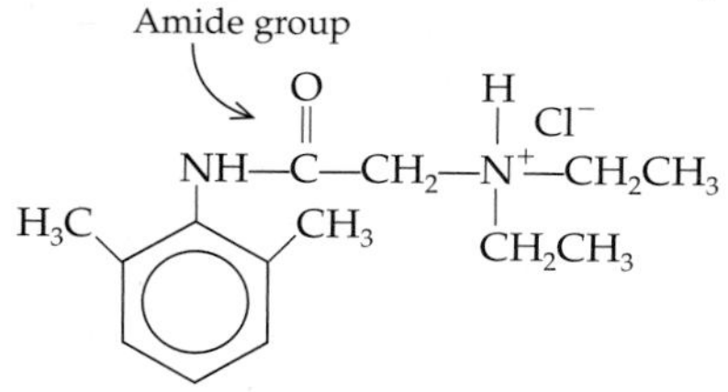

Amide group

$$\text{2,6-}(CH_3)_2C_6H_3-NH-\overset{O}{\overset{\|}{C}}-CH_2-\overset{H\ \ Cl^-}{\overset{|}{N^+}}(CH_2CH_3)-CH_2CH_3$$

Lidocaine hydrochloride

15.65

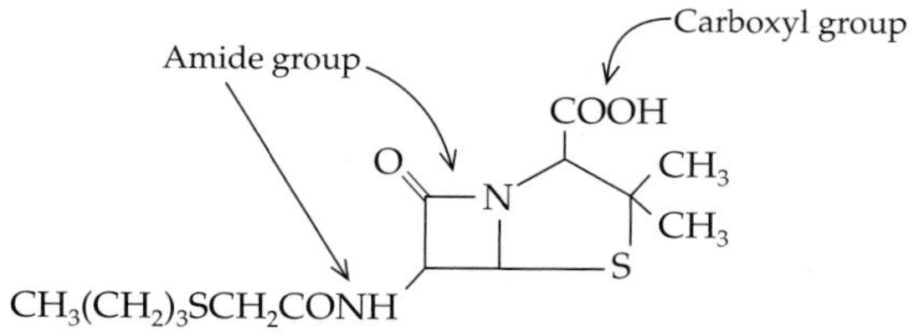

Amide group; Carboxyl group

$$CH_3(CH_2)_3SCH_2CONH-(\text{β-lactam ring with } C{=}O, N) \text{ fused to thiazolidine ring with } COOH, (CH_3)_2, S$$

Penicillin BT

15.67 a.

$$CH_3-\overset{O}{\overset{\|}{C}}-NHCH_3 + H_3O^+ \longrightarrow CH_3COOH + CH_3N^+H_3$$

N-Methylethanamide → Ethanoic acid + Methylammonium ion

b.

$$CH_3CH_2CH_2-\overset{O}{\overset{\|}{C}}-NH-CH_3 + H_3O^+ \longrightarrow CH_3CH_2CH_2COOH + CH_3N^+H_3$$

N-Methylbutanamide → Butanoic acid + Methylammonium ion

c.

$$CH_3\underset{}{\overset{CH_3}{\overset{|}{C}}}HCH_2-\overset{O}{\overset{\|}{C}}-NH-CH_2CH_3 + H_3O^+ \longrightarrow CH_3\underset{CH_3}{\underset{|}{C}}HCH_2COOH + CH_3CH_2N^+H_3$$

N-Ethyl-3-methylbutanamide → 3-Methylbutanoic acid + Ethylammonium ion

15.69 a.

$$CH_3CH_2-\overset{O}{\overset{\|}{C}}-O-\overset{O}{\overset{\|}{C}}-CH_2CH_3$$

b.

$$CH_3CH_2-\overset{O}{\overset{\|}{C}}-NH_2 + NH_4^+Cl^-$$

c.

$$CH_3CH_2CH_2-\overset{O}{\overset{\|}{C}}-Cl + 2CH_3CH_2NH_2$$

15.71

$$H_2N-\underset{R}{\underset{|}{\overset{H}{\overset{|}{C}}}}-\overset{O}{\overset{\|}{C}}-OH$$

15.73 Glycine:

$$H_2N-\underset{H}{\underset{|}{\overset{H}{\overset{|}{C}}}}-\overset{O}{\overset{\|}{C}}-OH$$

Alanine:

$$H_2N-\underset{CH_3}{\underset{|}{\overset{H}{\overset{|}{C}}}}-\overset{O}{\overset{\|}{C}}-OH$$

15.75

$$H_2N-\underset{CH_3}{\underset{|}{\overset{H}{\overset{|}{C^*}}}}-\overset{O}{\overset{\|}{C}}-OH$$

15.77 In an acyl group transfer reaction, the acyl group of an acid chloride is transferred from the Cl of the acid chloride to the N of an amine or ammonia. The product is an amide.

15.79 A chemical that carries messages or signals from a nerve to a target cell

15.81 a. Tremors, monotonous speech, loss of memory and problem-solving ability, and loss of motor function
b. Parkinson's disease
c. Schizophrenia, intense satiety sensations

15.83 In proper amounts, dopamine causes a pleasant, satisfied feeling. This feeling becomes intense as the amount of dopamine increases. Several drugs, including cocaine, heroin, amphetamines, alcohol, and nicotine increase the levels of dopamine. It is thought that the intense satiety response this brings about may contribute to addiction to these substances.

15.85 Epinephrine is a component of the flight or fight response. It stimulates glycogen breakdown to provide the body with glucose to supply the needed energy for this stress response.

15.87 The amino acid tryptophan

15.89 Perception of pain, thermoregulation, and sleep

15.91 Promotes the itchy skin rash associated with poison ivy and insect bites; the respiratory symptoms characteristic of hay fever; secretion of stomach acid

15.93 Inhibitory neurotransmitters

15.95 When acetylcholine is released from a nerve cell, it binds to receptors on the surface of muscle cells. This binding stimulates the muscle cell to contract. To stop the contraction, the acetylcholine is then broken down to choline and acetate ion. This is catalyzed by the enzyme acetylcholinesterase.

15.97 Organophosphates inactivate acetylcholinesterase by binding covalently to it. Since acetylcholine is not broken down, nerve transmission continues, resulting in muscle spasm. Pyridine aldoxime methiodide (PAM) is an antidote to organophosphate poisoning because it displaces the organophosphate, thereby allowing acetycholinesterase to function.

Chapter 16

16.1 It is currently recommended that 45–55% of the calories in the diet should be carbohydrates. Of that amount, no more than 10% should be simple sugars.

16.3 An aldose is a sugar with an aldehyde functional group. A ketose is a sugar with a ketone functional group.

16.5 a. Fischer projections (top to bottom):
- CH_3; $C{=}O$; $H-C^*-OH$; CH_2OH
- CH_3; $C{=}O$; $HO-C^*-H$; CH_2OH

b.
- CHO; $H-C^*-OH$; $H-C^*-OH$; $HO-C^*-H$; CH_2OH
- CHO; $HO-C^*-H$; $HO-C^*-H$; $H-C^*-OH$; CH_2OH

c.
- CH_2OH; $C{=}O$; $HO-C^*-H$; $H-C^*-OH$; $H-C^*-OH$; CH_2OH
- CH_2OH; $C{=}O$; $H-C^*-OH$; $HO-C^*-H$; $HO-C^*-H$; CH_2OH

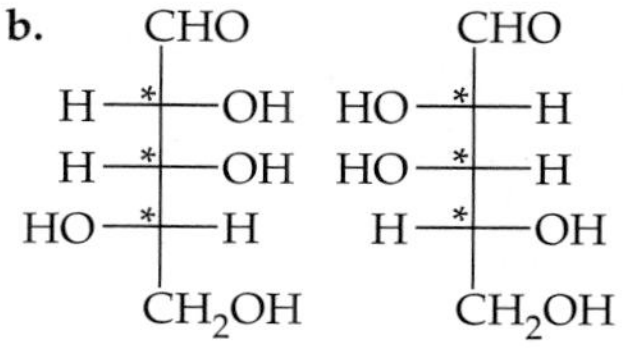

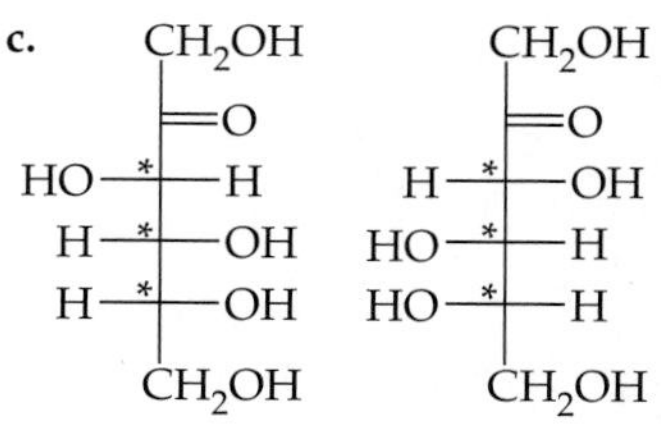

16.7 **a.** D-
b. L-
c. D-

16.9

CHO
H—OH
HO—H
HO—H
H—OH
CH_2OH

D-Galactose

16.11 α-Amylase and β-amylase are digestive enzymes that break down the starch amylose. α-Amylase cleaves glycosidic bonds of the amylose chain at random, producing shorter polysaccharide chains. β-Amylase sequentially cleaves maltose (a disaccharide of glucose) from the reducing end of the polysaccharide chain.

16.13 A monosaccharide is the simplest sugar and consists of a single saccharide unit. A disaccharide is made up of two monosaccharides joined covalently by a glycosidic bond.

16.15 Mashed potato flakes, rice, and corn starch contain amylose and amylopectin, both of which are polysaccharides. A candy bar contains sucrose, a disaccharide. Orange juice contains fructose, a monosaccharide. It may also contain sucrose if the label indicates that sugar has been added.

16.17 Four

16.19

O=C—H	CH_2OH
H—C—OH	C=O
HO—C—H	HO—C—H
HO—C—H	H—C—OH
H—C—OH	H—C—OH
CH_2OH	CH_2OH
D-Galactose (An aldohexose)	D-Fructose (A ketohexose)

16.21 An aldose is a sugar that contains an aldehyde (carbonyl) group.

16.23 A tetrose is a sugar with a four-carbon backbone.

16.25 A ketopentose is a sugar with a five-carbon backbone and containing a ketone (carbonyl) group.

16.27 **a.** β-D-Glucose
b. β-D-Fructose
c. α-D-Galactose

16.29

O=C—H	O=C—H
H—C—OH	HO—C—H
CH_2OH	CH_2OH
D-Glyceraldehyde	L-Glyceraldehyde

16.31 Stereoisomers are a pair of molecules that have the same structural formula and bonding pattern but that differ in the arrangement of the atoms in space.

16.33 A chiral carbon is one that is bonded to four different chemical groups.

16.35 A polarimeter converts monochromatic light into monochromatic plane-polarized light. This plane-polarized light is passed through a sample and into an analyzer. If the sample is optically active, it will rotate the plane of the light. The degree and angle of rotation are measured by the analyzer.

16.37 A Fischer Projection is a two-dimensional drawing of a molecule that shows a chiral carbon at the intersection of two lines. Horizontal lines at the intersection represent bonds projecting out of the page and vertical lines represent bonds that project into the page.

16.39 Diastereomers are a pair of stereoisomers that are not enantiomers.

16.41 Dextrose is a common name used for D-glucose.

16.43 D- and L-Glyceraldehyde are a pair of enantiomers, that is, they are nonsuperimposable mirror images of one another.

16.45

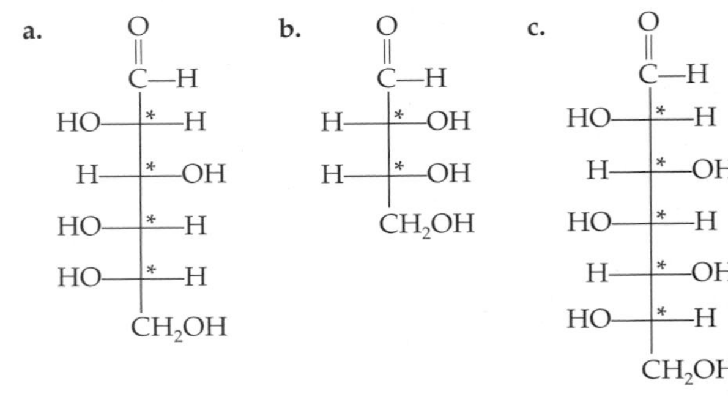

16.47 **a.**

HC=O	HC=O	HC=O	HC=O
H—OH	HO—H	HO—H	H—OH
H—OH	HO—H	H—OH	HO—H
HC=O	HC=O	CH=O	HC=O
A	B	C	D

The stereoisomers are A, C, and D. Compounds A and B are identical and they are meso compounds because they have an internal plane of symmetry. Compounds C and D are enantiomers. Compound A is a diastereomer to both compounds C and D.

b.

CH_2OH	CH_2OH	CH_2OH	CH_2OH
H—Br	Br—H	Br—H	H—Br
H—CH_3	H_3C—H	H—CH_3	H_3C—H
CH_2OH	CH_2OH	CH_2OH	CH_2OH
A	B	C	D

There are four possible stereoisomers. The two pairs of enantiomers are A with B and C with D. Compounds A and B are both diastereomers to compounds C and D.

16.49 **a.**

CH_2CH_3	CH_2CH_3	CH_2CH_3	CH_2CH_3
H—OH	HO—H	HO—H	H—OH
H—OH	HO—H	H—OH	HO—H
CH_2CH_3	CH_2CH_3	CH_2CH_3	CH_2CH_3
A	B	C	D

The stereoisomers are A, C, and D. Compounds A and B are identical and they are meso compounds because they have an internal plane of symmetry. Compounds C and D are enantiomers. Compound A is a diastereomer to both compounds C and D.

b.

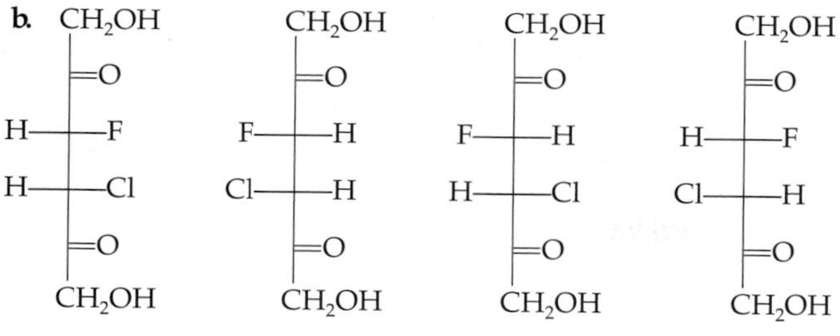

A	B	C	D
CH_2OH	CH_2OH	CH_2OH	CH_2OH
=O	=O	=O	=O
H—F	F—H	F—H	H—F
H—Cl	Cl—H	H—Cl	Cl—H
=O	=O	=O	=O
CH_2OH	CH_2OH	CH_2OH	CH_2OH

There are four possible stereoisomers. Compounds A and B are enantiomers, and compounds C and D are enantiomers. Compounds A and B are diastereomers to both compounds C and D.

16.51 Anomers are isomers that differ in the arrangement of bonds around the hemiacetal carbon.

16.53 A hemiacetal is a member of the family of organic compounds formed in the reaction of one molecule of alcohol with an aldehyde or a ketone.

16.55 When the carbonyl group at C-1 of d-glucose reacts with the C-5 hydroxyl group, a new chiral carbon is created (C-1). In the α-isomer of the cyclic sugar, the C-1 hydroxyl group is below the ring; and in the β-isomer, the C-1 hydroxyl group is above the ring.

16.57 β-Maltose and α-lactose would give positive Benedict's tests. Glycogen would give only a weak reaction because there are fewer reducing ends for a given mass of the carbohydrate.

16.59 Enantiomers are stereoisomers that are nonsuperimposable mirror images of one another. For instance:

D-Glyceraldehyde	L-Glyceraldehyde
CHO	CHO
H—OH	HO—H
CH_2OH	CH_2OH

16.61 An aldehyde sugar forms an intramolecular hemiacetal when the carbonyl group of the monosaccharide reacts with a hydroxyl group on one of the other carbon atoms.

16.63 A disaccharide is a simple carbohydrate composed of two monosaccharides.

16.65 A glycosidic bond is the bond formed between the hydroxyl group of the C-1 carbon of one sugar and a hydroxyl group of another sugar.

16.67

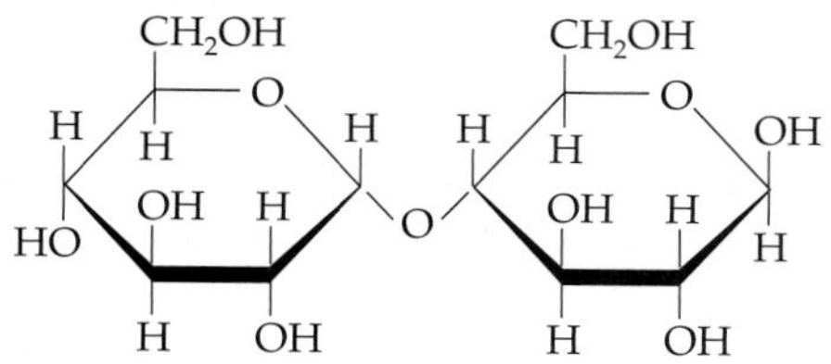

[Structure: two glucose rings (CH_2OH, O, H, OH, HO labels) joined through O]

β-Maltose

16.69 Milk

16.71 Eliminating milk and milk products from the diet

16.73 Lactose intolerance is the inability to produce the enzyme lactase that hydrolyzes the milk sugar lactose into its component monosaccharides, glucose and galactose.

16.75 A polymer is a very large molecule formed by the combination of many small molecules, called monomers.

16.77 Starch

16.79 Homopolysaccharides are a class of polysaccharides that are composed of a single monosaccharide.

16.81 Starch, glycogen, and cellulose are examples of homopolysaccharides. These homopolysaccharides are all made up of glucose.

16.83 The glucose units of amylose are joined by α (1 → 4) glycosidic bonds and those of cellulose are bonded together by β (1 → 4) glycosidic bonds.

16.85 Glycogen serves as a storage molecule for glucose.

16.87 The salivary glands and the pancreas

Chapter 17

17.1 a. $CH_3(CH_2)_7CH{=}CH(CH_2)_7COOH$
b. $CH_3(CH_2)_{10}COOH$
c. $CH_3(CH_2)_4CH{=}CH{-}CH_2{-}CH{=}CH(CH_2)_7COOH$
d. $CH_3(CH_2)_{16}COOH$

17.3

$$\underset{\text{Tetradecanoic acid}}{CH_3(CH_2)_{12}\overset{O}{\overset{\|}{C}}{-}OH} + \underset{\text{Ethanol}}{CH_3CH_2OH} \xrightarrow[\text{heat}]{H^+} \underset{\text{Ethyl tetradecanoate}}{CH_3(CH_2)_{12}\overset{O}{\overset{\|}{C}}{-}O{-}CH_2CH_3}$$

17.5

$$\underset{\text{Pentyl butanoate}}{CH_3CH_2CH_2\overset{O}{\overset{\|}{C}}{-}O{-}CH_2(CH_2)_3CH_3} \xrightarrow[\text{heat}]{H^+} \underset{\text{Butanoic acid}}{CH_3CH_2CH_2\overset{O}{\overset{\|}{C}}{-}OH} + \underset{\text{1-Pentanol}}{CH_3(CH_2)_3CH_2OH}$$

17.7

$$\underset{\text{Butyl acetate}}{CH_3\overset{O}{\overset{\|}{C}}{-}O{-}CH_2(CH_2)_2CH_3} + KOH \rightarrow \underset{\text{Potassium acetate}}{CH_3\overset{O}{\overset{\|}{C}}{-}O^-K^+} + \underset{\text{1-Butanol}}{CH_3(CH_2)_2CH_2OH}$$

17.9

$$\underset{\text{All } cis\text{-9,12,15-Octadecatrienoic acid}}{CH_3CH_2CH{=}CHCH_2CH{=}CHCH_2CH{=}CH(CH_2)_7COOH} + 3H_2 \xrightarrow{Ni} \underset{\text{Octadecanoic acid}}{CH_3(CH_2)_{16}COOH}$$

17.11 a.

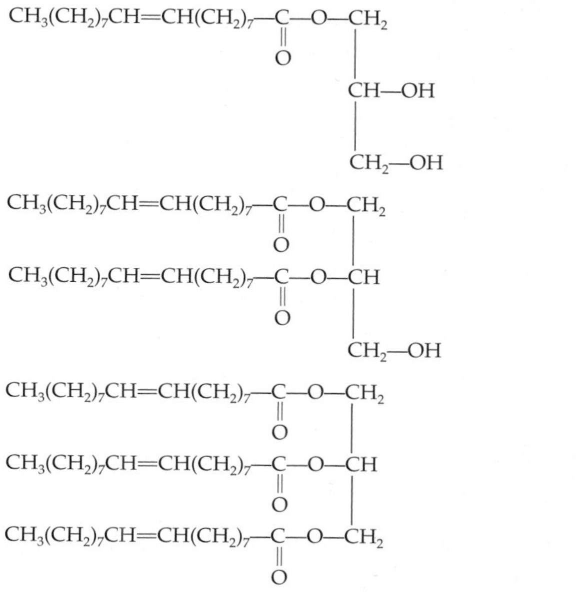

$$\begin{array}{l} CH_3(CH_2)_7CH{=}CH(CH_2)_7{-}\overset{O}{\overset{\|}{C}}{-}O{-}CH_2 \\ \qquad\qquad\qquad\qquad\qquad\qquad\quad |\\ \qquad\qquad\qquad\qquad\qquad\qquad\quad CH{-}OH \\ \qquad\qquad\qquad\qquad\qquad\qquad\quad |\\ \qquad\qquad\qquad\qquad\qquad\qquad\quad CH_2{-}OH \end{array}$$

$$\begin{array}{l} CH_3(CH_2)_7CH{=}CH(CH_2)_7{-}\overset{O}{\overset{\|}{C}}{-}O{-}CH_2 \\ CH_3(CH_2)_7CH{=}CH(CH_2)_7{-}\overset{O}{\overset{\|}{C}}{-}O{-}CH \\ \qquad\qquad\qquad\qquad\qquad\qquad\quad CH_2{-}OH \end{array}$$

$$\begin{array}{l} CH_3(CH_2)_7CH{=}CH(CH_2)_7{-}\overset{O}{\overset{\|}{C}}{-}O{-}CH_2 \\ CH_3(CH_2)_7CH{=}CH(CH_2)_7{-}\overset{O}{\overset{\|}{C}}{-}O{-}CH \\ CH_3(CH_2)_7CH{=}CH(CH_2)_7{-}\overset{O}{\overset{\|}{C}}{-}O{-}CH_2 \end{array}$$

b. $CH_3(CH_2)_8-C(=O)-O-CH_2$ / $CH-OH$ / CH_2-OH

$CH_3(CH_2)_8-C(=O)-O-CH_2$ / $CH_3(CH_2)_8-C(=O)-O-CH$ / CH_2-OH

$CH_3(CH_2)_8-C(=O)-O-CH_2$ / $CH_3(CH_2)_8-C(=O)-O-CH$ / $CH_3(CH_2)_8-C(=O)-O-CH_2$

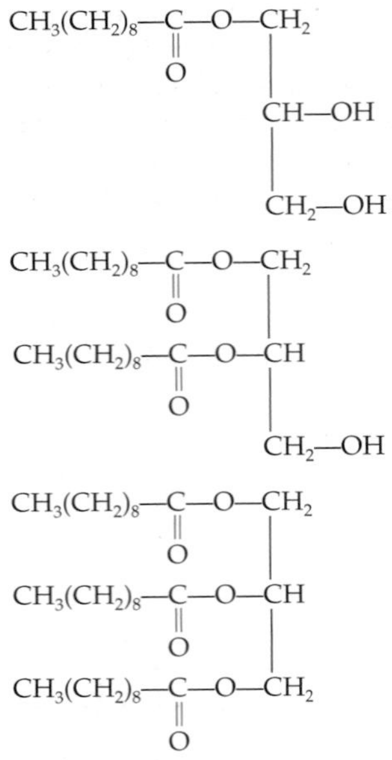

17.13

Rings A, B, C, D; carbons numbered 1–17

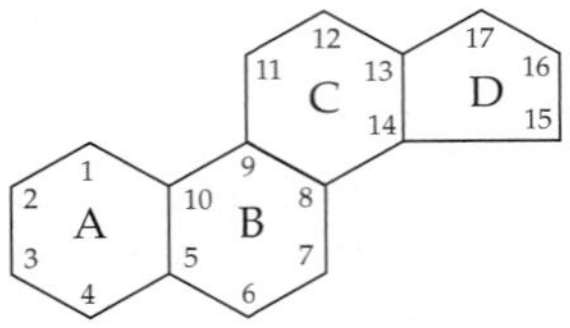

Steroid nucleus

17.15 Receptor-mediated endocytosis

17.17 Fatty acids, glycerides, nonglyceride lipids, and complex lipids

17.19 Lipid-soluble vitamins are transported into cells of the small intestine in association with dietary fat molecules. Thus, a diet low in fat reduces the amount of vitamins A, D, E, and K that enters the body.

17.21 A saturated fatty acid is one in which the hydrocarbon tail has only carbon-to-carbon single bonds. An unsaturated fatty acid has at least one carbon-to-carbon double bond.

17.23 The melting points increase.

17.25 The melting points of fatty acids increase as the length of the hydrocarbon chains increase. This is because the intermolecular attractive forces, including London dispersion forces, increase as the length of the hydrocarbon chain increases.

17.27 **a.** Decanoic acid $CH_3(CH_2)_8COOH$

b. Stearic acid $CH_3(CH_2)_{16}COOH$

17.29 **a.** IUPAC name: Hexadecanoic acid

Common name: Palmitic acid

b. IUPAC name: Dodecanoic acid

Common name: Lauric acid

17.31 Esterification of glycerol with three molecules of myristic acid:

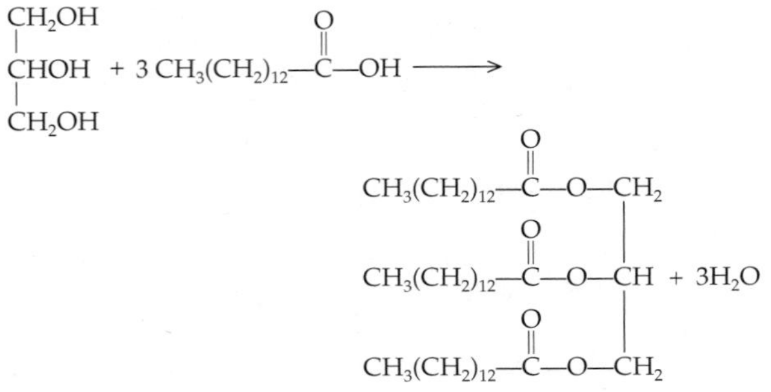

$$CH_2OH-CHOH-CH_2OH + 3\,CH_3(CH_2)_{12}-C(=O)-OH \longrightarrow$$

$$CH_3(CH_2)_{12}-C(=O)-O-CH_2 \,/\, CH_3(CH_2)_{12}-C(=O)-O-CH \,/\, CH_3(CH_2)_{12}-C(=O)-O-CH_2 + 3H_2O$$

17.33

$$H-C(H)-O-C(=O)-(CH_2)_7CH{=}CH(CH_2)_7CH_3$$
$$H-C-O-C(=O)-(CH_2)_7CH{=}CH(CH_2)_7CH_3 \quad + 3H_2O$$
$$H-C(H)-O-C(=O)-(CH_2)_7CH{=}CH(CH_2)_7CH_3$$

$\downarrow$ H^+, heat

$$H-C(H)-OH \quad + \quad HO-C(=O)-(CH_2)_7CH{=}CH(CH_2)_7CH_3$$
$$H-C-OH \quad + \quad HO-C(=O)-(CH_2)_7CH{=}CH(CH_2)_7CH_3$$
$$H-C(H)-OH \quad + \quad HO-C(=O)-(CH_2)_7CH{=}CH(CH_2)_7CH_3$$

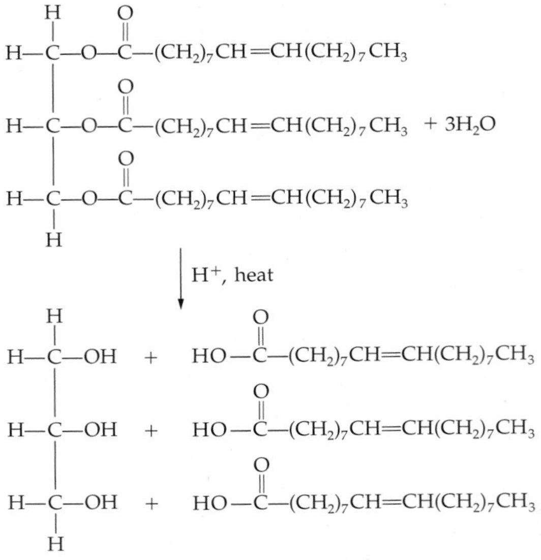

Glycerol   3 Oleic Acid Molecules

17.35

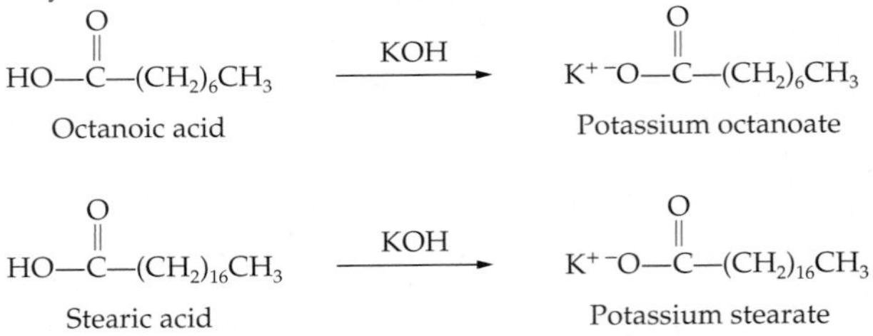

$$HO-C(=O)-(CH_2)_6CH_3 \xrightarrow{KOH} K^+\,{}^-O-C(=O)-(CH_2)_6CH_3$$

Octanoic acid   Potassium octanoate

$$HO-C(=O)-(CH_2)_{16}CH_3 \xrightarrow{KOH} K^+\,{}^-O-C(=O)-(CH_2)_{16}CH_3$$

Stearic acid   Potassium stearate

17.37 This line drawing of EPA shows the bends or "kinks" introduced into the molecule by the double bonds.

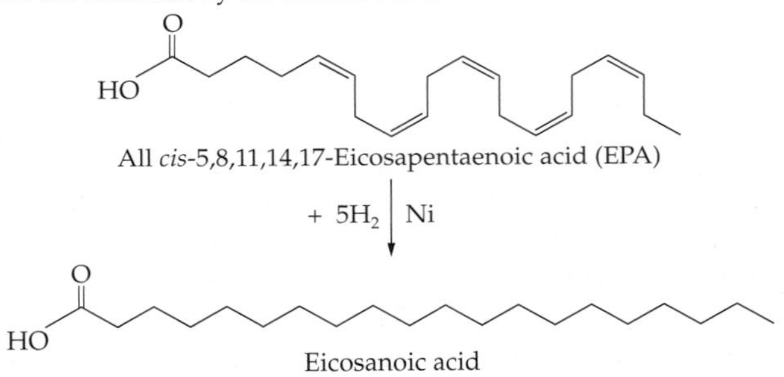

All *cis*-5,8,11,14,17-Eicosapentaenoic acid (EPA)

$\downarrow$ $+ 5H_2$ | Ni

Eicosanoic acid

17.39

$$H-C(H)-O-C(=O)-(CH_2)_{10}CH_3 \quad \text{Lauric acid}$$
$$H-C-O-C(=O)-(CH_2)_{16}CH_3 \quad \text{Stearic acid}$$
$$H-C(H)-O-C(=O)-(CH_2)_8CH_3 \quad \text{Capric acid}$$

$\downarrow$ NaOH

$$H-C(H)-OH \quad + \quad Na^{+\,-}O-C(=O)-(CH_2)_{10}CH_3$$
$$H-C-OH \quad + \quad Na^{+\,-}O-C(=O)-(CH_2)_{16}CH_3$$
$$H-C(H)-OH \quad + \quad Na^{+\,-}O-C(=O)-(CH_2)_8CH_3$$

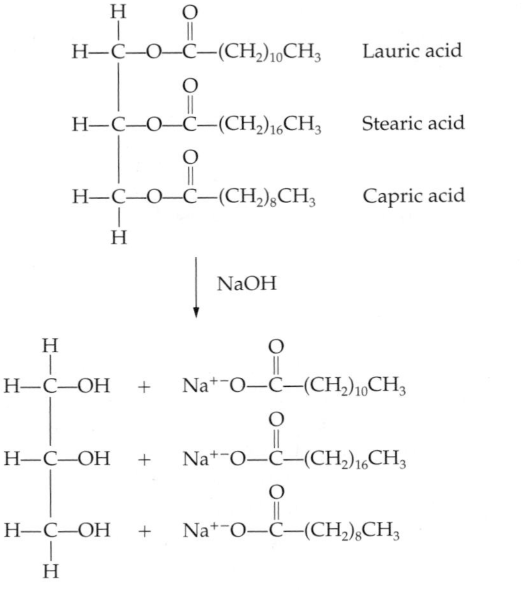

17.41

Glycerol $+$ $HO{-}C(=O){-}(CH_2)_8CH_3$ (Decanoic acid) $+$ $HO{-}C(=O){-}(CH_2)_{10}CH_3$ (Dodecanoic acid) $+$ $HO{-}C(=O){-}(CH_2)_{14}CH_3$ (Hexadecanoic acid)

$$\xrightarrow{H^+,\ heat}$$

$$CH_2{-}O{-}C(=O){-}(CH_2)_8CH_3$$
$$CH{-}O{-}C(=O){-}(CH_2)_{10}CH_3 \; + 3H_2O$$
$$CH_2{-}O{-}C(=O){-}(CH_2)_{14}CH_3$$

17.43 The essential fatty acid linoleic acid is required for the synthesis of arachidonic acid, a precursor for the synthesis of the prostaglandins, a group of hormonelike molecules.

17.45 Aspirin effectively decreases the inflammatory response by inhibiting the synthesis of all prostaglandins. Aspirin works by inhibiting cyclooxygenase, the first enzyme in prostaglandin biosynthesis. This inhibition results from the transfer of an acetyl group from aspirin to the enzyme. Because cyclooxygenase is found in all cells, synthesis of all prostaglandins is inhibited.

17.47 Smooth muscle contraction, enhancement of fever and swelling associated with the inflammatory response, bronchial dilation, inhibition of secretion of acid into the stomach.

17.49 The name of these fatty acids arises from the position of the double bond nearest the terminal *methyl group* of the molecule. The terminal methyl group is designated omega (ω). In ω-3 fatty acids the double bond nearest the ω methyl group is three carbons along the chain. In ω-6 fatty acids, the nearest double bond is six carbons from the end.

17.51 Omega-3 fatty acids reduce the risk of cardiovascular disease by decreasing blood clot formation, blood triglyceride levels, and growth of atherosclerotic plaque.

17.53 The decrease in blood clot formation, along with the reduced blood triglyceride levels and decreased atherosclerotic plaque result in improved arterial health. This, in turn, results in lower blood pressure and a decreased risk of sudden death and heart arrhythmias.

17.55 Omega-3 fatty acids are precursors of prostaglandins that exhibit anti-inflammatory effects. On the other hand, omega-6 fatty acids are precursors to prostaglandins that have inflammatory effects. To reduce the inflammatory response contribution to cardiovascular disease, it is logical to increase the amount of omega-3 fatty acids in the diet and to decrease the amount of omega-6 fatty acids.

17.57 A glyceride is a lipid ester that contains the glycerol molecule and from one to three fatty acids.

17.59 An emulsifying agent is a molecule that aids in the suspension of triglycerides in water. They are amphipathic molecules, such as lecithin, that serve as bridges holding together the highly polar water molecules and the nonpolar triglycerides.

17.61 A triglyceride with three saturated fatty acid tails would be a solid at room temperature. The long, straight fatty acid tails would stack with one another because of strong intermolecular and intramolecular London dispersion force attractions.

17.63

$$CH_3(CH_2)_{14}{-}C(=O){-}O{-}\overset{1}{C}H_2$$
$$CH_3(CH_2)_4CH_2{-}CH{=}CH{-}CH_2(CH_2)_6{-}C(=O){-}O{-}\overset{2}{C}H$$
$$CH_3(CH_2)_4CH_2{-}CH{=}CH{-}CH_2(CH_2)_6{-}C(=O){-}O{-}\overset{3}{C}H_2$$

(H and H on opposite sides of the C=C in the second chain; H and H on the same side in the third chain)

17.65

$$CH_3CH_2CH_2CH_2CH_2CH_2CH_2CH_2CH_2{-}C(=O){-}O{-}\overset{1}{C}H_2$$
$$CH_3CH_2CH_2CH_2CH_2CH_2CH_2CH_2CH_2CH_2CH_2{-}C(=O){-}O{-}\overset{2}{C}H$$
$$\overset{3}{C}H_2{-}O{-}P(=O)(O^-){-}O^-$$

17.67 Triglycerides consist of three fatty acids esterified to the three hydroxyl groups of glycerol. In phospholipids there are only two fatty acids esterified to glycerol. A phosphoryl group is esterified (phosphoester linkage) to the third hydroxyl group.

17.69 A sphingolipid is a lipid that is not derived from glycerol, but rather from sphingosine, a long-chain, nitrogen-containing (amino) alcohol. Like phospholipids, sphingolipids are amphipathic.

17.71 A glycosphingolipid or glycolipid is a lipid that is built on a ceramide backbone structure. Ceramide is a fatty acid derivative of sphingosine.

17.73 Sphingomyelins are important structural lipid components of nerve cell membranes. They are found in the myelin sheath that surrounds and insulates cells of the central nervous system.

17.75 Cholesterol is readily soluble in the hydrophobic region of biological membranes. It is involved in regulating the fluidity of the membrane.

17.77 Progesterone is the most important hormone associated with pregnancy. Testosterone is needed for development of male secondary sexual characteristics. Estrone is required for proper development of female secondary sexual characteristics.

17.79 Cortisone is used to treat rheumatoid arthritis, asthma, gastrointestinal disorders, and many skin conditions.

17.81 Myricyl palmitate (beeswax) is made up of the fatty acid palmitic acid and the alcohol myricyl alcohol—$CH_3(CH_2)_{28}CH_2OH$.

17.83 Isoprenoids are a large, diverse collection of lipids that are synthesized from the isoprene unit:

$$CH_2{=}C(CH_3){-}CH{=}CH_2$$

17.85 Steroids and bile salts, lipid-soluble vitamins, certain plant hormones, and chlorophyll

17.87 Chylomicrons, high-density lipoproteins, low-density lipoproteins, and very low density lipoproteins

17.89 The terms "good" and "bad" cholesterol refer to two classes of lipoprotein complexes. The high-density lipoproteins, or HDL, are considered to be "good" cholesterol because a correlation has been made between elevated levels of HDL and a reduced incidence of atherosclerosis. Low-density lipoproteins, or LDL, are considered to be "bad" cholesterol because evidence suggests that a high level of LDL is associated with increased risk of atherosclerosis.

17.91 Atherosclerosis results when cholesterol and other substances coat the arteries, causing a narrowing of the passageways. As the passageways become narrower, greater pressure is required to provide adequate blood flow. This results in higher blood pressure (hypertension).

17.93 If the LDL receptor is defective, it cannot function to remove cholesterol-bearing LDL particles from the blood. The excess cholesterol, along with other substances, will accumulate along the walls of the arteries, causing atherosclerosis.

17.95 The basic structure of a biological membrane is a bilayer of phospholipid molecules arranged so that the hydrophobic hydrocarbon tails are packed in the center and the hydrophilic head groups are exposed on the inner and outer surfaces.

17.97 A peripheral membrane protein is bound to only one surface of the membrane, either inside or outside the cell.

17.99 Cholesterol is freely soluble in the hydrophobic layer of a biological membrane. It moderates the fluidity of the membrane by disrupting the stacking of the fatty acid tails of membrane phospholipids.

17.101 Specific membrane proteins on human and mouse cells were labeled with red and green fluorescent dyes, respectively. The human and mouse cells were fused into single-celled hybrids and were observed using a microscope with an ultraviolet light source. The ultraviolet light caused the dyes to fluoresce. Initially the dyes were localized in regions of the membrane representing the original human or mouse cell. Within an hour, the proteins were evenly distributed throughout the membrane of the fused cell.

17.103 If the fatty acid tails of the membrane phospholipids are converted from saturated to unsaturated, the fluidity of the membrane will increase.

Chapter 18

18.1 **a.** Glycine (gly or G):

```
        COO⁻
        |
  H3⁺N—C—H
        |
        H
```

b. Proline (pro or P):

```
             COO⁻
             |
  H2⁺N———CH
   |         |
  H2C     CH2
      \ C /
        H2
```

c. Threonine (thr or T):

```
        COO⁻
        |
  H3⁺N—C—H
        |
     H—C—OH
        |
        CH3
```

d. Aspartate (asp or D):

```
        COO⁻
        |
  H3⁺N—C—H
        |
     H—C—H
        |
        COO⁻
```

e. Lysine (lys or K):

```
        COO⁻
        |
  H3⁺N—C—H
        |
     H—C—H
        |
     H—C—H
        |
     H—C—H
        |
     H—C—H
        |
        N⁺H3
```

18.3 **a.** Alanyl-phenylalanine:

```
        H  O  H  H
        |  ‖  |  |
  H3⁺N—C—C—N—C—COO⁻
        |        |
        CH3      CH2
                 |
               (C6H5)
```

b. Lysyl-alanine:

```
        H  O  H  H
        |  ‖  |  |
  H3⁺N—C—C—N—C—COO⁻
        |        |
        CH2      CH3
        |
        CH2
        |
        CH2
        |
        CH2
        |
        N⁺H3
```

c. Phenylalanyl-tyrosyl-leucine:

```
        H  O  H  H  O  H  H
        |  ‖  |  |  ‖  |  |
  H3⁺N—C—C—N—C—C—N—C—COO⁻
        |        |        |
        CH2      CH2      CH2
        |        |        |
      (C6H5)   (C6H4)     CHCH3
                 |        |
                 OH       CH3
```

18.5 The primary structure of a protein is the amino acid sequence of the protein chain. Regular, repeating folding of the peptide chain caused by hydrogen bonding between the amide nitrogens and carbonyl oxygens of the peptide bond is the secondary structure of a protein. The two most common types of secondary structure are the α-helix and the β-pleated sheet. Tertiary structure is the further folding of the regions of α-helix and β-pleated sheet into a compact, spherical structure. Formation and maintenance of the tertiary structure results from weak attractions between amino acid R groups. The binding of two or more peptides to produce a functional protein defines the quaternary structure.

18.7 Oxygen is efficiently transferred from hemoglobin to myoglobin in the muscle because myoglobin has a greater affinity for oxygen.

18.9 High temperature disrupts the hydrogen bonds and other weak interactions that maintain protein structure.

18.11 Vegetables vary in amino acid composition. No single vegetable can provide all of the amino acid requirements of the body.

By eating a variety of different vegetables, all the amino acid requirements of the human body can be met.

18.13 An enzyme is a protein that serves as a biological catalyst, speeding up biological reactions.

18.15 A transport protein is a protein that transports materials across the cell membrane or throughout the body.

18.17 Enzymes speed up reactions that might take days or weeks to occur on their own. They also catalyze reactions that might require very high temperatures or harsh conditions if carried out in the laboratory. In the body, these reactions occur quickly under physiological conditions.

18.19 Transferrin is a transport protein that carries iron from the liver to the bone marrow, where it is used to produce the heme group for hemoglobin and myoglobin. Hemoglobin transports oxygen in the blood.

18.21 Egg albumin is a nutrient protein that serves as a source of protein for the developing chick. Casein is the nutrient storage protein in milk, providing protein, a source of amino acids, for mammals.

18.23 The general structure of an L-α-amino acid has a carbon in the center that is referred to as the alpha carbon. Bonded to the alpha carbon are an amino group, a carboxyl group, a hydrogen atom, and a side chain, R.

COO^-
$H_3^+N—C—H$
R

18.25 A zwitterion is a neutral molecule with equal numbers of positive and negative charges. Under physiological conditions, amino acids are zwitterions.

18.27 A chiral carbon is one that has four different atoms or groups of atoms attached to it.

18.29 Interactions between the R groups of the amino acids in a polypeptide chain are important for the formation and maintenance of the tertiary and quaternary structures of proteins.

18.31

L-Serine: COO^- / $H_3^+N—C—H$ / CH_2 / OH

L-Threonine: COO^- / $H_3^+N—C—H$ / H—C—OH / CH_3

L-Cysteine: COO^- / $H_3^+N—C—H$ / CH_2 / SH

L-Tyrosine: COO^- / $H_3^+N—C—H$ / CH_2 / (benzene ring) / OH

L-Asparagine: COO^- / $H_3^+N—C—H$ / CH_2 / C(=O)NH_2

L-Glutamine: COO^- / $H_3^+N—C—H$ / CH_2 / CH_2 / C(=O)NH_2

18.33 A peptide bond is an amide bond between two amino acids in a peptide chain.

18.35 Linus Pauling and his colleagues carried out X-ray diffraction studies of protein. Interpretation of the pattern formed when X-rays were diffracted by a crystal of pure protein led Pauling to conclude that peptide bonds are both planar (flat) and rigid and that the N—C bonds are shorter than expected. In other words, they deduced that the peptide bond has a partial double bond character because it exhibits resonance. There is no free rotation about the amide bond because the carbonyl group of the amide bond has a strong attraction for the amide nitrogen lone pair of electrons. This can best be described using a resonance model:

[R—C(=Ö:)—N̈(H)—R′ ⟷ R—C(—Ö:⁻)=N⁺(H)—R′]

The partially double bonded character of the resonance structure restricts free rotation.

18.37

a. $H_3^+N—CH(CH_2C_6H_5)—C(=O)—N(H)—CH(CH(CH_3)—CH_3)—C(=O)—N(H)—CH(CH_2C_6H_4OH)—C(=O)—O^-$

b. $H_3^+N—CH(CH_3)—C(=O)—N(H)—CH(CH_2CH_2C(=O)O^-)—C(=O)—N(H)—CH(CH_2SH)—C(=O)—O^-$

c. $H_3^+N—CH(CH_2C(=O)NH_2)—C(=O)—N(H)—CH(CH_2CH(CH_3)CH_3)—C(=O)—N(H)—CH(H)—C(=O)—O^-$

18.39 The primary structure of a protein is the sequence of amino acids bonded to one another by peptide bonds.

18.41 The primary structure of a protein determines its three-dimensional shape and biological function because the location of R groups along the protein chain is determined by the primary structure. The interactions among the R groups, based on their location in the chain, will govern how the protein folds. This, in turn, dictates its three-dimensional structure and biological function.

18.43

$H_3^+N—CH(CH_2—CH(CH_3)—CH_3)—C(=O)—O^-$ + $H_3^+N—CH(CH_2CH_2CH_2—NH—C(=NH_2^+)—NH_2)—C(=O)—O^-$ ⟶ $H_3^+N—CH(CH_2—CH(CH_3)—CH_3)—C(=O)—N(H)—CH(CH_2CH_2CH_2—NH—C(=NH_2^+)—NH_2)—C(=O)—O^-$ + H_2O

18.45 The secondary structure of a protein is the folding of the primary structure into an α-helix or β-pleated sheet.

18.47 **a.** α-Helix

b. β-Pleated sheet

18.49 A fibrous protein is one that is composed of peptides arranged in long sheets or fibers.

18.51 A parallel β-pleated sheet is one in which the hydrogen bonded peptide chains have their amino-termini aligned head-to-head.

18.53 The tertiary structure of a protein is the globular, three-dimensional structure of a protein that results from folding the regions of secondary structure.

18.55

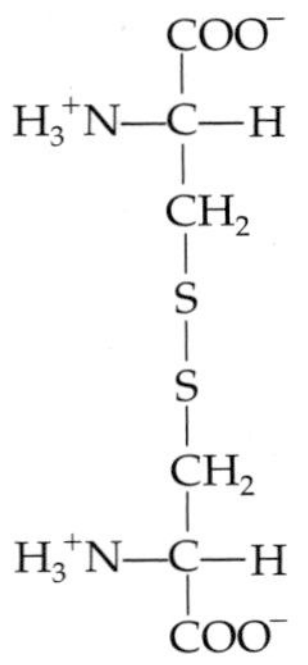

$$\begin{array}{c} COO^- \\ | \\ H_3^+N-C-H \\ | \\ CH_2 \\ | \\ S \\ | \\ S \\ | \\ CH_2 \\ | \\ H_3^+N-C-H \\ | \\ COO^- \end{array}$$

18.57 The tertiary structure is a level of folding of a protein chain that has already undergone secondary folding. The regions of α-helix and β-pleated sheet are folded into a globular structure.

18.59 Quaternary protein structure is the aggregation of two or more folded peptide chains to produce a functional protein.

18.61 A glycoprotein is a protein with covalently attached sugars.

18.63 Hydrogen bonding maintains the secondary structure of a protein and contributes to the stability of the tertiary and quaternary levels of structure.

18.65 The peptide bond exhibits resonance, which results in a partially double bonded character. This causes the rigidity of the peptide bond.

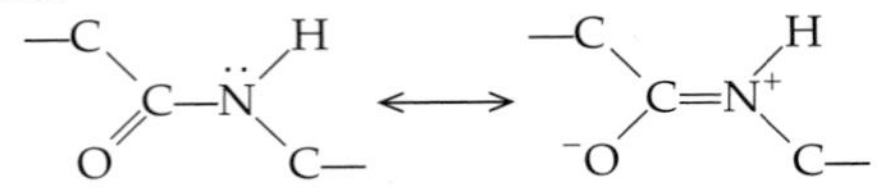

$$-C-C(=O)-\ddot{N}(H)-C- \longleftrightarrow -C-C(-O^-)=N^+(H)-C-$$

18.67 The code for the primary structure of a protein is carried in the genetic information (DNA).

18.69 The function of hemoglobin is to carry oxygen from the lungs to oxygen-demanding tissues throughout the body. Hemoglobin is found in red blood cells.

18.71 Hemoglobin is a protein composed of four subunits—two α-globin and two β-globin subunits. Each subunit holds a heme group, which in turn carries an Fe^{2+} ion.

18.73 The function of the heme group in hemoglobin and myoglobin is to bind to molecular oxygen.

18.75 Because carbon monoxide binds tightly to the heme groups of hemoglobin, it is not easily removed or replaced by oxygen. As a result, the effects of oxygen deprivation (suffocation) occur.

18.77 When sickle cell hemoglobin (HbS) is deoxygenated, the amino acid valine fits into a hydrophobic pocket on the surface of another HbS molecule. Many such sickle cell hemoglobin molecules polymerize into long rods that cause the red blood cell to sickle. In normal hemoglobin, glutamic acid is found in the place of the valine. This negatively charged amino acid will not "fit" into the hydrophobic pocket.

18.79 When individuals have one copy of the sickle cell gene and one copy of the normal gene, they are said to carry the sickle cell trait. These individuals will not suffer serious side effects, but may pass the trait to their offspring. Individuals with two copies of the sickle cell globin gene exhibit all the symptoms of the disease and are said to have sickle cell anemia.

18.81 Albumin

18.83 Albumin in the blood can serve as a carrier for Ca^{2+} because it contains acidic amino acids. The negative charges in the acidic amino acids can form salt bridges (or ionic bonds) with Ca^{2+}. Albumin can also serve as a carrier for fatty acids because it contains basic amino acids. The positive charges in the basic amino acids can form salt bridges with the anionic fatty acids.

18.85 Denaturation is the process by which the organized structure of a protein is disrupted, resulting in a completely disorganized, nonfunctional form of the protein.

18.87 Heat is an effective means of sterilization because it destroys the proteins of microbial life-forms, including fungi, bacteria, and viruses.

18.89 The low pH of the yogurt denatures the proteins of microbial contaminants, inhibiting their growth.

18.91 An essential amino acid is one that must be provided in the diet because it cannot be synthesized in the body.

18.93 A complete protein is one that contains all of the essential and nonessential amino acids.

18.95 Chymotrypsin catalyzes the hydrolysis of peptide bonds on the carbonyl side of aromatic amino acids.

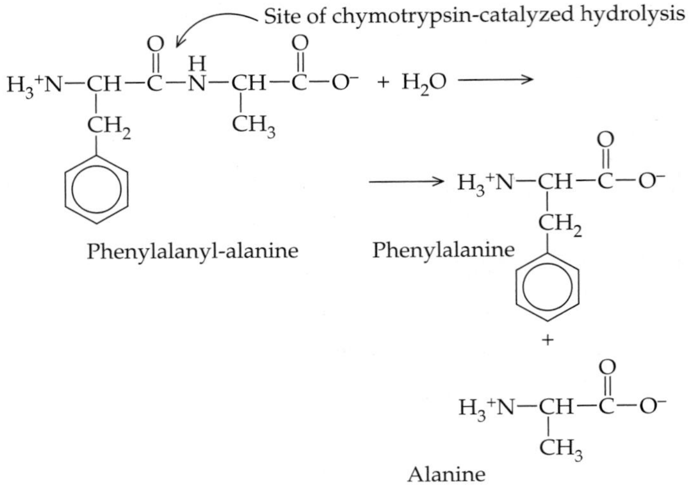

Site of chymotrypsin-catalyzed hydrolysis

$$H_3^+N-CH(CH_2C_6H_5)-C(=O)-NH-CH(CH_3)-C(=O)-O^- + H_2O \longrightarrow$$

Phenylalanyl-alanine

$$\longrightarrow H_3^+N-CH(CH_2C_6H_5)-C(=O)-O^- + H_3^+N-CH(CH_3)-C(=O)-O^-$$

Phenylalanine + Alanine

18.97 In a vegetarian diet, vegetables are the only source of dietary protein. Because individual vegetable sources do not provide all the needed amino acids, vegetables must be mixed to provide all the essential and nonessential amino acids in the amounts required for biosynthesis.

18.99 Synthesis of digestive enzymes must be carefully controlled because the active enzyme would digest, and thus destroy, the cell that produces it.

Chapter 19

19.1 **a.** Pyruvate kinase catalyzes the transfer of a phosphoryl group from phosphoenolpyruvate to adenosine diphosphate.

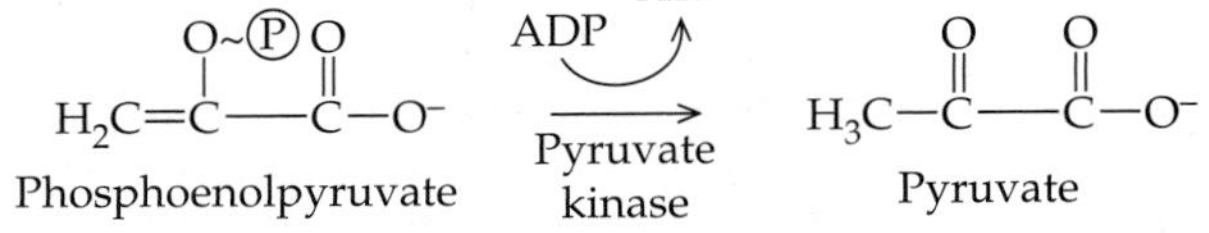

$$H_2C=C(O\sim P)-C(=O)-O^- \xrightarrow[\text{Pyruvate kinase}]{ADP \rightarrow ATP} H_3C-C(=O)-C(=O)-O^-$$

Phosphoenolpyruvate → Pyruvate

b. Alanine transaminase catalyzes the transfer of an amino group from alanine to α-ketoglutarate, producing pyruvate and glutamate.

$H_3^+N-CH(CH_3)-COO^-$ (Alanine) + $^-OOC-CH_2-CH_2-CO-COO^-$ (α-Ketoglutarate) $\xrightarrow{\text{Alanine transaminase}}$ $H_3C-CO-COO^-$ (Pyruvate) + $H_3^+N-CH(COO^-)-CH_2-CH_2-COO^-$ (Glutamate)

Alanine

Alanine transaminase

Pyruvate

α-Ketoglutarate

Glutamate

c. Triose phosphate isomerase catalyzes the isomerization of the ketone dihydroxyacetone phosphate to the aldehyde glyceraldehyde-3-phosphate.

$H_2C(O{\sim}P)-CO-CH_2OH$ $\xrightarrow{\text{Triose phosphate isomerase}}$ $H_2C(O{\sim}P)-CH(OH)-CHO$

Dihydroxyacetone phosphate — Glyceraldehyde-3-phosphate

d. Pyruvate dehydrogenase catalyzes the oxidation and decarboxylation of pyruvate, producing acetyl coenzyme A and CO_2.

$H_3C-CO-COO^-$ (Pyruvate) + H-S-CoA (Coenzyme A) $\xrightarrow{\text{Pyruvate dehydrogenase}}$ $H_3C-CO{\sim}S\text{-}CoA + CO_2$ (Acetyl coenzyme A)

19.3 a. Sucrose
b. Pyruvate
c. Succinate

19.5 The induced fit model assumes that the enzyme is flexible. Both the enzyme and the substrate are able to change shape to form the enzyme-substrate complex. The lock-and-key model assumes that the enzyme is inflexible (the lock) and the substrate (the key) fits into a specific rigid site (the active site) on the enzyme to form the enzyme-substrate complex.

19.7 An enzyme might distort a bond, thereby catalyzing bond breakage. An enzyme could bring two reactants into close proximity and in the proper orientation for the reaction to occur. Finally, an enzyme could alter the pH of the microenvironment of the active site, thereby serving as a transient donor or acceptor of H^+.

19.9 Water-soluble vitamins are required by the body for the synthesis of coenzymes that are required for the function of a variety of enzymes.

19.11 A decrease in pH will change the degree of ionization of the R groups within a peptide chain. This disturbs the weak interactions that maintain the structure of an enzyme, which may denature the enzyme. Less drastic alterations in the charge of R groups in the active site of the enzyme can inhibit enzyme-substrate binding or destroy the catalytic ability of the active site.

19.13 Irreversible inhibitors bind very tightly, sometimes even covalently, to an R group in enzyme active sites. They generally inhibit many different enzymes. The loss of enzyme activity impairs normal cellular metabolism, resulting in death of the cell or the individual.

19.15 A structural analog is a molecule that has a structure and charge distribution very similar to that of the natural substrate of an enzyme. Generally they are able to bind to the enzyme active site. This inhibits enzyme activity because the normal substrate must compete with the structural analog to form an enzyme-substrate complex.

19.17 a. Bond cleaved by chymotrypsin (the peptide bond after phe)

$H_3N^+-CH(CH_3)-CO-NH-CH(CH_2C_6H_5)-CO{\downarrow}-NH-CH(CH_3)-COO^-$

ala-phe-ala

b. Bond cleaved by chymotrypsin (the peptide bond after the first tyr)

$H_3N^+-CH(CH_2C_6H_4OH)-CO{\downarrow}-NH-CH(CH_3)-CO-NH-CH(CH_2C_6H_4OH)-COO^-$

tyr-ala-tyr

19.19 Chymotrypsin Elastase Elastase

$H_3^+N-CH(CH(CH_3)_2)-CO-NH-CH(CH_2C_6H_5)-CO{\downarrow}-NH-CH(CH_3)-CO{\downarrow}-NH-CH_2-CO{\downarrow}-NH-CH(CH_2-CH(CH_3)_2)-COO^-$

19.21 The common name of an enzyme is often derived from the name of the substrate and/or the type of reaction that it catalyzes.

19.23 1. Urease
2. Peroxidase
3. Lipase
4. Aspartase
5. Glucose-6-phosphatase
6. Sucrase

19.25 a. Citrate decarboxylase catalyzes the cleavage of a carboxyl group from citrate.
b. Adenosine diphosphate phosphorylase catalyzes the addition of a phosphate group to ADP.
c. Oxalate reductase catalyzes the reduction of oxalate.
d. Nitrite oxidase catalyzes the oxidation of nitrite.
e. *cis-trans* Isomerase catalyzes interconversion of *cis* and *trans* isomers.

19.27 A substrate is the reactant in an enzyme-catalyzed reaction that binds to the active site of the enzyme and is converted into product.

19.29 The activation energy of a reaction is the energy required for the reaction to occur.

19.31 The equilibrium constant for a chemical reaction is a reflection of the difference in energy of the reactants and products.
Consider the following reaction:

$$aA + bB \rightarrow cC + dD$$

The equilibrium constant for this reaction is:

$$K_{eq} = [D]^d[C]^c/[A]^a[B]^b = [\text{products}]/[\text{reactants}]$$

Because the difference in energy between reactants and products is the same regardless of what path the reaction takes, an enzyme does not alter the equilibrium constant of a reaction.

19.33 The rate of an uncatalyzed chemical reaction typically doubles every time the substrate concentration is doubled.

19.35 The rate-limiting step is that step in an enzyme-catalyzed reaction that is the slowest, and hence limits the speed with which the substrate can be converted into product.

19.37

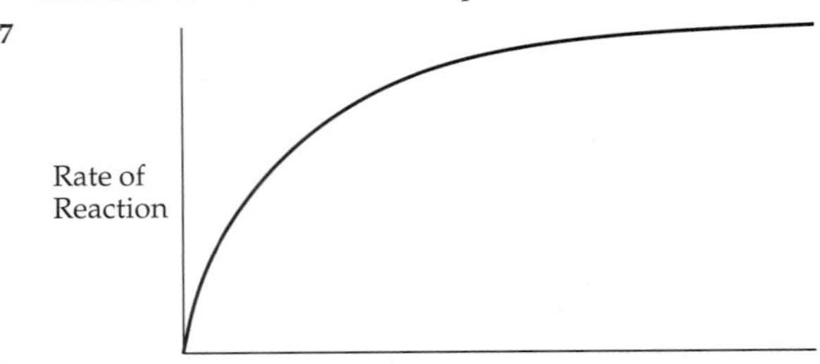

19.39 The enzyme-substrate complex is the molecular aggregate formed when the substrate binds to the active site of an enzyme.

19.41 The catalytic groups of an enzyme active site are those functional groups that are involved in carrying out catalysis.

19.43 Enzyme active sites are pockets in the surface of an enzyme that include R groups involved in binding and R groups involved in catalysis. The shape of the active site is complementary to the shape of the substrate. Thus, the conformation of the active site determines the specificity of the enzyme. Enzyme-substrate binding involves weak, noncovalent interactions.

19.45 The lock-and-key model of enzyme-substrate binding was proposed by Emil Fischer in 1894. He thought that the active site was a rigid region of the enzyme into which the substrate fit perfectly. Thus, the model purports that the substrate simply snaps into place within the active site, like two pieces of a jigsaw puzzle fitting together.

19.47 Enzyme specificity is the ability of an enzyme to bind to only one, or a very few, substrates and thus catalyze only a single reaction.

19.49 Group specificity means that an enzyme catalyzes reactions involving similar molecules having the same functional group.

19.51 Absolute specificity means that an enzyme catalyzes the reaction of only one substrate.

19.53 Hexokinase has group specificity. The advantage is that the cell does not need to encode many enzymes to carry out the phosphorylation of six-carbon sugars. Hexokinase can carry out many of these reactions.

19.55 Methionyl tRNA synthetase has absolute specificity. This is the enzyme that attaches the amino acid methionine to the transfer RNA (tRNA) that will carry the amino acid to the site of protein synthesis. If the wrong amino acid were attached to the tRNA, it could be incorporated into the protein, destroying its correct three-dimensional structure and biological function.

19.57 The first step of an enzyme-catalyzed reaction is the formation of the enzyme-substrate complex. In the second step, the transition state is formed. This is the state in which the substrate assumes a form intermediate between the original substrate and the product. In step 3 the substrate is converted to product and the enzyme-product complex is formed. Step 4 involves the release of the product and regeneration of the enzyme in its original form.

19.59 In a reaction involving bond breaking, the enzyme might distort a bond, producing a transition state in which the bond is stressed. An enzyme could bring two reactants into close proximity and in the proper orientation for the reaction to occur, producing a transition state in which the proximity of the reactants facilitates bond formation. Finally, an enzyme could alter the pH of the microenvironment of the active site, thereby serving as a transient donor or acceptor of H^+.

19.61 A cofactor helps maintain the shape of the active site of an enzyme.

19.63 Thiamine (B_1) is found in the coenzyme thiamine pyrophosphate. Riboflavin (B_2) is found in both flavin mononucleotide and flavin adenine dinucleotide. Niacin (B_3) is found in both nicotinamide adenine dinucleotide and nicotinamide adenine dinucleotide phosphate. Pyridoxine (B_6) is found in both pyridoxal phosphate and pyridoxamine phosphate. Cyanocobalamin (B_{12}) is found in deoxyadenosyl cobalamin. Folic acid is found in tetrahydrofolic acid. Pantothenic acid is found in coenzyme A. Biotin is found in biocytin.

19.65 At the temperature optimum, the enzyme is functioning optimally and the rate of the reaction is maximal. Above the temperature optimum, increasing temperature begins to denature the enzyme and stop the reaction.

19.67 Each of the following answers assumes that the enzyme was purified from an organism with optimal conditions for life near 37°C, pH 7.

a. Decreasing the temperature from 37°C to 10°C will cause the rate of an enzyme-catalyzed reaction to decrease because the frequency of collisions between enzyme and substrate will decrease as the rate of molecular movement decreases.

b. Increasing the pH from 7 to 11 will generally cause a decrease in the rate of an enzyme-catalyzed reaction. In fact, most enzymes would be denatured by a pH of 11 and enzyme activity would cease.

c. Heating an enzyme from 37°C to 100°C will destroy enzyme activity because the enzyme would be denatured by the extreme heat.

19.69 High temperature denatures bacterial enzymes and structural proteins. Because the life of the cell is dependent on the function of these proteins, the cell dies.

19.71 A lysosome is a membrane-bound vesicle in the cytoplasm of cells that contains approximately fifty hydrolytic enzymes. Some of the enzymes in the lysosomes can degrade proteins to amino acids, others hydrolyze polysaccharides into monosaccharides, and some degrade lipids and nucleic acids. The lysosome contains these enzymes to prevent degradation of large biological molecules that are important to maintain cell integrity.

19.73 Enzymes used for clinical assays in hospitals are typically stored at refrigerator temperatures to ensure that they are not denatured by heat. In this way they retain their activity for long periods.

19.75 **a.** Cells regulate the level of enzyme activity to conserve energy. It is a waste of cellular energy to produce an enzyme if its substrate is not present or if its product is in excess.

b. Production of proteolytic digestive enzymes must be carefully controlled because the active enzyme could destroy the cell that produces it. Thus, they are produced in an inactive form in the cell and are only activated at the site where they carry out digestion.

19.77 In positive allosterism, binding of the effector molecule turns the enzyme on. In negative allosterism, binding of the effector molecule turns the enzyme off.

19.79 A proenzyme is the inactive form of an enzyme that is converted to the active form at the site of its activity.

19.81 Blood clotting is a critical protective mechanism in the body, preventing excessive loss of blood following an injury. However, it can be a dangerous mechanism if it is triggered inappropriately. The resulting clot could cause a heart attack or stroke. By having a cascade of proteolytic reactions leading to the final formation of the clot, there are many steps at which the process can be regulated. This ensures that it will only be activated under the appropriate conditions.

19.83 Competitive enzyme inhibition occurs when a structural analog of the normal substrate occupies the enzyme active site so that the reaction cannot occur. The structural analog and the normal substrate compete for the active site. Thus, the rate of the reaction will depend on the relative concentrations of the two molecules.

19.85 A structural analog has a shape and charge distribution that are very similar to those of the normal substrate for an enzyme.

19.87 Irreversible inhibitors bind tightly to and block the active site of an enzyme and eliminate catalysis at the site.

19.89 The compound would be a competitive inhibitor of the enzyme.

19.91 A proteolytic enzyme catalyzes the cleavage of the peptide bond that maintains the primary protein structure.

19.93 The structural similarities among chymotrypsin, trypsin, and elastase suggest that these enzymes evolved from a single ancestral gene that was duplicated. Each copy then evolved independently.

19.95

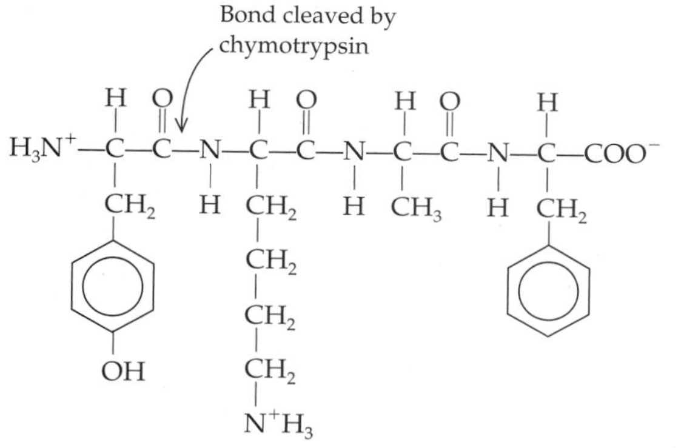

Bond cleaved by chymotrypsin

tyr-lys-ala-phe

19.97 Elastase will cleave the peptide bonds on the carbonyl side of alanine and glycine. Trypsin will cleave the peptide bonds on the carbonyl side of lysine and arginine. Chymotrypsin will cleave the peptide bonds on the carbonyl side of tryptophan and phenylalanine.

19.99 Analysis of blood serum for levels of certain enzymes can confirm a preliminary diagnosis that was made based on disease symptoms or a clinical picture. When cells die, they release their enzymes into the bloodstream. Enzyme assays can measure amounts of certain enzymes in the blood.

19.101 Creatine kinase-MB and aspartate aminotransferase (AST/SGOT)

19.103 Urease is used in the clinical analysis of urea in blood. In a test called the blood urea nitrogen test (BUN), urea is converted to ammonia using the enzyme urease; the ammonia becomes an indicator of urea. This allows for the levels of urea to be measured. This measurement is useful in the diagnosis of kidney malfunction.

Chapter 20

20.1 **a.** Adenosine diphosphate:

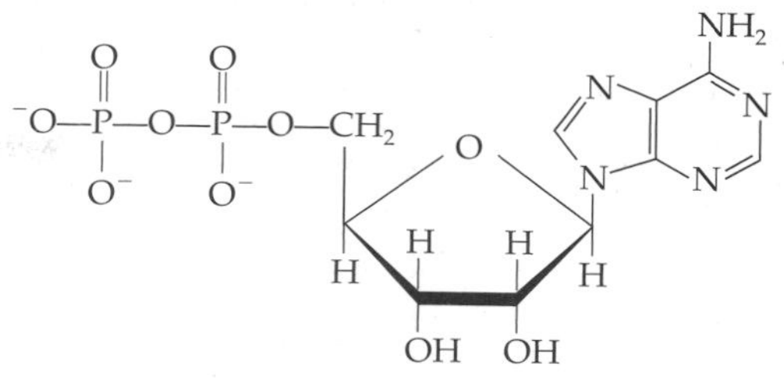

b. Deoxyguanosine triphosphate:

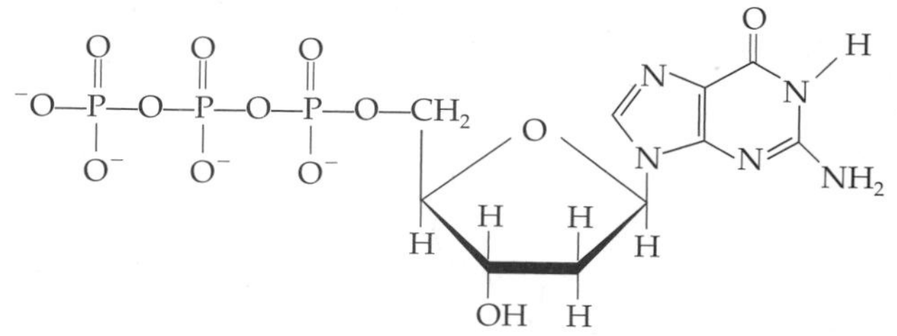

20.3 The RNA polymerase recognizes the promoter site for a gene, separates the strands of DNA, and catalyzes the polymerization of an RNA strand complementary to the DNA strand that carries the genetic code for a protein. It recognizes a termination site at the end of the gene and releases the RNA molecule.

20.5 The genetic code is said to be degenerate because several different triplet codons may serve as code words for a single amino acid.

20.7 The nitrogenous bases of the codons are complementary to those of the anticodons. As a result they are able to hydrogen bond to one another according to the base pairing rules.

20.9 The ribosomal P-site holds the peptidyl tRNA during protein synthesis. The peptidyl tRNA is the tRNA carrying the growing peptide chain. The only exception to this is during initiation of translation when the P-site holds the initiator tRNA.

20.11 The normal mRNA sequence, AUG-CCC-GAC-UUU, would encode the peptide sequence methionine-proline-aspartate-phenylalanine. The mutant mRNA sequence, AUG-CGC-GAC-UUU, would encode the mutant peptide sequence methionine-arginine-aspartate-phenylalanine. This would not be a silent mutation because a hydrophobic amino acid (proline) has been replaced by a positively charged amino acid (arginine).

20.13 A heterocyclic amine is a compound that contains nitrogen in at least one position of the ring skeleton.

20.15 It is the N-9 of the purine that forms the *N*-glycosidic bond with C-1 of the five-carbon sugar. The general structure of the purine ring is shown below:

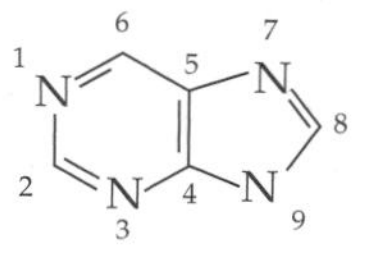

20.17 The ATP nucleotide is composed of the five-carbon sugar ribose, the purine adenine, and a triphosphate group.

20.19 The two strands of DNA in the double helix are said to be antiparallel because they run in opposite directions. One strand progresses in the $5' \rightarrow 3'$ direction, and the opposite strand progresses in the $3' \rightarrow 5'$ direction.

20.21 The DNA double helix is 2 nm in width. The nitrogenous bases are stacked at a distance of 0.34 nm from one another. One complete turn of the helix is 3.4 nm, or 10 base pairs.

20.23

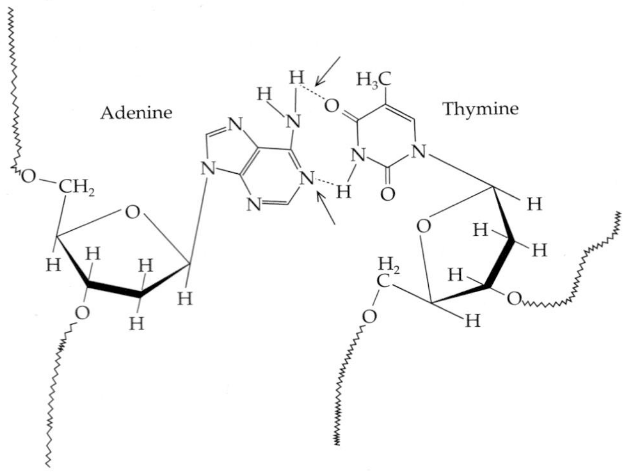

20.25

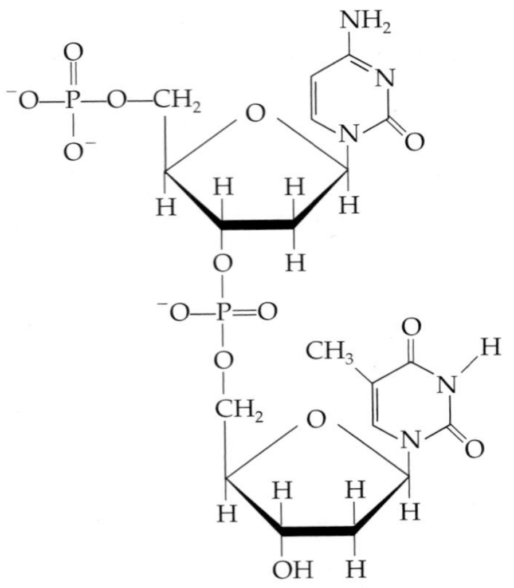

20.27 The prokaryotic chromosome is a circular DNA molecule that is supercoiled, that is, the helix is coiled on itself.

20.29 The term semiconservative DNA replication refers to the fact that each parental DNA strand serves as the template for the synthesis of a daughter strand. As a result, each of the daughter DNA molecules is made up of one strand of the original parental DNA and one strand of newly synthesized DNA.

20.31 The two primary functions of DNA polymerase III are to read a template DNA strand and catalyze the polymerization of a new daughter strand, and to proofread the newly synthesized strand and correct any errors by removing the incorrectly inserted nucleotide and adding the proper one.

20.33 3′-TACGGGCTCGACTAACTAGTCT-5′

20.35 The replication origin of a DNA molecule is the unique sequence on the DNA molecule where DNA replication begins.

20.37 The enzyme helicase separates the strands of DNA at the origin of DNA replication so that the proteins involved in replication can interact with the nitrogenous base pairs.

20.39 The RNA primer "primes" DNA replication by providing a 3′—OH which can be used by DNA polymerase III for the addition of the next nucleotide in the growing DNA chain.

20.41 DNA → RNA → Protein

20.43 Anticodons are found on transfer RNA molecules.

20.45 3′-AUGCCCGUAUCCGGAAUUUCGAUCGAA-5′

20.47 RNA splicing is the process by which the noncoding sequences (introns) of the primary transcript of a eukaryotic mRNA are removed and the protein coding sequences (exons) are spliced together.

20.49 Messenger RNA, transfer RNA, and ribosomal RNA

20.51 Spliceosomes are small ribonucleoprotein complexes that carry out RNA splicing.

20.53 The poly(A) tail is a stretch of 100–200 adenosine nucleotides polymerized onto the 3′ end of a mRNA by the enzyme poly(A) polymerase.

20.55 The cap structure is made up of the nucleotide 7-methylguanosine attached to the 5′ end of a mRNA by a 5′-5′ triphosphate bridge. Generally the first two nucleotides of the mRNA are also methylated.

20.57 Sixty-four

20.59 The reading frame of a gene is the sequential set of triplet codons that carries the genetic code for the primary structure of a protein.

20.61 Methionine and tryptophan

20.63 The codon 5′-UUU-3′ encodes the amino acid phenylalanine. The mutant codon 5′-UUA-3′ encodes the amino acid leucine. Both leucine and phenylalanine are hydrophobic amino acids, however, leucine has a smaller R group. It is possible that the smaller R group would disrupt the structure of the protein.

20.65 The ribosomes serve as a platform on which protein synthesis can occur. They also carry the enzymatic activity that forms peptide bonds.

20.67 5′-AUG GCU GGG CUU UGU AUG UGG UAU UCU AUU GGG UAA-3′

20.69 The sequence of DNA nucleotides in a gene is transcribed to produce a complementary sequence of RNA nucleotides in a messenger RNA (mRNA). In the process of translation the sequence of the mRNA is read sequentially in words of three nucleotides (codons) to produce a protein. Each codon calls for the addition of a particular amino acid to the growing peptide chain. If one of those codons has been altered by mutation, it may now call for the addition of the wrong amino acid to the growing peptide chain. This could result in improper folding of the protein and in loss of biological function.

20.71 An ester bond

20.73 A point mutation is the substitution of one nucleotide pair for another in a gene.

20.75 Some mutations are silent because the change in the nucleotide sequence does not alter the amino acid sequence of the protein. This can happen because there are many amino acids encoded by multiple codons.

20.77 UV light causes the formation of pyrimidine dimers, the covalent bonding of two adjacent pyrimidine bases. Mutations occur when the UV damage repair system makes an error during the repair process. This causes a change in the nucleotide sequence of the DNA.

20.79 **a.** A carcinogen is a compound that causes cancer. Cancers are caused by mutations in the genes responsible for controlling cell division.

b. Carcinogens cause DNA damage that results in changes in the nucleotide sequence of the gene. Thus, carcinogens are also mutagens.

20.81 A restriction enzyme is a bacterial enzyme that "cuts" the sugar–phosphate backbone of DNA molecules at a specific nucleotide sequence.

20.83 A selectable marker is a genetic trait that can be used to detect the presence of a plasmid in a bacterium. Many plasmids have antibiotic resistance genes as selectable markers. Bacteria containing the plasmid will be able to grow in the presence of the antibiotic; those without the plasmid will be killed.

20.85 Human insulin, interferon, human growth hormone, and human blood clotting factor VIII

20.87 4096 copies

20.89 The goals of the Human Genome Project were to identify and map all of the genes of the human genome and to determine the DNA sequences of the complete three billion nucleotide pairs.

20.91 A genome library is a set of clones that represents all of the DNA sequences in the genome of an organism.

20.93 A dideoxynucleotide is one that has hydrogen atoms rather than hydroxyl groups bonded to both the 2′ and 3′ carbons of the five-carbon sugar.

20.95 Sequences that these DNA sequences have in common are highlighted in bold.

a. 5′-**AGCTCCT**GATTTCATACAGTTTCTACT**ACCTACTA**-3′
b. 5′-AGACATTCTATCTACCTAGACTATG**TTCAGAA**-3′
c. 5′-**TTCAGAA**CTCATTCAGACCTACTACTATACCTTGG **GAGCTCCT**-3′
d. 5′-**ACCTACTA**GACTATACTACTACTAAGGGGACTATT CCAGACTT-3′

The 5′ end of sequence (a) is identical to the 3′ end of sequence (c). The 3′ end of sequence (a) is identical to the 5′ end of sequence (d). The 3′ end of sequence (b) is identical to the 5′ end of sequence (c). From 5′ to 3′, the sequences would form the following map:

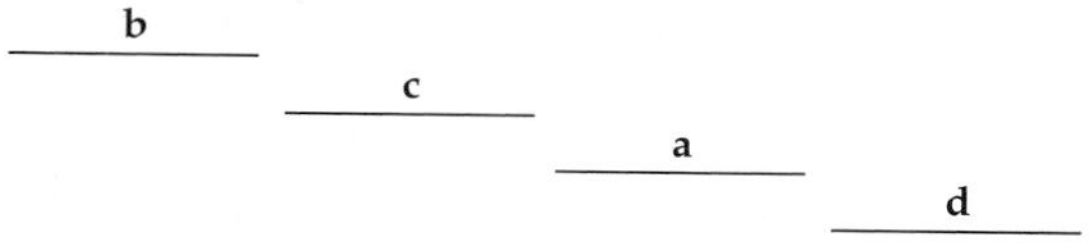

b
c
a
d

Chapter 21

21.1 ATP is called the universal energy currency because it is the major molecule used by all organisms to store energy.

21.3 The first stage of catabolism is the digestion (hydrolysis) of dietary macromolecules in the stomach and intestine.

In the second stage of catabolism, monosaccharides, amino acids, fatty acids, and glycerol are converted by metabolic reactions into molecules that can be completely oxidized.

In the third stage of catabolism, the two-carbon acetyl group of acetyl CoA is completely oxidized by the reactions of the citric acid cycle. The energy of the electrons harvested in these oxidation reactions is used to make ATP.

21.5 Substrate level phosphorylation is one way the cell can make ATP. In this reaction, a high-energy phosphoryl group of a substrate in the reaction is transferred to ADP to produce ATP.

21.7 Glycolysis is a pathway involving ten reactions. In reactions 1–3, energy is invested in the beginning substrate, glucose. This is done by transferring high-energy phosphoryl groups from ATP to the intermediates in the pathway. The product is fructose-1, 6-bisphosphate. In the energy-harvesting reactions of glycolysis, fructose-1,6-bisphosphate is split into two three-carbon molecules that begin a series of rearrangement, oxidation-reduction, and substrate-level phosphorylation reactions that produce four ATP, two NADH, and two pyruvate molecules. Because of the investment of two ATP in the early steps of glycolysis, the net yield of ATP is two.

21.9 Both the alcohol and lactate fermentations are anaerobic reactions that use the pyruvate and re-oxidize the NADH produced in glycolysis.

21.11 Gluconeogenesis (synthesis of glucose from noncarbohydrate sources) appears to be the reverse of glycolysis (the first stage of carbohydrate degradation) because the intermediates in the two pathways are the same. However, reactions 1, 3, and 10 of glycolysis are not reversible reactions. Thus, the reverse reactions must be carried out by different enzymes.

21.13 The enzyme glycogen phosphorylase catalyzes the phosphorolysis of a glucose unit at one end of a glycogen molecule. The reaction involves the displacement of the glucose by a phosphate group. The products are glucose-1-phosphate and a glycogen molecule that is one glucose unit shorter.

21.15 Glucokinase traps glucose within the liver cell by phosphorylating it. Because the product, glucose-6-phosphate, is charged, it cannot be exported from the cell.

21.17 Glucagon indirectly stimulates glycogen phosphorylase, the first enzyme of glycogenolysis. This speeds up glycogen degradation. Glucagon also inhibits glycogen synthase, the first enzyme in glycogenesis. This inhibits glycogen synthesis.

21.19 ATP

21.21

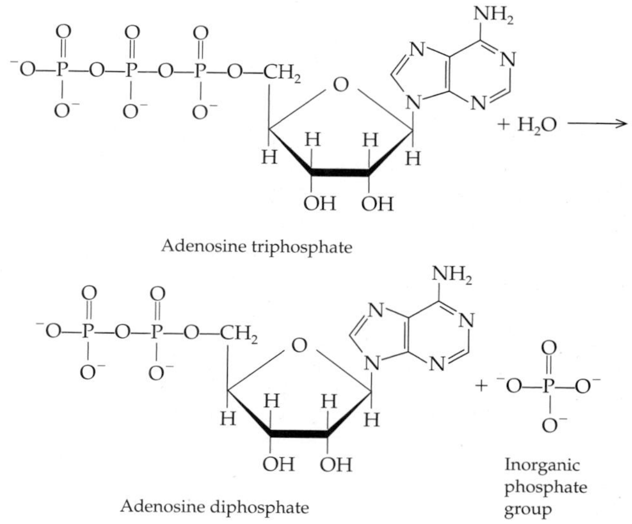

Adenosine triphosphate $+ H_2O \longrightarrow$

Adenosine diphosphate $+$ Inorganic phosphate group

21.23 A coupled reaction is one that can be thought of as a two-step process. In a coupled reaction, two reactions occur simultaneously. Frequently one of the reactions releases the energy that drives the second, energy-requiring, reaction.

21.25 Carbohydrates

21.27 The following equation represents the hydrolysis of maltose:

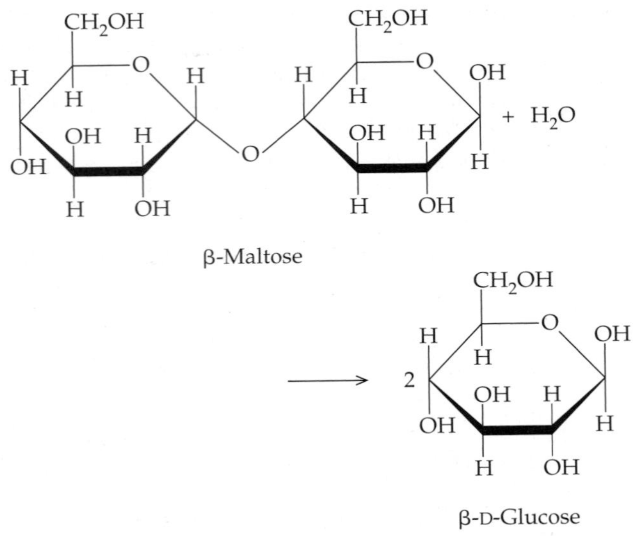

β-Maltose $+ H_2O \longrightarrow$ 2 β-D-Glucose

21.29

$H_3^+N{-}CH(CH_2C_6H_5){-}C(=O){-}HN{-}CH(CH_3){-}C(=O){-}HN{-}CH(CH_2CH_2C(=O)O^-){-}C(=O){-}HN{-}CH(CH_2CH_2SCH_3){-}C(=O){-}HN{-}CH(CH_2CH_2CH_2CH_2\overset{+}{N}H_3){-}C(=O){-}O^-$

$+ 4H_2O \downarrow$

$H_3^+N{-}CH(CH_3){-}C(=O){-}O^-$ + $H_3^+N{-}CH(CH_2CH_2SCH_3){-}C(=O){-}O^-$

$H_3^+N{-}CH(CH_2C_6H_5){-}C(=O){-}O^-$ + $H_3^+N{-}CH(CH_2CH_2C(=O)O^-){-}C(=O){-}O^-$ + $H_3^+N{-}CH(CH_2CH_2CH_2CH_2\overset{+}{N}H_3){-}C(=O){-}O^-$

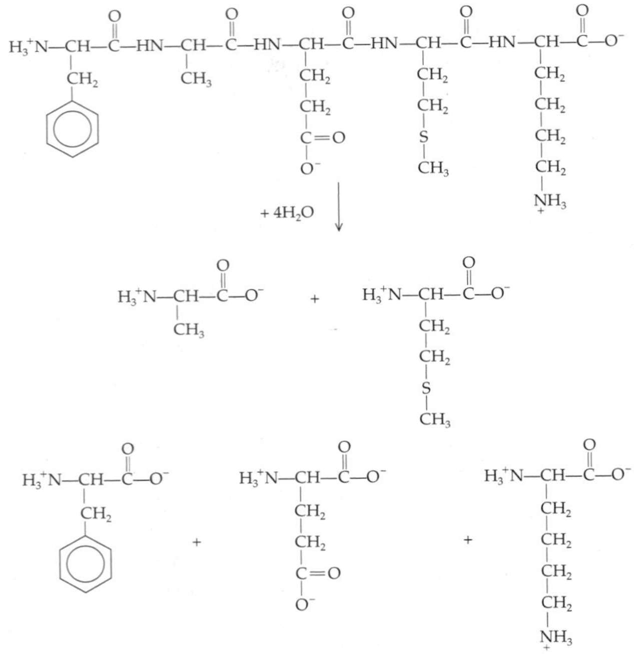

21.31 The hydrolysis of a triglyceride containing oleic acid, stearic acid, and linoleic acid is represented in the following equations:

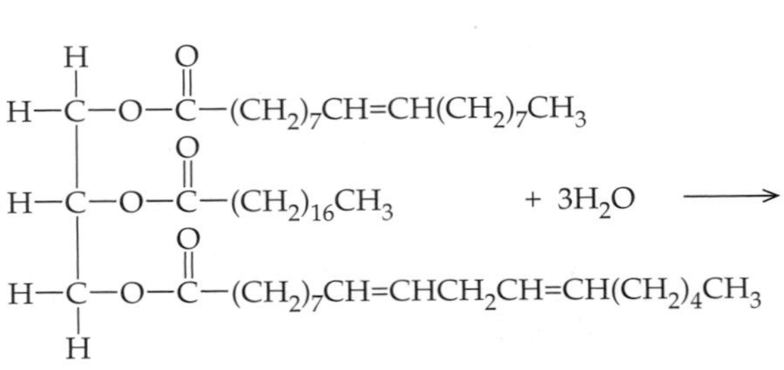

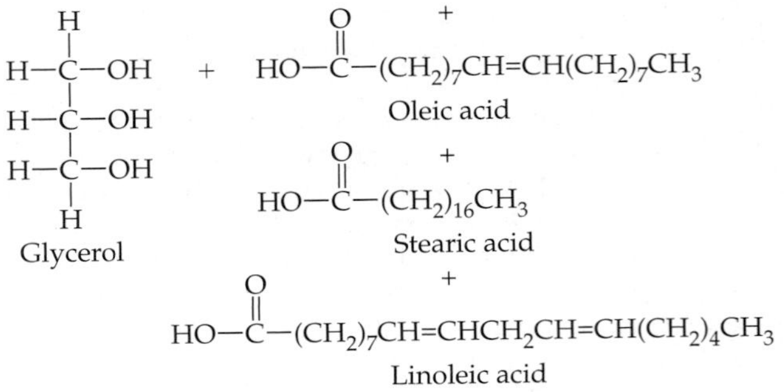

$H{-}C(H){-}O{-}C(=O){-}(CH_2)_7CH{=}CH(CH_2)_7CH_3$
$H{-}C{-}O{-}C(=O){-}(CH_2)_{16}CH_3 \quad + 3H_2O \longrightarrow$
$H{-}C(H){-}O{-}C(=O){-}(CH_2)_7CH{=}CHCH_2CH{=}CH(CH_2)_4CH_3$

$H{-}C(H)(OH){-}C(H)(OH){-}C(H)(OH){-}H$ (Glycerol) + $HO{-}C(=O){-}(CH_2)_7CH{=}CH(CH_2)_7CH_3$ (Oleic acid) + $HO{-}C(=O){-}(CH_2)_{16}CH_3$ (Stearic acid) + $HO{-}C(=O){-}(CH_2)_7CH{=}CHCH_2CH{=}CH(CH_2)_4CH_3$ (Linoleic acid)

21.33 The hydrolysis of the dipeptide alanyl leucine is represented in the following equation:

$H_3^+N{-}CH(CH_3){-}C(=O){-}N(H){-}CH(CH_2CH(CH_3)CH_3){-}C(=O){-}O^- + H_2O \longrightarrow$

Alanyl leucine

$H_3^+N{-}CH(CH_3){-}C(=O){-}O^-$ (Alanine) + $H_3^+N{-}CH(CH_2CH(CH_3)CH_3){-}C(=O){-}O^-$ (Leucine)

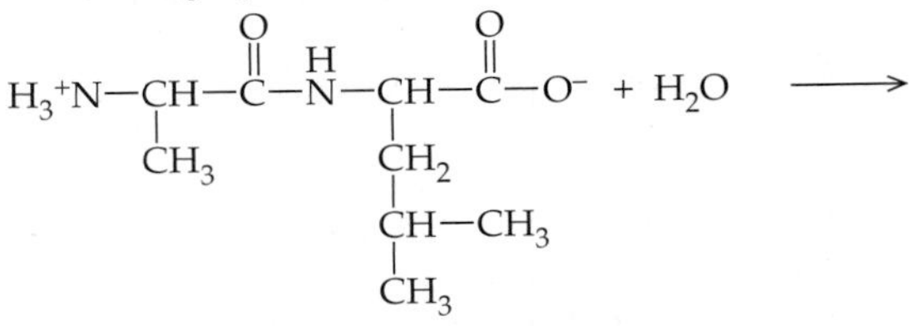

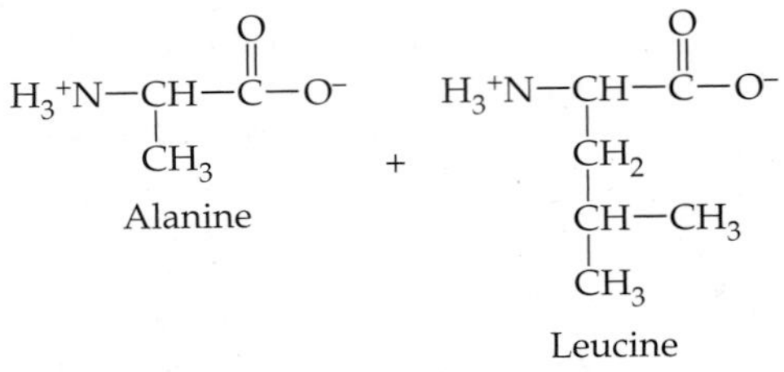

21.35 Glycolysis is the enzymatic pathway that converts a glucose molecule into two molecules of pyruvate. The pathway generates a net energy yield of two ATP and two NADH. Glycolysis is the first stage of carbohydrate catabolism.

21.37 Glycolysis requires NAD^+ for reaction 6 in which glyceraldehyde-3-phosphate dehydrogenase catalyzes the oxidation of glyceraldehyde-3-phosphate. NAD^+ is reduced.

21.39 Two ATP per glucose

21.41 Although muscle cells have enough ATP stored for only a few seconds of activity, glycolysis speeds up dramatically when there is a demand for more energy. If the cells have a sufficient supply of oxygen, aerobic respiration (the citric acid cycle and oxidative phosphorylation) will contribute large amounts of ATP. If oxygen is limited, the lactate fermentation will speed up. This will use up the pyruvate and re-oxidize the NADH produced by glycolysis and allow continued synthesis of ATP for muscle contraction.

21.43 $C_6H_{12}O_6 + 2ADP + 2P_i + 2NAD^+ \rightarrow 2C_3H_3O_3 + 2ATP + 2NADH + 2H_2O$
Glucose → Pyruvate

21.45
a. 7
b. 2
c. 6
d. 4
e. 1
f. 9
g. 5
h. 10
i. 3
j. 8

21.47 Myopathy and hemolytic anemia are symptoms associated with a genetic defect in some of the enzymes of glycolysis. Myopathy can lead to exercise intolerance, muscle breakdown, and blood in the urine. Tarui's disease is also caused by a deficiency in one of the enzymes of glycolysis. Its symptoms include muscle pain, exercise intolerance, respiratory failure, heart muscle disease, seizures, and blindness.

21.49 If a person is deficient in some of the enzymes of glycolysis, muscle cells may begin to die, which can lead to the release of myoglobin into the blood and the urine. This condition is called myoglobinuria, and it results in urine that is the color of cola soft drinks.

21.51 Isomerase

21.53 Enediol

21.55 A kinase transfers a phosphoryl group from one molecule to another.

21.57 NAD^+ is reduced, accepting a hydride anion.

21.59 To optimize efficiency and minimize waste, it is important that energy-harvesting pathways, such as glycolysis, respond to the energy demands of the cell. If energy in the form of ATP is abundant, there is no need for the pathway to continue at a rapid rate. When this is the case, allosteric enzymes that catalyze the reactions of the pathway are inhibited by binding to their negative effectors. Similarly, when there is a great demand for ATP, the pathway speeds up as a result of the action of allosteric enzymes binding to positive effectors.

21.61 ATP and citrate are allosteric inhibitors of phosphofructokinase, whereas AMP and ADP are allosteric activators.

21.63 Citrate, which is the first intermediate in the citric acid cycle, is an allosteric inhibitor of phosphofructokinase. The citric acid cycle is a pathway that results in the complete oxidation of the pyruvate produced by glycolysis. A high concentration of citrate signals that sufficient substrate is entering the citric acid cycle. The inhibition of phosphofructokinase by citrate is an example of feedback inhibition: the product, citrate, allosterically inhibits the activity of an enzyme early in the pathway.

21.65

$$CH_3{-}\overset{\displaystyle O}{\overset{\|}{C}}{-}H \xrightarrow{NADH \quad NAD^+} CH_3CH_2OH$$

Acetaldehyde — Ethanol

21.67 Lactate fermentation

21.69 Yogurt and some cheeses

21.71 Lactate dehydrogenase

21.73 This child must have the enzymes to carry out the alcohol fermentation. When the child exercised hard, there was not enough oxygen in the cells to maintain aerobic respiration. As a result, glycolysis and the alcohol fermentation were responsible for the majority of the ATP production by the child. The accumulation of alcohol (ethanol) in the child caused the symptoms of drunkenness.

21.75 The ribose-5-phosphate is used for the biosynthesis of nucleotides. The erythrose-4-phosphate is used for the biosynthesis of aromatic amino acids.

21.77 Gluconeogenesis is production of glucose from noncarbohydrate starting materials. This pathway can provide glucose when starvation or strenuous exercise leads to a depletion of glucose from the body.

21.79 The liver

21.81 Lactate is first converted to pyruvate.

21.83 Because steps 1, 3, and 10 of glycolysis are irreversible, gluconeogenesis is not simply the reverse of glycolysis. The reverse reactions must be carried out by different enzymes.

21.85 Steps 1, 3, and 10 of glycolysis are irreversible. Step 1 is the transfer of a phosphoryl group from ATP to carbon-6 of glucose and is catalyzed by hexokinase. Step 3 is the transfer of a phosphoryl group from ATP to carbon-1 of fructose-6-phosphate and is catalyzed by phosphofructokinase. Step 10 is the substrate-level phosphorylation in which a phosphoryl group is transferred from phosphoenolpyruvate to ADP and is catalyzed by pyruvate kinase.

21.87 The liver and pancreas

21.89 Hypoglycemia is the condition in which blood glucose levels are too low.

21.91 **a.** Insulin stimulates glycogen synthase, the first enzyme in glycogen synthesis. It also stimulates uptake of glucose from the bloodstream into cells and phosphorylation of glucose by the enzyme glucokinase.

b. This traps glucose within liver cells and increases the storage of glucose in the form of glycogen.

c. These processes decrease blood glucose levels.

21.93 Any defect in the enzymes required to degrade glycogen or export glucose from liver cells will result in a reduced ability of the liver to provide glucose at times when blood glucose levels are low. This will cause hypoglycemia.

21.95 Glycogen phosphorylase catalyzes phosphorylysis of a glucose at one end of a glycogen polymer. The reaction involves the displacement of a glucose unit of glycogen by a phosphate group. As a result, glucose-1-phosphate is produced.

$$\text{Glycogen(glucose)}_x + n\text{HPO}_4^{2-} \rightarrow \text{Glycogen(glucose)}_{n-x} + n\text{glucose-1-phosphate}$$

21.97 In glycogen degradation, phosphoglucomutase converts glucose-1-phosphate to glucose-6-phosphate. In glycogen synthesis, phosphoglucomutase converts glucose-6-phosphate to glucose-1-phosphate.

$$\text{(glucose-1-phosphate)} \xrightleftharpoons{\text{Phosphoglucomutase}} \text{(glucose-6-phosphate)}$$

21.99 Glucokinase converts glucose to glucose-6-phosphate as the first reaction of glycogen synthesis.

$$\text{(glucose)} + \text{ATP} \xrightarrow{\text{Glucokinase}} \text{(glucose-6-phosphate)} + \text{ADP} + \text{H}^+$$

Chapter 22

22.1 Mitochondria are the organelles responsible for aerobic respiration.

22.3

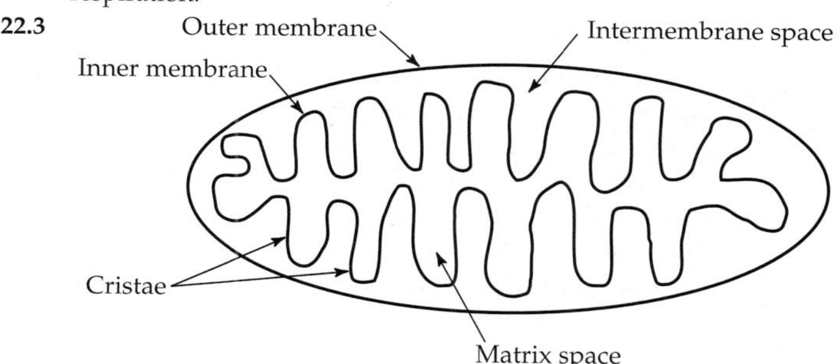

22.5 Pyruvate is converted to acetyl CoA by the pyruvate dehydrogenase complex. This huge enzyme complex requires four coenzymes, each of which is made from a different vitamin.

The four coenzymes are thiamine pyrophosphate (made from thiamine), FAD (made from riboflavin), NAD^+(made from niacin), and coenzyme A (made from the vitamin pantothenic acid). The coenzyme lipoamide is also involved in this reaction.

22.7 Oxidative phosphorylation is the process by which the energy of electrons harvested from oxidation of a fuel molecule is used to phosphorylate ADP to produce ATP.

22.9 $NAD^+ + H:^- \rightarrow NADH$

22.11 During transamination reactions, the α-amino group is transferred to the coenzyme pyridoxal phosphate. In the last part of the reaction, the α-amino group is transferred from pyridoxal phosphate to an α-keto acid.

22.13 The purpose of the urea cycle is to convert toxic ammonium ions to urea, which is excreted in the urine of land animals.

22.15 An amphibolic pathway is a metabolic pathway that functions both in anabolism and catabolism. The citric acid cycle is amphibolic because it has a catabolic function—it completely oxidizes the acetyl group carried by acetyl CoA to provide electrons for ATP synthesis. Because citric acid cycle intermediates are precursors for the biosynthesis of many other molecules, it also serves a function in anabolism.

22.17 The mitochondrion is an organelle that serves as the cellular power plant. The reactions of the citric acid cycle, the electron transport system, and ATP synthase function together within the mitochondrion to harvest ATP energy for the cell.

22.19 The intermembrane compartment is the location of the high-energy proton (H^+) reservoir produced by the electron transport system. The energy of this H^+ reservoir is used to make ATP.

22.21 The outer mitochondrial membrane is freely permeable to substances of molar mass less than 10,000 g/mol. The inner mitochondrial membrane is highly impermeable. Embedded within the inner mitochondrial membrane are the electron carriers of the electron transport system, and ATP synthase, the multisubunit enzyme that makes ATP.

22.23 Coenzyme A is a molecule derived from ATP and the vitamin pantothenic acid. It functions in the transfer of acetyl groups in lipid and carbohydrate metabolism.

22.25 Decarboxylation is a chemical reaction in which a carboxyl group is removed from a molecule.

22.27 Under aerobic conditions pyruvate is converted to acetyl CoA.

22.29 The coenzymes NAD^+, FAD, thiamine pyrophosphate, and coenzyme A are required by the pyruvate dehydrogenase complex for the conversion of pyruvate to acetyl CoA. These coenzymes are synthesized from the vitamins niacin, riboflavin, thiamine, and pantothenic acid, respectively. If the vitamins are not available, the coenzymes will not be available and pyruvate cannot be converted to acetyl CoA. Because the complete oxidation of the acetyl group of acetyl CoA produces the vast majority of the ATP for the body, ATP production would be severely inhibited by a deficiency of any of these vitamins.

22.31 A condensation is a reaction in which aldehydes or ketones react to form larger molecules.

22.33 Oxidation reduction

22.35 A dehydrogenation reaction is an oxidation reaction in which protons and electrons are removed from a molecule.

22.37 **a.** 1 **b.** 6 **c.** 2 **d.** 2 **e.** 4 **f.** 2 **g.** 5 **h.** 2

22.39 True

22.41 Three

22.43 Two ATP per glucose

22.45 The function of acetyl CoA in the citric acid cycle is to bring the two-carbon remnant (acetyl group) of pyruvate from glycolysis and transfer it to oxaloacetate. In this way the acetyl group enters the citric acid cycle for the final stages of oxidation.

22.47 The high-energy phosphoryl group of the GTP is transferred to ADP to produce ATP. This reaction is catalyzed by the enzyme dinucleotide diphosphokinase.

22.49 Fumarate contains an alkene carbon-carbon double bond. Addition of water to the double bond of fumarate gives malate. The enzyme fumarase catalyzes this reaction. When water is added to the alkene double bond, one of the carbons forms a new bond to $-OH$, and the other carbon forms a new bond to $-H$. As a result, the alkene becomes an alcohol.

22.51 First, pyruvate is converted to acetyl CoA:

$$H_3\overset{*}{C}-\overset{O}{\overset{\|}{C}}-COO^- \longrightarrow H_3\overset{*}{C}-\overset{O}{\overset{\|}{C}}\sim S-CoA$$

Pyruvate → Acetyl CoA

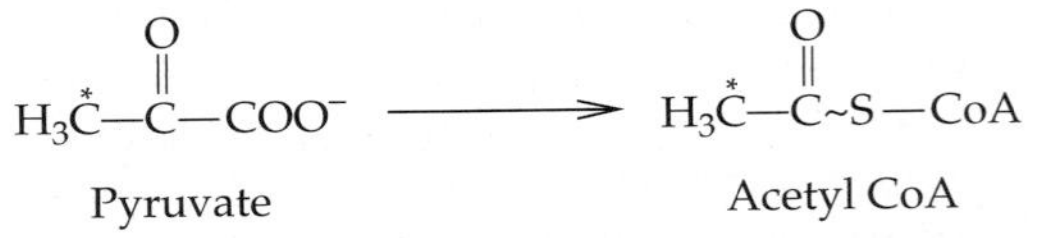

Then, citrate is formed from oxaloacetate and the radiolabeled acetyl CoA.

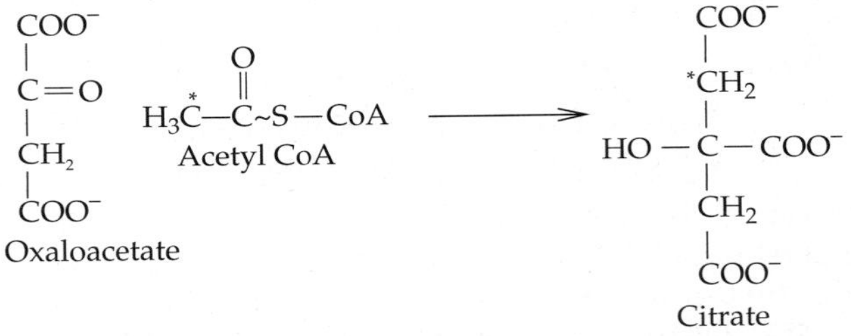

Oxaloacetate (COO^-–$C{=}O$–CH_2–COO^-) + Acetyl CoA ($H_3\overset{*}{C}-\overset{O}{\overset{\|}{C}}\sim S-CoA$) ⟶ Citrate ($COO^-$–$^*CH_2$–$HO-C-COO^-$–$CH_2$–$COO^-$)

The following structures are the intermediates of the citric acid cycle. An asterisk is on the radiolabeled carbon, and circles are on the $-COO^-$ groups that are released as CO_2.

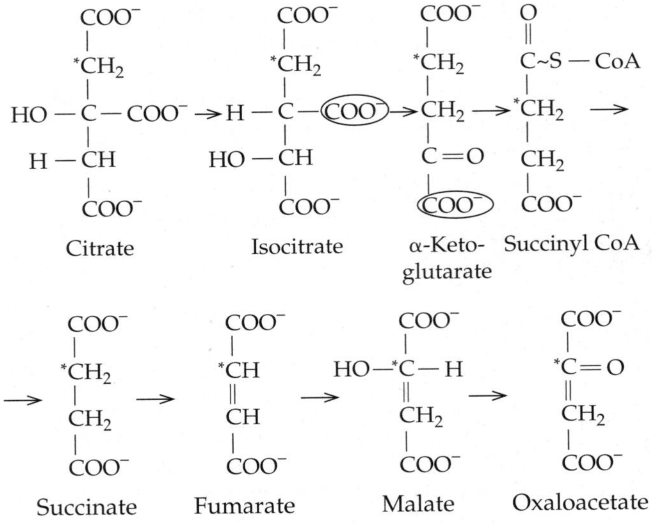

Citrate (COO^-–$^*CH_2$–$HO-C-COO^-$–$H-CH$–COO^-) → Isocitrate (COO^-–$^*CH_2$–$H-C-$(circled COO^-)–$HO-CH$–COO^-) → α-Keto-glutarate (COO^-–$^*CH_2$–CH_2–$C{=}O$–(circled COO^-)) → Succinyl CoA ($\overset{O}{\overset{\|}{C}}\sim S-CoA$–$^*CH_2$–$CH_2$–$COO^-$) →

→ Succinate (COO^-–$^*CH_2$–CH_2–COO^-) → Fumarate (COO^-–$^*CH$=CH–COO^-) → Malate (COO^-–$HO-^*C-H$–CH_2–COO^-) → Oxaloacetate (COO^-–$^*C{=}O$–CH_2–COO^-)

22.53 This reaction is an example of the oxidation of a secondary alcohol to a ketone. The two functional groups are the hydroxyl group of the alcohol and the carbonyl group of the ketone.

22.55 It is a kinase because it transfers a phosphoryl group from one molecule to another. Kinases are a specific type of transferase.

22.57 Mutations of the citric acid cycle enzymes frequently appear first in the central nervous system because of the high energy (ATP) demands of this tissue.

22.59 Deficiencies of citric acid cycle enzymes cause hypotonia because there is insufficient ATP.

22.61 An allosteric enzyme is one that has an effector binding site and an active site. Effector binding can change the shape of the active site, causing it to be active or inactive.

22.63 Allosteric enzymes are an efficient means to regulate a biochemical pathway because they bind to effectors, such as ATP or ADP, that alter the shape of the enzyme active site, either stimulating the rate of the reaction or inhibiting the reaction.

22.65 The citric acid cycle is regulated by the following four enzymes or enzyme complexes: pyruvate dehydrogenase complex, citrate synthase, isocitrate dehydrogenase, and the α-ketoglutarate dehydrogenase complex.

22.67 Energy-harvesting pathways, such as the citric acid cycle, must be responsive to the energy needs of the cell. If the energy requirements are high, as during exercise, the reactions must speed up. If energy demands are low and ATP is in excess, the reactions of the pathway slow down.

22.69 ADP

22.71 The electron transport system is a series of electron transport proteins embedded in the inner mitochondrial membrane that accept high-energy electrons from NADH and $FADH_2$ and transfer them in stepwise fashion to molecular oxygen (O_2).

22.73 Three ATP

22.75 The oxidation of a variety of fuel molecules, including carbohydrates, the carbon skeletons of amino acids, and fatty acids provides the electrons. The energy of these electrons is used to produce an H^+ reservoir. The energy of this proton reservoir is used for ATP synthesis.

22.77 The electron transport system passes electrons harvested during oxidation of fuel molecules to molecular oxygen. At three sites protons are pumped from the mitochondrial matrix into the intermembrane compartment. Thus, the electron transport system builds the high-energy H^+ reservoir that provides energy for ATP synthesis.

22.79 **a.** Two ATP per glucose (net yield) are produced in glycolysis, whereas the complete oxidation of glucose in aerobic respiration (glycolysis, the citric acid cycle, and oxidative phosphorylation) results in the production of 36 ATP per glucose.

b. Thus, aerobic respiration harvests nearly 40% of the potential energy of glucose, and anaerobic glycolysis harvests only about 2% of the potential energy of glucose.

22.81 Transaminases transfer amino groups from amino acids to ketoacids.

22.83 The glutamate family of transaminases is very important because the ketoacid corresponding to glutamate is α-ketoglutarate, one of the citric acid cycle intermediates. This provides a link between the citric acid cycle and amino acid metabolism. These transaminases provide amino groups for amino acid synthesis and collect amino groups during catabolism of amino acids.

22.85 **a.** Pyruvate **d.** Acetyl CoA
b. α-Ketoglutarate **e.** Succinate
c. Oxaloacetate **f.** α-Ketoglutarate

22.87 Transaminase binds to the amino acid in its active site. Then, the α-amino group is transferred to pyridoxal phosphate, producing pyridoxamine phosphate. The amino group is then transferred to an α-keto acid.

22.89 Hyperammonemia

22.91 **a.** The source of one amino group of urea is the ammonium ion and the source of the other is the α-amino group of the amino acid aspartate.

b. The carbonyl group of urea is derived from CO_2.

22.93 Anabolism is a term used to describe all of the cellular energy-requiring biosynthetic pathways.

22.95 α-Ketoglutarate

22.97 Citric acid cycle intermediates are the starting materials for the biosynthesis of many biological molecules.

22.99 An essential amino acid is one that cannot be synthesized by the body and must be provided in the diet.

22.101

$$CH_3-C(=O)-COO^- + CO_2 + ATP \longrightarrow {}^-OOC-CH_2-C(=O)-COO^- + ADP + P_i$$

Pyruvate Oxaloacetate

Chapter 23

23.1 Because dietary lipids are hydrophobic, they arrive in the small intestine as large fat globules. The bile salts emulsify these fat globules into tiny fat droplets. This greatly increases the surface area of the lipids, allowing them to be more accessible to pancreatic lipases and thus more easily digested.

23.3 Starvation, a diet low in carbohydrates, and diabetes mellitus are conditions that lead to the production of ketone bodies.

23.5 **(1)** Fatty acid biosynthesis occurs in the cytoplasm whereas β-oxidation occurs in the mitochondria.

(2) The acyl group carrier in fatty acid biosynthesis is acyl carrier protein while the acyl group carrier in β-oxidation is coenzyme A.

(3) The seven enzymes of fatty acid biosynthesis are associated as a multienzyme complex called *fatty acid synthase*. The enzymes involved in β-oxidation are not physically associated with one another.

(4) NADPH is the reducing agent used in fatty acid biosynthesis. NADH and $FADH_2$ are produced by β-oxidation.

23.7 The liver regulates blood glucose levels under the control of the hormones insulin and glucagon. When blood glucose levels are too high, insulin stimulates the uptake of glucose by liver cells and the storage of the glucose in glycogen polymers. When blood glucose levels are too low, the hormone glucagon stimulates the breakdown of glycogen and release of glucose into the bloodstream. Glucagon also stimulates the liver to produce glucose for export into the bloodstream by the process of gluconeogenesis.

23.9 Insulin stimulates uptake of glucose and amino acids by cells, glycogen and protein synthesis, and storage of lipids. It inhibits glycogenolysis, gluconeogenesis, breakdown of stored triglycerides, and ketogenesis.

23.11

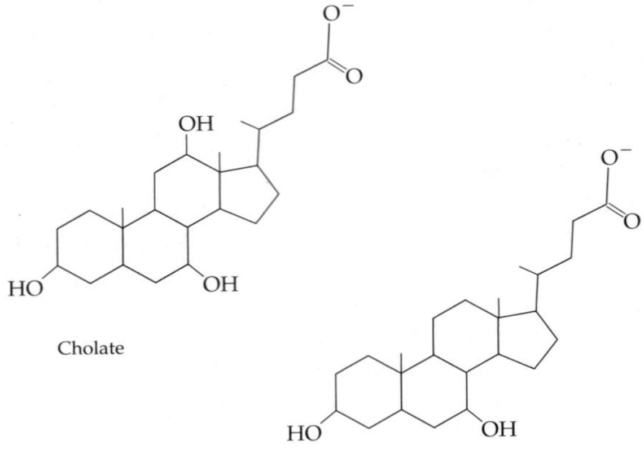

Cholate

Chenodeoxycholate

23.13 A micelle is an aggregation of molecules having nonpolar and polar regions; the nonpolar regions of the molecules aggregate, leaving the polar regions facing the surrounding water.

23.15 A triglyceride is a molecule composed of glycerol esterified to three fatty acids.

23.17 Triglycerides, cholesterol, and phospholipids are packaged into a protein-coated shell to produce the class of plasma lipoproteins called chylomicrons.

23.19 Triglycerides

23.21 The large fat globule that takes up nearly the entire cytoplasm

23.23 Lipases catalyze the hydrolysis of the ester bonds of triglycerides.

23.25 Acetyl CoA is the precursor for fatty acids, several amino acids, cholesterol, and other steroids.

23.27 Chylomicrons carry dietary triglycerides from the intestine to all tissues via the bloodstream.

23.29 Bile salts are detergents that emulsify the lipids, increasing their surface area and making them more accessible to digestive enzymes (pancreatic lipases).

23.31 When dietary lipids in the form of fat globules reach the duodenum, they are emulsified by bile salts. The triglycerides in the resulting tiny fat droplets are hydrolyzed into monoglycerides and fatty acids by the action of pancreatic lipases, assisted by colipase. The monoglycerides and fatty acids are absorbed by cells lining the intestine.

23.33 The hydrolysis of ATP into AMP and PP_i

23.35 Carnitine is a carrier molecule that brings fatty acyl groups into the mitochondrial matrix.

23.37 The following equation represents the reaction catalyzed by acyl-CoA dehydrogenase. Notice that the reaction involves the loss of two hydrogen atoms. Thus, this is an oxidation reaction.

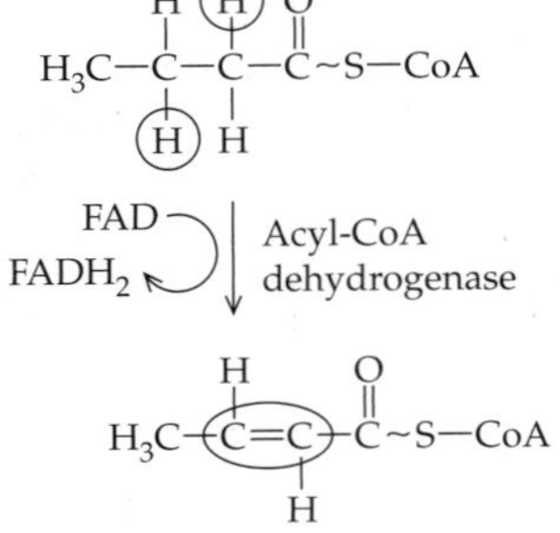

$$H_3C-CH_2-CH_2-\overset{O}{\overset{\|}{C}}\sim S-CoA \xrightarrow[\text{FAD} \rightarrow \text{FADH}_2]{\text{Acyl-CoA dehydrogenase}} H_3C-CH{=}CH-\overset{O}{\overset{\|}{C}}\sim S-CoA$$

23.39 An alcohol is the product of the hydration of an alkene.

23.41 Six acetyl CoA, one phenyl acetate, six NADH, and six $FADH_2$

23.43 112 ATP

23.45 95 ATP

23.47 The acetyl CoA produced by β-oxidation will enter the citric acid cycle.

23.49 Ketone bodies include the compounds acetone, acetoacetone, and β-hydroxybutyrate, which are produced from fatty acids in the liver via acetyl CoA.

23.51 Ketosis is an abnormal rise in the level of ketone bodies in the blood.

23.53 Matrix of the mitochondrion.

23.55

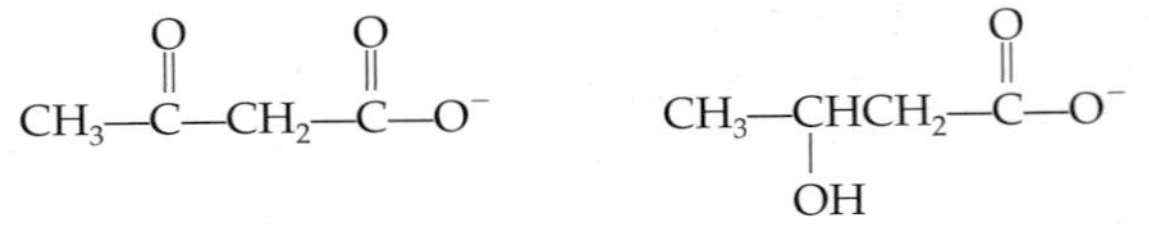

$$CH_3-\overset{O}{\overset{\|}{C}}-CH_2-\overset{O}{\overset{\|}{C}}-O^-$$

Acetoacetate

$$CH_3-\underset{OH}{\underset{|}{C}}HCH_2-\overset{O}{\overset{\|}{C}}-O^-$$

β-Hydroxybutyrate

23.57 In those suffering from uncontrolled diabetes, the glucose in the blood cannot get into the cells of the body. The excess glucose is excreted in the urine. Body cells degrade fatty acids because glucose is not available. β-oxidation of fatty acids yields enormous quantities of acetyl CoA, so much acetyl CoA, in fact, that it cannot all enter the citric acid cycle because there is not enough oxaloacetate available. Excess acetyl CoA is used for ketogenesis.

23.59 Ketone bodies are the preferred energy source of the heart.

23.61 Cytoplasm

23.63

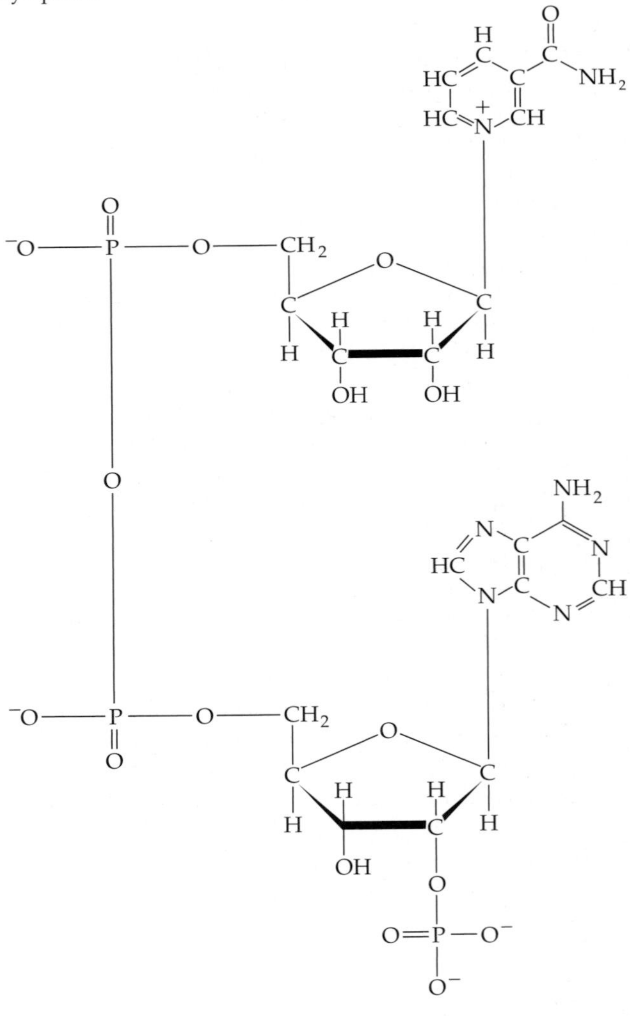

23.65 **a.** The phosphopantetheine group allows formation of a high-energy thioester bond with a fatty acid.
b. It is derived from the vitamin pantothenic acid.

23.67 Fatty acid synthase is a huge multienzyme complex consisting of the seven enzymes involved in fatty acid synthesis. It is found in the cell cytoplasm. The enzymes involved in β-oxidation are not physically associated with one another. They are free in the mitochondrial matrix space.

23.69 Glycogenesis is the synthesis of the polymer glycogen from glucose monomers.

23.71 Gluconeogenesis is the synthesis of glucose from noncarbohydrate precursors.

23.73 β-oxidation of fatty acids

23.75 The major metabolic function of the liver is to regulate blood glucose levels.

23.77 Ketone bodies are the major fuel for the heart. Glucose is the major energy source of the brain, and the liver obtains most of its energy from the oxidation of amino acid carbon skeletons.

23.79 Fatty acids are absorbed from the bloodstream by adipocytes. Using glycerol-3-phosphate, produced as a by-product of glycolysis, triglycerides are synthesized. Triglycerides are constantly being hydrolyzed and resynthesized in adipocytes. The rates of hydrolysis and synthesis are determined by lipases that are under hormonal control.

23.81 In general, insulin stimulates anabolic processes and inhibits catabolic processes.

23.83 A target cell is one that has a receptor for a particular hormone.

23.85 Decreased blood glucose levels

23.87 In the β-cells of the islets of Langerhans in the pancreas.

23.89 Insulin stimulates the uptake of glucose from the blood into cells. It enhances glucose storage by stimulating glycogenesis and inhibiting glycogen degradation and gluconeogenesis.

23.91 Insulin stimulates synthesis and storage of triglycerides.

23.93 Insulin is secreted when blood glucose levels are high. It facilitates the uptake and storage of glucose by target cells to restore normal blood glucose levels. Glucagon is secreted when blood glucose levels are too low. It stimulates release of glucose into the blood to restore normal levels.

Credits

Chapter 1

Opener: © Purestock/SuperStock RF; Page 3: © Digital Vision/PunchStock RF; p. 5: © Royalty Free/Corbis RF; 1.2a: © Afdam Gault/Getty Images RF; 1.2b: © Dr. Parvinder Sethi; 1.2c: © David Parker/Segate Microelectronics/SPL/Photo Researchers, Inc.; 1.2d: Courtesy APHIS, PPG, Otis Methods Development Center, USDA; 1.3a: © Design Pics/Corey Hochachka RF; 1.3b: © The McGraw-Hill Companies, Inc./Jeff Topping, photographer; 1.3c: © The McGraw-Hill Companies, Inc./Louis Rosenstock, photographer; 1.4(both): © The McGraw-Hill Companies, Inc./Ken Karp, photographer; 1.6a-b: © Image Source RF; 1.6c: © PhotoDisc/Getty Images RF; p. 11: © The McGraw-Hill Companies, Inc./John Thoeming, photographer; 1.7a-c, 1.9a-d: © The McGraw-Hill Companies, Inc./Louis Rosenstock, photographer; p. 21: © Adam Gault/Getty Images RF; p. 26: Dan Stober/Stanford News Service; p. 29: © Royalty-Free/Corbis RF; 1.12: © The McGraw-Hill Companies, Inc./Louis Rosenstock, photographer; p. 35: © Vol. 12/Getty Images RF.

Chapter 2

Opener: NASA; 2.1: © IBM Corporation, Almaden Research Center; 2.6: © Yoav Levy/Phototake.com; p. 54(left): © Earth Satellite Corp./SPL/Photo Researchers, Inc.; p. 54(right): © Scott Camazine/Photo Researchers, Inc.; p. 56: © PhotoDisc Vol.2/Getty Images RF; p. 58: © The McGraw-Hill Companies, Inc./Stephen Frisch, photographer; 2.14: © The McGraw-Hill Companies, Inc./Jacques Cornell photographer.

Chapter 3

Opener: © Javier Trueba/MSF/Photo Researchers, Inc.; 3.2c: © The McGraw Hill Companies, Inc./Dennis Strete, photographer; p. 88: © Comstock Images/Picture Quest RF; p. 99: © Pixtal/age fotostock RF; 3.15: © David Tietz/Editorial Image, LLC.

Chapter 4

Opener: © Monty Rakusen/Getty Images RF; 4.1, 4.3: © The McGraw-Hill Companies, Inc./Louis Rosenstock, photographer; p. 146(top): © The McGraw-Hill Companies/Charles D. Winters, photographer; p. 146(bottom): © The McGraw-Hill Companies, Inc./Louis Rosenstock, photographer; p. 147: © The McGraw-Hill Companies/Stephen Frisch, photographer.

Chapter 5

Opener: © Royalty Free/Corbis RF; p.168: © The Image Bank/Getty Images; 5.2a-b: © The McGraw-Hill Companies, Inc./Louis Rosenstock, photographer; 5.5: © Alamy Images RF; p. 181: © BrandX/Picture Quest RF; p. 187: © PhotoDisc/Getty Images RF.

Chapter 6

Opener: © Brand X Pictures/Punchstock RF; 6.1: © Kip Peticolas/Fundamental Photographs, NYC; p.198: © Martin Strmiska/Alamy RF; 6.4: © The McGraw-Hill Companies, Inc./Louis Rosenstock, photographer; 6.6a-c: © David M. Phillips/Visuals Unlimited; p. 214: Courtesy of Rita Colwell, National Science Foundation; 6.7: © Sean Justice/Corbis RF; 6.8a-b: © The McGraw-Hill Companies, Inc./Louis Rosenstock, photographer; p. 220: © AJPhoto/Photo Researchers, Inc.

Chapter 7

Opener: © The McGraw Hill Companies, Inc./Connie Mueller, photographer; p. 234(both): © The McGraw-Hill Companies, Inc./Louis Rosenstock, photographer; 7.9: © The McGraw-Hill Companies, Inc./Ken Karp, photographer; p. 241: © Design Pics/Punchstock RF; 7.15, 7.16: © The McGraw-Hill Companies, Inc./Ken Karp, photographer; p. 255: © The McGraw-Hill Companies, Inc./Louis Rosenstock, photographer.

Chapter 8

Opener: © Comstock/Jupiter Images RF; 8.1: © The McGraw-Hill Companies, Inc./Mark Dierker, photographer; 8.4a: © The McGraw-Hill Companies, Inc./Louis Rosenstock, photographer; 8.4b, 8.6a-b: © The McGraw Hill Companies, Inc./Stephen Frisch, photographer; p. 276, p. 277, p. 279: © The McGraw-Hill Companies, Inc./Louis Rosenstock, photographer; p. 283: © The McGraw Hill Companies, Inc./Auburn University Photographic Services; p. 285: © PhotoDisc/Getty Images RF; p. 286a: © The McGraw-Hill Companies, Inc./Louis Rosenstock, photographer; p. 286b: © The McGraw Hill Companies, Inc./Connie Mueller, photographer; p. 286c: © Brand X Pictures/Punchstock RF; 8.7: © The McGraw-Hill Companies, Inc./Stephen Frisch, photographer; p. 290: © AAA Photo/Phototake.com.

Chapter 9

Opener: © Royalty-Free/Corbis RF; 9.3: © Gianni Tortoli/Photo Researchers, Inc.; 9.6: © U.S. DOE/Science Source/Photo Researchers, Inc.; p. 312: NASA; p. 313: © Stockbyte/Punchstock RF; 9.7: © Blair Seitz/Photo Researchers, Inc.; p. 316(top): © The McGraw-Hill Companies, Inc./Louis Rosenstock, photographer; p. 316(middle): © Javier Larrea/age fotostock RF; 9.8b: Courtesy Bristol-Myers Squibb Medical Imaging; 9.9: © U.S. DoE/Mark Marten/Photo Researchers, Inc.; 9.10: © The McGraw-Hill Companies, Inc./Louis Rosenstock, photographer; 9.11: © Scott Camazine/Photo Researchers, Inc.

Chapter 10

Opener; © Digital Vision/Punchstock RF; p. 328 © Vol. 0S22/PhotoDisc/Getty Images RF; p. 330: Courtesy Ocean Drilling Program/NOAA; p. 338: © Vol. 43/PhotoDisc/Getty Images RF; p. 350(top): © Royalty Free/Corbis RF; p. 350(bottom): © OS23/Getty Images RF; p. 351: © Royalty Free/Corbis RF; p. 352: © Fotosearch RF; p. 354: © Royalty Free/Corbis RF.

Chapter 11

Opener: © Digital Vision/Getty Images RF; p. 364: © Vol. 12/PhotoDisc/Getty Images RF; p. 365(top): © Vol. 19/PhotoDisc/Getty Images RF; p. 365(bottom): © Banana Stock/Punchstock RF; p. 370: © Vol. 77/PhotoDisc/Getty Images RF; p. 371: © Steven P. Lynch; p.377(top): © Ingram Publishing/SuperStock RF; p. 377(center): © PhotoDisc/Getty Images RF; p. 377(bottom): © Steven P. Lynch; p. 378: © Digital Vision/Getty Images RF; p. 379: © PhotoDisc/Getty Images RF; 11.4: © The McGraw-Hill Companies, Inc./Ken Karp, photographer; p. 388: © Moodboard/Corbis RF.

Chapter 12

Opener: © C Squared Studios/Getty Images RF; p. 406: © Royalty-Free/Corbis RF; 12.3: © Vol. 12/PhotoDisc/Getty Images RF; p. 412: © Vol. 18/PhotoDisc/Getty Images RF; 12.4: © Royalty Free/Corbis RF; p. 421: © Damien Meyer/Getty Images; p. 424: © StockFood RF; 12.8: © Glow Wellness/Getty Images; 12.9: © Vol. OS22/PhotoDisc/Getty Images RF; p. 430: © PhotoDisc Collection/Getty Images RF.

Chapter 13

Opener: © Iconotec RF; p. 443, p. 446: © Vol. 12/PhotoDisc/Getty Images RF; 13.3(Almonds): © Goodshoot/Punchstock RF; 13.3(Vanilla): © Eisenhut & Mayer-Wien/Getty Images 13.3(Cinnamon): © IT Stock/PunchStock RF; 13.3(Lemon grass): © Studio Paggy/Getty Images RF; 13.3(Blueberries): © Dynamic Graphics Group/Punchstock RF; 13.3(Mushroom): © John Foxx/Imagestate Media RF; 13.4a-c: © The McGraw-Hill Companies/Charles D. Winters, photographer; 13.5: © Andrew Lambert Photography/Photo Researchers, Inc.; p. 456: © Michael Grayson/Getty Images RF.

Chapter 14

Opener: © Royalty Free/Corbis RF; p. 471: © Alamy RF; p. 473: © Royalty Free/Corbis RF; p. 476: © Reuters/Corbis; p. 488(Pineapple): © Vol. 19/PhotoDisc/Getty Images RF; p. 488(Raspberries): © Vol. OS49/PhotoDisc RF; p. 488(Bananas): © Vol. 30/PhotoDisc RF; p. 489(Oranges): © Royalty Free/Corbis RF; p. 489(Apples): © Royalty Free/Corbis RF; p. 489(Apricots): © Vol. 121/Corbis RF; p. 489(Strawberries): © Vol. 83/Corbis RF; p. 500(top): U.S. Dept. of Agriculture; p. 500(center): © Vol. 101/Corbis RF; p. 500(bottom): © Norm Thomas/Photo Researchers, Inc.

Chapter 15

Opener: © Dr. Parvinder Sethi; p. 512: © Vol. 59/ Getty Images RF; p. 517(top): © Duncan Smith/ SPL/Photo Researchers Inc. p. 517(bottom): © Creatas/Punchstock RF; 15.3a-b: © Vol. 94/ Corbis RF; 15.3c: © Getty Images RF; p. 526: © Steven P. Lynch; p. 536a: © Vol. 9/PhotoDisc RF; p. 536b: © Phil Larkin, CSIRO Plant Industry.

Chapter 16

Opener: © Phanie/Photo Researchers, Inc.; 16.1: U.S. Dept. of Agriculture; 16.2: © Vol. 67/ PhotoDisc RF; p. 551: © Stanley Flegler/Visuals Unlimited; 16.3b, p. 559: © Royalty Free/Corbis RF; p. 563: U.S. Dept. of Agriculture; p. 564(top): © The McGraw-Hill Companies, Inc./Jill Braaten, photographer; p. 564(bottom): © Getty Images RF; p. 566(left): © foodimagecollection/ Alamy;p. 566(right): © FoodCollection/ SuperStock Inc.; p. 569: © Pixtal/SuperStock RF; p. 570: © Jean Claude Revy-ISM/Phototake.com; p. 571: © Getty Images RF; p. 572: © Royalty Free/Corbis RF.

Chapter 17

Opener: © Steve Satushek/The Image Bank/ Getty Images; 17.2(top): © Getty Images RF; 17.2(bottom), p. 590: © Vol. 20/PhotoDisc/Getty Images RF; p. 597: © Greg Fitchett (http://www.geograph.org.uk/profile/61750); p. 601: © Vol. 12/PhotoDisc/Getty Images RF; p. 602: © Steven P. Lynch; p. 603: © Getty Images RF; 17.10a: © James Dennis/Phototake.com; p. 608: © Royalty Free/Corbis RF.

Chapter 18

Opener: © Fritz Polking/Visuals Unlimited; p. 627: © V258/Getty Images RF; 18.14: © Meckes/Ottawa/Photo Researchers, Inc.; p. 637: © Vol. 18/PhotoDisc RF; p. 638(top): © Getty Images RF; p. 638(center): © Vol. 20/ PhotoDisc/Getty Images RF; p. 638(bottom): © The McGraw-Hill Companies, Inc./Bob Coyle, photographer; p. 639: © Laszlo Selly/ FoodPix/Getty Images.

Chapter 19

Opener: Courtesy Dr. Robert E. Shoemaker; p. 651: © Comstock/Alamy RF; p. 656(left): © Stephanie Le/momofukufor2.com; p. 656(right): © & Courtesy of Adam Melonas/ www.madridlab.net/melonas/adam-melonas; p. 662: © Merck/Phil Degginger/Color-Pic, Inc.

Chapter 20

Opener: © Barbara Penoyar/Getty Images RF; p. 691: © Vol. 72/PhotoDisc/Getty Images RF; p. 711: © EP77/PhotoDisc/Getty Images RF; p. 718: Dr. Charles S. Helling/USDA; p. 719: Courtesy of Orchid Cellmark, Germantown, Maryland.

Chapter 21

Opener; © Chris Falkenstein/Getty Images RF; p. 731: © PhotoLink/Getty Images RF; p. 742: © SS07/Getty Images RF; p. 744: © The McGraw Hill Companies, Inc./Louis Rosenstock, photographer; p. 748: U.S. Air Force photo by Tech. Sgt. Tracy L. DeMarco.

Chapter 22

Opener: © Chris Falkenstein/PhotoDisc/ Getty Images RF; 22.1a: © CNRI/Phototake.com; p. 765(left): © DV/287/Getty Images RF; p. 765(right): © PhotoLink/Getty Images RF.

Chapter 23

Opener: © PhotoDisc/Getty Images RF; p. 807: © Vol. 11/PhotoDisc RF.

Index

Note: Page numbers followed by B indicate boxed material; those followed by F indicate figures; those followed by T indicate tables.

A

ABO blood types, 570B
absolute specificity, 660
absolute temperature (K), 170
accelerants, and arson, 338B
accuracy, in scientific measurement, 17
acetals, 457, 458, 459F, 567
acetaldehyde, 287–88, 444T, 453B. *See also* ethanal
acetamide. *See* ethanamide
acetaminophen, 500B, 531
acetate ion, 105–106
acetic acid. *See also* ethanoic acid
  buffer solutions, 278, 279, 280–82
  neutralization, 482
  nomenclature, 474T
  solubility, 471
  vinegar, 472, 478
  weak acids, 264, 265
acetic anhydride, 495
acetic caproic anhydride, 496
acetic valeric anhydride, 495
acetic propanoic anhydride, 495
acetoacetate, 805, 806F, 808
acetoacetyl ACP, 809F
acetoacetyl CoA, 805
acetone, 805, 806F, 812B. *See also* propanone
"acetone breath," and diabetes, 806F, 811B, 812B
acetone fermentation, 745B
acetylcholine, 539–40, 672B, 673B
acetylcholinesterase, 539, 672B, 673B
acetyl coenzyme A (acetyl CoA)
  aerobic respiration and conversion of pyruvate to, 764–67
  carbohydrate metabolism, 732
  citric acid cycle, 772
  structure of, 803
  thioesters, 499, 501
  thiols, 430
β-D-*N*-acetylgalactosamine, 564
N-acetylglucosamine, 573B
acetylsalicylic acid, 480, 500B. *See also* aspirin
achiral molecule, 558
acid(s), and bases. *See also* acetic acid; acid-base reactions; citric acid cycle; fatty acids; hydrochloric acid; pH and pH scale; strong acids and bases; sulfuric acid; weak acids and bases
  acid-base properties of water, 263
  Arrhenius theory, 262
  Brønsted-Lowry theory, 263
  buffers, 278–82
  conjugate, 264–67
  dissociation of water, 267
  Henderson-Hasselbalch equation, 282–83
  reactions between, 273–78
  strength of, 263–64
acid anhydrides, 495–98
acid-base reactions, 146–47, 482–83
acid chlorides, 494–95
acid hydrolysis, 592–93
acidosis, 283. *See also* lactic acidosis
acid rain, 272, 276B
aconitase, 768T, 769
ACP. *See* acyl carrier protein
acquired immune deficiency syndrome (AIDS), 285B, 662B
acrylic acid, 387B
acrylonitrile, 388T
actinide series, 59
activated complex, 240
activation energy, 239–40
activation reaction, 799
active transport, 219, 729T, 732. *See also* transport proteins
acute myocardial infarction (AMI), 676
acylcarnitine, 801F
acyl carrier protein (ACP), 808, 809F. *See also* butyryl ACP; β-hydroxybutyryl ACP; malonyl ACP
acyl CoA, 800, 801F
acyl-CoA dehydrogenase, 802
acyl-CoA ligase, 800
acyl group, 470, 497, 501, 531
Adams, Mike, 650
addiction, and neurotransmitters, 535. *See also* drug abuse
addition, of significant figures, 17–18
addition polymers, 386
addition reactions, 378, 413, 455–59
adenine (A), 686
adeno-associated virus (AAV), 720B
adenosine, 687
adenosine diphosphate (ADP), 460, 653, 688T, 730
adenosine monophosphate, 688T
adenosine triphosphate (ATP)
  allosteric enzymes, 669–70
  cofactors and coenzymes, 663
  exercise and energy metabolism, 764B
  glycolysis, 735
  nomenclature, 668T
  phosphoesters, 498–99
  as universal energy currency, 728–31
adipic acid. *See* hexanedioic acid
adipocere, 597B
adipocytes, 582, 795–96
adipose tissue, 591, 795, 807–808B, 812. *See also* fat(s)
ADP. See adenosine diphosphate
aerobic conditions, and glycolysis,
aerobic respiration. *See also* citric acid cycle; glycolysis
  anabolism, 786–87
  conversion of pyruvate to acetyl CoA, 764–67
  degradation of amino acids, 778–82
  mitochondria, 762–63
  overview of, 767–68
  oxidation phosphorylation, 774–78
  urea cycle, 782–85
Africa, and relationship between sickle cell trait and malaria, 636
African Americans, and sickle cell anemia, 636
agarose gel electrophoresis, 712
agglutination, 570B
agriculture, pH scale and pH control, 272. *See also* plants; soils
AIDS. *See* acquired immune deficiency syndrome
air. *See also* air pollution
  atmospheric pressure, 179
  density, 30T
  as solution, 9, 194
air bags, in automobiles, 152B
air pollution, radon and indoor, 320B. *See also* acid rain; greenhouse effect; smog
ALA. *See* linolenic acid
alanine
  abbreviation for, 622T
  anabolism, 786
  classes of amino acids, 620
  as nonessential amino acid, 642T
  structure of, 621F, 628
D-alanine and L-alanine, 619
alanine aminotransferase/serum glutamate-pyruvate transaminase (ALT/SGPT), 677
alanine transaminase, 780
alanyl-glycine, 623
alanyl-glycyl-valine, 623
albumin, 220, 637
Alcaligenes eutrophus,
alchemy, 290B
Alcmaeon (ancient Greece), 26B
alcohol(s). *See also* alcohol fermentation; alcoholic beverages; ethanol
  blood levels of, 421
  carboxylic acids and esterification, 484
  chemical reactions involving, 413–19
  functional groups, 331, 332T
  medically important, 411–13
  nomenclature, 409–11
  oxidation-reduction reactions, 449
  structure and physical properties, 407–409
alcohol abuse, 453B. *See also* alcohol-related automobile accidents; drug abuse
alcohol dehydrogenase, 743
alcohol fermentation, 743, 744–45B
alcoholic beverages, 411, 419, 421B, 743. *See also* alcohol abuse; fetal alcohol syndrome; wine making
alcohol-related automobile accidents, 421B, 453B
aldehydes
  chemical reactions involving, 449–60
  functional groups, 332T
  hydration, 384
  important forms of, 447–48
  nomenclature, 442–45
  preparation of alcohol by hydrogenation of, 413–14
  structure and physical properties of, 441–42
aldohexose, 559
aldolase, 737
aldose, 550
aldosterone, 604
aldotetrose, 550
aliphatic hydrocarbons, 329
alkali metals, 59, 146T
alkaline earth metals, 59
alkaloids, 526
alkalosis, 283
alkanamide, 529T
alkanamine (alkylamine), 516, 518T

alkanes
- alkyl groups, 336–37
- arson investigations, 338B
- chemical reactions, 351–53
- classification of hydrocarbons, 329F, 331
- conformations of, 348–50
- nomenclature, 338–43
- physical properties of, 335–36
- structural isomers, 344–45
- structure of, 331–34, 364

alkenes
- chemical reactions, 378–87
- classification of hydrocarbons, 329F, 330
- functional groups, 331, 332T
- in nature, 376–78
- nomenclature, 366–69
- physical properties of, 365–66
- structure of, 364–65

alkylamine. *See* alkanamine
alkylammonium ion, 521
alkylammonium salts, 522, 524
alkyl groups, 336–37
alkyl halide, 352, 353, 385
alkynes
- chemical reactions, 378–87
- classification of hydrocarbons, 329F, 330
- functional groups, 332T
- nomenclature, 366–69
- physical properties of, 364–65
- structure of, 364–65

allicin, 430B
alliin, 430B
allinase, 430B
allosteric enzymes, 669–70, 741
allotropic forms, of carbon, 327–28
alloys, of metals, 195
alpha decay, 301–302
alpha particles, 299
alpha-particle scattering experiment, 51F
alpha radiation, 300, 318
alternative energy sources, 276B, 340B
ALT/SGPT. *See* alanine aminotransferase/serum glutamate-pyruvate transaminase
aluminum
- density, 33B
- ionic compounds, 86–87
- Lewis structure, 110, 113
- as metal, 59
- oxidation-reduction processes, 286
- pH and soil chemistry, 277B

aluminum nitrate, 139
aluminum oxide, 286
alveoli, 583B, 667B
Alzheimer's disease (AD), 637
American Civil War, 625B
American College of Cardiology, 676
American Heart Association (AHA), 480, 589
American Medical Association, 412B
Ames, Bruce, 710B
Ames test, 710B
amide(s), 332T, 521, 527–34
amide bond, 528, 622
amines. *See also* heterocyclic amines
- chemical reactions involving, 520–25
- definition of, 512, 513
- functional groups, 332T
- medically important, 519–20
- nomenclature, 516–19
- structure and properties of, 513–16

amino acids. *See also* proteins
- aerobic respiration and degradation of, 778–82
- classes of, 620
- codons, 703
- definition of, 428, 512–13, 534–35
- essential and nonessential, 642
- metabolic effects of insulin and glucagon, 814T
- stereoisomers of, 619–20
- structure of, 618–19, 621F

α-amino acids, 618–22, 779–80
aminoacyl group, 535
aminoacyl tRNA, 535, 705
aminoacyl tRNA binding site (A site), 705, 706F
aminoacyl tRNA synthetases, 660, 705
aminobutyric acid (GABA), 538–39
amino sugars, 573B
ammonia
- amines, 513
- boiling point, 184
- chemical equation, 137
- chemical equilibrium, 252, 253
- density, 30T
- diffusion, 169F
- endothermic reactions, 229, 230
- formula of, 97
- Haber process and synthesis of, 242F
- Lewis structure, 102–103, 114
- melting and boiling points, 120T
- solubility, 117

ammonium, 146T. *See also* ammonium ions
ammonium chloride, 236, 531
ammonium cyanate, 327
ammonium ions, 782, 783F
ammonium nitrate, 144
ammonium sulfate, 134, 144
amniocentesis, 693B
amorphous solids, 98, 185
amphetamines, 519
amphibolic pathways, 786
amphipathic molecule, 595
amphiprotic water, 263
amipicillin, 532B, 714
Amtrak, 340B
amu. *See* atomic mass unit
amylase, 677, 732
α-amylase and β-amylase, 571
amyloid plaques, 637
amylopectin, 571, 572F
amylose, 571
anabolic steroids, 600
anabolism, 728, 786–87. *See also* aromatic hydrocarbons; catabolism
anaerobic conditions, and glycolysis, 733
anaerobic threshold, 743
analgesics, 500B, 519, 526–27
analytical balance, 12F
analytical chemistry, 2
anaplerotic reaction, 787
Andersen's disease, 755B
anesthetics, 354B, 426, 519, 526
aniline, 264, 390, 517
animals. *See also* bears; cat(s); dogs; skunks; whales
- body temperature and membrane lipids, 609
- digestion of cellulose, 572
- DNA fingerprinting and genetic diversity of, 719B
- lipid metabolism in, 794–98

anion(s), 70, 71, 74, 92
anionic detergents, 492B
anisole, 390
anode, 50, 289
anomer(s), 561
anorexia nervosa, 536
ant(s), chemicals produced by, 409, 471F, 478
antabuse, 453B
anthracene, 393
anthrax, 49B
antibiotics, 430B
antibodies, 220, 610B, 618, 640B
anticodon, 698, 705
antidotes, for poisoning, 673B
antifreeze, 208, 413
antigens, 570B, 618, 640B
antihistamines, 512, 538, 548
antiobesity vaccine, 807–808B
antiparallel β-pleated sheet, 628
antiparallel strands, of DNA, 689–90
antipyretics, 500B
antiseptics, 285B, 525
antitrypsin, 637, 667B, 720B
apoenzyme, 663
aqueous solutions, 194, 208–10, 215–20
arachidic acid, 585T
arachidonic acid, 585T, 587, 588, 589F, 590
archaeology, 308–309
Arctic Ocean, 608
arginine
- abbreviation for, 622T
- essential and nonessential amino acids, 642T, 786
- neurotransmitters, 540
- structure of, 621F
- urea cycle, 783F, 784

arginosuccinate, 783F, 784
arginosuccinate lyase, 783F, 784
arginosuccinate synthase, 783F, 784
argon, 66, 179
Aristotle, 685
aromatic carboxylic acids, 477
aromatic hydrocarbons, 329, 331, 388–94
Arrhenius theory of acids and bases, 262
arsenic, 671
arson, and alkanes, 338B
artificial flavors, 488B
artificial radioactivity, 315
artwork, and ultraviolet light, 245B
ascorbic acid, 664T
asparagine, 620, 621F, 622T, 642T, 786
aspartame, 406, 532–33
aspartate, 620, 621F, 622T, 642T
aspartate aminotransferase/serum glutamate-oxaloacetate transaminase (AST/SGOT), 677
aspartate transaminase, 780
aspartic acid, 533
aspirin (acetylsalicylic acid), 339, 480, 500B, 588–89
asthma, 588
AST/SGOT. *See* aspartate aminotransferase/serum glutamate-oxaloacetate transaminase
atherosclerosis, 594, 601, 607–608, 812B
atmosphere, and depletion of ozone, 157. *See also* air; atmospheric pressure; greenhouse effect
atmosphere (atm), as unit of measurement, 167
atmospheric pressure, 167, 179
atom(s). *See also* atomic theory; electrons; Lewis structures; molecules; neutrons; nucleus; protons
- composition of, 44–48
- definition of, 44
- mole concept, 128–33
- octet rule, 70–73
- quantum mechanical, 61
- size of, 73
- structure of, 52–57
- trends in periodic table, 73–75
- valence electrons, 73

atomic mass, 46–48, 60
atomic mass unit (amu), 128
atomic number (Z), 45, 60, 298
atomic orbital, 56, 62
atomic theory, 48, 50–51, 55–57. *See also* atom(s)
atomic weight, 128
ATP. *See* adenosine triphosphate
ATP synthase, 763, 775

atrial natriuretic factor, 716T
aufbau principle, 63–64
autoclaves and autoclaving, 668
autoionization, of water, 267
automobiles
air bags, 152B
alcohol-related accidents, 421B, 453B
antifreeze, 413
brake lines, 180
catalytic converter, 245B
chemical reaction in battery, 229
energy efficiency, 230B
investigation of accidents, 421B
average kinetic energy, 182
aviation industry, 340B
Avogadro, Amadeo, 129, 167
Avogadro's law, 174–75
Avogadro's number, 128–30
Aztecs (Mexico), 395B

B

background radiation, 317, 321F
bacteria. *See also Clostridium perfringens; Clostridium welchii; Escherichia coli; Salmonella typhimurium; Streptococcus mutans; Streptococcus pyogenes; Thermus aquaticus*
adipocere, 597B
cloning and cloning vectors, 714, 716
DNA replication, 695–96
fermentation, 743, 745B
mitochondria, 763
origins of life, 650
RNA splicing, 701
sterilization, 668
tooth decay, 551B
balance(s), and instruments of measurement, 12F
balancing, of equations, 140–44, 273
balloons, 172
ball-and-stick models, of molecules, 4–5, 407, 423, 555
Bangham, Alec, 610B
barbital, 531
barbiturates, 480, 529
bariatric surgery, 807B
barium-131, 314T
barium hydroxide, 278
barium sulfate, 139
barometer, 167
base(s). *See* acids and bases; acid-base reactions; pH and pH scale; strong acids and bases; weak acids and bases
base pairs, 689
batteries, 229, 289–90, 291F. *See also* voltaic cells
Bayer and Company, 480
beans, and vegetarian diet, 643
bears, and hibernation, 794
Bechler, Steve, 520
Becquerel, Henri, 309B
behavior modification, and weight loss, 807B
benadryl, 538
bends, and scuba diving, 198B
Benedict's reagent, 565–67
Benedict's test, 451, 452
bent (angular) structure, 114
benzaldehyde, 390, 448F, 451
benzalkonium chloride, 525
benzedrine, 519
benzenamine. *See* aniline
benzene, 30T, 331, 391–92, 393–94
benzene ring, 390, 391F
benzenesulfonic acid, 393
benzodiazopines, 539
benzoic acid, 390, 451, 475–76, 482
benzoic anhydride, 495
benzopyrene, 393
benzoyl peroxide, 285B
benzyl alcohol, 392
benzyl chloride, 392
beryl, 187B
beryllium, 65, 110, 113
Berzelius, Jöns Jakob, 327
beta decay, 302
beta particles, 299–300
beta radiation, 300, 318
BHT. *See* butylated hydroxytoluene
bicarbonates, 146T, 219, 278, 283
big bang theory, 301B
bile, 794–95
bile salts, 602–603, 732, 794, 796F
bilirubin, 2
binding energy, of nucleus, 306
binding site, of enzyme, 658
biochemistry, 2. *See also* chemistry
biocytin, 664T
biodegradable plastics, 478B
bioethanol, 383–84
biofuels, 340B
bioinformatics, 721
biological systems. *See also* animals; fish; humans; insects; plants
disaccharides, 567–69
electrolytes in solution, 217, 219–20
elements important in, 59T
lipids, 582–84
monosaccharides, 559–67
oxidation and reduction in, 419–21
radiation, 300, 317–18
structure of membranes, 608–11
biomarkers, 676–77
Biopol, 478B
biosynthesis, 536–37B, 729T
biotin, 664T, 787
birds. *See* hummingbirds
birth control, 603–604
1,3-bisphosphoglycerate, 735, 738, 739
bladder, and stone formation, 88B
bleaching, 287
blimps, 168B
blood. *See also* blood pressure
alcohol levels in, 421B
clotting, 587
control of pH, 283
electrolyte concentrations, 219–20
gases in and respiration, 181B
glucose levels, 349, 567, 571, 752B, 810, 812B, 814
nuclear medicine, 314T
plasma and osmosis, 212–13
proteins in, 636–37
specific gravity, 34–35
types, 570B
urea levels in, 677
blood pressure, 72B, 102B, 395B, 601
blood sugar, 349, 451–52. *See also* blood; glucose
blood urea nitrogen (BUN) test, 677
Blumenthal, Heston, 656B
B lymphocytes, 640B
boat conformation, 350, 351F
body-mass index (BMI), 34B
body temperature, 609, 776–77B
Boeing Corporation, 340B
Bohr atom, 55, 61
Bohr, Niels, 53, 55
boiling point
alcohols, 408, 516T
aldehydes and ketones, 441
alkanes, 336T
amines, 515T, 516T
aqueous solutions and calculation of, 208–10
definition of, 98
hydrogen bonding, 183–84
molecular geometry, 119–20
solution concentration, 207–208
vapor pressure, 182
of water, 7
bomb calorimeter, 237–38
bond(s). *See* chemical bonding
bond energy, 107
bonding process, and electron configuration, 61
bond order, 107
bone
density, 30T
dietary calcium, 72B
nuclear medicine, 314
Borgia, Lucretia, 671
boron, 65, 110
boron trifluoride, 113
Boyle, Robert, 167, 169, 411
Boyle's law, 169–70
brain
fatty acid metabolism, 813
nuclear medicine, 314T
opium poppy and peptides in, 625–26B
study of, 26B
branched alkanes, 353
branching enzyme, 753
bread making, 743, 744–45B
breathalyzer test, 421B
breeder reactors, 312
Bright's disease, 35B
British Anti-Lewisite (BAL), 429
bromide, 75
bromine, 137, 380, 381, 393
bromination, of alkenes, 382
bromobenzene, 390, 393
α-bromobenzoic acid, 476
β-bromocaproic acid, 475
bromochlorofluoromethane, 554, 555
3-bromocyclohexanol, 410
2-bromo-3,3-dimethylpentane, 341
bromoethane, 385
2-bromo-3-hexyne, 367
bromomethane, 353
1-bromo-4-methylhexane, 343
4-bromopentanal, 445
1-bromopropane, 353, 385
2-bromopropane, 340, 353, 385
3-bromopropanoyl chloride, 494
γ-bromovaleraldehyde, 445
bronchioles, 667B
Brønsted-Lowry theory of acids and bases, 263
Brookhaven National Laboratory (New York), 315
brown fat, 776–77B
browning reactions, and foods, 528B
buckminsterfullerene, 327–28
buffer(s), acid-base, 278–83
buffer capacity, 279
bulimia, 536
buprenorphine, 536–37B
buret, 273
burns, and collagen, 631B
butanal (butyraldehyde), 444T, 449
butanamine, 516
butane
atomic structure, 335F
balancing of equations, 143–44
boiling point, 441
ethers, 423
isomers, 108
molecular formula, 331, 333
butanedione, 566B
butanoic acid, 470, 478

2-butanol, 415
butanoyl chloride (butyryl chloride), 494
1-butene, 365T, 367, 415
2-butene, 372, 380–81, 415
trans-2-butene, 372, 380–81
trans-2-butene-1-thiol, 427F
1-butyne and 2-butyne, 365T
butyryl ACP, 809F
burets, 13F
butanal, 454
butanamine, 515T
butane, 329T, 471
butanoic acid. *See* butyric acid
butanoic anhydride, 496
butanol, 745B
butanone, 444, 447
t-butyl, 337
butyl alcohol. *See* 1-butanol
butylated hydroxytoluene (BHT), 423
butyl propyl ketone. *See* 4-octanone
butyraldehyde. *See* butanal
butyric acid
  fermentation, 745B
  hydrolysis of amides, 534
  odors and fragrances, 472, 478, 488B
  sources of, 474T

C

calcium, 72B, 88B, 141–42, 218
calcium carbonate, 72B, 137, 138, 245
calcium chloride, 210
calcium hydroxide, 133, 153–54
calcium hypochlorite, 285B
calcium oxalate, 88B, 145
calcium phosphate, 88B, 136
calorie(s) (cal), 28, 29B, 237, 807B. *See also* kilocalorie
calorimeter, 235
calorimetry, 228, 235–38
cancer. *See also* medicine and medical perspective
  carcinogens, 709, 710B
  chocolate, 395B
  dietary calcium and colon, 72B
  radiation therapy, 54B, 313
  tanning and skin cancer, 711
capillin, 370B, 371B
capric acid, 474T, 585T. *See also* decanoic acid
caproic acid, 474T, 479. *See also* hexanoic acid
caprylic acid, 474T, 479. *See also* octanoic acid
capsaicin, 422B
cap structure, of RNA, 700
carbamoyl phosphate, 782, 783F
carbamoyl phosphate synthase, 782
carbinol carbon, 407
carbohydrate(s). *See also* carbohydrate metabolism; dissacharides; monosaccharides; polysaccharides
  combustion reactions and energy from foods, 237
  stereoisomers and stereochemistry, 552–59
  types of, 548–49
carbohydrate metabolism. *See also* metabolism
  ATP as cellular energy currency, 728–31
  fermentations, 742–45
  gluconeogenesis, 746–48
  glycogen synthesis and degradation, 748–55
  glycolysis, 733–42
  insulin, 814
  overview of catabolic processes, 731–32
  pentose phosphate pathway, 744–45
  regulation of, 810–13
carbolic acid, 423
carbo-loading, 748
carbon
  alkyl groups, 336
  chiral molecules, 553, 556, 557, 558
  covalent bonding, 89
  electron configuration, 65
  isotopes, 299
  organic compounds, 327–28
  oxidation-reduction reactions, 286
  tetrahedral structure, 334
α-carbon, 618–19
carbon-11, 302
carbon-12, 128–29, 299, 308
carbon-14, 299, 306T, 308
carbonate(s), 104–105, 146T
carbonated beverages, 193F, 197
carbon dioxide (CO_2)
  alcohol fermentation, 744B
  atmosphere, 179
  blood pH, 283
  chemical reaction, 7, 146
  density, 30T
  fire extinguishers, 241
  greenhouse effect and climate change, 179B
  Lewis structures, 100–101
  nonpolar molecules, 117
  respiration, 181B
  solubility, 197
  theoretical yield, 157
carbonic acid, 264, 278, 283
carbon monoxide, 155B, 179
carbon skeletons, 782
carbonyl group, 440, 441
carboxylases, 654
carboxylic acids
  aldehydes and oxidation reactions, 450
  chemical reactions involving, 481–84
  in daily life, 470
  functional groups, 332T
  important forms of, 478–81
  medical uses of, 500B
  nomenclature, 472–77
  structure and physical properties of, 471–72
carcinogens, 709, 710B
cardiac biomarkers, 676–77
cardiac troponin I, 676
cardiotonic steroids, 602B
cardiovascular disease, 314, 590. *See also* heart disease
carnitine, 801F, 802B
L-carnitine, 800, 802B
carnitine acyltransferase I, 800
carnitine acyltransferase II, 801
carvacrol, 423
carvone, 548
cat(s), 651
catabolism, 728, 731–32, 786. *See also* anabolism
catalyst, and rate of chemical reaction, 241–42, 254
catalytic converter, 245B
catalytic cracking and re-forming, of petroleum, 350B
catechin, 395B
catecholamines, 535–36
cathode, 50, 289
cathode rays, 50
cationic detergents, 493B
cations, 70, 73, 92
cell membrane, 211, 582
cellulase, 572
cellulose, 572
Celsius temperature scale, 27, 171
Centers for Disease Control and Prevention, 285B, 453B, 662B
centi- (prefix), 11T
central atoms, 100, 103–104
central dogma of molecular biology, 698
cephalin, 595, 596F
cerebrosides, 598–99
Cerezyme, 678
cetyl palmitate, 605
cetylpyridinium chloride, 525
Chadwick, James, 51
chain elongation, and RNA translation, 705–707
chain reaction, 310
chair conformation, 349–50
Challenger (space shuttle), 107
champagne, 411F
chaos, and second law of thermodynamics, 231
Chargaff, Irwin, 688, 689
Charles, Jacques, 167, 170
Charles's law, 170–72, 639B
chemical bonding. *See also* covalent bonds; double bonds; glycosidic bonds; hydrogen bonding; ionic bonds; thioester bonds
  definition of, 84
  endothermic and exothermic reactions, 229
  Lewis symbols, 84
  polar covalent bonding and electronegativity, 89–91
  principal types of, 84–89
chemical change, 7, 136–48
chemical equations
  balancing of, 140–44
  calculations using, 149
  conversion factors, 149–56
  definition of, 136
  experimental basis of, 137–38
  features of, 137
  net ionic, 147–48
  strategies for writing, 138–39
  theoretical and percent yield, 156–59
chemical equilibrium, 247–51
chemical formula, 133–34. *See also* formulas
chemical kinetics, 238–39
chemical properties, 7. *See also* properties
chemical reactions. *See also* addition reactions; oxidation-reduction reactions
  alcohols, 413–19
  aldehydes and ketones, 449–60
  alkanes and cycloalkanes, 351–53
  alkenes and alkynes, 378–87
  amides, 531–34
  amines, 520–25
  benzene, 393–94
  carboxylic acids, 481–84
  chemical kinetics, 238–40
  chemical properties, 7
  citric acid cycle, 769–72
  classification of, 145–47
  enzymes, 656–62
  equilibrium, 244–54
  esters, 485–94
  experimental determination of energy change in, 235–38
  fatty acids, 592–95
  glycolysis, 736–40
  β-oxidation, 799–804
  reaction rate, 241–44, 254
  thermodynamics, 227–28
chemical warfare, 429
chemistry. *See also* biochemistry; crime scenes; green chemistry; medicine and medical perspective
  definition of, 2
  major areas of, 2–3
  models, 4–6
chemotherapy, 610B
chenodeoxycholate, 603, 794, 795F
Chernobyl nuclear accident, 230B
children. *See also* genetic disorders; infants
  diarrhea and oral rehydration therapy, 214B
  kidney stones, 88B
chili peppers, 422B

China, ancient, 364, 512
chiral molecules, 552, 553, 556, 557, 558
chlorates, 146T
chloride, 219, 284
chlorine
 atomic mass, 46–47
 chemical equations, 137
 as disinfectant and antiseptic, 285B
 halogenation, 380, 381
 oxidation-reduction processes, 284
4-chlorobenzoyl chloride, 494
2-chloro-2-butene, 367
chlorocyclohexane, 345–46, 369
chloroethane, 354B
chlorofluorocarbon (CFC), 341
chloroform, 354B
chloromethane, 354B
3-chloro-4-methyl-3-hexene, 367
2-chloro-2-methylpropane, 353
1-chloropentane and 2-chloropentane, 386
chlorophyll, 7, 394, 526
γ-chlorovaleric acid, 475
chocolate, 395B, 424B
cholate, 603, 794, 795F
cholera, 214B
cholesterol, 375, 600–603, 605, 607, 794
choline, 525
chondroitin sulfate, 573B
chorionic villus sampling, 693B
chromate, 146T, 262F
chromic acid, 416
chromium, 187B, 291, 304
chromosomes, 685, 690–91
chromosome walking, 718
chylomicrons, 605, 606F, 795, 796F
chymotrypsin, 642, 675–76
chymotrypsinogen A, 671T
cicutoxin, 371B
cigarette smoking, 667B, 709, 710B
cimetidine, 394, 538
cinnamaldehyde, 448F
citral, 448F
citrate, 742, 770F, 772
citrate lyase, 651
citric acid, 480
citric acid cycle
 adenosine triphosphate (ATP), 501
 aerobic respiration, 764, 767, 768–69
 biosynthetic intermediates, 786–87
 carbohydrate metabolism, 732
 carboxylic acids, 480
 chemical reactions, 769–72
 control of, 772–73
 exercise and energy metabolism, 764B
 hydration, 383
 regulation of glycolysis, 742
citrulline, 782, 783F, 784
classification. *See also* nomenclature
 of chemical reactions, 145–47
 of elements on periodic table, 57–61
 of matter, 6–10
clathrate, 330B
clear versus colorless, 195
climate
 acid rain, 272, 276B
 global warming, 179B, 330B, 352
 water in environment, 28, 255B
cloning and cloning vectors, 714, 715F, 716
Clostridium perfringens, 488B
Clostridium welchii, 597B
coagulation, of proteins, 638
coal, 276B, 328F. *See also* fossil fuels
cobalt-60, 306T, 313
coca plants (*Erythroxylum* spp.), 718B
cocaine, 524–25, 526, 718B
cocamido DEA, 216B
codeine, 526–27, 536B
codons, 698, 702–703
coefficient, 140
coenzyme(s), 420, 429, 499, 539, 663–66. *See also* acetoacetyl CoA; acetyl coenzyme A; acyl CoA; coenzyme A; succinyl CoA
coenzyme A, 664T, 732, 765, 766
cold adaptation, and brown fat, 776B. *See also* freezing point; ice
cold packs, 234B
Coleman, Douglas, 797B
colipase, 794
collagen, 573B, 631–32B
colligative properties, 206
colloid(s), 195–96
colloidal suspension, 195
Colombia, 718B
colon cancer, 72B
color
 Benedict's reagent, 567
 breathalyzer test, 421B
 bromination of alkenes, 382
 fluid mosaic membrane, 611
 pH indicators, 274F
colorless, use of term, 195
combination reactions, 138
combined gas law, 172–74
combustion, of hydrocarbons, 351–52
common names, and nomenclature systems
 alcohols, 410–11
 aldehydes and ketones, 443, 444, 445, 446
 amines, 518
 aromatic compounds, 391
 carboxylic acids, 474, 475
 esters, 485
 ionic compounds, 92
 iron and copper ions, 93T
compass, 63F
competitive inhibition, 450B, 539, 673
complementary strands, of DNA, 689
complete protein, 642
complex carbohydrates, 549
complex lipids, 582, 605–608
composition, of matter, 9–10
compounds. *See also* covalent compounds; ionic compounds; nitro compounds
 definition of, 9
 naming and writing formulas of, 91–98
 organic compared to inorganic, 328–29
compressibility, and physical properties of gases, liquids, and solids, 166T, 168, 180
computerized tomography (CT) imaging, 54B, 319
concentration, of solutions
 acid strength, 263
 chemical equilibrium, 248, 252
 measurement of, 30–33
 moles, 202–206
 percent by mass, 198–200
 properties dependent on, 206–14
 rate of chemical reactions, 241
concentration gradient, 211
condensation, 182
condensation polymers, 491–94
condensation reaction, 426, 486
condensed formula, 332–33
conductivity, of metallic solids, 186
conformations, of alkanes and cycloalkanes, 348–50
congestive heart failure, 602B
coniine, 526F
conjugate acids and bases, 264–67
conservation of energy, law of, 230B
conservation of mass, law of, 136, 140, 154F
constitutional isomers. *See* structural isomers
continental drift, 330B
contour maps, and microbial forensics, 49B
conversion factors, 22–26, 149–56
cookbook approach, to chemical laboratories, 3
copper
 common names for ions, 93T
 cooking pots, 639B
 fireworks, 56B
 ionic forms, 72
 metallic solids, 186
 molar mass, 130F
 oxidation-reduction reactions, 147, 288, 289
 single-replacement reaction, 139
 Wilson's disease and deficiency of, 60B
copper hydroxide, 451
copper sulfate, 134, 139
Cori Cycle, 743, 747F, 748
Cori's disease, 755B
Cornwell, Patricia, 476B
coronary artery, 314T
corrosion, 146, 286
cortisone, 604
corundum, 187B
cosmeceuticals, 610B
cosmetics industry, 610B, 631B
covalent bonds, 84, 88–89, 328, 629
covalent compounds
 definition of, 89
 Lewis structures, 100–103, 111–12
 naming of, 96–98
 properties of, 98–99
 rate of chemical reactions, 241
covalent solids, 186
crack cocaine, 524–25
creatine kinase-MB (CK-MB), 676, 677
creatine phosphate, 764B
C-reactive protein (CRP), 608
cresol, 391
Crick, Francis, 686, 687, 688, 693, 702
crime scenes
 adipocere and mummies of soap, 597B
 arson and alkanes, 338B
 automobile accidents, 421B
 blood group antigens, 570B
 carboxylic acids and forensic anthropology, 476B
 DNA fingerprinting, 718–19B
 enzymes, nerve agents, and poisoning, 672–73B
 explosives at airports, 184B
 methamphetamines, 523B
 microbial forensics, 49B
cristae, 762
Crookes, William, 50
crotonyl ACP, 809F
CRP. *See* C-reactive protein
crystal lattice, 87, 98
crystalline solids, 98, 185–87
C-terminal amino acid (C-terminus), 622
CT scan. *See* computerized tomography imaging
cube, 13
Curie, Marie and Pierre, 309B, 320B
curie (unit of measurement), 320–21
curiosity, and scientific discovery, 26B
curium-245, 303
cyanide, 775
cyanocobalamin, 664T
cyclic AMP (cAMP), 625B
cycloalkanes, 329F, 331, 345–53, 474
cyclobutane, 346F
cyclohexanal ethanal, 456
cyclohexane, 331, 346F, 349, 351
cyclohexanecarboxylic acid, 474
cyclooxygenase, 500B, 588, 589
cyclopropane, 174, 346F

cysteine
- abbreviation for, 622T
- citric acid cycle, 786
- nonessential amino acids, 642T
- oxidation reactions, 630F
- polar neutral amino acids, 620
- structure of, 621F
- thiols, 428

cystine, 629, 630F
cytidine, 687
cytochrome *c*, 287
cytochrome oxidase, 775
cytosine, 686

D

Dalton, John, 48, 167, 227
Dalton's law of partial pressures, 178–80
Dalton's theory, 48, 50
data, 4
DDT, 245B, 354B
death
- alcohol abuse, 453B
- carboxylic acids and forensic research, 476B

debranching enzyme, 749
decanal, 440
decane, 333T
decanoic acid,
decarboxylases, 654
deci- (prefix), 11T
decomposition reactions, 138–39
decongestants, 519–20
defense proteins, 618
degenerate code, 702
degradation
- of amino acids, 778–82
- of fatty acids, 798–804

dehydration, and alcohols, 415–16
dehydrogenases, 654
dehydrogenation reaction, 801–802
deka- (prefix), 11T
deletion mutations, 708
α-demascone, 448F
demerol, 519
denaturation
- of alcohols, 411
- of enzymes, 638
- of proteins, 637–41

density
- gases, 32B, 168, 175–76
- liquids, 32–33B
- measurement of, 30
- physical properties of gases, liquids, and solids, 166T

dental caries, 99B. *See also* teeth
dental plaque, 551B
dentistry, 245B, 290B. *See also* teeth
2′-deoxyadenosine, 687
deoxyadenosine diphosphate, 688T
deoxyadenosine monophosphate, 688T
deoxyadenosine triphosphate, 688T
deoxyadenosyl cobalamin, 664T
2′-deoxycytidine, 687
2′-deoxyguanosine, 687
deoxyribonucleotides, 687, 688
deoxyribose, 564–65
2′-deoxyribose, 686, 687
2″-deoxythymidine, 687F
Department of Agriculture (USDA), 406, 718B
Department of Energy, 330B, 717
dephosphorylation, of enzyme, 670–71
depression, 536
detergents, 216B, 492–93B, 641, 794. *See also* soaps
deuterium, 46, 299, 301B, 310
dextran, 551B
dextrorotatory compounds, 554
DHA. *See* docosahexaenoic acid
DHAP. *See* dihydroxyacetone phosphate
diabetes and diabetes mellitus
- acetone and "acetone breath," 805, 806F
- Benedict's reagent, 565–66
- blood glucose levels, 559, 567, 752B
- composition of urine, 35
- diagnosis of, 752B
- elevated sodium levels in blood, 219
- ketone bodies, 811–12B
- *trans*-fatty acids, 375

diabetic retinopathy, 812B
dialysis, 220B
diamonds, 186, 187B, 327–28
diarrhea, 214B, 219
diastereomers, 556–57
diastolic blood pressure, 102B
diatomic chlorine, 284
diatomic hydrogen, 88
diatomic molecule, 89, 117
dibromethane, 353
2,3-dibromobutane, 381
cis-1,2-dibromocyclopentane, 348
2,5-dibromohexane, 341
dicarboxylic acids, 479
1,2-dichlorocyclohexane and *trans*-1,2-dichlorocyclohexane, 347
1,1-dichloroethene, 372
cis-1,2-dichloroethene and *trans*-1,2-dichloroethene, 372
trans-3,4-dichloro-3-heptene, 373
1,2-dichloropentane, 381
dideoxyadenosine triphosphate (ddA), 719
dideoxynucleotides, 719–21
diet. *See also* estimated safe and adequate daily dietary intake (ESADDI); food; obesity; weight loss
- atherosclerosis, 607–608
- blood pressure and excess salt, 102B
- calcium, 72B, 88B
- carbohydrates, 549
- collagen, 631B
- drug delivery, 272B
- fat intake, 582
- electrolyte concentrations in blood, 219
- kidney stones and excess salt, 88B
- omega-3 fatty acids, 589, 590
- protein and protein digestion, 641–43, 778
- pyruvate carboxylase deficiency, 785B
- sources of energy, 728
- sugars in, 406, 549, 569

diethyl ether, 425, 426
diffusion
- of gases, 168, 169F
- of solutes, 210–11

DIFP. *See* diisopropyl fluorophosphate
digestion and digestive tract
- fats, 732
- hydrolysis reactions in, 732, 733F
- lipids, 796F
- proenzymes, 671T
- proteins, 641–43, 732
- triglycerides, 794–95

digitalis and digitoxin, 581F, 602B
diglycerides, 590–91
dihydroxyacetone, 550
dihydroxyacetone phosphate (DHAP), 653, 737, 738, 740, 741B
diisopropyl fluorophosphate (DIFP), 539
dilution, of solutions, 204–206
dimensional analysis, and unit conversion, 21–22
dimethylamine, 518. *See also* *N*-methylmethanamine
2,3-dimethylbutanal, 445
2,2- and 2,3-dimethylbutane, 336T
3,3-dimethylbutyl group, 533
α, β-dimethylbutyraldehyde, 445
trans-1,3-dimethylcyclohexane, 348
dimethyl ether, 116, 425, 426
2,2-dimethyl-3-hexyne, 368
N,*N*-dimethylmethanamine, 513, 515T, 517, 518T, 521
6,8-dimethyl-2-nonanone, 446
2,6-dimethyl-3-octene, 367
2,2-dimethylpropanal, 417
6,10-dimethyl-5,9-undecadien-2-one, 440
dinitrogen pentoxide, 242–43
dinitrogen tetroxide, 97–98
dinucleotide diphosphokinase, 771
dipeptide, 622–23
diphosphate, 688
dipole, 117
dipole-dipole interactions, 183
diprotic acid, 277
disaccharides, 458, 549, 567–69
disease, as chemical system, 138. *See also* cancer; diabetes and diabetes mellitus; genetic disorders; heart disease; medicine and medical perspective
dishwashers, and surfactants, 216B
disinfectants, 285B, 450B, 480, 525. *See also* sterilization
dissociation
- acid strength and degree of, 263, 264
- of ionic solid, 99
- of water, 267

distance, and radiation safety, 318
distillation, of petroleum, 350B
disulfide and disulfide bonds, 428, 429
disulfiram, 453B
divergent evolution, 675, 676
division, of significant figures, 19
D- and L- system of terminology, 552, 558, 619–20
DNA (deoxyribonucleic acid)
- chemical composition of, 686
- heterocyclic aromatic compounds, 394
- replication, 693–97
- structure of, 526, 565, 688–90

DNA fingerprinting, 338B, 718–19B
DNA helicase, 696F
DNA ligase, 652, 696
DNA polymerase, 695, 696, 697F, 717
DNA primer, 717
DNA sequencing, 718–21
docosahexaenoic acid (DHA), 589, 590
cis-7-dodecenyl acetate, 500B
dogs, and detection of scents, 184B, 440
Domagk, Gerhard, 674
dopamine, 520, 523B, 535
double bonds, 364, 584, 624
double helix, and structure of DNA, 688–90
double-labeled periodic tables, 58
double-replacement reaction, 139
Down syndrome, 691
Drake, Mary Anne, 443
drug(s). *See also* analgesics; anesthetics; antibiotics; antihistamines; drug abuse; nonsteroidal anti-inflammatory drugs; pharmaceutical industry
- chemical reactions, 239
- delivery systems for, 272B, 610B
- HIV protease inhibitors and design of, 662B
- weight of water taken up by formulations of, 4

drug abuse, 523B, 535. *See also* alcohol abuse; cocaine; heroin; methamphetamine
dry ice, 188
Dufresne, Wylie, 656B

Duve, Christian de, 666
dynamic equilibrium, 197, 246, 247
dysmenorrhea, 588

E

ECG. *See* epicathechin gallate
eclipsed conformation, of alkanes, 349
EcoR1, 711–12
Edward syndrome, 691
effective collisions, 241
effector binding, 741
effector molecules, 669
EGCG. *See* epigallocatechin gallate
eggs, and coagulation of proteins, 638F, 639B
Egypt, ancient, 411, 480
eicosanoids, 587–90
eicosapentaenoic acid (EPA), 589, 590
Einstein, Albert, 52, 309
elaidic acid, 375
elastase, 675–76, 720B
elastin, 667B
electricity, energy sources for generation of, 230B
electrochemical cells, and voltaic cells, 288, 290B
electrolytes, 99, 217–20, 267
electrolysis, and oxidation-reduction reactions, 290–91
electrolytic solution, 99
electromagnetic radiation, 52, 300
electromagnetic spectrum, 52
electron(s). *See also* electron transport system; orbitals; valence electrons
  affinity, 75
  arrangement of and periodic table, 61–69
  carriers, 809
  configuration, 63–69
  definition of, 44–45
  density, 56
  evidence for, 50
  properties based on structure of, 119–20
  spin, 63
  sublevels, 63
electronegativity, 90–91
electronic balances, 12F
electron transport system, 783, 774–75
electroplating, 291
electrostatic force, and ionic bond, 85
element(s). *See also* periodic table
  biological systems, 59T
  composition of atom, 45
  definition of, 9
  Lewis structures for molecules, 100
  origin of universe and, 301B
  periodic table and classification of, 57–61
El Gamal, Abbas, 26B
elimination reaction, 415. *See also* dehydration
elongation, and RNA transcription, 699F, 707
EmbdenMeyerhof Pathway, 733. *See also* glycolysis
emeralds, 187B
emission spectrum, 53, 55
emphysema, 667B
emulsifying agent, 595
emulsion, 491
enantiomers, 552, 557
encephalopathy, 768
endothermic reactions, 229, 240
energy. *See also* aerobic respiration; carbohydrate metabolism; energy levels; fossil fuels
  alternative sources of, 230B, 276B, 340B
  biofuels, 340B
  carbohydrates, 548
  chemical reactions, 235–38
  definition of, 2
  exercise and metabolism, 764–65B
  ionization, 74, 75F
  lipids, 582
  measurement of, 28–29
  nuclear power, 309–10
  sources of in diet, 728
  thermodynamics, 227–28
  triglycerides, 794
energy levels, and Bohr atom, 55
English ivy, 370B
English system of measurement, 11, 21T, 167
enkephalins, 625B
enol and enol form, 384, 459–60
enolase, 739
enoyl-CoA hydrase, 802
enthalpy, of chemical reactions, 229–31
Enthrane, 426
entropy, 231–32
environment. *See also* air pollution; climate; global warming; green chemistry; lakes; seawater
  acid rain, 272, 276B
  atmospheric smog, 157
  effects of water on, 28, 255B
  enzymes, 666–68
  equilibrium in systems, 245
  ozone layer, 341
  plastic recycling, 388–89B, 478B
enzyme(s). *See also* coenzyme(s); enzyme assays; enzyme-substrate complex
  chemical reactions, 656–58
  classification of, 650–52, 653
  cofactors, 663–66
  definition of, 571, 618
  denaturation of, 638
  environmental effects, 666–68
  fatty acid synthesis, 808
  inhibition of activity, 671–75
  medical uses of, 676–78
  nomenclature, 652, 654
  proteolytic, 675–76
  regulation of, 668–71
enzyme assays, 676
enzyme-substrate complex, 657–62
EPA. *See* eicosapentaenoic acid
ephedra, 512, 520
ephedrine, 512, 519, 523B
epicatechin gallate (ECG), 423
epigallocatechin gallate (EGCG), 423
epinephrine, 535F, 536, 748
equations. *See* chemical equations
equilibrium. *See also* equilibrium constant; equilibrium reactions
  chemical reactions, 244–54
  solubility, 197
equilibrium constant, 247, 248, 657
equivalence point, 273
equivalent (eq), 217
error, in scientific measurement, 16–17
erythropoietin, 716T
erythrose-4-phosphate, 744
Escherichia coli, 694, 711, 714
essential amino acids, 642, 786
essential fatty acids, 587
ester(s). See also esterification; phosphoesters
  chemical reactions, 485–94
  functional groups, 332T
  nomenclature, 484–85
  odors, 479
  structure and physical properties of, 484
esterification, 484, 486, 592
estimated safe and adequate daily dietary intake (ESADDI), 60B, 102B
estrone, 603
ethanal, 419, 443, 444T, 447. *See also* acetaldehyde
ethanamide, 527, 529
ethanamine, 515T, 516, 518, 521
ethane, 103–104, 331, 333, 366F
1,2-ethanediol. *See* ethylene glycol
ethanoic acid, 419, 471, 472, 481, 495. *See also* acetic acid
ethanoic anhydride, 495
ethanoic hexanoic anhydride, 496
ethanoic pentanoic anhydride, 495
ethanoic propanoic anhydride, 495
ethanol. *See also* alcoholic beverages; ethyl alcohol
  addition reactions, 457
  alcohol fermentation, 744B
  balanced equation for combustion of, 153
  boiling point, 515, 516T
  dehydration of, 415
  as gasoline additive, 383–84
  hydration of ethene and production of, 382
  medical uses, 411, 450B
  metabolism, 287–88, 419
  molecular structure, 407
  nomenclature, 410
  rate laws, 244
ethene
  dehydration of, 415
  hydration and production of ethanol, 383–84
  hydrohalogenation, 385
  physical properties of, 365T
  ripening of fruit, 364, 365F, 376
  structure of, 366F
ethers, 332T, 406, 424–27
ethnobotany, 511
ethyl acetate, 484, 566B
ethyl alcohol, 30T, 97. *See* also ethanol
ethylamine. *See* ethanamine
ethylbenzene, 390
ethyl butanoate (ethyl butyrate), 485, 486, 488B
ethylene. *See* ethane
ethylene glycol, 208, 209, 410, 412–13
ethyl ethanoate, 484, 566B
ethyl isopropyl ether, 425
ethylmethylamine. *See* *N*-methylethanamine
ethyl methyl ether. *See* methoxyethane
4-ethyl-3-methyloctane, 341, 368
17-ethynylestradiol, 370B
4-ethyloctane, 340
ethyl pentyl ketone, 446
ethyl propanoate (ethyl propionate), 487
ethyne, 365T, 366F
eukaryotes
  chromosomes, 690–91, 692F
  DNA replication, 696
  post-transcriptional processing of RNA, 701
  ribosomes, 704
Europe, and renewable energy sources, 340B
evaporation, of liquids, 182
evolution, and primary structure of proteins, 626. *See also* divergent evolution
exact numbers, 20
excitatory neurotransmitters, 535
excited state, and atomic structure, 55
exercise
  carboxylic acids, 470
  energy metabolism, 764–65B
  ketones, 455
  lactate fermentation, 742–43
  lactic acid, 480
  weight loss, 29B, 591, 807B
exons, 701
EXOSURF Neonatal, 583B
exothermic reactions, 228, 229, 240
expanded octet, 110–12
experiments and experimentation, 3, 137–38
explosives, and airport security, 184B

exponent(s), 24–25B, 248
extensive property, 8
eyes. *See* diabetic retinopathy

F

Fabry's disease, 601B
factor-label method, of unit conversion, 21–22
factor VIII, 656B, 716T
factor IX, 716T
FAD. *See* flavin adenine dinucleotide
Fahrenheit scale, 27, 171
falcarinol, 370B, 371B
familial emphysema, 667B, 720B
families (groups), and periodic table, 58
farnesol, 378
fast-twitch muscle fibers, 765B
fat(s). *See also* adipose tissue; fatty acids
  brown fat, 776–77B
  dietary intake, 582
  digestion of, 732
  soaps and saponification, 490–91
  storage of excess calories as, 29B
fatty acid(s). *See also* fatty acid metabolism; fatty acid synthase; glycerides; lipid(s)
  carboxylic acids, 472, 479
  chemical reactions, 592–95
  citric acid cycle, 732
  double and single bonds and saturation of, 364
  eicosanoids, 587–89
  geometric isomers, 374–75
  hydrogenation, 375, 379F, 380
  omega-3 and omega-6, 589–90
  structure and properties, 584–87
fatty acid metabolism
  digestion and absorption of lipids, 794–95
  fatty acid degradation, 798–804
  fatty acid synthesis, 808–10
  insulin and glucagon, 813–14
  ketone bodies, 804–808
  lipid storage, 795–97
  regulation of lipid and carbohydrate metabolism, 810–13
fatty acid methyl or ethyl esters (FAMES), 340B
fatty acid synthase, 808
Federal Bureau of Investigation (FBI), 49B, 338B
Federal Communications Commission (FCC), 54B
feedback inhibition, 669F, 670, 742
feedforward activation, 742
fermentation, 411, 742–45
fetal alcohol syndrome, 412B
fetal hemoglobin, 635–36
F_0 F_1 complex, 775
fibrils, 572
fibrinogen, 637
fibrous proteins, 627F, 628
film badges, 320
fingerprinting. *See* DNA fingerprinting
fire extinguishers, 241
firefly, 229
fireworks, 56B
first law of thermodynamics, 228–31
Fischer, Emil, 554, 558, 658, 685
Fischer Projection, 554–55
fish, 590
fission, 310
flavin adenine dinucleotide (FAD), 664T, 665F, 666, 766, 772
flavin mononucleotide (FMN), 664T
flavors, of foods, 443, 446F, 488B
Fleming, Alexander, 5B, 532B
Flotte, Terry, 720B
fluid mosaic structure, of biological membranes, 608–11
fluorescence microscope, 26B
fluoride, 184
fluorine, 45, 66, 71, 89, 184, 298
3-fluoro-2,4-dimethylhexane, 341
fluoxetine, 538
FMN. *See* flavin mononucleotide
folic acid, 664T, 673
folk medicine, 422B, 602B
food, and food industry. *See also* bread making; chocolate; diet; eggs; fish; flavors; fruits; garlic; milk; truffles; vinegar
  aldehydes and ketones, 447
  browning reactions, 528B
  calories in, 29B
  carboxylic acids, 472, 478, 480
  chemical processes and shelf life of, 239
  conversion into cellular energy, 731F
  esters, 484, 488–89B
  fermentation, 743
  fuel value of, 237, 238
  hydrogenation, 379, 380, 594
  ketones, 446F
  osmotic pressure, 214, 215F
  phenols, 422B
  "sugar-free," 406
  transaminases, 656B
Food and Drug Administration (FDA), 520, 531, 533, 588, 603
forensics, 49B, 440. *See also* crime scenes
forests, and acid rain, 276B
formaldehyde, 450B. *See also* methanal
formalin, 447, 450B
formic acid, 471F, 472, 474T, 478
formula(s), 91–96. *See also* chemical formulas; formula mass; formula unit; structural formulas
formula mass, 134–36
formulation of question, and scientific method, 3
formula unit, 133
fossil fuels, 145–46, 230B, 276B, 286–87, 352. *See also* acid rain; coal; gasoline; petroleum industry
Fourth of July, and fireworks, 56B
fragrance, chemistry of, 488–89B. *See also* odor
Franklin, Rosalind, 688
free basing, of cocaine, 524
free energy, 233–34
freeze-fracture technique, 609
freezing point, 207–10, 341
Friedman, Jeffrey, 797B
Friedrich ataxia, 768T, 769
frozen methane, 330B
fructokinase, 740
fructose, 458, 459F, 563, 740, 741B
D-fructose, 550, 558, 563
fructose-1,6-biphosphate, 669, 737, 741B, 742, 747
fructose-1-phosphate, 740
fructose-6-phosphate, 737, 740
fruits
  esters and flavors of, 488B
  ethene and ripening of, 364, 365F, 376
  fructose, 563
fuel value, 237, 238
Fukushima Daiichi nuclear plant (Japan), 230B, 318
Fuller, Buckminster, 328
fumarase, 651, 768
fumarate, 651, 770F, 772, 783F, 784
functional groups, 331, 332T
fungi. *See* mushrooms; truffles
furan, 394, 566B
fused ring structures, 526, 600
fusion, 310
fusion reactions, 301B

G

GABA (γ-aminobutyric acid), 538–39
galactocerebroside, 599
galactose, 564, 568
galactosemia, 568
α-galactosidase A, 601B
β-galactosidase substrate X-gal, 714
gallium-67, 315
gamma radiation, 54B, 300, 302–303, 313, 318
Gamow, George, 702
Gane, R., 364
gangliosides, 599, 600F
garlic, 430B
gas(es)
  alkanes, 335
  Avogadro's law, 174–75
  Boyle's law, 169–70
  Charles's law, 170–72
  combined gas law, 172–74
  covalent and ionic compounds, 98
  Dalton's law of partial pressures, 178–80
  definition of, 6
  density, 32B, 168, 175–76
  ideal gas concept, 166–67
  ideal versus real, 180
  kinetic molecular theory, 167–69
  measurement of, 167
  molar volume, 175
  physical properties of, 166T
  solubility, 197
gas chromatography, 338B
gas gangrene, 472, 478, 488B, 745B
gasoline, 30T, 181, 350B, 383–84
gastrointestinal tract, and prostaglandins, 588
Gaucher's disease, 601B, 677–78
Gay-Lussac, Joseph-Louis, 167
Geiger, Hans, 51
Geiger counter, 319
gelatin, 631B
gemstones, 187B
gene therapy, 693B
genetic(s). *See* genetic disorders; genetic diversity; molecular genetics; mutations
genetic code, 702–703
genetic counseling, 693B
genetic disorders
  aerobic respiration, 762
  chromosome numbers, 691
  genetic mutations, 709
  glycolysis, 735–36
  molecular genetics and detection of, 693B
  obesity, 797B
  sphingolipid metabolism, 601B
  urea cycle, 785
genetic diversity, 719B
genome, 690, 717–21
genomic library, 717–18
Genzyme Corporation, 678
geometric isomers, 346–47, 369–76
geraniol, 376–77, 427F
germicides, 423
ghrelin, 479, 797B, 807B, 808B
ginger, and gingerol, 422B
glaciers, 3F
Glaxo-Wellcome Company, 583B
global warming, 179B, 330B, 352
β-globin gene, 716
globular proteins, 629, 630, 637

glucagon
blood glucose levels, 559, 754
diabetes, 812B, 814
glycogen metabolism, 754F
regulation of metabolism, 810
synthesis and degradation of, 748
glucocerebrosidase, 677–78
glucocerebroside, 598–99, 601B, 677–78
glucokinase, 751
gluconeogenesis, 746–48, 810, 814T
D-glucosamine, 573B
glucose
biological roles of, 559, 561
blood levels of, 220, 349, 567, 571, 810, 812B, 814
in brain, 813
calculation of molarity from mass, 203
as energy source, 548
formula, 97
fuel value of foods, 238
gluconeogenesis, 746–48
Haworth projection, 562–63
hemiacetal formation, 458, 459F
mass/volume percent composition, 199
as nonelectrolyte, 208
osmotic pressure, 211
oxidation reactions, 451
phosphoesters, 498
phosphorylation of, 730
urine levels of, 452, 566–67
D-glucose, 550, 558, 559–60, 561
glucose oxidase, 567
glucose-1-phosphate, 749, 750F, 751
glucose-6-phosphatase, 755B
glucose-6-phosphate
gluconeogenesis, 747, 755B
glycogenesis, 751
glycogen storage disease, 755B
glycolysis, 736, 737
hydrolysis of adenosine triphosphate (ATP), 730
glucose tolerance test, 752B
glucosyl transferase, 551B
glutamate
abbreviation for, 622T
classes of amino acids, 620
nitric oxide, 540
as nonessential amino acid, 642T
structure of, 621F
transamination, 780
glutamate dehydrogenase, 780–81
glutamic acid, 708–709
glutamine, 620, 621F, 622T
glutaric acid, 480
glyceraldehyde, 553, 555, 558
D-glyceraldehyde, 550, 553F, 619
L-glyceraldehyde, 553F, 619
glyceraldehyde-3-phosphate (G3P)
carbohydrate metabolism, 732
classification of enzymes, 653
glycolysis, 735, 737, 738, 740
high fructose corn syrup, 741B
glyceraldehyde-3-phosphate dehydrogenase, 738
glycerides, 582, 590–96
glycerol, 180–81, 490. *See also* 1,2,3-propanetriol
glycerol-3-phosphate, 812
glycine
abbreviation for, 622T
citric acid cycle, 786
classes of amino acids, 619, 620
collagen, 631B
neurotransmitters, 538–39
nonessential amino acids, 642T
silk fibroin, 628
structure of, 621F
glycogen, 571, 572F, 748–55, 814T
glycogenesis, 810
glycogen granules, 748
glycogenolysis, 748–55, 810, 814T
glycogen phosphorylase, 671, 748
glycogen storage diseases, 755B
glycogen synthase, 671, 748, 752
glycolysis, 498, 653, 669, 733–42, 764B
glycoproteins, 610, 632
glycosaminoglycans, 573B
glycosidase, 749
glycosides, 567
glycosidic bonds
amylopectin, 571
disaccharides, 567, 568F, 569F
monosaccharides, 458, 549
β-N-glycosidic linkage, 686
glycosphingolipids, 598
glycyl-alanine, 622
gold, 30T, 130F
gold-198, 315
Goldstein, Eugene, 50
Goodyear blimp, 168B
Gore-Tex, 387B
graduated cylinders, 13F
grain alcohol. *See* ethanol
gram (g), 132, 149–56
graphite, 327–28
gravity, 12
Greater Baltimore Medical Center, 319F
Greece, ancient, 811B
green chemistry. *See also* environment
acid rain, 276B
alternative energy sources, 230B
biofuels, 340B
electromagnetic radiation, 54B
frozen methane, 330B
greenhouse effect and global warming, 179B
nuclear waste disposal, 312B
petroleum industry and gasoline production, 350B
plants, pH, and soil chemistry, 277B
plastic recycling, 388–89B, 478B
radon and indoor air pollution, 320B
greenhouse effect, 179B, 330B
green tea, 423
ground state, of atom, 55
groups, and periodic table, 58
group specificity, of enzymes, 660
guanine (G), 686
guanosine, 687
guanosine triphosphate (GTP), 747
gypsum, 83F

H

Haber process, 242F
hair, structure of, 628, 685
Halaas, Jeff, 797B
half-cells, and oxidation-reduction reactions, 289
half-life, of radioactive isotopes, 306–308, 317
half reactions, and oxidation-reduction process, 284, 286
halides, 146T, 332T
haloalkane, 352
halogen(s), 59, 353
halogenated ethers, 426
halogenation, 352–53, 380–82
halothane, 354 B
Hanford (Washington) nuclear storage facility, 318F
hangover, from alcohol consumption, 419
"hard" water, 594
Harrison Act (1914), 625B
Haworth projection, 561–63
HDL. *See* high-density lipoproteins
HDPE. *See* high-density polyethylene
headspace gas chromatography, 338B
heart attack, 677
heartburn, 538
heart failure, 219
heart disease
blood pressure, 102B, 601
chocolate, 395B
cholesterol, 375
enzymes and treatment of, 676–77
nuclear medicine, 314T
steroids and treatment of, 602B
heat. *See also* cardiovascular disease; temperature
chemical equilibrium, 252–53
definition of, 228
energy measurement, 28
halogenation, 352–53
heat flow, 228
heavy metals, 590, 641
helicase, 695, 697F
helium
airships and blimps, 168B
alpha particles, 299
Charles's law, 172
combined gas law, 174
density of, 176
emission spectrum, 53F
electron configuration of atom, 64–65
molar volume, 177
octet rule, 70
origin of elements, 301B
scuba tanks, 198B
α-helix, 627–28, 630
heme group, 632, 634
hemiacetals, 455, 456, 457, 458, 561
hemodialysis, 220B
hemoglobin
blood pH, 283
carbon monoxide poisoning, 155B
heterocyclic amines, 526
heterocyclic aromatic compounds, 394
osmosis, 219
oxygen transport, 634–35
post-transcriptional processing of RNA, 701
sickle cell anemia, 636
structure of proteins, 633F
hemolytic anemia, 393, 736
Henderson-Hasselbalch equation, 282–83
Henry's law, 197–98
hepatitis B virus (HBV) vaccine, 716T
2,4-heptadiene, 367
heptane, 333T, 350B
heptanoic acid, 479
2-heptanone, 446F
heroin, 527
heterocyclic amines, 525–27
heterocyclic aromatic compounds, 394
heterogeneous mixture, 9, 10F
heteropolymers, 478B, 492
heteropolysaccharides, 571, 573B
hexachlorophene, 423
hexadecanoic acid, 471
2,4-hexadiene, 367
hexanal and *trans*-2-hexanal, 443
hexanamine, 516
hexane, 333T, 336T, 344, 351–52
hexanedioic acid, 473, 479T, 480
hexanoic acid, 479
2-hexanone, 449
hexokinase, 653, 660, 730, 736, 742
hexosaminidase, 601B
hexylresorcinol, 423
hexose, 550
hibernation, 776B, 794

high-density lipoproteins (HDL), 605–608
high-density polyethylene (HDPE), 388B, 389T
high-energy bond, 729–30, 800
high entropy, 231
high fructose corn syrup, 741B
Hindenburg (airship), 168B
hinge regions, 630
Hippocrates, 536B
histamine, 512, 538
histidine, 538, 642T, 710B
HIV (human immunodeficiency virus), 662B
HMG-CoA, 805
Hoebel, Bart, 741B
holoenzyme, 663
homogeneous mixture, 9, 10F
homopolysaccharides, 570–71
hormones, 583, 588. *See also* glucagon; insulin; steroids
hot packs, 234B
Hughes, John, 625B
human(s), and genetics, 691, 717–21. *See also* biological systems; children; infants
Human Genome Project, 717–21
human growth hormone, 716T
human immunodeficiency virus. *See* HIV
hummingbirds, 794
Hund's rule, 64
"hunger hormone," 479
hyaluronic acid, 573B
hybridization, and recombinant DNA technology, 712–14
hydrate, 139
hydration. *See also* dehydration
  of alcohols, 413
  of alkenes, 382–85
hydrocarbons, 107–108, 118, 216B, 329. *See also* aromatic hydrocarbons; unsaturated hydrocarbons hydrochloric acid
  acid-base reactions, 146
  Arrhenius theory, 262
  Brønsted-Lowry theory, 263
  calculating quantity of reactant, 153–54
  conjugate acids, 265
  concentration of solution, 275
  double-replacement reactions, 139
  hydrohalogenation of alkanes, 385–86
  measurement of pH, 269
  neutralization, 273
hydrogen
  acid-base reactions, 146
  boiling point, 184
  chemical equilibrium, 247
  definition of acids, 262
  density, 30T
  covalent bonding, 88, 89F
  dipole, 183
  electron configuration, 64
  emission spectrum, 53F
  isotopes, 46, 299
  Lewis structure, 100, 107, 117
  molar mass, 130
  origin of universe, 301B
hydrogen-3, 306T
hydrogenases, 654
hydrogenation
  alcohols, 413–14
  alkenes and alkynes, 379–81
  catalysis, 242
  definition of, 378
  fatty acids, 375, 594–95
  reduction reactions, 452–54
hydrogen bonding
  amines, 513
  boiling and melting temperatures, 183–85
  carboxylic acids, 471F
  definition of, 183
  physical properties of aldehydes and ketones, 442
  structure of proteins, 620, 629
hydrogen bromide, 385
hydrogen chloride, 138, 140, 141–42, 169F
hydrogen fluoride, 184–85
hydrogen gas, 133, 142, 168B
hydrogen iodide, 253
hydrogen ion gradient, and electron transport system, 774–75
hydrogen peroxide, 140, 245B, 285B, 567
hydrohalogenation, of alkenes, 385–86
hydrolases, 651, 653
hydrolysis, 487, 490–91, 496, 534, 731F, 732. *See also* acid hydrolysis
hydrometer, 35B
hydronium ion, 263, 267, 270
hydrophilic amino acids, 620
hydrophilic molecules, 408, 491
hydrophobic amino acids, 620, 621F
hydrophobic molecules, 408, 491
hydrophobic pocket, 675
hydroxide, 146T, 262, 267, 270
L-β-hydroxyacyl-CoA dehydrogenase, 803
hydroxyapatite, 99B, 631B
β-hydroxybutyrate, 805, 806F, 808
β-hydroxybutyric acid, 475, 478B
β-hydroxybutyryl ACP, 809F
4-hydroxyheptanal, 458
hydroxyl group, 407
hydroxylysine, 631B, 632B
β-hydroxy-β-methylglutaryl CoA (HMG-CoA), 805
hydroxyproline, 631B, 632B
2-hydroxypropanoic acid, 472
α-hydroxypropionic acid, 475
β-hydroxyvaleric acid, 478B
hyperammonemia, 785
hypercholesterolemia, 607
hyperglycemia, 754
hypertension, 72B, 102B, 601. *See also* blood pressure
hyperthyroidism, 307–308
hypertonic solution, 213
hyperventilation, 283
hypoglycemia, 752B, 754
hypothalamus, and appetite control, 797B
hypothesis, and scientific method, 3
hypotonia, 768
hypotonic solution, 213

I

ibuprofen, 500B
ice
  environmental impact of properties of, 255B
  exothermic and endothermic reactions, 229
  frozen methane, 330B
  molecular solids, 186
ichthyothereol, 370B, 371B
ideal gases, 180
ideal gas law, 176–78
imidazole, 394, 525
immune system, 640–41B. *See also* antibodies; antigens
immunoglobulin(s), 220, 640–41B
immunoglobulin A (IgA), immunoglobulin D (IgD), and immunoglobulin E (IgE), 641B
immunoglobulin G (IgG) and immunoglobulin M (IgM), 640B
incomplete octet, 110
incomplete protein, 642
indicator, and pH, 273
indigo, 517F
indole, 526
indoor air pollution, 320B
induced fit model, of enzyme activity, 658
industry and industrial uses, 242, 272. *See also* cosmetics industry; foods and food industry; petroleum industry; pharmaceutical industry
inert gases, 70
inexact numbers, 20
infants. *See also* children
  brown fat and temperature regulation, 776B
  jaundice, 2
  pulmonary surfactant, 583B
  pyruvate carboxylase deficiency, 785B
  respiratory distress syndrome, 583B
  ultraviolet light and treatment of jaundice, 2
inflammatory response, 587–88
influenza vaccine, 716T
information summarization, and scientific method, 3
infrared (IR) lamps, 54B
inhibitory neurotransmitters, 535
initiation, and molecular genetics, 698, 699F, 705
initiation factors, 705, 707F
inner mitochondrial membrane, 762–63
inorganic chemistry, 2
inorganic compounds, compared to organic compounds, 328–29
insect(s), and pheromones, 500B, 517F. *See also* ants; DDT; firefly; tsetse fly
insecticides, 354B, 539
insect repellants, 377
insertion mutations, 708
instantaneous dipole, 183
insulin
  blood glucose levels, 566
  cellular metabolism, 813–14
  diabetes, 811–12B
  genetic engineering, 716T
  glycogenesis, 750–51, 754
  monosaccharides, 559
  thiols, 428–29
intensive property, 8
interferon, 716T
interleukin-2, 716T
intermolecular distance, and physical properties of gases, liquids, and solids, 166T
intermolecular forces, 119
International Union of Pure and Applied Chemistry (IUPAC), 58. *See also* nomenclature
intramolecular forces, 119
intramolecular hemiacetal, 561
intramolecular hydrogen bonding, 409
intravenous solutions, 213–14
introns, 701
iodine-127, 313
iodine-131, 302–303, 306T, 307–308, 313, 314T
m-iodobenzoic acid, 476
ion(s), 70–73. *See also* ionic bonds; ionic compounds; ion pairs; ion product for water
ionic bonds, 84, 85–87, 328–29, 629
ionic compounds
  naming and formulas of, 91–96
  properties of, 98–99
  rate of chemical reactions, 241
  solubility, 146T
ionic equation, 147
ionic solids, 185
ionization energy, 74, 75F
ionizing radiation, 300, 313
ion pairs, 85, 87
ion product for water, 267
iron, 93T, 130, 158–59
iron-59, 306T

iron oxide, 234B, 286
irreversible enzyme inhibitors, 671
ischemia, 676
isoamyl acetate. *See* methyl butanoate
isobutane, 108
isobutyl, 337
isobutyl methanoate (isobutyl formate), 488B
isocitrate, 770F, 771, 773
isocitrate dehydrogenase, 769
isoelectronic ion, 71
isoleucine, 620, 621F, 622T, 642T
isomer(s), 107–108, 328. *See also* geometric isomers; isomerases; stereoisomers; structural isomers
isomerases, 652, 654
cis-trans isomerism, 346–48, 370–73
isooctane, 350B
isoprene, 368, 376, 387B, 600
isoprenoids, 376, 600
isopropyl alcohol, 410. *See also* propanol
isopropyl benzoate, 484
isopropyl group, 337
3-isopropylhexane, 336
isotonic solutions, 213
isotopes, 46, 49B, 298–99, 314T, 315–16. *See also* radioisotopes
IUPAC. *See* International Union of Pure and Applied Chemistry

J

jaundice, in infants, 2
Jeffries, Alec, 718B

K

karyotype, 691
Kekulé, Friedrich, 390
Kelvin scale, 27, 171
α-keratins, 628
kerosene, 30T
α-keto acid(s), 779–80
ketoacidosis, 805, 812B
9-keto-*trans*-2-decenoic acid, 500B
keto-enol tautomers, 459–60
ketogenesis, 805–806, 808, 814T
α-ketoglutarate, 770F, 771, 773, 786
α-ketoglutarate dehydrogenase, 768, 771
ketone(s). *See also* ketone bodies
  alcohol and hydrogenation of, 414
  chemical reactions involving, 449–60
  functional groups, 332T
  hydration of alkynes, 384
  important forms of, 447–48
  nomenclature, 444–47
  structure and physical properties of, 441–42
ketone bodies, 804–808, 811–12B
ketose, 550
ketosis, 805
kidney(s). *See also* kidney stones
  analysis of, 35B
  composition of urine, 35
  diabetes and failure of, 812B
  dialysis and failure of, 220
  nuclear medicine, 314T
  prostaglandins, 588
  urea levels in, 677
kidney stones, 88B, 145
kilo- (prefix), 11T
kilocalorie (kcal), 28, 237, 548
kilograms, 133
kinase, 651
kinetic energy, 28, 238–44, 245B
kinetic molecular theory, 167–69, 227–28
Klinefelter syndrome, 691
Knoop, Franz, 798
Koshland, Daniel E., Jr., 658
Kossel, Albrecht, 685
Krebs, Sir Hans, 764
Krebs cycle, 764, 768–69. *See also* citric acid cycle

L

lactase, 568
lactate, 764B
lactate dehydrogenase, 455, 650, 742
lactate fermentation, 742–43, 764B
lactic acid, 478B, 480
lactic acidosis, 785B
lactose, 568, 732
lactose intolerance, 568
lac Z gene, 714, 716
lagging strand, 695–96, 697F
lakes
  acid rain, 276B
  pH of water sample from, 271
Landsteiner, Karl, 570B
lanolin, 605
lanthanide series, 59
lauric acid, 585T
laws, scientific. *See also* theory
  Avogadro's, 174–75
  Boyle's, 169–70
  Charles's, 170–72, 639B
  combined gas, 172–74
  conservation of energy, 230B
  conservation of mass, 136, 140, 154F
  conservation of matter, 3
  Dalton's of partial pressures, 178–80
  definition of, 3
  Henry's, 197–98
  ideal gas, 176–78
  Le Chatelier's principle, 246, 252–54, 278, 279, 283, 482
  multiple proportions, 155B
  periodic, 57, 58
  Raoult's, 206–207
  thermodynamics, 228–34
LDL. *See* low-density lipoproteins
L-dopa, 520, 535
LDPE. *See* low-density polyethylene
lead, 30T, 130, 202, 641
leading strand, 695–96, 697F
lead sulfate, 144
LeBel, J. A., 554
Leber's hereditary optic neuropathy (LHON), 762
Le Chatelier's principle
  acid-base reactions, 482
  buffer process, 278, 279
  control of blood pH, 283
  equilibrium reactions, 246
  stress and changes in equilibrium, 252–54
lecithin, 595, 596F, 796F
Leigh disease, 768T, 768
length, and units of measurement, 11T, 12
leptin, 741B, 797B
Leroux, Henri, 480
lethal dose (LD), of radiation, 321
leucine, 620, 621F, 622T, 642T, 702
leucine enkephalin, 625B
leukotrienes, 587, 588
Levene, Phoebus, 685, 687
levorotatory compounds, 554
Lewis, G. N., 84
lewisite, 429
Lewis structures
  definition of, 84
  exceptions to octet rule, 110–12
  methane, 333, 334F
  molecular geometry and VSEPR theory, 112–15
  molecules, 89, 99–104
  polarity, 117–18
  polyatomic ions, 104–106
  for representative elements, 85F
  resonance, 108–10
  stability, multiple bonds, and bond energies, 107
life, origins of, 650
ligases, 652
light. *See also* ultraviolet light
  atomic structure, 52–53
  colloid particles, 196
  halogenation, 352–53
  photosynthesis, 7
  plane-polarized, 553–54
  speed of, 53
limiting reactant, 157–59
limonene, 377, 548
linear molecular structure, 113
linkage specificity, of enzyme, 660
linoleic acid, 585T, 587, 590, 594
linolenic acid, 379, 585T
lipases, 651, 677, 732, 794
lipid(s). *See also* complex lipids; fatty acids; glycerides; lipid metabolism
  biological membranes, 608–11
  medical uses of, 583B
  nonglyceride forms of, 598–605
  storage of, 795–97
  types if, 582–84
lipid metabolism, 794–98, 810–13, 814
Lipkin, Martin, 72B
lipoamide, 766
lipogenesis, 814T
lipolysis, 814T
lipoproteins, 606F
liposomes, 610B
liquid(s)
  alkanes, 335
  boiling points, 119
  compressibility, 180
  covalent and ionic compounds, 98
  density and mass of, 31–32B
  density and volume of, 32–33B
  hydrogen bonding, 183–85
  physical properties compared to gases and solids, 166T
  states of matter, 6
  surface tension, 181
  van der Waals forces,
  vapor pressure, 182–83
  viscosity, 180–81
  liquid solutions, 195
liquified oxygen, 178
Lister, Joseph, 285B, 423
liter (L), 13
lithium, 58, 65
lithium sulfide, 92
liver
  ethanol, 419
  degradation of amino acids, 778
  enzymes and diseases of, 677
  fatty acid metabolism, 810
  glycogen storage diseases, 755B
  glycogen synthesis and degradation, 571
  lipoprotein receptors, 607
  metabolism, 287–88
  monosaccharides, 573B
  nuclear medicine, 314T
  plasma proteins, 637
local anesthetic, 354B
lock-and-key model, of enzyme activity, 658
London, Fritz, 183
London dispersion forces, 183, 335, 366

lone electron pairs, 89
Love, Jennifer, 476B
low-density lipoproteins (LDL), 605–608
low-density polyethylene (LDPE), 388B, 389T
low entropy, 231
lung(s), 583B, 634–35, 667B, 720B. *See also* respiration and respiratory system
lyases, 651–52
lysergic acid diethylamide (LSD), 526, 527F
lysine, 620, 621F, 622T, 632B, 642T
lysosomes, 607, 666

M

macromolecules, 731F, 732
magic numbers, and radioisotopes, 306
magnesium, 71, 137, 284
magnesium carbonate, 138
magnesium phosphate, 95–96
magnetic resonance imaging (MRI), 316B
magnetism, 63
Maillard, Louis Camille, 528B
Maillard reaction, 528B
malaria, 636
malate, 651, 770F, 772
malate dehydrogenase, 653, 772
malic acid, 480
malonic acid. *See* propanedioic acid
malonyl ACP, 809F
maltase, 571, 732
maltol, 566B
maltose, 568
manganese, 72
manganese(IV) oxide, 92–93
mannitol, 406
marijuana, 535
Markovnikov, Vladimir, 383
Markovnikov's rule, 383, 384, 385, 386
mass, 12, 31–32B. *See also* mass number; molar mass; percent by mass
mass/mass percent (m/m), 200–201
mass number, 45, 298
mass/volume percent (m/V), 199
matrix space, 762, 763F
matter, 2, 6–10. *See also* gas(es); liquid(s); solid(s)
Maya (Mexico), 395B
McArdle's disease, 755B
McCarron, David, 72B
McGrayne, Sharon Bertsch, 309B
measurement
  English and metric systems of, 11–13
  gases, 167
  numbers of, 14–20
  pH scale, 267–72
  radiation, 318–21
  scientific method, 127F
  temperature, 27–28
  unit conversion, 20–26
meat glue, 655–56B
mechanical stress, and protein conformation, 641
medicine and medical perspective. *See also* cancer; diabetes; disease; drugs; folk medicine; heart disease
  alcohols, 411–13
  alkynes and toxic plants, 370–71B
  amides, 529, 531
  amines, 519–20
  blood gases and respiration, 181B
  blood pressure and sodium ion/potassium ion ratio, 102B
  capsaicins, 422B
  carbon monoxide poisoning, 156B
  carboxylic acids, 480
  carnitine, 802B
  collagen, 631–32B
  copper deficiency and Wilson's disease, 60B
  crystal formation, 88B
  dietary calcium, 72B
  drug delivery, 272B, 610B
  drug design, 662B
  electrochemical reactions and dental fillings, 290B
  electromagnetic radiation and spectroscopy, 54B
  enzymes, 676–78
  familial emphysema, 667B, 720B
  fetal alcohol syndrome, 412B
  formaldehyde and methanol poisoning, 450B
  genetic engineering, 716T
  glycogen storage diseases, 755B
  heart disease, 602B
  hemodialysis, 220B
  high fructose corn syrup, 741B
  HIV protease inhibitors, 662B
  hot and cold packs, 234B
  immunoglobulins and immune response, 640–41B
  lipids, 583B
  magnetic resonance imaging, 316B
  molecular genetics and genetic disorders, 693B
  monosaccharide derivatives and heteropolysaccharides, 573B
  obesity and genetics, 797B
  opiate biosynthesis and opium poppy, 536–37B
  oral rehydration therapy, 214B
  oxidizing agents, 285B
  pharmaceutical chemistry, 158B
  polyhalogenated hydrocarbons as anesthetics, 354B
  pyruvate carboxylase deficiency, 785B
  radioactivity, 313–16
  rebuilding of teeth, 99B
  resveratrol, 424B
  semisynthetic penicillins, 532B
  sphingolipid metabolism disorders, 601B
mega- (prefix), 11T
melanin, 685
Melona, Adam, 656B
melting point
  alkanes, 336T
  definition of, 98
  fatty acids, 585T, 586
  molecular geometry, 119–20
  of water, 7
membranes. *See* biological systems; cell membranes; mitochondria; semi-permeable membranes
memory, and immune response, 640B
Mendel, Gregor, 685
Mendeleev, Dmitri, 57, 58
mercury, 27, 30T, 167, 641, 671
Meselson, Matthew, 694
meso compounds, 557–58
meso-tartaric acid, 558
messenger RNA (mRNA), 698, 701, 702, 704
metabolic decompensation, 802B
metabolism. *See also* carbohydrate metabolism; fatty acid metabolism; lipid metabolism
  citric acid cycle, 383
  coenzyme A, 429
  exercise, 764–65B
  oxidation-reduction reactions, 287–88
  sphingolipids and disorders of, 601B
metal(s). *See also* metalloids; nonmetals
  alloys, 195
  ion formation, 70
  magnesium as, 284
  periodic table, 59
metal hydroxides, 263–64
metallic bonds, 186
metallic solids, 186–87
metalloids, 59
metastable isotope, 302
methadone, 537B
methamphetamines, 520, 523B
methanal, 411, 417, 443, 444T, 447
methanamide, 529T
methanamine, 513, 515T, 516T, 517, 534
methane
  atmosphere, 179
  carbon monoxide poisoning, 155B
  chemical reactions, 146, 351, 353
  condensed formula, 333
  formula units, 134F
  fossil fuel combustion, 286–87
  frozen as fuel source, 330B
  geometrically correct model of, 4–5
  greenhouse effect, 179B
  molecular formula, 331
  tetrahedral structure, 113, 114F, 334F
  thermal energy and combustion of, 228, 230
methanthiol, 406
methanol. *See also* methyl alcohol
  addition reactions, 457
  boiling point, 516T
  condensation reaction, 426
  oxidation reactions, 417
  toxicity of and poisoning, 411, 450B
  uses of, 411
methedrine, 519
methicillin, 532B
methionine, 620, 621F, 622T, 642T, 667B, 702
methionine enkephalin, 625B
methoxyethane, 423, 441, 471
methoxymethane, 406, 425
3-methoxynonane, 425
methyl acetate. *See* methyl ethanoate
methyl alcohol, 406, 407. *See also* methanol
methylamine, 264, 514F, 518
methylammonium chloride, 522
2-methyl-1,3-,butadiene, 368, 387B
3-methylbutanal, 443, 454
N-methylbutanamide, 531
3-methyl-1-butanethiol, 427F
methyl butanoate (methyl butyrate), 489B
3-methyl-2-butanol, 416
2-methyl-2-butene, 416
3-methyl-1-butene, 416
methylbutyl ethanoate, 488B
3-methyl-1,4-cyclohexadiene, 367
methylcyclopentane, 345–46
3-methylcyclopentene, 369
N-methylethanamide (*N*-methylacetamide), 529T
N-methylethanamine, 517, 518
methyl ethanoate, 484
methyl group, 589
4-methyl-3-heptanol, 410
4-methyl 2-heptanone, 446
6-methyl-5-hepten-2-one, 440
methyl methacrylate, 388T
N-methylmethanamide, 529T
N-methylmethanamine, 513, 515T, 517
cis-3-methyl-3-octene, 373
2-methylpentanal, 443, 444
3-methylpentanal, 444
2- and 3-methylpentane, 336T, 340
2-methyl-2-pentanol, 449
3-methyl-2-pentene, 374
2-methylpropanal, 443
N-methylpropanamide, 529
N-methylpropanamine, 518, 520
methylpropane, 333, 353
methyl propanoate, 486

2-methyl-2-propanol, 407, 408
methylpropene, 365T
methyl propyl ether, 425
methyl propyl ketone, 446
methyl thiobutanoate (methyl thiobutyrate), 489B
methylurea, 659–60
metric system of measurement, 11, 12, 21T, 24B
Mexico, 395B
Meyer, Lothar, 57
micelles, 491, 794, 795F, 796F
micro- (prefix), 11T
microbes. See bacteria
microbial forensics, 49B
microfibril, 628
microliters, 13
microscope, 26b
microwave radiation, 54B
Miescher, Friedrich, 685, 687
milk, 564, 568, 638, 743
milk of magnesia, 155–56
milli- (prefix), 11T
milliequivalents/liter (meq/L), 217
milliliters, 13
miniature fluorescence microscope, 26B
mirrors, 451
mitochondria, 762–63
mixture, 9
models, use of in chemistry, 4–6
molality (m), 207–208
molarity, 202–204, 207, 248
molar mass, 129, 134–36
molar volume, of gas, 175
mole (mol)
  atoms and concept of, 128–29, 130, 131, 133
  concentration based on, 202–206
  conversion factors, 149–56
  definition of, 107
mole concept, 128–33
molecular biology, central dogma of, 698
molecular formulas, 331–32. *See also* chemical formula
molecular gastronomy, 639B
molecular genetics. *See also* DNA; genetic disorders; recombinant DNA technology; RNA
  DNA replication, 693–97
  genetic code, 702–703
  Human Genome Project, 717–21
  information flow, 698–701
  mutation, ultraviolet light, and DNA repair, 708–11
  polymerase chain reaction, 717
  protein synthesis, 703–708
  structure of DNA and RNA, 688–93
  structure of nucleotide, 685–88
molecular geometry, 112–15, 119–20
molecular solids, 186
Molecular Targets Drug Discovery Program, 370B
molecules. *See also* macromolecules; molecular formula; molecular geometry
  covalent compounds, 89
  Lewis structures, 99–104
  optical activity and structure of, 554
  periodic table and structure of, 115–17
  rate of chemical reaction and shape or orientation of, 241
  resonance and stability of, 109
molé sauce, 395B
molybdenum-99, 306T, 316B
monatomic ions, 93
monoglycerides, 590–91
monomers, 386, 491, 731F, 732
monophosphate, 688
monoprotic acid, 277
monosaccharides
  addition reactions, 458
  biologically important forms of, 559–67
  hydrolysis of polysaccharides, 732
  medical uses of, 573B
  types of carbohydrates, 549, 550
morphine, 526–27, 536B, 625–26B
Morton, William, 426
mothballs, 393
motility, and cellular energy, 729T
movement proteins, 618
MRI. *See* magnetic resonance imaging
Mulder, Johannes, 618
multilayer plastics, 389T
multiple bonds, 107
multiple proportions, law of, 155B
multiplication, of significant figures, 19
municipal services, and pH, 272
muscles and muscle cells, 735, 812–13
mushrooms, 407, 448F. *See also* truffles
mutagens, 708, 709
mutations, genetic, 702, 703, 708–709
Mylar, 494
myelin sheath, 598
myglobin, 526, 634, 635F, 676, 765B
myoglobinuria, 735
myopathy, 735
myrcene, 377
myricyl palmitate, 605
myristic acid, 585T

N

NAD. *See* nicotinamide adenine dinucleotide
NADH. *See* nicotinamide adenine dinucleotide
NADH dehydrogenase, 762
NADP. *See* nicotinamide adenine dinucleotide phosphate
NADPH. *See* nicotinamide adenine dinucleotide phosphate
nalbuphine, 536B
naloxone, 536B, 537B
naltrexone, 536B
names and naming. *See* nomenclature
nano- (prefix), 11T
naphthalene, 188, 393
naproxen, 500B
National Aeronautics and Space Administration (NASA), 26, 330B, 340B
National Institutes of Health, 590, 717
Native Americans, 480, 643, 785B
natural abundance, of isotopes, 46
natural radioactivity, 51, 298–301, 315
negative allosterism, 669, 741
negatively charged amino acids, 620, 621F
neon, 47–48, 66, 68
neotame, 533
nerve agents, and poisoning, 672–73B
nerve gases, 671
nerve synapses, 672B
nervous system, 598, 599. *See* also neurotransmitters
net ionic equations, 147–48, 273
neuromuscular junction, 672B
neuropathy, and diabetes, 812B
neurotransmitters, 535–40, 672B, 728
neutral glycerides, 590–91
neutralization, of acids and bases, 273, 482, 483, 522, 524–25. *See also* acid-base reactions
neutrons, 44–45, 50–51
niacin, 663, 664T
nickel, 242, 378
nicotinamide adenine dinucleotide (NAD/NADH). *See also* NADH dehydrogenase
  aerobic respiration and conversion of pyruate to acetyl CoA, 766
  as coenzyme, 663, 664T, 665F, 666
  glycolysis, 735, 738
  lactate fermentation, 742
  oxidation-reduction reactions, 420–21, 455
nicotinamide adenine dinucleotide phosphate (NADP/NADPH)
  as coenzyme, 663, 664T, 666
  fatty acid synthesis and degradation, 809, 810F
  structure of, 665F
nicotine, 394, 526, 527F, 539. *See also* cigarette smoking
Niemann-Pick disease, 601B
nitrate(s), 146T
nitrate ion, 109
nitric acid, 263, 272, 393–94
nitric oxide (NO), 276B, 540
nitrobenzene, 390, 394
nitro compounds, 520–21
nitrogen
  automobile air bags, 152B
  chemical equilibrium, 247
  covalent bonding, 89
  density of gas, 176
  electron configuration, 65
  ion formation, 71
  Lewis structure, 107
  melting and boiling points, 120T
  scuba diving and bends, 198B
nitrogen-16, 302
nitrogen compounds, 641
nitrogen dioxide, 242, 276B
nitrogen oxides, 276B
Nobel Prize, 90, 309B, 316B
noble gases, 59, 68, 70, 74
nomenclature. *See also* classification; common nomenclature system; International Union of Pure and Applied Chemistry Nomenclature System; prefixes; suffixes
  acid anhydrides, 495, 496–97
  acid chlorides, 494
  alcohols, 409–11
  aldehydes, 442–44
  alkanes, 338–43
  alkenes and alkynes, 366–69
  amides, 529, 530
  amines, 516–19
  aromatic hydrocarbons, 390–92
  carboxylic acids, 472–77, 483
  compounds, 91–98
  D- and L- system of, 552, 558
  enzymes, 652, 654
  esters, 484–85
  isomers, 345
  ketones, 444–47
  nucleotides, 687–88
  peptides, 622
  prostaglandins, 587
  thiols, 427–28
2,5-nonadiene, 367
nonanal, 440
nonane, 333T, 336, 339
2-nonanone, 446F
nonelectrolytes, 99, 195
4-nonene, 373
nonessential amino acids, 642
nonglyceride lipids, 582, 598–605
nonionic detergents, 493B
nonmetals, 59, 70
nonpolar molecules, 117
nonreducing sugars, 568
nonshivering thermogenesis, 776B
nonspontaneous reactions, 231
nonsteroidal anti-inflammatory drugs (NSAIDs), 500B, 573B

norepinephrine, 523B, 535F, 536
norlutin, 603
normal boiling point, 182
19-norprogesterone, 603
nothing, as distinct from zero, 18
novocaine, 519, 524
N-terminal amino acid, 622
nuclear decay, 303–305
nuclear equation, 301–305. *See also* molecular formula
nuclear fission, 50, 310
nuclear fusion, 50, 310, 312
nuclear imaging, 313
nuclear medicine, 313–16
nuclear power, 230B, 309–12, 315. *See also* nuclear waste and nuclear waste disposal
nuclear reactors, 311F, 315
nuclear stability, 306
nuclear symbols, 298
nuclear waste and nuclear waste disposal, 245B, 312B, 318
nuclein, 685
nucleosides, 686–87
nucleosome, 691
nucleotide, 685–88, 729
nucleus, of atom, 44, 51, 306
nuclide, 299, 301
numbers, of measurement, 14–20
nutrient proteins, 618
nutritional calorie (C), 237
nylon, 480

O

Oak Ridge National Laboratory (Tennessee), 311F, 476B
obesity. *See also* weight loss
  body-mass index, 34B
  factors contributing to, 237
  as genetic disorder, 797B
  high fructose corn syrup, 741B
  kidney stones, 88B
  sugar in diet, 406
obestatin, 797B
obligate anaerobes, 745B
observation, and scientific method, 3
Occupational Safety and Health Administration (OSHA), 300
oceans. *See* Arctic Ocean; seawater
octadecanoic acid, 594. *See also* stearic acid
cis-9-octadecenoic acid and *trans*-9-octadecenoic acid, 375
octane
  of gasoline, 350B
  molecular formula, 333T
octanoic acid, 479
1-octanol and 3-octanol, 407
2-octanone, 448F
3-octanone, 453
octet rule, 70–73, 85, 89, 100, 110–12
octyl ethanoate (oxtyl acetate), 489B
odd-electron molecules, 110
odor. *See also* fragrance
  aldehydes and ketones, 440
  carboxylic acids, 478–79
oil. *See* fossil fuels; gasoline; petroleum industry
oleic acid, 364F, 365F, 374–75, 585T
oligosaccharides, 549
omega-3 and omega-6 fatty acids, 589, 590
opiates, biosynthesis of, 536–37B
opium poppy, 536–37B, 625–26B
optical activity, and molecular structure, 554
oral contraceptives, 603–604
oral rehydration therapy, 214B
orbital(s), of electrons, 62
orbital diagrams, 64
organelles, 762. *See also* mitochondria
organic chemistry, 2
organic compounds, 327–31
organic solvents, 639
organophosphates, 539, 673B
organ transplantation, 812B
ornithine, 783F, 784
ornithine transcarbamoylase, 782
orthotolidine, 567
osmolarity, 212–14
osmosis, 210–14, 219
osmotic pressure, 211–12
osteoarthritis, 573B
outer mitochondrial membrane, 762, 763F
oxacillin, 532B
oxalic acid, 479
oxaloacetate
  aerobic respiration and degradation of amino acids, 780
  citric acid cycle, 770F, 772, 785B, 786–87
  classification of enzymes, 653
  ketone bodies, 804–805
  pyruvate carboxylase deficiency, 785B
oxazoles, 528B
oxidases, 650
β-oxidation, 499, 798–804, 808
oxidation half-reaction, 284
oxidation-reduction reactions
  alcohols, 416–19
  aldehydes and ketones, 449, 450–55
  applications of, 286–87
  biological processes, 287–88
  carboxylic acids, 481
  definitions of terms, 146–47
  electrolysis, 290–91
  in living systems, 419–21
  oxidation and reduction processes, 284, 286
  voltaic cells, 288–90
oxidative deamination, of α-amino groups, 780–81
oxidative phosphorylation, 735, 768, 774–78
oxidizing agents, 284, 285B
oxidoreductases, 420, 650, 653
oxycodone, 536B
oxygen
  chemical reactions, 145–46
  converting mass to volume, 178
  converting moles to grams, 150–51
  covalent bonding, 89
  electron configuration, 66
  hemoglobin and transport of, 634–36
  ion formation, 71
  ionic compounds, 86
  Lewis structure, 107
  melting and boiling points, 120T
  myoglobin and storage of, 634, 635F
  oxidation-reduction processes, 286
  respiration, 181B
oxygen-18 and oxygen-16, 49B
oxygen gas, 142, 149–50, 176–77
oxymorphone, 536B
ozone, 157
ozone layer, 341

P

PABA. *See* para-aminobenzoic acid
PAH. *See* polynuclear aromatic hydrocarbons
paired electrons, 63
palladium, 378
palmitic acid, 474T, 585T, 804F
palmitoleic acid, 585
PAM. *See* pyridine aldoxime methiodide
pancreas transplants, 812B
pancreatic serine proteases, 675–76
pancreatitis, 677
pantothenic acid, 664T
paraffin wax, 604
paraganglioma, 768T, 769
parallel β-pleated sheet, 628
para-aminobenzoic acid (PABA), 673–74
parent compound, and nomenclature, 339
Parkes, Alexander, 388B
Parkinson's disease, 523B, 535
parsalmide, 370B
partial hydrogenation, 594
partial pressures, 179
particle accelerators, 315
particle motion, and physical properties of gases, liquids, and solids, 166T
parts per thousand (ppt) and parts per million (ppm), 201–202
Pascal, Blaise, 167
pascal, as unit of measurement, 167
passive transport, 732
Pasteur, Louis, 2, 554, 556, 743
Patau syndrome, 691
pattern recognition, and scientific method, 3
Pauli, Wolfgang, 64
Pauli exclusion principle, 64
Pauling, Linus, 90, 624
PCR. *See* polymerase chain reaction
PEN. *See* polyethylene naphthalate
penicillin, 5B, 338, 532B, 671
1,4-pentadiene, 367
pentaerythrityl palmitate, 493B
pentanal, 444T
2-pentanamine, 517
pentane, 333T, 339
n-pentane, 108
pentanoic acid, 478–79
1-pentanol and 2-pentanol, 384
2-pentanone, 451
3-pentanone, 454
1-pentene, 374, 380–81, 384, 385–86
pentose, 550
pentose phosphate pathway, 744
Pentrane, 426
pentyl butanoate (pentyl butyrate), 485, 489B
N-pentylpropanamide, 530
1-pentyne, 367
pepsin, 642, 666
pepinsogen, 642, 670, 671T
peptidase, 653
peptide(s), 535, 625–26B, 708
peptide bond, 534, 622–26
peptidyl transferase, 706, 708
peptidyl tRNA binding site (P-site), 705
percent by mass, 198–200
percent yield, 156–59
periodic law, 57
periodic table
  atomic weights in amu, 128
  classification of elements, 57–61
  covalent bonding, 90
  electron arrangement, 61–69
  molecular structure, 115–17
  predictive power, 75
  trends in, 73–75
peripheral membrane proteins, 609
PETE. *See* polyethylene terephthalate
petroleum industry, 350B. *See also* fossil fuels; gasoline
pH and pH scale
  amino acids, 618, 621F
  of blood, 283
  buffers, 279–82

calculation of, 268–71
definition of, 267–68
enzymes, 662, 666
importance of, 272
measurement of, 268
plants and soil chemistry, 277B
proteins, 638
pharmaceutical industry, 158B, 352, 662B. *See also* drug(s)
pharmacology, 272B. *See also* drug(s)
phenacetin, 531
phenanthrene, 393
phenol(s), 390, 395B, 406, 421–23
phenolphthalein, 275
phenylalanine, 533, 620, 621F, 622T, 642T
2-phenylbutane, 392
3-phenyl-1-butene, 392
10-phenyldecanoic acid, 799
phenylephrine, 520
phenylethanolamine-N-methyltransferase (PNMT), 651
phenyl group, 392, 477
phenylketonuria (PKU), 533
4-phenylpentanoic acid, 477
o-phenylphenol, 423
3-phenylpropanoic acid, 477
pheromones, 409, 500B, 517F
phosphatases, 671
phosphates, 146T, 218
phosphatidate, 595, 596F
phosphatidylcholine, 595, 596F. *See also* lecithin
phosphatidylethanolamine, 595, 596F. *See also* cephalin
phosphatidylserine, 596F
phosphoanhydride bond, 499, 729–30
phosphoenolpyruvate, 460, 735, 739, 747
phosphoesters, 498–501
phosphofructokinase, 669, 736, 737, 742
phosphoglucomutase, 749, 751
phosphoglucose isomerase, 737
2-phosphoglycerate and 3-phosphoglycerate, 739
phosphoglycerate kinase, 736, 738
phosphoglycerate mutase, 652, 736, 739
phosphoglycerides, 595–96
phospholipids, 608
phosphopantetheine group, 808, 809F
phosphoric acid, 277, 278
phosphorolysis, 748–49
phosphorus, 71
phosphorus pentafluoride, 111
phosphoryl, 499
phosphorylation
of enzymes, 670–71
of glucose, 730
photography, 245B, 319
photons, 52
photosynthesis, 7, 179B, 549F
phthalic acid, 476
physical change, 7
physical chemistry, 2
physical equilibrium, 246
physical properties. *See* properties
physical states, of ionic and covalent compounds, 98, 241
physiology, and pH, 272
Phytochemistry (journal), 719B
pipets, 13F
PKU. *See* phenylketonuria
PLA. *See* polyacetic acid
Planck, Max, 52
plane-polarized light, 553–54
plants. *See also* agriculture; beans; coca plants; English ivy; fruits; opium poppy; photosynthesis; roses; water hemlock; willow bark
alkenes, 376–78
biofuels, 340B
cellulose, 572
DNA fingerprinting and genetic diversity of, 719B
drugs from, 581F, 602B
neurotoxins, 526F
pentanoic (valeric) acid, 478–79
pH and soil chemistry, 277B
polysaccharides, 571
toxic alkynes, 370–71B
plasma lipoproteins, 605
plasmid vector, 714
plasminogen, 677
plastics, recycling of, 388–89B, 478B
platinum, 200–201, 378
β-pleated sheet, 628, 629F, 630
plutonium, 312B, 318
PNMT. *See* phenylethanolamine-*N*-methyltransferase
point mutation, 708
poisoning
cyanide, 775
enzymes and nerve agents, 672–73B
methanol, 450B
polar compounds, 441
polar covalent bond, 89–90
polarimeter, 553, 554
polarity, and Lewis structures, 117–18
polar molecules, 117
polar neutral amino acids, 620, 621F
polio, and polio vaccine, 450B
pollution. *See* air pollution; nuclear waste and nuclear waste disposal; oil spills
polonium, 320B
polyacrylonitrile (orlon), 388T
polyatomic ions, 93–94, 104–106
polyenes, 376
polyesters, 492, 494
polyethylene, 386, 387B
polyethylene naphthalate (PEN), 494
polyethylene terephthalate (PETE), 388B, 389T, 481, 494
polyhalogenated hydrocarbons, 354B
polyhydroxyaldehydes, 550
polyhydroxyketones, 550
polylactic acid (PLA), 478B
polymer(s) , 386–87, 388T, 478B, 491
polymerase chain reaction (PCR), 717
polymethyl methacrylate, 388T
polynuclear aromatic hydrocarbons (PAH), 393
polyphenols, 423
poly(A) polymerase, 700–701
polypropylene (PP), 386, 388B, 389T
polyprotic substances, 277–78
polysaccharides, 549, 570–73, 732
polysomes, 704–705
polystyrene (PS), 388–89B
poly(A) tail, 700–701
polytetrafluoroethylene, 388T. *See also* Teflon
polyurethane, 480
polyvinyl chloride (PVC), 388B, 389T, 480
poppy. *See* opium poppy
p orbitals, 62
porphyrin, 394, 526
positive allosterism, 669, 741
positive feedback loop, 540
positively charged amino acids, 620, 621F
positron, 300, 302
postsynaptic membrane, 672B
post-transcriptional processing, of RNA, 700–701
potash, 491
potassium, 102B, 217, 303
potassium bromide, 120T
potassium chromate, 450
potassium cyanide, 151
potassium hydroxide, 264
potassium nitrate, 196
potassium perchlorate, 56B
potassium permanganate, 416, 450
potential energy, 28
precipitate, 145, 197
precipitation reactions, 145, 147–48
precision, in scientific measurement, 17
prefixes. *See also* nomenclature
alkanes, 339
aromatic hydrocarbons, 391
carboxylic acids, 472
covalent compounds, 96
electron configurations, 67
metric system, 11T
pregnancy, 412B, 635–36, 693B. *See also* infants; reproductive system
preimplantation diagnosis, of genetic disorders, 693B
premenstrual syndrome (PMS), 72B
pressure. *See also* atmospheric pressure; standard temperature and pressure; vapor pressure
Boyle's law, 169–70
equilibrium reactions, 253–54
gases, 167, 169
scuba diving, 198B
solubility, 197
presynaptic membrane, 672B
primary alcohol, 407, 449
primary amine, 513–15
primary transcript, 700
primase, 695, 696, 697F
principal energy levels, 61, 62
prism, 52F,
problem solving, and unit conversion, 20–21
procarboxypeptidases, 671T
products, of chemical reaction, 7, 136, 137
proelastase, 671T
proenzymes, 670, 671T
progesterone, 603
prokaryotes, 690
proline
abbreviation for, 622T
classes of amino acids, 620
collagen, 632B
as nonessential amino acid, 642T
structure of, 621F, 630
promoter, and RNA polymerase, 698
propanal, 414, 443, 444T
propanamide, 529
propanamine, 515T, 516T, 517, 518T
propane
balancing equations, 142–43
boiling point, 515
bromination of, 353
condensed formula, 333
conversion of moles of reactants to moles of products, 150–51
functional groups, 331
molecular formula, 331
nomenclature, 339
propanedioic acid, 473, 479T, 480
1,2,3-propanetriol, 413, 593. *See also* glycerol
propanoate anion, 451
propanoic acid, 478, 481, 483. *See also* propionic acid
propanoic anhydride, 496
propanol, 441, 457, 471, 516T. *See also* isopropyl alcohol
1-propanol, 415, 423, 441, 471
2-propanol, 407, 410, 412, 639

propanone, 418, 441, 444, 447, 457, 471. *See also* acetone
propene, 365T, 383, 385, 415
propenyl disulfide, 430B
propenyl sulfenic acid, 430B
properties, of matter. *See also* boiling point; freezing point; gas(es); liquids; melting point; solids; solubility
- classification of matter, 6
- definition of, 7
- electronic structure and molecular geometry, 119–20
- intensive and extensive, 8
- ionic and covalent compounds, 98–99
- organic and inorganic compounds, 329T
- solutions, 194–98

propion aldehyde. *See* propanol
propionamide, 529
propionibacteria, 745B
propionic acid, 470, 472, 474T. *See also* propanoic acid
propyl alcohol. *See* propanol
propylamine. *See* propanamine
N-propylbutanamide, 530
propyl decanoate, 592
propylene. *See* propene
propyl ethanoate, 486
N-propylhexanamide, 529
propyne, 365T
prostacyclin, 587, 590
prostaglandins, 500B, 587–88
prostate specific antigen (PSA), 637
prosthetic group, 632
protease(s), 660
protease inhibitors, 662B
protein(s). *See also* amino acids; protein synthesis
- amino acids and structure of, 535, 618–22
- in blood, 636–37
- denaturation of, 637–41
- diet and digestion of, 641–43, 732, 778
- insulin and metabolism of, 814
- myoglobin and hemoglobin, 634–36
- overview of structure and function, 633–34
- peptide bond, 622–26
- primary structure of, 626, 633
- quaternary structure of, 632, 633
- secondary structure of, 626–28, 633
- tertiary structure of, 629–32, 633
- types of, 618

protein kinases, 671
protein modification, by enzymes, 670–71
protein synthesis, 703–708
proteolytic enzymes, 675–76
protium, 299
protofibril, 628
protons, 44–45, 50, 263
Prozac, 538
PSA. *See* prostate specific antigen
pseudoephedrine, 520, 523B
P-site. *See* peptidyl tRNA binding site
pulmonary disease, and nuclear medicine, 314
pure substance, 9, 10F, 195
purine, 394, 526, 686
PVC. *See* polyvinyl chloride
pyrazines, 528B
pyridines, 264, 394, 525, 528B
pyridine aldoxime methiodide (PAM), 539, 673B
pyridoxal phosphate, 664T, 780
pyridoxamine phosphate, 664T
pyridoxine, 664T
pyrimidine, 394, 525, 686
pyrimidine dimer, 709, 711
pyrolysis, 338B
pyrophosphorylase, 751
pyrrole, 394, 525
pyruvate
- aerobic respiration and conversion to acetyl CoA, 764–67
- citric acid cycle, 772, 787
- glycolysis, 498, 734F, 735, 739
- transamination, 780

pyruvate carboxylase, 747, 787
pyruvate carboxylase deficiency, 785B
pyruvate decarboxylase, 743
pyruvate dehydrogenase complex, 766
pyruvate kinase, 739

Q

quantum mechanics, 61
quartz, 98
quaternary ammonium salts, 525
"quats," 525
quinine, 527

R

Rabi, Isidor, 316B
racemate, 556
racemic mixtures, 556
rad (unit of measurement), 320, 321
radiation and radioactivity. *See also* alpha radiation; beta radiation; gamma radiation
- biological effects of, 317–18
- Dalton's theory, 50
- decay of, 245B
- definition of, 298
- isotopes, 46, 305–309
- measurement of, 318–21
- medical applications of, 313–16
- nuclear equation, 301–305
- nuclear power, 309–12
- properties of radioisotopes, 305–309
- radiation therapy for cancer, 54B

radiocarbon dating, 308–309
radio frequencies (RF), 54B
radioisotopes, 46, 305–309
radio waves, 54B
radium, 51, 309B, 320B
radius, of atom, 73
rainbow, 52
Raleigh, Sir Walter, 710B
random error, 16
Raoult's law, 206–207
rate constant, 243
rate laws, 243–44
rate-limiting step, and enzyme-catalyzed reactions, 658
RBE. *See* relative biological effect
reactants, of chemical reaction, 7, 136, 137
reaction order, 243
reaction rate, for chemical reactions, 241–44
receptor-mediated endocytosis, 605, 607F
Reckitt Benckiser company, 536B
recombinant DNA technology, 677, 678, 711–12. *See also* molecular genetics
recycling
- of plastics, 388–89B, 478B, 494
- separation based on physical properties, 7F

red blood cells (RBCs), 213, 283, 570B, 608
redox reactions. *See* oxidation
reductases, 650
reducing agent, 284
reducing sugars, 565–67, 568
reduction. *See* oxidation-reduction reactions
reduction half-reaction, 284
refrigeration, 245B
regulation
- of body temperature, 776–77B
- of citric acid cycle, 772–73
- of enzymes, 668–71
- of gluconeogenesis, 747
- of glycolysis, 741–42, 747
- of lipid and carbohydrate metabolism, 810–13

regulatory proteins, 618
relative biological effect (RBE), 321
relaxation, of atom, 55
release factor, 708
rem (unit of measurement), 320, 321
remineralization, of teeth, 99B
repair endonuclease, 711
replacement reactions, 139
replacement therapy, and enzymes, 677–78
replication, of mitochondria, 763
replication fork, 695, 697F
replication origin, 695
representative elements, 58
reproductive system, 588, 603. *See also* infants; pregnancy
resonance, and Lewis structures, 108–10
resonance hybrids, 108–109, 528
respiration and respiratory tract. *See also* aerobic respiration; lungs; pulmonary disease
- acidosis and alkalosis, 283
- blood gases, 181B
- Henry's law, 197
- nuclear medicine, 314T
- oxidation-reduction processes, 287
- prostaglandins, 588

respiratory distress syndrome (RDS), 583B
respiratory electron transport system, 774
restriction enzymes, 711–12
results, of scientific experiments, 4
resveratrol, 424B
reticuline, 536B
retinol, 378
retroviruses, 716
reversibility, of chemical reactions, 244–46
reversible, competitive enzyme inhibitors, 672–74
reversible, noncompetitive enzyme inhibitors, 674–75
reversible reaction, 246
R groups, 619, 620, 621F
rhabdomyolysis, 735
riboflavin, 664T, 666
ribonucleotides, 687, 688, 692
ribose, 564–65, 686, 692
ribosomal RNA (rRNA), 698, 704
ribosomes, 704–705, 783
RNA (ribonucleic acid)
- chemical composition of, 686
- classes of, 698
- heterocyclic amines, 526
- heterocyclic aromatic compounds, 394
- post-transcriptional modification, 700–701
- protein synthesis, 535
- ribose and structure of, 564
- structure of, 692–93
- transcription, 698, 700

RNA polymerase, 698, 700
RNA primers, 695, 697F
RNA splicing, 701
rock, and equilibrium composition, 254
roentgen, 320, 321
Romans, and history of soap, 490–91
roses, scent of, 427F
rounding off, of numbers, 20
(R) and (S) system of terminology, 552
rubbing alcohol, 412, 639

rubies, 187B
rust, 286
Rutherford, Ernest, 51, 320B

S

safety
  acid and base solutions, 267
  nuclear power, 312
  radiation, 300, 317–18
salicylic acid, 480
saliva, and tooth decay, 551B
Salmonella typhimurium, 710B
salt. *See also* bile salts; quaternary ammonium; sodium chloride
  carboxylic acids, 483
  dietary intake of, 88B, 102B
  freezing point of water, 207
Sandoz Company, 430B
saponification, 490, 593–94
sapphires, 187B
Sarin (isopropylmethylfluorophosphate), 672B
saturated fatty acids, 584, 586T
saturated hydrocarbons, 329–30
saturated solution, 196
Schnitzer, Mark, 26B
schizophrenia, 535
Schröedinger, Erwin, 61
scientific law. *See* laws, scientific
scientific method, 3, 5B, 127F. *See also* laws; theory
scientific notation, 15–16
Scripps Research Institute, 807–808B
scuba diving, 198B
scurvy, 632B
SDS. *See* sodium dodecylsulfate
seasonal affective disorder (SAD), 536
seawater
  classification of matter, 10B
  osmotic pressure, 214
second(s), 13
secondary alcohol, 407, 418, 449
secondary amine, 513–15
second law of thermodynamics, 231–34
selectable marker, 714
selectively permeable membranes, 211
self, recognition of by immune system, 640B
self-replication, of mitochondria, 763
semiconservative replication, 694
semipermeable membranes, 211
semisynthetic penicillins, 532B
Semmelweis, Ignatz, 285B
separation, and physical properties, 7F
serine
  abbreviation for, 622T
  citric acid cycle, 786
  classes of amino acids, 620
  genetic code, 702
  as nonessential amino acid, 642T
  structure of, 621F, 628
serine proteases, 667B
serotonin, 536–38
serotonin reuptake inhibitors (SSRIs), 538
shagaol, 422B
shape
  of orbital, 62
  physical properties of gases, liquids, and solids, 166T
shared electron pairs, 89
shielding, and radiation, 318
shorthand method, for electron configurations, 67–68, 70
Shroud of Turin, 308F
sickle cell anemia, 470, 636, 709, 714, 716
side chains, of amino acids, 620
side effects, of drugs, 272B
significant digits, 15
significant figures, 14–15
silent mutations, 708–709
silicon, 67, 69, 113, 301B
silk and silk fibers, 617F, 628, 629F
silver, 130F, 186, 291, 451
single-replacement reaction, 139
single-strand binding protein, 695, 696
size, of atom, 73–74
skin cancer, 711
skunks, and odor molecules, 427F
slow-twitch muscle fibers, 765B
small intestine, and digestion of fats, 732
small nuclear ribonucleoproteins (snRNPs), 701
smog, atmospheric, 157
smoking. *See* cigarette smoking
snake venoms, 671
soaps, 483, 490–91, 492B, 593–94. *See also* detergents
Socrates, 526F
sodium. *See also* sodium chloride
  Avogadro's number and molar mass, 129
  biological systems, 217
  electron configuration, 66
  emission spectrum, 53F
  fireworks, 56B
  ionic compound, 86
  ion formation, 70, 71
  ionization energy, 74
  periodic table, 58
sodium-24, 306T
sodium acetate, 278, 280–82
sodium azide, 152B
sodium benzoate, 482
sodium bicarbonate, 94
sodium chloride. *See also* salt
  balancing chemical equations, 140
  chemical formula, 133
  formula units, 134F
  freezing and boiling points of water, 208
  ionic bonding, 85, 87
  melting point, 98, 120T
  nomenclature, 92
  physical properties of, 329T
  solutions, 195
sodium dodecylbenzenesulfonate, 492B
sodium dodecylsulfate (SDS), 492B
sodium ethanoate, 484
sodium hydrogen phosphate, 94
sodium hydroxide
  acid-base reactions, 146
  Arrhenius theory, 262
  calculation of reactant quantities, 155–56
  neutralization, 273, 275, 483
  as strong base, 264, 483
sodium hypochlorite, 285B, 287
sodium ion/potassium ion ratio, and blood pressure, 102B
sodium propanoate, 483, 534
sodium propionate, 483
sodium sulfate, 95, 135
soil
  equilibrium composition, 254
  pH and chemistry of, 277B
solar energy, 54B, 230B
solid(s)
  alkanes, 335
  crystalline solids, 185–87
  definition of, 6
  density, 31B
  ionic compounds, 98
  melting points, 119–20
  physical properties of, 166T, 185
  sublimation, 187–88
solubility. *See also* solutions; solvents
  alcohols, 408
  amines, 515
  carboxylic acids, 471
  degree of, 196–97
  of ionic compounds, 146T
  of molecules, 119
  solutes, 194
  surfactants and dishwashers, 216B
solutions. *See also* aqueous solutions; solubility; solvents
  buffers, 279–82
  definition of, 9
  ionic and covalent compounds, 98–99
  percent by mass and concentration of, 198–200
  properties of, 194–98, 206–14
solvents, 215–17, 377
sorbitol, 406
Southern blotting, 712–14
specific gravity, 33–35
specific heat, 235
specificity, of enzyme-substrate complex, 659–60
spectator ions, 147, 273
spectral line, on emission spectrum, 55
spectrophotometer, 52
spectroscopy, 52, 54B
speed
  of chemical reactions, 238
  of light, 52
sphingolipids, 598–99, 601B
sphingomyelin, 598
sphingomyelinase, 601B
sphingosine, 598
spliceosomes, 701
spontaneous reactions, 231
staggered conformation, of alkanes, 349
Stahl, Franklin, 694
stalactites and stalagmites, 245
standard mass, 12
standard solution, 273, 274F
standard temperature and pressure (STP), 175
starch, 549, 570–71
starvation, and gluconegenesis, 746
stearic acid, 379, 474T, 585T, 594, 803–804
stereochemical specificity, 660
stereochemistry, 548, 552
stereoisomers, 347, 552–59, 619–20
sterilization, 668. *See also* disinfectants
Stern, Otto, 316B
steroids, 600–604
sticky ends, 712
Stock system, 92, 93T
stoichiometry, 148
stomach acid, 538
STP. *See* standard temperatures and pressure
stream water, concentration of lead in, 202
Streptococcus mutans, 551B
Streptococcus pyogenes, 677
streptokinase, 677, 716T
strong acids and bases, 263, 265, 482, 483
strontium, 56B, 306T, 314T
structural analogs, 673
structural formulas, 332, 342
structural isomers, 344–45
structural proteins, 618
structure-properties concept, 5–6
strychnine, 527
styrene, 388T
sublevels, of electron orbitals, 62, 63
sublimation, of solids, 187–88
Suboxone, 536B
subscripts, and chemical equations, 140
substituted hydrocarbons, 329, 331
substitution reactions, 352, 393

subtraction, of significant figures, 17–18
substrates, of enzymes, 657–62
succinate, 770F, 771, 772
succinate dehydrogenase, 768T, 769, 772
succinic acid, 479T, 480
succinylcholine, 539, 540
succinyl CoA, 770F, 771, 773
succotash, 643
sucrase, 660
sucrose
  acetal formation, 459F
  biological roles of, 568–69
  in diet, 406, 549
  enzyme-substrate complex, 660–61
  heating of, 566B
  high fructose corn syrup compared to, 741B
  hydrolysis, 732
  observable properties and structure of, 215
suffixes. *See also* nomenclature
  alkanes, 339
  alkenes and alkynes, 366
  amines, 518
  carboxylic acids, 472, 474, 476, 482
  ionic compounds, 92
  ketones, 444
  thiols, 427
sugar(s). *See also* fructose; glucose; reducing sugars; sucrose
  in diet, 406, 549, 569
  dynamic equilibrium, 246
  oxidation reactions, 451–52
  tooth decay, 406, 551B
sugar-phosphate backbone, of DNA structure, 688
sulfa drugs, 520, 673–74
sulfanilamide, 520
sulfates, 146T
sulfatides, 599
sulfhydryl group, 427
sulfides, 146T
sulfur, 86–87, 131, 132, 133
sulfur dioxide, 108, 276B
sulfuric acid, 272, 276B, 277, 278, 393
sulfur oxides, 204, 276B
sulfur trioxide, 276B, 393
Sun. *See* solar energy
superabsorbers, and polymers, 387B
superoxide radical, 285B
supersaturated solution, 197
surface tension, 181
surfactants, 181, 216B, 492B
surroundings, and thermodynamics, 228
suspensions, 196
symmetrical acid anhydrides, 495
synthetic opioids, 536B
synthetic polymers, 494
system(s), and thermodynamics, 228, 231
systematic error, 17
Système International (S. I. system), 11
systolic blood pressure, 102B

T

table of elements. *See* periodic table
Tagamet, 538. *See also* cimetidine
tanzanite, 187B
Taq polymerase, 717
target cells, 813
tartaric acid, 480, 557
Tarui's disease, 736
Tasmania, 536B
tautomers, 459
Tay-Sachs disease, 600F, 601B
TCA. *See also* tricarboxylic acid cycle
technetium-99m, 306T, 307F, 314, 316B, 317F
teeth. *See also* dental caries; dental plaque; dentistry
  decay of and sugar in diet, 406, 551B
  rebuilding of, 99B
Teflon, 387B
temperature. *See also* body temperature; boiling point; cold adaptation; freezing point; heat; melting point; standard temperature and pressure
  definition of, 27
  enzymes, 667–68
  equilibrium constant expressions, 248
  gases, 169, 171, 180
  intensive and extensive properties, 8–9
  measurement of, 27–28
  proteins, 637–38
  rate of chemical reactions, 241
  solubility, 196–97
  vapor pressure of liquids, 182
  viscosity of liquids, 181
  water in environment, 255B
terephthalic acid, 481
terminal electron acceptor, 775
termination, of RNA transcription and translation, 699F, 700, 708
termination codons, 708
terpenes, 376, 600
tertiary alcohol, 407, 418, 449
tertiary amine, 513–15
testosterone, 603
tetrabromomethane, 353
tetradecenyl acetate, 500B
tetraethylthiuram disulfide, 453B
tetrafluoroethene, 387B, 388T
tetrahaloalkane, 381
tetrahedral structure, 113, 334
tetrahydrofolic acid, 664T
tetrose, 550
thalidomide, 548
thallium-201, 314
thebaine, 537B
theobromine, 395B
theoretical yield, 156–59
theory, scientific, 3, 57. *See also* Arrhenius theory; atomic theory; Brønsted-Lowry theory; VSEPR theory
thermal energy, 228
thermochemical equation, 228
thermocycler, 717
thermodynamics, 227–34
thermogenesis, 776B, 777B
thermogenin, 776B, 777B
thermography, 776B
thermometer, 27
thermophiles, 608F
Thermus aquaticus, 717
thiamine, 664T
thiamine pyrophosphate, 766
thiazoles, 528B
thioester(s), 498–501
thioester bonds, 429, 799–800
thiolase, 803
thiolysis, 803
thiophenes, 528B
30 nm fiber, 691
This, Hervé, 639B
Thomson, J. J., 50
Three Mile Island nuclear accident, 230B
threonine, 620, 621F, 622T, 642T
thromboxanes, 587
thrombus, 677
thymidine, 687
thymine, 686
thymol, 423
thymosin α-1, 716T
thyroid, and nuclear medicine, 314T
Thys-Jacobs, Susan, 72B
time
  of exposure to radiation, 318
  measurement of, 13
tin, 66–67, 68
tissue-type plasminogen activator (TPA), 677, 716T
titration, 273, 274F
Tollen's test, 451, 452F
toluene, 390
m-toluic acid, 476
m-toluidine, *o*-toluidine, and *p*-toluidine , 517
top-loading singe-pan electronic balance, 12F
topoisomerase, 695, 696, 697F
Torricelli, Evangelista, 167
toxicity, of alkynes, 370–71B
TPA. *See* tissue-type plasminogen activator
tracers, medical, 313–14
transaminase, 651, 779
transamination, of α-amino groups, 779–80, 781F
transcription, and molecular genetics, 698, 700
transferases, 651, 653
transfer RNA (tRNA), 535, 698, 699F, 705
transglutaminase, 655–56B
transition elements, 58
transition metals, 71–72
transition state, of enzyme-substrate complex, 660–62
translation, and molecular genetics, 698, 703–708
translocase, 801F
translocation, of RNA, 707
transmembrane proteins, 609–10
transmethylase, 651
transport proteins, 618. *See also* active transport
triacylglycerol lipase, 671
tribromomethane, 353
3,5,7-tribromooctanoic acid, 473
tricarboxylic acid (TCA) cycle, 764
2,3,4-trichlorobutanal, 556
trichloromethane, 354B
triesters, 490–91
triethylamine, 516
triglycerides, 479, 590–91, 605, 794–95, 812
trigonal planar structure, 113, 365
trigonal pyramidal molecule, 114
trimethylamine, 116, 515, 518. *See also N,N*-dimethylmethanamine
3,5,7-trimethyldecane, 341
trimethylhexadecyl ammonium bromide, 493B
2,2,4-trimethylpentane, 334–35, 342, 350B
triolein, 380F
triose, 550
triose phosphate isomerase, 654, 738
tripeptides, 623
triphosphate, 688
triple bond, 107
triple helix, 631B
triprotic acid, 277
tristearin, 380F
tritium, 46, 299, 310
true solution, 195
truffles, 456B
trypsin, 642, 666, 675–76
trypsinogen, 671T
tryptophan
  abbreviation for, 622T
  classes of amino acids, 620
  as essential amino acids, 642T
  genetic code, 702
  serotonin synthesis, 537–38
  structure of, 621F
tumor necrosis factor, 716T
Turner syndrome, 691

200 nm fiber, 691
two-pan comparison balance, 12F
tyloxapol, 583B
Tyndall effect, 196
tyrosine
  abbreviation for, 622T
  anabolism, 786
  classes of amino acids, 620
  as nonessential amino acid, 642T
  opiate biosynthesis, 536B
  structure of, 621F

U

ultraviolet (UV) lamps, 54B
ultraviolet (UV) light, 2, 245B, 709, 711
uncertainty, in scientific measurement, 17
undecanal, 440
unit conversion, 20–26
U.S. Dietary Guidelines, 582
U.S. Geological Survey, 330B
U.S. Surgeon General, 412B
units of measurement, 11–13
universal energy currency, and adenosine triphosphate, 728
universal solvent, 215
universe, origin of, 301B
University of Tennessee Anthropological Research Facility, 476B
unsaturated fatty acids, 584, 585, 586T, 608
unsaturated hydrocarbons, 329–30, 369–76, 394. *See also* alkenes; alkynes; aromatic hydrocarbons
unsymmetrical anhydrides, 495
uracil (U), 686, 687, 692
uranium-235, 306T, 310, 311F
uranium-238, 312
urea, 220B, 327, 677
urea cycle, 782–85
urease, 651, 652, 659, 677
uric acid, 220B
uridine, 687
uridine triphosphate (UTP), 751–52, 753F
urine
  glucose levels in, 452, 566–67
  specific gravity, 34–35
urinometer, 35B
uronates, 573B
UTP. *See* uridine triphosphate

V

vaccines and vaccination, 450B, 640B, 716T, 807–808B
valence electrons, 69, 84, 100. *See also* VSEPR theory
valeraldehyde. *See* pentanal
valeric acid, 474T, 478–79
valine
  abbreviation for, 622T
  classes of amino acids, 620
  as essential amino acid, 642T
  sickle cell anemia, 636, 709
  structure of, 621F
Valonia (alga), 572
vanadium, 72, 187B
van der Waals forces, 183, 629
vanillin, 447, 448F
van't Hoff, J. H., 554
vaporization, of water, 255B
vapor pressure, 182–83, 184B, 206–207
variable number tandem repeats (VNTRs), 718B
Vass, Arpad, 476B
vectors. *See* clones and cloning vectors
vegetarian diet, 642–43
very low density lipoproteins (VLDL), 605, 606F, 810
Vibrio cholera, 214B
vinegar, 472, 478
vinyl chloride, 388T
virus(es). *See* acquired autoimmune deficiency syndrome; adeno-associated virus; HIV; retroviruses
viscosity, of liquids, 180–81
vitamin(s). *See also* specific vitamins
  aerobic respiration, 766–67
  coenzymes, 663, 664T
  lipids, 583
vitamin A, 364, 378
vitamin B, 527
vitamin C, 632B, 663, 802B
vitamin D, 72B
vitamin K, 364
VLDL. *See* very low density lipoproteins
VNTRs. *See* variable number tandem repeats
volatile esters, 488B
volcanoes, 165F
voltaic cells, 288–90
volume, 11T, 13, 32–33B, 166T. *See also* Boyle's law; Charles's law
volumetric flask, 13F
von Gierke's disease, 755B
VSEPR (valence-shell electron-pair repulsion) theory, 112–15, 333

W

waste disposal. *See* nuclear waste and nuclear waste disposal; recycling
water. *See also* ice; lakes; seawater; stream water
  acid-base properties of, 263
  boiling point, 7, 120T, 184
  chemical formula, 133, 140
  climate and environment, 28, 255B
  common names of covalent compounds, 97
  dissociation of in acids and bases, 267
  dynamic equilibrium in sugar solution, 246
  formula mass and molar mass, 134, 135
  hydrates, 139
  hydration of alkenes, 382–85
  Lewis structure, 118
  melting point, 7, 120T
  microbial forensics, 49B
  molecular geometry, 114, 115F
  physical properties and physical change, 7
  solutions and solubility, 119, 215–17, 408
  specific gravity, 33
water hemlock (*Cicuta maculata*), 371B
Watson, James, 686, 687, 688, 693
wavelengths, 52
waxes, 604–605
weak acids and bases, 263, 482, 521
weight, 11T, 12. *See also* weight loss
weight loss, 29B, 807–808B. *See also* obesity
whales, 605
white fat, 776B
Wilkins, Maurice, 688
willow bark, 480
Wilson's disease, 60B
wind energy, 230B
wine making, 35B, 288, 411, 424B, 554, 743, 744B
withdrawal, and drug addiction, 625–26B
Withering, William, 602B
Wöhler, Friedrich, 327
wonder drug, 158B
wood alcohol. *See* methanol

X

xenon, 303, 305, 314
xeroderma pigmentosum, 711
X-rays, 54B, 624
xylene, 391

Y

yeast, 745B
Yellowstone National Park, 608F, 649F, 668, 717

Z

Zaitsev, Alexander, 415–16
Zaitsev's rule, 416
zeros, and significant figures, 18
zinc, 139, 147, 288, 289
zingerone, 422B
zwitterion, 618